2024 EDITION

Greenberg's GUIDES®

LIONEL® TRAINS
POCKET PRICE GUIDE
1901-2024

Edited by Roger Carp

Kalmbach Media

Kalmbach Media
21027 Crossroads Circle
Waukesha, Wisconsin 53186
www.KalmbachHobbyStore.com

Published in 2023
Forty-third Edition

Manufactured in the United States of America

ISBN: 978-1-62700-993-5
EISBN: 978-1-62700-994-2

Front cover photo: Lionel Milwaukee Road steam engine, courtesy Jack Sommerfeld, Sommerfeld's Trains & Hobbies, Butler, Wis.

Back cover photo: Lionel No. 193 Industrial Water Tower, courtesy Joe Algozzini

Lionel® brand name and logo used with permission.
Lionel does not set prices and valuations; these are developed independently as third party estimates.

We constantly strive to improve Greenberg's Pocket Price Guides. If you find missing items or detect misinformation, please contact us.
Send your comments, new information, or corrections via e-mail to books@kalmbach.com or by mail to Lionel Pocket Price Guide Editor at the address above.

CONTENTS

INTRODUCTION

Whether you are a longtime Lionel enthusiast or a newcomer to the toy train hobby, this guide contains the information you need to identify and evaluate thousands of items made by Lionel since 1901. Most of all, you'll have at your fingertips the most up-to-date prices for locomotives, freight cars, passenger cars, stations, tunnels, signals, track sections, transformers, and other items.

What is listed

Almost every Lionel Standard, O, O-27, and OO gauge toy train and accessory produced over the years is listed in the pages that follow.

This edition of the *Lionel Pocket Price Guide* contains information about new additions to the product line as described in Lionel catalogs, press releases, and other sources. Any additions that Lionel makes to its line after this book is printed will be reported in the next edition.

In addition, the *Lionel Pocket Price Guide* provides information about items associated with Lionel yet not mentioned in its catalogs. These uncataloged or promotional items include unique models and specially decorated locomotives and cars that Lionel produces for national and regional toy train collecting and operating groups, museums, local railroad clubs, and other customers.

When to consult this guide

Many readers of the *Lionel Pocket Price Guide* use it after the fact. They already have some trains and accessories and now want to identify and evaluate those items. Maybe someone lucked upon a bridge at a garage sale and wants to know whether it's a No. 300 Hellgate Bridge or a No. 314 Deck Girder Bridge. Somebody else needs to provide his or her insurance agent with a complete list of O gauge locomotives that includes their conditions and current values. This guide contains the information needed to identify that bridge as well as determining present values for that engine roster.

In addition, the *Lionel Pocket Price Guide* can help you think about what to acquire in the future. That's really when the fun begins! You just have to spend some time considering how you want to approach the hobby. Collect, operate, or both? Prewar, postwar, or modern? Particular types of locomotives or cars? Favorite railroads? Promotional items?

Once you have a general idea of how to enjoy this hobby, you can make informed decisions about which trains you want.

UNDERSTANDING VALUES

The values presented here are an averaged reflection of prices for items bought and sold across the country during the year prior to the publication of this edition. These values are offered as guidelines and should be viewed as starting points that buyers and sellers can use to begin informed and reasonable negotiations.

In a listing for a steam locomotive, the value includes a tender, even if the tender is not listed in the description. The value of steam locomotives, particularly prewar items, may be affected significantly by the type of tender included.

Values for individual items may differ from what is listed in this price guide due to a few key factors. Where collectible trains are scarce and demand outruns supply, actual values may exceed what is shown. Values may also rise where certain items are especially popular, often because of their road names. And as with all collectibles, national and local economic conditions will impact values, which tend to drop when times are tough and demand falls.

Original packaging

Items in Like New or better condition require their original packaging to maintain their high level of value. The values given for items in Good and Excellent condition are not based on the expectation that a box and other associated items are present.

Items that do have their original packaging, especially if it is complete and undamaged, command a premium among collectors of prewar and postwar trains. No hard-and-fast rules can be stated as to how much higher their value is over the same items in Excellent condition. Generally speaking, though, boxed items in Like New condition are valued about 50 percent above the same item without a box.

Using the values

The values listed are what a consumer would pay—more or less—to get a particular item in a specific condition. One collector selling that item to another would probably ask the stated value and expect to get something close to it.

However, someone selling that same item to a person or business that intends to resell it (a train dealer) is unlikely to receive the stated value. Experience shows that sellers get about half the amount. Dealers offer less so they can earn a profit when reselling an item.

When buying or selling a toy train, you should learn more about it. Start by consulting this price guide and then look for more about it in a reference guide or website on toy trains. You can also ask more experienced hobbyists for their opinion about the item's condition and value.

FINDING A PRODUCT

The *Lionel Pocket Price Guide* has been divided into eight major sections.

Section 1: Prewar 1901–1942

Section 1 of the *Lionel Pocket Price Guide* is devoted to the pre-World War II period. The entries cover just about every train, accessory, and transformer associated with Lionel's line during its first 42 years.

The only outfits (sets) listed are those of articulated streamlined trains that consist of a powered unit and attached unpowered cars.

In an item's listing, the basic description specifies its gauge (the distance between the inside of the outermost rails). During this time, Lionel catalogued models in four sizes. It is noted in parentheses whether an item is 2⅞-inch, Standard (2⅛ inches), O (1¼ inches), or OO (¾ inches). O gauge models intended to run on tighter 27-inch-diameter track belong to Lionel's O-27 gauge line and are identified as such.

Transformers, rheostats, and many accessories were not limited to a single gauge, so their descriptions do not specify a gauge.

Section 2: Postwar 1945–1969

Section 2 concentrates on the post-World War II period of production. Nearly every train and accessory (except outfits) that Lionel cataloged between 1945 and 1969 has its own listing. By this time, Lionel no longer made trains in 2⅞-inch, Standard, or OO gauge. Instead, it offered trains that ran on track that had a diameter of either 31 inches (O gauge) or 27 inches (O-27 gauge). However, the entries in this section do not distinguish between O and O-27 since only a handful of locomotives and cars could operate solely on the wider curves.

Section 3: Modern Era 1970–2023

Section 3 shows the trains, accessories, transformers, and other items that Lionel has cataloged since 1970. The modern era encompasses the products of three companies: General Mills (Model Products Corp. and Fundimensions divisions), 1970–85; Lionel Trains Inc. (LTI), 1986–95; and Lionel LLC (LLC), 1996–2023.

These incarnations of Lionel are responsible for an enormous inventory of trains, rolling stock, transformers, and accessories. Cataloged and uncataloged O gauge items (ranging from the near-scale Standard O to the toy-like O-27) can be found within the pages of this section. All items in Section 3 are arranged according to their Lionel catalog number (omitting the numeral 6 used as a prefix). The descriptions of products made during the modern era may include information that relates to where in the product line a particular item belongs. Models derived from older designs have been described as traditional. Rolling stock whose dimensions and features approach scale realism may be designated as Standard O (abbreviated as std O). Locomotives equipped with TrainMaster Command Control or its successor, Legacy, are identified with the abbreviation CC.

Section 4: Lionel Corporation Tinplate

Section 4 features 800 products developed jointly by Lionel and MTH Electric Trains since 2009. These Lionel Corporation trains and accessories are reproductions of Lionel (and some American Flyer) tinplate items from the prewar era. You'll find trains here that operate as tinplate trains did prior to 1942 as well as others that have been updated with modern features and technology, such as Proto-Sound. The retail prices are listed for these products.

Section 5: Modern tinplate

Section 4 covers a category of modern-era trains that is referred to as modern tinplate. Here you'll find reissues of Standard and O gauge trains and accessories dating from the prewar period that LTI and LLC brought out for the purpose of satisfying a growing market. Also included in this section are a few Standard gauge trains that Lionel LLC has created, based on new designs.

Section 6: Club Cars and Special Production

Section 5 gathers the various items, principally locomotives and rolling stock, Lionel has made or sponsored for different hobby organizations, museums, and businesses since the 1970s. These uncataloged club cars and special production items are arranged according to the groups that offered them for sale. These groups are listed alphabetically; regional divisions of national organizations follow the parent organization's listing. Within each subordinate section, items are listed in numerical (not chronological) order, with a description similar to that used for cataloged entries.

Section 7: Boxes

Over the past 25 years, original boxes and other forms of packaging have assumed significance for some collectors. These hobbyists insist that the trains they buy come in the boxes and have the paperwork and ancillary pieces (inserts, instruction sheets, and envelopes) that the manufacturer packed with them before offering them for sale.

Cardboard boxes, inserts, and assorted sheets of paper are more fragile than die-cast metal or plastic trains. They were also deemed to be less important to the children playing with toy trains long ago and so were not treated with the same care. Instruction sheets were lost, and boxes were discarded. As a result, fewer boxes and instruction sheets have survived than have the trains and accessories that went with them. In some cases, the box that a particular locomotive, car, or even set came in is now valued more than the item itself. Boxes are evaluated according to standards and conditions established by the Train Collectors Association, similar to those developed for toy trains and accessories:

P-10   **Mint:** Brand new, complete, all original as made, and unused. Flaps appear to never have been opened, and edges are crisp. No tears, fading, or wear marks. Contains original contents and all applicable sealing tape, wrap, and staples.

P-9   **Store New:** Complete, all original, and unused. May have merchant additions such as store stamps and price tags. Must have appropriate inner liners.

P-8   **Like New:** Complete and all original. There is evidence of light use and aging. Box may have notations (discrete) added since leaving the manufacturer.

P-7   **Excellent:** Complete and all original. Box shows moderate signs of being opened and closed including edge and corner wear. All flaps must be intact.

P-6   **Very Good:** Complete and all original. Box shows signs of usage such as minor abrasions, small tears, color changes, and minor soiling. Inner liners may be missing, and inner flaps may require strengthening. The box can still safely store its original contents.

P-5   **Good:** Box shows substantial wear, and edges may be damaged. Box may have extensive color fading but no evident water damage or cardboard deterioration. Exterior flaps are present, but their connection to the box may require repair. Inner liners may be missing. With care, the box can still store contents. (Any box that has been repaired cannot be graded above P-5.)

P-4   **Fair:** Box shows heavy damage and may have been repaired. Inner flaps may be missing. Box cannot store its original contents. Water damage may be present.

Values for postwar boxes in this section are shown for Good (P-5) and Excellent (P-7) conditions.

Lionel used these box types during the postwar years:

Art Deco: Original postwar box with bold orange and blue design and lettering. It was used in 1946 and 1947.

Classic: More understated design than Art Deco. It was the main component box from 1948 through 1958. Boxes can be divided into Early (1948–49), Middle (1949–55), and Late (1956–58) Classic designs, which are marked by minor lettering changes.

Orange Perforated: This was a significant change from the Classic design. The solid orange box features white lettering and a tear-out perforated front panel. It was used in 1959 and 1960.

Orange Picture: Instead of a perforated panel, this version of the Orange Perforated box features an illustration of a steam locomotive and an F3 diesel on the front. It was used from 1961 to 1964.

Hillside Orange Picture: Similar to an Orange Picture box, it is labeled with Hillside, N.J., where Lionel's plant was located. It was used in 1965.

Cellophane: Used in 1966, this box features a clear cellophane window on the front.

Hagerstown Checkerboard: It has a Lionel checkerboard pattern and Hagerstown, Maryland, printed on end flap bottoms. The box was used in 1968.

Hillside Checkerboard: This 1969 box is the same as the Hagerstown Checkerboard box, but with Hillside, New Jersey, printed on it.

Lionel also used brown corrugated and plain white boxes.

Section 8: Sets

This section lists boxed train sets cataloged by Lionel during the postwar years, 1945–69. When collecting sets, it is important that the sets, or outfits, contain all the items, including ancillary ones, that Lionel packed with them. These items include the locomotive (and tender if a steam engine) rolling stock, any accessories, track, transformer, instructions and other paper pieces, component boxes, and the set box.

The listings include the set's catalog number, a short description, and product numbers for the locomotives, rolling stock, and any major accessories. Sets came with O-27 gauge, O gauge, or Super O track. O-27 and Super O track are listed in the set's description. If no track is listed, the set came with O gauge.

Set values are listed for Excellent (C-7) condition. The presence and condition of original component boxes, set boxes, inserts and other packaging materials can have a significant effect on a set's value. The values reflect the inclusion of these materials. Values of individual set and component boxes can be found in Section 7.

Due to space constraints, not every item found in a set is listed in the description. You can find more complete information on a set's contents on various websites and in the third volume of *Greenberg's Guide to Lionel Trains 1945–1969: Cataloged Sets* by Paul Ambrose and Harold J. Lovelock. Even though the book is out of print, copies can be found from booksellers on the internet.

USING THE GUIDE

Number	Description	Condition ➞ Good	Exc	
2561	Vista Valley Observation Car, 59–61 *	75	230	___
X6454	NYC Boxcar, 48			
	(A) Brown body	15	35	___
	(B) Orange body	50	140	___
	(C) Tan body	20	60	___
6475	Libby's Crushed Pineapple Vat Car, 63u	35	90	___

Identifying a catalog number

A Lionel catalog number is usually stamped, printed, or painted on an item. However, some products do not contain a catalog number. In these cases, you can match the product with its catalog number using a comprehensive reference book or website, including Lionel.com, which contains current and some past catalogs.

Two-, three-, and four-digit numbers predominated during the prewar (1901–42) and postwar (1945–69) periods. Four- and five-digit numbers, and now seven digit numbers, have been most common during the modern era (1970–2023).

On the models, catalog numbers often double as road numbers, although sometimes separate road numbers were added.

Locating an item

Sections are arranged in numerical order of catalog numbers. Items having one or more zeroes as placeholders are listed before those without placeholders. For example, a 004 4-6-4 Locomotive is listed before a 4 Electric Locomotive.

In the prewar and postwar sections, some items, such as transformers and track pieces, are identified by a letter. These products follow the numbered items.

Reading an entry

Every entry begins with the product's catalog number assigned by Lionel. (Club and special production cars may have numbers that were assigned by the group.)

A basic description of the model follows. It gives the type of product, lists the name of any railroad identified with it, and includes identifying characteristics, such as color or lettering. If the item has a road number that differs from its catalog number, that number is shown in quotation marks. (Most of these are seen in Section 3). Abbreviations used in the descriptions, including those of railroad names, are listed at the back of the price guide.

Next, you'll find the year or years during which that item was part of Lionel's cataloged product line. The years are shown in italics. If a year is followed by a u, this item is considered to be uncataloged. It was not part of the cataloged line but a promotional item that Lionel made or sponsored for an outside business or group.

Entries that show an asterisk (*) after the year have had one or more reissues of the item made.

Many entries feature variations, each indicated by a separate letter (A, B, and so forth). Variations amount to slight yet noteworthy differences in appearance that distinguish models that otherwise seem identical. These differences can relate to color, lettering, and details that were added or deleted. For items having many variations, an entry may not include every variation.

An entry concludes with an indication of the value of the item for several common conditions.

Condition

Lionel enthusiasts should be familiar with the condition and grading standards established by the Train Collectors Association, which are used as the basis for evaluating the condition of toy trains and accessories:

C-10 **Mint:** Brand new—all original, unused, and unblemished.

C-9 **Factory New:** Same condition as Mint but with evidence of factory rubs or slight signs of handling, shipping, and being test run at the factory.

C-8 **Like New:** Complete and all original with no rust or no missing parts; may show effects of being displayed or signs of age and may have been run.

C-7 **Excellent:** All original and may have minute scratches and paint nicks; no rust, no missing parts, and no distortion of component parts.

C-6 **Very Good:** Has minor scratches, paint nicks, or minor spots of surface rust; is free of dents and may have minor parts replaced.

C-5 **Good:** Shows evidence of heavy use and signs of play wear—small dents, scratches, minor paint loss, and minor surface rust.

C-4 **Fair:** Shows evidence of heavy use—scratches and dents, moderate paint loss, missing parts, and surface rust.

C-3 **Poor:** Requires major body repair and is a candidate for restoration; major rust, missing parts, and heavily scratched.

C-2 **Restoration:** Needs to be restored.

C-1 **Junk:** Parts value only.

Values are listed for prewar and postwar trains in Good (C-5) and Excellent (C-7) conditions. For modern-era trains, including special production and club cars, the values for Excellent (C-7) and Mint (C-10) are shown.

You may also see NRS listed as a value. NRS (No Reported Sales) refers to an item with limited pricing data since only a handful of these scarce items may have been reported.

Determining a model's condition

Look over a model carefully to see whether it has suffered serious damage, including warping and breaking. Then note whether any parts are missing. Feel for dents in metal and cracks in plastic. Check for areas marred by rust, mildew, or chipped paint.

The TCA condition standards will assist you in evaluating your model, such as deciding whether a prewar or postwar model falls below Good or above Excellent.

The assessment of a toy train's value is based on the expectations that it has not been modified and that all parts are present and original to it. Repainting or relettering a model seriously undermines a train's value, regardless of how beat-up and scratched it may have been before undergoing modification. Any model that has been altered should be labeled as a restoration; potential buyers deserve to be informed about how it has been modified, so they do not mistake it for an original.

A model that is missing some parts should be sold as is or have those parts replaced by identical originals. A tank car cataloged in 1935 that needs a brake wheel must have a part from 1935 put on it to be considered a true original. Adding a brake wheel from 1936 undermines the car's legitimacy as much as adding one from 2023 does.

The same rule applies to the ancillary items that came with various models. The value of a flatcar may depend largely on the miniature airplane or rocket packed with it; therefore, having a load that is a genuine original is essential to maintaining the value of that flatcar. Similarly, freight loaders must have whatever cargo came with them (coal, logs, trailers, and so forth). Reproductions should be identified as such.

NOTES

Section 1
PREWAR 1901–1942

			Good	Exc
___	001	4-6-4 Locomotive (OO), 38-42	195	360
___	1	Bild-A-Motor (O), 28-31	60	140
___	1	Trolley (std), 06-14		
___		(A) Cream body, orange band and roof	1900	4750
___		(B) White body, blue band and roof	1750	4750
___		(C) Cream body, blue band and roof	1300	3150
___		(D) Cream body, blue band and roof, Curtis Bay	2150	5550
___		(E) Blue, cream band, blue roof	1450	3150
___	1/111	Trolley Trailer (std), 06-14	1000	2700
___	002	4-6-4 Locomotive (OO), 39-42	160	285
___	2	Bild-A-Motor (std), 28-31	100	180
___	2	Trolley (std), 06-16*		
___		(A) Yellow, red band	1200	3575
___		(B) Red, yellow band	1200	2250
___	2/200	Trolley Trailer (std), 06-16	1000	1800
___	003	4-6-4 Locomotive (OO), 39-42		
___		(A) 003W whistling Tender	190	395
___		(B) 003T nonwhistling Tender	175	355
___	3	Trolley (std), 06-13		
___		(A) Cream, orange band	1400	3100
___		(B) Cream, dark olive green band	1400	3100
___		(C) Orange, dark olive green band	1400	3100
___		(D) Dark green, cream windows	1400	3100
___		(E) Green, cream windows, Bay Shore	1650	3700
___	3/300	Trolley Trailer (std), 06-13	1500	3500
___	004	4-6-4 Locomotive (OO), 39-42		
___		(A) 004W whistling Tender	210	350
___		(B) 004T nonwhistling Tender	190	310
___	4	Electric Locomotive 0-4-0 (O), 28-32*		
___		(A) Orange, black frame	550	875
___		(B) Gray, apple green stripe	580	1050
___	4	Trolley (std), 06-12		
___		(A) Cream, dark olive green band	3000	4950
___		(B) Green or olive green, cream roof	3000	4950
___	4U	No. 4 Kit Form (O), 28-29	1150	1600
___	5	0-4-0 Locomotive, no tender, early (std), 06-07		
___		(A) NYC & HRR	1000	1450
___		(B) Pennsylvania	1400	2300
___		(C) NYC & HRRR (3 Rs)	1250	2050
___		(D) B&O RR	1500	2400
___	5	0-4-0 Locomotive, tender, early Special (std), 06-09	980	1300
___	5	0-4-0 Locomotive, no tender, later (std), 10-11	750	1150
___	5	0-4-0 Locomotive, tender, later Special (std), 10-11	920	1200

PREWAR 1901-1942		Good	Exc	
5	0-4-0 Locomotive, tender, latest (std), 12-23	800	1100	___
6	4-4-0 Locomotive (std), 06-23	860	1250	___
6	0-4-0 Locomotive Special (std), 08-09	2050	2950	___
7	Steam 4-4-0 Locomotive (std), 10-23*	1850	2300	___
8	Electric Locomotive 0-4-0 (std), 25-32			___
	(A) Maroon or mojave, brass windows and trim	130	250	___
	(B) Olive green, brass windows	155	205	___
	(C) Red, brass or cream windows	137	250	___
	(D) Peacock, orange windows	520	750	___
8	Trolley (std), 08-14*			___
	(A) Cream, orange band and roof	3000	5400	___
	(B) Dark green, cream windows	3450	5400	___
8E	Electric Locomotive 0-4-0 (std), 26-32			___
	(A) Mojave, brass windows and trim	175	250	___
	(B) Red, brass or cream windows	150	225	___
	(C) Peacock, orange windows	370	590	___
	(D) Pea green, cream stripe	465	670	___
9	Electric Locomotive 0-4-0 (std), 29*	1200	2150	___
9	Motor Car (std), 09-12		NRS	___
9	Trolley (std), 9	3000	5400	___
9E	Electric Locomotive (std), 28-35*			___
	(A) 0-4-0, orange	700	1250	___
	(B) 2-4-2, two-tone green	880	1600	___
	(C) 2-4-2, gunmetal gray	653	1100	___
9U	Electric Locomotive 0-4-0 Kit (std), 28-29	975	1975	___
10	Electric Locomotive 0-4-0 (std), 25-29*			___
	(A) Mojave, brass trim	145	215	___
	(B) Gray, brass trim	125	228	___
	(C) Peacock, brass inserts	145	165	___
	(D) Red, cream stripe	580	880	___
10	Interurban (std), 10-16			___
	(A) Maroon	3000	5750	___
	(B) Dark olive green	1200	2150	___
10E	Electric Locomotive 0-4-0 (std), 26-30			___
	(A) Olive green, black frame		NRS	___
	(B) Peacock, dark green or black frame	245	400	___
	(C) State brown, dark green frame	435	630	___
	(D) Gray, black frame	165	220	___
	(E) Red, cream stripe	620	890	___
11	Non derailing switches, 33-37	18	38	___
11	Flatcar, early (std), 06-08	150	360	___
11	Flatcar, later (std), 09-15	45	90	___
11	Flatcar, latest (std), 16-18	50	90	___
11	Flatcar, Lionel Corp. (std), 18-26	50	80	___
12	Switches, pair (O), 27-33	20	40	___
12	Gondola, early (std), 06-08	150	360	___

	PREWAR 1901-1942	Good	Exc
___ 12	Gondola, later (std), 09-15	50	100
___ 12	Gondola, latest (std), 16-18	33	70
___ 12	Gondola, Lionel Corp. (std), 18-26	50	70
___ 13	012 Switches and 439 panel board, 27-33	120	190
___ 13	Cattle Car, early (std), 06-08	300	450
___ 13	Cattle Car, later (std), 09-15	150	225
___ 13	Cattle Car, latest (std), 16-18	65	115
___ 13	Cattle Car, Lionel Corp. (std), 18-26	65	115
___ 0014	Boxcar (OO), 38-42		
___	(A) Yellow, Lionel Lines	80	155
___	(B) Tuscan, Pennsylvania	40	75
___ 14	Boxcar, early (std), 06-08	195	435
___ 14	Boxcar, later (std), 09-15	80	105
___ 14	Boxcar, latest (std), 16-18	75	105
___ 14	Boxcar, Lionel Corp. (std), 18-26	80	105
___ 0015	Tank Car (OO), 38-42		
___	(A) Silver, Sunoco	40	90
___	(B) Black, Shell	50	83
___ 15	Oil Car, early (std), 06-08	200	360
___ 15	Oil Car, later (std), 09-15	75	115
___ 15	Oil Car, latest (std), 16-18	75	115
___ 15	Oil Car, Lionel Corp. (std), 18-26	75	115
___ 0016	Hopper Car (OO), 38-42		
___	(A) Gray	75	160
___	(B) Black	58	115
___ 16	Ballast Dump Car, early (std), 06-11	400	700
___ 16	Ballast Dump Car, later (std), 09-15	95	175
___ 16	Ballast Dump Car, latest (std), 16-18	95	175
___ 16	Ballast Dump Car, Lionel Corp. (std), 18-26	95	175
___ 17	Caboose (OO), 38-42	40	90
___ 17	Caboose, early (std), 06-08	220	440
___ 17	Caboose, later (std), 09-15	70	135
___ 17	Caboose, latest (std), 16-18	75	135
___ 17	Caboose, Lionel Corp. (std), 18-26	50	90
___ 18	Pullman Car (std), 08		
___	(A) Dark olive green, nonremovable roof	700	2150
___	(B) Dark olive green, removable roof	88	215
___	(C) Yellow-orange, removable roof	315	870
___	(D) Orange, removable roof	90	205
___	(E) Mojave, removable roof	305	890
___ 18	Pullman Car (std), 11-13	600	900
___ 18	Pullman Car (std), 13-15	150	270
___ 18	Pullman Car (std), 15-18	150	270
___ 18	Pullman Car (std), 18-22	90	155
___ 18	Pullman Car (std), 23-26	270	530

		Good	Exc	
19	Combine Car (std), 08			___
	(A) Dark olive green, nonremovable roof	1100	2600	___
	(B) Dark olive green, removable roof	80	148	___
	(C) Yellow-orange, removable roof	260	430	___
	(D) Orange, removable roof	115	205	___
	(E) Mojave, removable roof	305	890	___
19	Combine Car (std), 11-13	600	900	___
19	Combine Car (std), 13-15	200	270	___
19	Combine Car (std), 15-18	200	270	___
19	Combine Car (std), 18-22	90	155	___
19	Combine Car (std), 23-26	265	520	___
20	90-degree Crossover (O), 15-42	4	13	___
020X	45-degree Crossover (O), 17-42	3	10	___
20	90-degree Crossover (std), 09-32	4	10	___
20	Direct Current Reducer, 06	95	195	___
20X	45-degree Crossover (std), 28-32	5	10	___
21	Switches, pair (O), 15-37	20	50	___
21	90-degree Crossover (std), 06	10	20	___
21	Switches, pair (std), 15-25	35	70	___
22	Remote Control Switches, pair (O), 38-42	40	70	___
22	Manual Switches, pair (std), 06-25	45	75	___
23	Bumper (O), 15-33	15	35	___
23	Bumper (std), 06-23	15	40	___
0024	Pennsylvania Boxcar (OO), 39-42	45	75	___
24	Railway Station (std), 06		NRS	___
25	Bumper (O), 28-42	17	40	___
0025	Tank Car (OO), 39-42			___
	(A) Black, Shell	40	90	___
	(B) Silver, Sunoco	40	80	___
25	Open Station (std), 06		NRS	___
25	Bumper (std), 27-42	25	45	___
26	Passenger Bridge (std), 06	15	40	___
0027	Caboose (OO), 39-42	40	70	___
27	Lighting Set, 11-23	15	40	___
27	Station (std), 09-12		NRS	___
28	Double Station with dome, 09-12		NRS	___
29	Day Coach (std), 07-22			___
	(A) Dark olive green, 9 windows	1500	3000	___
	(B) Maroon, 10 windows	1200	1500	___
	(C) Dark green, 10 windows	3000	4500	___
	(D) Dark olive green, 10 windows	680	1000	___
	(E) Dark green, 10 windows	450	900	___
31	2-rail 13" Curve Track (OO), 39-42	5	10	___
31	Combine Car (std), 21-25			___
	(A) Maroon	70	90	___
	(B) Orange	125	195	___

		Good	Exc
___	(C) Dark olive green	65	90
___	(D) Brown	75	95
___ 32	2-rail 12" Straight Track (OO), 39-42	10	15
___ 32	Mail Car (std), 21-25		
___	(A) Maroon	85	125
___	(B) Orange	120	185
___	(C) Dark olive green	65	85
___	(D) Brown	70	90
___ 32	Miniature Figures, 09-18	95	250
___ 33	Electric Locomotive 0-6-0, early (std), 13		
___	(A) Dark olive green, NYC in oval	105	188
___	(B) Black, NYC	320	950
___	(C) Dark olive green, NYC	440	950
___	(D) Pennsylvania RR	580	1250
___ 33	Electric Locomotive 0-4-0, later (std), 13-24	40	150
___	(A) Dark olive green or black, NYC	105	170
___	(B) Black, lettered C&O	395	720
___	(C) Maroon, red, or peacock	340	620
___ 34	2-rail 13" Curve Track, electrical connectors (OO), 39-42	10	15
___ 34	Electric Locomotive 0-6-0, early (std), 12	520	860
___ 34	Electric Locomotive 0-4-0 (std), 13	200	385
___ 35	Pullman Car (std), 12-13		
___	(A) Dark blue	470	900
___	(B) Dark olive green	170	235
___ 35	Pullman Car (std), 14-16		
___	(A) Dark olive green, maroon windows	35	70
___	(B) Maroon, green windows	75	105
___	(C) Orange, maroon windows	125	195
___ 35	Pullman Car (std), 15-18	40	70
___ 35	Pullman Car (std), 18-23		
___	(A) Dark olive green, maroon windows	30	50
___	(B) Maroon, green windows	25	45
___	(C) Orange, maroon windows	120	210
___	(D) Brown, green windows	30	50
___ 35	Boulevard Street Lamp, 6 1/8" high, 40-42	27	50
___ 35	Pullman Car (std), 24	40	55
___ 35	Pullman Car (std), 25-26	40	55
___ 36	Observation Car (std), 12-13		
___	(A) Dark blue	315	810
___	(B) Dark olive green	145	205
___ 36	Observation Car (std), 14-16		
___	(A) Dark olive green, maroon windows	60	95
___	(B) Maroon, green windows	50	70
___	(C) Orange, maroon windows	180	290
___	(D) Brown, green windows	50	75
___ 36	Observation Car (std), 15-18	60	80

| --- | --- | --- | --- |
36	Observation Car (std), 18-23			___
	(A) Dark olive green, maroon windows	40	55	
	(B) Maroon, green windows	40	55	
	(C) Orange, maroon windows	130	215	
	(D) Brown, green windows	40	55	
36	Observation Car (std), 24	40	55	___
36	Observation Car (std), 25-26	40	55	___
38	Electric Locomotive 0-4-0 (std), 13-24			___
	(A) Black	100	163	
	(B) Red	475	680	
	(C) Mojave or pea green	405	540	
	(D) Dark green	270	360	
	(E) Brown	270	315	
	(F) Red, cream trim	405	540	
	(G) Maroon	170	270	
	(H) Gray	70	125	
41	Accessory Contactor, 37-42	3	9	___
42	Switches, pair (O), 38-42	15	40	___
42	Electric Locomotive 0-4-4-0, square hood, early (std), 12*	760	1650	
42	Electric Locomotive 0-4-4-0, round hood, later (std), 13-23			___
	(A) Black or gray	300	510	
	(B) Maroon	1250	2050	
	(C) Dark gray	375	600	
	(D) Dark green or mojave	500	800	
	(E) Peacock	1100	1800	
	(F) Olive or dark olive green	750	1200	
043/43	Bild-A-Motor Gear Set, 29	40	85	___
0044	Boxcar (OO), 39-42	40	80	___
0044K	Boxcar Kit (OO), 39-42	75	120	___
0045	Tank Car (OO), 39-42			___
	(A) Black, Shell	40	95	
	(B) Silver, Sunoco	40	80	
0045K	Tank Car Kit (OO), 39-42	75	120	
45	Automatic Gateman (O), 35-36	15	35	
45	Automatic Gateman (std), 35-36	20	45	
45N	Automatic Gateman (std, O), 37-42	40	118	___
0046	Hopper Car (OO), 39-42	50	90	
0046K	Hopper Car Kit (OO), 39-42			___
	(A) Southern Pacific	75	135	___
	(B) Reading		NRS	___
46	Single Crossing Gate, 39-42	75	120	
0047	Caboose (OO), 39-42	30	60	___
0047K	Caboose Kit (OO), 39-42	75	135	
47	Double Crossing Gate, 39-42	70	140	
48W	Whistle Station, 37-42	20	65	___

	PREWAR 1901-1942	Good	Exc
___ 50	Electric Locomotive 0-4-0 (std), 24		
___	(A) Dark green or dark gray	133	250
___	(B) Maroon	315	600
___	(C) Mojave	175	345
___ 50	Cardboard Train, Cars, Accessory (O), 43*	200	360
___ 0051	7" Curve Track (OO), 39-42	5	15
___ 51	0-4-0 Locomotive, late, 8-wheel (std), 12-23	675	1150
___ 0052	7" Straight Track (OO), 39-42	10	15
___ 52	Lamp Post, 33-41	45	83
___ 53	Electric Locomotive 0-4-4-0, early (std), 12-14	1200	2450
___ 53	Electric Locomotive 0-4-0, later (std), 15-19		
___	(A) Maroon	550	950
___	(B) Mojave	670	1350
___	(C) Dark olive green	560	1150
___ 53	Electric Locomotive 0-6-6-0, early (std), 11		NRS
___ 53	Electric Locomotive 0-4-0, latest (std), 20-21	200	450
___ 53	Lamp Post, 31-42	30	50
___ 0054	7" Curve Track, electrical connectors (OO), 39-42	10	15
___ 54	Electric Locomotive 0-4-4-0, early (std), 12*	2500	4050
___ 54	Electric Locomotive 0-4-4-0, late (std), 13-23	1800	2700
___ 54	Lamp Post, 29-35	60	108
___ 56	Lamp Post, removable lens and cap, 24-42		
___	(A) Mojave	85	185
___	(B) Dark gray	55	110
___	(C) 45N Gateman green	25	45
___	(D) Pea green	30	50
___	(E) Aluminum	30	45
___	(F) Copper	60	160
___	(G) Dark green	30	45
___ 57	Lamp Post with street names, 22-42		
___	(A) Orange post, Main St. & Broadway	35	55
___	(B) Orange post, Fifth Ave. & 42nd St.	40	95
___	(C) Orange post, Broadway & 21st St.	45	90
___	(D) Orange post, Broadway, 42nd St., Fifth Ave. & 21st St.	70	130
___	(E) Yellow post, Main St. & Broadway	35	89
___ 58	Lamp Post, 7 3/8" high, 22-42		
___	(A) Cream	28	60
___	(B) Peacock	30	60
___	(C) Pea green	30	60
___	(D) Maroon	33	85
___	(E) Dark green	28	50
___	(F) Orange	30	60
___ 59	Lamp Post, 8 3/4" high, 20-36	40	100
___ 60	Telegraph Post (O), 29-42	10	25
___ 60	Telegraph Post (std), 20-28	10	25
___ 60	Electric Locomotive 0-4-0, FAO Schwartz (std), 15 u		NRS

PREWAR 1901-1942		Good	Exc	
61	7" Curve Track, tubular (OO), 38	3	10	
61	Lamp Post, one globe, 14-36	35	65	
61	Electric Locomotive 0-4-4-0, FAO Schwartz (std), 15 u		NRS	
0062	7" Straight Track, tubular (OO), 38	5	10	
62	Semaphore, 20-32	30	50	
62	Electric Locomotive 0-4-0, FAO Schwartz (std), 24-32 u		NRS	
0063	Half Curve Track, tubular (OO), 38-42	8	15	
63	Semaphore, single arm, 15-21	25	50	
63	Lamp Post, two globes, 33-42	135	265	
0064	7" Curve Track, tubular, electrical connectors (OO), 38	8	15	
64	Lamp Post, 40-42	35	70	
64	Semaphore, double arm, 15-21	30	60	
0065	Half Straight Track, tubular (OO), 38-42	10	15	
65	Semaphore, one-arm, 15-26	30	60	
65	Whistle Controller, 35	8	15	
0066	5 5/8" Straight Track (OO), 38-42	10	15	
66	Semaphore, two-arm, 15-26	35	70	
66	Whistle Controller, 36-39	5	10	
67	Lamp Post, 15-32	85	145	
67	Whistle Controller, 36-39	12	30	
68	Warning Signal (O), 25-42	10	25	
68	Warning Signal (std), 20-39	12	30	
69	Electric Warning Bell Signal (O), 21-35	37	75	
69	Electric Warning Bell Signal (std), 21-35	40	76	
69N	Electric Warning Bell Signal (std, O), 36-42	35	70	
70	90-degree Crossing, 38-42	5	10	
70	Outfit: 62 (2), 59 (1), 68 (1), 21-32	60	130	
71	060 Telegraph Post Set, 6 pieces (O), 29-42	70	160	
71	60 Telegraph Post Set, 6 pieces (std), 21-31	35	145	
72	Remote Control Switches, pair (OO), 38-42	155	290	
0072L	Remote Control Switch, left hand (OO), 38-42	50	95	
0072R	Remote Control Switch, right hand (OO)	50	95	
0074	Boxcar (OO), 39-42	35	85	
0075	Tank Car (OO), 39-42	50	145	
76	Block Signal (O), 23-28	35	105	
76	Warning Bell and Shack, 39-42	47	180	
0077	Caboose (OO), 39-42	30	60	
77/077	Automatic Crossing Gate, 23-35	14	50	
78/078	Train Signal, 24-32	40	100	
79	Flashing Signal, 28-42	97	175	
80/080	Semaphore, 26-35	50	120	
81	Controlling Rheostat, 27-33	5	17	
82/082	Semaphore, 27-35	40	120	
83	Flashing Traffic Signal, 27-42	65	195	
84	Semaphore (O), 27-32	60	100	
84	Semaphore (std), 27-32	43	85	

	PREWAR 1901-1942	Good	Exc
___ 85	Telegraph Pole (std), 29-42	18	30
___ 86	Telegraph Poles, 6 pieces, 29-42	60	135
___ 87	Flashing Crossing Signal, 27-42	168	308
___ 88	Rheostat, 15-27	3	10
___ 88	Direction Controller, 33-42	4	12
___ 89	Flagpole, 23-34	40	88
___ 90	Flagpole, 27-42	40	98
___ 91	Circuit Breaker, 30-42	30	50
___ 92	Signal Tower, 23-27	85	190
___ 92	Floodlight Tower, 31-42*	118	215
___ 93	Water Tower, 31-42	60	110
___ 94	High Tension Tower, 32-42*	150	290
___ 95	Controlling Rheostat, 34-42	5	15
___ 96	Telegraph Post (O), 34-35	15	25
___ 96	Coal Elevator, manual, 38-40	165	220
___ 97	Telegraph Post and Signal Set (O), 34-35	45	75
___ 97	Coal Elevator, 38-42	118	240
___ 98	Coal Bunker, 38-40	107	320
___ 99N	Train Control Block Signal, 36-42	45	180
___ 100	Wooden Gondola (2 7/8"), 01		NRS
___ 100	Bridge Approaches, 2 ramps (std), 20-31	20	40
___ 100	Electric Locomotive (2 7/8"), 03-05*	2900	5200
___ 100	Trolley (std), 10-16		
___	(A) Blue, white windows	1300	2700
___	(B) Blue, cream windows	1850	3600
___	(C) Red, cream windows	1300	2700
___ 101	Bridge, span (104) and 2 approaches (100), 20-31	65	120
___ 101	Summer Trolley (std), 10-13	1300	2700
___ 102	Bridge, 2 spans (104) and 2 approaches (100), 20-31	70	175
___ 103	Bridge (std), 13-16	40	75
___ 103	Bridge, 3 spans (104) and 2 approaches (100), 20-31	60	145
___ 104	Bridge Center Span (std), 20-31	20	45
___ 104	Tunnel, papier mache (std), 09-14	50	135
___ 105	Bridge (std), 11-14	40	70
___ 105	Bridge Approaches, 2 ramps (O), 20-31	50	70
___ 106	Bridge, span (110) and 2 approaches (105), 20-31	30	72
___ 106	Rheostat, 11-14	3	10
___ 107	DC Reducer, 110V, 23-32		NRS
___ 108	Bridge, 2 spans (110) and 2 approaches (105), 20-31	50	90
___ 109	Bridge, 3 spans, (110) and 2 approaches (105), 20-32	50	115
___ 109	Tunnel, papier mache (std), 13-14	30	70
___ 110	Bridge Center Span (O), 20-31	10	25
___ 111	Box of 50 Bulbs, 20-31	55	105
___ 112	Gondola, early (std), 10-12	225	400
___ 112	Gondola, later (std), 12-16	40	65
___ 112	Gondola, latest (std), 16-18	40	65

		Good	Exc	
112	Gondola, Lionel Corp. (std), 18-26	40	65	___
112	Station, 31-35	145	270	___
113	Cattle Car, later (std), 12-16	50	70	___
113	Cattle Car, latest (std), 16-18	50	70	___
113	Cattle Car, Lionel Corp. (std), 18-26	30	55	___
113	Station with light fixtures, 31-34	150	310	___
114	Boxcar, later (std), 12-16	50	90	___
114	Boxcar, latest (std), 16-18	40	70	___
114	Boxcar, Lionel Corp. (std), 18-26	40	70	___
114	Station with light fixtures, 31-34	530	1200	___
115	Station with train control, 35-42*	185	370	___
116	Ballast Car, early and later (std), 10-16	85	115	___
116	Ballast Car, latest (std), 16-18	65	105	___
116	Ballast Car, Lionel Corp. (std), 18-26	55	95	___
116	Station with train control, 35-42*	470	920	___
117	Caboose, early (std), 12	40	75	___
117	Caboose, later (std), 12-16	40	75	___
117	Caboose, latest (std), 16-18	40	75	___
117	Caboose, Lionel Corp. (std), 18-26	30	60	___
117	Station, 36-42	125	235	___
118	Tunnel, metal, 8" long (O), 20-32	23	65	___
118L	Tunnel, metal, lighted, 8" long, 27	20	55	___
119	Tunnel, metal, 12" long, 20-42	25	60	___
119L	Tunnel, metal, lighted, 12" long, 27-33	20	55	___
120	Tunnel, metal, 17" long, 22-27	30	75	___
120L	Tunnel, metal, lighted, 17" long, 27-42	75	140	___
121	Station, lighted (std), 09-16			___
	(A) 14" x 10" x 9"		NRS	___
	(B) 13" x 9" x 13"	150	300	___
121	Station (std), 20-26	75	165	___
121X	Station (std), 17-19	110	255	___
122	Station (std), 20-30	80	190	___
123	Station (std), 20-23	75	210	___
123	Tunnel, paperboard base, 18 1/2" long (O), 33-42	105	235	___
124	Lionel City Station, 20-36*			___
	(A) Tan or gray base, pea green roof	90	240	___
	(B) Pea green base, red roof	200	360	___
125	Lionelville Station, 23-25	80	185	___
125	Track Template, 38	1	5	___
126	Lionelville Station, 23-36	95	205	___
127	Lionel Town Station, 23-36	95	160	___
128	115 Station and 129 Terrace, 35-42*	900	1900	___
128	124 Station and 129 Terrace, 31-34*	900	1900	___
129	Terrace, 28-42*	600	1100	___
130	Tunnel, 26" long (O), 20-36	100	415	___
130L	Tunnel, lighted, 26" long, 27-33	150	450	___

PREWAR 1901-1942		Good	Exc
____ **131**	Corner Display, 24-28	125	295
____ **132**	Corner Grass Plot, 24-28	125	295
____ **133**	Heart-shaped Plot, 24-28	125	295
____ **134**	Lionel City Station with stop, 37-42	173	445
____ **134**	Oval-shaped Plot, 24-28	125	300
____ **135**	Circular Plot, 24-28	125	295
____ **136**	Large Elevation, 24-28		NRS
____ **136**	Lionelville Station with stop, 37-42	85	180
____ **137**	Station with stop, 37-42	97	160
____ **140L**	Tunnel, lighted, 37" long, 27-32	460	1050
____ **150**	Electric Locomotive 0-4-0, early (O), 17	93	180
____ **150**	Electric Locomotive 0-4-0, late (O), 18-25		
____	(A) Brown, brown or olive windows	95	225
____	(B) Maroon, dark olive windows	90	135
____ **152**	Electric Locomotive 0-4-0 (O), 17-27		
____	(A) Dark green	90	135
____	(B) Gray	100	160
____	(C) Mojave	340	680
____	(D) Peacock	340	680
____ **152**	Crossing Gate, 40-42	20	40
____ **153**	Block Signal, 40-42	25	45
____ **153**	Electric Locomotive 0-4-0 (O), 24-25		
____	(A) Dark green	100	160
____	(B) Gray	100	160
____	(C) Mojave	100	160
____ **154**	Electric Locomotive 0-4-0 (O), 17-23	100	180
____ **154**	Highway Signal, 40-42		
____	(A) Black base	25	50
____	(B) Orange base	123	245
____ **155**	Freight Shed, 30-42*		
____	(A) Cream base, terra cotta floor	168	320
____	(B) Ivory base, red floor	180	400
____ **156**	Electric Locomotive 0-4-0 (O), 17-23	400	720
____ **156**	Station Platform, 39-42	78	115
____ **156**	Electric Locomotive 4-4-4 (O), 17-23		
____	(A) Dark green	475	810
____	(B) Maroon	540	890
____	(C) Olive green	600	1050
____	(D) Gray	670	1200
____ **156X**	Electric Locomotive 0-4-0 (O), 23-24		
____	(A) Maroon	330	495
____	(B) Olive green	200	400
____	(C) Gray	530	710
____	(D) Brown	420	600
____ **157**	Hand Truck, 30-32	20	40

		Good	Exc	
158	Electric Locomotive 0-4-0 (O), 19-23			___
	(A) Gray or red windows	75	205	___
	(B) Black	95	250	___
158	Station Set: 136 Station and 2 platforms (156), 40-42	120	280	___
159	Block Actuator, 40	10	30	___
161	Baggage Truck, 30-32*	40	80	___
162	Dump Truck, 30-32*	40	80	___
163	Freight Accessory Set: 2 hand trucks (157), baggage truck (161), and dump truck (162), 30-42*	220	360	___
164	Log Loader, 40-42	120	225	___
165	Magnetic Crane, 40-42	182	240	___
165-22	Scrap Steel with bag, 40-42	50	125	___
165-83	Steel Blanks with bag, 40-42	50	110	___
166	Whistle Controller, 40-42	3	10	___
167	Whistle Controller, 40-42	8	25	___
167X	Whistle Controller (OO), 40-42	5	15	___
168	Magic Electrol Controller, 40-42	25	75	___
169	Controller, 40-42	4	18	___
170	DC Reducer, 220V, 14-38	5	10	___
171	DC to AC Inverter, 110V, 36-42	5	15	___
172	DC to AC Inverter, 229V, 39-42	3	7	___
180	Pullman Car (std), 11-13			___
	(A) Maroon body and roof	145	205	___
	(B) Brown body and roof	145	255	___
180	Pullman Car (std), 13-15	80	160	___
180	Pullman Car (std), 15-18	80	160	___
180	Pullman Car (std), 18-22	80	135	___
181	Combine Car (std), 11-13			___
	(A) Maroon, dark olive doors	145	205	___
	(B) Brown, dark olive doors	145	205	___
	(C) Yellow-orange, orange doors	350	495	___
181	Combine Car (std), 13-15	80	160	___
181	Combine Car (std), 15-18	80	160	___
181	Combine Car (std), 18-22	80	135	___
182	Observation Car (std), 11-13			___
	(A) Maroon, dark olive doors	145	205	___
	(B) Brown, dark olive doors	145	205	___
	(C) Yellow-orange, orange doors	300	495	___
182	Observation Car (std), 13-15	80	160	___
182	Observation Car (std), 15-18	80	160	___
182	Observation Car (std), 18-22	80	135	___
184	Bungalow, illuminated, 23-32*	65	123	___
185	Bungalow, 23-24	50	115	___
186	184 Bungalows, set of 5, 23-32	195	610	___
186	Log Loader Outfit, 40-41	130	340	___
187	185 Bungalows, set of 5, 23-24	170	590	___

PREWAR 1901-1942		Good	Exc
___ 188	Elevator and Car Set, 38-41	115	370
___ 189	Villa, illuminated, 23-32*	117	225
___ 190	Observation Car (std), 08		
___	(A) Dark olive green, nonremovable roof	1150	2600
___	(B) Dark olive green, removable roof	115	205
___	(C) Yellow-orange, removable roof	320	620
___	(D) Orange, removable roof	115	205
___	(E) Mojave, removable roof	345	870
___ 190	Observation Car (std), 11-13	600	900
___ 190	Observation Car (std), 13-15	200	295
___ 190	Observation Car (std), 15-18	200	295
___ 190	Observation Car (std), 18-22	80	135
___ 190	Observation Car (std), 23-26	230	475
___ 191	Villa, illuminated, 23-32*	125	325
___ 192	Illuminated Villa Set: 189, 191, 184 (2), 27-32	400	800
___ 193	Automatic Accessory Set (O), 27-29	150	325
___ 194	Automatic Accessory Set (std), 27-29	100	325
___ 195	Terrace, 27-30	350	740
___ 196	Accessory Set, 27	200	335
___ 200	Electric Express (2 7/8"), 03-05*	4000	6300
___ 200	Trailer, matches No. 2 Trolley (std), 11-16	1200	2400
___ 200	Turntable (std), 28-33*	85	190
___ 201	0-6-0 Locomotive (O), 40-42		
___	(A) 2201B Tender, bell	341	760
___	(B) 2201T Tender, no bell	345	690
___ 202	Summer Trolley (std), 10-13		
___	(A) Electric Rapid Transit	1300	2700
___	(B) Preston St.	3250	4500
___ 203	Armored 0-4-0 (O), 17-21	1100	1800
___ 203	0-6-0 Locomotive (O), 40-42		
___	(A) 2203B Tender, bell	400	495
___	(B) 2203T Tender, no bell	375	550
___ 204	2-4-2 Locomotive (O), 40-42 u		
___	(A) Black	55	105
___	(B) Gunmetal gray	80	165
___ 205	Merchandise Containers, 3 pieces, 30-38*	130	320
___ 206	Sack of Coal, 38-42	5	20
___ 208	Tool Set: 6 assorted tools, 34-42*	65	150
___ 209	Barrels, wood, 6 pieces (O), 34-42		
___	(A) Solid barrels	10	25
___	(B) 2-piece barrels	53	153
___ 209	Barrels, wood, 4 pieces (std), 34-42	10	103
___ 210	Switches, pair (std), 26, 34-42	40	75
___ 211	Flatcar (std), 26-40*	125	195
___ 212	Gondola (std), 26-40*		
___	(A) Gray or light green	100	205

PREWAR 1901-1942		Good	Exc	
	(B) Maroon	75	243	___
213	Cattle Car (std), 26-40*			___
	(A) Mojave, maroon roof	160	365	___
	(B) Terra-cotta, pea green roof	130	290	___
	(C) Cream, maroon roof	300	650	___
214	Boxcar (std), 26-40*			___
	(A) Terra-cotta, dark green roof	195	458	___
	(B) Cream body, orange roof	150	298	___
	(C) Yellow, brown roof	300	495	___
214R	Refrigerator Car (std), 29-40*			___
	(A) Ivory or white, peacock roof	263	495	___
	(B) White, light blue roof	435	790	___
215	Tank Car (std), 26-40*			___
	(A) Pea green	150	215	___
	(B) Ivory	220	360	___
	(C) Aluminum	315	720	___
216	Hopper Car (std), 26-38*			___
	(A) Dark green, brass plates	153	335	___
	(B) Dark green, nickel plates	445	1100	___
217	Caboose (std), 26-40*			___
	(A) Orange, maroon roof	325	510	___
	(B) Red, peacock roof	95	239	___
	(C) Red body and roof, ivory doors	150	320	___
217	Lighting Set, 14-23		NRS	___
218	Dump Car (std), 26-38*	220	365	___
219	Crane Car (std), 26-40*			___
	(A) Peacock, red boom	143	255	___
	(B) Yellow, light green or red boom	185	440	___
	(C) Ivory, light green boom	205	520	___
220	Floodlight Car (std), 31-40*			___
	(A) Terra-cotta base	208	385	___
	(B) Green base	340	485	
220	Switches, pair (std), 26*	25	90	___
222	Switches, pair (std), 26-32	40	100	___
223	Switches, pair (std), 32-42	35	120	___
224/224E	2-6-2 Locomotive (0), 38-42			___
	(A) Black, die-cast 2224 Tender	140	333	___
	(B) Black, plastic 2224 Tender	110	195	___
	(C) Gunmetal, die-cast 2224 Tender	385	950	___
	(D) Gunmetal, sheet-metal 2689 Tender	120	306	___
225	222 Switches and 439 Panel, 29-32	115	260	___
225/225E	2-6-2 Locomotive (0), 38-42			___
	(A) Black, 2235 or 2245 Tender	210	370	___
	(B) Black, 2235 plastic Tender	185	320	___
	(C) Gunmetal, 2225 or 2265 Tender	210	360	___
	(D) Gunmetal, 2235 die-cast Tender	285	1040	___

	PREWAR 1901-1942		Good	Exc
___	**226/226E**	2-6-4 Locomotive (O), 38-41	275	630
___	**227**	0-6-0 Locomotive (O), 39-42		
___		(A) 2227B Tender, bell	600	1576
___		(B) 2227T Tender, no bell	555	1200
___	**228**	0-6-0 Locomotive (O), 39-42		
___		(A) 2228B Tender, bell	600	1250
___		(B) 2228T Tender, no bell	600	1150
___	**229**	2-4-2 Locomotive (O), 39-42		
___		(A) Black or gunmetal, 2689W whistle Tender	155	240
___		(B) Black or gunmetal, 2689T nonwhistling Tender	120	200
___		(C) Black, 2666W whistle Tender	155	280
___		(D) Black, 2666T nonwhistling Tender	120	200
___	**230**	0-6-0 Locomotive (O), 39-42	1100	2050
___	**231**	0-6-0 Locomotive (O), 39	1000	1800
___	**232**	0-6-0 Locomotive (O), 40-42	1000	1800
___	**233**	0-6-0 Locomotive (O), 40-42	1000	1800
___	**238**	4-4-2 Locomotive (O), 39-40 u	430	710
___	**238E**	4-4-2 Locomotive (O), 36-38		
___		(A) 265W or 2225W whistle Tender	280	345
___		(B) 265 or 2225T nonwhistling Tender	275	360
___	**248**	Electric Locomotive 0-4-0 (O), 27-32	150	240
___	**249/249E**	2-4-2 Locomotive (O), 36-39		
___		(A) Gunmetal, 265T nonwhistling or 265W whistle Tender	100	270
___		(B) Black, 265W whistle Tender	110	210
___	**250**	Electric Locomotive 0-4-0, early (O), 26	125	220
___	**250**	Electric Locomotive 0-4-0, late (O), 34		
___		(A) Yellow-orange body, terra-cotta frame	145	245
___		(B) Terra-cotta body, maroon frame	160	270
___	**250E**	4-4-2 Hiawatha Locomotive (O), 35-42*	400	1100
___	**250W**	Hiawatha Tender (O), 35-42*	125	250
___	**251**	Electric Locomotive 0-4-0 (O), 25-32		
___		(A) Gray body, red windows	190	340
___		(B) Red body, ivory stripe	215	410
___		(C) Red body, no ivory stripe	200	380
___	**251E**	Electric Locomotive 0-4-0 (O), 27-32		
___		(A) Red body, ivory stripe	225	425
___		(B) Red body, no ivory stripe	215	395
___		(C) Gray, red trim	195	513
___	**252**	Electric Locomotive 0-4-0 (O), 26-32		
___		(A) Peacock or olive green	87	187
___		(B) Terra-cotta or yellow-orange	113	560
___	**252E**	Electric Locomotive 0-4-0 (O), 33-35		
___		(A) Terra-cotta	145	250
___		(B) Yellow-orange	125	205
___	**253**	Electric Locomotive 0-4-0 (O), 24-32		
___		(A) Maroon	180	430

		Good	Exc	
	(B) Dark green	105	250	___
	(C) Mojave	105	235	___
	(D) Terra-cotta	180	430	___
	(E) Peacock	95	195	___
	(F) Red	210	475	___
253E	Electric Locomotive 0-4-0 (O), 31-36			___
	(A) Green	150	205	___
	(B) Terra-cotta	190	305	___
254	Electric Locomotive 0-4-0 (O), 24-32	240	340	___
254E	Electric Locomotive 0-4-0 (O), 27-34	180	283	___
255E	2-4-2 Locomotive (O), 35-36	485	1000	___
256	Electric Locomotive 0-4-4-0 (O), 24-30*			___
	(A) Rubber-stamped lettering	470	1175	___
	(B) No outline around Lionel	425	770	___
	(C) Lionel Lines and No. 256 on brass	388	1050	___
257	2-4-0 Locomotive (O), 30-35 u			___
	(A) Black tender	145	300	___
	(B) Black crackle-finish tender	240	435	___
258	2-4-0 Locomotive, early (O), 30-35 u			___
	(A) 4-wheel 257 Tender	85	170	___
	(B) 8-wheel 258 Tender	100	195	___
258	2-4-2 Locomotive, late (O), 41 u			___
	(A) Black	60	100	___
	(B) Gunmetal	85	135	___
259	2-4-2 Locomotive (O), 32	70	148	___
259E	2-4-2 Locomotive (O), 33-42	80	165	___
259T	Tender	15	30	___
260E	2-4-2 Locomotive (O), 30-35*			___
	(A) Black body, green or black frame	385	475	___
	(B) Dark gunmetal body and frame	440	640	___
261	2-4-2 Locomotive (O), 31	125	210	___
261E	2-4-2 Locomotive (O), 35	190	285	___
262	2-4-2 Locomotive (O), 31-32	185	320	___
262E	2-4-2 Locomotive (O), 33-36			___
	(A) Gloss black, copper and brass trim	110	210	___
	(B) Satin black, nickel trim	125	260	___
263E	2-4-2 Locomotive (O), 36-39*			___
	(A) Gunmetal gray	315	610	___
	(B) 2-tone blue, from Blue Comet	415	950	___
263W	Tender, gunmetal	99	200	___
264E	2-4-2 Locomotive (O), 35-36			___
	(A) Red, Red Comet	135	295	___
	(B) Black	220	380	___
265E	2-4-2 Locomotive (O), 35-40			___
	(A) Black or gunmetal	170	330	___
	(B) Light blue, Blue Streak	460	800	___

			Good	Exc
___ 265T	Tender		15	28
___ 267E/W	Set: 616, 617 (2), 618, 35-41		275	560
___ 270	Bridge, 10" long (O), 31-42		27	85
___ 270	Lighting Set, 15-23			NRS
___ 271	270 Bridges, set of 2, 31-33, 35-40		65	150
___ 271	Lighting Set, 15-23			NRS
___ 272	270 Bridges, set of 3, 31-33, 35-40		60	165
___ 280	Bridge, 14" long (std), 31-42		50	115
___ 281	280 Bridges, set of 2, 31-33, 35-40		90	205
___ 282	280 Bridges, set of 3, 31-33, 35-40		105	265
___ 289E	2-4-2 Locomotive (O), 37 u		120	305
___ 300	Electric Trolley Car (2 7/8"), 01-05		2000	3600
___ 300	Hellgate Bridge (std), 28-42*			
	(A) Cream towers, green truss		800	1350
	(B) Ivory towers, aluminum truss		765	1600
___ 303	Summer Trolley, 10-13		1500	3150
___ 308	Signs, set of 5 (O), 40-42		30	70
___ 309	Electric Trolley Trailer (2 7/8"), 01-05		2500	4050
___ 309	Pullman Car (std), 26-39			
___	(A) Maroon body and roof, mojave windows		100	160
___	(B) Mojave body and roof, maroon windows		100	160
___	(C) Light brown body, dark brown roof		120	190
___	(D) Medium blue body, dark blue roof		170	280
___	(E) Apple green body, dark green roof		170	280
___	(F) Pale blue body, silver roof		100	185
___	(G) Maroon body, terra-cotta roof		130	195
___ 310	Rails and Ties, complete section (2 7/8"), 01-02			NRS
___ 310	Baggage Car (std), 26-39			
___	(A) Maroon body and roof, mojave windows		100	160
___	(B) Mojave body and roof, maroon windows		85	160
___	(C) Light brown body, dark brown roof		115	185
___	(D) Medium blue body, dark blue roof		170	280
___	(E) Apple green body, dark green roof		170	280
___	(F) Pale blue body, silver roof		100	175
___ 312	Observation Car (std), 24-39			
___	(A) Maroon body and roof, mojave windows		100	160
___	(B) Mojave body and roof, maroon windows		85	160
___	(C) Light brown body, dark brown roof		120	185
___	(D) Medium blue body, dark blue roof		170	280
___	(E) Apple green body, dark green roof		170	280
___	(F) Pale blue body, silver roof		100	175
___	(G) Maroon body, terra-cotta roof		130	195
___ 313	Bascule Bridge (O), 40-42			
___	(A) Silver bridge		235	500
___	(B) Gray bridge		280	590
___ 314	Girder Bridge (O), 40-42		20	40

PREWAR 1901-1942		Good	Exc	
315	Illuminated Trestle Bridge (O), 40-42	30	80	___
316	Trestle Bridge (O), 40-42	25	50	___
318	Electric Locomotive 0-4-0 (std), 24-32			___
	(A) Gray, dark gray, or mojave	150	300	___
	(B) Pea green	150	250	___
	(C) State brown	250	395	___
318E	Electric Locomotive 0-4-0, 26-35			___
	(A) Gray, mojave, or pea green	150	250	___
	(B) State brown	275	440	___
	(C) Black	550	1275	___
319	Pullman Car (std), 24-27	105	175	___
320	Baggage Car (std), 25-27	100	175	___
320	Switch and Signal (2 7/8"), 02-05		NRS	___
322	Observation Car (std), 24-27, 29-30 u	100	175	___
330	90-degree Crossing (2 7/8"), 02-05		NRS	___
332	Baggage Car (std), 26-33			___
	(A) Red body and roof, cream doors	80	120	___
	(B) Peacock body and roof, orange doors	75	115	___
	(C) Gray body and roof, maroon doors	75	115	___
	(D) Olive green body and roof, red doors	90	145	___
	(E) State brown body, dark brown roof	190	430	___
337	Pullman Car (std), 25-32			___
	(A) Red body and roof, cream doors	95	190	___
	(B) Mojave body and roof, maroon doors	95	190	___
	(C) Olive green body and roof, red doors	105	225	___
	(D) Olive green body and roof, maroon doors	95	190	___
	(E) Pea green body and roof, cream doors	210	500	___
338	Observation Car (std), 25-32			___
	(A) Red body and roof, cream doors	95	190	___
	(B) Mojave body and roof, maroon doors	95	190	___
	(C) Olive green body and roof, red doors	105	225	___
	(D) Olive green body and roof, maroon doors	95	190	___
339	Pullman Car (std), 25-33			___
	(A) Peacock body and roof, orange doors	55	90	___
	(B) Gray body and roof, maroon doors	55	100	___
	(C) State brown body, dark brown roof	135	380	___
	(D) Peacock body, dark green roof	75	130	___
	(E) Mojave body, maroon roof and doors	145	230	___
340	Suspension Bridge (2 7/8"), 02-05*		NRS	___
341	Observation Car (std), 25-33			___
	(A) Peacock body and roof, orange doors	50	70	___
	(B) Gray body and roof, maroon doors	50	70	___
	(C) State brown body, dark brown roof	75	160	___
	(D) Peacock body, dark green roof	65	95	___
	(E) Mojave body, maroon roof and doors	135	165	___
350	Track Bumper (2 7/8"), 02-05	225	550	___

	PREWAR 1901-1942	Good	Exc
___ 380	Elevated Pillars (2 7/8"), 04-05*	30	70
___ 380	Electric Locomotive 0-4-0 (std), 23-27	310	440
___ 380E	Electric Locomotive 0-4-0 (std), 26-29		
___	(A) Mojave	445	630
___	(B) Maroon	295	400
___	(C) Dark green	370	460
___ 381	Electric Locomotive 4-4-4 (std), 28-29*	1600	2100
___ 381E	Electric Locomotive 4-4-4 (std), 28-36*		
___	(A) State green, apple green subframe	1112	2385
___	(B) State green, red subframe	1900	3250
___ 381U	Electric Locomotive 4-4-4 Kit (std), 28-29	1600	4100
___ 384	2-4-0 Locomotive (std), 30-32*	415	730
___ 384E	2-4-0 Locomotive (std), 30-32*	425	650
___ 385E	2-4-2 Locomotive (std), 33-39*	370	670
___ 390	2-4-2 Locomotive (std), 29*	460	820
___ 390E	2-4-2 Locomotive (std), 29-31*		
___	(A) Black, with or without orange stripe	460	690
___	(B) 2-tone blue, cream-orange stripe	650	1050
___	(C) 2-tone green, orange or green stripe	990	2050
___ 392E	4-4-2 Locomotive (std), 32-39*		
___	(A) Black, 384 Tender	750	1250
___	(B) Black, large 12-wheel tender	1050	1850
___	(C) Gunmetal gray	1000	1800
___ 400	Express Trail Car (2 7/8"), 03-05*	3500	5850
___ 400E	4-4-4 Locomotive (std), 31-39*		
___	(A) Black	1400	2150
___	(B) Blue	1550	2350
___	(C) Gunmetal or light blue	1650	2800
___	(D) Black crackle finish	1600	3500
___ 402	Electric Locomotive 0-4-4-0 (std), 23-27	408	570
___ 402E	Electric Locomotive 0-4-4-0 (std), 26-29	345	550
___ 404	Summer Trolley (std), 10		NRS
___ 408E	Electric Locomotive 0-4-4-0 (std), 27-36*		
___	(A) Apple green or mojave, red pilots	770	1370
___	(B) State brown, brown pilots	2000	3000
___	(C) State green, red pilots	2000	3800
___ 412	California Pullman Car (std), 29-35*		
___	(A) Light green body, dark green roof	590	1750
___	(B) Light brown body, dark brown roof	735	2100
___ 413	Colorado Pullman Car (std), 29-35*		
___	(A) Light green body, dark green roof	590	1750
___	(B) Light brown body, dark brown roof	620	2100
___ 414	Illinois Pullman Car (std), 29-35*		
___	(A) Light green body, dark green roof	590	1750
___	(B) Light brown body, dark brown roof	620	2050

		Good	Exc	
416	New York Observation Car (std), 29-35*			___
	(A) Light green body, dark green roof	590	1750	___
	(B) Light brown body, dark brown roof	620	2100	___
418	Pullman Car (std), 23-32*	225	320	___
419	Combination (std), 23-32*	190	280	___
420	Faye Pullman Car (std), 30-40*			___
	(A) Brass trim	485	900	___
	(B) Nickel trim	500	1200	___
421	Westphal Pullman Car (std), 30-40*			___
	(A) Brass trim	500	900	___
	(B) Nickel trim	500	1200	___
422	Tempel Observation Car (std), 30-40*			___
	(A) Brass trim	485	900	___
	(B) Nickel trim	500	1200	___
424	Liberty Bell Pullman Car (std), 31-40*			___
	(A) Brass trim	350	530	___
	(B) Nickel trim	385	650	___
425	Stephen Girard Pullman Car (std), 31-40*			___
	(A) Brass trim	350	530	___
	(B) Nickel trim	385	650	___
426	Coral Isle Observation Car (std), 31-40*			___
	(A) Brass trim	350	530	___
	(B) Nickel trim	385	650	___
428	Pullman Car (std), 26-30*			___
	(A) Dark green body and roof	250	385	___
	(B) Orange body and roof, apple green windows	390	890	___
429	Combine Car (std), 26-30*			___
	(A) Dark green body and roof	250	385	___
	(B) Orange body and roof, apple green windows	390	890	___
430	Observation Car (std), 26-30*			___
	(A) Dark green body and roof	250	385	___
	(B) Orange body and roof, apple green windows	390	890	___
431	Diner (std), 27-32*			___
	(A) Mojave body, screw-mounted roof	350	540	___
	(B) Mojave body, hinged roof	465	720	___
	(C) Dark green body, orange windows	410	720	___
	(D) Orange body, apple green windows	410	720	___
	(E) Apple green body, red windows	410	720	___
435	Power Station, 26-38*	168	400	___
436	Power Station, 26-37*			___
	(A) Power Station plate	135	265	___
	(B) Edison Service plate	270	610	___
437	Switch Signal Tower, 26-37*	190	430	___
438	Signal Tower, 27-39*			___
	(A) Mojave base, orange house	185	325	___
	(B) Black base, white house	325	640	___

			Good	Exc
___	**439**	Panel Board, 28-42*	85	145
___	**440/0440**	Signal Bridge, 32-35*	180	470
___	**440C**	Panel Board, 32-42	90	145
___	**441**	Weighing Station (std), 32-36	495	1325
___	**442**	Landscaped Diner, 38-42	117	215
___	**444**	Roundhouse (std), 32-35*	1350	2850
___	**444-18**	Roundhouse Clip, 33		NRS
___	**450**	Electric Locomotive 0-4-0, Macy's (O), 30 u		
___		(A) Red, black frame	295	700
___		(B) Apple green, dark green frame	415	880
___	**450**	Set: 450, matching 605, 606 (2), 30 u	750	1800
___	**490**	Observation Car (std), 23-32*	190	255
___	**500**	Electric Derrick Car (2 7/8"), 03-04*	5000	6750
___	**511**	Flatcar (std), 27-40		
___		(A) Dark green	65	95
___		(B) Medium green	75	165
___	**512**	Gondola (std), 27-39		
___		(A) Peacock	35	60
___		(B) Light green	50	95
___	**513**	Cattle Car (std), 27-38		
___		(A) Olive green, orange roof	70	195
___		(B) Orange, pea green roof	60	110
___		(C) Cream, maroon roof	80	250
___	**514**	Boxcar (std), 29-40		
___		(A) Cream, orange roof	90	303
___		(B) Yellow, brown roof	115	285
___	**514**	Refrigerator Car, ivory or white, peacock roof, (std), 27-28	240	400
___	**514R**	Refrigerator Car (std), 29-40		
___		(A) Ivory, peacock roof	140	190
___		(B) White, light blue roof	350	545
___	**515**	Tank Car (std), 27-40		
___		(A) Terra-cotta	90	145
___		(B) Ivory	105	230
___		(C) Aluminum	90	325
___		(D) Orange, red Shell decal	340	750
___	**516**	Hopper Car (std), 28-40		
___		(A) Red	170	280
___		(B) Red, rubber-stamped data	200	300
___		(C) Light red, nickel trim	200	325
___	**517**	Caboose (std), 27-40		
___		(A) Pea green body, red roof	50	133
___		(B) Red body and roof	105	155
___		(C) Red body, black roof, orange windows	355	640
___	**520**	Floodlight Car (std), 31-40		
___		(A) Terra-cotta base	110	210
___		(B) Green base	110	240

Number	Description	Good	Exc	
529	Pullman Car (O), 26-32			___
	(A) Olive green body and roof	25	45	___
	(B) Terra-cotta body and roof	25	60	
530	Observation Car (O), 26-32			___
	(A) Olive green body and roof	25	45	___
	(B) Terra-cotta body and roof	25	60	
550	Miniature Figures, boxed (std), 32-36*	175	455	___
551	Engineer (std), 32	25	45	___
552	Conductor (std), 32	20	40	___
553	Porter with stool (std), 32	25	50	___
554	Male Passenger (std), 32	25	45	___
555	Female Passenger (std), 32	25	45	___
556	Red Cap with suitcase (std), 32	25	65	___
600	Derrick Trailer (2 7/8"), 03-04*	5000	8550	___
600	Pullman Car, early (O), 15-23			___
	(A) Dark green	65	170	___
	(B) Maroon or brown	45	85	___
600	Pullman Car, late (O), 33-42			___
	(A) Light red or gray, red roof	50	90	___
	(B) Light blue, aluminum roof	70	120	___
	(C) Light blue body-aluminum roof	70	120	___
601	Observation Car, late (O), 33-42			___
	(A) Light red body and roof	50	85	___
	(B) Light gray, red roof	50	90	___
	(C) Light blue body, aluminum roof	70	120	___
601	Pullman Car, early (O), 15-23	50	70	___
602	Lionel Lines Baggage Car, late (O), 33-42			___
	(A) Light red or gray, red roof	60	110	___
	(B) Light blue, aluminum roof	90	150	___
602	NYC Baggage Car (O), 15-23	33	45	___
602	Observation Car (O), 22 u	30	45	___
603	Pullman Car, early (O), 22 u	40	70	___
603	Pullman Car, later (O), 20-25	20	45	___
603	Pullman Car, latest (O), 31-36			___
	(A) Light red body and roof	45	85	___
	(B) Red body, black roof	35	60	___
	(C) Stephen Girard green body, dark green roof	35	60	___
	(D) Maroon body and roof, Macy Special	60	125	___
604	Observation Car, later (O), 20-25	35	60	___
604	Observation Car, latest (O), 31-36			___
	(A) Light red body and roof	45	85	___
	(B) Red body, black roof	35	60	___
	(C) Yellow-orange body, terra-cotta roof	35	60	___
	(D) Stephen Girard green body, dark green roof	35	60	___
	(E) Maroon body and roof	70	150	___

| --- | --- | --- | --- |
___ 605	Pullman Car (O), 25-32		
___	(A) Gray, Lionel Lines	85	170
___	(B) Gray, Illinois Central	85	170
___	(C) Red, Lionel Lines	170	255
___	(D) Red, Illinois Central	255	340
___	(E) Orange, Lionel Lines	170	255
___	(F) Orange, Illinois Central	300	430
___	(G) Olive green, Lionel Lines	255	340
___ 606	Observation Car (O), 25-32		
___	(A) Gray, Lionel Lines	130	215
___	(B) Gray, Illinois Central	90	170
___	(C) Red, Lionel Lines	170	255
___	(D) Red, Illinois Central	255	340
___	(E) Orange, Lionel Lines	170	255
___	(F) Orange, Illinois Central	170	255
___	(G) Olive green, Lionel Lines	255	340
___ 607	Pullman Car (O), 26-27		
___	(A) Peacock, Lionel Lines	50	70
___	(B) Peacock, Illinois Central	75	115
___	(C) 2-tone green, Lionel Lines	50	75
___	(D) Red, Lionel Lines	75	110
___ 608	Observation Car (O), 26-37		
___	(A) Peacock, Lionel Lines	50	70
___	(B) Peacock, Illinois Central	75	115
___	(C) 2-tone green, Lionel Lines	50	75
___	(D) Red, Lionel Lines	75	110
___ 609	Pullman Car (O), 37	60	85
___ 610	Pullman Car, early (O), 15-25		
___	(A) Dark green body and roof	50	65
___	(B) Maroon body and roof	60	95
___	(C) Mojave body and roof	60	95
___ 610	Pullman Car, late (O), 26-30		
___	(A) Olive green body and roof	65	80
___	(B) Mojave body and roof	55	80
___	(C) Terra-cotta body, maroon roof	100	155
___	(D) Pea green body and roof	70	115
___	(E) Light blue body, aluminum roof	130	260
___	(F) Light red body, aluminum-painted roof	100	155
___ 611	Observation Car (O), 37	55	80
___ 612	Observation Car, early (O), 15-25		
___	(A) Dark green body and roof	40	60
___	(B) Maroon body and roof	70	90
___	(C) Mojave body and roof	70	90
___ 612	Observation Car, late (O), 26-30		
___	(A) Olive green body and roof	55	80
___	(B) Mojave body and roof	55	80

		Good	Exc	
	(C) Terra-cotta body, maroon roof	100	155	___
	(D) Pea green body and roof	70	115	___
	(E) Light blue body, aluminum roof	130	260	___
	(F) Light red body, aluminum-painted roof	100	155	___
613	Pullman Car (O), 31-40*			___
	(A) Terra-cotta body, maroon/terra-cotta roof	85	195	___
	(B) Light red body, light red/aluminum roof	175	350	___
	(C) Blue, two-tone blue roof	115	225	___
614	Observation Car (O), 31-40*			___
	(A) Terra-cotta body, maroon/terra-cotta roof	100	190	___
	(B) Light red body, light red/aluminum roof	175	350	___
	(C) Blue, two-tone blue roof	115	225	___
615	Baggage Car (O), 33-40*	150	260	___
616E/W	Diesel only (O), 35-41	90	215	___
616E/W	Set: 616, 617 (2), 618	225	570	___
617	Coach (O), 35-41			___
	(A) Blue and white	55	85	___
	(B) Chrome, gunmetal skirts	55	85	___
	(C) Chrome, chrome skirts	55	85	___
	(D) Silver-painted	55	85	___
618	Observation Car (O), 35-41			___
	(A) Blue and white	55	85	___
	(B) Chrome, gunmetal skirts	55	85	___
	(C) Chrome, chrome skirts	55	85	___
	(D) Silver-painted	55	85	___
619	Combine Car (O), 36-38			___
	(A) Blue, white windows band	100	205	___
	(B) Chrome, chrome skirts	100	205	___
620	Floodlight Car (O), 37-42	39	85	___
629	Pullman Car (O), 24-32			___
	(A) Dark green body and roof	25	40	___
	(B) Orange body and roof	25	40	___
	(C) Red body and roof	20	35	___
	(D) Light red body and roof	30	55	___
630	Observation Car, 24-32			___
	(A) Dark green body and roof	25	40	___
	(B) Orange body and roof	25	40	___
	(C) Red body and roof	20	35	___
	(D) Light red body and roof	30	55	___
636W	Diesel only (O), 36-39	90	175	___
636W	Set: 636W, 637 (2), 638, 36-39	375	640	___
637	Coach (O), 36-39	70	105	___
638	Observation Car (O), 36-39	70	105	___
651	Flatcar (O), 35-40	30	65	___
652	Gondola (O), 35-40	28	55	___
653	Hopper Car (O), 34-40	35	65	___

PREWAR 1901-1942		Good	Exc
___ 654	Tank Car (O), 34-42		
___	(A) Orange or aluminum	35	60
___	(B) Gray	40	75
___ 655	Boxcar (O), 34-42		
___	(A) Cream, maroon roof	35	60
___	(B) Cream, tuscan roof	45	75
___ 656	Cattle Car (O), 35-40		
___	(A) Light gray, vermilion roof	40	100
___	(B) Burnt orange, tuscan roof	70	125
___ 657	Caboose (O), 34-42		
___	(A) Red body and roof	20	35
___	(B) Red body, tuscan roof	25	40
___ 659	Dump Car (O), 35-42	40	90
___ 700	Electric Locomotive 0-4-0 (O), 15-16	360	690
___ 700E	4-6-4 NYC Hudson "5344," scale (O), 37-42*	1400	2950
___ 700K	4-6-4 Locomotive, unbuilt gray primer (O), 38-42	4400	5950
___ 701	0-6-0 PRR Locomotive "8976", 41	900	2100
___ 701	Electric Locomotive 0-4-0 (O), 15-16	376	660
___ 702	Baggage Car (O), 17-21	115	305
___ 703	Electric Locomotive 4-4-4 (O), 15-16	711	1194
___ 706	Electric Locomotive 0-4-0 (O), 15-16	375	630
___ 708	0-6-0 PRR Locomotive "8976" (O), 39-42*	1450	2850
___ 710	Pullman Car (O), 24-34		
___	(A) Red, Lionel Lines	200	300
___	(B) Orange, Lionel Lines	150	225
___	(C) Orange, New York Central	175	225
___	(D) Orange, Illinois Central	300	450
___	(E) 2-tone blue, Lionel Lines	300	415
___	(F) Orange, New York Central	200	260
___ 711	Remote Control Switches, pair (072), 35-42	83	236
___ 712	Observation Car (O), 24-34		
___	(A) Red, Lionel Lines	185	355
___	(B) Orange, Lionel Lines	140	265
___	(C) Orange, New York Central	160	310
___	(D) Orange, Illinois Central	315	530
___	(E) 2-tone blue, Lionel Lines	280	485
___ 714	Boxcar (O), 40-42*	350	610
___ 714K	Boxcar, unbuilt (O), 40-42	220	480
___ 715	Tank Car (O), 40-42*		
___	(A) SEPS 8124 decal	340	610
___	(B) SUNX 715 decal	435	880
___ 715K	Tank Car, unbuilt (O), 40-42	250	530
___ 716	Hopper Car (O), 40-42*	290	400
___ 716K	Hopper Car, unbuilt (O), 40-42	350	730
___ 717	Caboose (O), 40-42*	340	510
___ 717K	Caboose, unbuilt (O), 40-42	275	590

720	90-degree Crossing (072), 35-42	20	40	___
721	Manual Switches, pair (072), 35-42	50	105	___
730	90-degree Crossing (072), 35-42	20	40	___
731	Remote Control Switches, pair, T-rail (072), 35-42	80	135	___
751E/W	Set: 752, 753 (2), 754 (O), 34-41*	640	1050	___
752E	Diesel only (O), 34-41*			___
	(A) Yellow and brown	170	355	___
	(B) Aluminum	145	340	___
753	Coach (O), 36-41			___
	(A) Yellow and brown	85	185	___
	(B) Aluminum	75	180	___
754	Observation Car (O), 36-41			___
	(A) Yellow and brown	80	185	___
	(B) Aluminum	75	180	___
760	Curved Track, 16 pieces, (072), 35-42	40	80	___
761	Curved Track (072), 34-42	1	2	___
762	Straight Track (072), 34-42	1	2	___
762S	Insulated Straight Track (072), 34-42	2	5	___
763E	4-6-4 Locomotive (O), 37-42			___
	(A) Gunmetal, 263 or 2263W Tender	1000	3163	___
	(B) Gunmetal, 2226X or 2226WX Tender	1150	2950	___
	(C) Black, 2226WX Tender	965	2725	___
771	Curved Track, T-rail (072), 35-42	3	10	___
772	Straight Track, T-rail (072), 35-42	5	25	___
772S	Insulated Straight Track, T-rail (072), 35-42	15	30	___
773	Fishplate Set, 50 plates (072), 36-42	15	30	___
782	Hiawatha Combine Car (O), 35-41*	230	380	___
783	Hiawatha Coach (O), 35-41*	140	290	___
784	Hiawatha Observation Car (O), 35-41*	205	445	___
792	Rail Chief Combine Car (O), 37-41*	215	580	___
793	Rail Chief Coach (O), 37-41*	290	800	___
794	Rail Chief Observation Car (O), 37-41*	250	800	___
800	Boxcar (2 7/8"), 04-05*	2500	4050	___
800	Boxcar (O), 15-26			___
	(A) Light orange body, brown-maroon roof	45	70	___
	(B) Orange body and roof, PRR	25	45	___
801	Caboose (O), 15-26	30	50	___
802	Stock Car (O), 15-26	40	60	___
803	Hopper Car, early (O), 23-28	25	55	___
803	Hopper Car, late (O), 29-34	30	55	___
804	Tank Car (O), 23-28	11	45	___
805	Boxcar (O), 27-34			___
	(A) Pea green, terra-cotta roof	35	55	___
	(B) Pea green, maroon roof	45	115	___
	(C) Orange, maroon roof	45	95	___

			Good	Exc
___	**806**	Stock Car (0), 27-34		
___		(A) Pea green, terra-cotta roof	40	75
___		(B) Orange, various color roofs	35	50
___	**807**	Caboose (0), 27-40		
___		(A) Peacock body, dark green roof	20	35
___		(B) Red body, peacock roof	20	93
___		(C) Light red body and roof	20	40
___	**809**	Dump Car (0), 31-41		
___		(A) Orange bin	40	136
___		(B) Green bin	40	85
___	**810**	Crane Car (0), 30-42		
___		(A) Terra-cotta cab, maroon roof	170	270
___		(B) Cream cab, vermilion roof	130	205
___	**811**	Flatcar (0), 26-40		
___		(A) Maroon	40	83
___		(B) Aluminum	50	100
___	**812**	Gondola (0), 26-42	40	70
___	**812T**	Tool Set: pick, shovel, hammer, 30-41	40	105
___	**813**	Stock Car (0), 26-42		
___		(A) Orange body, pea green roof	76	145
___		(B) Orange body, maroon roof	55	135
___		(C) Cream body, maroon roof	100	225
___		(D) Tuscan body and roof	800	1600
___	**814**	Boxcar (0), 26-42		
___		(A) Cream, orange roof	50	145
___		(B) Cream, maroon roof	118	140
___		(C) Yellow, brown roof	95	120
___	**814R**	Refrigerator Car (0), 29-42		
___		(A) Ivory, peacock roof	100	213
___		(B) White, light blue roof	103	230
___		(C) Flat white, brown roof	600	900
___	**815**	Tank Car (0), 26-42		
___		(A) Pea green, maroon frame	250	510
___		(B) Pea green, black frame	70	155
___		(C) Aluminum, black frame	50	100
___		(D) Orange-yellow, black frame	150	255
___	**816**	Hopper Car (0), 27-42		
___		(A) Olive green	85	155
___		(B) Red body	65	140
___		(C) Black body	370	680
___	**817**	Caboose (0), 26-42		
___		(A) Peacock body, dark green roof	45	70
___		(B) Red body, peacock roof	45	80
___		(C) Light red body and roof	45	80
___	**820**	Boxcar (0), 15-26		
___		(A) Orange, Illinois Central	40	80

		Good	Exc	
	(B) Orange, Union Pacific	50	105	___
820	Floodlight Car (0), 31-42			___
	(A) Terra-cotta	100	180	___
	(B) Green	100	175	___
	(C) Light green	105	180	___
821	Stock Car (0), 15-16, 25-26	45	85	___
822	Caboose (0), 15-26	35	65	___
831	Flatcar (0), 27-34	20	130	___
840	Industrial Power Station, 28-40*	1138	3050	___
900	Ammunition Car (0), 17-21	120	340	___
900	Box Trail Car (2 7/8"), 04-05*	2000	3600	___
901	Gondola (0), 19-27	25	50	___
902	Gondola (0), 27-34	25	45	___
910	Grove of Trees, 32-42	70	239	___
911	Country Estate, 32-42	195	720	___
912	Suburban Home	263	620	___
913	Landscaped Bungalow, 40-42	168	348	___
914	Park Landscape, 32-35	90	205	___
915	Tunnel, 65" or 60" long, 32-33, 35	160	435	___
916	Tunnel, 29¼" long, 35	95	180	___
917	Scenic Hillside, 34" x 15", 32-36	90	205	___
918	Scenic Hillside, 30" x 10", 32-36	90	205	___
919	Park Grass, cloth bag, 32-42	10	20	___
920	Village, 32-33	600	1600	___
921	Scenic Park, 3 pieces, 32-33	980	2600	___
921C	Park Center, 32-33	400	1050	___
922	Terrace, 32-36	90	290	___
923	Tunnel, 40¼" long, 33-42	125	225	___
924	Tunnel, 30" long (072), 35-42	50	135	___
925	Lubricant, 35-42	25	120	___
927	Flag Plot, 37-42	70	148	___
1000	Passenger Car (2 7/8"), 05*	4500	6750	___
1000	Trolley Trailer (std), 10-16	1400	2250	___
1010	Electric Locomotive 0-4-0, Winner Lines (0), 31-32	90	160	___
1010	Interurban Trailer (std), 10-16	1000	1800	___
1011	Pullman Car, Winner Lines (0), 31-32	45	75	___
1012	Station, 32	40	70	___
1015	0-4-0 Locomotive (0), 31-32	100	205	___
1017	Winner Station, 33	25	70	___
1019	Observation Car (0), 31-32	50	70	___
1020	Baggage Car (0), 31-32	65	110	___
1021	90-degree Crossover (027), 32-42	1	5	___
1022	Tunnel, 18¾" long (0), 35-42	15	30	___
1023	Tunnel, 19" long, 34-42	20	40	___
1024	Switches, pair (027), 37-42	5	33	___
1025	Bumper (027), 40-42	15	25	___

			Good	Exc
___	1027	Transformer Station, 34	50	115
___	1028	Transformer, 40 watts, 39	3	10
___	1029	Transformer, 25 watts, 36	5	20
___	1030	Electric Locomotive 0-4-0 (O), 32	75	135
___	1030	Transformer, 40 watts, 35-38	6	25
___	1035	0-4-0 Locomotive (O), 32	75	115
___	1037	Transformer, 40 watts, 40-42	7	25
___	1038	Transformer, 30 watts, 40	2	5
___	1039	Transformer, 35 watts, 37-40	7	20
___	1040	Transformer, 60 watts, 37-39	10	30
___	1041	Transformer, 60 watts, 39-42	15	30
___	1045	Watchman, 38-42	30	65
___	1050	Passenger Car Trailer (2 7/8"), 05*	5000	7200
___	1100	Summer Trolley Trailer (std), 10-13		NRS
___	1100	Mickey Mouse Handcar, 35-37*		
___		(A) Red base	425	640
___		(B) Apple green base, orange shoes	500	880
___		(C) Orange base	600	1225
___	1103	Peter Rabbit Handcar (O), 35-37*	330	820
___	1105	Santa Claus Handcar (O), 35-35*		
___		(A) Red base	660	1050
___		(B) Green base	720	1200
___	1107	Transformer Station, 33	25	70
___	1107	Donald Duck Handcar (O), 36-37*		
___		(A) White dog house, red roof	475	1200
___		(B) White dog house, green roof	450	1100
___		(C) Orange dog house, green roof	640	1850
___	1121	Switches, pair (O27), 37-42	15	35
___	1506L	0-4-0 Locomotive (O), 33-34	95	125
___	1506M	0-4-0 Locomotive (O), 35	250	430
___	1508	0-4-0 Commodore Vanderbilt with 1509 Mickey Mouse stoker Tender, 35	420	690
___	1511	0-4-0 Locomotive (O), 36-37	110	160
___	1512	Gondola (O), 31-33, 36-37	25	33
___	1514	Boxcar (O), 31-37	25	40
___	1515	Tank Car (O), 33-37	25	40
___	1517	Caboose (O), 31-37	25	40
___	1518	Mickey Mouse Circus Dining Car (O), 35	120	260
___	1519	Mickey Mouse Band Car (O), 35	120	260
___	1520	Mickey Mouse Circus Car (O), 35	120	260
___	1536	Mickey Mouse Circus Set: 1508, 1509, 1518, 1519, 1520, 35	770	1350
___	1550	Switches, for windup trains, pair, 33-37	2	5
___	1555	90-degree Crossover, for windup trains, 33-37	1	2
___	1560	Station, 33-37	15	35
___	1569	Accessory Set, 8 pieces, 33-37	35	70

PREWAR 1901-1942		Good	Exc	
1588	0-4-0 Locomotive (O), 36-37	150	250	___
1630	Pullman Car (O), 38-42			___
	(A) Aluminum windows	35	70	___
	(B) Light gray windows	45	80	___
1631	Observation Car (O), 38-42			___
	(A) Aluminum windows	35	70	___
	(B) Light gray windows	45	80	___
1651E	Electric Locomotive 0-4-0 (O), 33	130	240	___
1661E	2-4-0 Locomotive (O), 33	75	160	___
1662	0-4-0 Locomotive (O27), 40-42	154	365	___
1663	0-4-0 Locomotive (O27), 40-42	200	385	___
1664/E	2-4-2 Locomotive (O27), 38-42			___
	(A) Gunmetal	60	100	___
	(B) Black	60	95	___
1666/E	2-6-2 Locomotive (O27), 38-42			___
	(A) Gunmetal	115	170	___
	(B) Black	95	145	___
1668/E	2-6-2 Locomotive (O27), 37-41			___
	(A) Gunmetal	75	115	___
	(B) Black	75	130	___
1673	Coach (O), 36-37			___
	(A) Aluminum windows	35	75	___
	(B) Light gray windows	45	90	___
1674	Pullman Car (O), 36-37	35	75	___
1675	Observation Car (O), 36-37	30	70	___
1677	Gondola (O), 33-35, 39-42			___
	(A) Light blue, Ives	40	60	___
	(B) Blue or red, Lionel	20	40	___
1679	Boxcar (O), 33-42			___
	(A) Cream, Ives	25	40	___
	(B) Cream, Lionel	25	40	___
	(C) Cream or yellow, Baby Ruth	20	40	___
1680	Tank Car (O), 33-42			___
	(A) Aluminum, Ives Tank Lines	60	95	___
	(B) Aluminum, no Ives lettering	11	35	___
	(C) Orange, Shell Oil	15	37	___
1681	2-4-0 Locomotive (O), 34-35			___
	(A) Black, red frame	55	120	___
	(B) Red, red frame	110	145	___
1681E	2-4-0 Locomotive (O), 34-35			___
	(A) Black, red frame	65	130	___
	(B) Red, red frame	130	165	___
1682	Caboose (O), 33-42			___
	(A) Vermilion, Ives	35	70	___
	(B) Red or tuscan, Lionel	6	40	___

PREWAR 1901-1942		Good	Exc
___ 1684	2-4-2 Locomotive (027), 41-42		
___	(A) Black	45	70
___	(B) Gunmetal	45	70
___ 1685	Coach (O), 33-37 u		
___	(A) Gray, maroon roof	240	495
___	(B) Red, maroon roof	170	335
___	(C) Blue, silver roof	170	315
___ 1686	Baggage Car (O), 33-37 u		
___	(A) Gray, maroon roof	240	495
___	(B) Red, maroon roof	170	335
___	(C) Blue, silver roof	170	315
___ 1687	Observation Car (O), 33-37 u		
___	(A) Gray, maroon roof	170	315
___	(B) Red, maroon roof	180	315
___	(C) Blue, silver roof	170	315
___ 1688/E	2-4-2 Locomotive (027), 36-46	50	125
___ 1689E	2-4-2 Locomotive (027), 36-37		
___	(A) Gunmetal	75	115
___	(B) Black	60	100
___ 1689T	Tender, black, nonwhistling	15	38
___ 1690	Pullman Car (O), 33-40	35	60
___ 1691	Observation Car (O), 33-40	35	60
___ 1692	Pullman Car (027), 39 u	45	70
___ 1693	Observation Car (027), 39 u	45	70
___ 1700E	Diesel, power unit only (027), 35-37	45	70
___ 1700E	Set: 1700, 1701 (2), 1702, 35-37 u		
___	(A) Aluminum and light red	140	250
___	(B) Chrome and light red	140	250
___	(C) Orange and gray	155	285
___ 1701	Coach (027), 35-37		
___	(A) Chrome sides and roof	20	45
___	(B) Silver sides and roof	30	55
___	(C) Orange and gray	75	150
___ 1702	Observation Car (027), 35-37		
___	(A) Chrome sides and roof	20	45
___	(B) Silver sides and roof	30	55
___	(C) Orange and gray	75	150
___ 1703	Observation Car, hooked coupler, 35-37 u	50	110
___ 1717	Gondola (O), 33-40 u	30	50
___ 1717X	Gondola (O), 40 u	25	50
___ 1719	Boxcar (O), 33-40 u	30	50
___ 1719X	Boxcar (O), 41-42 u	30	50
___ 1722	Caboose (O), 33-42 u	25	50
___ 1722X	Caboose (O), 39-40 u	25	40
___ 1766	Pullman Car (std), 34-40*		
___	(A) Terra-cotta, maroon roof, brass trim	300	650

| --- | --- | --- | --- |
	(B) Red, maroon roof, nickel trim	300	540
1767	Baggage Car (std), 34-40*		
	(A) Terra-cotta, maroon roof, brass trim	295	850
	(B) Red, maroon roof, nickel trim	295	700
1768	Observation Car (std), 34-40*		
	(A) Terra-cotta, maroon roof, brass trim	300	650
	(B) Red, maroon roof, nickel trim	300	540
1811	Pullman Car (O), 33-37	35	70
1812	Observation Car (O), 33-37	30	65
1813	Baggage Car (O), 33-37	60	135
1816/W	Diesel (O), 35-37	100	240
1817	Coach (O), 35-37	25	50
1818	Observation Car (O), 35-37	25	50
1835E	2-4-2 Locomotive (std), 34-39	470	730
1910	Electric Locomotive 0-6-0, early (std), 10-11	920	1550
1910	Electric Locomotive 0-6-0, late (std), 12	550	1350
1910	Pullman Car (std), 09-10 u	860	1800
1911	Electric Locomotive 0-4-0, early (std), 10-12	860	1700
1911	Electric Locomotive 0-4-0, late (std), 13	700	1100
1911	Electric Locomotive 0-4-4-0 Special (std), 11-12	860	2500
1912	Electric Locomotive 0-4-4-0 (std), 10-12*		
	(A) New York, New Haven & Hartford	1550	3200
	(B) New York Central Lines	1300	2700
1912	Electric Locomotive 0-4-4-0 Special (std), 11*	2500	4500
2200	Summer Trolley Trailer (std), 10-13	1100	2250
2203B	Tender	40	99
2224W	Tender	55	137
2225W	Tender	30	60
2228B	Tender	140	280
2235W	Tender	25	50
2600	Pullman Car (O), 38-42	80	155
2601	Observation Car (O), 38-42	60	115
2602	Baggage Car (O), 38-42	90	185
2613	Pullman Car (O), 38-42*		
	(A) Blue, 2-tone blue roof	100	300
	(B) State green, 2-tone green roof	200	440
2614	Observation Car (O), 38-42*		
	(A) Blue, 2-tone blue roof	100	300
	(B) State green, 2-tone green roof	200	440
2615	Baggage Car (O), 38-42*		
	(A) Blue, 2-tone blue roof	115	300
	(B) State green, 2-tone green roof	200	420
2620	Floodlight Car (O), 38-42	65	100
2623	Pullman Car (O), 41-42		
	(A) Irvington	175	335
	(B) Manhattan	220	310

	PREWAR 1901-1942		Good	Exc
___	2624	Pullman Car (O), 41-42	750	1700
___	2630	Pullman Car (O), 38-42	30	70
___	2631	Observation Car (O), 38-42	30	70
___	2640	Pullman Car, illuminated (O), 38-42		
___		(A) Light blue, aluminum roof	30	120
___		(B) State green, dark green roof	30	70
___	2641	Observation Car, illuminated (O), 38-42		
___		(A) Light blue, aluminum roof	30	100
___		(B) State green, dark green roof	30	70
___	2642	Pullman Car (O), 41-42	30	70
___	2643	Observation Car (O), 41-42	30	65
___	2651	Flatcar (O), 38-42	30	80
___	2652	Gondola (O), 38-41	25	65
___	2653	Hopper Car (O), 38-42		
___		(A) Stephen Girard green	35	70
___		(B) Black	60	130
___	2654	Tank Car (O), 38-42		
___		(A) Aluminum, Sunoco	35	60
___		(B) Orange, Shell	35	60
___		(C) Light gray, Sunoco	40	70
___	2655	Boxcar (O), 38-42		
___		(A) Cream, maroon roof	35	65
___		(B) Cream, tuscan roof	40	70
___	2656	Stock Car (O), 38-41		
___		(A) Light gray, red roof	45	75
___		(B) Burnt orange, tuscan roof	39	67
___	2657	Caboose (O), 40-41	30	45
___	2657X	Caboose (O), 40-41	25	40
___	2659	Dump Car (O), 38-41	40	70
___	2660	Crane Car (O), 38-42	85	214
___	2672	Caboose (O27), 41-42	20	50
___	2677	Gondola (O27), 39-41	25	40
___	2679	Boxcar (O27), 38-42	15	30
___	2680	Tank Car (O27), 38-42		
___		(A) Aluminum, Sunoco	15	40
___		(B) Orange, Shell	15	40
___	2682	Caboose (O27), 38-42	6	30
___	2682X	Caboose (O27), 38-42	20	35
___	2689T	Tender	15	35
___	2689W	Tender	35	50
___	2717	Gondola (O), 38-42 u	20	40
___	2719	Boxcar (O), 38-42 u	30	50
___	2722	Caboose (O), 38-42 u	25	50
___	2755	Tank Car (O), 41-42	76	180
___	2757	Caboose (O), 41-42	25	53
___	2757X	Caboose (O), 41-42	25	40

PREWAR 1901-1942		Good	Exc	
2758	Automobile Boxcar (O), 41-42	35	60	___
2810	Crane Car (O), 38-42	145	210	___
2811	Flatcar (O), 38-42	50	95	___
2812	Gondola (O), 38-42			___
	(A) Green	40	85	___
	(B) Dark orange	45	95	___
2813	Stock Car (O), 38-42	120	225	___
2814	Boxcar (O), 38-42			___
	(A) Cream, maroon roof	85	150	___
	(B) Orange, brown roof, rubber-stamped lettering	200	700	___
2814R	Refrigerator Car (O), 38-42			___
	(A) White, light blue roof, nickel plates	138	260	___
	(B) White, brown roof, no plates	375	660	___
2815	Tank Car (O), 38-42			___
	(A) Aluminum	85	165	___
	(B) Orange	113	215	___
2816	Hopper Car (O), 35-42			___
	(A) Red	100	190	___
	(B) Black	110	220	___
2817	Caboose (O), 36-42			___
	(A) Light red body and roof	78	140	___
	(B) Flat red body, tuscan roof	115	180	___
2820	Floodlight Car (O), 38-42			___
	(A) Stamped nickel searchlights	110	205	___
	(B) Gray die-cast searchlights	120	260	___
2954	Boxcar (O), 40-42*	145	425	___
2955	Sunoco Tank Car (O), 40-42*			___
	(A) Shell decal	225	500	___
	(B) Sunoco decal	340	690	___
2956	Hopper Car (O), 40-42*	218	400	___
2957	Caboose (O), 40-42*	110	326	___
3300	Summer Trolley Trailer (std), 10-13	1400	2250	___
3651	Operating Lumber Car (O), 39-42	25	55	___
3652	Operating Gondola (O), 39-42	27	75	___
3659	Operating Dump Car (O), 39-42	20	40	___
3811	Operating Lumber Car (O), 39-42	35	88	___
3814	Operating Merchandise Car (O), 39-42	85	195	___
3859	Operating Dump Car (O), 38-42	45	90	___

Other Transformers and Motors

		Good	Exc	
A	Miniature Motor, 4	50	95	___
A	Transformer, 40, 60 watts, 21-37	10	41	___
B	New Departure Motor, 06-16	75	135	___
B	Transformer, 50, 75 watts, 16-38	7	25	___
C	New Departure Motor, 06-16	100	180	___
D	New Departure Motor, 06-14	100	180	___

PREWAR 1901-1942		Good	Exc
E	New Departure Motor, 06-14	100	180
F	New Departure Motor, 06-14	100	180
G	Fan Motor, battery-operated, 06-14	100	180
K	Transformer, 150, 200 watts, 13-38	18	73
L	Transformer, 50, 75 watts, 13-16, 33-38	10	25
M	Peerless Motor, battery-operated, 15-20	30	80
N	Transformer, 50 watts, 41-42	7	20
Q	Transformer, 50 watts, 14-15	10	21
Q	Transformer, 75 watts, 38-42	12	28
R	Peerless Motor, battery-operated, reversing, 15-20	30	75
R	Transformer, 100 watts, 38-42	20	45
S	Transformer, 50 watts, 14-17	13	28
T	Transformer, 75, 100, 150 watts, 14-28	8	30
U	Transformer, Aladdin, 32-33	5	15
V	Transformer, 150 watts, 39-42	40	75
W	Transformer, 75 watts, 32-33	10	35
Y	Peerless Motor, battery-operated, 3-speed, 15-20	40	80
Z	Transformer, 250 watts, 39-42	64	118

Track, Lockons, and Contactors

		Good	Exc
	O Straight		1
	O Curve		1
	072 Straight	1	3
	072 Curve	1	3
	027 Straight		1
	027 Curve		1
	Standard Straight	1	3
	Standard Curve	1	2
	Standard Insulated Straight, 33-42	2	4
	Standard Insulated Curve, 33-42	1	2
	O Gauge Lockon	0	4
	Standard Gauge Lockon		1
	UTC Lockon		1
	145C Contactor	3	9
	153C Contactor	3	7
	Track Clips, dozen (O), 37	5	10

		Good	Exc	
5C	Test Set	768	1523	___
5D	Test Set, 54	1238	2386	___
5E	Electronic Set Tester, 46-49	1189	2945	___
5F	Test Set	907	1905	___
011-11	Fiber Pins, dozen (O), 46-50	1	3	___
011-43	Insulating Pins, dozen (O), 61	1	3	___
20	90-degree Crossover (O), 45-61	2	6	___
020X	45-degree Crossover (O), 46-59	3	8	___
22	Remote Control Switches, pair (O), 45-69	20	46	___
022-500	Adapter Set (O), 57-61	2	7	___
022A	Remote Control Switches, pair (O), 47	22	55	___
022C-1	Switch Controller	6	11	___
25	Bumper (O), 46-47	5	15	___
26	Bumper, 48-50			___
	(A) Red, 49-50	5	13	___
	(B) Gray, 48	16	50	___
027C-1	Track Clips, box of 12 (O27), 47, 49	4	13	___
027C-1	Track Clips, box of 50 (O27)	13	39	___
30	Water Tower, 47-50			___
	(A) Single-walled	19	66	___
	(B) Double-walled	28	82	___
31	Curved Track (Super O), 57-66	1	4	___
31-5	Track Ground Pins, Dozen (Super O), 57-60	2	5	___
31-7	Power Blade Connection, dozen (Super O), 57-60	7	11	___
31-15	Ground Rail Pin, dozen (Super O), 57-66	3	11	___
31-45	Power Blade Connection, dozen (Super O), 61-66	4	10	___
32	Straight Track (Super O), 57-66	2	5	___
32-10	Insulating Pin, dozen (Super O), 57-60	4	11	___
32-20	Power Blade Insulator, dozen (Super O), 57-60	3	10	___
32-25	Insulating Pin (Super O), 57-61		1	___
32-30	Ground Pin (Super O), 57-61		1	___
32-31	Power Pin, Dozen (Super O), 57-61	1	10	___
32-32	Insulating Pin, Dozen (Super O), 57-61	1	6	___
32-33	Ground Pin, Dozen (Super O), 57-61	1	8	___
32-34	Power Pin (Super O), 57-61	1	8	___
32-35	Insulating Pin, dozen (Super O to O27), 57-61	2	5	___
32-45	Power Blade Insulators, dozen (Super O), 61-66	3	11	___
32-55	Insulating Pins, dozen (Super O), 61-66	3	10	___
33	Half Curved Track (Super O), 57-66	2	5	___
34	Half Straight Track (Super O), 57-66	3	6	___
35	Boulevard Lamp, 45-49	12	32	___
36	Operating Car Remote Control Set (Super O), 57-66	10	31	___
37	Uncoupling Track Set (Super O), 57-66	10	18	___

| --- | --- | --- | --- |
___ 38	Operating Water Tower, 46-47	80	247
___ 38-85	Accessory Adapter Tracks, pair (Super O), 57-61	7	33
___ 39	Operating Set (Super O), 57	4	8
___ 39-5	Operating Set (Super O), 57-58	4	9
___ 39-6	Operating Set (Super O), 57-58	4	9
___ 39-10	Operating Set (Super O), 58	4	8
___ 39-15	Operating Set with blade (Super O), 57-58	4	8
___ 39-20	Operating Set (Super O), 57-58	4	8
___ 39-25	Operating Set (Super O), 61-66	8	16
___ 39-35	Operating Set (Super O), 59	8	24
___ 40	Hookup Wire, 50-51, 53-63		
___	(A) Single reel, orange or gray, with tape	7	41
___	(B) 8 sealed reels in dealer box	100	465
___ 40-25	Conductor Wire with envelope, 56-59	9	38
___ 40-50	Cable Reel with envelope, 60-61	13	51
___ 41	U.S. Army Switcher, 55-57		
___	(A) Unpainted black body	51	108
___	(B) Black-painted body	307	942
___ 042/42	Manual Switches, pair (O), 46-59	11	37
___ 42	Picatinny Arsenal Switcher, 57	74	264
___ 43	Power Track (Super O), 59-66	5	18
___ 44	U.S. Army Mobile Launcher, 59-62	58	183
___ 44-80	Missiles, 59-60	10	29
___ 45	U.S. Marines Mobile Launcher, 60-62	78	249
___ 45	Automatic Gateman, 46-49	13	41
___ 45N	Automatic Gateman, 45	13	39
___ 48	Insulated Straight Track (Super O), 57-66	4	11
___ 49	Insulated Curved Track (Super O), 57-66	4	9
___ 50	Section Gang Car, 54-64		
___	(A) Gray bumpers, rotating blue man and fixed olive men, center horn, 54	226	798
___	(B) Blue bumpers, rotating olive man and fixed blue men, center horn	27	57
___	(C) Blue bumpers, rotating olive man and fixed blue men, off-center horn	22	46
___ 51	Navy Yard Switcher, 56-57	61	176
___ 52	Fire Car, 58-61	71	166
___ 53	Rio Grande Snowplow, 57-60		
___	(A) Backward "a" in Rio Grande	66	200
___	(B) Correctly printed "a"	155	451
___ 54	Ballast Tamper, 58-61, 66, 68-69	55	150
___ 55	PRR Tie-Jector Car, 57-61		
___	(A) Ventilation slot behind motorman	48	141
___	(B) No slot behind motorman	39	104
___ 55-150	Ties, 24 pieces, 57-60	15	29
___ 56	Lamp Post, 46-49	17	39
___ 56	M&StL Mine Transport, 58	125	342

		Good	Exc	
57	AEC Switcher, 59-60	148	449	___
58	GN Snowplow, 59-61	122	367	___
58	Lamp Post, 46-50	14	64	___
59	Minuteman Switcher, 62-63	167	473	___
60	Lionelville Rapid Transit Trolley, 55-58			___
	(A) Metal motorman silhouettes	82	235	___
	(B) No motorman silhouettes	38	95	___
61	Ground Lockon (Super O), 57-66	2	6	___
61-25	Super O Ground clips, dozen, with dealer envelope	8	18	___
62	Power Lockon (Super O), 57-66	2	6	___
64	Highway Lamp Post, 45-49	12	57	___
65	Handcar, 62-66			___
	(A) Light yellow	72	262	___
	(B) Dark yellow	64	228	___
68	Executive Inspection Car, 58-61	63	148	___
69	Maintenance Car, 60-62	88	198	___
70	Yard Light, 49-50	10	34	___
71	Lamp Post, 49-59	7	13	___
75	Goose Neck Lamps, set of 2, 61-63	10	30	___
76	Boulevard Street Lamps, set of 3, 59-66, 68-69	15	103	___
80	Controller, 60	7	20	___
88	Controller, 46-60	7	24	___
89	Flagpole, 56-58	15	76	___
90	Controller, 55-66			___
	(A) Metal clip	6	13	___
	(B) No metal clip	6	9	___
91	Circuit Breaker, 57-60	10	28	___
92	Circuit Breaker, 59-66, 68-69	8	16	___
93	Water Tower, 46-49	17	84	___
96C	Controller, 45-54	4	8	___
97	Coal Elevator, 46-50	45	132	___
108	Trestle Set, 12 black piers	9	21	___
109	Partial Trestle Set, 61	5	16	___
110	Graduated Trestle Set, 22 or 24 piers, 55-69	8	22	___
110-75	Graduated Trestle Set with 110-78 envelope	10	22	___
111	Elevated Trestle Set, 10 A piers, 56-69	9	15	___
111-100	Elevated Trestle Piers, set of 2, 60-63	11	29	___
112	Remote Control Switches, pair (Super O), 57-66	40	170	___
114	Newsstand with horn, 57-59	33	82	___
115	Passenger Station, 46-49	107	275	___
118	Newsstand with whistle, 57-58	35	94	___
119	Landscaped Tunnel, 57-58	200	400	___
120	90-degree Crossing (Super O), 57-66	5	14	___
121	Landscaped Tunnel, 59-66	200	400	___
122	Lamp Assortment, 48-52	336	579	___
123	Lamp Assortment, 55-59	250	443	___

			Good	Exc
___ 123-60	Lamp Assortment, 60-63		34	198
___ 125	Whistle Shack, 50-55			
___	(A) Gray base		15	47
___	(B) Green base		21	48
___ 128	Animated Newsstand, 57-60		51	84
___ 130	60-degree Crossing (Super O), 57-66		7	17
___ 131	Curved Tunnel, 59-66		255	360
___ 132	Passenger Station, 49-55		26	142
___ 133	Passenger Station, 57, 61-62, 66		19	41
___ 138	Water Tower, 53-57		21	121
___ 140	Automatic Banjo Signal, 54-66		13	32
___ 142	Manual Switches, pair (Super O), 57-66		23	54
___ 145	Automatic Gateman, 50-66			
___	(A) Red roof		13	31
___	(B) Maroon roof		10	29
___ 145C	Contactor, 50-60		4	24
___ 147	Whistle Controller, 61-66		2	6
___ 148	Dwarf Trackside Signal, 57-60		22	107
___ 148-100	Controller (SPDT switch), 57-60		5	19
___ 150	Telegraph Pole Set, 47-50		20	38
___ 151	Automatic Semaphore, 47-69			
___	(A) Green base, yellow blade, 47		22	47
___	(B) Black base, yellow blade, 47		13	36
___	(C) Black base, red blade, 47		177	418
___	(D) Green base, yellow blade with raised lenses		21	49
___ 152	Automatic Crossing Gate, 45-49		10	55
___ 153	Automatic Block Control Signal, 45-59		14	26
___ 153C	Contactor		3	10
___ 154	Automatic Highway Signal, 45-69		11	25
___ 154C	Contactor		4	7
___ 155	Blinking Light Signal with bell, 55-57		21	120
___ 156	Station Platform, 46-49		32	95
___ 156-5	Station Platform Fence with envelope		26	55
___ 157	Station Platform, 52-59			
___	(A) Maroon base		15	35
___	(B) Red base		27	112
___ 157-23	Station Platform Fence with envelope		16	40
___ 160	Unloading Bin, 52-57			
___	(A) Black plastic, long		2	7
___	(B) Black metal, short		42	73
___	(C) Multicolor Bakelite, short		6	28
___	(D) Black Bakelite, short		3	9
___ 161	Mail Pickup Set, 61-63		33	105
___ 163	Single Target Block Signal, 61-69		14	37
___ 164	Log Loader, 46-50		47	139
___ 164-64	Log Set, 5 pieces, separate sale w/box, 52-58		25	63

		Good	Exc	
167	Whistle Controller, 45-50, 52-57	3	8	___
175	Rocket Launcher, 58-60	51	203	___
175-50	Extra Rocket, 59-60	10	21	___
182	Magnetic Crane, 46-49	117	239	___
182-22	Steel Scrap with bag, 46-49	46	121	___
192	Operating Control Tower, 59-60	89	243	___
193	Industrial Water Tower, 53-55			___
	(A) Red	43	95	___
	(B) Black, 53	63	182	___
195	Floodlight Tower, 57-69			___
	(A) Medium tan base, rubber-stamped lettering	25	82	___
	(B) All other variations	23	65	___
195-75	Floodlight Extension, 8-bulb (with box), 58-60	25	68	___
196	Smoke Pellets, 46-47	30	115	___
197	Rotating Radar Antenna, 57-59			___
	(A) Orange platform	42	95	___
	(B) Gray platform	27	107	___
197-75	Separate Sale Radar Head with box	55	140	___
199	Microwave Relay Tower, 58-59	24	54	___
202	UP Alco Diesel A Unit, 57	27	68	___
204	Santa Fe Alco Diesel AA Units, 57	70	380	___
205	Missouri Pacific Alco Diesel AA Units, 57-58			___
	(A) Pilot without support	55	119	___
	(B) Pilot with painted metal support	71	168	___
206	Artificial Coal, large bag, 46-68	12	20	___
207	Artificial Coal, small bag, 46-48	6	13	___
208	Santa Fe Alco Diesel AA Units, 58-59	69	312	___
209	New Haven Alco Diesel AA Units, 58	191	620	___
209	Wood Barrels, set of 6, 46-50	9	15	___
210	Texas Special Alco Diesel AA Units, 58	58	132	___
211	Texas Special Alco Diesel AA Units, 62-66	60	239	___
212	Santa Fe Alco Diesel AA Units, 64-66			___
	(A) With Built Date 8-57, 64-65	43	112	___
	(B) Without Built Date, 66	61	145	___
212T	Santa Fe Alco Diesel Dummy A Unit, 64-66			___
	(A) With Built Date 8-57, 64-65	21	46	___
	(B) Without Built Date, 66	30	64	___
212	USMC Alco Diesel A Unit, 58-59	58	135	___
212T	USMC Diesel Dummy A Unit, 58 u	375	1148	___
213	M&StL Alco Diesel AA Units, 64	74	184	___
214	Plate Girder Bridge, 53-69	9	30	___
215	Santa Fe Alco Diesel Units, 65 u			___
	(A) AB Units	63	130	___
	(B) AA Units	79	157	___
215	Santa Fe Alco Diesel Powered A Unit, 65 u	25	54	___
216	Burlington Alco Diesel A Unit, 58	118	280	___

		Good	Exc
___ 216	M&StL Alco Diesel AA Units (213T dummy A unit), 64 u	67	179
___ 217	B&M Alco Diesel AB Units, 59	83	199
___ 217C	B&M Alco Diesel B Unit, 59	30	70
___ 218	Santa Fe Alco Diesel Units, 59-63		
___	(A) AA Units	75	471
___	(B) AB Units	64	210
___	(C) AA Units, solid nose decal	71	200
___ 218C	Santa Fe Alco B Unit, 61-63	39	87
___ 219	Missouri Pacific Alco Diesel AA Units, 59 u	69	154
___ 220	Santa Fe Alco Diesel Units, 60-61		
___	(A) A Unit	43	100
___	(B) AA Units	66	170
___ 221	2-6-4 Locomotive, 221W Tender, 46-47		
___	(A) Gray body, black drivers	65	141
___	(B) Black body, nickel-rimmed black drivers, 47	70	151
___	(C) Gray body, cast-aluminum drivers, 46	114	243
___ 221	Rio Grande Alco Diesel A Unit, 63-64	32	61
___ 221	Santa Fe Alco Diesel A Unit, 63-64 u	254	653
___ 221	U.S. Marine Corps Alco Diesel A Unit, 63-64 u	199	625
___ 221T	Tender (no whistle)		
___	(A) Gray	18	37
___	(B) Black	19	43
___ 221W	Whistle Tender	26	60
___ 222	Rio Grande Alco Diesel A Unit, 62	30	72
___ 223	Santa Fe Alco Diesel AB Units, 63	64	190
___ 224	2-6-2 Locomotive, 2466W or 2466WX Tender, 45-46		
___	(A) Blackened handrails, 45	117	236
___	(B) Silver handrails	72	142
___ 224	US Navy Alco Diesel B Unit, 60	43	80
___ 224	U.S. Navy Alco Diesel AB Units, 60	129	237
___ 225	C&O Alco Diesel A Unit, 60	35	71
___ 226	B&M Alco Diesel AB Units, 60 u	81	181
___ 226C	B&M Alco Diesel B Unit, 60 u	31	73
___ 227	CN Alco Diesel A Unit, 60 u	59	130
___ 228	CN Alco Diesel A Unit, 61 u	63	134
___ 229	M&StL Alco Diesel Units, 61-62		
___	(A) A Unit, 61	43	131
___	(B) AB Units, 62	78	186
___ 229C	M&StL Alco Diesel B Unit, 61-62	30	93
___ 230	C&O Alco Diesel A Unit, 61	38	172
___ 231	Rock Island Alco Diesel A Unit, 61-63		
___	(A) With red stripe	43	101
___	(B) Without red stripe	142	404
___ 232	New Haven Alco Diesel A Unit, 62	51	129
___ 233	2-4-2 Scout Locomotive, 233W Tender, 61-62	30	66
___ 233W	Whistle Tender	19	39

		Good	Exc	
234T	Lionel Lines Tender	8	22	___
234T	Pennsylvania Tender	17	42	___
234W	Lionel Whistle Tender	22	47	___
234W	Pennsylvania Whistle Tender	36	92	___
235	2-4-2 Scout Locomotive, 1130T or 1060T Tender, 60 u	68	212	___
236	2-4-2 Scout Locomotive, 61-62			___
	(A) 1050T Slope-back Tender	15	39	___
	(B) 1130T Tender	15	37	___
237	2-4-2 Scout Locomotive, 63-66			___
	(A) 1060T Tender	25	56	___
	(B) 234W Tender	31	78	___
238	2-4-2 Scout Locomotive, stripe on running board, 234W Tender, 63-64	49	132	___
239	2-4-2 Scout Locomotive, 234W Tender, 65-66	37	77	___
240	2-4-2 Scout Locomotive, 242T Tender, 64 u	83	251	___
241	2-4-2 Scout Locomotive, 65 u			___
	(A) Narrow stripe, 234W Tender	32	77	___
	(B) Wide stripe, 1130T Tender	25	60	___
242	2-4-2 Scout Locomotive, 1060T or 1062T Tender, 62-66	24	47	___
243	2-4-2 Scout Locomotive, 243W Tender, 60	34	78	___
243W	Whistle Tender	18	45	___
244	2-4-2 Scout Locomotive, 244T or 1130T Tender, 60-61	20	48	___
244T	Tender	8	29	___
245	2-4-2 Scout Locomotive, 1130T Tender, 59 u	25	63	___
246	2-4-2 Scout Locomotive, 244T or 1130T Tender, 59-61	16	93	___
247	2-4-2 Scout Locomotive, 247T Tender, 59			___
	(A) Closed pilot	19	62	___
	(B) Open pilot	34	128	___
247T	B&O Tender	15	50	___
248	2-4-2 Scout Locomotive, 1130T Tender, 58	25	65	___
42	IMCO PS-2 2-bay Covered Hopper, 95		50	___
249	2-4-2 Scout Locomotive, 250T Tender, 58	20	48	___
250	2-4-2 Scout Locomotive, 250T Tender, 57	21	51	___
250T	Tender	10	21	___
251	2-4-2 Scout Locomotive, 66 u			___
	(A) 1062T Slope-back Tender	73	181	___
	(B) 250T-type Tender	73	179	___
252	Crossing Gate, 50-62	8	21	___
253	Block Control Signal, 56-59	12	38	___
256	Illuminated Freight Station, 50-53			___
	(A) Dark green roof	23	42	___
	(B) Light green roof	44	104	___
257	Freight Station with diesel horn, 56-57			___
	(A) Maroon base	30	66	___
	(B) Brown base	40	87	___
	(C) Maroon or brown base, light green roof	60	129	___

|---|---|---|---|
___ 260	Bumper, 51-69		
___	(A) Die-cast	6	13
___	(B) Black plastic	13	36
___ 262	Highway Crossing Gate, 62-69	14	35
___ 264	Operating Forklift Platform, 57-60	63	208
___ 282	Portal Gantry Crane, 54-57	78	175
___ 282R	Portal Gantry Crane, 56-57	65	161
___ 299	Code Transmitter Beacon Set, 61-63	34	89
___ 308	Railroad Sign Set, die-cast, 45-49	20	48
___ 309	Yard Sign Set, plastic, 50-59	7	18
___ 309-100	Yard Sign Set in Plastic Packaging, 66-69 u		67
___ 310	Billboard Set, 50-68	9	33
___ 313	Bascule Bridge, 46-49	77	276
___ 313-82	Fiber Pins, dozen, 46-60	1	2
___ 313-121	Fiber Pins, dozen, 61	1	3
___ 314	Scale Model Girder Bridge, 45-50	10	26
___ 315	Illuminated Trestle Bridge, 46-48	31	85
___ 316	Trestle Bridge, 49	16	34
___ 317	Trestle Bridge, 50-56	14	32
___ 321	Trestle Bridge, 58-64	15	37
___ 321-100	Trestle Bridge	22	50
___ 332	Arch-Under Trestle Bridge, 59-66	16	35
___ 334	Operating Dispatching Board, 57-60	66	158
___ 342	Culvert Loader, 56-58	48	162
___ 345	Culvert Unloader, 57-59	48	415
___ 346	Culvert Unloader, manual, 65 u	46	179
___ 347	Cannon Firing Range Set, 64 u	301	743
___ 348	Culvert Unloader, manual, 66-69	59	140
___ 350	Engine Transfer Table, 57-60	112	225
___ 350-50	Transfer Table Extension, 57-60	55	139
___ 352	Ice Depot with 6352 Ice Car, 55-57	75	137
___ 353	Trackside Control Signal, 60-61	11	29
___ 356	Operating Freight Station, 52-57		
___	(A) Dark green roof, 52-57	36	81
___	(B) Light green roof, 57	63	186
___ 362	Barrel Loader, 52-57		
___	(A) Gold lettering	23	119
___	(B) Red lettering	94	298
___ 362-78	Wood Barrels, 6 pieces, 52-57		
___	(A) Brown	8	21
___	(B) Red	96	225
___ 364	Conveyor Lumber Loader, 48-57	25	69
___ 364C	On/Off Switch, 48-64	6	10
___ 365	Dispatching Station, 58-59	37	92
___ 365-35	Set of Delivery Carts, 52	10	32
___ 375	Turntable, 62-64	61	168

		Good	Exc
390C	Switch, double-pole, double-throw, 60-64	6	16 ___
394	Rotary Beacon, 49-53		___
	(A) Steel tower, red platform	17	42 ___
	(B) Steel tower, green platform	34	81 ___
	(C) Aluminum tower, platform, and base	15	36 ___
	(D) Aluminum tower, red steel base	31	141 ___
	(E) Steel tower, red platform, stick-on nameplate	32	77 ___
395	Floodlight Tower, 49-56		___
	(A) Light green, silver, or unpainted aluminum	12	43 ___
	(B) Red	33	102 ___
	(C) Dark green	81	243 ___
	(D) Yellow	43	107 ___
397	Diesel-type Coal Loader, 48-57		___
	(A) Yellow generator, 48	125	543 ___
	(B) Blue generator, 49-57	31	107 ___
400	B&O Passenger Rail Diesel Car, 56-58	71	211 ___
404	B&O Baggage-Mail Rail Diesel Car, 57-58	121	276 ___
410	Billboard Blinker, 56-58	18	51 ___
413	Countdown Control Panel, 62	17	87 ___
415	Diesel Fueling Station, 55-57	44	123 ___
419	Heliport Control Tower, 62	138	335 ___
443	Missile Launching Platform with ammo dump, 60-62	27	62 ___
445	Switch Tower, lighted, 52-57	21	58 ___
448	Missile Firing Range Set, 61-63	47	234 ___
450	Operating Signal Bridge, 52-58	25	53 ___
450L	Signal Light Head, 52-58	12	38 ___
452	Overhead Gantry Signal, 61-63	40	143 ___
455	Operating Oil Derrick, 50-54		___
	(A) Dark green tower, green top	49	269 ___
	(B) Dark green tower, red top	59	248 ___
	(C) Apple green tower, red top	94	287 ___
456	Coal Ramp with 3456 Hopper, 50-55		___
	(A) Light gray ramp	42	108 ___
	(B) Dark gray ramp	64	143 ___
456C	Coal Ramp Controller	11	25 ___
460	Piggyback Transportation Set, 55-57		___
	(A) Metal stick-on signs on lift truck	52	101 ___
	(B) Rubber-stamped lettering on lift truck	60	122 ___
460P	Piggyback Platform, 55-57	18	46 ___
460-150	Separate Sale 2 Trailers in Box	48	222 ___
461	Platform with truck and trailer, 66	62	169 ___
462	Derrick Platform Set, 61-62	119	337 ___
464	Lumber Mill, 56-60	44	106 ___
465	Sound Dispatching Station, 56-57	37	84 ___
470	Missile Launching Platform w/6470 exploding boxcar, 59-62	57	97 ___

			Good	Exc
___	479-1	Truck for 6362 Truck Car with envelope, 55-56	25	66
___	480-25	Conversion Magnetic Coupler, 50-60	1	5
___	480-32	Conversion Magnetic Coupler, 61-69	1	8
___	494	Rotating Beacon, 54-66		
___		(A) Painted steel	20	41
___		(B) Unpainted aluminum	17	51
___	497	Coaling Station, 53-58	45	101
___	497C	Controller, 53-58	11	25
___	520	LL Boxcab Electric Locomotive, 56-57		
___		(A) Black pantograph	32	73
___		(B) Copper-colored pantograph	39	84
___	600	MKT NW2 Switcher, 55		
___		(A) Black frame, black end rails	50	106
___		(B) Gray frame, yellow or black end rails	77	196
___	601	Seaboard NW2 Switcher, 56		
___		(A) Red stripes with square ends	73	180
___		(B) Red stripes with round ends	77	157
___	602	Seaboard NW2 Switcher, 57-58	77	155
___	610	Erie NW2 Switcher, 55		
___		(A) Black frame, one-axle Magne-Traction	58	144
___		(B) Black frame, two-axle Magne-Traction	84	299
___		(C) Yellow frame, two-axle Magne-Traction	174	543
___		(D) Replacement body with nameplates	92	262
___	611	Jersey Central NW2 Switcher, 57-58	60	136
___	613	UP NW2 Switcher, 58	76	423
___	614	Alaska NW2 Switcher, 59-60		
___		(A) Plastic bell, no brake	77	176
___		(B) No bell, yellow brake	110	260
___		(C) "Built by Lionel" outlined in yellow near nose	153	309
___	616	Santa Fe NW2 Switcher, 61-62		
___		(A) Open E-unit slot and bell/horn slots	83	176
___		(B) Plugged E-unit slot and open bell/horn slots	97	222
___		(C) Plugged E-unit slot and bell/horn slots	106	237
___	617	Santa Fe NW2 Switcher, 63	112	261
___	621	Jersey Central NW2 Switcher, 56-57	67	121
___	622	Santa Fe NW2 Switcher, 49-50		
___		(A) Large GM decal on cab	116	246
___		(B) Small GM decal on side	94	207
___	623	Santa Fe NW2 Switcher, 52-54	72	152
___	624	C&O NW2 Switcher, 52-54	69	167
___	625	LV GE 44-ton Switcher, 57-58	42	98
___	626	B&O GE 44-ton Switcher, 56-57, 59	122	284
___	627	LV GE 44-ton Switcher, 56-57	30	90
___	628	NP GE 44-ton Switcher, 56-57	41	87
___	629	Burlington GE 44-ton Switcher, 56	140	512
___	633	Santa Fe NW2 Switcher, 62	64	176

| --- | --- | --- | --- |
634	Santa Fe NW2 Switcher, 63, 65-66		___
	(A) Safety stripes	74	147 ___
	(B) No safety stripes	48	92 ___
635	UP NW2 Switcher, 65 u	59	112 ___
637	2-6-4 Locomotive, 2046 736W Tender, 59-63		___
	(A) 2046W Lionel Lines Tender	54	136 ___
	(B) 736W Pennsylvania Tender	70	339 ___
638-2361	Van Camp's Pork & Beans Boxcar, 62 u	14	36 ___
645	Union Pacific NW2 Switcher, 69	78	486 ___
646	4-6-4 Locomotive, 2046W Tender, 54-58	88	382 ___
665	4-6-4 Locomotive, 2046W, 6026W, or 736W Tender, 54-59, 66	74	251 ___
671	6-8-6 Steam Turbine Locomotive, 46-49		___
	(A) Bulb smoke unit, 671W Tender, 46	40	147 ___
	(B) E-unit slot, heater smoke unit, 671W Tender, 47	59	163 ___
	(C) Thin nickel rims, 2671WX Tender with functioning backup lights, 48	63	208 ___
	(D) Thin nickel rims, 2671W Tender, nonfunctioning backup lights, 48	56	135 ___
	(E) Thin nickel rims, 2671W Tender, no backup light lenses, 48	52	113 ___
	(F) No rims on drivers, 49	50	110 ___
671-75	Smoke Lamp, 12 volt, 46	11	18 ___
671R	6-8-6 Steam Turbine Locomotive, 4424W or 4671 Tender, 46-49	170	317 ___
671RR	6-8-6 Steam Turbine Locomotive, 2046W-50 Tender, 52	85	205 ___
671S	Smoke Conversion Kit	25	106 ___
671W	Whistle Tender, 46-48	27	67 ___
675	2-6-2 Locomotive, 2466WX or 6466WX Tender, 47-49		___
	(A) Aluminum smokestack, 47	67	190 ___
	(B) Black smokestack, 48-49	56	163 ___
675	2-6-4 Locomotive, 2046W Tender, 52	68	171 ___
681	6-8-6 Steam Turbine Locomotive		___
	(A) 2671W Tender, 50-51	68	157 ___
	(B) 2046W-50 Tender, 53	48	144 ___
682	6-8-6 Steam Turbine Locomotive, 2046W-50 Tender, 54-55	138	303 ___
685	4-6-4 Hudson Locomotive, 6026W Tender, 53	79	208 ___
703-10	Smoke Lamp, 18 volt, 46	11	22 ___
726	2-8-4 Berkshire, 46-49		___
	(A) Turned stanchions, no front coupler, bulb smoke unit, 2426W Tender, 46	233	599 ___
	(B) Cotter pin stanchions, E-unit slot, no front coupler, heater smoke unit, 2426W Tender, 47	200	419 ___
	(C) Simulated front coupler, 2426W Tender, 48-49	105	342 ___
726RR	2-8-4 Berkshire Locomotive, 2046W Tender, 52	126	303 ___
726S	Smoke Conversion Kit	31	93 ___
736	2-8-4 Berkshire Locomotive, 50-66		___

| --- | --- | --- | --- |
____	(A) No headlight wedge brace, hexagonal flagstaff base, 2671WX Tender , 50-51	120	311
____	(B) Headlight wedge brace, round flagstaff brace, 2046W Tender, 53-54	134	216
____	(C) Sheet metal and plastic trailing truck, 55-56	113	198
____	(D) Smaller typeface on cab number, 57-60	110	169
____	(E) 736W Tender, 61-66	73	184
____ 736W	PRR Whistle Tender	40	74
____ 746	N&W 4-8-4 Class J Northern, 57-60		
____	(A) Tender with long stripe	451	947
____	(B) Tender with short stripe	313	1208
____ 746W	N&W Tender		
____	(A) Short stripe	56	166
____	(B) Long stripe	100	190
____ 760	Curved Track, 16 sections (O72), 54-57	26	78
____ 773	4-6-4 Hudson Locomotive, 50, 64-66		
____	(A) Valve guides cast in steam chest, 2426W Tender, 50	788	1314
____	(B) No valve guides in steam chest, 736W Pennsylvania Tender, 64	548	955
____	(C) No valve guides in steam chest, 773W New York Central Tender, 64-66	555	1040
____ 773W	NYC Whistle Tender, 64-66		
____	(A) Closed spaced lettering	250	500
____	(B) Widely spaced lettering	175	350
____ 902	Elevated Trestle Set, 60, u	31	96
____ 908	Union Station, 59, u		899
____ 909	Smoke Fluid, large or small bottle, 57-66, 68-69		
____	(A) 1/2-ounce bottle	8	33
____	(B) 2-ounce bottle	15	36
____ B909	Smoke Fluid, 2-ounce bottle in blister pack, 66	100	285
____ 919	Artificial Grass, 46-64	8	16
____ 920	Scenic Display Set, 57-58	33	80
____ 920-2	Tunnel Portals, pair, 58-59	13	35
____ 920-3	Green Grass, 57	4	11
____ 920-4	Yellow Grass, 57	7	15
____ 920-5	Artificial Rock, 57-58	4	21
____ 920-6	Dry Glue, 57-58	3	10
____ 920-8	Dyed Lichen, 57-58	4	15
____ 925	Lubricant, 2-ounce tube, 46-69	3	30
____ 925-1	Lubricant, 1-ounce tube, 50-69	2	5
____ 926	Lubricant, 1/2-ounce tube, 55	2	3
____ 926-5	Instruction Booklet, 46-48	1	4
____ 927	Lubricating Kit, 50-59	10	43
____ 927-3	Track Cleaner	4	14
____ 928	Maintenance and Lubricating Kit, 60-63	23	48
____ 943	Ammo Dump, 59-61	16	38
____ 950	U.S. Railroad Map, 58-66	14	45

POSTWAR 1945-1969		Good	Exc
951	Farm Set, 13 pieces, 58	44	95 ___
952	Figure Set, 30 pieces, 58	28	96 ___
953	Figure Set, 32 pieces, 59-62	41	80 ___
954	Swimming Pool and Playground Set, 30 pieces, 59	40	153 ___
955	Highway Set, 22 pieces, 58	30	63 ___
956	Stockyard Set, 18 pieces, 59	40	85 ___
957	Farm Building and Animal Set, 35 pieces, 58	54	120 ___
958	Vehicle Set, 24 pieces, 58	43	112 ___
959	Barn Set, 23 pieces, 58	37	166 ___
960	Barnyard Set, 29 pieces, 59-61	50	108 ___
961	School Set, 36 pieces, 59	43	94 ___
962	Turnpike Set, 24 pieces, 58	58	128 ___
963	Frontier Set, 18 pieces, 59-60	63	128 ___
963-100	Boxed Frontier Set, 60	125	400 ___
964	Factory Site Set, 18 pieces, 59	70	169 ___
965	Farm Set, 36 pieces, 59	56	117 ___
966	Firehouse Set, 45 pieces, 58	68	142 ___
967	Post Office Set, 25 pieces, 58	49	130 ___
968	TV Transmitter Set, 28 pieces, 58	55	113 ___
969	Construction Set, 23 pieces, 60	60	122 ___
970	Ticket Booth, 58-60	29	105 ___
971	Lichen with box, 60-64	29	94 ___
972	Landscape Tree Assortment, 61-64	25	149 ___
973	Complete Landscaping Set, 60-64	42	218 ___
974	Scenery Set, 58	70	197 ___
980	Ranch Set, 14 pieces, 60	45	110 ___
981	Freight Yard Set, 10 pieces, 60	51	131 ___
982	Suburban Split Level Set, 18 pieces, 60	42	334 ___
983	Farm Set, 7 pieces, 60-61	29	75 ___
984	Railroad Set, 22 pieces, 61-62	51	114 ___
985	Freight Area Set, 32 pieces, 61	38	113 ___
986	Farm Set, 20 pieces, 62	43	305 ___
987	Town Set, 24 pieces, 62	30	253 ___
988	Railroad Structure Set, 16 pieces, 62	40	236 ___
1001	2-4-2 Scout Locomotive, plastic body, 1001T Tender, 48		___
	(A) Silver rubber-stamped cab number	30	73 ___
	(B) White heat-stamped cab number	15	39 ___
1001T	Tender (no whistle)	6	14 ___
1002	Gondola, 48-52		___
	(A) Black, white lettering	4	9 ___
	(B) Blue, white lettering	5	10 ___
	(C) Silver, black lettering	139	460 ___
	(D) Yellow, black lettering	132	451 ___
	(E) Red, white lettering	133	442 ___
X1004	PRR Baby Ruth Boxcar, 48-52	4	10 ___
1005	Sunoco 1-D Tank Car, 48-50	3	10 ___

		Good	Exc
1007	LL SP-type Caboose, 48-52		
___	(A) Red body	2	8
___	(B) Red body, raised board on catwalk	10	28
___	(C) Tuscan body	188	548
1008	Uncoupling Unit (O27), 57-62	2	5
1008-50	Uncoupling Track Section (O27), 57-62	1	5
1009	Manumatic Track Section (O27), 48-52	2	5
1010	Transformer, 35 watts, 61-66	5	11
1011	Transformer, 25 watts, 48-49	3	9
1012	Transformer, 35 watts, 50-54	5	9
1013	Curved Track (O27), 45-69		1
1013-17	Steel Pins, dozen (O27), 46-60		1
1013-42	Steel Pins, dozen (O27), 61-68		2
1014	Transformer, 40 watts, 55	5	11
1015	Transformer, 45 watts, 56-60	6	11
1016	Transformer, 35 watts, 59-60	4	8
1018	Half Straight Track (O27), 55-69		1
1018	Straight Track (O27), 45-69		1
1019	Remote Control Track Set (O27), 46-48	2	8
1020	90-degree Crossing (O27), 55-69	2	5
1021	90-degree Crossing (O27), 45-54	2	4
1022	Manual Switches, pair (O27), 53-69	6	11
1023	45-degree Crossing (O27), 56-69	2	5
1024	Manual Switches, pair (O27), 46-52	5	11
1025	Illuminated Bumper (O27), 46-47	5	11
1025	Transformer, 45 watts, 61-69	4	10
1026	Transformer, 25 watts, 61-64	2	6
1032	Transformer, 75 watts, 48	9	20
1033	Transformer, 90 watts, 48-56	19	30
1034	Transformer, 75 watts, 48-54	11	65
1035	Transformer, 60 watts, 47	7	56
1037	Transformer, 40 watts, 46-47	4	8
1041	Transformer, 60 watts, 45-46	8	16
1042	Transformer, 75 watts, 47-48	12	22
1043	Transformer, 50 watts, 53-57	6	14
1043-500	Transformer, 60 watts, ivory, 57-58	72	140
1044	Transformer, 90 watts, 57-69	16	36
1045	Operating Watchman, 46-50	17	118
1045C	Contactor	4	9
1047	Operating Switchman, 59-61	27	150
1050	0-4-0 Scout Locomotive, 1050T Tender, 59 u	40	100
1050T	Tender (no whistle)	6	15
1053	Transformer, 60 watts, 56-60	7	15
1055	Texas Special Alco Diesel A Unit, 59-60	24	57
1060	2-4-2 Locomotive, 1050T or 1060T Tender, 60-62	15	30
1060T	Lionel Lines Tender (no whistle)	6	12

		Good	Exc	
1060T-50	Southern Pacific Tender, 63-64 u	12	24	___
1061	0-4-0 or 2-4-2 Scout Locomotive, 1061T Tender, 64, 69			___
	(A) Slope-back Lionel Lines tender	8	22	___
	(B) Paper number labels	41	118	___
	(C) No number stamped on cab	24	59	___
1061T	Tender	4	16	___
1062	0-4-0 or 2-4-2 Scout Locomotive, 63-64			___
	(A) Streamlined Southern Pacific Tender	25	53	___
	(B) Other tenders	15	38	___
1063	Transformer, 75 watts, 60-64	11	27	___
1063	Transformer 75 watt, with green whistle control	155	206	___
1065	Union Pacific Alco Diesel A Unit, 61	27	68	___
1066	Union Pacific Alco Diesel A Unit, 64 u	29	64	___
1073	Transformer, 60 watts, 61-66	7	16	___
1101	Transformer, 25 watts, 48	3	6	___
1101	2-4-2 Scout Locomotive, 1001T Tender, 48 u			___
	(A) Cab correctly marked "1101"	15	35	___
	(B) Cab marked "1001"	85	202	___
1110	2-4-2 Locomotive, 1001T Tender, 49, 51-52	14	31	___
1120	2-4-2 Scout Locomotive, 1001T Tender, 50	17	32	___
1121	Remote Control Switches, pair (O27), 46-51	11	28	___
1122	Remote Control Switches, pair (O27), 52-53	12	26	___
1122-34	Remote Control Switches, pair, 52-53	11	26	___
1122-500	Gauge Adapter (O27), 57-66	3	8	___
1122E	Remote Control Switches, pair (O27), 53-69	11	26	___
1130	2-4-2 Locomotive, 6066T or 1130T Tender, 53-54			___
	(A) Plastic body	15	41	___
	(B) Die-cast body	34	87	___
1130T	Tender (no whistle)			___
	(A) Black-painted shell	28	67	___
	(B) Black plastic shell	6	16	___
1130T-500	Tender, pink, from Girls Set	101	237	___
1144	Transformer, 75 watts, 61-66	10	25	___
1232	Transformer, 75 watts, made for export, 48	18	41	___
1615	0-4-0 Locomotive, 1615T Tender, 55-57			___
	(A) No grab irons	63	127	___
	(B) Grab irons on locomotive and tender	106	216	___
1615T	Tender (no whistle)	15	30	___
1625	0-4-0 Locomotive, 1625T Tender, 58	140	353	___
1625T	Tender (no whistle)	24	51	___
1640-100	Presidential Kit, 60	45	126	___
1654	2-4-2 Locomotive, 1654W Tender, 46-47	35	76	___
1654T	Tender (no whistle)	10	28	___
1654W	Whistle Tender	15	34	___
1655	2-4-2 Locomotive, 6654W Tender, 48-49	35	74	___

			Good	Exc
___	**1656**	0-4-0 Locomotive, 6403B Tender, 48-49		
___		(A) Large silver cab number	120	338
___		(B) Small silver cab number	122	280
___	**1665**	0-4-0 Locomotive, 2403B Tender, 46	168	334
___	**1666**	2-6-2 Locomotive, 2466W or 2466WX Tender, 46-47		
___		(A) Number plate and two-piece bell	60	120
___		(B) Rubber-stamped number and one-piece bell	70	135
___	**1666T**	Tender (no whistle)	10	25
___	**1862**	4-4-0 Civil War General, 1862T Tender, 59-62		
___		(A) Gray smokestack	80	148
___		(B) Black smokestack	82	163
___	**1862T**	Tender (no whistle)	21	41
___	**1865**	Western & Atlantic Coach, 59-62	23	46
___	**1866**	Western & Atlantic Mail-Baggage Car, 59-62	22	49
___	**1872**	4-4-0 Civil War General, 1872T Tender, 59-62	102	301
___	**1872T**	Tender (no whistle)	28	49
___	**1875**	Western & Atlantic Coach, 59-62	75	287
___	**1875W**	Western & Atlantic Coach, whistle, 59-62	51	133
___	**1876**	Western & Atlantic Baggage Car, 59-62	36	134
___	**1877**	Flatcar with fence and horses, 59-62	46	101
___	**1882**	4-4-0 Civil War General, 1882T Tender, 60 u	187	380
___	**1882T**	Tender, 60 u	39	84
___	**1885**	Western & Atlantic Coach, 60 u	105	250
___	**1887**	Flatcar with fences and horses, 60 u	70	153
___	**2001**	Track Make-up Kit (O27), 63	288	703
___	**2002**	Track Make-up Kit (O27), 63	495	1181
___	**2003**	Track Make-up Kit (O27), 63	600	1900
___	**2016**	2-6-4 Locomotive, 6026W Tender, 55-56	43	95
___	**2018**	2-6-4 Locomotive, 56-59, 61		
___		(A) 6026T Tender	33	59
___		(B) 6026W Tender	44	88
___		(C) 1130T Tender	35	65
___	**2020**	6-8-6 Steam Turbine Locomotive, 2020W or 2466WX Tender, smoke lamp, 46	84	172
___	**2020**	6-8-6 Steam Turbine Locomotive, 2020W or 6020W Tender, 47-49	72	167
___	**2020W**	Whistle Tender	31	61
___	**2023**	Union Pacific Alco Diesel AA Units, 50-51		
___		(A) Yellow body	75	289
___		(B) Gray nose and side frames	1128	3494
___		(C) Silver body	73	170
___	**2024**	C&O Alco Diesel A Unit, 69	30	71
___	**2025**	2-6-2 Locomotive, 2466WX or 6466WX Tender, 47-49		
___		(A) Black smokestack, 48-49	75	165
___		(B) Aluminum smokestack, 47	80	180
___	**2025**	2-6-4 Locomotive, 6466W Tender, 52	76	212

		Good	Exc	
2026	2-6-2 Locomotive, 6466WX Tender, 48-49	47	89	___
2026	2-6-4 Locomotive, 6466W, 6466T, or 6066T Tender, 51-53	38	69	___
2028	Pennsylvania GP7 Diesel, 55			___
	(A) Gold lettering	138	279	___
	(B) Yellow lettering	85	193	___
	(C) Tan frame	208	435	___
2029	2-6-4 Locomotive, 64-69			___
	(A) 234W Lionel Lines Tender	49	106	___
	(B) LL Tender with "Hagerstown" on bottom	61	127	___
	(C) 234W Pennsylvania Tender	77	169	___
2031	Rock Island Alco Diesel AA Units, 52-54	72	253	___
2032	Erie Alco Diesel AA Units, 52-54	88	355	___
2033	Union Pacific Alco Diesel AA Units, 52-54	66	170	___
2034	2-4-2 Scout Locomotive, 6066T Tender, 52	28	59	___
2035	2-6-4 Locomotive, 6466W Tender, 50-51	59	126	___
2036	2-6-4 Locomotive, 6466W Tender, 50	43	93	___
2037	2-6-4 Locomotive, 54-55, 57-63			___
	(A) 6026T or 1130T Tender	35	78	___
	(B) 6026W, 233W, or 234W Whistle Tender	51	112	___
2037-500	2-6-4 Locomotive, pink, 1130T-500 Tender, 57-58	316	989	___
2041	Rock Island Alco Diesel AA Units, 69	61	145	___
2046	4-6-4 Locomotive, 2046W Tender, 50-51, 53	85	208	___
2046T	Tender, for export	67	192	___
2046W	Whistle Tender	28	108	___
2046W-50	PRR Whistle Tender	31	171	___
2055	4-6-4 Locomotive, 2046W or 6026W Tender, 53-55	73	131	___
2056	4-6-4 Locomotive, 2046W Tender, 52	72	242	___
2065	4-6-4 Locomotive, 2046W or 6026W Tender, 54-56	74	204	___
2203B	Tender with bell	52	114	___
2203T	Tender, 45-46	36	54	___
2224W	Whistle Tender	26	67	___
2240	Wabash F3 AB Units, 56	166	381	___
2242	New Haven F3 AB Units, 58-59	205	643	___
2242C	New Haven F3 B Unit, 58-59	66	261	___
2243	Santa Fe F3 AB Units, 55-57	26	39	___
	(A) Gray body mold, raised molded cab door ladder	114	296	___
	(B) Typical molded cab door ladder	84	187	___
2243C	Santa Fe F3 B Unit, 55-57	53	162	___
2245	Texas Special F3 AB Units, 54-55	140	666	___
	(A) B Unit with portholes, 54	207	624	___
	(B) B Unit without portholes, 55	228	603	___
2257	SP-type caboose, 47			___
	(A) Red body, no smokestack	5	15	___
	(B) Tuscan body and smokestack	104	299	___
	(C) Red body and smokestack	171	401	___

| --- | --- | --- | --- |
2321	Lackawanna FM Train Master Diesel, 54-56		
	(A) Gray roof	155	425
	(B) Maroon roof	164	572
2322	Virginian FM Train Master Diesel, 65-66		
	(A) Unpainted blue body, yellow stripes	228	424
	(B) Blue or black body, painted blue and yellow stripes	292	629
2328	Burlington GP7 Diesel, 55-56	89	288
2329	Virginian GE E-33/EL-C Electric Locomotive, 58-59	163	369
2330	Pennsylvania GG1 Electric Locomotive, green, 50	356	963
2331	Virginian FM Train Master Diesel, 55-58		
	(A) Black and yellow stripes, gray mold, 55	319	644
	(B) Yellow stripes, blue mold, 56-58	227	564
	(C) Blue and yellow stripes, gray mold	477	941
2332	Pennsylvania GG1 Electric Locomotive, 47-49		
	(A) Black	546	1228
	(B) Dark green	164	606
2333	NYC F3 Diesel AA Units, 48-49		
	(A) Rubber-stamped lettering	216	796
	(B) Heat-stamped lettering	163	476
2333	Santa Fe F3 Diesel AA Units, 48-49	177	464
2337	Wabash GP7 Diesel, 58	92	211
2338	Milwaukee Road GP7 Diesel, 55-56		
	(A) Orange band around shell	430	1150
	(B) Interrupted orange band	77	272
2339	Wabash GP7 Diesel, 57	126	233
2340	Pennsylvania GG1 Electric Locomotive, 55		
	(A) Tuscan	402	1038
	(B) Dark green	282	738
2341	Jersey Central FM Train Master Diesel, 56		
	(A) High-gloss orange	901	2625
	(B) Dull orange	811	1882
2343	Santa Fe F3 Diesel AA Units, 50-52	150	455
2343C	Santa Fe F3 B Unit, 50-55		
	(A) Screen roof vents	92	227
	(B) Louver roof vents	69	187
2344	NYC F3 Diesel AA Units, 50-52	179	406
2344C	NYC F3 B Unit, 50-55	95	255
2345	Western Pacific F3 Diesel AA Units, 52	439	1151
2346	B&M GP9 Diesel, 65-66	122	268
2347	C&O GP7 Diesel, 65 u	1635	3879
2348	M&StL GP9 Diesel, 58-59	137	260
2349	Northern Pacific GP9 Diesel, 59-60	156	461
2350	New Haven EP-5 Electric Locomotive, 56-58		
	(A) Painted nose trim, white N and orange H	199	472
	(B) Decaled nose trim, white N and orange H	116	354
	(C) Painted nose trim, orange N and black H	757	2796

		Good	Exc
	(D) Decaled nose trim, orange N and black H	382	841 ___
	(E) Orange and white stripes go through doorjambs	306	1058 ___
2351	Milwaukee Road EP-5 Electric Locomotive, 57-58	150	547 ___
2352	Pennsylvania EP-5 Electric Locomotive, 58-59		___
	(A) Tuscan body	162	391 ___
	(B) Chocolate brown body	222	397 ___
2353	Santa Fe F3 Diesel AA Units, 53-55	173	388 ___
2354	NYC F3 Diesel AA Units, 53-55	226	403 ___
2355	Western Pacific F3 Diesel AA Units, 53	406	770 ___
2356	Southern F3 Diesel AA Units, 54-56	333	766 ___
2356C	Southern F3 B Unit, 54-56	128	324 ___
2357	SP-type Caboose, 47-48		___
	(A) Red body and smokestack	178	481 ___
	(B) Tuscan body and smokestack	13	55 ___
	(C) Tile red, no smokestack, "6357" stamped on bottom	68	166 ___
2358	Great Northern EP-5 Electric Locomotive, 59-60	211	471 ___
2359	Boston & Maine GP9 Diesel, 61-62	102	428 ___
2360	Pennsylvania GG1 Electric Locomotive, 56-58, 61-63		___
	(A) Tuscan, 5 gold stripes	501	1213 ___
	(B) Dark green, 5 gold stripes	352	776 ___
	(C) Tuscan, gold stripe, heat-stamped lettering	376	697 ___
	(D) Tuscan, gold stripe, decaled lettering	364	665 ___
2363	Illinois Central F3 Diesel AB Units, 55-56		___
	(A) Black lettering	292	671 ___
	(B) Brown lettering	369	838 ___
2363C	Illinois Central F3 Diesel B Unit, 55-56	90	160 ___
2365	C&O GP7 Diesel, 62-63	119	393 ___
2367	Wabash F3 Diesel AB Units, 55	305	630 ___
2367C	Wabash F3 Diesel B Unit, 55	80	213 ___
2368	B&O F3 Diesel AB Units, 56	453	1350 ___
2368C	B&O F3 Diesel B Unit, 56	145	510 ___
2373	CP F3 Diesel AA Units, 57	656	1388 ___
2378	Milwaukee Road F3 Diesel AB Units, 56		___
	(A) Yellow roof line stripes	487	1098 ___
	(B) No roof line stripes	433	938 ___
2378C	Milwaukee Road F3 B Unit, yellow roof line stripe, 56	237	442 ___
2379	Rio Grande F3 Diesel AB Units, 57-58	347	896 ___
2379C	Rio Grande F3 Diesel B Unit, 57-58	65	275 ___
2383	Santa Fe F3 Diesel AA Units, 58-66	193	446 ___
2400	Maplewood Pullman Car, green, 48-49	35	87 ___
2401	Hillside Observation Car, green, 48-49	29	75 ___
2402	Chatham Pullman Car, green, 48-49	37	88 ___
2403B	Tender, 46	20	47 ___
2404	Santa Fe Vista Dome Car, 64-65	26	62 ___
2405	Santa Fe Pullman Car, 64-65	26	64 ___

| --- | --- | --- | --- |
___ 2406	Santa Fe Observation Car, 64-65	22	54
___ 2408	Santa Fe Vista Dome Car, 66	33	74
___ 2409	Santa Fe Pullman Car, 66	37	76
___ 2410	Santa Fe Observation Car, 66	28	61
___ 2411	Lionel Lines Flatcar, 46-48		
___	(A) With pipes, 46	30	66
___	(B) With logs, 47-48	15	37
___ 2412	Santa Fe Vista Dome Car, 59-63	31	115
___ 2414	Santa Fe Pullman Car, 59-63	39	116
___ 2416	Santa Fe Observation Car, 59-63	28	88
___ 2419	DL&W Work Caboose, 46-47	20	45
___ 2420	DL&W Work Caboose with searchlight, 46-48		
___	(A) Light or dark gray, heat-stamped lettering	42	86
___	(B) Light or dark gray, rubber-stamped lettering	59	125
___ 2421	Maplewood Pullman Car, 50-53		
___	(A) Gray roof	26	60
___	(B) Silver roof	24	68
___ 2422	Chatham Pullman Car, 50-53		
___	(A) Gray roof	29	66
___	(B) Silver roof	23	49
___ 2423	Hillside Observation Car, 50-53		
___	(A) Gray roof	25	59
___	(B) Silver roof	21	46
___ 2426W	Whistle Tender, 50	134	297
___ 2429	Livingston Pullman Car, 52-53	45	142
___ 2430	Pullman Car, blue, 46-47	22	86
___ 2431	Observation Car, blue, 46-47	22	69
___ 2432	Clifton Vista Dome Car, 54-58	30	145
___ 2434	Newark Pullman Car, 54-58	32	173
___ 2435	Elizabeth Pullman Car, 54-58	42	141
___ 2436	Mooseheart Observation Car, 57-58	30	67
___ 2436	Summit Observation Car, 54-56	25	68
___ 2440	Pullman Car, green, 46-47		
___	(A) Silver lettering	31	63
___	(B) White lettering	25	53
___ 2441	Observation Car, green, 46-47		
___	(A) Silver lettering	31	63
___	(B) White lettering	23	48
___ 2442	Clifton Vista Dome Car, 56	36	74
___ 2442	Pullman Car, brown, 46-48		
___	(A) Silver lettering	34	70
___	(B) White lettering	27	77
___ 2443	Observation Car, brown, 46-48		
___	(A) Silver lettering	33	64
___	(B) White lettering	28	80
___ 2444	Newark Pullman Car, 56	41	88

POSTWAR 1945-1969		Good	Exc
2445	Elizabeth Pullman Car, 56	82	186 ___
2446	Summit Observation Car, 56	40	84 ___
2452	Pennsylvania Gondola, 45-47		___
	(A) Whirly wheels, 45	22	53 ___
	(B) Regular wheels	9	19 ___
	(C) Early flying shoe trucks, two holes in floor, 45	42	111 ___
2452X	Pennsylvania Gondola, 46-47	8	17 ___
X2454	Baby Ruth Boxcar, PRR logo, 46-47	16	39 ___
X2454	Pennsylvania Boxcar, 46		___
	(A) Brown door	63	184 ___
	(B) Orange door	138	434 ___
2456	Lehigh Valley Hopper, 48		___
	(A) Flat black, 2 lines of data, 48	12	33 ___
	(B) Flat black, 3 lines of data, 48	83	220 ___
2457	PRR N5-type Caboose "477618," tinplate, 45-47		___
	(A) Brown body, white lettering centered, red window frames, 45	15	45 ___
	(B) Brown body, white lettering not centered, 45	88	332 ___
	(C) Red body, red window frames, 46-47	10	28 ___
	(D) Red body, black window frames, 46-47	13	46 ___
	(E) Red body, no "Eastern Division" markings, 46-47	10	20 ___
	(F) Same as E, but black smokejack, 46-47	10	21 ___
X2458	PRR Automobile Boxcar, 46-48	25	52 ___
2460	Bucyrus Erie Crane Car, 12-wheel, 46-50		
	(A) Gray cab	95	232 ___
	(B) Black cab	33	79 ___
2461	Transformer Car, die-cast, 47-48		___
	(A) Red transformer	29	79 ___
	(B) Black transformer	25	62 ___
	(C) Red transformer, number rubber-stamped on bottom	49	134 ___
2465	Sunoco 2-D Tank Car, 46-48		___
	(A) Gas, Sunoco, and Oils in diamond, centered	169	628 ___
	(B) Sunoco in diamond	6	15 ___
	(C) Sunoco extends beyond diamond	6	16 ___
	(D) Sunoco in diamond, centered	63	120 ___
2466T	Tender (no whistle)	16	36 ___
2466W	Whistle Tender, 46-48		___
	(A) Number heat-stamped on front, 46	64	151 ___
	(B) Number missing from front, 47-48	12	30 ___
2466WX	Whistle Tender, 45-48	25	58 ___
2472	PRR N5-type Caboose, tinplate, 46-47	13	26 ___
2481	Plainfield Pullman Car, yellow, 50	89	230 ___
2482	Westfield Pullman Car, yellow, 50	89	241 ___
2483	Livingston Observation Car, yellow, 50	73	216 ___
2521	President McKinley Observation Car, 62-66	63	156 ___
2522	President Harrison Vista Dome Car, 62-66	73	174 ___

| --- | --- | --- | --- |
2523	President Garfield Pullman Car, 62-66	89	175
2530	REA Baggage Car, 54-60		
	(A) Large doors	162	663
	(B) Small doors	67	328
2531	Silver Dawn Observation Car, 52-60		
	(A) Ribbed channels, round rivets	32	98
	(B) Ribbed channels, hex rivets	39	85
	(C) Ribbed channels, hex rivets, red center taillight	70	138
	(D) Flat channels, glued nameplates	48	177
2532	Silver Range Vista Dome Car, 52-60	55	115
	(A) Ribbed channels, hex rivets	36	86
	(B) Flat channels, glued nameplates	44	183
2533	Silver Cloud Pullman Car, 52-59		
	(A) Ribbed channels, hex rivets	33	82
	(B) Flat channels, glued nameplates	46	106
2534	Silver Bluff Pullman Car, 52-59		
	(A) Ribbed channels, hex rivets	39	100
	(B) Flat channels, glued nameplates	39	97
2541	Alexander Hamilton Observation Car, 55-56*	66	138
2542	Betsy Ross Vista Dome Car, 55-56*	67	149
2543	William Penn Pullman Car, 55-56*	68	157
2544	Molly Pitcher Pullman Car, 55-56*	67	153
2550	B&O Baggage-Mail Rail Diesel Car, 57-58	143	377
2551	Banff Park Observation Car, 57*	96	210
2552	Skyline 500 Vista Dome Car, 57*	114	255
2553	Blair Manor Pullman Car, 57*	159	353
2554	Craig Manor Pullman Car, 57*	164	355
2555	Sunoco 1-D Tank Car, 46-48	21	52
2559	B&O Passenger Rail Diesel Car, 57-58	129	262
2560	Lionel Lines Crane Car, 8-wheel, 46-47		
	(A) Black boom	23	89
	(B) Brown boom	27	72
	(C) Green boom	32	81
2561	Vista Valley Observation Car, 59-61*	82	195
2562	Regal Pass Vista Dome Car, 59-61*	88	230
2563	Indian Falls Pullman Car, 59-61*	88	212
2625	Irvington Pullman Car, 46-50*		
	(A) No silhouettes	64	146
	(B) Silhouettes	77	209
2625	Madison Pullman Car, 46-47*	58	159
2625	Manhattan Pullman Car, 46-47*	58	159
2627	Madison Pullman Car, 48-50*		
	(A) No silhouettes	56	165
	(B) Silhouettes	77	207
2628	Manhattan Pullman Car, 48-50*		
	(A) No silhouettes	58	151

	(B) Silhouettes	81	292 ___
2666T	Tender	9	18 ___
2671T	PRR Tender, for export	46	129 ___
2671W	Whistle Tender	38	113 ___
2671W	PRR Tender with silver letters and back-up light	169	384 ___
2671WX	Whistle Tender	42	269 ___
2755	Sunoco 1-D Tank Car, 45	26	61 ___
X2758	PRR Automobile Boxcar, 45-46	26	57 ___
2855	Sunoco 1-D Tank Car, 46-47		___
	(A) Black	69	214 ___
	(B) Black, decal without Gas and Oils	59	175 ___
	(C) Gray	48	139 ___
3309	Turbo Missile Launch Car, red body, 63-64	17	46 ___
3309-50	Turbo Missile Launch Car, olive body, 63-64	169	467 ___
3330	Flatcar with submarine kit, 60-62	60	162 ___
3330-100	Operating Submarine Kit with box, 60-61	102	475 ___
3349	Turbo Missile Launch Car, red body, 62-65	16	101 ___
3356	Operating Horse Car and Corral Set, 56-60, 64-66	45	230 ___
3356	Operating Horse Car only, 56-60, 64-66		___
	(A) Built date, bar-end trucks, 56-60	60	320 ___
	(B) No built date, AAR trucks, 64-66	45	98 ___
3356-100	Black Horses, 9 pieces, 56-59	17	47 ___
3356-150	Horse Car Corral, 57-60	18	208 ___
3357	Hydraulic Maintenance Car, 62-64		___
	(A) Blue, 62-64	10	33 ___
	(B) Teal, 62-64	40	91 ___
3357-27	Trestle Components for Hydraulic Maintenance Car, 62	26	49 ___
3359	Lionel Lines Twin-bin Coal Dump Car, 55-58	17	44 ___
3360	Operating Burro Crane, self-propelled, 56-57	67	158 ___
3361	Operating Log Dump Car, 55-58	15	83 ___
3362	Helium Tank Unloading Car, 61-63, 69	24	64 ___
3364	Operating Dump Car with 3 logs, 65-66, 68	16	62 ___
3366	Circus Car Corral Set, 59-62	109	236 ___
3366	Circus Car Corral only, 59-62	18	95 ___
3366	Circus Car only, 59-62	44	95 ___
3366-100	White Horses, 9 pieces, 59-62	33	66 ___
3370	W&A Sheriff and Outlaw Car, 61-64		___
	(A) AAR trucks	17	44 ___
	(B) Archbar trucks	25	60 ___
3376	Bronx Zoo Car, 60-66, 69		___
	(A) Blue, white lettering	20	51 ___
	(B) Green, yellow lettering	27	55 ___
	(C) Blue, yellow lettering	81	221 ___
3386	Bronx Zoo Car, 60	25	62 ___
3409	Helicopter Car, 61	32	93 ___
3410	Helicopter Car, 61-63		___

			Good	Exc
___		(A) Two operating couplers, gray Navy helicopter	29	72
___		(B) One operating coupler, yellow helicopter, 63	57	120
___	**3413**	Mercury Capsule Car, 62-64	43	150
___	**3419**	Helicopter Car, 59-65	35	80
___	**3424**	Wabash Operating Boxcar, 56-58	22	76
___	**3424-75**	Low Bridge Signal, 56-57	72	219
___	**3424-100**	Low Bridge Signal Set, 56-58	20	133
___	**3428**	U.S. Mail Operating Boxcar, 59-60	38	108
___	**3429**	USMC Helicopter Car, 60	199	405
___	**3434**	Poultry Dispatch Car, 59-60, 64-66		
___		(A) Gray man	49	245
___		(B) Blue man	50	103
___	**3435**	Traveling Aquarium Car, 59-62		
___		(A) Gold lettering, tank designations, and circle around L	425	900
___		(B) Gold lettering, tank designations, no circle around L	250	590
___		(C) Gold lettering, no tank designations, no circle around L	105	230
___		(D) Yellow lettering, no tank designations, no circle around L	48	121
___	**3444**	Erie Operating Gondola, 57-59	29	66
___	**3451**	Operating Log Dump Car, 46-48		
___		(A) Heat-stamped lettering	15	36
___		(B) Rubber-stamped lettering	21	65
___	**3454**	PRR Operating Merchandise Car, 46-47		
___		(A) Red lettering	1005	3646
___		(B) Blue lettering	35	197
___	**3456**	N&W Operating Hopper, 50-55	21	58
___	**3459**	LL Operating Coal Dump Car, 46-48		
___		(A) Aluminum bin	115	372
___		(B) Black bin	19	42
___		(C) Green bin	25	68
___	**3460**	Flatcar with trailers, 55-57	29	74
___	**3461**	LL Operating Log Car, 49-55		
___		(A) Black car, heat-stamped lettering	20	40
___		(B) Black car, rubber-stamped lettering	159	390
___	**3461-25**	LL Operating Log Car, green	20	52
___	**3462**	Automatic Milk Car, 47-48		
___		(A) Flat white or cream, steel base mechanism	12	50
___		(B) Flat white or cream, brass base mechanism	25	65
___		(C) Glossy cream	53	196
___	**3462-70**	Magnetic Milk Cans, 52-59	10	16
___	**3462P**	Milk Car Platform, 47-48	6	19
___	**X3464**	ATSF Operating Boxcar, 49-52		
___		(A) Orange body, corner steps, 49	8	14
___		(B) Orange body, no steps, 50-52	8	35
___		(C) Tan body	444	1088
___	**X3464**	NYC Operating Boxcar, 49-52		

		Good	Exc	
	(A) Corner steps, 49	8	15	___
	(B) No steps, 50-52	6	13	___
3469	LL Operating Coal Dump Car, 49-55	16	96	___
3470	Target Launching Car, dark blue, 62-64	24	195	___
3470-100	Target Launching Car, light blue, 63	66	198	___
3472	Automatic Milk Car, 49-53	39	55	___
3474	Western Pacific Operating Boxcar, 52-53	22	57	___
3482	Automatic Milk Car, 54-55			___
	(A) "RT3472" on right	41	90	___
	(B) "RT3482" on right	20	60	___
3484	Pennsylvania Operating Boxcar, 53	22	56	___
3484-25	ATSF Operating Boxcar, 54			
	(A) White lettering	32	73	___
	(B) Black lettering	490	1219	___
3494-1	NYC Operating Boxcar, 55	36	90	___
3494-150	MP Operating Boxcar, 56	49	132	___
3494-275	State of Maine Operating Boxcar, 56-58			___
	(A) "3494275" on side	37	86	___
	(B) No number on side	60	131	___
3494-550	Monon Operating Boxcar, 57-58	192	424	___
3494-625	Soo Operating Boxcar, 57-58	185	453	___
3509	Satellite Launching Car, 61			___
	(A) Chrome satellite cover	31	73	___
	(B) Gray satellite cover	75	208	___
3510	Satellite Launching Car, 62	39	92	___
3512	Fireman and Ladder Car, 59-61			___
	(A) Black extension ladder	37	95	___
	(B) Silver extension ladder	65	177	___
3519	Satellite Launching Car, 61-64	23	65	___
3520	Searchlight Car, 52-53			___
	(A) Serif lettering	19	45	___
	(B) Sans serif lettering	15	32	___
3530	GM Generator Car, 56-58			___
	(A) Blue fuel tank	44	181	___
	(B) Black fuel tank	39	108	___
	(C) 3530 underscored	598	1690	___
3530-50	Searchlight with pole and base, 56-56	19	93	___
3535	Security Car with searchlight, 60-61	43	97	___
3540	Operating Radar Car, 59-60	35	101	___
3545	Operating TV Monitor Car, 61-62	50	166	___
3559	Operating Coal Dump Car, 46-48			___
	(A) Black coil housing	15	56	___
	(B) Brown coil housing	38	87	___
3562-1	ATSF Operating Barrel Car, 54			___
	(A) Black, black unloading trough	66	189	___

			Good	Exc
		(B) Black, yellow unloading trough	59	178
		(C) Gray, red lettering	1150	2885
___	3562-25	ATSF Operating Barrel Car, gray, 54		
___		(A) Red lettering, no bracket tab	168	428
___		(B) Blue lettering, no bracket tab	18	103
___		(C) Blue lettering, bracket tab	25	76
___	3562-50	ATSF Operating Barrel Car, yellow, 55-56		
___		(A) Painted	36	102
___		(B) Unpainted	26	90
___	3562-75	ATSF Operating Barrel Car, orange, 57-58	36	181
___	3619	Helicopter Reconnaissance Car, 62-64		
___		(A) Light yellow	48	107
___		(B) Dark yellow	66	171
___	3620	Searchlight Car, orange generator, 54-56		
___		(A) Unpainted gray plastic searchlight	20	36
___		(B) Gray-painted gray plastic searchlight	27	47
___		(C) Unpainted orange plastic searchlight	47	113
___		(D) Gray-painted orange plastic searchlight	63	225
___	3650	Extension Searchlight Car, 56-59		
___		(A) Light gray	28	70
___		(B) Dark gray	48	149
___		(C) Olive gray	96	265
___	3656	Operating Cattle Car, some with an open coil, 49-55		
___		(A) Black letters, Armour sticker	126	315
___		(B) White letters, Armour sticker	23	54
___		(C) Black letters, no Armour sticker	92	202
___		(D) White letters, no Armour sticker	19	52
___	3656	Stockyard with cattle, 49-55	28	47
___	3656-34	Cattle, black, 9 pieces, 49-58		
___		(A) Rounded ridge on base, 49	57	84
___		(B) Plain base	15	27
___	3656-150	Corral Platform, yellow tray with box	215	769
___	3662	Automatic Milk Car, 55-60, 64-66	34	112
___	3662-79	Nonmagnetic Milk Cans, 7 pieces, white envelope	20	43
___	3662-80	Nonmagnetic Milk Cans, 7 pieces, manila envelope	18	40
___	3665	Minuteman Operating Car, 61-64		
___		(A) Medium blue roof	60	219
___		(B) Dark blue roof	36	78
___	3666	Minuteman Boxcar with cannon, 64 u	196	470
___	3672	Bosco Operating Milk Car, 59-60		
___		(A) Unpainted yellow body	81	171
___		(B) Painted yellow body	120	267
___	3672-79	Bosco Can Set, 7 pieces in envelope, 59-60	28	81
___	3820	USMC Operating Submarine Car, 60-62	91	229
___	3830	Operating Submarine Car, 60-63	38	110

| --- | --- | --- | --- |
3854	Automatic Merchandise Car, 46-47	186	414 ___
3927	Lionel Lines Track Cleaning Car, 56-60	26	49 ___
3927-38	Track Cleaning Fluid Bottle	6	15 ___
3927-50	Track Wiping Cylinders, 25 pieces, 57-60	16	31 ___
3927-75	Track-Clean Detergent, can, 56-69	5	14 ___
4357	SP-type Caboose, electronic, die-cast stack, 48-49		___
	(A) Die-cast metal smokestack	75	194 ___
	(B) Matching plastic smokestack	112	258 ___
	(C) Matching plastic smokestack, raised board on roofwalk	110	255 ___
4452	PRR Gondola, electronic, 46-49	49	120 ___
4454	Baby Ruth PRR Boxcar, electronic, 46-49	55	139 ___
4457	PRR N5-type Caboose, tinplate, electronic, 46-47	55	146 ___
4671W	Whistle Tender	79	178 ___
5102	Railroad and Roadway Crossing	10	45 ___
5159-50	Maintenance and Lube Kit, 66-69	25	63 ___
5160	Viewing Stand, 63	40	142 ___
5459	LL Coal Dump Car, electronic, 46-49	57	137 ___
6001T	Tender	6	15 ___
6002	NYC Gondola, 50	4	7 ___
X6004	Baby Ruth PRR Boxcar, 50	4	8 ___
6007	Lionel Lines SP-type Caboose, 50	3	6 ___
6009	Remote Control Uncoupling Track, 53-54	2	5 ___
6012	Gondola, 51-56	2	6 ___
6014	Bosco PRR Boxcar, 58		___
	(A) White body	20	38 ___
	(B) Red body	4	12 ___
	(C) Orange body	4	7 ___
6014	Chun King Boxcar, 57 u	43	121 ___
6014	Frisco Boxcar, 57, 63-69		___
	(A) White body	5	52 ___
	(B) Red body	5	8 ___
	(C) White body, coin slot	16	40 ___
	(D) Orange body, 57	13	37 ___
	(E) Orange body, 69	9	19 ___
X6014	Baby Ruth PRR Boxcar, 51-56		___
	(A) White body	5	9 ___
	(B) Red body	4	8 ___
6014-100	Airex Boxcar, 60 u	15	36 ___
6014-150	Wix Boxcar, 59 u	69	169 ___
6015	Sunoco 1-D Tank Car, 54-55		___
	(A) Painted tank	70	303 ___
	(B) Unpainted tank	5	10 ___
6017	Lionel Lines SP-type Caboose, 51-62		___
	(A) Unpainted red or Tuscan body	4	13 ___
	(B) Glossy Tuscan-painted, orange mold	23	71 ___

			Good	Exc
___		(C) Semi-glossy Tuscan-painted, orange mold	14	35
___		(D) Light or dark tile red-painted, blue mold	14	35
___		(E) Brown painted body	2	8
___	**6017**	Lionel SP-type Caboose, unpainted maroon, 56	10	27
___	**6017-50**	U.S. Marine Corps SP-type Caboose, 58	26	66
___	**6017-85**	Lionel Lines SP-type Caboose, gray-painted, 58	23	61
___	**6017-100**	B&M SP-type Caboose, 59, 62, 65-66		
___		(A) Dark purple-blue	81	381
___		(B) Medium or light blue	15	37
___	**6017-185**	ATSF SP-type Caboose, gray-painted, 59-60	14	39
___	**6017-200**	U.S. Navy SP-type Caboose, 60	56	164
___	**6017-235**	ATSF SP-type Caboose, red-painted, 62	17	44
___	**6019**	Remote Control Track (O27), 48-66	2	10
___	**6020W**	Whistle Tender	28	60
___	**6024**	Nabisco Shredded Wheat Boxcar, 57	10	30
___	**6024**	RCA Whirlpool Boxcar, 57 u	20	60
___	**6025**	Gulf 1-D Tank Car, 56-58		
___		(A) Gray body, blue lettering	5	15
___		(B) Orange body, blue lettering	6	22
___		(C) Black body, red-orange Gulf emblem	5	14
___	**6026T**	Tender (no whistle)	13	39
___	**6026W**	Whistle Tender	23	79
___	**6027**	Alaska SP-type Caboose, 59	29	64
___	**6029**	Remote Control Uncoupling Track, 55-63	2	9
___	**6032**	Short Gondola, black (O27), 52-54	2	6
___	**X6034**	Baby Ruth PRR Boxcar, 53-54		
___		(A) Orange, blue lettering	5	15
___		(B) Orange, black lettering	6	11
___	**6035**	Sunoco 1-D Tank Car, 52-53	4	10
___	**6037**	Lionel Lines SP-type Caboose, 52-54		
___		(A) Tuscan	3	6
___		(B) Red	4	8
___	**6042**	Short Gondola, 59-61, 62-64	4	8
___	**6044**	Airex Boxcar, orange lettering, 59-60 u		
___		(A) Medium blue	10	23
___		(B) Teal blue	26	66
___		(C) Purple-blue	93	265
___	**6044-1X**	Nestles/McCall's Boxcar, 62-63 u	335	1397
___	**6045**	Lionel Lines 2-D Tank Car, 59-64		
___		(A) Gray	10	22
___		(B) Orange	15	28
___		(C) Beige	10	21
___	**6045**	Cities Service 2-D Tank, 60 u	12	29
___	**6047**	Lionel Lines SP-type Caboose, 62		
___		(A) Unpainted medium red	2	7

		Good	Exc	
	(B) Painted brown	173	557	___
	(C) Unpainted coral pink	15	45	___
6050	Lionel Savings Bank Boxcar, 61			___
	(A) Type I body, Blt by Lionel	18	41	___
	(B) Type I body, Built by Lionel	42	132	___
	(C) Type IIa body, Blt by Lionel	125	260	___
6050-110	Swift Boxcar, 62-63			___
	(A) Red body	9	39	___
	(B) Dark red body, 2 open holes in roof	44	101	___
6050-175	Libby's Tomato Juice Boxcar, 63 u			___
	(A) Green stems on tomatoes	15	40	___
	(B) Green stems missing	24	58	___
	(C) No white lines between glass and tomatoes	25	67	___
6057	LL SP-type Caboose, 59-62			___
	(A) Unpainted red	3	19	___
	(B) Painted red	26	75	___
	(C) Unpainted coral pink	20	50	___
6057-50	LL SP-type Caboose, orange, 62	19	63	___
6058	C&O SP-type Caboose, 61			___
	(A) Blue lettering	18	45	___
	(B) Black lettering	29	62	___
6059	M&StL SP-type Caboose, 61-69			___
	(A) Painted red	15	32	___
	(B) Unpainted red	5	17	___
	(C) Unpainted maroon	6	12	___
6062	NYC Gondola with 3 cable reels, 59-62			___
	(A) No metal undercarriage	13	28	___
	(B) Metal undercarriage	23	57	___
	(C) No metal undercarriage, no paint on bottom	38	73	___
6062-50	NYC Gondola with 2 canisters, 69	10	20	___
6066T	Tender (no whistle)	10	20	___
6067	SP-type Caboose, unmarked, 61-62			___
	(A) Red	3	7	___
	(B) Yellow	6	12	___
	(C) Brown	7	21	___
6076	ATSF Hopper, 63 u	8	21	___
6076	Lehigh Valley Hopper, short, 63			___
	(A) Gray body	8	17	___
	(B) Black body	7	14	___
	(C) Red body	8	15	___
	(D) Yellow body, painted	371	1060	___
6076-100	Hopper, gray, unmarked, 63	9	27	___
6110	2-4-2 Locomotive, 6001T Tender, 50-51	19	37	___
6111	Flatcar with logs, 55-57			___
	(A) Yellow with black lettering	10	35	___

|---|---|---|---|
	(B) Yellow with white lettering	95	370
6112	Short Gondola with 4 canisters, 56-58		
	(A) Black body	6	21
	(B) Blue body	7	17
	(C) White body	16	43
6112-5	Canister, 56-58		
	(A) Red or white	2	3
	(B) Red with black letters	20	46
6112-25	Canister Set, 4 pieces, red or white, with box, 56-58	27	64
6119	DL&W Work Caboose, red, 55-56	11	23
6119-25	DL&W Work Caboose, orange, 56-59	19	44
6119-50	DL&W Work Caboose, brown, 56	22	78
6119-75	DL&W Work Caboose, 57		
	(A) Heat-stamped letters on frame	15	55
	(B) Closely spaced rubber-stamped letters on frame	64	216
	(C) Widely spaced rubber-stamped letters on frame	59	200
6119-100	DL&W Work Caboose, red cab, gray tool tray, 57-66, 69		
	(A) Black frame, white letters	10	23
	(B) Built By Lionel builders plate, 66	24	66
	(C) Black frame, red-painted cab	56	161
	(D) Santa Fe cab, gray tool box	10	34
6119-125	Rescue Caboose, unpainted olive tray, black frame, white lettering, 64	68	246
6120	Work Caboose, yellow, unmarked, 61-62	7	13
6121	Flatcar with pipes, 56-57		
	(A) Yellow, red, or gray	13	51
	(B) Maroon	18	64
6130	ATSF Work Caboose, 61, 65-69		
	(A) Red painted, no builders plate	15	39
	(B) Red unpainted, builders plate	10	31
	(C) Red painted, builders plate	67	226
6139	Remote Control Uncoupling Track (O27), 63	1	4
6142	Short Gondola, green, blue, or black, with 2 canisters, 63-66, 69	7	15
6142-175	Short Gondola, olive drab, with 2 canisters	60	190
6149	Remote Control Uncoupling Track (O27), 64-69	1	4
6151	Flatcar with patrol truck, 58		
	(A) Yellow frame	35	86
	(B) Orange frame	28	64
	(C) Cream frame	35	84
6162	NYC Gondola with 3 white canisters, 59-68		
	(A) Blue body	9	38
	(B) Red body	76	282
	(C) Teal body/or green body	30	65
6162-60	Alaska Gondola with 3 red canisters, 59	38	90
6162-100	NYC Gondola, 59-68		

POSTWAR 1945-1969		Good	Exc
	(A) Red body with 3 red canisters	80	160 ___
	(B) Teal or green body with 3 white canisters	15	33 ___
6167	LL SP-type Caboose, red, 63-64		___
	(A) Unpainted	5	9 ___
	(B) Painted	36	100 ___
6167	SP-type Caboose, unmarked, no end rails, 63-64		___
	(A) Red body	4	8 ___
	(B) Brown body	8	18 ___
6167-50	SP-type Caboose, unmarked, yellow	5	14 ___
6167-85	Union Pacific SP-type Caboose, 69	10	27 ___
6167-175	SP-type Caboose, unmarked, olive	96	293 ___
6175	Flatcar with rocket, 58-61		___
	(A) Black frame	27	62 ___
	(B) Red frame	26	58 ___
6176	Hopper, unmarked, 63-69		___
	(A) Dark yellow	11	27 ___
	(B) Gray	8	15 ___
	(C) Red	10	22 ___
	(D) Bright yellow	23	54 ___
6176-75	Lehigh Valley Hopper, 64-66, 69		___
	(A) Dark yellow	5	15 ___
	(B) Gray	6	11 ___
	(C) Black	4	9 ___
	(D) Red	12	28 ___
	(E) Bright yellow	22	56 ___
6176-100	Olive Drab Hopper, unmarked	50	130 ___
6219	C&O Work Caboose, 60	20	47 ___
6220	Santa Fe NW2 Switcher, 49-50		___
	(A) Large GM decal on cab	112	241 ___
	(B) Small GM decal on side	80	184 ___
6250	Seaboard NW2 Switcher, 54-55		___
	(A) Seaboard decal	84	393 ___
	(B) Widely spaced rubber-stamped letters	101	306 ___
	(C) Closely spaced rubber-stamped letters	136	406 ___
6257	SP-type Caboose, 48-52		___
	(A) Dark red, matching plastic smokestack	155	329 ___
	(B) All other variations	8	15 ___
6257-25	SP-type Caboose, circle-L logo, 53-55		___
	(A) Red painted	7	16 ___
	(B) Red unpainted	5	11 ___
6257-50	SP-type Caboose, 56	5	11 ___
6257-100	Lionel Lines SP-type Caboose, smokestack, 63-64	9	25 ___
6257X	SP-type Caboose, red, 2 couplers, with box, 48	27	173 ___
6262	Flatcar with wheel load, 56-57		___
	(A) Black frame, 56-57	27	55 ___
	(B) Red frame, 56	361	672 ___

		Good	Exc
___ 6264	Flatcar with lumber for 264 Fork Lift Platform, 57-60		
___	(A) Bar-end trucks	26	59
___	(B) Plastic trucks	29	64
	(C) Separate-sale box and envelope	113	329
___ 6311	Flatcar with 3 pipes, 55	20	47
___ 6315	Gulf 1-D Chemical Tank Car, 56-59, 68-69		
___	(A) Early, painted	30	77
___	(B) Late, unpainted	23	49
___	(C) Late, unpainted, built date	44	104
___ 6315	Lionel Lines 1-D Tank Car, 63-66		
___	(A) Unpainted orange body	15	38
___	(B) Painted orange body	91	279
___ 6342	NYC Gondola with culvert channel and 7 pipes, 56-58, 64-66	19	102
___ 6343	Barrel Ramp Car with 6 barrels, 61-62	20	83
___ 6346	Alcoa Quad Hopper, 56	28	66
___ 6352-1	PFE Ice Car from 352 Ice Depot, 55-57		
___	(A) 3 lines of data	57	115
___	(B) 4 lines of data	35	95
___	(C) Separate-sale box	696	2982
___ 6356	NYC Stock Car, 2-level, 54-55		
___	(A) Heat-stamped lettering	21	43
___	(B) Rubber-stamped lettering	28	80
___ 6357	SP-type Caboose, SP logo, 48-53		
___	(A) Tile red, Tuscan, or maroon	13	28
___	(B) Tile red, extra board on catwalk	125	478
___ 6357	SP-type Caboose, no logo, 57-61		
___	(A) Number to left	10	29
___	(B) Number to right	20	56
___ 6357-25	SP-type Caboose, circle-L logo, 53-56		
___	(A) Maroon or Tuscan body, black metal smokestack	12	25
___	(B) Maroon body, maroon metal smokestack	96	336
___ 6357-50	ATSF SP-type Caboose, lighted, 60	411	1147
___ 6361	Timber Transport Car, 60-61, 64-69		
___	(A) White lettering	32	74
___	(B) No lettering	53	147
___ 6362	Truck Car with 3 trucks, 55-56		
___	(A) Shiny orange	23	53
___	(B) Dull orange	35	75
___ 6376	LL Circus Stock Car, 56-57	27	78
___ 6401	Flatcar, no load, gray, 60	4	45
___ 6401-25	Gray flatcar with load, 64-67		
___	(A) Jeep and cannon	113	235
___	(B) Tank	95	213
___	(C) Payton automobile	23	48
___	(D) Logs	11	26

		Good	Exc
6402	Flatcar with 2 Cable Reels, 62, 64-66, 69		___
	(A) Gray car with orange reels	5	13 ___
	(B) Maroon car with orange reels	6	13 ___
	(C) Brown car with gray or orange reels	8	15 ___
	(D) Gray car with gray reels	8	15 ___
	(E) Gray car with green reels	10	25 ___
6402	Flatcar with blue boat, 69	28	67 ___
6402-25	Flatcar with 2 cable reels (gray or orange), 62, 64-66	12	25 ___
6402-150	Maroon Flatcar with white trailer	18	35 ___
6403B	Tender	35	79 ___
6404	Black Flatcar with auto, 60 u		___
	(A) Red auto	30	62 ___
	(B) Yellow auto	58	112 ___
	(C) Brown auto	88	220 ___
	(D) Green auto	104	249 ___
6405	Flatcar with piggyback van, 61	20	44 ___
6406	Flatcar with auto, 61		___
	(A) Maroon frame, red auto	32	61 ___
	(B) Maroon frame, yellow auto	63	128 ___
	(C) Gray frame, dark brown auto	116	249 ___
	(D) Gray frame, green auto	134	277 ___
	(E) Gray frame, yellow auto	60	109 ___
	(F) Gray frame, red auto	26	50 ___
6407	Flatcar with rocket, 63	164	510 ___
6408	Flatcar with pipes, 63 u	19	39 ___
6408-50	Flatcar with 2 orange cable reels, 67 u	16	36 ___
6409-25	Flatcar with pipes, 63 u	16	51 ___
6410-25	Flatcar with 2 automobiles, 63 u		___
	(A) Yellow autos	153	381 ___
	(B) Brown autos	195	480 ___
6411	Flatcar with logs, 48-50	15	36 ___
6413	Mercury Capsule Carrying Car, 62-63		___
	(A) Medium blue frame	68	165 ___
	(B) Aquamarine frame	88	198 ___
	(C) Teal frame	99	236 ___
6414	Evans Auto Loader with 4 cars, 55-66		___
	(A) Premium cars (chrome bumpers, windows, rubber wheels): red, yellow, blue-green, and white	42	109 ___
	(B) Cheapie cars (no wheels): 2 red and 2 yellow	155	297 ___
	(C) Red cars with gray bumpers	79	175 ___
	(D) Yellow cars with gray bumpers	206	395 ___
	(E) Brown cars with gray bumpers	282	768 ___
	(F) Green cars with gray bumpers	460	960 ___
	(H) Metal trucks, number right of Lionel without nubs on axle	54	127 ___

		Good	Exc
____	(G) Metal trucks, number right of Lionel, premium cars with nubs on axle first run	61	138
____ 6414-25	Set of 4 Automobiles, separate-sale box, 55-58	136	365
____ 6415	Sunoco 3-D Tank Car, 53-55, 64-66, 69	15	39
____ 6416	Boat Transport Car, 4 boats, 61-63	118	255
____ 6417	PRR N5c Porthole Caboose, 53-57		
____	(A) New York Zone	19	35
____	(B) Without New York Zone	123	245
____ 6417-25	Lionel Lines N5c Porthole Caboose, 54	15	63
____ 6417-50	LV N5c Porthole Caboose, 54		
____	(A) Gray	57	178
____	(B) Tuscan	422	1821
____ 6418	Machinery Car with 2 girders, 55-57		
____	(A) Black girders, Lionel in raised letters	57	114
____	(B) Orange girders, Lionel in raised letters	50	101
____	(C) Pinkish orange girders, U.S. Steel	65	122
____	(D) Black girders, U.S. Steel	65	123
____ 6419	DL&W Work Caboose, 48-50, 52-55	15	60
____ 6419-25	DL&W Work Caboose, one coupler, 54-55	18	46
____ 6419-50	DL&W Work Caboose, short smokestack, 56-57	16	40
____ 6419-75	DL&W Work Caboose, one coupler, 56-57	15	35
____ 6419-100	N&W Work Caboose, 57-58	46	130
____ 6420	DL&W Work Caboose with searchlight, 48-50		
____	(A) Heat-stamped serif lettering	41	81
____	(B) Rubber-stamped sans serif lettering	65	136
____ 6424	Twin Auto Flatcar, 56-59		
____	(A) Black frame, premium cars	27	64
____	(B) 6805 slots, no rail stops	51	113
____	(C) AAR trucks, number on right	31	66
____ 6424-110	Twin Auto Flatcar, 6805 slots and rail stops, 58-59	80	183
____ 6425	Gulf 3-D Tank Car, 56-58	12	35
____ 6427	Lionel Lines N5c Porthole Caboose, 54-60	15	52
____ 6427-60	Virginian N5c Porthole Caboose, 58	206	418
____ 6427-500	PRR N5c Porthole Caboose, sky blue, from Girls Set, 57-58*	152	330
____ 6428	U.S. Mail Boxcar, 60-61, 65-66	20	74
____ 6429	DL&W Work Caboose, AAR trucks, 63	108	269
____ 6430	Flatcar with 2 trailers, 56-58		
____	(A) Gray Cooper-Jarrett trailers	27	94
____	(B) White Cooper-Jarrett trailers	31	95
____	(C) Green Fruehauf trailers	27	56
____	(D) Gray Cooper-Jarrett trailers with Fruehauf stickers	35	81
____ 6431	Flatcar with 2 vans and Midgetoy tractor, 66		
____	(A) White vans, 66	69	155
____	(B) Yellow vans, 66	149	352
____ 6434	Poultry Dispatch Stock Car, 58-59	31	80

		Good	Exc
6436-1	LV Open Quad Hopper, black, 55-56, 66		___
	(A) No spreader brace holes	50	117 ___
	(B) Spreader brace with holes	10	36 ___
6436-25	LV Open Quad Hopper, maroon, 55-57		___
	(A) No spreader brace holes	105	253 ___
	(B) Spreader brace with holes	20	77 ___
6436-110	LV Quad Hopper, red, 63-68		___
	(A) No built date	19	43 ___
	(B) Built date New 3-55	39	88 ___
6436-500	LV Open Quad Hopper, lilac, from Girls Set, 57-58*		___
	(A) No spreader brace holes	153	390 ___
	(B) Spreader brace with holes	112	290 ___
6436-1969	TCA (Train Collectors Association) Open Quad Hopper, 69u	47	110 ___
6437	PRR N5c Porthole Caboose, 61-68	17	67 ___
6440	Flatcar with gray vans, 61-63	34	80 ___
6440	Green Pullman Car, 48-49	33	79 ___
6441	Green Observation Car, 48-49	29	71 ___
6442	Brown Pullman Car, 49	35	76 ___
6443	Brown Observation Car, 49	27	67 ___
6445	Fort Knox Gold Reserve Boxcar with coin slot, 61-63	43	94 ___
6446	N&W Covered Quad Hopper, black or gray, 54-55	28	57 ___
6446-25	N&W Covered Quad Hopper, 55-57		___
	(A) Black, white lettering	27	78 ___
	(B) Gray, black lettering	32	71 ___
	(C) Gray, AAR truck, spreader brace holes	64	136 ___
6446-60	LV Covered Quad Hopper, 63	84	201 ___
6447	PRR N5c Porthole Caboose, 63	124	316 ___
6448	Exploding Target Range Boxcar, 61-64		___
	(A) Red sides, white roof and ends	15	63 ___
	(B) White sides, red roof and ends	14	35 ___
6452	Pennsylvania Gondola, black, 48-49		___
	(A) Numbered "6462," 48	18	43 ___
	(B) Numbered "6452," 49	8	16 ___
X6454	Baby Ruth PRR Boxcar, 48	81	245 ___
X6454	Santa Fe Boxcar, 48	13	32 ___
X6454	NYC Boxcar, 48		___
	(A) Brown body	13	30 ___
	(B) Orange body	52	146 ___
	(C) Tan body	21	56 ___
X6454	Erie Boxcar, 49-52		___
	(A) Corner steps, 49	14	34 ___
	(B) No steps, 50-52	10	26 ___
X6454	PRR Boxcar, 49-52		___
	(A) Corner steps, 49	15	32 ___
	(B) No steps, 50-52	10	26 ___

			Good	Exc
___ X6454	SP Boxcar, 49-52			
___	(A) Steps, break in herald circle between R and N, 49		28	83
___	(B) No steps, full circle in herald, 50		16	60
___	(C) No steps, red-brown body, 51-52		16	37
___ 6456	Lehigh Valley Short Hopper, 48-55			
___	(A) Black		11	22
___	(B) Maroon		9	18
___ 6456-25	Lehigh Valley Short Hopper, gray, 54-55		19	93
___ 6456-50	Lehigh Valley Short Hopper, enamel red, white lettering, 54		241	704
___ 6456-75	Lehigh Valley Short Hopper, enamel red, yellow lettering, 54		66	137
___ 6457	SP-type Caboose, 49-52			
___	(A) Tuscan body and plastic smokejack		14	25
___	(B) Tuscan body and brown metal smokejack		9	15
___	(C) Tuscan body and black metal smokejack		12	22
___	(D) Maroon body and black metal smokejack		12	20
___ 6460	Bucyrus Erie Crane Car, black cab, 8-wheel, 52-54		20	39
___ 6460-25	Bucyrus Erie Crane Car, red cab, 8-wheel, 54		39	92
___ 6461	Transformer Car, 49-50		30	68
___ 6462	NYC Gondola, black or red, with 6 barrels, 49-54		9	20
___ 6462-25	NYC Gondola, green, with 6 barrels, 54-57			
___	(A) N in second panel, 2 lines of data		12	30
___	(B) N in third panel, 3 lines of data		16	45
___ 6462-75	NYC Gondola, red-painted, with 6 barrels, 52-55		12	31
___ 6462-125	NYC Gondola, red plastic, with 6 barrels, 55-57		8	29
___ 6462-500	NYC Gondola, pink, from Girls Set, with 4 canisters, 57-58*		79	184
___ 6463	Rocket Fuel 2-D Tank Car, 62-63		20	61
___ 6464-1	WP Boxcar, 53-54			
___	(A) Blue lettering		26	69
___	(B) Red lettering		534	1509
___ 6464-25	GN Boxcar, 53-54		34	79
___ 6464-50	M&StL Boxcar, 53-56		28	67
___ 6464-75	RI Boxcar, green, 53-54, 69			
___	(A) Built date, 53-54		29	80
___	(B) No built date, 69		39	91
___ 6464-100	Western Pacific Boxcar, 54-55			
___	(A) Silver body, yellow feather		41	217
___	(B) Orange body, blue feather		231	752
___ 6464-125	NYC Pacemaker Boxcar, 54-56		40	127
___ 6464-150	MP Boxcar, 54-55, 57			
___	(A) Unpainted royal blue or navy blue body		42	94
___	(B) Painted royal blue or navy blue body		40	92
___	(C) Herald in fifth panel (first panel to left of door)		500	1200
___	(D) New 3 54 on left and XME on lower right		45	98

		Good	Exc
6464-175	Rock Island Boxcar, 54-55		___
	(A) Blue lettering	39	266 ___
	(B) Black lettering	414	1040 ___
6464-200	Pennsylvania Boxcar, 54-55, 69		___
	(A) Built date NEW 5-53	60	130 ___
	(B) No built date	56	127 ___
6464-225	SP Boxcar, 54-56	44	113 ___
6464-250	WP Boxcar, 66	69	243 ___
6464-275	State of Maine Boxcar, 55, 57-59		
	(A) Striped doors	39	83 ___
	(B) Solid doors	57	124 ___
	(C) Striped doors, AAR trucks, 59	22	46 ___
6464-300	Rutland Boxcar, 55-56		___
	(A) Rubber-stamped lettering	46	103 ___
	(B) Split door with bottom painted green	385	1124 ___
	(C) Rubber-stamped lettering with solid shield	2165	3958 ___
	(D) Heat-stamped lettering	74	214 ___
	(E) Painted yellow body, rubber-stamped lettering	500	1500 ___
	(E) Painted yellow body, heat-stamped lettering	1350	4150 ___
	(F) Blue body painted yellow and green, heat-stamped lettering	350	750 ___
6464-325	B&O Sentinel Boxcar, 56	185	445 ___
6464-350	MKT Boxcar, 56	136	257 ___
6464-375	Central of Georgia Boxcar, 56-57, 66		___
	(A) Unpainted maroon body, 56-57	41	100 ___
	(B) Painted red body, 66	775	3071 ___
6464-400	B&O Time-Saver Boxcar, 56-57, 69		___
	(A) BLT 5-54	42	89 ___
	(B) BLT 2-56	112	287 ___
	(C) No built date	45	143 ___
	(D) 54 built date on one side/56 built date on other	500	975 ___
6464-425	New Haven Boxcar, 56-58, 69	29	54 ___
6464-450	Great Northern Boxcar, 56-57, 66	68	139 ___
6464-475	B&M Boxcar, 57-60, 65-66, 68		___
	(A) Medium blue-painted or unpainted plastic	34	97 ___
	(B) Dark purple-painted, gray or blue mold	76	258 ___
	(C) Dark blue-painted, yellow mold	168	425 ___
6464-500	Timken Boxcar, white side band and charcoal lettering, 57-59, 69		___
	(A) Unpainted yellow body	45	128 ___
	(B) Painted yellow body, Type II	149	391 ___
	(C) Painted yellow body, Type IV	54	162 ___
6464-510	NYC Pacemaker Boxcar (pastel blue), 57-58	314	609 ___
6464-515	MKT Boxcar (pastel yellow), 57-58	321	643 ___
6464-525	M&StL Boxcar, 57-58, 64-66		___
	(A) Red, white lettering	30	94 ___
	(B) Maroon, white lettering	120	328 ___

| --- | --- | --- | --- |
6464-650	D&RGW Boxcar, 57-58, 66		
	(A) Yellow body, silver roof, black stripe	65	150
	(B) Yellow body, type II, silver roof, no black stripe	549	1304
	(C) Painted yellow body and yellow roof	775	2304
	(D) Yellow body, silver roof, no black stripe on one side only	400	1100
	(E) Yellow body, type IV, silver roof, black stripe on one side only	400	1100
6464-700	Santa Fe Boxcar, 61, 66	47	153
6464-725	New Haven Boxcar, 62-66, 68		
	(A) Orange body	31	59
	(B) Black body	69	208
6464-825	Alaska Boxcar, 59-60	113	305
6464-900	NYC Boxcar, 60-66		
	(A) Green Doors	33	65
	(B) Black Doors	30	62
6465	Gulf 2-D Tank Car, 58		
	(A) Black tank	14	46
	(B) Gray tank	11	27
6465	Sunoco 2-D Tank Car, 48-56		
	(A) Silver tank, rubber-stamped 6465	6	15
	(B) Silver tank, rubber-stamped 6455	19	56
	(C) Silver tank, no number on frame	7	16
	(D) Glossy gray tank	10	29
6465-85	LL 2-D Tank Car, black, 59	18	292
6465-110	Cities Service 2-D Tank, 60-62	22	77
6465-160	LL 2-D Tank Car, orange with black ends, 63-64	11	34
6466T	Tender, 49-53 (no whistle)	15	30
6466W	Whistle Tender, 49-53	21	46
6466WX	Whistle Tender, 49-53	25	50
6467	Miscellaneous Car, 56	23	50
6468	B&O Auto Boxcar, blue, 53-55	16	41
6468X	B&O Auto Boxcar, Tuscan, 53-55	120	302
6468-25	NH Auto Boxcar, 56-58		
	(A) Black N over white H, black doors	25	58
	(B) White N over black H, black doors	75	300
	(C) Black N over white H, painted Tuscan doors	41	108
6469	Liquified Gas Tank Car, 63	38	87
6470	Explosives Boxcar, 59-60	12	36
6472	Refrigerator Car, 50-53	12	24
6473	Horse Transport Car, 62-69	15	27
6475	Libby's Crushed Pineapple Vat Car, 63 u	42	135
6475	Pickles Vat Car, 60-62	22	80
6476	LV Short Hopper, 57-63		
	(A) Red body	6	17
	(B) Gray body	8	21
	(C) Black body	6	16

| --- | --- | --- | --- |
6476-75	LV Short Hopper, black, Type VI body, 63	8	17 ___
6476-135	LV Short Hopper, yellow, 64-66, 68	16	55 ___
6476-160	LV Short Hopper, black, 69	6	17 ___
6476-185	LV Short Hopper, yellow, 69	6	17 ___
6477	Miscellaneous Car with pipes, 57-58	24	65 ___
6480	Explosives Boxcar, red, 61	16	36 ___
6482	Refrigerator Car, 57	18	39 ___
6500	Flatcar with Bonanza airplane, 62, 65		___
	(A) Plane, red top and wings	332	647 ___
	(B) Plane, white top and wings	458	1003 ___
6501	Flatcar with jet boat, 62-63	55	135 ___
6502	Flatcar with Girder, 62	6	30 ___
	(A) Black flatcar	21	70 ___
	(B) Red flatcar	31	82 ___
6502-50	Flatcar, blue or teal, no lettering, with bridge girder, 62	16	39 ___
6511	Flatcar with pipes, 53-56		___
	(A) Die-cast metal truck plates, 53	18	56 ___
	(B) Red car, stamped metal truck plates	15	67 ___
	(C) Brown car, stamped metal truck plates	7	25 ___
6511-24	Set of 6 pipes with box, 55-58	53	163 ___
6512	Cherry Picker Car, 62-63	29	80 ___
6517	LL Bay Window Caboose, 55-59		___
	(A) Built date underscored	26	66 ___
	(B) Built date not underscored	20	96 ___
	(C) Built date not underscored, lettering higher	21	53 ___
6517-75	Erie Bay Window Caboose, 66	164	486 ___
6518	Transformer Car, 56-58	22	76 ___
6519	Allis-Chalmers Flatcar, 58-61		___
	(A) Dark or medium orange base	24	78 ___
	(B) Dull light orange base	39	98 ___
6520	Searchlight Car, 49-51		___
	(A) Tan generator	694	1468 ___
	(B) Green generator	111	260 ___
	(C) Maroon generator	18	43 ___
	(D) Orange generator	15	37 ___
	(E) Green generator, black searchlight housing	116	282 ___
6530	Firefighting Instruction Car, 60-61		___
	(A) Red body, white lettering	27	70 ___
	(B) Black body, white lettering	118	309 ___
6536	M&StL Open Quad Hopper, 58-59, 63		___
	(A) AAR trucks, 59, 63	26	60 ___
	(B) Bar-end trucks, 58	45	113 ___
6544	Missile Firing Car, 4 missiles, 60-64		___
	(A) White-lettered console	48	222 ___
	(B) Black-lettered console	105	295 ___
6555	Sunoco 1-D Tank Car, 49-50	14	83 ___

|---|---|---|
__ **6556** MKT Stock Car, 58	143	274
__ **6557** SP-type Smoking Caboose, 58-59		
(A) Tuscan, with non-reverse lettering	100	222
(B) Brown, with reverse lettering	509	1283
__ **6560** Bucyrus Erie Crane Car, smokestack, 55-58, 68-69		
(A) Black frame, unpainted red-orange cab	34	92
(B) Black frame, painted red cab, no 6560	45	168
(C) Black frame, unpainted gray cab	22	55
(D) Black frame, unpainted red cab, closed crank spokes	11	21
(E) Black frame, unpainted red cab, no 6560 on frame	13	24
(F) Black frame, unpainted red cab, open crank spokes	10	20
(G) Black frame, black cab	57	144
(H) Dark blue frame, bronze hook	19	56
__ **6560-25** Bucyrus Erie Crane Car, 8-wheel, marked 656025, 56	32	142
__ **6561** Cable Car, 2 reels, 53-56		
(A) Orange reels	17	60
(B) Gray reels	25	79
__ **6562** NYC Gondola with 4 red canisters, 56-58		
(A) Gray body, 56	17	133
(B) Red body, 56, 58	13	30
(C) Black body, 57	14	28
__ **6572** REA Refrigerator Car, 58-59, 63		
(A) Passenger trucks	77	188
(B) Bar-end trucks	37	96
(C) AAR trucks, 63	28	68
__ **6630** Missile Launching Car, 61	25	61
__ **6636** Alaska Open Quad Hopper, 59-60	34	78
__ **6640** USMC Missile Launching Car, 60	74	196
__ **6646** Lionel Lines Stock Car, 57	14	41
__ **6650** IRBM Rocket Launcher, 59-63		
(A) 6650 stamped on left	19	75
(B) 6650 stamped on right	88	246
__ **6650-80** Missile, 60	5	10
__ **6651** USMC Cannon Car, 64 u	76	210
__ **6654W** Whistle Tender	19	37
__ **6656** Lionel Lines Stock Car, 49-55		
(A) Brown Armour decal	21	49
(B) No decal	10	22
__ **6657** Rio Grande SP-type Caboose, 57-58		
(A) With ladder slots	54	177
(B) Without ladder slots	130	331
__ **6660** Boom Car, 58	25	133
__ **6670** Derrick Car, 59-60		
(A) 6670 stamped on left	25	62
(B) 6670 stamped on right	66	206

| --- | --- | --- | --- |
6672	Santa Fe Refrigerator Car, 54-56		___
	(A) Blue lettering, 2 lines of data	20	46 ___
	(B) Black lettering, 2 lines of data	25	55 ___
	(C) Blue lettering, 3 lines of data	86	253 ___
6736	Detroit & Mackinac Open Quad Hopper, 60-62	18	73 ___
6800	Flatcar with airplane, 57-60		___
	(A) Plane, black top and wings	39	84 ___
	(B) Plane, yellow top and wings	50	100 ___
6800-60	Airplane, separate sale w/box, 57-58	87	231 ___
6801	Flatcar with boat, white hull, brown deck, 57	26	61 ___
6801-50	Flatcar with boat, yellow hull, white deck, 58-60	40	78 ___
6801-60	Boat, separate sale w/box, 57-58	41	111 ___
6801-75	Flatcar with boat, blue hull, white deck, 58-60	34	81 ___
6802	Flatcar with 2 U.S. Steel girders, 58-59	20	64 ___
6803	Flatcar with USMC tank and sound truck, 58-59	108	224 ___
6804	Flatcar with USMC antiaircraft and sound trucks, 58-59	114	223 ___
6805	Atomic Energy Disposal Flatcar, 58-59	46	268 ___
6806	Flatcar with USMC radar and medical trucks, 58-59	101	227 ___
6807	Flatcar with amphibious vehicle, 58-59	67	203 ___
6808	Flatcar with USMC tank and searchlight truck, 58-59	109	257 ___
6809	Flatcar with USMC antiaircraft and medical trucks, 58-59	101	227 ___
6810	Flatcar with trailer, 58	21	43 ___
6812	Track Maintenance Car, 59		___
	(A) Dark yellow superstructure	20	67 ___
	(B) Black base, gray platform and crank handle	20	60 ___
	(C) Gray base, black platform and crank handle	19	62 ___
	(D) Cream superstructure	49	198 ___
	(E) Light yellow superstructure	22	64 ___
6814	Rescue Caboose, 59-61	41	112 ___
6816	Flatcar with Allis-Chalmers bulldozer, 59-60		___
	(A) Red car	169	575 ___
	(B) Black car	625	1205 ___
6816-100	Allis-Chalmers Bulldozer, 59-60		___
	(A) No box	81	246 ___
	(B) Separate-sale box	257	594 ___
6817	Flatcar with Allis-Chalmers motor scraper, 59-60		___
	(A) Red car	175	419 ___
	(B) Black car	652	1175 ___
6817-100	Allis-Chalmers motor scraper, 59-60		___
	(A) No box	140	286 ___
	(B) Separate-sale box	255	659 ___
6818	Flatcar with transformer, 58	19	56 ___
6819	Flatcar with helicopter, 59-60	23	56 ___
6820	Aerial Missile Transport Car with helicopter, 60-61		___
	(A) Light blue frame	88	218 ___
	(B) Medium blue frame	69	185 ___

			Good	Exc
___ 6821	Flatcar with crates, 59-60		16	56
___ 6822	Searchlight Car, 61-69			
___	(A) Black base, gray light		15	45
___	(B) Gray base, black light		22	39
___ 6823	Flatcar with 2 IRBM missiles, 59-60		28	77
___ 6824	USMC Work Caboose, 60		94	249
___ 6824-50	Rescue Caboose, white, 64		39	101
___ 6825	Flatcar with arch trestle bridge, 59-62		17	46
___ 6826	Flatcar with Christmas trees, 59-60		30	105
___ 6827	Flatcar with Harnischfeger power shovel, 60-63		82	286
___ 6827-100	Harnischfeger power shovel, 60			
___	(A) No box		62	125
___	(B) Separate-sale box		115	257
___ 6828	Flatcar with Harnischfeger crane, 60-63, 66			
___	(A) Black flatcar, light yellow crane cab		76	235
___	(B) Black flatcar, dark yellow crane cab		79	271
___	(C) Red flatcar, dark yellow crane cab		419	1174
___ 6828-100	Harnischfeger Construction Crane, 60			
___	(A) No box		45	110
___	(B) Separate-sale box		97	252
___ 6830	Flatcar with submarine, 60-61		49	113
___ 6844	Missile Carrying Car, 6 missiles, 59-60			
___	(A) Black frame		29	76
___	(B) Red frame		411	1170

Other Track, Transformers, and Assorted Items

		Good	Exc
___ A	Transformer, 90 watts, 47-48	13	34
___ CO-1	Track Clips, dozen, with envelope (O), 49	5	53
___ CO-1	Track Clips, box of 50 (O), 49	28	73
___ CO-1	Track Clips, box of 100 (O), 49	42	115
___ CTC	Lockon (O and O27), 47-69	1	3
___ CTC-14	Lockons, dozen, with envelope	11	33
___ ECU-1	Electronic Control Unit, 46	35	91
___ KW	Transformer, 190 watts, 50-65	38	80
___ LTC	Lockon (O and O27), 50-69	2	16
___ LW	Transformer, 125 watts, 55-56	35	63
___ OC	Curved Track (O), 45-61	1	3
___ OC1/2	Half Section Curved Track (O), 45-66	0	2
___ OCS	Curved Insulated Track (O), 46-50	6	15
___ OS	Straight Track (O), 45-61	0	2
___ OSS	Straight Insulated Track, 46-50	5	18
___ OTC	Lockon Track (O and O27)	2	3
___ Q	Transformer, 75 watts, 46	11	24
___ R	Transformer, 110 watts, 46-47	16	33
___ RCS	Remote Control Track (O), 45-48	3	10
___ RW	Transformer, 110 watts, 48-54	14	35

		Good	Exc
RX	Transformer, 100 watts, 47-48	13	29 ___
S	Transformer, 80 watts, 47	10	26 ___
SP	Smoke Pellets, bottle, 48-69		___
	(A) Tall, light amber bottle	12	36 ___
	(B) Tall, dark amber bottle	12	35 ___
	(C) Short, light amber bottle	17	39 ___
	(D) All other bottles	6	26 ___
	(E) Bottle on blister pack, 65	23	58 ___
SP-12	Dealer Display Box with 12 full smoke bottles	115	300 ___
ST-295	Nut Driver, 5/32-inch		29 ___
ST-296	Nut Driver, 3/16-inch		43 ___
ST-297	Nut Driver, 7/32-inch		58 ___
ST-300	Nut Driver Set with holder, service station item	557	946 ___
ST-301	Wheel Puller, service station item	63	139 ___
ST-302	Spring Adjusting Tool	100	179 ___
ST-303	E Unit Spreader, service station item	46	83 ___
ST-311	Wheel Puller, service station item	77	172 ___
ST-320	Phillips Screwdriver, service station item	107	213 ___
ST-321	Flathead Screwdriver, short, service station item	137	254 ___
ST-322	Flathead Screwdriver, long, service station item	40	113 ___
ST-325	Screwdriver Set, service station item	400	875 ___
ST-342	Track Pliers, service station item	73	144 ___
ST-343	O Gauge Track Pliers, service station item	213	491 ___
ST-350	Rivet Press, service station item	414	679 ___
ST-350-6	Rivet Press Tool Block with tools, service station item	312	528 ___
ST-350-17	Sliding Shoe Anvil, service station item	17	31 ___
ST-375	Wheel Cup Tool Set, service station item	436	769 ___
ST-378	E-Unit Vice, service station item	131	319 ___
ST-384	Track Pliers, service station item	127	215 ___
SW	Transformer, 130 watts, 61-66	27	94 ___
TW	Transformer, 175 watts, 53-60	39	82 ___
TOC	Curved Track (O), 62-66, 68-69	1	2 ___
TOC1/2	Half Section Straight Track (O), 62-66	1	2 ___
TOS	Straight Track (O), 62-69	1	3 ___
UCS	Remote Control Track (O), 45-69	5	15 ___
UTC	Lockon (O, O27, Standard), 45	2	4 ___
V	Transformer, 150 watts, 46-47	34	71 ___
VW	Transformer, 150 watts, 48-49	38	78 ___
Z	Transformer, 250 watts, 45-47	62	105 ___
ZW	Transformer, 250 watts, 48-49	57	339 ___
ZW	Transformer, 275 watts, 50-56	77	146 ___
ZW	Transformer, 275 watts, R type, 57-66	91	206 ___

Section 3
MODERN 1970–2023

			Exc	Mint
___	366	Menards C&NW 4-4-2 Locomotive with tender, 09	45	75
___	400	Menards C&NW Chicago Combine Car, 09	25	40
___	403	Menards C&NW Lake Superior Observation Car, 09	25	40
___	410	Menards C&NW Lake Michigan Coach, 09	40	65
___	0512	Toy Fair Reefer, 81 u	60	70
___	550C	31" Diameter Curved Track (O), 70	1	2
___	550S	Straight Track (O), 70	1	2
___	665E	Johnny Cash Blue Train 4-6-4 Locomotive, 71 u		NRS
___	1050	New Englander Set, 80-81	155	205
___	1051	Texas & Pacific Diesel Set, 80	150	175
___	1052	Chesapeake Flyer Set, 80	140	150
___	1053	James Gang Set, 80-82	145	195
___	1070	Royal Limited Set, 80	238	350
___	1071	Mid Atlantic Limited Set, 80	225	230
___	1072	Cross Country Express Set, 80-81	197	385
___	1081	Wabash Cannonball Set, 70-72	105	120
___	1082	Yard Boss Set, 70	110	165
___	1083	Pacemaker Set, 70	105	120
___	1084	Grand Trunk Western Freight Set, 70	120	140
___	1085	Santa Fe Express Diesel Freight Set, 70	175	190
___	1086	Mountaineer Train Set, 70	120	145
___	1087	Midnight Express Train Set, 70	125	150
___	1091	Sears Special Steam Freight Set, 70 u	150	165
___	1092	Sears GTW Steam Freight Set, 70 u	150	165
___	1100	Happy Huff n' Puff, 74-75 u	55	70
___	1150	L.A.S.E.R. Train Set, 81-82	153	203
___	1151	Union Pacific Thunder Freight Set, 81-82	150	175
___	1153	JCPenney Thunderball Freight Set, 81 u	165	180
___	1154	Reading Yard King Set, 81-82	170	190
___	1155	Cannonball Freight Set, 82	75	85
___	1157	Lionel Leisure Wabash Cannonball Set, 81 u		250
___	1158	Maple Leaf Limited Set, 81	405	435
___	1159	Toys 'R' Us Midnight Flyer Set, 81 u	135	145
___	1160	Great Lakes Limited Set, 81	178	330
___	T-1171	CN Locomotive Set, 71 u	240	275
___	T-1172	Yardmaster Set, 71 u		200
___	T-1173	Grand Trunk Western Freight Set, 71-73 u	175	195
___	T-1174	Canadian National Set, 71-73 u	265	300
___	1182	Yardmaster Set, 71-72	85	105
___	1183	Silver Star Set, 71-72	65	80
___	1184	Allegheny Set, 71	120	150
___	1186	Cross Country Express Set, 71-72	210	260
___	1187	Illinois Central Set (SSS), 71	400	485
___	1190	Sears Special #1 Set, 71 u	88	103
___	1195	JCPenney Special Set, 71 u	150	165
___	1198	Unnamed Set, 71 u		175
___	1199	Ford-Autolite Allegheny Set, 71 u	187	207
___	1200	Gravel Gus, 75 u	75	100
___	1223	Seattle & North Coast Hi-Cube Boxcar, 86	25	225
___	1250	New York Central Set (SSS), 72	315	380

		Exc	Mint	
1252	Heavy Iron Set, 82-83	90	130	___
1253	Quicksilver Express Set, 82-83	265	340	___
1254	Black Cave Flyer Set, 82	75	105	___
1260	Continental Limited Set, 82	183	388	___
1261	Sears Black Cave Flyer Set, 82 u	165	195	___
1262	Toys 'R' Us Heavy Iron Set, 82 u	150	165	___
1263	JCPenney Overland Freight Set, 82 u	150	165	___
1264	NIBCO Express Set, 82 u	190	215	___
1265	Tappan Special Set, 82 u	130	155	___
T-1272	Yardmaster Set, 72-73 u	150	165	___
T-1273	Silver Star Set, 72-73 u	90	115	___
1280	Kickapoo Valley & Northern Set, 72	55	75	___
1284	Allegheny Set, 72	140	165	___
1285	Santa Fe Twin Diesel Set, 72	95	140	___
1287	Pioneer Dockside Switcher Set, 72	95	100	___
1290	Sears Steam Freight Set, 72 u	150	165	___
1291	Sears Steam Freight Set, 72 u	150	165	___
1300	Gravel Gus Junior, 75 u	70	90	___
1350	Canadian Pacific Set (SSS), 73	460	620	___
1351	Baltimore & Ohio Set, 83-84	205	280	___
1352	Rocky Mountain Freight Set, 83-84	75	95	___
1353	Southern Streak Set, 83-85	75	95	___
1354	Northern Freight Flyer Set, 83-85	230	280	___
1355	Commando Assault Train, 83-84	175	262	___
1359	Display Case for Set 1355, 83 u	75	95	___
1361	Gold Coast Limited Set, 83	265	400	___
1362	Lionel Leisure BN Express Set, 83 u	200	300	___
1380	U.S. Steel Industrial Switcher Set, 73-75	55	83	___
1381	Cannonball Set, 73-75	70	75	___
1382	Yardmaster Set, 73-74	110	135	___
1383	Santa Fe Freight Set, 73-75	100	125	___
1384	Southern Express Set, 73-76	75	120	___
1385	Blue Streak Freight Set, 73-74	100	120	___
1386	Rock Island Express Set, 73-74	120	140	___
1387	Milwaukee Road Special Set, 73	146	285	___
1388	Golden State Arrow Set, 73-75	215	240	___
1390	Sears 7-unit Steam Freight Set, 73 u	170	190	___
1392	Sears 8-unit Steam Freight Set, 73 u	150	165	___
1393	Sears 6-unit Diesel Freight Set, 73 u	150	165	___
1395	JCPenney Set, 73 u	150	165	___
1400	Happy Huff n' Puff Junior, 75 u	130	140	___
1402	Chessie System Set, 84-85	125	150	___
1403	Redwood Valley Express Set, 84-85	170	205	___
1450	D&RGW Set (SSS), 74	233	404	___
1451	Erie-Lackawanna Limited Set, 84	293	443	___
1460	Grand National Set, 74	300	330	___
1461	Black Diamond Set, 74 u, 75	100	120	___
1463	Coca-Cola Special Set, 74 u, 75	229	289	___
1487	Broadway Limited Set, 74-75	160	255	___
1489	Santa Fe Double Diesel Set, 74-76	140	165	___
1492	Sears 7-unit Steam Freight Set, 74 u	150	165	___
1493	Sears 7-unit Steam Freight Set, 74 u	150	165	___
1499	JCPenney Great Express Set, 74 u	150	165	___
1501	Midland Freight Set, 85-86	75	95	___

			Exc	Mint
___	**1502**	Yard Chief Set, 85-86	205	230
___	**1506**	Sears Centennial Chessie System Set, 85 u	165	195
___	**1512**	JCPenney Midland Freight Set, 85 u	90	115
___	**1549**	Toys 'R' Us Heavy Iron Set, 85-89 u	160	218
___	**1552**	Burlington Northern Limited Set, 85	450	570
___	**1560**	North American Express Set, 75	275	365
___	**1562**	Fast Freight Flyer Set, 85 u	120	140
___	**1577**	Liberty Special Set, 75 u	212	275
___	**1579**	Milwaukee Road Set (SSS), 75	325	410
___	**1581**	Thunderball Freight Set, 75-76	90	100
___	**1582**	Yard Chief Set, 75-76	115	155
___	**1584**	N&W "Spirit of America" Set, 75	140	180
___	**1585**	75th Anniversary Special Set, 75-77	159	227
___	**1586**	Chesapeake Flyer Set, 75-77	160	190
___	**1587**	Capitol Limited Set, 75	270	300
___	**1593**	Sears Set, 75 u		100
___	**1595**	Sears 6-unit Diesel Freight Set, 75 u	150	165
___	**1602**	Nickel Plate Special Set, 86-91	120	125
___	**1606**	Sears Centennial Nickel Plate Set, 86 u	165	195
___	**1608**	American Express General Set, 86 u	205	320
___	**1615**	Cannonball Express Set, 86-90	65	75
___	**1632**	Santa Fe Work Train (SSS), 86	174	210
___	**1652**	B&O Freight Set, 86	140	185
___	**1658**	Town House TV and Appliances Set, 86 u	80	95
___	**1660**	Yard Boss Set, 76	100	115
___	**1661**	Rock Island Line Set, 76-77	80	100
___	**1662**	Black River Freight Set, 76-78	75	95
___	**1663**	Amtrak Lake Shore Limited Set, 76-77	193	265
___	**1664**	Illinois Central Freight Set, 76-77	265	355
___	**1665**	NYC Empire State Express Set, 76	229	417
___	**1672**	Northern Pacific Set (SSS), 76	215	280
___	**1685**	True Value Freight Flyer Set, 86-87 u	60	75
___	**1686**	Kay Bee Toys Freight Flyer Set, 86 u	150	165
___	**1687**	Freight Flyer Set, 87-90	39	47
___	**1693**	Toys 'R' Us Rock Island Line Set, 76 u	110	130
___	**1694**	Toys 'R' Us Black River Freight Set, 76 u	115	135
___	**1696**	Sears Steam Freight Set, 76 u	110	130
___	**1698**	True Value Rock Island Line Set, 76 u	125	145
___	**1760**	Trains n' Truckin' Steel Hauler Set, 77-78	105	110
___	**1761**	Trains n' Truckin' Cargo King Set, 77-78	95	165
___	**1762**	Wabash Cannonball Set, 77	135	190
___	**1764**	Heartland Express Set, 77	185	240
___	**1765**	Rocky Mountain Special Set, 77	210	315
___	**1766**	B&O Budd Car Set (SSS), 77	335	390
___	**1776**	Seaboard U36B Diesel w/wo printing on chassis, 74-76	74	123
___	**1790**	Lionel Leisure Steel Hauler Set, 77 u	150	200
___	**1791**	Toys 'R' Us Steel Hauler Set, 77 u	130	175
___	**1792**	True Value Rock Island Line Set, 77 u	100	135
___	**1793**	Toys 'R' Us Black River Freight Set, 77 u	120	155
___	**1796**	JCPenney Cargo Master Set, 77 u		200
___	**1860**	"Workin' on the Railroad" Timberline Set, 78	65	85
___	**1862**	"Workin' on the Railroad" Logging Empire Set, 78	85	110
___	**1864**	Santa Fe Double Diesel Set, 78-79	155	190

		Exc	Mint	
1865	Chesapeake Flyer Set, 78-79	155	180	___
1866	Great Plains Express Set, 78-79	172	285	___
1867	Milwaukee Road Limited Set, 78	175	275	___
1868	M&StL Set (SSS), 78	215	255	___
1892	JCPenney Logging Empire Set, 78 u	95	125	___
1893	Toys 'R' Us Logging Empire Set, 78 u	175	225	___
1960	Midnight Flyer Set, 79-81	55	75	___
1962	Wabash Cannonball Set, 79	90	105	___
1963	Black River Freight Set, 79-81	75	85	___
1965	Smokey Mountain Line Set, 79	65	85	___
1970	Southern Pacific Limited Set, 79 u	213	365	___
1971	Quaker City Limited Set, 79	182	335	___
1990	Mystery Glow Midnight Flyer Set, 79 u	75	90	___
1991	JCPenney Wabash Cannonball Deluxe Express Set, 79 u	150	165	___
1993	Toys 'R' Us Midnight Flyer Set, 79 u	115	135	___
2110	Graduated Trestle Set, 22 pieces, 70-88	9	13	___
2111	Elevated Trestle Set, 10 pieces, 70-88	8	11	___
2113	Tunnel Portals, pair, 84-87	11	16	___
2115	Dwarf Signal, 84-87	9	13	___
2117	Block Target Signal, 84-87	23	29	___
2122	Extension Bridge, rock piers, 76-87	24	34	___
2125	Whistling Freight Shed, 71	36	43	___
2126	Whistling Freight Shed, 76-87	18	26	___
2127	Diesel Horn Shed, 76-87	25	30	___
2128	Operating Switchman, 83-86	26	29	___
2129	Illuminated Freight Station, 83-86	30	33	___
2133	Lighted Freight Station, 72-78, 80-84	34	38	___
2140	Automatic Banjo Signal, 70-84	17	21	___
2145	Automatic Gateman, 72-84	31	47	___
2151	Operating Semaphore, 78-82	15	19	___
2152	Automatic Crossing Gate, 70-84	21	25	___
2154	Automatic Highway Flasher, 70-87	19	24	___
2156	Illuminated Station Platform, 70-71	26	34	___
2162	Crossing Gate and Signal "262," 70-87, 94, 96-98, 05	16	27	___
2163	Block Target Signal, 70-78	14	19	___
2170	Street Lamps, set of 3, 70-87	13	19	___
2171	Gooseneck Street Lamps, set of 2, 80-81, 83-84	15	18	___
2175	"Sandy Andy" Gravel Loader Kit, 76-79	34	55	___
2180	Road Signs, 16 pieces, 77-98		6	___
2181	Telephone Pole Set "150," 77-98		5	___
2195	Floodlight Tower, 70-71	38	50	___
2199	Microwave Tower, 72-75	30	39	___
2214	Girder Bridge, 70-71, 72 u, 73-87	5	9	___
2256	Station Platform, 73-81	12	18	___
2260	Illuminated Bumper, 70-71, 72 u, 73	23	35	___
2280	Nonilluminated Bumpers, set of 3, 73-84	2	4	___
2282	Die-cast Bumpers, pair, 83 u	12	18	___
2283	Die-cast Illuminated Bumpers "260,", 84-99	10	16	___
2290	Illuminated Bumpers, pair, 75 u, 76-86	7	11	___
2292	Station Platform, 85-87	5	9	___
2300	Operating Oil Drum Loader, 83-87	80	90	___
2301	Operating Sawmill, 80-84	60	65	___
2302	Union Pacific Manual Gantry Crane, 80-82	24	31	___

		Exc	Mint
___ 2303	Santa Fe Manual Gantry Crane, 80-81, 83 u	17	21
___ 2305	Getty Operating Oil Derrick, 81-84	105	115
___ 2306	Operating Ice Station with 6700 Ice Car, 82-83	90	125
___ 2307	Lighted Billboard, 82-86	12	13
___ 2308	Animated Newsstand, 82-83	82	120
___ 2309	Mechanical Crossing Gate, 82-92	4	7
___ 2310	Mechanical Crossing Gate, 73-77	2	4
___ 2311	Mechanical Semaphore, 82-92	4	7
___ 2312	Mechanical Semaphore, 73-77	2	4
___ 2313	Floodlight Tower, 75-86	22	27
___ 2314	Searchlight Tower, 75-84	22	27
___ 2315	Operating Coaling Station, 83-84	80	89
___ 2316	N&W Operating Gantry Crane, 83-84	90	125
___ 2317	Operating Drawbridge, 75 u, 76-81	100	130
___ 2318	Operating Control Tower, 83-86	40	52
___ 2319	Illuminated Watchtower, 75-78, 80	29	56
___ 2320	Flagpole Kit, 83-87	10	14
___ 2321	Operating Sawmill, 84, 86-87	115	133
___ 2323	Operating Freight Station, 84-87	43	47
___ 2324	Operating Switch Tower, 84-87	60	65
___ 2390	Lionel Mirror, 82 u	93	125
___ 2494	Rotary Beacon, 72-74	37	44
___ 2709	Rico Station Kit, 81-98		42
___ 2710	Billboards, set of 5, 70-84	4	10
___ 2714	Tunnel, 75 u, 76-77	36	43
___ 2716	Short Extension Bridge, 88-98	3	8
___ 2717	Short Extension Bridge, 77-87	2	4
___ 2718	Barrel Platform Kit, 77-84	3	5
___ 2719	Watchman Shanty Kit, 77-87	3	5
___ 2720	Lumber Shed Kit, 77-84, 87	3	5
___ 2721	Operating Log Mill Kit, 78	2	4
___ 2722	Barrel Loader Kit, 78	2	4
___ 2783	Freight Station Kit, 84	6	10
___ 2784	Freight Platform Kit, 81-90	5	8
___ 2785	Engine House Kit, 73-77	31	39
___ 2786	Freight Platform Kit, 73-77	4	6
___ 2787	Freight Station Kit, 73-77, 83	7	10
___ 2788	Coal Station Kit, 75 u, 76-77	18	30
___ 2789	Water Tower Kit, 75-77, 80	19	24
___ 2791	Cross Country Set, 70-71	22	30
___ 2792	Whistle Stop Set, 70-71	24	34
___ 2792	Layout Starter Pack, 80-84	9	21
___ 2793	Alamo Junction Set, 70-71	22	30
___ 2796	Grain Elevator Kit, 76 u, 77	43	47
___ 2797	Rico Station Kit, 76-77	23	37
___ 2900	Lockon, 70-98	3	8
___ 2901	Track Clips, dozen (027), 71-98		8
___ 2905	Lockon and Wire, 74-00		3
___ 2909	Smoke Fluid, 70-98		8
___ 2910	OTC Contactor, 84-86, 88	4	7
___ 2911	Smoke Pellets, 70-73	18	35
___ 2925	Lubricant, 70-71, 72 u, 73-75		2
___ 2927	Maintenance Kit, 70, 78-98		11
___ 2928	Oil, 71		2

		Exc	Mint	
2951	Track Layout Book, 70-86	1	2	___
2952	Train and Accessory Manual, 70-74	1	2	___
2953	Train and Accessory Manual, 75-86	1	2	___
2960	Lionel 75th Anniversary Book, 75 u, 76	15	30	___
2980	Magnetic Conversion Coupler, 70-71	1	2	___
2985	The Lionel Train Book, 86-98		18	___
3100	Great Northern 4-8-4 (FARR 3), 81	335	388	___
4044	Transformer, 45-watt, 70-71	2	7	___
4045	Safety Transformer, 70-71	2	3	___
4050	Safety Transformer, 72-79	2	3	___
4060	Power Master Transformer, 80-93	4	13	___
4090	Power Master Transformer, 70-84	50	65	___
4125	Transformer, 25-watt, 72	2	3	___
4150	Trainmaster Transformer, 72-73, 75-77	6	15	___
4250	Trainmaster Transformer, 74	5	10	___
4651	Trainmaster Transformer, 78-79	1	2	___
4690	MW Transformer, 86-89	60	80	___
4851	AC Transformer, red or black, 85-91, 94-96	5	10	___
5012	27" Diameter Curved Track, card of 4 (027), 70-96		17	___
5013	27" Diameter Curved Track (027), 70-78		1	___
5014	Half Curved Track (027), 70-98		1	___
5016	36" Straight Track (027), 87-88	1	2	___
5017	Straight Track, card of 4 (027), 70-96		4	___
5018	Straight Track (027), 70-78		1	___
5019	Half Straight Track (027), 70-98		1	___
5020	90-degree Crossover (027), 70-98		7	___
5021	27" Manual Switch, left hand (027), 70-98		15	___
5022	27" Manual Switch, right hand (027), 70-98		15	___
5023	45-degree Crossover (027), 70-98		6	___
5024	35" Straight Track (027), 88-98, 05		3	___
5025	Manumatic Uncoupler, 71-72	1	2	___
5027	27" Manual Switches, pair (027), 74-84	13	21	___
5030	Track Expander Set (027), 71-84	18	26	___
5031	Ford-Autolite Layout Expander Set, 71 u	50	65	___
5033	27" Diameter Curved Track (027), 79-98		1	___
5038	Straight Track (027), 79-98		1	___
5041	Insulator Pins, dozen (027), 70-98		1	___
5042	Steel Pins, dozen (027), 70-98		1	___
5045	54" Diameter Curved Track Ballast (027), 87-88	1	2	___
5046	27" Diameter Curved Track Ballast (027), 87-88	1	2	___
5047	Straight Track Ballast (027), 87-88	1	2	___
5049	42" Diameter Curved Track (027), 88-98	1	2	___
5090	27" Manual Switches, 3 pair (027), 78-84	55	70	___
5113	54" Diameter Curved Track (027), 79-98	1	2	___
5121	27" Remote Switch, left hand (027), 70-98	18	22	___
5122	27" Remote Switch, right hand (027), 70-98	20	22	___
5125	27" Remote Switches, pair (027), 71-83	20	30	___
5132	31" Remote Switch, right hand (0), 80-94	29	30	___
5133	31" Remote Switch, left hand (0), 80-94	22	30	___
5149	Remote Uncoupling Section (027), 70-98		15	___
5165	72" Remote Switch, right hand (0), 87-98	23	65	___
5166	72" Remote Switch, left hand (0), 87-98	23	75	___
5167	42" Remote Switch, right hand (027), 88-98	25	37	___

| --- | --- | --- | --- |
5168	42" Remote Switch, left hand (027), 88-98	25	37
5193	27" Remote Switches, 3 pair (027), 78-83	80	95
5500	10" Straight Track (O), 71-98		1
5501	31" Diameter Curved Track (O), 71-98		1
5502	Remote Uncoupling Section (O), 71-72	7	9
5504	Half Curved Track (O), 83-98		1
5505	Half Straight Track (O), 83-98		1
5520	90-degree Crossover (O), 71-72	6	9
5522	36" Straight, 87-88		3
5523	40" Straight Track (O), 88-98		4
5530	Remote Uncoupling Section (O), 81-98	10	19
5540	90-degree Crossover (O), 81-98		10
5543	Insulator Pins, dozen (O), 70-98		1
5545	45-degree Crossover (O), 83-98		11
5551	Steel Pins, dozen (O), 70-98		1
5554	54" Diameter Curved Track (O), 90-98		2
5560	72" Diameter Curved Track Ballast (O), 87-88	1	2
5561	31" Diameter Curved Track Ballast (O), 87-88	1	2
5562	Straight Track Ballast (O), 87-88	1	2
5572	72" Diameter Curved Track (O), 79-98	2	3
5600	Curved Track (Trutrack), 73-74	1	2
5601	Curved Track, card of 4 (Trutrack), 73-74	6	10
5602	Curved Track Ballast, card of 4 (Trutrack), 73-74	5	9
5605	Straight Track (Trutrack), 73-74	1	2
5606	Straight Track, card of 4 (Trutrack), 73-74	5	9
5607	Straight Track Ballast, card of 4 (Trutrack), 73-74	5	9
5620	Manual Switch, left hand (Trutrack), 73-74	4	13
5625	Remote Switch, left hand (Trutrack), 73-74	9	17
5630	Manual Switch, right hand (Trutrack), 73-74	4	13
5635	Remote Switch, right hand (Trutrack), 73-74	9	17
5640	Left Switch Ballast, card of 2 (Trutrack), 73-74	5	9
5650	Right Switch Ballast, card of 2 (Trutrack), 73-74	5	9
5655	Lockon (Trutrack), 73-74	1	2
5660	Terminal Track with lockon (Trutrack), 74	1	3
5700	Oppenheimer Reefer, 81	32	39
5701	Dairymen's League Reefer, 81	21	23
5702	National Dairy Despatch Reefer, 81	16	21
5703	North American Despatch Reefer, 81	22	26
5704	Budweiser Reefer, 81-82	69	78
5705	Ball Glass Jars Reefer, 81-82	30	35
5706	Lindsay Brothers Reefer, 81-82	26	29
5707	American Refrigerator Transit Reefer, 81-82	17	20
5708	Armour Reefer, 82-83	16	21
5709	REA Reefer, 82-83	22	26
5710	Canadian Pacific Reefer, 82-83	22	25
5711	Commercial Express Reefer, 82-83	13	15
5712	Lionel Lines Reefer, 82 u	47	75
5713	Cotton Belt Reefer, 83-84	19	22
5714	Michigan Central Reefer, 83-84	17	24
5715	Santa Fe Reefer, 83-84	19	26
5716	Vermont Central Reefer, 83-84	20	23
5717	Santa Fe Bunk Car, 83	22	30
5719	Canadian National Reefer, 84	11	17

		Exc	Mint	
5720	Great Northern Reefer, 84	75	90	___
5721	Soo Line Reefer, 84	21	23	___
5722	NKP Reefer, 84	16	18	___
5724	PRR Bunk Car, 84	15	23	___
5726	Southern Bunk Car, 84 u	22	27	___
5727	USMC Bunk Car, 84-85	25	30	___
5728	Canadian Pacific Bunk Car, 86	17	24	___
5730	Strasburg Reefer, 85-86	20	27	___
5731	L&N Reefer, 85-86	19	24	___
5732	Jersey Central Reefer, 85-86	18	24	___
5733	Lionel Lines Bunk Car, 86 u	18	24	___
5735	NYC Bunk Car, 85-86	33	35	___
5739	B&O Tool Car, 86	32	37	___
5745	Santa Fe Bunk Car (SSS), 86	39	45	___
5760	Santa Fe Tool Car (SSS), 86	30	35	___
5900	AC/DC Converter, 79-83	3	10	___
6076	LV Hopper (O27), 70 u	17	21	___
6100	Ontario Northland Covered Quad Hopper, 81-82	30	34	___
6101	BN Covered Quad Hopper, 81-82	17	31	___
6102	GN Covered Quad Hopper (FARR 3), 81	26	28	___
6103	Canadian National Covered Quad Hopper, 81	35	39	___
6104	Southern Quad Hopper with coal (FARR 4), 83	39	60	___
6105	Reading Operating Hopper, 82	34	40	___
6106	N&W Covered Quad Hopper, 82	30	40	___
6107	Shell Covered Quad Hopper, 82	13	26	___
6109	C&O Operating Hopper, 83	29	41	___
6110	MP Covered Quad Hopper, 83-84	17	27	___
6111	L&N Covered Quad Hopper, 83-84	13	20	___
6113	Illinois Central Hopper (O27), 83-85	15	25	___
6114	C&NW Covered Quad Hopper, 83	54	80	___
6115	Southern Hopper (O27), 83-86	15	19	___
6116	Soo Line Ore Car, 84	21	27	___
6117	Erie Operating Hopper, 84	29	39	___
6118	Erie Covered Quad Hopper, 84	31	45	___
6122	Penn Central Ore Car, 84	20	25	___
6123	PRR Covered Quad Hopper (FARR 5), 84-85	55	105	___
6124	D&H Covered Quad Hopper, 84	19	32	___
6126	Canadian National Ore Car, 86	18	24	___
6127	Northern Pacific Ore Car, 86	20	24	___
6131	Illinois Terminal Covered Quad Hopper, 85-86	15	21	___
6134	BN 2-bay ACF Hopper (std O), 86 u	95	115	___
6135	C&NW 2-bay ACF Hopper (std O), 86 u	65	80	___
6137	NKP Hopper (O27), 86-91	13	17	___
6138	B&O Quad Hopper with coal, 86	21	28	___
6142	Gondola, black, 70	20	33	___
6150	Santa Fe Hopper (O27), 85-86, 92 u	10	15	___
6177	Reading Hopper (O27), 86-90	14	19	___
6200	FEC Gondola with canisters, 81-82	13	24	___
6201	Union Pacific Animated Gondola, 82-83	19	25	___
6202	WM Gondola with coal, 82	34	36	___
6203	Black Cave Gondola (O27), 82	2	4	___
6205	CP Gondola with canisters, 83	18	26	___
6206	C&IM Gondola with canisters, 83-85	18	26	___

			Exc	Mint
___	**6207**	Southern Gondola with canisters (027), 83-85	6	8
___	**6208**	Chessie System Gondola with canisters, 83 u	21	24
___	**6209**	NYC Gondola with coal (std O), 84-85	42	46
___	**6210**	Erie-Lackawanna Gondola with canisters, 84	21	30
___	**6211**	C&O Gondola with canisters, 84-85	6	10
___	**6214**	Lionel Lines Gondola with canisters, 84 u	38	45
___	**6230**	Erie-Lackawanna Reefer (std O), 86 u	95	120
___	**6231**	Railgon Gondola with coal (std O), 86 u	66	76
___	**6232**	Illinois Central Boxcar (std O), 86 u	65	80
___	**6233**	CP Flatcar with stakes (std O), 86 u	36	43
___	**6234**	Burlington Northern Boxcar (std O), 85	55	75
___	**6235**	Burlington Northern Boxcar (std O), 85	33	43
___	**6236**	Burlington Northern Boxcar (std O), 85	33	43
___	**6237**	Burlington Northern Boxcar (std O), 85	33	49
___	**6238**	Burlington Northern Boxcar (std O), 85	33	43
___	**6239**	Burlington Northern Boxcar (std O), 86 u	38	55
___	**6251**	NYC Coal Dump Car, 85	25	42
___	**6254**	NKP Gondola with canisters, 86-91	6	11
___	**6258**	Santa Fe Gondola with canisters (027), 85-86, 92 u	3	5
___	**X6260**	NYC Gondola with canisters, 85-86	13	15
___	**6272**	Santa Fe Gondola with cable reels (SSS), 86	20	25
___	**6300**	Corn Products 3-D Tank Car, 81-82	19	25
___	**6301**	Gulf 1-D Tank Car, 81	20	26
___	**6302**	Quaker State 3-D Tank Car, 81	42	46
___	**6304**	GN 1-D Tank Car (FARR 3), 81	32	53
___	**6305**	British Columbia 1-D Tank Car, 81	46	64
___	**6306**	Southern 1-D Tank Car (FARR 4), 83	45	50
___	**6307**	PRR 1-D Tank Car (FARR 5), 84-85	70	75
___	**6308**	Alaska 1-D Tank Car (027), 82-83	27	35
___	**6310**	Shell 2-D Tank Car (027), 83-84	19	24
___	**6312**	C&O 2-D Tank Car (027), 84-85	18	26
___	**6313**	Lionel Lines 1-D Tank Car, 84 u	40	50
___	**6314**	B&O 3-D Tank Car, 86	31	38
___	**6317**	Gulf 2-D Tank Car (027), 84-85	18	22
___	**6357**	Frisco 1-D Tank Car, 83	42	50
___	**6401**	Virginian Bay Window Caboose, 81	37	47
___	**6403**	Amtrak Vista Dome Car (027), 76-77	24	31
___	**6404**	Amtrak Passenger Coach (027), 76-77	24	31
___	**6405**	Amtrak Passenger Coach (027), 76-77	24	31
___	**6406**	Amtrak Observation Car (027), 76-77	22	29
___	**6410**	Amtrak Passenger Coach (027), 77	28	48
___	**6411**	Amtrak Passenger Coach (027), 77	24	35
___	**6412**	Amtrak Vista Dome Car (027), 77	22	33
___	**6420**	Reading Transfer Caboose, 81-82	20	28
___	**6421**	Joshua L. Cowen Bay Window Caboose, 82	34	40
___	**6422**	DM&IR Bay Window Caboose, 81	32	38
___	**6425**	Erie-Lackawanna Bay Window Caboose, 83-84	35	43
___	**6426**	Reading Transfer Caboose, 82-83	14	24
___	**6427**	BN Transfer Caboose, 83-84	12	21
___	**6428**	C&NW Transfer Caboose, 83-85	22	25
___	**6430**	Santa Fe SP-type Caboose, 83-89	4	14
___	**6431**	Southern Bay Window Caboose (FARR 4), 83	42	55
___	**6432**	Union Pacific SP-type Caboose, 81-82	6	10

		Exc	Mint	
6433	Canadian Pacific Bay Window Caboose, 81	50	70	___
6435	U.S. Marines Transfer Caboose, 83-84	9	17	___
6438	GN Bay Window Caboose (FARR 3), 81	48	65	___
6439	Reading Bay Window Caboose, 84-85	22	30	___
6441	Alaska Bay Window Caboose, 82-83	45	50	___
6446-25	N&W Covered Quad Hopper, 70 u	203	333	___
6449	Wendy's N5c Caboose, 81-82	64	74	___
6464-500	Timken Boxcar, orange, 70 u	225	319	___
6464-500	Timken Boxcar, yellow, 70 u	210	358	___
6476-135	LV Hopper "25000," (O27), 70-71 u	6	11	___
6478	Black Cave SP-type Caboose, 82	5	9	___
6482	NIBCO Express SP-type Caboose, 82 u	26	34	___
6485	Chessie System SP-type Caboose, 84-85	6	10	___
6486	Southern SP-type Caboose, 83-85	5	7	___
6490	NKP N5c Caboose, 84 u		NRS	___
6491	Erie-Lackawanna Transfer Caboose, 85-86	9	17	___
6493	L&C Bay Window Caboose, 86-87	21	36	___
6494	Santa Fe Bobber Caboose, 85-86	7	9	___
6496	Santa Fe Work Caboose (SSS), 86	21	29	___
6504	L.A.S.E.R. Flatcar with helicopter (O27), 81-82	18	26	___
6505	L.A.S.E.R. Radar Car, 81-82	17	25	___
6506	L.A.S.E.R. Security Car, 81-82	18	26	___
6507	L.A.S.E.R. Flatcar with cruise missile, 81-82	21	30	___
6508	Canadian Pacific Crane Car, 81	50	70	___
6509	Depressed Center Flatcar with girders, 81	60	85	___
6510	Union Pacific Crane Car, 82	55	60	___
6515	Union Pacific Flatcar (O27), 83-84, 86	5	13	___
6521	NYC Flatcar with stakes (std O), 84-85	29	35	___
6522	C&NW Searchlight Car, 83-85	27	30	___
6524	Erie Crane Car, 84	55	60	___
6526	Searchlight Car, 84-85	23	25	___
6529	NYC Searchlight Car, 85-86	21	27	___
6531	Express Mail Flatcar with trailers, 85-86	23	32	___
6560	Bucyrus Erie Crane Car, 71	100	130	___
6561	Flatcar with cruise missile (O27), 83-84	13	26	___
6562	Flatcar with fences (O27), 83-84	13	21	___
6564	U.S. Marines Flatcar with 2 tanks (O27), 83-84	13	21	___
6573	Redwood Valley Express Log Dump Car (O27), 84-85	8	13	___
6574	Redwood Valley Express Crane Car (O27), 84-85	7	13	___
6575	Redwood Valley Express Flatcar with fences (O27), 84-85	7	13	___
6576	Santa Fe Crane Car (O27), 85-86, 92 u	7	10	___
6579	NYC Crane Car, 85-86	36	44	___
6585	PRR Flatcar with fences (O27), 86-90	5	9	___
6587	W&ARR Flatcar with horses, 86 u	18	26	___
6593	Santa Fe Crane Car (SSS), 86	41	48	___
6700	PFE Ice Car, 82-83	45	70	___
6900	N&W Extended Vision Caboose, 82	60	65	___
6901	Ontario Northland Extended Vision Caboose, 82 u	44	55	___
6903	Santa Fe Extended Vision Caboose, 83	80	95	___
6904	Union Pacific Extended Vision Caboose, 83	115	135	___

		Exc	Mint
___ 6905	NKP Extended Vision Caboose, 83 u	50	65
___ 6906	Erie-Lackawanna Extended Vision Caboose, 84	75	90
___ 6907	NYC Wood-sided Caboose (std O), 86 u	90	92
___ 6908	PRR N5c Caboose (FARR 5), 84-85	43	47
___ 6910	NYC Extended Vision Caboose, 84 u	55	60
___ 6912	Redwood Valley Express SP-type Caboose, 84-85	9	16
___ 6913	Burlington Northern Extended Vision Caboose, 85	60	90
___ 6916	NYC Work Caboose, 85-86	16	22
___ 6917	Jersey Central Extended Vision Caboose, 86	36	50
___ 6918	B&O SP-type Caboose, 86	10	15
___ 6919	Nickel Plate Road SP-type Caboose, 86-91	5	9
___ 6920	B&A Wood-sided Caboose (std O), 86 u	65	80
___ 6921	PRR SP-type Caboose, 86-90	5	9
___ 7200	Quicksilver Passenger Coach (027), 82-83	26	34
___ 7201	Quicksilver Passenger Coach (027), 82-83	26	34
___ 7202	Quicksilver Observation Car (027), 82-83	26	34
___ 7203	N&W Diner "491," 82 u	130	180
___ 7204	Southern Pacific Diner, 82 u	190	235
___ 7207	NYC Diner, 83 u	70	140
___ 7208	PRR Diner, 83 u	80	90
___ 7210	Union Pacific Diner, 84	85	110
___ 7211	Southern Pacific Vista Dome Car, 83 u	145	185
___ 7215	B&O Passenger Coach, 83-84	43	50
___ 7216	B&O Passenger Coach, 83-84	43	50
___ 7217	B&O Baggage Car, 83-84	43	50
___ 7220	Illinois Central Baggage Car, 85, 87	105	135
___ 7221	Illinois Central Combination Car, 85, 87	85	105
___ 7222	Illinois Central Passenger Coach, 85, 87	85	105
___ 7223	Illinois Central Passenger Coach, 85, 87	85	105
___ 7224	Illinois Central Diner, 85, 87	75	90
___ 7225	Illinois Central Observation Car, 85, 87	95	115
___ 7227	Wabash Diner (FF 1), 86-87	115	130
___ 7228	Wabash Baggage Car (FF 1), 86-87	90	100
___ 7229	Wabash Combination Car (FF 1), 86-87	90	100
___ 7230	Wabash Passenger Coach (FF 1), 86-87	90	100
___ 7231	Wabash Passenger Coach (FF 1), 86-87	90	100
___ 7232	Wabash Observation Car (FF 1), 86-87	88	98
___ 7241	W&ARR Passenger Coach, 86 u	43	50
___ 7242	W&ARR Baggage Car, 86 u	43	50
___ 7301	Norfolk & Western Stock Car, 82	34	45
___ 7302	Texas & Pacific Stock Car (027), 83-84	9	14
___ 7303	Erie Stock Car, 84	41	50
___ 7304	Southern Stock Car (FARR 4), 83 u	41	45
___ 7309	Southern Stock Car (027), 85-86	12	16
___ 7312	W&ARR Stock Car (027), 86 u	25	30
___ 7401	Chessie System Stock Car (027), 84-85	13	17
___ 7404	Jersey Central Boxcar, 86	26	40
___ 7500	Lionel 75th Anniversary U36B Diesel, 75-77	153	181
___ 7501	Lionel 75th Anniversary Boxcar, 75-77	28	39
___ 7502	Lionel 75th Anniversary Reefer, 75-77	30	41
___ 7503	Lionel 75th Anniversary Reefer, 75-77	41	47
___ 7504	Lionel 75th Anniversary Covered Quad Hopper, 75-77	28	40
___ 7505	Lionel 75th Anniversary Boxcar, 75-77	41	50

	MODERN 1970-2023	Exc	Mint	
7506	Lionel 75th Anniversary Boxcar, 75-77	20	25	
7507	Lionel 75th Anniversary Reefer, 75-77	27	39	
7508	Lionel 75th Anniversary N5c Caboose, 75-77	24	29	
7509	Kentucky Fried Chicken Reefer, 81-82	81	91	
7510	Red Lobster Reefer, 81-82	74	83	
7511	Pizza Hut Reefer, 81-82	70	81	
7512	Arthur Treacher's Reefer, 82	69	76	
7513	Bonanza Reefer, 82	70	78	
7514	Taco Bell Reefer, 82	74	319	
7515	Denver Mint Car, 81	64	81	
7517	Philadelphia Mint Car, 82	38	39	
7518	Carson City Mint Car, 83	34	43	
7519	Toy Fair Reefer, 82 u	35	42	
7520	NIBCO Express Boxcar, 82 u	265	440	
7521	Toy Fair Reefer, 83 u	50	65	
7522	New Orleans Mint Car, 84	33	38	
7523	Toy Fair Reefer, 84 u	44	49	
7524	Toy Fair Reefer, 85 u	55	60	
7525	Toy Fair Boxcar, 86 u	65	80	
7530	Dahlonega Mint Car, 86	37	48	
7600	Frisco "Spirit of '76" N5c Caboose, 74-76	33	39	
7601	Delaware Boxcar, 74-76	11	21	
7602	Pennsylvania Boxcar, 74-76	11	27	
7603	New Jersey Boxcar, 74-76	13	24	
7604	Georgia Boxcar, 74 u, 75-76	22	26	
7605	Connecticut Boxcar, 74 u, 75-76	11	32	
7606	Massachusetts Boxcar, 74 u, 75-76	25	29	
7607	Maryland Boxcar, 74 u, 75-76	13	34	
7608	South Carolina Boxcar, 75 u, 76	38	50	
7609	New Hampshire Boxcar, 75 u, 76	38	46	
7610	Virginia Boxcar, 75 u, 76	155	200	
7611	New York Boxcar, 75 u, 76	50	65	
7612	North Carolina Boxcar, 75 u, 76	35	60	
7613	Rhode Island Boxcar, 75 u, 76	36	50	
7700	Uncle Sam Boxcar, 75 u	44	51	
7701	Camel Boxcar, 76-77	68	78	
7702	Prince Albert Boxcar, 76-77	65	84	
7703	Beechnut Boxcar, 76-77	39	58	
7704	Toy Fair Boxcar, 76 u	110	120	
7705	Canadian Toy Fair Boxcar, 76 u	130	145	
7706	Sir Walter Raleigh Boxcar, 77-78	56	88	
7707	White Owl Boxcar, 77-78	71	80	
7708	Winston Boxcar, 77-78	70	85	
7709	Salem Boxcar, 78	70	78	
7710	Mail Pouch Boxcar, 78	69	79	
7711	El Producto Boxcar, 78	44	75	
7712	Santa Fe Boxcar (FARR 1), 79	30	50	
7800	Pepsi Boxcar, 76 u, 77	83	93	
7801	A&W Boxcar, 76 u, 77	54	67	
7802	Canada Dry Boxcar, 76 u, 77	44	57	
7803	Trains n' Truckin' Boxcar, 77 u	20	26	
7806	Season's Greetings Boxcar, 76 u	70	95	
7807	Toy Fair Boxcar, 77 u	70	95	

			Exc	Mint
___	7808	Northern Pacific Stock Car, 77	37	43
___	7809	Vernors Boxcar, 77 u, 78	50	65
___	7810	Orange Crush Boxcar, 77 u, 78	45	60
___	7811	Dr Pepper Boxcar, 77 u, 78	51	65
___	7813	Season's Greetings Boxcar, 77 u	65	90
___	7814	Season's Greetings Boxcar, 78 u	70	95
___	7815	Toy Fair Boxcar, 78 u	65	85
___	7816	Toy Fair Boxcar, 79 u	65	85
___	7817	Toy Fair Boxcar, 80 u	95	105
___	7900	D&RGW Operating Cowboy Car (O27), 82-83	22	26
___	7901	LL Cop and Hobo Car (O27), 82-83	24	27
___	7902	Santa Fe Boxcar (O27), 82-85	5	9
___	7903	Rock Island Boxcar (O27), 83	8	13
___	7904	San Diego Zoo Giraffe Car (O27), 83-84	44	55
___	7905	Black Cave Boxcar (O27), 82	6	9
___	7908	Tappan Boxcar (O27), 82 u	39	55
___	7909	L&N Boxcar (O27), 83-84	40	49
___	7910	Chessie System Boxcar (O27), 84-85	18	23
___	7912	Toys 'R' Us Giraffe Car (O27), 82-84 u	70	80
___	7913	Turtleback Zoo Giraffe Car (O27), 85-86	50	60
___	7914	Toys 'R' Us Giraffe Car (O27), 85-89 u	70	90
___	7920	Sears Centennial Boxcar (O27), 85-86 u	39	44
___	7925	Erie-Lackawanna Boxcar (O27), 86-90	10	18
___	7926	NKP Boxcar (O27), 86-91	8	10
___	7930	True Value Boxcar (O27), 86-87 u	34	50
___	7931	Town House TV and Appliances Boxcar (O27), 86 u	31	39
___	7932	Kay Bee Toys Boxcar (O27), 86-87 u	40	49
___	8001	NKP 2-6-4 Locomotive, 80 u	55	65
___	8002	Union Pacific 2-8-4 Locomotive (FARR 2), 80	310	345
___	8003	Chessie System 2-8-4 Locomotive, 80	360	540
___	8004	Rock Island 4-4-0 Locomotive, 80-82	190	220
___	8005	Santa Fe 4-4-0 Locomotive, 80-82	65	75
___	8006	ACL 4-6-4 Locomotive, 80 u	223	340
___	8007	NYNH&H 2-6-4 Locomotive, 80-81	65	75
___	8008	Chessie System 4-4-2 Locomotive, 80	65	75
___	8010	Santa Fe NW2 Switcher, 70, 71 u	48	79
___	8020	Santa Fe Alco Diesel A Unit, dummy, 70	45	60
___	8020	Santa Fe Alco Diesel A Unit, 70-72, 74-76	65	85
___	8021	Santa Fe Alco Diesel B Unit, 71-72, 74-76	49	67
___	8022	Santa Fe Alco Diesel A Unit, 71 u	80	105
___	8025	CN Alco Diesel A Unit, 71-73 u	85	105
___	8025	CN Alco Diesel A Unit, dummy, 71-73 u	45	65
___	8030	Illinois Central GP9 Diesel, 70-72	75	140
___	8031	Canadian National GP7 Diesel, 71-73 u	80	150
___	8031	Illinois Central GP9 Diesel, unpowered, 70	40	127
___	8040	Canadian National 2-4-2 Locomotive, 71 u	43	85
___	8040	NKP 2-4-2 Locomotive, 70-72	26	34
___	8041	NYC 2-4-2 Locomotive, 70	55	65
___	8041	PRR 2-4-2 Locomotive, 71 u	55	65
___	8042	GTW 2-4-2 Locomotive, 70, 71-73 u	26	34
___	8043	NKP 2-4-2 Locomotive, 70 u	45	65
___	8050	D&H U36C Diesel, 80	105	220
___	8051	D&H U36C Diesel Dummy Unit, 80	95	115

		Exc	Mint	
8054	Burlington F3 Diesel AA Set, 80	360	385	___
8056	C&NW FM Train Master Diesel, 80	137	202	___
8057	Burlington NW2 Switcher, 80	100	115	___
8059	Pennsylvania F3 Diesel B Unit, 80 u	190	290	___
8060	Pennsylvania F3 Diesel B Unit, 80 u	335	420	___
8061	Chessie System U36C Diesel, 80	93	140	___
8062	Burlington F3 Diesel B Unit, 80 u	205	255	___
8063	Seaboard SD9 Diesel, 80	80	100	___
8064	Florida East Coast GP9 Diesel, 80	150	200	___
8065	Florida East Coast GP9 Diesel Dummy Unit, 80	95	120	___
8066	TP&W GP20 Diesel, 80-81, 83 u	65	80	___
8071	Virginian SD18 Diesel, 80 u	135	155	___
8072	Virginian SD18 Diesel Dummy Unit, 80 u	75	110	___
8100	Norfolk & Western 4-8-4 "611," 81	330	402	___
8101	Chicago & Alton 4-6-4 Locomotive "659," 81	275	445	___
8102	Union Pacific 4-4-2 Locomotive, 81-82	49	65	___
8104	Union Pacific 4-4-0 Locomotive "3," 81 u	180	235	___
8111	DT&I NW2 Switcher, 71-74	55	65	___
8140	Southern 2-4-0 Locomotive, 71 u	22	30	___
8141	PRR 2-4-2 Locomotive, 71-72	41	43	___
8142	C&O 4-4-2 Locomotive, 71-72	45	55	___
8150	PRR GG1 Electric Locomotive "4935," 81	260	395	___
8151	Burlington SD28 Diesel, 81	120	145	___
8152	Canadian Pacific SD24 Diesel, 81	155	185	___
8153	Reading NW2 Switcher, 81-82	100	155	___
8154	Alaska NW2 Switcher, 81-82	120	160	___
8155	Monon U36B Diesel, 81-82	110	135	___
8156	Monon U36B Diesel Dummy Unit, 81-82	50	65	___
8157	Santa Fe FM Train Master, 81	280	325	___
8158	DM&IR GP35 Diesel, 81-82	90	150	___
8159	DM&IR GP35 Diesel Dummy Unit, 81-82	55	75	___
8160	Burger King GP20 Diesel, 81-82	106	128	___
8161	L.A.S.E.R. Switcher, 81-82	23	55	___
8162	Ontario Northland SD18 Diesel, 81 u	150	210	___
8163	Ontario Northland SD18 Diesel Dummy Unit, 81 u	95	140	___
8164	Pennsylvania F3 Diesel B Unit, 81 u	340	370	___
8182	NIBCO Express NW2 Switcher, 82 u	90	130	___
8190	Diesel Horn Kit, 81 u		30	___
8200	Kickapoo Dockside 0-4-0T, 72	28	39	___
8203	PRR 2-4-2 Locomotive, 72, 74 u, 75	26	34	___
8204	C&O 4-4-2 Locomotive, 72	55	60	___
8206	NYC 4-6-4 Locomotive, 72-75	140	155	___
8209	Pioneer Dockside 0-4-0T with tender, 72	45	65	___
8209	Pioneer Dockside 0-4-0T, no tender, 73-76	42	55	___
8210	Joshua L. Cowen 4-6-4 Locomotive, 82	245	350	___
8212	Black Cave 0-4-0 Locomotive, 82	30	49	___
8213	D&RGW 2-4-2 Locomotive, 82-83, 84-91 u	65	70	___
8214	Pennsylvania 2-4-2 Locomotive, 82-83	55	65	___
8215	Nickel Plate Road 2-8-4 Locomotive "779," 82 u	245	285	___
8250	Santa Fe GP9 Diesel, 72, 74-75	120	145	___
8251-50	Horn/Whistle Controller, 72-74	1	2	___
8252	D&H Alco Diesel A Unit, 72	85	125	___
8253	D&H Alco Diesel B Unit, 72	50	70	___

	MODERN 1970-2023	Exc	Mint
___	8254 Illinois Central GP9 Diesel Dummy Unit, 72	60	65
___	8255 Santa Fe GP9 Diesel Dummy Unit, 72	60	65
___	8258 Canadian National GP7 Diesel Dummy Unit, 72-73 u	65	85
___	8260/62 Southern Pacific F3 Diesel AA Set, 82	490	520
___	8261 Southern Pacific F3 Diesel B Unit, 82 u	330	395
___	8263 Santa Fe GP7 Diesel, 82	65	80
___	8264 CP Vulcan Switcher Snowplow, 82	80	100
___	8265 Santa Fe SD40 Diesel, 82	165	225
___	8266 Norfolk & Western SD24 Diesel, 82	113	225
___	8268 Quicksilver Alco Diesel A Unit, 82-83	85	105
___	8269 Quicksilver Alco Diesel A Unit, dummy, 82-83	55	65
___	8272 Pennsylvania EP-5 Electric Locomotive, 82 u	205	265
___	8300 Santa Fe 2-4-0 Locomotive, 73-74	22	25
___	8302 Southern 2-4-0 Locomotive, 73-76	29	30
___	8303 Jersey Central 2-4-2 Locomotive, 73-74	55	59
___	8304 B&O 4-4-2 Locomotive, 75	75	105
___	8304 Rock Island 4-4-2 Locomotive, 73-75	85	105
___	8304 Pennsylvania 4-4-2 Locomotive, 74-75	75	105
___	8304 C&O 4-4-2 Locomotive, 75-77	75	105
___	8305 Milwaukee Road 4-4-2 Locomotive, 73	95	120
___	8307 Southern Pacific 4-8-4 Locomotive "4449," 83	490	560
___	8308 Jersey Central 2-4-2 Locomotive, 73-74 u	36	43
___	8309 Southern 2-8-2 Locomotive "4501," (FARR 4), 83	385	495
___	8310 Nickel Plate Road 2-4-0 Locomotive, 73 u	26	50
___	8310 Santa Fe 2-4-0 Locomotive, 74-75 u	26	34
___	8310 Jersey Central 2-4-0 Locomotive, 74-75 u	26	50
___	8311 Southern 0-4-0 Locomotive, 73 u	26	34
___	8313 Santa Fe 0-4-0 Locomotive, 83-84	13	17
___	8314 Southern 2-4-0 Locomotive, 83-85	17	21
___	8315 B&O 4-4-0 Locomotive, 83-84	85	120
___	8341 ACL SP-type Caboose, 86 u, 87-90	6	8
___	8350 U.S. Steel Switcher, 73-75	18	26
___	8351 Santa Fe Alco Diesel A Unit, 73-75	60	65
___	8352 Santa Fe GP20 Diesel, 73-75	65	105
___	8353 Grand Trunk Western GP7 Diesel, 73-75	90	120
___	8354 Erie NW2 Switcher, 73, 75	80	105
___	8355 Santa Fe GP20 Diesel Dummy Unit, 73-74	65	90
___	8356 Grand Trunk Western GP7 Diesel Dummy Unit, 73-75	65	75
___	8357 PRR GP9 Diesel, 73-75	100	120
___	8358 PRR GP9 Diesel Dummy Unit, 73-75	55	100
___	8359 Chessie System GP7 Diesel "GM50," 73	95	120
___	8360 Long Island GP20 Diesel, 73-74	70	105
___	8361 Western Pacific Alco Diesel A Unit, 73-75	50	70
___	8362 Western Pacific Alco Diesel B Unit, 73-75	45	65
___	8363 B&O F3 Diesel A Unit, 73-75	280	310
___	8364 B&O F3 Diesel A Unit, dummy, 73-75	120	160
___	8365/66 CP F3 Diesel AA Set (SSS), 73	355	405
___	8367 Long Island GP20 Diesel Dummy Unit, 73-75	80	100
___	8368 Alaska Vulcan Switcher, 83	120	129
___	8369 Erie-Lackawanna GP20 Diesel, 83-85	125	140
___	8370/72 NYC F3 Diesel AA Set, 83	330	435
___	8371 NYC F3 Diesel B Unit, 83	105	150
___	8374 Burlington Northern NW2 Switcher, 83-85	105	120

		Exc	Mint	
8375	C&NW GP7 Diesel, 83-85	135	165	___
8376	Union Pacific SD40 Diesel, 83	175	200	___
8377	U.S. Marines Switcher, 83-84	55	65	___
8378	Wabash FM Train Master Diesel "550," 83 u	500	690	___
8379	PRR Fire Car, 83 u	80	100	___
8380	Lionel Lines SD28 Diesel, 83 u	235	315	___
8402	Reading 4-4-2 Locomotive, 84-85	47	55	___
8403	Chessie System 4-4-2 Locomotive, 84-85	55	65	___
8404	PRR 6-8-6 Turbine "6200," (FARR 5), 84-85	360	460	___
8406	NYC 4-6-4 Locomotive "783," 84	445	571	___
8410	Redwood Valley Express 4-4-0 Locomotive, 84-85	34	50	___
8452	Erie Alco Diesel A Unit, 74-75	75	95	___
8453	Erie Alco Diesel B Unit, 74-75	55	75	___
8454	D&RGW GP7 Diesel, 74-75	80	110	___
8455	D&RGW GP7 Diesel Dummy Unit, 74-75	50	85	___
8458	Erie-Lackawanna SD40 Diesel, 84	160	190	___
8459	D&RGW Vulcan Rotary Snowplow, 84	125	146	___
8460	MKT NW2 Switcher, 74-75	45	65	___
8463	Chessie System GP20 Diesel, 74 u	130	200	___
8464/65	D&RGW F3 Diesel AA Set (SSS), 74	220	325	___
8466	Amtrak F3 Diesel A Unit, 74-76	225	250	___
8467	Amtrak F3 Diesel A Unit, dummy, 74-76	80	90	___
8468	B&O F3 Diesel B Unit, 74-75	95	100	___
8469	CP F3 Diesel B Unit (SSS), 74	85	110	___
8470	Chessie System U36B Diesel, 74	80	110	___
8471	Pennsylvania NW2 Switcher, 74-76	170	195	___
8473	Coca-Cola NW2 Switcher, 74 u, 75	120	130	___
8474	D&RGW F3 Diesel B Unit (SSS), 74	110	125	___
8475	Amtrak F3 Diesel B Unit, 74	85	105	___
8477	NYC GP9 Diesel, 84 u	150	205	___
8480/82	Union Pacific F3 Diesel AA Set, 84	280	365	___
8481	Union Pacific F3 Diesel B Unit, 84	150	155	___
8485	USMC NW2 Switcher, 84-85	105	135	___
8500	Pennsylvania 2-4-0 Locomotive, 75-76	17	21	___
8502	Santa Fe 2-4-0 Locomotive, 75	17	21	___
8506	PRR 0-4-0 Locomotive, 75-77	75	90	___
8507	Santa Fe 2-4-0 Locomotive, 75 u	25	30	___
8512	Santa Fe 0-4-0T Locomotive, 85-86	22	30	___
8516	NYC 0-4-0 Locomotive, 85-86	115	140	___
8550	Jersey Central GP9 Diesel, 75-76	120	155	___
8551	Pennsylvania EP-5 Electric Locomotive, 75-76	115	120	___
8552 /53 /54	SP Alco Diesel ABA Set, 75-76	170	245	___
8555/57	Milwaukee Road F3 Diesel AA Set (SSS), 75	240	315	___
8556	Chessie System NW2 Switcher, 75-76	115	160	___
8558	Milwaukee Road EP-5 Electric Locomotive, 76-77	128	185	___
8559	N&W GP9 Diesel "1776," 75	115	145	___
8560	Chessie System U36B Diesel Dummy Unit, 75	75	115	___
8561	Jersey Central GP9 Diesel Dummy Unit, 75-76	70	95	___
8562	Missouri Pacific GP20 Diesel, 75-76	95	138	___
8563	Rock Island Alco Diesel A Unit, 75-76 u	65	90	___
8564	Union Pacific U36B Diesel, 75	110	155	___
8565	Missouri Pacific GP20 Diesel Dummy Unit, 75-76	48	70	___

			Exc	Mint
___	8566	Southern F3 Diesel A Unit, 75-77	220	370
___	8567	Southern F3 Diesel A Unit, dummy, 75-77	105	135
___	8568	Preamble Express F3 Diesel A Unit, 75 u	90	115
___	8569	Soo Line NW2 Switcher, 75-77	60	65
___	8570	Liberty Special Alco Diesel A Unit, 75 u	75	90
___	8571	Frisco U36B Diesel, 75-76	58	95
___	8572	Frisco U36B Diesel Dummy Unit, 75-76	23	55
___	8573	Union Pacific U36B Diesel Dummy Unit, 75 u	103	138
___	8575	Milwaukee Road F3 Diesel B Unit (SSS), 75	105	160
___	8576	Penn Central GP7 Diesel, 75 u, 76-77	90	120
___	8578	NYC Ballast Tamper, 85, 87	85	90
___	8580/82	Illinois Central F3 Diesel AA Set, 85, 87	420	485
___	8581	Illinois Central F3 Diesel B Unit, 85, 87	130	155
___	8585	Burlington Northern SD40 Diesel, 85	355	385
___	8587	Wabash GP9 Diesel "484," 85 u	250	280
___	8600	NYC 4-6-4 Locomotive, 76	175	195
___	8601	Rock Island 0-4-0 Locomotive, 76-77	13	33
___	8602	D&RGW 2-4-0 Locomotive, 76-78	16	26
___	8603	C&O 4-6-4 Locomotive, 76-77	135	190
___	8604	Jersey Central 2-4-2 Locomotive, 76 u	39	44
___	8606	B&A 4-6-4 Locomotive "784," 86 u	720	760
___	8610	Wabash 4-6-2 "672" (FF 1), 86-87	324	610
___	8615	L&N 2-8-4 Locomotive "1970," 86 u	540	630
___	8616	Santa Fe 4-4-2 Locomotive, 86	60	65
___	8617	Nickel Plate Road 4-4-2 Locomotive, 86-91	60	65
___	8625	Pennsylvania 2-4-0 Locomotive, 86-90	21	34
___	8630	W&ARR 4-4-0 Locomotive "3," 86 u	125	150
___	8635	Santa Fe 0-4-0 (SSS), 86	80	100
___	8650	Burlington Northern U36B Diesel, 76-77	100	145
___	8651	Burlington Northern U36B Diesel Dummy Unit, 76-77	60	93
___	8652	Santa Fe F3 Diesel A Unit, 76-77	260	510
___	8653	Santa Fe F3 Diesel A Unit, dummy, 76-77	135	160
___	8654	Boston & Maine GP9 Diesel, 76-77	143	178
___	8655	Boston & Maine GP9 Diesel Dummy Unit, 76-77	90	115
___	8656	Canadian National Alco Diesel A Unit, 76	150	193
___	8657	Canadian National Alco Diesel B Unit, 76	60	75
___	8658	CN Alco Diesel A Unit, dummy, 76	85	170
___	8659	Virginian Electric Locomotive, 76-77	113	134
___	8660	CP Rail NW2 Switcher, 76-77	112	138
___	8661	Southern F3 Diesel B Unit, 76	145	165
___	8662	B&O GP7 Diesel, 86	120	130
___	8664	Amtrak Alco Diesel A Unit, 76-77	85	120
___	8665	BAR Jeremiah O'Brien GP9 Diesel "1776," 76 u	100	170
___	8666	Northern Pacific GP9 Diesel (SSS), 76	128	183
___	8667	Amtrak Alco Diesel B Unit, 76-77	60	80
___	8668	Northern Pacific GP9 Diesel Dummy Unit (SSS), 76	100	130
___	8669	Illinois Central Gulf U36B Diesel, 76-77	118	153
___	8670	Chessie System Switcher, 76	30	55
___	8679	Northern Pacific GP20 Diesel, 86	90	105
___	8687	Jersey Central FM Train Master Diesel, 86	189	258
___	8690	Lionel Lines Trolley, 86	105	115
___	8701	W&ARR 4-4-0 Locomotive "3," 77-79	157	210
___	8702	Southern 4-6-4 Locomotive, 77-78	280	398

		Exc	Mint	
8703	Wabash 2-4-2 Locomotive, 77	22	30	___
8750	Rock Island GP7 Diesel, 77-78	110	125	___
8751	Rock Island GP7 Diesel Dummy Unit, 77-78	50	70	___
8753	Pennsylvania GG1 Electric Locomotive, 77 u	290	315	___
8754	New Haven Electric Locomotive, 77-78	100	115	___
8755	Santa Fe U36B Diesel, 77-78	130	150	___
8756	Santa Fe U36B Diesel Dummy Unit, 77-78	75	95	___
8757	Conrail GP9 Diesel, 76 u, 77-78	111	138	___
8758	Southern GP7 Diesel Dummy Unit, 77 u, 78	75	95	___
8759	Erie-Lackawanna GP9 Diesel, 77-79	117	175	___
8760	Erie-Lackawanna GP9 Diesel Dummy Unit, 77-79	95	115	___
8761	GTW NW2 Switcher, 77-78	95	130	___
8762	Great Northern EP-5 Electric Locomotive, 77-78	130	140	___
8763	Norfolk & Western GP9 Diesel, 76 u, 77-78	110	120	___
8764	B&O Budd RDC Passenger (SSS), 77	110	135	___
8765	B&O Budd RDC Baggage Dummy Unit (SSS), 77	80	100	___
8766	B&O Budd RDC Baggage (SSS), 77		310	___
8767	B&O Budd RDC Passenger Dummy Unit (SSS), 77	85	105	___
8768	B&O Budd RDC Passenger Dummy Unit (SSS), 77	85	105	___
8769	Republic Steel Switcher, 77-78	22	39	___
8770	NW2 Switcher, 77-78	50	65	___
8771	Great Northern U36B Diesel, 77	110	130	___
8772	GM&O GP20 Diesel, 77	85	95	___
8773	Mickey Mouse U36B Diesel, 77-78	497	655	___
8774	Southern GP7 Diesel, 77 u, 78	115	135	___
8775	Lehigh Valley GP9 Diesel, 77 u, 78	85	105	___
8776	C&NW GP20 Diesel, 77 u, 78	87	129	___
8777	Santa Fe F3 Diesel B Unit (SSS), 77	160	175	___
8778	Lehigh Valley GP9 Diesel Dummy Unit, 77 u, 78	90	110	___
8779	C&NW GP20 Diesel Dummy Unit, 77 u, 78	73	109	___
8800	Lionel Lines 4-4-2 Locomotive, 78-81	58	105	___
8801	Blue Comet 4-6-4 Locomotive, 78-80	385	505	___
8803	Santa Fe 0-4-0 Locomotive, 78	14	24	___
8850	Penn Central GG1 Electric Locomotive, 78 u, 79	215	305	___
8851/52	New Haven F3 Diesel AA Set, 78 u, 79	320	430	___
8854	CP Rail GP9 Diesel, 78-79	100	120	___
8855	Milwaukee Road SD18 Diesel, 78		115	___
8857	Northern Pacific U36B Diesel, 78-80	140	180	___
8858	Northern Pacific U36B Diesel Dummy Unit, 78-80	55	85	___
8859	Conrail Electric Locomotive, 78-82	105	150	___
8860	Rock Island NW2 Switcher, 78-79	85	100	___
8861	Santa Fe Alco Diesel A Unit, 78-79	65	85	___
8862	Santa Fe Alco Diesel B Unit, 78-79	36	43	___
8864	New Haven F3 Diesel B Unit, 78	85	105	___
8866	M&StL GP9 Diesel (SSS), 78	85	120	___
8867	M&StL GP9 Diesel Dummy Unit (SSS), 78	65	95	___
8868	Amtrak Budd RDC Baggage, 78, 80	195	235	___
8869	Amtrak Budd RDC Passenger Dummy Unit, 78, 80	75	95	___
8870	Amtrak Budd RDC Passenger Dummy Unit, 78, 80	85	115	___
8871	Amtrak Budd RDC Baggage Dummy Unit, 78, 80	85	105	___
8872	Santa Fe SD18 Diesel, 78 u	125	155	___
8873	Santa Fe SD18 Diesel Dummy Unit, 78 u	60	85	___
8900	Santa Fe 4-6-4 Locomotive (FARR 1), 79	270	310	___

	MODERN 1970-2023	Exc	Mint
___	**8902** ACL 2-4-0 Locomotive, 79-82, 86 u, 87-90	13	17
___	**8903** D&RGW 2-4-2 Locomotive, 79-81	17	21
___	**8904** Wabash 2-4-2 Locomotive, 79, 81 u	30	34
___	**8905** Smokey Mountain Dockside 0-4-0T Locomotive, 79	9	17
___	**8950** Virginian FM Train Master Diesel, 79	210	285
___	**8951** Southern Pacific FM Train Master Diesel, 79	194	335
___	**8952/53** PRR F3 Diesel AA Set, 79	350	500
___	**8955** Southern U36B Diesel, 79	120	195
___	**8956** Southern U36B Diesel Dummy Unit, 79	80	125
___	**8957** Burlington Northern GP20 Diesel, 79	120	150
___	**8958** Burlington Northern GP20 Diesel Dummy Unit, 79	85	90
___	**8960** Southern Pacific U36C Diesel, 79 u	130	180
___	**8961** Southern Pacific U36C Diesel Dummy Unit, 79 u	70	80
___	**8962** Reading U36B Diesel, 79	115	130
___	**8970/71** PRR F3 Diesel AA Set, 79 u, 80	330	425
___	**9001** Conrail Boxcar (027), 86-87 u, 88-90	5	10
___	**9010** GN Hopper (027), 70-71	6	8
___	**9011** GN Hopper (027), 70 u, 75-76, 78-83	8	10
___	**9012** TA&G Hopper (027), 71-72	7	8
___	**9013** Canadian National Hopper (027), 72-76	5	8
___	**9015** Reading Hopper (027), 73-75	17	21
___	**9016** Chessie System Hopper (027), 75-79, 87-88, 89 u	4	6
___	**9017** Wabash Gondola with canisters (027), 78-82	3	5
___	**9018** DT&I Hopper (027), 78-79, 81-82	6	7
___	**9019** Flatcar (027), 78	2	3
___	**9020** Union Pacific Flatcar (027), 70-78	3	5
___	**9021** Santa Fe Work Caboose, 70-71, 73-75	20	29
___	**9022** Santa Fe Bulkhead Flatcar (027), 70-72, 75-79	7	13
___	**9023** MKT Bulkhead Flatcar (027), 73-74	7	10
___	**9024** C&O Flatcar (027), 73-75	3	6
___	**9025** DT&I Work Caboose, 71-74, 77-78	8	10
___	**9026** Republic Steel Flatcar (027), 75-82	5	7
___	**9027** Soo Line Work Caboose, 75-76	7	9
___	**9030** Kickapoo Gondola (027), 72, 79	5	9
___	**9031** NKP Gondola with canisters (027), 73-75, 82-83, 84-91 u	5	8
___	**9032** SP Gondola with canisters (027), 75-78	3	5
___	**9033** PC Gondola with canisters (027), 76-78, 82, 86 u, 87-90, 92 u	3	5
___	**9034** Lionel Leisure Hopper (027), 77 u	30	34
___	**9035** Conrail Boxcar (027), 78-82	5	12
___	**9036** Mobilgas 1-D Tank Car (027), 78-82	7	19
___	**9037** Conrail Boxcar (027), 78 u, 80	7	10
___	**9038** Chessie System Hopper (027), 78 u, 80	15	19
___	**9039** Mobilgas 1-D Tank Car (027), 78 u, 80	10	15
___	**9040** General Mills Wheaties Boxcar (027), 70-72	9	13
___	**9041** Hershey's Boxcar (027), 70-71, 73-76	18	28
___	**9042** Ford-Autolite Boxcar (027), 71 u, 72 74-76	13	21
___	**9043** Erie-Lackawanna Boxcar (027), 73-75	13	20
___	**9044** D&RGW Boxcar (027), 75-76	5	8
___	**9045** Toys 'R' Us Boxcar (027), 75 u	35	42
___	**9046** True Value Boxcar (027), 76 u	26	34
___	**9047** Toys 'R' Us Boxcar (027), 76 u	40	43
___	**9048** Toys 'R' Us Boxcar (027), 76 u	33	41
___	**9049** Toys 'R' Us Boxcar (027), 78 u		87

		Exc	Mint	
9050	Sunoco 1-D Tank Car (027), 70-71	17	23	___
9051	Firestone 1-D Tank Car (027), 74-75, 78	15	19	___
9052	Toys 'R' Us Boxcar (027), 77 u	26	34	___
9053	True Value Boxcar (027), 77 u	28	40	___
9054	JCPenney Boxcar (027), 77 u	14	19	___
9055	Republic Steel Gondola with canisters, 78 u	9	10	___
9057	CP Rail SP-type Caboose, 78-79	10	15	___
9058	Lionel Lines SP-type Caboose, 78-79, 83	5	7	___
9059	Lionel Lines SP-type Caboose, 79 u, 81 u	7	9	___
9060	Nickel Plate Road SP-type Caboose, 70-72	5	7	___
9061	Santa Fe SP-type Caboose, 70-76	5	8	___
9062	Penn Central SP-type Caboose, 70-72, 74-76	7	9	___
9063	GTW SP-type Caboose, 70, 71-73 u	15	19	___
9064	C&O SP-type Caboose, 71-72, 75-77	7	10	___
9065	Canadian National SP-type Caboose, 71-73 u	19	24	___
9066	Southern SP-type Caboose, 73-76	7	9	___
9067	Kickapoo Valley Bobber Caboose, 72	6	9	___
9068	Reading Bobber Caboose, 73-76	5	7	___
9069	Jersey Central SP-type Caboose, 73-74, 75-76 u	5	8	___
9070	Rock Island SP-type Caboose, 73-74	13	17	___
9071	Santa Fe Bobber Caboose, 74 u, 77-78	7	9	___
9073	Coca-Cola SP-type Caboose, 74 u, 75	33	38	___
9075	Rock Island SP-type Caboose, 75-76 u	13	17	___
9076	"We The People" SP-type Caboose, 75 u	19	28	___
9077	D&RGW SP-type Caboose, 76-83, 84-91 u	7	8	___
9078	Rock Island Bobber Caboose, 76-77	5	7	___
9079	GTW Hopper (027), 77	28	32	___
9080	Wabash SP-type Caboose, 77	9	10	___
9085	Santa Fe Work Caboose, 79-82	4	5	___
9090	General Mills Mini-Max Car, 71	27	32	___
9106	Miller Vat Car, 84-85	33	52	___
9107	Dr Pepper Vat Car, 86-87	30	36	___
9110	B&O Quad Hopper, 71			___
	(A) White Lettering	25	30	___
	(B) Gray Lettering	25	35	___
	(C) Yellow Lettering	50	70	___
9111	N&W Quad Hopper, 72-75	15	20	___
9112	D&RGW Covered Quad Hopper, 73-75	20	23	___
9113	Norfolk & Western Quad Hopper (SSS), 73	27	32	___
9114	Morton Salt Covered Quad Hopper, 74-76	18	27	___
9115	Planter's Covered Quad Hopper, 74-76	21	33	___
9116	Domino Sugar Covered Quad Hopper, 74-76	22	29	___
9117	Alaska Covered Quad Hopper (SSS), 74-76	29	33	___
9118	Corning 4-Bay Covered Hopper, 74 u		45	___
9119	Detroit & Mackinac Covered Hopper, 75 u		20	___
9120	Northern Pacific Flatcar with trailers, 70-71	33	38	___
9121	L&N Flatcar with bulldozer and scraper, 71-79	47	54	___
9122	Northern Pacific Flatcar with trailers, 72-75	19	32	___
9123	C&O Auto Carrier, 3-tier, 72 u, 73-74	18	27	___
9124	P&LE Flatcar with logs, 73-74	18	25	___
9125	Norfolk & Western Auto Carrier, 2-tier, 73-77	23	28	___
9126	C&O Auto Carrier, 3-tier, 73-75	23	34	___
9128	Heinz Vat Car, 74-76	19	36	___

		Exc	Mint
9129	N&W Auto Carrier, 3-tier, 75-76	17	19
9130	B&O Quad Hopper, 70	20	24
9131	D&RGW Gondola with canisters, 73-77	5	8
9132	Libby's Vat Car (SSS), 75-77	16	23
9133	BN Flatcar with trailers, 76-77, 80	20	28
9134	Virginian Covered Quad Hopper, 76-77	21	32
9135	N&W Covered Quad Hopper, 70 u, 71, 75	12	26
9136	Republic Steel Gondola with canisters, 72-76, 79	9	11
9138	Sunoco 3-D Tank Car (SSS), 78	33	37
9139	PC Auto Carrier, 3-tier, 76-77	21	29
9140	Burlington Gondola with canisters, 70, 73-82, 87-89	7	9
9141	BN Gondola with canisters, 70-72	8	10
9142	Republic Steel Gondola w/2 canisters, 77 u	15	23
9143	CN Gondola with canisters, 71-73 u	30	34
9144	D&RGW Gondola with canisters (SSS), 74-76	9	13
9145	ICG Auto Carrier, 3-tier, 77-80	21	29
9146	Mogen David Vat Car, 77-81	21	26
9147	Texaco 1-D Tank Car, 77-78	46	63
9148	Du Pont 3-D Tank Car, 77-81	25	28
9149	CP Rail Flatcar with trailers, 77-78	22	35
9150	Gulf 1-D Tank Car, 70 u, 71	22	28
9151	Shell 1-D Tank Car, 72	27	31
9152	Shell 1-D Tank Car, 73-76	25	34
9153	Chevron 1-D Tank Car, 74-76	32	39
9154	Borden 1-D Tank Car, 75-76	33	47
9155	Monsanto 1-D Tank Car, 75 u	38	47
9156	Mobilgas 1-D Tank Car, 76-77	30	40
9157	C&O Crane Car, 76-78, 81-82	35	44
9158	PC Flatcar with shovel, 76-77, 80	40	55
9159	Sunoco 1-D Tank Car, 76	35	50
9160	Illinois Central N5c Caboose, 70-72	17	23
9161	CN N5c Caboose, 72-74	14	25
9162	PRR N5c Caboose, 72-76	25	30
9163	Santa Fe N5c Caboose, 73-76	17	24
9165	Canadian Pacific N5c Caboose (SSS), 73	21	30
9166	D&RGW SP-type Caboose (SSS), 74-75	20	25
9167	Chessie System N5c Caboose, 74-76	24	31
9168	Union Pacific N5c Caboose, 75-77	17	19
9169	Milwaukee Road SP-type Caboose (SSS), 75	18	35
9170	N&W N5c Caboose "1776," 75	27	30
9171	MP SP-type Caboose, 75 u, 76-77	19	20
9172	Penn Central SP-type Caboose, 75 u, 76-77	23	31
9173	Jersey Central SP-type Caboose, 75 u, 76-77	22	33
9174	NYC (P&E) Bay Window Caboose, 76	65	70
9175	Virginian N5c Caboose, 76-77	24	26
9176	BAR N5c Caboose, 76 u	16	30
9177	Northern Pacific Bay Window Caboose (SSS), 76	20	35
9178	ICG SP-type Caboose, 76-77	19	24
9179	Chessie System Bobber Caboose, 76	7	11
9180	Rock Island N5c Caboose, 77-78	12	23
9181	B&M N5c Caboose, 76 u, 77	28	49
9182	N&W N5c Caboose, 76 u, 77-80	20	26
9183	Mickey Mouse N5c Caboose, 77-78	32	54

		Exc	Mint	
9184	Erie Bay Window Caboose, 77-78	24	30	___
9185	GTW N5c Caboose, 77	21	28	___
9186	Conrail N5c Caboose, 76 u, 77-78	27	29	___
9187	Gulf, Mobile & Ohio SP-type Caboose, 77	10	16	___
9188	GN Bay Window Caboose, 77	22	27	___
9189	Gulf 1-D Tank Car, 77	40	60	___
9193	Budweiser Vat Car, 83-84	92	121	___
9200	Illinois Central Boxcar, 70-71	19	25	___
9201	Penn Central Boxcar, 70	17	25	___
9202	Santa Fe Boxcar, 70	20	24	___
9203	Union Pacific Boxcar, 70	17	21	___
9204	Northern Pacific Boxcar, 70	17	21	___
9205	Norfolk & Western Boxcar, 70	22	25	___
9206	Great Northern Boxcar, 70-71	15	20	___
9207	Soo Line Boxcar, 71	11	18	___
9208	CP Rail Boxcar, 71	21	23	___
9209	Burlington Northern Boxcar, 71-72	16	25	___
9210	B&O DD Boxcar, 71	16	20	___
9211	Penn Central Boxcar, 71	17	28	___
9212	Seaboard Coast Line Flatcar with trailers, 76 u	22	31	___
9213	M&StL Covered Quad Hopper (SSS), 78	20	29	___
9214	Northern Pacific Boxcar, 71-72	16	21	___
9215	Norfolk & Western Boxcar, 71	19	24	___
9216	Great Northern Auto Carrier, 3-tier, 78	25	39	___
9217	Soo Line Operating Boxcar, 82-84	29	36	___
9218	Monon Operating Boxcar, 81	23	33	___
9219	Missouri Pacific Operating Boxcar, 83	29	37	___
9220	Borden Operating Milk Car, 83-86	95	113	___
9221	Poultry Dispatch Operating Chicken Car, 83-85	45	50	___
9222	L&N Flatcar with trailers, 83-84	38	60	___
9223	Reading Operating Boxcar, 84	33	40	___
9224	Churchill Downs Operating Horse Car, 84-86	85	110	___
9225	Conrail Operating Barrel Car, 84	42	55	___
9226	Delaware & Hudson Flatcar with trailers, 84-85	31	34	___
9228	Canadian Pacific Operating Boxcar, 86	23	42	___
9229	Express Mail Operating Boxcar, 85-86	21	27	___
9230	Monon Boxcar (SSS), 71, 72 u	17	24	___
9231	Reading Bay Window Caboose, 79	24	32	___
9232	Allis-Chalmers Condenser Car, 80-81, 83 u	42	50	___
9233	Depressed Center Flatcar with transformer, 80	55	65	___
9234	Radioactive Waste Car, 80	53	78	___
9235	Union Pacific Derrick Car, 83-84	16	22	___
9236	C&NW Derrick Car, 83-85	22	30	___
9237	UPS Express Operating Boxcar, 84	32	99	___
9238	Northern Pacific Log Dump Car, 84	16	24	___
9239	Lionel Lines N5c Caboose, 83 u	50	60	___
9240	NYC Operating Hopper, 86	32	39	___
9240	NYC Hopper (O27), 87 u	20	29	___
9241	PRR Log Dump Car, 85-86	21	27	___
9250	WaterPoxy 3-D Tank Car, 70-71	23	34	___
9260	Reynolds Aluminum Covered Quad Hopper, 75-77	19	22	___
9261	Sun-Maid Raisins Covered Quad Hopper, 75 u, 76	25	31	___
9262	Ralston Purina Covered Quad Hopper, 75 u, 76	36	58	___

		Exc	Mint
9263	PRR Covered Quad Hopper, 75 u, 76-77	23	30
9264	Illinois Central Covered Quad Hopper, 75 u, 76-77	28	39
9265	Chessie System Covered Quad Hopper, 75 u, 76-77	21	27
9266	Southern "Big John" Covered Quad Hopper, 76	46	65
9267	Alcoa Covered Quad Hopper (SSS), 76	20	25
9268	Northern Pacific Bay Window Caboose, 77 u	30	40
9269	Milwaukee Road Bay Window Caboose, 78	37	59
9270	Northern Pacific N5c Caboose, 78	14	27
9271	M&StL Bay Window Caboose (SSS), 78-79	18	30
9272	New Haven Bay Window Caboose, 78-80	20	34
9273	Southern Bay Window Caboose, 78 u	36	45
9274	Santa Fe Bay Window Caboose, 78 u	40	47
9276	Peabody Quad Hopper, 78	19	28
9277	Cities Service 1-D Tank Car, 78	41	45
9278	Life Savers 1-D Tank Car, 78-79	80	156
9279	Magnolia 3-D Tank Car, 78, 79 u	13	19
9280	Santa Fe Operating Stock Car (O27), 77-81	16	24
9281	Santa Fe Auto Carrier, 3-tier, 78-80	21	27
9282	GN Flatcar with trailers, 78-79, 81-82	22	28
9283	Union Pacific Gondola with canisters, 77	15	21
9284	Santa Fe Gondola with canisters, 77	16	27
9285	ICG Flatcar with trailers, 77	47	48
9286	B&LE Covered Quad Hopper, 77	14	26
9287	Southern N5c Caboose, 77 u, 78	18	30
9288	Lehigh Valley N5c Caboose, 77 u, 78, 80	25	31
9289	C&NW N5c Caboose, 77 u, 78, 80	25	36
9290	Union Pacific Operating Barrel Car, 83	65	75
9300	PC Log Dump Car, 70-75, 77	18	24
9301	U.S. Mail Operating Boxcar, 73-84	32	42
9302	L&N Searchlight Car, 72 u, 73-78	21	24
9303	Union Pacific Log Dump Car, 74-78, 80	17	22
9304	C&O Coal Dump Car, 74-78	11	25
9305	Santa Fe Operating Cowboy Car (O27), 80-82	16	23
9306	Santa Fe Flatcar with horses, 80-82	18	26
9307	Erie Animated Gondola, 80-84	55	70
9308	Aquarium Car, 81-84	125	129
9309	TP&W Bay Window Caboose, 80-81, 83 u	19	25
9310	Santa Fe Log Dump Car, 78 u, 79-83	13	24
9311	Union Pacific Coal Dump Car, 78 u, 79-82	13	24
9312	Conrail Searchlight Car, 78 u, 79-83	18	27
9313	Gulf 3-D Tank Car, 79 u	43	50
9315	Southern Pacific Gondola with canisters, 79 u	16	23
9316	Southern Pacific Bay Window Caboose, 79 u	47	50
9317	Santa Fe Bay Window Caboose, 79	21	36
9320	Fort Knox Mint Car, 79 u	110	135
9321	Santa Fe 1-D Tank Car (FARR 1), 79	25	31
9322	Santa Fe Covered Quad Hopper (FARR 1), 79	30	38
9323	Santa Fe Bay Window Caboose (FARR 1), 79	39	49
9324	Tootsie Roll 1-D Tank Car, 79-81	69	98
9325	Norfolk & Western Flatcar with fences, 79-81 u	6	10
9326	Burlington Northern Bay Window Caboose, 79-80	34	44
9327	Bakelite 3-D Tank Car, 80	19	29
9328	Chessie System Bay Window Caboose, 80	33	42

		Exc	Mint	
9329	Chessie System Crane Car, 80	40	47	___
9330	Kickapoo Dump Car, 72, 79	3	7	___
9331	Union 76 1-D Tank Car, 79	39	44	___
9332	Reading Crane Car, 79	37	50	___
9333	Southern Pacific Flatcar with trailers, 79-80	33	47	___
9334	Humble 1-D Tank Car, 79	21	26	___
9335	B&O Log Dump Car, 86	16	22	___
9336	CP Rail Gondola with canisters, 79	16	29	___
9338	Pennsylvania Power & Light Quad Hopper, 79	60	75	___
9339	GN Boxcar (O27), 79-83, 85 u, 86	8	10	___
9340	Illinois Central Gondola with canisters (O27), 79-81, 82 u, 83	5	9	___
9341	ACL SP-type Caboose, 79-82, 86 u 87-90	6	8	___
9344	Citgo 3-D Tank Car, 80	23	38	___
9345	Reading Searchlight Car, 84-85	20	25	___
9346	Wabash SP-type Caboose, 79	6	10	___
9347	Niagara Falls 3-D Tank Car, 79 u	38	46	___
9348	Santa Fe Crane Car (FARR 1), 79 u	60	70	___
9349	San Francisco Mint Car, 80	55	70	___
9351	PRR Auto Carrier, 3-tier, 80	23	40	___
9352	Trailer Train Flatcar with C&NW trailers, 80	29	55	___
9353	Crystal Line 3-D Tank Car, 80	18	26	___
9354	Pennzoil 1-D Tank Car, 80, 81 u	60	85	___
9355	Delaware & Hudson Bay Window Caboose, 80	37	45	___
9357	Smokey Mountain Bobber Caboose, 79	8	10	___
9359	National Basketball Association Boxcar (O27), 79-80 u	19	24	___
9360	National Hockey League Boxcar (O27), 79-80 u	21	26	___
9361	C&NW Bay Window Caboose, 80	47	50	___
9362	Major League Baseball Boxcar (O27), 79-80 u	17	21	___
9363	N&W Log Dump Car "9325" (O27), 79	4	7	___
9364	N&W Crane Car "9325" (O27), 79	7	9	___
9365	Toys 'R' Us Boxcar (O27), 79 u	30	37	___
9366	UP Covered Quad Hopper (FARR 2), 80	19	23	___
9367	Union Pacific 1-D Tank Car (FARR 2), 80	21	30	___
9368	Union Pacific Bay Window Caboose (FARR 2), 80	30	36	___
9369	Sinclair 1-D Tank Car, 80	60	85	___
9370	Seaboard Gondola with canisters, 80	19	21	___
9371	Atlantic Sugar Covered Quad Hopper, 80	19	22	___
9372	Seaboard Bay Window Caboose, 80	35	40	___
9373	Getty 1-D Tank Car, 80-81, 83 u	31	42	___
9374	Reading Covered Quad Hopper, 80-81, 83 u	39	40	___
9376	Soo Line Boxcar (O27), 81 u	40	50	___
9378	Derrick Car, 80-82	18	22	___
9379	Santa Fe Gondola with canisters, 80-81, 83 u	22	30	___
9380	NYNH&H SP-type Caboose, 80-81	7	10	___
9381	Chessie System SP-type Caboose, 80	7	9	___
9382	Florida East Coast Bay Window Caboose, 80	34	48	___
9383	UP Flatcar with trailers (FARR 2), 80 u	27	34	___
9384	Great Northern Operating Hopper, 81	50	55	___
9385	Alaska Gondola with canisters, 81	27	34	___
9386	Pure Oil 1-D Tank Car, 81	38	50	___
9387	Burlington Bay Window Caboose, 81	46	52	___
9388	Toys 'R' Us Boxcar (O27), 81 u	38	45	___
9389	Radioactive Waste Car, 81-82	65	78	___

		Exc	Mint
9398	PRR Coal Dump Car, 83-84	28	38
9399	C&NW Coal Dump Car, 83-85	17	22
9400	Conrail Boxcar, 78	14	20
9401	Great Northern Boxcar, 78	18	23
9402	Susquehanna Boxcar, 78	30	36
9403	Seaboard Coast Line Boxcar, 78	12	17
9404	NKP Boxcar, 78	19	21
9405	Chattahoochee Boxcar, 78	14	19
9406	D&RGW Boxcar, 78-79	17	21
9407	Union Pacific Stock Car, 78	18	25
9408	Lionel Lines Circus Stock Car (SSS), 78	31	40
9411	Lackawanna Phoebe Snow Boxcar, 78	35	43
9412	RF&P Boxcar, 79	21	27
9413	Napierville Junction Boxcar, 79	18	24
9414	Cotton Belt Boxcar, 79	19	23
9415	Providence & Worcester Boxcar, 79	17	25
9416	MD&W Boxcar, 79, 81	13	19
9417	CP Rail Boxcar, 79	45	50
9418	FARR Boxcar, 79 u	50	60
9419	Union Pacific Boxcar (FARR 2), 80	22	31
9420	B&O Sentinel Boxcar, 80	21	26
9421	Maine Central Boxcar, 80	10	17
9422	EJ&E Boxcar, 80	12	20
9423	NYNH&H Boxcar, 80	14	22
9424	TP&W Boxcar, 80	17	21
9425	British Columbia DD Boxcar, 80	26	35
9426	Chesapeake & Ohio Boxcar, 80	19	30
9427	Bay Line Boxcar, 80-81	12	17
9428	TP&W Boxcar, 80-81, 83 u		23
9429	"The Early Years" Boxcar, 80	13	27
9430	"The Standard Gauge Years" Boxcar, 80	12	25
9431	"The Prewar Years" Boxcar, 80	13	25
9432	"The Postwar Years" Boxcar, 80	32	55
9433	"The Golden Years" Boxcar, 80	33	43
9434	Joshua Lionel Cowen "The Man" Boxcar, 80 u	29	37
9436	Burlington Boxcar, 81	25	30
9437	Northern Pacific Stock Car, 81	22	36
9438	Ontario Northland Boxcar, 81	25	31
9439	Ashley Drew & Northern Boxcar, 81	11	19
9440	Reading Boxcar, 81	50	65
9441	Pennsylvania Boxcar, 81	32	42
9442	Canadian Pacific Boxcar, 81	12	31
9443	Florida East Coast Boxcar, 81	19	24
9444	Louisiana Midland Boxcar, 81	14	18
9445	Vermont Northern Boxcar, 81	14	17
9446	Sabine River & Northern Boxcar, 81	15	21
9447	Pullman Standard Boxcar, 81	16	21
9448	Santa Fe Stock Car, 81-82	34	40
9449	Great Northern Boxcar (FARR 3), 81	22	35
9450	Great Northern Stock Car (FARR 3), 81 u	50	60
9451	Southern Boxcar (FARR 4), 83	26	32
9452	Western Pacific Boxcar, 82-83	12	16
9453	MPA Boxcar, 82-83	14	19

		Exc	Mint	
9454	New Hope & Ivyland Boxcar, 82-83	21	27	___
9455	Milwaukee Road Boxcar, 82-83	15	29	___
9456	PRR DD Boxcar (FARR 5), 84-85	24	30	___
9461	Norfolk & Southern Boxcar, 82	25	43	___
9462	Southern Pacific Boxcar, 83-84	18	23	___
9463	Texas & Pacific Boxcar, 83-84	15	19	___
9464	NC&StL Boxcar, 83-84	16	22	___
9465	Santa Fe Boxcar, 83-84	12	19	___
9466	Wanamaker Boxcar, 82 u	60	70	___
9467	Tennessee World's Fair Boxcar, 82 u	26	31	___
9468	Union Pacific DD Boxcar, 83	31	34	___
9469	NYC Pacemaker Boxcar (std O), 84-85	37	53	___
9470	Chicago Beltline Boxcar, 84	15	20	___
9471	Atlantic Coast Line Boxcar, 84	13	20	___
9472	Detroit & Mackinac Boxcar, 84	22	26	___
9473	Lehigh Valley Boxcar, 84	13	28	___
9474	Erie-Lackawanna Boxcar, 84	31	35	___
9475	D&H "I Love NY" Boxcar, 84 u	28	37	___
9476	PRR Boxcar (FARR 5), 84-85	27	36	___
9480	MN&S Boxcar, 85-86	15	18	___
9481	Seaboard System Boxcar, 85-86	15	18	___
9482	Norfolk & Southern Boxcar, 85-86	13	17	___
9483	Manufacturers Railway Boxcar, 85-86	14	19	___
9484	Lionel 85th Anniversary Boxcar, 85	22	26	___
9486	GTW "I Love Michigan" Boxcar, 86	23	34	___
9490	Christmas Boxcar for Lionel Employees, 85 u	140	300	___
9491	Christmas Boxcar, 86 u	26	37	___
9492	Lionel Lines Boxcar, 86	23	29	___
9500	Milwaukee Road Passenger Coach, 73	28	75	___
9501	Milwaukee Road Passenger Coach, 73 u, 74-76	33	37	___
9502	Milwaukee Road Observation Car, 73	30	48	___
9503	Milwaukee Road Passenger Coach, 73	33	48	___
9504	Milwaukee Road Passenger Coach, 73 u, 74-76	33	37	___
9505	Milwaukee Road Passenger Coach, 73 u, 74-76	35	38	___
9506	Milwaukee Road Combination Car, 74 u, 75-76	32	37	___
9507	PRR Passenger Coach, 74-75	34	55	___
9508	PRR Passenger Coach, 74-75	32	50	___
9509	PRR Observation Car, 74-75	41	60	___
9510	PRR Combination Car, 74 u, 75-76	30	47	___
9511	Milwaukee Road Passenger Coach, 74 u	33	48	___
9513	PRR Passenger Coach, 75-76	25	44	___
9514	PRR Passenger Coach, 75-76	23	36	___
9515	PRR Passenger Coach, 75-76	22	34	___
9516	B&O Passenger Coach, 76	27	42	___
9517	B&O Passenger Coach, 75	45	65	___
9518	B&O Observation Car, 75	45	65	___
9519	B&O Combination Car, 75	55	85	___
9521	PRR Baggage Car, 75 u, 76	65	95	___
9522	Milwaukee Road Baggage Car, 75 u, 76	65	80	___
9523	B&O Baggage Car, 75 u, 76	60	70	___
9524	B&O Passenger Coach, 76	27	37	___
9525	B&O Passenger Coach, 76	30	43	___
9527	Milwaukee Road Campaign Observation Car, 76 u	38	60	___

			Exc	Mint
___	9528	PRR Campaign Observation Car, 76 u	48	75
___	9529	B&O Campaign Observation Car, 76 u	35	59
___	9530	Southern Baggage Car, 77-78	45	65
___	9531	Southern Combination Car, 77-78	29	37
___	9532	Southern Passenger Coach, 77-78	33	47
___	9533	Southern Passenger Coach, 77-78	27	38
___	9534	Southern Observation Car, 77-78	31	47
___	9536	Blue Comet Baggage Car, 78-80	39	55
___	9537	Blue Comet Combination Car, 78-80	35	50
___	9538	Blue Comet Passenger Coach, 78-80	35	47
___	9539	Blue Comet Passenger Coach, 78-80	35	48
___	9540	Blue Comet Observation Car, 78-80	16	40
___	9541	Santa Fe Baggage Car, 80-82	21	30
___	9545	Union Pacific Baggage Car, 84	135	200
___	9546	Union Pacific Combination Car, 84	85	105
___	9547	Union Pacific Observation Car, 84	85	105
___	9548	UP Placid Bay Passenger Coach, 84	90	110
___	9549	UP Ocean Sunset Passenger Coach, 84	85	105
___	9551	W&ARR Baggage Car, 77 u, 78-80	36	48
___	9552	W&ARR Passenger Coach, 77 u, 78-80	46	60
___	9553	W&ARR Flatcar with horses, 77 u, 78-80	32	50
___	9554	Chicago & Alton Baggage Car, 81	55	85
___	9555	Chicago & Alton Combination Car, 81	50	75
___	9556	Chicago & Alton Wilson Passenger Coach, 81	50	75
___	9557	Chicago & Alton Webster Groves Passenger Coach, 81	45	65
___	9558	Chicago & Alton Observation Car, 81	50	75
___	9559	Rock Island Baggage Car, 81-82	42	65
___	9560	Rock Island Passenger Coach, 81-82	43	65
___	9561	Rock Island Passenger Coach, 81-82	42	65
___	9562	N&W Baggage Car "577," 81	80	110
___	9563	N&W Combination Car "578," 81	80	105
___	9564	N&W Passenger Coach "579," 81	90	100
___	9565	N&W Passenger Coach "580," 81	85	100
___	9566	N&W Observation Car "581," 81	90	95
___	9567	N&W Vista Dome Car "582," 81 u	160	255
___	9569	PRR Combination Car, 81 u	115	160
___	9570	PRR Baggage Car, 79	85	115
___	9571	PRR Passenger Coach, 79	125	145
___	9572	PRR Passenger Coach, 79	110	125
___	9573	PRR Vista Dome Car, 79	95	120
___	9574	PRR Observation Car, 79	75	100
___	9575	PRR Passenger Coach, 79-80 u	100	135
___	9576	Burlington Baggage Car, 80	145	175
___	9577	Burlington Passenger Coach, 80	95	105
___	9578	Burlington Passenger Coach, 80	105	110
___	9579	Burlington Vista Dome Car, 80	95	110
___	9580	Burlington Observation Car, 80	95	110
___	9581	Chessie System Baggage Car, 80	55	62
___	9582	Chessie System Combination Car, 80	47	55
___	9583	Chessie System Passenger Coach, 80	40	47
___	9584	Chessie System Passenger Coach, 80	31	37
___	9585	Chessie System Observation Car, 80	55	65
___	9586	Chessie System Diner, 86 u	85	90

		Exc	Mint	
9588	Burlington Vista Dome Car, 80 u	110	120	___
9589	Southern Pacific Baggage Car, 82-83	110	135	___
9590	Southern Pacific Combination Car, 82-83	90	105	___
9591	Southern Pacific Pullman Passenger Coach, 82-83	85	105	___
9592	Southern Pacific Pullman Passenger Coach, 82-83	85	105	___
9593	Southern Pacific Observation Car, 82-83	100	130	___
9594	NYC Baggage Car, 83-84	76	130	___
9595	NYC Combination Car, 83-84	75	85	___
9596	NYC Wayne County Passenger Coach, 83-84	80	95	___
9597	NYC Hudson River Passenger Coach, 83-84	70	85	___
9598	NYC Observation Car, 83-84	75	85	___
9599	Chicago & Alton Diner, 86 u	80	90	___
9600	Chessie System Hi-Cube Boxcar, 75 u, 76-77	19	25	___
9601	ICG Hi-Cube Boxcar, 75 u, 76-77	20	21	___
9602	Santa Fe Hi-Cube Boxcar, 75 u, 76-77	17	20	___
9603	Penn Central Hi-Cube Boxcar, 76-77	12	18	___
9604	Norfolk & Western Hi-Cube Boxcar, 76-77	23	26	___
9605	NH Hi-Cube Boxcar, 76-77	17	21	___
9606	Union Pacific Hi-Cube Boxcar, 76 u, 77	10	17	___
9607	Southern Pacific Hi-Cube Boxcar, 76 u, 77	12	15	___
9608	Burlington Northern Hi-Cube Boxcar, 76 u, 77	21	23	___
9610	Frisco Hi-Cube Boxcar, 77	25	34	___
9620	NHL Wales Boxcar, 80	27	35	___
9621	NHL Campbell Boxcar, 80	27	34	___
9622	NBA Western Boxcar, 80	24	30	___
9623	NBA Eastern Boxcar, 80	26	34	___
9624	National League Baseball Boxcar, 80	27	34	___
9625	American League Baseball Boxcar, 80	27	35	___
9626	Santa Fe Hi-Cube Boxcar, 82-84	10	14	___
9627	Union Pacific Hi-Cube Boxcar, 82-83	15	21	___
9628	Burlington Northern Hi-Cube Boxcar, 82-84	14	19	___
9629	Chessie System Hi-Cube Boxcar, 83-84	24	36	___
9660	Mickey Mouse Hi-Cube Boxcar, 77-78	34	46	___
9661	Goofy Hi-Cube Boxcar, 77-78	57	66	___
9662	Donald Duck Hi-Cube Boxcar, 77-78	38	49	___
9663	Dumbo Hi-Cube Boxcar, 77 u, 78	43	58	___
9664	Cinderella Hi-Cube Boxcar, 77 u, 78	56	86	___
9665	Peter Pan Hi-Cube Boxcar, 77 u, 78	49	77	___
9666	Pinocchio Hi-Cube Boxcar, 78	120	175	___
9667	Snow White Hi-Cube Boxcar, 78	365	473	___
9668	Pluto Hi-Cube Boxcar, 78	149	193	___
9669	Bambi Hi-Cube Boxcar, 78 u	67	105	___
9670	Alice In Wonderland Hi-Cube Boxcar, 78 u	61	91	___
9671	Fantasia Hi-Cube Boxcar, 78 u	56	91	___
9672	Mickey Mouse 50th Anniversary Hi-Cube Boxcar, 78 u	379	479	___
9700	Southern Boxcar, 72-73	22	30	___
9700	Hoboken Shore RR Boxcar "1029," 98 u		20	___
9701	B&O DD Boxcar, 72	14	19	___
9702	Soo Line Boxcar, 72-73	15	21	___
9703	CP Rail Boxcar, 72	30	40	___
9704	Norfolk & Western Boxcar, 72	10	17	___
9705	D&RGW Boxcar, 72	13	20	___
9706	C&O Boxcar, 72	11	19	___

			Exc	Mint
___	**9707**	MKT Stock Car, 72-75	14	22
___	**9708**	U.S. Mail Toy Fair Boxcar, 73 u	85	95
___	**9708**	U.S. Mail Boxcar, 72-75	18	23
___	**9709**	BAR State of Maine Boxcar (SSS), 72-74	29	32
___	**9710**	Rutland Boxcar (SSS), 72-74	24	28
___	**9711**	Southern Boxcar, 74-75	19	25
___	**9712**	B&O DD Boxcar, 73-74	31	34
___	**9713**	CP Rail "Season's Greetings" Boxcar, 74 u	95	120
___	**9713**	CP Rail Boxcar, 73-74	24	30
___	**9714**	D&RGW Boxcar, 73-74	16	20
___	**9715**	C&O Boxcar, 73-74	17	22
___	**9716**	Penn Central Boxcar, 73-74	15	20
___	**9717**	Union Pacific Boxcar, 73-74	18	28
___	**9718**	Canadian National Boxcar, 73-74	23	31
___	**9719**	New Haven DD Boxcar, 73 u	23	32
___	**9723**	Western Pacific Toy Fair Boxcar, 74 u	20	60
___	**9723**	Western Pacific Boxcar (SSS), 73-74	27	29
___	**9724**	Missouri Pacific Boxcar (SSS), 73-74	21	24
___	**9725**	MKT Stock Car (SSS), 73-75	15	18
___	**9726**	Erie-Lackawanna Boxcar (SSS), 78	25	30
___	**9729**	CP Rail Boxcar, black, 78	30	34
___	**9730**	CP Rail Boxcar, silver, 74-75	23	27
___	**9731**	Milwaukee Road Boxcar, 74-75	18	28
___	**9732**	Southern Pacific Boxcar, 79 u	24	31
___	**9734**	Bangor & Aroostook Boxcar, 79	30	38
___	**9735**	Grand Trunk Western Boxcar, 74-75	15	21
___	**9737**	Vermont Central Boxcar, 74-76	27	34
___	**9738**	Illinois Terminal Boxcar, 82	33	45
___	**9739**	D&RGW Boxcar (SSS), 74-76	17	25
___	**9740**	Chessie System Boxcar, 74-75	15	19
___	**9742**	M&StL Boxcar, 73 u	12	19
___	**9742**	M&StL "Season's Greetings" Boxcar, 73 u	85	105
___	**9743**	Sprite Boxcar, 74 u, 75	19	27
___	**9744**	Tab Boxcar, 74 u, 75	17	24
___	**9745**	Fanta Boxcar, 74 u, 75	19	29
___	**9747**	Chessie System DD Boxcar, 75-76	24	28
___	**9748**	CP Rail Boxcar, 75-76	16	20
___	**9749**	Penn Central Boxcar, 75-76	16	21
___	**9750**	DT&I Boxcar, 75-76	13	20
___	**9751**	Frisco Boxcar, 75-76	15	23
___	**9752**	L&N Boxcar, 75-76	20	23
___	**9753**	Maine Central Boxcar, 75-76	16	22
___	**9754**	NYC Pacemaker Boxcar (SSS), 75-77	20	30
___	**9755**	Union Pacific Boxcar, 75-76	20	24
___	**9757**	Central of Georgia Boxcar, 74 u	16	17
___	**9758**	Alaska Boxcar (SSS), 75-77	24	31
___	**9759**	Paul Revere Boxcar, 75 u	36	43
___	**9760**	Liberty Bell Boxcar, 75 u	30	40
___	**9761**	George Washington Boxcar, 75 u	36	43
___	**9762**	Toy Fair Boxcar, 75 u	125	170
___	**9763**	D&RGW Stock Car, 76-77	15	20
___	**9764**	GTW DD Boxcar, 76-77	40	63
___	**9767**	Railbox Boxcar, 76-77	15	20

		Exc	Mint	
9768	B&M Boxcar, 76-77	18	27	___
9769	B&LE Boxcar, 76-77	13	21	___
9770	Northern Pacific Boxcar, 76-77	14	18	___
9771	Norfolk & Western Boxcar, 76-77	16	24	___
9772	Great Northern Boxcar, 76	49	81	___
9773	NYC Stock Car, 76	32	39	___
9775	M&StL Boxcar (SSS), 76	19	23	___
9776	SP Overnight Boxcar (SSS), 76	32	34	___
9777	Virginian Boxcar, 76-77	19	25	___
9778	"Season's Greetings" Boxcar, 75 u	165	185	___
9780	Johnny Cash Boxcar, 76 u	50	61	___
9781	Delaware & Hudson Boxcar, 77-78	19	23	___
9782	Rock Island Boxcar, 77-78	14	17	___
9783	B&O Time-Saver Boxcar, 77-78	18	27	___
9784	Santa Fe Boxcar, 77-78	13	17	___
9785	Conrail Boxcar, 77-78	20	23	___
9786	C&NW Boxcar, 77-79	18	27	___
9787	Jersey Central Boxcar, 77-79	12	19	___
9788	Lehigh Valley Boxcar, 77-79	17	21	___
9789	Pickens Boxcar, 77	25	33	___
9801	B&O Sentinel Boxcar (std 0), 73-75	18	26	___
9802	Miller High Life Reefer (std 0), 73-75	30	38	___
9803	Johnson Wax Boxcar (std 0), 73-75	27	33	___
9805	Grand Trunk Western Reefer (std 0), 73-75	20	31	___
9806	Rock Island Boxcar (std 0), 74-75	38	46	___
9807	Stroh's Beer Reefer (std 0), 74-76	72	85	___
9808	Union Pacific Boxcar (std 0), 75-76	36	50	___
9809	Clark Reefer (std 0), 75-76	33	41	___
9811	Pacific Fruit Express Reefer (FARR 2), 80	26	33	___
9812	Arm & Hammer Reefer, 80	24	30	___
9813	Ruffles Reefer, 80	20	28	___
9814	Perrier Reefer, 80	21	30	___
9815	NYC "Early Bird" Reefer (std 0), 84-85	34	40	___
9816	Brach's Candy Reefer, 80	21	26	___
9817	Bazooka Bubble Gum Reefer, 80	24	31	___
9818	Western Maryland Reefer, 80	18	23	___
9819	Western Fruit Express Reefer (FARR 3), 81	22	29	___
9820	Wabash Gondola with coal (std 0), 73-74	24	38	___
9821	SP Gondola with coal (std 0), 73-75	28	32	___
9822	GTW Gondola with coal (std 0), 74-75	24	29	___
9823	Santa Fe Flatcar with crates (std 0), 75-76	34	44	___
9824	NYC Gondola with coal (std 0), 75-76	41	56	___
9825	Schaefer Reefer (std 0), 76-77	45	60	___
9826	P&LE Boxcar (std 0), 76-77	34	39	___
9827	Cutty Sark Reefer, 84	41	51	___
9828	J&B Reefer, 84	37	49	___
9829	Dewar's White Label Reefer, 84	45	51	___
9830	Johnnie Walker Red Label Reefer, 84	36	44	___
9831	Pepsi Cola Reefer, 82	87	98	___
9832	Cheerios Reefer, 82	162	190	___
9833	Vlasic Pickles Reefer, 82	23	29	___
9834	Southern Comfort Reefer, 83-84	34	47	___
9835	Jim Beam Reefer, 83-84	48	62	___

		Exc	Mint
9836	Old Grand-Dad Reefer, 83-84	44	54
9837	Wild Turkey Reefer, 83-84	70	103
9840	Fleischmann's Gin Reefer, 85	39	44
9841	Calvert Gin Reefer, 85	44	49
9842	Seagram's Gin Reefer, 85	44	49
9843	Tanqueray Gin Reefer, 85	45	50
9844	Sambuca Reefer, 86	37	49
9845	Baileys Irish Cream Reefer, 86	62	86
9846	Seagram's Vodka Reefer, 86	41	49
9847	Wolfschmidt Vodka Reefer, 86	38	43
9849	Lionel Lines Reefer, 83 u	20	32
9850	Budweiser Reefer, 72 u, 73-75	58	70
9851	Schlitz Reefer, 72 u, 73-75	30	36
9852	Miller Reefer, 72 u, 73-77	32	38
9853	Cracker Jack Reefer, 72 u, 73-75		
	(A) White body, black border on logo	24	34
	(B) Caramel body, clear background logo	23	28
	(C) Caramel body, white background logo	23	28
9854	Baby Ruth Reefer, 72 u, 73-76	22	26
9855	Swift Reefer, 72 u, 73-77	16	28
9856	Old Milwaukee Reefer, 75-76	33	40
9858	Butterfinger Reefer, 73 u, 74-76	22	28
9859	Pabst Reefer, 73 u, 74-75	43	50
9860	Gold Medal Reefer, 73 u, 74-76	12	21
9861	Tropicana Reefer, 75-77	23	35
9862	Hamm's Reefer, 75-76	35	42
9863	REA Reefer (SSS), 74-76	24	28
9866	Coors Reefer, 76-77	42	58
9867	Hershey's Reefer, 76-77	80	93
9869	Santa Fe Reefer (SSS), 76	32	37
9870	Old Dutch Cleanser Reefer, 77-78, 80	15	21
9871	Carling Black Label Reefer, 77-78, 80	33	45
9872	Pacific Fruit Express Reefer, 77-79	24	28
9873	Ralston Purina Reefer, 78	25	38
9874	Miller Lite Beer Reefer, 78-79	58	63
9875	A&P Reefer, 78-79	23	31
9876	Vermont Central Reefer, 78	26	31
9877	Gerber Reefer, 79-80	68	78
9878	Good and Plenty Reefer, 79	24	31
9879	Hills Bros. Reefer, 79-80	24	29
9880	Santa Fe Reefer (FARR 1), 79	27	31
9881	Rath Packing Reefer, 79 u	22	31
9882	NYC "Early Bird" Reefer, 79	25	29
9883	Nabisco Oreo Reefer, 79	92	98
9884	Fritos Reefer, 81-82	26	34
9885	Lipton Tea Reefer, 81-82	30	38
9886	Mounds Reefer, 81-82	24	30
9887	Fruit Growers Express Reefer (FARR 4), 83	29	38
9888	Green Bay & Western Reefer, 83	42	49
11000	Holiday Express Freight Set, 08		280
11004	NASCAR Diesel Freight Set, 06-07	150	325
11005	Dale Earnhardt Jr. Diesel Freight Set, 06-07		240
11006	Lionel Lion Set, 03 u		230

		Exc	Mint	
11006	Kasey Kahne Expansion Pack, 06-07		130	___
11007	Dale Earnhardt Sr. Expansion Pack, 06-07		130	___
11008	Dale Earnhardt Jr. Expansion Pack, 06-07		130	___
11009	Tony Stewart Expansion Pack, 06-07		130	___
11010	Jimmie Johnson Expansion Pack, 06-07		130	___
11011	Jeff Gordon Expansion Pack, 06-07		130	___
11020	Harry Potter Hogwarts Express Steam Passenger Set, 08-13		330	___
11025	Jimmie Johnson 2006 Champion Boxcar, 07		45	___
11038	Snow-covered Straight Track 4-pack, 08		14	___
11041	Holiday Calliope Car, 08		45	___
11067	Lionel Bear, 08		25	___
11077	Harry Potter Figures, 08		27	___
11096	Engineer Hat, 08		20	___
11098	Holiday Toy Soldier Car, 08		50	___
11099	Pennsylvania Flyer Steam Freight Set, 08	136	210	___
11100	PRR 2-8-2 Mikado Locomotive "9631," CC, 07		370	___
11101	LL 2-8-4 Berkshire Locomotive "737," CC, 06		350	___
11103	Southern PS-4 4-6-2 Pacific Locomotive "1403," CC, 06		1000	___
11104	UP Big Boy Locomotive "4014," CC, 06		1800	___
11105	NYC L-2A 4-8-2 Mohawk Locomotive "2770," CC, 06		1100	___
11106	N&W 4-8-4 Northern Locomotive "746," CC, 06-07	610	750	___
11107	LionMaster SP Cab Forward "4276," RailSounds, 06-07		850	___
11108	C&O F-19 4-6-2 Pacific Locomotive "494," CC, 06-07		1160	___
11109	C&O 0-8-0 Locomotive "79," TrainSounds, 06		420	___
11110	NYC 0-8-0 Locomotive "7805," TrainSounds, 06		420	___
11114	NYC 4-8-2 Mohawk Locomotive "2795," CC, 06		1000	___
11116	UP 4-8-4 FEF-3 Locomotive "844," gray, CC, 08-09		1160	___
11117	Santa Fe E6 4-4-2 Atlantic Locomotive "1484," CC, 07-09		600	___
11119	Southern 0-8-0 Locomotive "6535," TrainSounds, 07	113	420	___
11122	UP Big Boy Locomotive "4024," CC, 06		1700	___
11123	UP Big Boy Locomotive "4023," CC, 06		1700	___
11126	UP Big Boy Locomotive "4012," CC, 06		1700	___
11127	SP GS-4 4-8-4 Northern Locomotive "4436," CC, 07-09		1200	___
11128	C&O F-19 4-6-2 Pacific Locomotive "490," CC, 07		1160	___
11129	C&O 2-8-4 Berkshire Locomotive "2696," CC, 07		1160	___
11129	C&O 2-8-4 Berkshire Locomotive "2699," CC, 07-09		1200	___
11130	Postwar "736" 2-8-4 Berkshire Locomotive, 07		300	___
11131	UP 4-8-4 FEF-3 Locomotive "844," black, CC, 08-09		1160	___
11132	Reading 2-8-0 Consolidation "1914," RailSounds, 08		450	___
11133	NYC 2-8-0 Consolidation "1149," RailSounds, 08		450	___
11134	WM 2-8-0 Consolidation Locomotive "729," RailSounds, 08		450	___
11135	B&O 2-8-0 Consolidation "2784," RailSounds, 08		450	___
11136	WP 2-8-2 Mikado Locomotive "322," CC, 08		800	___
11137	UP 2-8-2 Mikado Locomotive "1925," CC, 08		800	___
11138	ATSF 2-8-2 Mikado Locomotive "3156," CC, 08		800	___
11139	MILW 2-8-2 Mikado Locomotive "462," CC, 08		800	___
11140	Cass Scenic Shay Locomotive "7," CC, 07		800	___
11141	Birch Valley Lumber Shay Locomotive "5," CC, 07		800	___
11142	Hogwarts Express Add-on 2-pack, 09-10		120	___
11143	SP AC-4 Cab Forward Locomotive "4100," CC, 08		1670	___
11145	CNJ G3s 4-6-2 Pacific Locomotive "835," CC, 08		1290	___
11146	Pere Marquette 2-8-4 Berkshire Locomotive "1225," CC, 08		1290	___
11147	PRR 4-8-2 Mib Locomotive "6750," CC, 08		1290	___

			Exc	Mint
	MODERN 1970-2023			
___	11148	NYC Dreyfuss J-3a 4-6-4 Hudson "5448," CC, 08		1130
___	11149	LionMaster UP Big Boy 4-8-8-4 Locomotive ""4006," CC, 08		860
___	11150	NYC F-12e 4-6-0 Ten-Wheeler Locomotive "827," CC, 08		700
___	11151	Polar Express Tender, RailSounds, 08-10		440
___	11152	D&RGW LionMaster 4-6-6-4 Challenger "3805," CC, 09		900
___	11153	Stourbridge Lion Steam Locomotive, 09-10		430
___	11154	PRR CC2s 0-8-8-0 Mallet Locomotive "8183," CC, 09-10		2000
___	11155	ATSF 2-10-10-2 Mallet Locomotive "3000," CC, 09-10		2500
___	11156	C&O 4-6-0 Ten-Wheeler Locomotive, CC, 10	213	740
___	11157	WM Shay Locomotive "6," CC, 10		800
___	11162	Lone Ranger Add-on 3-pack, 10		165
___	11164	Dewitt Clinton Passenger Set, 10		630
___	11165	Dewitt Clinton Add-on Coach, 10		70
___	11166	CSX Merger Freight 2-pack #1, 10-11		130
___	11167	CSX Merger Freight 2-pack #2, 10-11		105
___	11168	CSX Merger Freight 2-pack #3, 10-11		130
___	11169	Strasburg Freight Add-on 2-pack, 10		100
___	11170	Three Rivers Fast Freight Set, 10-12		400
___	11172	Santa Fe 4-4-2 Steam Freight Set, 13		200
___	11173	Texan Freight Add-on 2-pack, 10-11		130
___	11174	Maple Leaf Freight Add-on 2-pack, 10-11		110
___	11175	Operation Eagle Justice Add-on 2-pack, 10-11		125
___	11180	Motor City Express Diesel Freight Train Set, CC, 12-13		1175
___	11181	CN GP9 Diesel Piggyback Train Set, CC, 12		850
___	11182	Dixie Special FT Diesel Freight Set, 11		700
___	11183	Lincoln Funeral Train, 13		1140
___	11194	Texas Special Diesel Passenger Set, CC, 13-14		1110
___	11195	PRR Diesel Passenger Set, CC, 13-14		1110
___	11196	BNSF Gondola "670591," 13		35
___	11197	ATSF Caboose "999471," 13		48
___	11199	UP NW2 Diesel Switcher Work Train Set, CC, 12		600
___	11200	UP LionMaster Challenger Locomotive "3985," CC, 10		900
___	11201	WM LionMaster Challenger Locomotive "1204," CC, 10		900
___	11202	CP 4-6-0 Ten-Wheeler Locomotive "914," CC, 10		740
___	11203	Pere Marquette Berkshire Locomotive "1225," CC, 09		980
___	11204	Pere Marquette Tender, RailSounds, 09-10		440
___	11206	DeWitt Clinton Locomotive and Tender, 11		800
___	11207	PRR LionMaster T1 Duplex Locomotive "5511," CC, 10		800
___	11208	UP LionMaster Big Boy Locomotive "4011," CC, 10		900
___	11209	Vision NYC Hudson Locomotive "5344," CC, 10		1600
___	11210	UP Challenger Locomotive "3967," CC, 10		1825
___	11211	UP 4-6-6-4 Challenger Locomotive "3976," CC, 10		1825
___	11212	NKP Berkshire Locomotive "765," CC, 10		1350
___	11215	LV 4-6-0 Camelback Locomotive "1598," CC, 10		550
___	11216	Jersey Central 4-6-0 Camelback Locomotive, CC, 10		550
___	11217	PRR 4-6-0 Camelback Locomotive "822," CC, 10		550
___	11218	Vision NYC Hudson Locomotive "5331," CC, 10		1600
___	11219	Clinchfield Challenger Locomotive "672," CC, 10		1825
___	11220	UP Challenger Locomotive "3989," CC, 10		1825
___	11221	UP Challenger Locomotive "3983," CC, 10		1825
___	11224	PRR Atlantic Locomotive "460," CC, 10-11		700
___	11225	B&O Atlantic Locomotive "1440," CC		700
___	11226	UP Water Tender, black, CC, 11		300

		Exc	Mint
11227	UP Water Tender, gray, CC, 11		300 ___
11228	Clinchfield Water Tender, CC, 11		300 ___
11229	MILW 4-8-4 Northern Locomotive "261," CC, 11		995 ___
11230	MILW 4-8-4 Northern Locomotive "267," CC, 11		995 ___
11232	Reading Atlantic Locomotive "351," CC, 11		700 ___
11233	Pennsylvania Power & Light 2-Truck Shay, CC, 11		900 ___
11234	Pennsylvania Power & Light 2-Truck Shay Locomotive, 11		750 ___
11235	West Side Lumber 2-Truck Shay Steam Locomotive, CC, 11		900 ___
11236	West Side Lumber 2-Truck Shay Steam Locomotive, 11		750 ___
11237	Sugar Pine Lumber Shay Locomotive "4," CC, 11		900 ___
11238	Sugar Pine Lumber Shay Locomotive "5," 11		750 ___
11239	Merrill & Ring Lumber 2-Truck Shay Steam, CC, 11		900 ___
11240	Merrill & Ring Lumber 2-Truck Shay Steam Locomotive, 11		750 ___
11247	Erie USRA 0-8-0 Steam Switcher "121," CC, 11-12		700 ___
11248	Erie USRA 0-8-0 Steam Switcher "127," 11-12		550 ___
11249	L&N USRA 0-8-0 Steam Switcher "2119," CC, 11-12		700 ___
11250	L&N USRA 0-8-0 Steam Switcher "2121," 11-12		550 ___
11251	Pere Marquette USRA 0-8-0 Switcher "1300," CC, 11-12		700 ___
11252	Pere Marquette USRA 0-8-0 Steam Switcher "1307," 11-12		550 ___
11253	NH 0-8-0 Steam Switcher "3603," CC, 11-13		700 ___
11254	NH 0-8-0 Steam Switcher "3606," 11-13		550 ___
11255	C&O 2-8-2 Mikado Steam Locomotive "1062," CC, 12		900 ___
11256	NH 2-8-2 Mikado Steam Locomotive "3021," CC, 12		900 ___
11257	PRR 2-8-2 Mikado Steam Locomotive "8631," CC, 12		900 ___
11258	Southern 2-8-2 Mikado Steam Locomotive "4501" CC, 12		900 ___
11259	UP 2-8-2 Mikado Steam Locomotive "2840," CC, 12		900 ___
11260	Rio Grande 2-8-2 Mikado Steam Locomotive "1207," CC, 12		900 ___
11261	DM&I 2-8-2 Mikado Steam Locomotive "1305," CC, 12		900 ___
11262	Erie 2-8-2 Mikado Steam Locomotive "3007," CC, 12		900 ___
11264	PRR K4 4-6-2 Pacific Steam Locomotive "1361," CC, 11		900 ___
11265	PRR K4 4-6-2 Pacific Steam Locomotive "1330," CC, 11		900 ___
11266	PRR K4 4-6-2 Pacific Locomotive "1361," 11		750 ___
11267	Undecorated S-3 4-8-4 Northern Locomotive, CC, 11		995 ___
11268	Strasburg 2-6-0 Mogul Steam Locomotive "89", 11		550 ___
11269	RI 2-6-0 Mogul Steam Locomotive "750," 11-13		550 ___
11270	GN 2-6-0 Mogul Steam Locomotive "453,", 11		550 ___
11271	C&O 2-6-0 Mogul Steam Locomotive "49," 11-12		550 ___
11272	ATSF 2-6-0 Mogul Steam Locomotive "573," 11		550 ___
11273	Central Pacific 2-6-0 Mogul Steam Locomotive "1470," 11-13		550 ___
11274	MKT USRA 0-8-0 Steam Switcher "46," CC, 11-12		700 ___
11275	MKT 0-8-0 Steam Switcher "51," CC, 11		550 ___
11276	Lionelville & Western 0-8-0 Steam Switcher "1," CC, 11-13		700 ___
11277	Lionelville & Western 0-8-0 Steam Switcher "2", 11-13		550 ___
11278	WP 2-8-2 Mikado Steam Locomotive "322," CC, 11		900 ___
11279	WP 2-8-2 Mikado Steam Locomotive "327," 11		750 ___
11280	B&O 2-8-2 Mikado Steam Locomotive "4507," CC, 11		900 ___
11281	B&O 2-8-2 Mikado Steam Locomotive '451," 11		750 ___
11282	GN 2-8-2 Mikado Locomotive "3125," CC, 11		900 ___
11283	GN 2i-8-2 Mikado Locomotive "3130," traditional, 11		750 ___
11284	MP 2-8-2 Mikado Locomotive "1310," CC, 11		900 ___
11285	MP 2-8-2 Mikado Locomotive "1312," traditional, 11		750 ___
11286	RI 2-8-2 Mikado Steam Locomotive "2302," CC, 11		900 ___

		Exc	Mint
___ 11287	RI 2-8-2 Mikado Steam Locomotive "2305," 11		750
___ 11288	T&P 2-8-2 Mikado Steam Locomotive "552," CC, 11		900
___ 11289	T&P 2-8-2 Mikado Steam Locomotive "557," 11		750
___ 11290	Bethlehem Steel 2-6-0 Mogul Steam Locomotive "28," 11		550
___ 11291	Weyerhaeuser 2-6-0 Mogul Locomotive "288," 11-13		550
___ 11292	Nashville 4-4-0 General Locomotive, 13		500
___ 11295	Elk River Lumber 2-Truck Shay Locomotive "1," CC, 11		900
___ 11296	Elk River Lumber 2-Truck Shay Locomotive "2," 11		750
___ 11297	P. Bunyan Lumber 2-Truck Shay Locomotive "18," CC, 11		900
___ 11298	P. Bunyan Lumber 2-Truck Shay Locomotive "23," 11		750
___ 11299	C&O 2-6-6-2 Mallet Steam Locomotive "875," CC, 12		1300
___ 11300	PRR 2-10-4 Texas Steam Locomotive "6479," CC, 11		1300
___ 11301	PRR 2-10-4 Texas Steam Locomotive "6498," CC, 11		1300
___ 11303	C&O 2-10-4 Texas Steam Locomotive "3011," CC, 11		1300
___ 11304	C&O 2-10-4 Texas Steam Locomotive "3025," CC, 11		1300
___ 11306	NKP 2-10-4 Texas Steam Locomotive "801," CC, 11		1300
___ 11308	Erie 2-10-4 Texas Steam Locomotive "3405," CC, 11		1300
___ 11310	Pere Marquette 2-10-4 Texas Locomotive "1241," CC, 11		1300
___ 11312	MILW S3 4-8-4 Northern Steam Locomotive "265," CC, 11		995
___ 11315	Pennsylvania-Reading Seashore Atlantic Locomotive, 11		550
___ 11316	PRR 4-4-2 Atlantic Steam Locomotive "272,", 11		550
___ 11317	Southern 4-4-2 Atlantic Steam Locomotive "1910," 11		550
___ 11318	CN 4-4-2 Atlantic Steam Locomotive "1630," 11		550
___ 11319	PRR K4 4-6-2 Pacific Locomotive "5409," 13		900
___ 11320	PRR K4 4-6-2 Pacific Locomotive, "5436," 13		750
___ 11321	C&O 2-6-6-2 Mallet Steam Locomotive "1525," CC, 12		1300
___ 11322	NKP 2-6-6-2 Mallet Steam Locomotive "943," CC, 12		1300
___ 11323	W&LE 2-6-6-2 Mallet Steam Locomotive "8002," CC, 12		1300
___ 11327	PRR Prewar K4 4-6-2 Pacific Locomotive "3667," CC, 11		900
___ 11328	PRR Prewar K4 4-6-2 Pacific Locomotive "3672," CC, 11		900
___ 11329	PRR Prewar K4 4-6-2 Pacific Locomotive "3678," 11		750
___ 11330	Polar K4 4-6-2 Pacific Locomotive, CC, 11-14		900
___ 11331	Polar K4 4-6-2 Pacific Locomotive, 11		750
___ 11332	ATSF 4-8-4 Northern Steam Locomotive "3751," CC, 12	413	1300
___ 11333	ATSF 4-8-4 Northern Steam Locomotive "3759," CC, 12		1300
___ 11334	Southern Crescent Limited 4-6-2 Pacific Locomotive, CC, 12		1100
___ 11335	Blue Comet 4-6-2 Pacific Locomotive "832," CC, 12		1100
___ 11336	Undecorated EM-1 2-8-8-4 Pilot Locomotive, CC, 12		1300
___ 11337	B&O 2-8-8-4 Steam Locomotive "7621," CC, 12		1300
___ 11338	Alton Limited 4-6-2 Pacific Steam Locomotive "657," CC, 12		1100
___ 11339	N&W 2-6-6-2 Mallet Steam Locomotive "1409," CC, 12		1300
___ 11340	B&O 2-8-8-4 Steam Locomotive "659," CC, 12		1300
___ 11341	Pilot 4-12-2 Locomotive, CC, 13		1300
___ 11342	UP 4-12-2 Steam Locomotive "9004," CC, 12-13		1300
___ 11343	UP 4-12-2 Steam Locomotive, black, "9000," CC, 12-13		1300
___ 11344	UP 4-12-2 Steam Locomotive, greyhound, "9000," CC, 12		1300
___ 11363	Cass Scenic RR 2-Truck Shay Steam Locomotive "3," CC, 12		900
___ 11364	Meadow River 2-Truck Shay Steam Locomotive "1," CC, 12-13		900
___ 11365	Weyerhaeuser 2-Truck Shay Steam Locomotive "3," CC, 12-13		900
___ 11366	Pickering Lumber 2-Truck Shay Steam Locomotive "3," CC, 12-13		900
___ 11367	CP 2-Truck Shay Steam Locomotive "111," CC, 12-13		900
___ 11368	WM 2-Truck Shay Steam Locomotive "2," CC, 12		900

		Exc	Mint
11369	Bethlehem Steel 2-Truck Shay Steam Locomotive "5," CC, 12-13		900 ___
11374	DM&I 2-8-8-4 Steam Locomotive "223," CC, 12		1300 ___
11375	WP 2-8-8-4 Steam Locomotive "258," CC, 12		1300 ___
11376	NP 2-8-8-4 Steam Locomotive "5000," CC, 12		1300 ___
11377	GN 2-8-8-4 Steam Locomotive "2060," CC, 12		1300 ___
11379	PRR 0-4-0 Shifter Steam Locomotive "112," 12		450 ___
11380	PRR 0-4-0 Shifter Steam Locomotive "94," 12		450 ___
11381	North Pole Central 0-4-0 Switcher (std O), 12		450 ___
11382	Transylvania 0-4-0 Shifter Steam Locomotive "1," 12		450 ___
11383	Bethlehem Steel 0-4-0 Shifter Steam Locomotive "134," 12		450 ___
11384	ATSF 0-4-0 Shifter Steam Locomotive "2301," 13		450 ___
11385	UP 0-4-0 Shifter Steam Locomotive "206," 13		450 ___
11386	B&M 2-8-4 Berkshire Steam Locomotive "4018," CC, 12-13		1250 ___
11387	ATSF 2-8-4 Berkshire Steam Locomotive "4199," CC, 12-13		1250 ___
11388	SP 2-8-4 Berkshire Steam Locomotive "3505," CC, 12-13		1250 ___
11389	B&A 2-8-4 Berkshire Steam Locomotive "1404," CC, 12-13		1250 ___
11390	Lima Demonstrator 2-8-4 Berkshire Locomotive "1," CC, 12-13		1250 ___
11391	IC 2-8-4 Berkshire Steam Locomotive "7020," CC, 12-13		1250 ___
11392	Michigan Central 2-8-4 Berkshire Locomotive "1420," CC, 12-13		1250 ___
11399	UP H7 Class 2-8-8-2 Steam Locomotive "3595," CC, 13-14		1350 ___
11400	C&O H7 Class 2-8-8-2 Steam Locomotive "1578," CC, 13-14		1350 ___
11401	Pilot H7 Class 2-8-8-2 Locomotive, CC, 14-15		1350 ___
11402	Virginian USRA Y3 2-8-8-2 Locomotive, CC, 13-14		1350 ___
11403	Pilot USRA 2-8-8-2 Locomotive, CC, 13-15		1350 ___
11404	ATSF USRA Y3 2-8-8-2 Locomotive, CC, 13-14		1350 ___
11405	N&W USRA Y3 2-8-8-2 Locomotive, CC, 13-14		1350 ___
11410	Pilot 4-8-2 Mohawk Locomotive, CC, 13-15		1300 ___
11411	NYC 4-8-2 Mohawk Locomotive "2854," CC, 12-13		1300 ___
11412	NYC 4-8-2 Mohawk Locomotive "2867," CC, 12-13		1300 ___
11413	Pilot 4-8-4 J-Class Locomotive, CC, 13-15		1300 ___
11414	N&W 4-8-4 Steam Locomotive "612," CC, 12-13		1300 ___
11415	Pilot S2 6-8-6 Turbine Locomotive, CC, 14-15		1300 ___
11416	PRR S2 6-8-6 Steam Turbine Locomotive "6200," CC, 12-14		1300 ___
11417	PRR S2 6-8-6 Steam Turbine Locomotive "6200," CC, 12-13		1300 ___
11418	Pilot GS-6 Locomotive, CC, 13-14		1300 ___
11419	SP 4-8-4 GS-2 Locomotive, black, CC, 12-13		1300 ___
11420	SP 4-8-4 GS-2 Locomotive, Daylight, CC, 12		1300 ___
11421	SP 4-8-4 GS-6 Locomotive, black, CC, 12		1300 ___
11422	WP 4-8-4 GS-64 Locomotive "482," CC, 12		1300 ___
11423	CNJ Blue Comet Locomotive "833," CC, 12-13		1100 ___
11425	Alaska 0-4-0 Locomotive, RailSounds, 12-13		1100 ___
11426	Rio Grande 0-4-0 Locomotive, RailSounds, 12-13		450 ___
11427	SP 0-4-0 Locomotive "14," RailSounds, 12-13		450 ___
11428	MILW 0-4-0 Locomotive, RailSounds, 12-13		450 ___
11429	Southern 0-4-0 Locomotive, RailSounds, 12-13		450 ___
11430	GN 0-4-0 Locomotive "1066," RailSounds, 12-13		450 ___
11431	N&W 4-8-4 Locomotive "611," CC, 12		1300 ___
11432	LL S2 6-8-6 Steam Turbine Locomotive, CC, 13-14		1300 ___
11433	PRR S2 6-8-6 Steam Turbine Locomotive CC, 13-14		1300 ___
11434	UP Big Boy Locomotive "4006," CC, 14		2700 ___
11435	UP Big Boy Locomotive "4018," CC, 14		2700 ___

		Exc	Mint
___ 11436	UP Big Boy Locomotive "4005," CC, 14		2700
___ 11437	UP Big Boy Locomotive '4014," CC, 14		2700
___ 11438	UP Big Boy Locomotive "4017," CC, 14		2700
___ 11446	UP USRA Y3 2-8-8-2 Locomotive "3671," CC, 13-14		1350
___ 11447	PRR USRA Y3 2-8-8-2 Locomotive "376," CC, 13-14		1350
___ 11448	UP Big Boy Locomotive "4012," CC, 14		2700
___ 11449	UP Big Boy Locomotive "4004," CC, 14		2700
___ 11450	Polar Express Berkshire Scale Locomotive, gold, CC, 14		1500
___ 11451	Polar Express Berkshire Scale Locomotive, black, CC, 14		1500
___ 11452	C&O 2-8-4 Berkshire Locomotive "2687," CC, 14		1500
___ 11453	Erie 2-8-4 Berkshire Locomotive "3321," CC, 14		1500
___ 11454	NKP 2-8-4 Berkshire Locomotive "765," CC, 14		1500
___ 11455	Pere Marquette 2-8-4 Berkshire Locomotive "1225," CC, 14		1500
___ 11456	Pere Marquette 2-8-4 Berkshire Locomotive "1227," CC, 14		1500
___ 11462	SP AC-12 Cab-Forward Locomotive "4291," CC, 14		1700
___ 11463	SP AC-12 Cab-Forward Locomotive "4286," CC, 14		1700
___ 11464	SP AC-12 Cab-Forward Locomotive "4294," CC, 14		1700
___ 11465	SP AC-12 Cab-Forward Locomotive "4275," CC, 14		1700
___ 11469	Pilot AC-12 Cab-Forward Locomotive, CC, 14-15		1700
___ 11528	Frosty the Snowman Figure Pack, 14, 16		30
___ 11650	Alderney Dairy General American Milk Car 2-pack (std O), 07		130
___ 11651	Freeport General American Milk Car 2-pack (std O), 07		130
___ 11652	BNSF Mechanical Reefer 2-pack (std O), 07-09		140
___ 11653	SPFE Mechanical Reefer 2-pack (std O), 07		140
___ 11654	UPFE Mechanical Reefer 2-pack (std O), 07		140
___ 11655	GN WFE Mechanical Reefer 2-pack (std O), 07		140
___ 11657	PFE Wood-sided Reefer 3-pack (std O), 06		190
___ 11658	John Bull Add-on Coach, 08		80
___ 11700	Conrail Limited Set, 87	203	370
___ 11701	Rail Blazer Set, 87-88	30	114
___ 11702	Black Diamond Set, 87	168	265
___ 11703	Iron Horse Freight Set, 88-91	100	105
___ 11704	Southern Freight Runner Set (SSS), 87	170	285
___ 11705	Chessie System Unit Train, 88	245	450
___ 11706	Dry Gulch Line Set (SSS), 88	195	260
___ 11707	Silver Spike Set, 88-89	175	245
___ 11708	Midnight Shift Set, 88 u, 89	60	83
___ 11710	CP Rail Freight Set, 89	321	415
___ 11711	Santa Fe F3 Diesel ABA Set, 91	545	745
___ 11712	Great Lakes Express Set (SSS), 90	260	340
___ 11713	Santa Fe Dash 8-40B Set, 90	279	480
___ 11714	Badlands Express Set, 90-91	49	60
___ 11715	Lionel 90th Anniversary Set, 90	186	373
___ 11716	Lionelville Circus Special Set, 90-91	155	190
___ 11717	CSX Freight Set, 90	230	240
___ 11718	Norfolk Southern Dash 8-40C Unit Train, 92	445	481
___ 11719	Coastal Freight Set (SSS), 91	165	215
___ 11720	Santa Fe Special Set, 91	49	60
___ 11721	Mickey's World Tour Train Set, 91, 92 u	105	154
___ 11722	Girls Train Set, 91	583	826
___ 11723	Amtrak Maintenance Train, 91, 92 u	210	245
___ 11724	GN F3 Diesel ABA Set, 92	730	840
___ 11726	Erie-Lackawanna Freight Set, 91 u	225	275

		Exc	Mint	
11727	Coastal Limited Set, 92	90	110	____
11728	High Plains Runner Set, 92	120	130	____
11733	Feather River Set (SSS), 92	260	330	____
11734	Erie Alco Diesel ABA Set (FF 7), 93	200	305	____
11735	NYC Flyer Freight Set "1735WS," 93-99	88	160	____
11736	Union Pacific Express Set, 93-95	110	130	____
11738	Soo Line Set (SSS), 93	250	280	____
11739	Super Chief Set, 93-94	135	165	____
11740	Conrail Consolidated Set, 93	200	240	____
11741	Northwest Express Set, 93	130	155	____
11742	Coastal Limited Set, 93 u	90	115	____
11743	Chesapeake & Ohio Freight Set, 94	240	280	____
11744	NYC Passenger/Freight Set (SSS), 94	272	335	____
11745	U.S. Navy Set, 94-95	186	264	____
11746	Seaboard Freight Set, 94, 95 u	90	183	____
11747	Lionel Lines Steam Set, 95	310	340	____
11748	Amtrak Alco Diesel Passenger Set, 95-96	145	235	____
11749	Western Maryland Set (SSS), 95	223	300	____
11750	McDonald's Nickel Plate Special Set, 87 u	143	153	____
11751	Sears PRR Passenger Set, 87 u	120	155	____
11752	JCPenney Timber Master Set, 87 u	75	115	____
11753	Kay Bee Toys Rail Blazer Set, 87 u	80	100	____
11754	Key America Set, 87 u	150	165	____
11755	Timber Master Set, 87 u	150	165	____
11756	Hawthorne Freight Flyer Set, 87-88 u	65	85	____
11757	Chrysler Mopar Express Set, 88 u	327	387	____
11758	Desert King Set (SSS), 89	195	250	____
11759	JCPenney Silver Spike Set, 88 u	175	250	____
11761	JCPenney Iron Horse Freight Set, 88 u	120	125	____
11762	True Value Cannonball Express Set, 89 u	95	145	____
11763	United Model Freight Hauler Set, 88 u	135	145	____
11764	Sears Iron Horse Freight Set, 88 u	155	190	____
11765	Spiegel Silver Spike Set, 88 u	175	250	____
11767	Shoprite Freight Flyer Set, 88 u	80	125	____
11769	JCPenney Midnight Shift Set, 89 u	100	175	____
11770	Sears Circus Set, 89 u	185	220	____
11771	K-Mart Microracers Set, 89 u	80	110	____
11772	Macy's Freight Flyer Set, 89 u	170	220	____
11773	Sears NYC Passenger Set, 89 u	175	200	____
11774	Ace Hardware Cannonball Express Set, 89 u	145	175	____
11775	Anheuser-Busch Set, 89-92 u	261	355	____
11776	Pace Iron Horse Freight Set, 89 u	115	135	____
11777	Sears Lionelville Circus Set, 90 u	175	190	____
11778	Sears Badlands Express Set, 90 u	49	60	____
11779	Sears CSX Freight Set, 90 u	190	230	____
11780	Sears NP Passenger Set, 90 u	155	190	____
11781	True Value Cannonball Express Set, 90 u	75	115	____
11783	Toys 'R' Us Heavy Iron Set, 90-91 u	138	165	____
11784	Pace Iron Horse Freight Set, 90 u	115	135	____
11785	Costco Union Pacific Express Set, 90 u	200	230	____
11789	Sears Illinois Central Passenger Set, 91 u	170	200	____
11793	Santa Fe Set, 91 u	49	60	____
11794	Mickey's World Tour Set, 91 u	80	100	____

		Exc	Mint
___ 11796	Union Pacific Express Set, 91 u	150	160
___ 11797	Sears Coastal Limited Set, 92 u	80	100
___ 11800	Toys 'R' Us Heavy Iron Thunder Limited Set, 92-93 u	238	298
___ 11803	Nickel Plate Special Set, 92 u	135	145
___ 11804	K-Mart Coastal Limited Set, 92 u	80	100
___ 11809	Village Trolley Set, 95-97	55	85
___ 11810	Budweiser Modern Era Set, 93-94 u	220	231
___ 11811	United Auto Workers Set, 93 u	189	447
___ 11812	Coastal Limited Special Set, 93 u	95	115
___ 11813	Crayola Activity Train Set, 94 u, 95	122	148
___ 11814	Ford Limited Edition Set, 94 u	222	266
___ 11818	Chrysler Mopar Set, 94 u	173	268
___ 11819	Georgia Power Set, 95 u	540	563
___ 11820	Red Wing Shoes NYC Flyer Set, 95 u	264	324
___ 11821	Sears Zenith Set, 95 u	363	790
___ 11822	Chevrolet Set, 96 u	287	337
___ 11825	Bloomingdale's Set, 96 u	150	333
___ 11826	Sears NYC Zenith Express Freight Set, 95-96 u	380	776
___ 11827	Zenith Employees Set, 96 u	340	823
___ 11828	NJ Transit Passenger Set, 96 u	70	180
___ 11833	NJ Transit GP38 Diesel Passenger Set, 97	275	300
___ 11837	Union Pacific GP9 Diesel Set, 97	113	520
___ 11838	ATSF Warhorse Hudson Freight Set, 97		810
___ 11839	SP&S 4-6-2 Steam Freight Set, 97		280
___ 11841	Bloomingdale's Set, 97 u	157	332
___ 11843	Boston & Maine GP9 Diesel ABA Set, 98		510
___ 11844	Union Pacific Die-cast Ore Cars 4-pack, 98		225
___ 11846	Kal Kan Pet Care Train Set, 97 u	271	879
___ 11849	Lionel Centennial Series Reefer 4-pack, 98	80	123
___ 11850	Rice A Roni Trolley Set, 02 u		271
___ 11851	PFE Reefer 6-pack (std O), 02	225	255
___ 11852	Clinchfield PS-2 2-bay Hopper, 04		70
___ 11853	B&M PS-2 2-bay Hopper 2-pack, 05		128
___ 11854	N&W PS-2 Covered Hopper 2-pack, 04		70
___ 11855	GN Offset Hopper with coal, 2-pack, 05		120
___ 11856	Green Bay & Western Offset Hopper 2-pack, 05		120
___ 11857	Baltimore & Ohio Offset Hopper 2-pack, 05		120
___ 11858	PRR PS-4 Flatcar with trailers, 2-pack (std O), 05		160
___ 11859	GN PS-4 Flatcar with trailers (std O), 05		160
___ 11860	SP PS-4 Flatcar with trailers (std O), 05		160
___ 11861	C&O PS-4 Flatcar with trailers (std O), 05		160
___ 11863	Southern Pacific GP9 Diesel "2383," 98		225
___ 11864	New York Central GP9 Diesel "2383," 98		275
___ 11865	Alaska GP7 Diesel "1802," 98-99		90
___ 11866	Govt. of Canada Cylindrical Hopper 2-pack (std O), 05		120
___ 11867	CN Cylindrical Hopper 2-pack (std O), 05		120
___ 11868	BN Husky Stack Car 2-pack (std O), 05		160
___ 11869	SP Husky Stack Car 2-pack (std O), 05		160
___ 11870	CSX Husky Stack Car 2-pack (std O), 05		220
___ 11871	TTX Trailer Train Stack Car 2-pack (std O), 05		160
___ 11872	PFE Orange Steel-sided Reefer 3-pack (std O), 05		130
___ 11873	C&O Offset Hopper 3-pack (std O), 05		130
___ 11874	PFE Orange Steel-sided Reefer 3-pack (std O), 05		130

		Exc	Mint	
11875	NP Steel-sided Reefer 3-pack (std O), 05	68	131	___
11876	PFE Silver Steel-sided Reefer 3-pack (std O), 05		130	___
11877	C&NW Steel-sided Reefer 3-pack (std O), 05		130	___
11878	Santa Fe PS-2 2-bay Covered Hopper 3-pack (std O), 06		125	___
11879	MKT PS-2 2-bay Covered Hopper 3-pack (std O), 06		125	___
11880	Boraxo PS-2 2-bay Covered Hopper 3-pack (std O), 06		125	___
11881	PRR PS-2 2-bay Covered Hopper 3-pack (std O), 06		125	___
11882	RI Offset Hopper with gravel, 3-pack (std O), 06		125	___
11883	CNJ Offset Hopper 3-pack (std O), 06		145	___
11884	Maine Central Offset Hopper 3-pack (std O), 06		145	___
11891	Pennsylvania 3-bay Hopper 3-pack (std O), 06		155	___
11892	Conrail ACF 3-bay Hopper 3-pack (std O), 06		155	___
11893	N&W 3-bay Hopper 3-pack (std O), 06		155	___
11894	UP 3-bay Hopper 3-pack (std O), 06		155	___
11895	GN Steel-sided Reefer 3-pack (std O), 06		145	___
11896	Santa Fe Steel-sided Reefer 3-pack (std O), 06		145	___
11897	Pepper Packing Steel-sided Reefer 3-pack (std O), 06		145	___
11900	SF Steam Freight Set, 96-01		130	___
11903	ACL F3 Diesel ABA Set, 96		716	___
11905	U.S. Coast Guard Set, 96	148	205	___
11906	Factory Selection Special Set, 95 u	43	93	___
11909	N&W J 4-8-4 Warhorse Set, 96	480	720	___
11910	Lionel Lines Set (O27), 96	100	160	___
11912	"57" Switcher Service Exclusive, 96	129	310	___
11913	SP GP9 Diesel Freight Set, 97	100	440	___
11914	NYC GP9 Diesel Freight Set, 97		370	___
11918	Conrail SD20 Service Exclusive "X1144" (SSS), 97	60	255	___
11919	Docksider Set, 97		70	___
11920	Port of Lionel City Dive Team Set, 97		185	___
11921	Lionel Lines Freight Set, 97		130	___
11929	ATSF Warbonnet Passenger Set, 97-99		132	___
11930	ATSF Warbonnet Passenger Car 2-pack, 97-99		80	___
11931	Chessie Flyer Freight Set "1931S," 97-99	105	185	___
11933	Dodge Motorsports Freight Set, 96 u	189	323	___
11934	Virginian Electric Locomotive Freight Set, 97-99		260	___
11935	NYC Flyer Freight Set, 97		155	___
11936	Little League Baseball Steam Set, 97	250	321	___
11939	SP&S 4-6-2 Steam Freight Set, 97		220	___
11940	Southern Pacific SD40 Warhorse Coal Set, 98		600	___
11944	Lionel Lines 4-4-2 Steam Freight Set, 98		175	___
11956	UP GP9 Diesel Set, 97	330	380	___
11957	Mobil Oil Steam Special Set, 97	75	448	___
11971	D&H 4-4-2 Steam Freight Set, 98	125	155	___
11972	Alaska GP7 Diesel Set, 98-99	165	215	___
11974	Station Accessory Set, 98		22	___
11975	Freight Accessory Pack, 98		23	___
11977	NP Freight Cars 4-pack, 98	60	185	___
11979	N&W 4-4-2 Steam Freight Set, 98	38	120	___
11981	1998 Holiday Trolley Set, 98		75	___
11982	New Jersey Transit Ore Car Set, 98		250	___
11983	Farmrail GP7 Agricultural Freight Set, 99	269	493	___
11984	Corvette GP7 Diesel Set, 99	138	424	___
11988	NYC Firecar "18444" and Instruction Car "19853," 99		210	___

			Exc	Mint
___	12000	NY Yankees Berkshire Passenger Set , 13		380
___	12004	Philadelphia Phillies Berkshire Passenger Set, 13	188	388
___	12008	Boston Red Sox Berkshire Passenger Set , 13		380
___	12012	Chicago Cubs Berkshire Passenger Set , 13	175	380
___	12013	NY Mets and Yankees Subway Series Set, 13		400
___	12014	FasTrack 10" Straight Track, 03-23		6
___	12015	FasTrack O36 Curved Track, 03-23		6
___	12016	FasTrack 10" Terminal Track, 03-23		10
___	12017	FasTrack O36 Manual Switch, left hand, 03-23		55
___	12018	FasTrack O36 Manual Switch, right-hand, 03-23		55
___	12019	FasTrack 90-degree Crossover, 03-23		29
___	12020	FasTrack 5" Uncoupling Track, 03-23		46
___	12022	FasTrack O36 Half Curved Track, 03-23		5
___	12023	FasTrack O36 Quarter Curved Track, 03-23		5
___	12024	FasTrack 5" Straight Track, 03-23		5
___	12025	FasTrack 4½" Straight Track, 03-23		5
___	12026	FasTrack 1¾" Straight Track, 03-23		5
___	12027	FasTrack 10" Insulated Track, 03-23		5
___	12028	FasTrack Inner Passing Loop Track Pack, 03-23		127
___	12029	FasTrack Accessory Activator Pack, 03-23		23
___	12030	FasTrack Figure 8 Track Pack, 03-23		83
___	12031	FasTrack Outer Passing Loop Track Pack, 03-23		160
___	12032	FasTrack 10" Straight Track,4-pack, 03-23		25
___	12033	FasTrack O36 Curved Track, 4-pack, 03-23		25
___	12035	FasTrack Lighted Bumper, 2-pack, 05-23		37
___	12036	FasTrack Grade Crossing, 2-pack, 05-23		22
___	12037	FasTrack Graduated Trestle Set, 05-23		94
___	12038	FasTrack Elevated Trestle Set, 05-23		50
___	12039	FasTrack Railer, 04-23		11
___	12040	FasTrack O Gauge Transition Piece, 04-23		11
___	12041	FasTrack O72 Curved Track, 04-23		8
___	12042	FasTrack 30" Straight Track, 04-23		19
___	12043	FasTrack O48 Curved Track, 04-23		7
___	12044	FasTrack Siding Track Add-on Track Pack, 04-23		132
___	12045	O36 Remote Switch, left hand (FasTrack), 04-17		95
___	12046	O36 Remote Switch, right hand (FasTrack), 04-17		95
___	12047	O72 Wye Remote Switch (FasTrack), 04-14		97
___	12048	O72 Remote Switch, left hand (FasTrack), 04-14		104
___	12049	O72 Remote Switch, right hand (FasTrack), 04-14		104
___	12050	FasTrack 22.5-degree Crossover, 04-23		55
___	12051	FasTrack 45-degree Crossover, 04-23		33
___	12052	FasTrack Grade Crossing w/Flashers, 05-23		110
___	12053	FasTrack Accessory Power Wire, 04-23		4
___	12054	FasTrack 10" Straight Uncoupling Track, 05-23		50
___	12055	FasTrack O72 Half Curved Track , 04-23		7
___	12056	FasTrack O60 Curved Track, 05-23		8
___	12057	O60 Remote Switch, left hand, 05-14		110
___	12058	O60 Remote Switch, right hand (FasTrack), 05-14		110
___	12059	FasTrack Earthen Bumper, 04-23		15
___	12060	FasTrack Block Section, 05-23		13
___	12061	FasTrack O84 Curved Track, 05-23		8
___	12062	FasTrack Grade Crossing w/Gates and Flashers, 06-23		187
___	12065	O48 Remote Switch, left hand (FasTrack), 07-14		104

			Exc	Mint	
12066	048 Remote Switch, right hand (FasTrack), 07-14			104	___
12073	FasTrack 1 3/8" Track Section, 07-23			5	___
12074	FasTrack 1 3/8" Track Section, no roadbed, 07-23			5	___
12080	42" Path Remote Switch, right hand, 07-12			80	___
12081	42" Path Remote Switch, left hand, 07-12			80	___
12700	Erie Magnetic Gantry Crane, 87		125	150	___
12701	Operating Fueling Station, 87		60	74	___
12702	Control Tower, 87		60	75	___
12703	Icing Station, 88-89		60	65	___
12704	Dwarf Signal, 88-93		9	11	___
12705	Lumber Shed Kit, 88-99			9	___
12706	Barrel Loader Building Kit, 87-99			10	___
12707	Billboards, set of 3, 87-99			5	___
12708	Street Lamps, set of 3, 88-93		6	9	___
12709	Banjo Signal, 87-91, 95-00			29	___
12710	Engine House Kit, 87-91		21	25	___
12711	Water Tower Kit, 87-99			13	___
12712	Automatic Ore Loader, 87-88		17	21	___
12713	Automatic Gateman, 87-88, 94-00		30	40	___
12714	No. 252 Crossing Gate, 87-23			55	___
12715	Illuminated Bumpers, set of 2, 87-15			18	___
12716	Searchlight Tower, 87-89, 91-92		15	22	___
12717	Nonilluminated Bumpers, set of 3, 87-17			7	___
12718	Barrel Shed Kit, 87-99			10	___
12719	Animated Refreshment Stand, 88-89		65	70	___
12720	Rotary Beacon, 88-89		40	45	___
12721	Illuminated Extension Bridge, rock piers, 89		26	38	___
12722	Roadside Diner, smoke, 88-89		27	38	___
12723	Microwave Tower, 88-91, 94-95		14	19	___
12724	Double Signal Bridge, 88-90		39	50	___
12725	Lionel Tractor and Trailer, 88-89		10	18	___
12726	Grain Elevator Kit, 88-91, 94-99			31	___
12727	Operating Semaphore, 89-99			26	___
12728	Illuminated Freight Station, 89		29	38	___
12729	Mail Pickup Set, 88-91, 95		12	16	___
12730	Lionel Girder Bridge, 88-03, 08-23			21	___
12731	Station Platform, 88-00			8	___
12732	Coal Bag, 88-23			8	___
12733	Watchman Shanty Kit, 88-99			5	___
12734	Passenger/Freight Station Kit, 89-99		16	39	___
12735	Diesel Horn Shed, 88-91		19	24	___
12736	Coaling Station Kit, 88-91		21	31	___
12737	Whistling Freight Shed, 88-99			28	___
12739	Lionel Gas Company Tractor and Tanker, 89		20	25	___
12740	Genuine Wood Logs, set of 3, 88-92, 94-95, 97-99			5	___
12741	Union Pacific Intermodal Crane, 89		165	185	___
12742	Gooseneck Lamps, set of 2, 89-00			21	___
12743	Track Clips, dozen (O), 89-16			12	___
12744	Rock Piers, set of 2, 89-23			19	___
12745	Barrel Pack, set of 6, 89-23			10	___
12746	Operating/Uncoupling Track (O27), 89-16			10	___
12748	Illuminated Passenger Platform, 89-99			18	___
12749	Rotary Radar Antenna, 89-92, 95		28	38	___

			Exc	Mint
	MODERN 1970-2023			
___	12750	Crane Kit, 89-91	8	10
___	12751	Shovel Kit, 89-91	8	10
___	12752	History of Lionel Trains Video, 89-92, 94	19	21
___	12753	Ore Load, set of 2, 89-91, 95	1	2
___	12754	Graduated Trestle Set, 22 pieces, 89-15		27
___	12755	Elevated Trestle Set, 10 pieces, 89-15	0	34
___	12756	The Making of the Scale Hudson Video, 91-94	20	22
___	12759	Floodlight Tower, 90-00		25
___	12760	Automatic Highway Flasher, 90-91	23	27
___	12761	Animated Billboard, 90-91, 93, 95	12	23
___	12763	Single Signal Bridge, 90-91, 93	31	35
___	12767	Steam Clean and Wheel Grind Shop, 92-93, 95	240	290
___	12768	Burning Switch Tower, 90, 93	85	94
___	12770	Arch-Under Bridge, 90-03, 08-23		30
___	12771	Mom's Roadside Diner, smoke, 90-91	40	68
___	12772	Truss Bridge, flasher and piers, 90-16, 18, 20		70
___	12773	Freight Platform Kit, 90-98		32
___	12774	Lumber Loader Kit, 90-99		19
___	12777	Chevron Tractor and Tanker, 90-91	9	15
___	12778	Conrail Tractor and Trailer, 90	9	16
___	12779	Lionelville Grain Company Tractor and Trailer, 90	11	19
___	12780	RS-1 50-watt Transformer, 90-93	95	130
___	12781	N&W Intermodal Crane, 90-91	145	160
___	12782	Lift Bridge, 91-92	428	518
___	12783	Monon Tractor and Trailer, 91	11	19
___	12784	Intermodal Containers, set of 3, 91	12	17
___	12785	Lionel Gravel Company Tractor and Trailer, 91	9	15
___	12786	Lionel Steel Company Tractor and Trailer, 91	10	16
___	12791	Animated Passenger Station, 91	45	60
___	12794	Lionel Tractor, 91	7	13
___	12795	Cable Reels, pair, 91-98	3	5
___	12798	Forklift Loader Station, 92-95	33	44
___	12800	Scale Hudson Replacement Pilot Truck, 91 u	13	17
___	12802	Chat & Chew Roadside Diner, smoke and lights, 92-95	41	50
___	12804	Highway Lights, 4-pack, 92-04, 13-23	9	35
___	12805	Intermodal Containers, set of 3, 92	10	14
___	12806	Lionel Lumber Company Tractor and Trailer, 92	10	15
___	12807	Little Caesars Tractor and Trailer, 92	9	14
___	12808	Mobil Tractor and Tanker, 92	8	13
___	12809	Animated Billboard, 92-93	12	22
___	12810	American Flyer Tractor and Trailer, 94	12	18
___	12811	Alka Seltzer Tractor and Trailer, 92	11	19
___	12812	Illuminated Freight Station, 93-00	18	27
___	12818	Animated Freight Station, 92, 94-95	50	60
___	12819	Inland Steel Tractor and Trailer, 92	9	16
___	12821	Lionel Catalog Video, 92	13	17
___	12826	Intermodal Containers, set of 3, 93	10	16
___	12831	Rotary Beacon, 93-95	20	41
___	12832	Block Target Signal, 93-98	14	25
___	12833	RoadRailer Tractor and Trailer, 93	9	15
___	12834	Pennsylvania Magnetic Gantry Crane, 93	130	170
___	12835	Operating Fueling Station, 93	55	60
___	12836	Santa Fe Quantum Tractor and Trailer, 93	8	14

		Exc	Mint	
12837	Humble Oil Tractor and Tanker, 93	9	16	___
12838	Crate Load, set of 2, 93-97		3	___
12839	Grade Crossings, set of 2, 93-16		7	___
12840	Insulated Straight Track (O), 93-16		8	___
12841	Insulated Straight Track (O27), 93-16		5	___
12842	Dunkin' Donuts Tractor and Trailer, 92 u	13	25	___
12843	Die-cast Sprung Trucks, pair, 93-99		10	___
12844	Coil Covers, pair (O), 93-98		3	___
12847	Animated Ice Depot, 94-99	50	65	___
12848	Lionel Oil Company Derrick, 94	55	75	___
12849	Lionel Controller with wall pack, 94, 95 u	22	40	___
12852	Die-cast Intermodal Trailer Frame, 94-01		6	___
12853	Coil Covers, pair (std O), 94-98		7	___
12854	U.S. Navy Tractor and Tanker, 94-95		33	___
12855	Intermodal Containers, set of 3, 94-95	9	13	___
12860	Lionel Visitor's Center Tractor and Trailer, 94 u	10	14	___
12861	Lionel Leasing Company Tractor, 94	8	13	___
12862	Oil Drum Loader, 94-95	75	85	___
12864	Little Caesars Tractor and Trailer, 94	8	14	___
12865	Wisk Tractor and Trailer, 94	12	55	___
12866	TMCC 135-watt PowerHouse Power Supply, 94 u, 95-03	15	46	___
12867	TMCC 135-watt PowerMaster Power Distribution Center, 94 u, 95-04	15	49	___
12868	TMCC CAB-1 Remote Controller, 94 u, 95-09		115	___
12869	Marathon Oil Tractor and Tanker, 94	15	22	___
12873	Operating Sawmill, 95-97	40	95	___
12874	Classic Street Lamps, set of 3, 94-00		13	___
12877	Operating Fueling Station, 95	75	85	___
12878	Control Tower, 95	49	60	___
12881	Chrysler Mopar Tractor and Trailer, 94 u	46	57	___
12882	Lighted Billboard, 95	9	14	___
12883	No. 148 Dwarf Signal, 95-23		30	___
12884	Truck Loading Dock Kit, 95-98		16	___
12885	40-watt Control System, 94 u, 95-05		35	___
12886	Floodlight Tower, 95-98		31	___
12888	No. 154 Railroad Crossing Flasher, 95-23		60	___
12889	Operating Windmill, 95-98	15	47	___
12890	Big Red Control Button, 94 u, 95-00		43	___
12891	Lionel Refrigerator Lines Tractor and Trailer, 95	12	16	___
12892	Automatic Flagman, 95-96		25	___
12893	TMCC PowerMaster Adapter Cable, 94 u, 95-23		25	___
12894	Signal Bridge, 95-01		22	___
12895	Double-track Signal Bridge, 95-00	13	49	___
12896	Tunnel Portals, pair, 95-23		22	___
12897	Engine House Kit, 96-98		29	___
12898	Flagpole, 95-97		9	___
12899	Searchlight Tower, 95-98	10	25	___
12900	Crane Kit, 95-98		9	___
12901	Shovel Kit, 95-98		7	___
12902	Marathon Oil Derrick, 94 u, 95	109	161	___
12903	Diesel Horn Shed, 95-98		29	___
12904	Coaling Station Kit, 95-98		19	___
12905	Factory Kit, 95-98		20	___

		Exc	Mint
___ 12906	Maintenance Shed Kit, 95-98		20
___ 12907	Intermodal Containers, set of 3, 95	9	14
___ 12911	TMCC Command Base, 95-09		80
___ 12912	Oil Pumping Station, 95-98	38	65
___ 12914	SC-1 Switch and Accessory Controller, 95-98		35
___ 12915	Log Loader, 96	40	120
___ 12916	Water Tower, 96-97		56
___ 12917	Animated Switch Tower, 96-98		29
___ 12922	NYC Operating Gantry Crane, coil covers, 96	75	90
___ 12923	Red Wing Shoes Tractor and Trailer, 95 u	34	38
___ 12925	42" Diameter Curved Track Section (O), 96-16		4
___ 12926	Black Globe Street Lamps, 3-pack, 96-03, 08-09, 16-23		30
___ 12927	Yard Lights, 3-pack, 96-23		35
___ 12929	Rail-truck Loading Dock, 96		44
___ 12930	Lionelville Oil Company Derrick, 95 u, 96	55	75
___ 12931	Electrical Substation, 96		22
___ 12932	Laimbeer Packaging Tractor and Trailer Set, 96		14
___ 12933	GM Parts Tractor and Trailer, 95	17	29
___ 12935	Zenith Tractor and Trailer, 96		25
___ 12936	SP Intermodal Crane, 97		195
___ 12937	NS Intermodal Crane, 97		200
___ 12938	PowerStation Controller and PowerHouse 135-watt Supply, 97-00		150
___ 12943	Illuminated Station Platform, 97-00		24
___ 12944	Sunoco Oil Derrick, 97		85
___ 12945	Sunoco Pumping Oil Station, 97		80
___ 12948	Bascule Bridge, 97	75	315
___ 12949	Billboards, set of 3, 97-00		7
___ 12951	Airplane Hangar Kit, 97-98		29
___ 12952	Big L Diner Kit, 97		24
___ 12953	Linex Gas Tall Oil Tank, 97		9
___ 12954	Linex Gas Wide Oil Tank, 97		10
___ 12955	Road Runner and Wile E. Coyote Ambush Shack, 97		100
___ 12958	Industrial Water Tower, 97-98		50
___ 12960	Rotary Radar Antenna, 97		26
___ 12961	Newsstand with diesel horn, 97		30
___ 12962	LL Passenger Service Train Whistle, 97-99		30
___ 12964	Donald Duck Radar Antenna, 97	60	77
___ 12965	Goofy Rotary Beacon, 97		58
___ 12966	Rotary Aircraft Beacon, 97-00		35
___ 12968	Girder Bridge Building Kit, 97		22
___ 12969	TMCC Command Set, 97-09		148
___ 12974	Blinking Light Billboard, 97-00		15
___ 12975	Steiner Victorian Building Kit, 97-98		33
___ 12976	Dobson Victorian Building Kit, 97-98		24
___ 12977	Kindler Victorian Building Kit, 97-98		35
___ 12982	Culvert Loader, conventional, 98-00	38	170
___ 12983	Culvert Unloader, conventional, 99		185
___ 12987	Intermodal Containers, set of 3, 98		15
___ 12989	Lionel Tractor and Trailer, 98		16
___ 12991	Linex Gas Tractor-Tanker, 98		16
___ 14000	Operating Forklift Platform, 00		160
___ 14001	Operating Belt Lumber Loader, 00		95

		Exc	Mint	
14002	ZW Amp/Volt Meter, 00-04		80	___
14003	80-watt Transformer/Controller, 00-03		70	___
14004	Operating Coal Loader, 00	45	135	___
14005	Operating Coal Ramp, 00	50	165	___
14018	ElectroCoupler Kit for Command Upgradeable GP9s, 00		20	___
14062	31" Path Remote Switch, left hand, 01-14		55	___
14063	31" Path Remote Switch, right hand, 01-14		75	___
14065	Nuclear Reactor, 00		233	___
14071	Yard Light 3-pack, 00-18		35	___
14072	Haunted House, 01		181	___
14073	History of Lionel, The First 90 Years Video, 00		15	___
14075	A Century of Lionel, 1900-1969 Video, 00		15	___
14076	A Century of Lionel, 1970-2000 Video, 00		15	___
14077	ZW Amp/Volt Meter, 00-03		70	___
14078	Die-cast Sprung Trucks, 2-pack, 00-23		35	___
14079	Operating North Pole Pylon, 01		70	___
14080	Hobo Hotel, 01	30	65	___
14081	Shell Oil Derrick, 01		100	___
14082	Pedestrian Walkover, speed sensor, 01-03		50	___
14083	Pedestrian Walkover, 01-03, 08, 12-16		55	___
14084	Lionel Heliport, 01		85	___
14085	Newsstand, 01		75	___
14086	Water Tower, 00		105	___
14087	Lighthouse, 01		95	___
14090	No. 140 Banjo Signal, 01-23		60	___
14091	Automatic Gateman, 01-03, 07-09		38	___
14092	Floodlight Tower, 01-05, 08-16		48	___
14093	Single Signal Bridge, 01-04, 08		22	___
14094	Double Signal Bridge, 01-04, 08		30	___
14095	Illuminated Station Platform, 01-04		20	___
14096	Station Platform, 01-04		10	___
14097	Rotary Aircraft Beacon, 01-04, 07-10	15	50	___
14098	Auto Crossing Gate 2-pack, 01-23		120	___
14099	Block Target Signal, 01-04, 07-08		22	___
14100	Blinking Light Billboard, 01-03		23	___
14101	Red Baron Pylon, 01		85	___
14102	Rocket Launcher, 01	160	280	___
14104	Burning Switch Tower, 00		70	___
14105	Aquarium, 01		175	___
14106	Operating Freight Station, 00	25	85	___
14107	Coaling Station, 01-03		95	___
14109	Carousel, 01		230	___
14110	Operating Ferris Wheel, 01-02, 04		170	___
14111	1531R Controller, 00-23	20	53	___
14112	Lighted Lockon, 01-10, 13-16		6	___
14113	Engine Transfer Table, 01		210	___
14114	Engine Transfer Table Extension, 01		75	___
14116	PRR Die-cast Girder Bridge, 01		20	___
14117	NYC Die-cast Girder Bridge, 01		20	___
14119	Gooseneck Lamps, set of 2, 01-04, 07		22	___
14121	Classic Billboards, set of 3, 01-03		10	___
14124	ZW Controller with 2 transformers, 01		300	___
14125	Christmas Tree with 400E Train, 00		65	___

MODERN 1970-2023			Exc	Mint
____	14126	Exploding Ammo Dump		55
____	14133	Madison Hobby Shop, 01	223	368
____	14134	Triple Action Magnetic Crane, 01		230
____	14135	NS Black Die-cast Girder Bridge, 02		15
____	14137	Die-cast Girder Bridge, 01-07		25
____	14138	Snap-On Tool Animated Billboard, 01 u	27	40
____	14142	Industrial Smokestack, 02-04		50
____	14143	Industrial Tank, 02-04		40
____	14145	Operating Lumberjacks, 02-03		65
____	14147	Die-cast Old Style Clock Tower, 02-04, 08-23		30
____	14148	Operating Billboard Signmen, 02-03		60
____	14149	Scale-sized Banjo Signal, 02-05		40
____	14151	Mainline Dwarf Signal, 02-08		43
____	14152	Passenger Station, 02-04		37
____	14153	Lion Oil Derrick, 02-03		50
____	14154	Water Tower, 01-02		65
____	14155	Floodlight Tower, 02-03		55
____	14156	Lion Oil Diesel Fueling Station, 02-03		70
____	14157	Coal Loader, 01-03		120
____	14158	Icing Station, 01-02		75
____	14159	Animated Billboard, 02-04		20
____	14160	Frank's Hotdog Stand, 03-04		55
____	14161	Smoking Hobo Shack, 02		60
____	14162	Missile Launching Platform, 02-03		48
____	14163	Industrial Power Station, 02-03		550
____	14164	Lionelville Bandstand, 02		140
____	14166	Train Orders Building, 04-05		49
____	14167	Operating Lift Bridge, 02		380
____	14168	Operating Harry's Barber Shop, 02-04		100
____	14170	Amusement Park Swing Ride, 03-04		150
____	14171	Pirate Ship Ride, 02-04		130
____	14172	NYC Railroad Tugboat, 02		180
____	14173	Drawbridge, 02-04		70
____	14175	Santa Fe Die-cast Girder Bridge, 01-03		17
____	14176	Norfolk Southern Die-cast Girder Bridge, 02-03		18
____	14178	TMCC Direct Lockon, 02-03		25
____	14179	TMCC Track Power Controller, 02-13		230
____	14180	B&O Railroad Tugboat, 02-03		155
____	14181	TMCC Action Recorder Controller, 02-13	60	115
____	14182	TMCC Accessory Switch Controller, 02-13		115
____	14183	TMCC Accessory Motor Controller, 02-13		115
____	14184	TMCC Block Power Controller, 02-12		90
____	14185	TMCC Operating Track Controller, 02-13		100
____	14186	TMCC Accessory Voltage Controller, 02-13		160
____	14187	TMCC How-to Video, 02-04		11
____	14189	TMCC Track Power Controller, 02-13		175
____	14190	The Lionel Train Book, 04-14		30
____	14191	TMCC Command Base Cable, 6 feet, 02-13		14
____	14192	TMCC 3-wire Command Base Cable, 02-13		15
____	14193	TMCC Controller to Controller Cable, 1 foot, 02-13		6
____	14194	TMCC TPC Cable Set, 02-13		16
____	14195	TMCC Command Base Cable, 20 feet, 02-07		12
____	14196	TMCC Controller to Controller Cable, 6 feet, 02-13		9

		Exc	Mint	
14197	TMCC Controller to Controller Cable, 20 feet, 02-07		9	___
14198	CW-80 80-watt Transformer, 03-18	65	150	___
14199	Playground Swings, 03-04, 08-09		50	___
14201	Burning Switch Tower, 05		70	___
14202	Water Tower, 05		140	___
14203	Amusement Park Swing Ride, 06-07		230	___
14209	U.S. Steel Gantry Crane, 05		180	___
14210	Pony Ride, 06-07		70	___
14211	Road Crew, 07-08		90	___
14214	Lionelville Mini Golf, 06		80	___
14215	Tug-of-War, 06-08		60	___
14217	Helicopter Pylon, 06-09		140	___
14218	Downtown People Pack, 06-19		27	___
14219	Ice Rink, 06-08		80	___
14220	Lionelville Water Tower, 06-08		21	___
14221	Witches Cauldron, 06-08		70	___
14222	Die-cast Girder Bridge, 06-09		30	___
14225	Sunoco Industrial Tank, 06-09		70	___
14227	Yard Tower, 06-08		45	___
14229	Crossing Shanty, 06-09		20	___
14230	Milk Bottle Toss Midway Game, 06		20	___
14231	Cotton Candy Midway Booth, 06		20	___
14236	Operating Freight Station, 06-07		105	___
14237	Rocket Launcher, 06-07		320	___
14240	Ice Block 10-Pack, 06-23		7	___
14241	Work Crew People Pack, 06-19		27	___
14242	Hard Rock Cafe, 06		50	___
14243	U.S. Army Water Tower, 06-08		95	___
14244	Ammo Loader, 06-07		105	___
14251	Die-cast Sprung Trucks, rotating bearing caps, 07-23		40	___
14255	Sand Tower, 06-18		35	___
14257	Passenger Station, 06-13		60	___
14258	North Pole Passenger Station, 06-10		53	___
14259	Christmas People Pack, 06-12		23	___
14260	Christmas Tractor and Trailer, 06-08		25	___
14261	Christmas Tree Lot, 06		70	___
14262	Elevated Tank, 07		70	___
14265	Sawmill with sound, 08		130	___
14267	Sir Topham Hatt Gateman, 07-12		80	___
14273	Polar Express Add-on Figures, 06-07, 12-23		30	___
14289	Operating Santa Gateman, 08		80	___
14290	UPS Store, 06		30	___
14291	Operating Milk Loading Depot, K-Line, 08		100	___
14294	993 Legacy Expansion Set, 07-16, 18-20		335	___
14295	990 Legacy Command Set, 07-16, 18-20	175	567	___
14297	Halloween Witch Pylon, 07-08	80	150	___
14500	KCS F3 Diesel AA Set, Railsounds, CC, 01	380	660	___
14512	F3 Diesel ABA Demonstrator "291," CC, 01	360	425	___
14517	Santa Fe F3 Diesel B Unit "2343C," powered, 01		280	___
14518	CP F3 Diesel B Unit "2373C," RailSounds, CC, 01		345	___
14520	Texas Special F3 Diesel B Unit, RailSounds, 01		360	___
14521	Rock Island E6 Diesel AA Set, 01	340	530	___
14524	Atlantic Coast Line E6 Diesel AA Set, 01		630	___

|---|---|---|---|
	14536 Santa Fe F3 Diesel AA Set, RailSounds, CC, 03-04		800
	14539 Santa Fe F3 Diesel B Unit, 03		300
	14540 D&RGW F3 Diesel B Unit, RailSounds, CC, 01		315
	14541 C&O F3 Diesel B Unit, RailSounds, CC, 01		300
	14542 KCS F3 Diesel B Unit "2388C," RailSounds, CC, 01		375
	14543 SP F3 Diesel B Unit, RailSounds, CC, 01		282
	14544 Southern E6 AA Diesel Set, CC, 02		560
	14547 Burlington E5 AA Diesel Set, CC, 02		570
	14552 NYC F3 Diesel AA Set, RailSounds, CC, 03-04		740
	14555 NYC F3 Diesel B Unit, 03		200
	14557 WP F3 Diesel B Unit, nonpowered, 03-04		190
	14558 B&O F3 Diesel B Unit, nonpowered, 03-04		155
	14559 D&RGW F3 Diesel AA Set, 01		620
	14560 NP F3 Diesel A Unit "2390B," freight, 02		175
	14561 NP F3 Diesel A Unit "2390B," passenger, 02		190
	14562 Milwaukee Road F3 Diesel A Unit "75C," 02	80	190
	14563 Erie-Lackawanna F3 Diesel A Unit "7094," 02		175
	14564 CP F3 Diesel B Unit "237C," CC, 02		350
	14565 B&O F3 Diesel AA Set, 03-04		650
	14568 WP F3 Diesel AA Set, 03-04		780
	14571 Santa Fe PA Diesel AA Set, CC, 03		660
	14574 D&H PA Diesel AA Set, CC, 03		580
	14579 UP Alco PA-1 Diesel A Unit "600," powered, 03		450
	14580 UP Alco PA-1 Diesel B Unit "600B," unpowered, 03		150
	14581 UP Alco PA-1 Diesel A Unit "601," unpowered, 03		150
	14584 Wabash F3 Diesel A Unit, nonpowered, 03		180
	14586 D&H PB Unit, 03		125
	14587 Santa Fe PB Unit, 03		125
	14588 Santa Fe F3 Diesel ABA Set, CC, 04-05		980
	14592 PRR F3 Diesel ABA Set, CC, 04-05		750
	14596 NH Alco PA Diesel AA Set, 04-05		700
	14599 NH Alco PB Diesel B Unit "0767-B," 04-05		150
	15000 D&RGW Waffle-sided Boxcar, 95	12	18
	15001 Seaboard Waffle-sided Boxcar, 95	14	19
	15002 Chesapeake & Ohio Waffle-sided Boxcar, 96	16	20
	15003 Green Bay & Western Waffle-sided Boxcar, 96	16	20
	15004 Bloomingdale's Boxcar, 97 u		40
	15005 "I Love NY" Boxcar, 97 u		65
	15008 CP Rail Boxcar		30
	15013 L&N Waffle-sided Boxcar "102402," 00		29
	15014 Seaboard Waffle-sided Boxcar "125925," 00		25
	15015 C&NW Waffle-sided Boxcar "161013," 03		18
	15016 IC Waffle-sided Boxcar "12981," 04		20
	15017 CSX Waffle-sided Boxcar, 05		27
	15018 D&H Waffle-sided Boxcar "24052," 06		30
	15020 NH Waffle-sided Boxcar, 07		30
	15021 MKT Waffle-sided Boxcar, 08		35
	15024 UP Waffle Boxcar "960860," 09-11		40
	15028 Southern Waffle-sided Boxcar "539889," 10		40
	15029 Western & Atlantic Wood-sided Reefer, 10		53
	15033 MTK Stock Car, 10		65
	15036 NPC Bass Pro Shops Boxcar, 11		22
	15038 CSX Hi-Cube Boxcar, 11-12		40

		Exc	Mint
15039	NS Waffle-sided Boxcar, 11-12		40 ___
15041	BNSF Hi-Cube Boxcar, 10		50 ___
15042	CSX Waffle-sided Boxcar, 11		40 ___
15051	Lionel Lines Boxcar, 11-12		40 ___
15052	Amtrak Hi-Cube Boxcar, 11-12		40 ___
15053	REA Waffle-sided Boxcar, 11-12		40 ___
15054	C&NW Wood-sided Reefer, 11-12		40 ___
15060	K-Line Boxcar, 06		40 ___
15063	U.S.A.F. Minuteman Boxcar, 11		55 ___
15069	Coke Wood-sided Reefer #1, 09-16		65 ___
15071	Coca-Cola Christmas Boxcar, 12		70 ___
15072	Halloween Boxcar, 09-11		55 ___
15074	Mr. Goodbar Wood-sided Reefer, 09-11		55 ___
15075	Boy Scouts of America Eagle Scout Boxcar, 11-14		60 ___
15077	ATSF Stock Car, 11		55 ___
15078	Pabst Wood-sided Reefer, 11		65 ___
15079	Schlitz Wood-sided Reefer, 11		58 ___
15080	C&O 40' Boxcar, 11		55 ___
15083	CP Rail Waffle-sided Boxcar, 13		43 ___
15084	GN Hi-Cube Boxcar, 13-14		43 ___
15086	Alaska Wood-Sided Reefer, 12		40 ___
15091	Angela Trotta Thomas "High Hopes" Hi-Cube Boxcar, 12		55 ___
15094	Sleepy Hollow Halloween Reefer, 14-15		60 ___
15095	1953 Lionel Catalog Art Reefer, 13		55 ___
15096	Hershey's Kisses Christmas Boxcar, 12		70 ___
15097	Peanuts Christmas Boxcar, 12-13		70 ___
15098	Lone Ranger Boxcar, 12-14		60 ___
15100	Amtrak Passenger Coach, 95-97		35 ___
15101	Reading Baggage Car (027), 96		34 ___
15102	Reading Combination Car (027), 96		23 ___
15103	Reading Passenger Coach (027), 96		23 ___
15104	Reading Vista Dome Car (027), 96		26 ___
15105	Reading Full Vista Dome Car (027), 96		26 ___
15106	Reading Observation Car (027), 96		23 ___
15107	Amtrak Vista Dome Car, 96		38 ___
15108	Northern Pacific Vista Dome Car, 96		34 ___
15109	ATSF Combine Car "2407," 97		35 ___
15110	ATSF Vista Dome Car 2404," 97		35 ___
15111	ATSF Observation Car "2406," 97		35 ___
15112	ATSF Albuquerque Coach "2405," 97		34 ___
15113	ATSF Culebra Vista Dome Car "2404," 97		34 ___
15114	NJ Transit Coach "5610," 96 u		45 ___
15115	NJ Transit Coach "5611," 96 u		45 ___
15116	NJ Transit Coach "5612," 96 u		45 ___
15117	Annie Passenger Coach, 97		26 ___
15118	Clarabel Passenger Coach, 97		26 ___
15122	NJ Transit Passenger Coach "5613," 97 u		45 ___
15123	NJ Transit Passenger Coach "5614," 97 u		45 ___
15124	NJ Transit Passenger Coach "5615," 97 u		45 ___
15125	Amtrak Observation Car, 97 u		50 ___
15126	Stars & Stripes Abraham Lincoln General Coach, 99		60 ___
15127	Stars & Stripes Ulysses S. Grant General Coach, 99		60 ___
15128	Pride of Richmond Robert E. Lee General Coach, 99		60 ___

	MODERN 1970-2023	Exc	Mint
___	15129	Pride of Richmond Jefferson Davis General Coach, 99		60
___	15136	Custom Series Short Observation Car, blue, 99		40
___	15137	Custom Series Short Observation Car, red, 99		34
___	15138	Pratt's Hollow Baggage Car, 98		100
___	15139	Pratt's Hollow Vista Dome Car, 98		100
___	15140	Pratt's Hollow Coach, 98		100
___	15141	Pratt's Hollow Observation, 98		100
___	15142	U.S. Army Baby Heavyweight Coach, 00		50
___	15143	U.S. Army Baby Heavyweight Coach, 00		50
___	15153	Pullman Baby Madison Set 4-pack, 01		190
___	15163	T&P Baby Heavyweight Coach, 01		30
___	15166	Union Pacific Whistling Baggage Car, 04		41
___	15169	C&O Streamliner Car 4-pack, 03	55	140
___	15170	L&N Streamliner Car 4-pack, 03		140
___	15180	NYC Streamliner Car 4-pack, 04		340
___	15185	UP Streamliner Car 4-pack, 04		340
___	15300	NYC Superliner Aluminum Passenger Car 4-pack, 02		360
___	15301	NYC Manhattan Superliner Passenger Coach, 02		90
___	15302	NYC Queens Superliner Passenger Coach, 02		90
___	15304	NYC Staten Island Superliner Passenger Coach, 02		90
___	15305	NYC Brooklyn Superliner Passenger Coach, 02		90
___	15311	CB&Q California Zephyr Aluminum Passenger Car 4-pack, 03		350
___	15312	Santa Fe Super Chief Aluminum Passenger Car 4-pack, 03		275
___	15313	D&H Aluminum Passenger Car 4-pack, 03		415
___	15314	Amtrak Superliner 2-pack, 03		220
___	15315	Santa Fe Superliner 2-pack, 03		200
___	15316	NYC Superliner 2-pack, 03		195
___	15317	Southern Aluminum Passenger Car 4-pack, 03		350
___	15318	Lionel Lines Aluminum Passenger Car 2-pack, 03		125
___	15319	Santa Fe Superliner Aluminum Passenger Car 2-pack, 03		145
___	15326	NYC 20th Century Limited Aluminum Passenger Car 6-pack, 02		485
___	15333	N&W Powhatan Arrow Aluminum Car 6-pack, 02-03		435
___	15334	N&W Powhatan Arrow Aluminum Baggage Car "117," 02-03		70
___	15335	N&W Powhatan Arrow Aluminum Combine, 02-03		70
___	15336	N&W Powhatan Arrow Aluminum Coach "537," 02-03		70
___	15337	N&W Powhatan Arrow Aluminum Coach "553," 02-03		70
___	15338	N&W Powhatan Arrow Aluminum Coach "641," 02-03		70
___	15339	N&W Powhatan Arrow Aluminum Observation, 02-03		70
___	15340	PRR South Wind Aluminum Passenger Car 6-pack, 02-03		435
___	15341	PRR South Wind Aluminum Baggage Car "6529," 02-03		100
___	15342	PRR South Wind Aluminum Combine "6700," 02-03		100
___	15343	PRR South Wind Aluminum Coach "4021," 02-03		100
___	15344	PRR South Wind Aluminum Coach "4022," 02-03		100
___	15345	PRR South Wind Aluminum Coach "4022," 02-03		100
___	15346	PRR South Wind Aluminum Observation "1126," 02-03		100
___	15350	Amtrak Superliner Aluminum Sleeper, 02-03		100
___	15351	Amtrak Superliner Aluminum Lounge Car, 02-03		100
___	15352	ATSF Superliner Hi-Level Sleeper "712," 03		100
___	15353	ATSF Superliner Hi-Level Lounge Car "575," 03		100
___	15364	ATSF Super Chief Aluminum Baggage Car "3425," 03		100
___	15365	ATSF Super Chief Aluminum Sleeper "Palm Leaf," 03		100
___	15366	ATSF Super Chief Aluminum Vista Dome, 03		100
___	15368	UP Streamlined Aluminum Baggage Car "5608," 03		100

		Exc	Mint
15369	UP Streamlined Aluminum Combination Car "Clifton," 03		100
15370	UP Streamlined Aluminum Diner w/StationSounds, 03		230
15371	UP Streamlined Aluminum Coach "Chatham," 03		100
15372	UP Streamlined Aluminum Offset Dome Car "Plainfield," 03		100
15373	UP Streamlined Aluminum Offset Dome Car "Westfield"		100
15374	UP Streamlined Aluminum Observation "Elizabeth," 03		100
15375	Southern Aluminum Combination Car "Mississippi," 03		100
15376	Southern Aluminum Coach "North Carolina," 03		100
15377	Southern Aluminum Coach "Maryland," 03		100
15378	Southern Aluminum Observation "Louisiana," 03		100
15379	Lionel Lines Silver Valley Aluminum Combination Car, 03		100
15380	Lionel Lines Silver Spoon Aluminum Diner, 03		100
15381	Santa Fe Aluminum Baggage Car "2571," 03		100
15382	Santa Fe Regal Dome Aluminum Vista Dome Car, 03		100
15383	NYC 20th Century Limited Diner, StationSounds, 03		195
15384	N&W Powhatan Arrow Diner, StationSounds, 03		190
15385	Pennsylvania South Wind Diner, StationSounds, 03		190
15394	Amtrak Streamliner Car 4-pack, 03-04		450
15395	Alaska Streamliner Car 4-pack, 03-04		355
15396	Amtrak Superliner Diner, StationSounds, 03		220
15397	Santa Fe Superliner Diner, StationSounds, 03		200
15398	NYC Superliner Diner, StationSounds, 03		200
15405	50th Anniversary Hillside Heavyweight Diner, StationSounds, 02		195
15406	Blue Comet Giacobini Heavyweight Diner, StationSounds, 02		300
15504	Alton Limited Diner, StationSounds, 03		230
15506	Alton Limited Heavyweight Baggage Car "R.S. Brauer," 03		115
15506	Alton Limited Heavyweight Coach "Oak Park," 03		115
15507	Phantom III Passenger Car 4-pack, 02		245
15508	Phantom III Baggage Car, 02		65
15509	Phantom II Vista Dome, 02		65
15510	Phantom III Coach, 02		65
15511	Phantom III Observation, 02		65
15512	Phantom II Passenger Car 4-pack, 02		250
15517	Southern Crescent Limited Heavyweight Car 2-pack, 03-04		205
15520	Southern Crescent Limited Diner, StationSounds, 03-04		220
15521	NYC 20th Century Limited Heavyweight Car 4-pack, 04		345
15526	Santa Fe Chief Heavyweight Passenger Car 4-pack, 04		370
15538	NYC 20th Century Limited Heavyweight Car 2-pack, 04		200
15541	NYC 20th Century Limited Heavyweight Diner, StationSounds, 04		200
15542	Santa Fe Chief Heavyweight Passenger Car 2-pack, 04		195
15545	Santa Fe Chief Heavyweight Diner, StationSounds, 04		200
15546	Napa Valley Wine Train Heavyweight 2-pack, 05		250
15547	Napa Valley Wine Train Heavyweight Coach "1015," 05		125
15548	Napa Valley Wine Train Heavyweight Coach "1100," 05		125
15549	Napa Valley Wine Train Diner, StationSounds, 05		280
15550	Napa Valley Wine Train Heavyweight Combo Car "1052," 05		100
15551	Napa Valley Wine Train Heavyweight Coach "1017," 05		100
15552	Napa Valley Wine Train Heavyweight Coach "1014," 05		100
15553	Napa Valley Wine Train Heavyweight Observation "1011," 05		100
15554	Pennsylvania Heavyweight Car 3-pack (std O), 05		375
15558	Pennsylvania Heavyweight Add-on Coach (std O), 05		140
15559	PRR Reading Seashore Heavyweight Car 3-pack (std O), 05		370

| --- | --- | --- | --- | --- |
____	15563	PRR Reading Seashore Heavyweight Add-on Coach, 05		130
____	15564	LIRR Heavyweight Car 3-pack (std O), 05		370
____	15568	LIRR Heavyweight Add-on Coach (std O), 05		130
____	15570	LIRR Heavyweight Car 3-pack (std O), 06		230
____	15574	LIRR Heavyweight Car Add-on (std O), 06		140
____	15575	C&O Heavyweight Diner, StationSounds (std O), 06-07		295
____	15576	C&O Heavyweight Passenger Car 2-pack (std O), 06-07		265
____	15577	NYC Heavyweight 3-pack (std O), 05-06		370
____	15581	NYC Heavyweight Add-on Coach (std O), 05-06		130
____	15584	Amtrak Acela Passenger Car 3-pack (std O), 06		670
____	15588	Southern Heavyweight Passenger Car 4-pack, 06		495
____	15593	Southern Heavyweight Passenger Car 2-pack, 06		265
____	15596	Southern Heavyweight Diner, StationSounds, 06		295
____	15597	C&O Heavyweight Passenger Car 4-pack (std O), 06-07		495
____	15906	RailSounds Trigger Button, 90-95		12
____	16000	PRR Vista Dome Car (O27), 87-88	37	55
____	16001	PRR Passenger Coach (O27), 87-88	33	41
____	16002	PRR Passenger Coach (O27), 87-88	24	29
____	16003	PRR Observation Car (O27), 87-88	24	29
____	16009	PRR Combination Car (O27), 88	36	38
____	16010	Virginia & Truckee Passenger Coach (SSS), 88	36	47
____	16010	Railbox Modern Boxcar 6-pack, LionScale, 16		360
____	16011	Virginia & Truckee Passenger Coach (SSS), 88	36	47
____	16012	Virginia & Truckee Baggage Car (SSS), 88	36	47
____	16013	Amtrak Combination Car (O27), 88-89	21	34
____	16014	Amtrak Vista Dome Car (O27), 88-89	21	34
____	16015	Amtrak Observation Car (O27), 88-89	21	34
____	16016	NYC Baggage Car (O27), 89	36	55
____	16017	NYC Combination Car (O27), 89	21	29
____	16018	NYC Passenger Coach (O27), 89	21	29
____	16019	NYC Vista Dome Car (O27), 89	21	29
____	16020	NYC Passenger Coach (O27), 89	23	33
____	16020	BNSF Modern Boxcar 6-pack, LionScale, 16		360
____	16021	NYC Observation Car (O27), 89	20	28
____	16022	Pennsylvania Baggage Car (O27), 89	27	38
____	16023	Amtrak Passenger Coach (O27), 89	21	30
____	16024	Northern Pacific Diner (O27), 92	39	44
____	16027	LL Combination Car (O27, SSS), 90	39	48
____	16028	LL Passenger Coach (SSS, O27), 90	32	42
____	16029	LL Passenger Coach (SSS, O27), 90	35	42
____	16030	LL Observation Car (SSS, O27), 90	35	42
____	16030	CSX Modern Boxcar 6-pack, LionScale, 16		360
____	16031	Pennsylvania Diner (O27), 90	35	39
____	16033	Amtrak Baggage Car (O27), 90	28	38
____	16034	NP Baggage Car (O27), 90-91	30	45
____	16035	NP Combination Car (O27), 90-91	18	26
____	16036	NP Passenger Coach (O27), 90-91	21	30
____	16037	NP Vista Dome Car (O27), 90-91	18	26
____	16038	NP Passenger Coach (O27), 90-91	17	25
____	16039	NP Observation Car (O27), 90-91	21	30
____	16040	Southern Pacific Baggage Car, 90-91	22	30
____	16040	NS Modern Boxcar 6-pack, LionScale, 16		360
____	16041	NYC Diner (O27), 91	37	47

	MODERN 1970-2023	Exc	Mint	
16042	Illinois Central Baggage Car (027), 91	24	34	___
16043	Illinois Central Combination Car (027), 91	22	30	___
16044	Illinois Central Passenger Coach (027), 91	24	34	___
16045	Illinois Central Vista Dome Car (027), 91	22	30	___
16046	Illinois Central Passenger Coach (027), 91	24	34	___
16047	Illinois Central Observation Car (027), 91	24	34	___
16048	Amtrak Diner (027), 91-92	33	40	___
16049	Illinois Central Diner (027), 92	27	38	___
16050	C&NW Baggage Car "6620," 93	44	55	___
16050	AT&SF 3-bay Offset Hopper 6-pack, LionScale, 16		330	___
16051	C&NW Combination Car "6630," 93	40	50	___
16052	C&NW Passenger Coach "6616," 93	34	42	___
16053	C&NW Passenger Coach "6602," 93	37	46	___
16054	C&NW Observation Car "6603," 93	38	47	___
16055	Santa Fe Passenger Coach (027), 93-94	29	38	___
16056	Santa Fe Vista Dome Car (027), 93-94	25	32	___
16057	Santa Fe Passenger Coach (027), 93-94	30	40	___
16058	Santa Fe Combination Car (027), 93-94	27	35	___
16059	Santa Fe Vista Dome Car (027), 93-94	26	34	___
16060	Santa Fe Observation Car (027), 93-94	25	31	___
16060	B&O 3-bay Offset Hopper 6-pack, LionScale, 16		330	___
16061	N&W Baggage Car "6061," 94	60	85	___
16062	N&W Combination Car "6062," 94	38	50	___
16063	N&W Passenger Coach "6063," 94	43	55	___
16064	N&W Passenger Coach "6064," 94	43	55	___
16065	N&W Observation Car "6065," 94	36	48	___
16066	NYC Combination Car "6066" (SSS), 94	55	70	___
16067	NYC Passenger Coach "6067" (SSS), 94	38	47	___
16068	UP Baggage Car "6068" (027), 94	50	65	___
16069	UP Combination Car "6069" (027), 94	36	43	___
16070	UP Passenger Coach "6070" (027), 94	36	43	___
16070	B&M 3-bay Offset Hopper 6-pack, LionScale, 16		330	___
16071	UP Diner "6071" (027), 94	36	46	___
16072	UP Vista Dome Car "6072" (027), 94	36	43	___
16073	UP Passenger Coach "6073" (027), 94	36	42	___
16074	UP Observation Car "6074" (027), 94	36	43	___
16075	Missouri Pacific Baggage Car "6620," 95	44	55	___
16076	Missouri Pacific Combination Car "6630," 95	34	41	___
16077	Missouri Pacific Passenger Coach "6616," 95	34	41	___
16078	Missouri Pacific Passenger Coach "7805," 95	34	39	___
16079	Missouri Pacific Observation Car "6609," 95	34	41	___
16080	New Haven Baggage Car "6080" (027), 95	35	44	___
16080	C&O 3-bay Offset Hopper 6-pack #1, LionScale, 16		330	___
16081	New Haven Combination Car "6081" (027), 95	28	37	___
16082	New Haven Passenger Coach "6082" (027), 95	28	37	___
16083	New Haven Vista Dome Car "6083" (027), 95	30	39	___
16084	New Haven Full Vista Dome Car "6084" (027), 95	33	39	___
16086	New Haven Observation Car "6086" (027), 95	31	40	___
16087	NYC Baggage Car "6087" (SSS), 95	48	65	___
16088	NYC Passenger Coach "6088" (SSS), 95	36	43	___
16089	NYC Diner "6089" (SSS), 95	36	43	___
16090	NYC Observation Car "6090" (SSS), 95	38	46	___
16090	C&O 3-bay Offset Hopper 6-pack #2, LionScale, 16		330	___

			Exc	Mint
	MODERN 1970-2023			
___	16091	NYC Passenger Cars, set of 4 (SSS), 95	140	165
___	16092	Santa Fe Full Vista Dome Car (027), 95	30	38
___	16093	Illinois Central Full Vista Dome Car (027), 95	29	38
___	16094	Pennsylvania Full Vista Dome Car (027), 95	30	39
___	16095	Amtrak Combination Car (027), 95	19	23
___	16096	Amtrak Vista Dome Car (027), 95	19	23
___	16097	Amtrak Observation Car (027), 95	19	23
___	16098	Amtrak Passenger Coach, 95-97	20	33
___	16099	Amtrak Vista Dome Car, 95-97	20	33
___	16100	Alaska RR 3-bay 9-panel Hopper 6-pack, LionScale, 16		330
___	16102	Southern 3-D Tank Car (SSS), 87	23	30
___	16103	Lehigh Valley 2-D Tank Car (027), 88	19	25
___	16104	Santa Fe 2-D Tank Car (027), 89	19	23
___	16105	D&RGW 3-D Tank Car (SSS), 89	48	65
___	16106	Mopar Express 3-D Tank Car, 88 u	105	156
___	16107	Sunoco 2-D Tank Car (027), 90	16	20
___	16108	Racing Fuel 1-D Tank Car "6108" (027), 89 u, 92 u	9	13
___	16109	B&O 1-D Tank Car (SSS), 91	29	34
___	16110	Circus Animals Operating Stock Car "1989" (027), 89 u	24	34
___	16110	Chessie 3-bay 9-panel Hopper 6-pack, LionScale, 16		330
___	16111	Alaska 1-D Tank Car (027), 90-91	22	27
___	16112	Dow Chemical 3-D Tank Car, 90	20	26
___	16113	Diamond Shamrock 2-D Tank Car (027), 91	20	25
___	16114	Hooker Chemicals 1-D Tank Car (027), 91	13	17
___	16115	MKT 3-D Tank Car, 92	13	16
___	16116	U.S. Army 1-D Tank Car, 91 u	36	42
___	16119	MKT 2-D Tank Car (027), 92, 93 u	14	19
___	16120	Southern 3-bay 9-panel Hopper 6-pack, LionScale, 16		330
___	16121	C&NW Stock Car (SSS), 92	33	43
___	16123	Union Pacific 3-D Tank Car, 93-95	16	22
___	16124	Penn Salt 3-D Tank Car, 93	21	26
___	16125	Virginian Stock Car, 93	19	24
___	16126	Jefferson Lake 3-D Tank Car, 93	22	26
___	16127	Mobil 1-D Tank Car, 93	28	33
___	16128	Alaska 1-D Tank Car, 94	24	29
___	16129	Alaska 1-D Tank Car (027), 93 u, 94	21	28
___	16130	SP Stock Car (027), 93 u, 94	10	13
___	16130	WM 3-bay 9-panel Hopper 6-pack, LionScale, 16		330
___	16131	T&P Reefer, 94	19	24
___	16132	Deep Rock 3-D Tank Car, 94	25	30
___	16133	Santa Fe Reefer, 94	22	28
___	16134	Reading Reefer, 94	17	21
___	16135	C&O Stock Car, 94	23	27
___	16136	B&O 1-D Tank Car, 94	28	32
___	16137	Ford 1-D Tank Car "12," 94 u	34	39
___	16138	Goodyear 1-D Tank Car, 95	28	34
___	16140	Domino Sugar 1-D Tank Car, 95	24	29
___	16140	Klemme Coop PS-2CD Covered Hopper 6-pack, LionScale, 16		360
___	16141	Erie Stock Car, 95	22	30
___	16142	Santa Fe 1-D Tank Car, 95	26	30
___	16143	Reading Reefer, 95	18	23
___	16144	San Angelo 3-D Tank Car, 95	22	25
___	16146	Dairy Despatch Reefer, 95	15	20

		Exc	Mint	
16147	Clearly Canadian 1-D Tank Car (027), 94 u	25	40	___
16149	Zep Chemical 1-D Tank Car (027), 95 u	68	81	___
16150	Sunoco 1-D Tank Car "6315," 97	35	38	___
16150	D&RGW PS-2CD Covered Hopper 6-pack, LionScale, 16		360	___
16152	Sunoco 3-D Tank Car "6415," 97		26	___
16153	AEC Reactor Fluid 1-D Tank Car "6515-1," 97		94	___
16154	AEC Reactor Fluid 1-D Tank Car "6515-2," 97	39	107	___
16155	AEC Reactor Fluid 1-D Tank Car "6515-3," 97	60	109	___
16157	Gatorade Little League Baseball 1-D Tank Car "6315," 97 u	30	64	___
16160	AEC Tank Car "6515" with reactor fluid, 98		85	___
16160	MILW PS-2CD Covered Hopper 6-pack, LionScale, 16		360	___
16162	Hooker 1-D Tank Car "6315-1," 97		50	___
16163	Hooker 1-D Tank Car "6315-2," 97		50	___
16164	Hooker 1-D Tank Car "6315-3," 97		50	___
16165	Mobilfuel 3-D Tank Car "6415," 97 u		50	___
16170	RFMX PS-2CD Covered Hopper 6-pack, LionScale, 16		360	___
16171	Alaska 1-D Tank Car "6171," 98-99		33	___
16173	Harold the Helicopter Flatcar, 98	45	60	___
16175	NJ Transit Port Morris Ore Car "9125," 98		45	___
16176	NJ Transit Raritan Yard Ore Car "9126," 98 u		45	___
16177	NJ Transit Gladstone Yard Ore Car "9127," 98 u		45	___
16178	NJ Transit Bay Head Yard Ore Car "9128," 98 u	7	45	___
16179	NJ Transit Dover Yard Ore Car "9129," 98 u		45	___
16180	Tabasco 1-D Tank Car, 98	67	84	___
16181	Biohazard Tank Car with Lights, 98	50	90	___
16182	Gatorade 1-D Tank Car "6315," 98 u		64	___
16187	Linex 3-D Tank Car "6425," 99		30	___
16188	Kodak 1-D Tank Car "6515," 99	74	93	___
16199	UP 1-D Tank Car "6035," 99-00		25	___
16200	Rock Island Boxcar (027), 87-88	5	10	___
16201	Wabash Boxcar (027), 88-91	7	10	___
16203	Key America Boxcar (027), 87 u	45	65	___
16204	Hawthorne Boxcar (027), 87 u	50	85	___
16205	Mopar Express Boxcar "1987" (027), 87-88 u	55	65	___
16206	D&RGW Boxcar (SSS), 89	37	42	___
16207	True Value Boxcar (027), 88 u	32	115	___
16208	PRR Auto Carrier, 3-tier, 89	24	37	___
16209	Disney Magic Boxcar (027), 88 u	90	110	___
16211	Hawthorne Boxcar (027), 88 u	45	65	___
16213	Shoprite Boxcar (027), 88 u	55	80	___
16214	D&RGW Auto Carrier, 90	22	32	___
16215	Conrail Auto Carrier, 90	27	38	___
16217	Burlington Northern Auto Carrier, 92	24	36	___
16219	True Value Boxcar (027), 89 u	55	75	___
16220	Ace Hardware Boxcar (027), 89 u	58	81	___
16221	Macy Boxcar (027), 89 u	55	80	___
16222	Great Northern Boxcar (027), 90-91	8	15	___
16223	Budweiser Reefer, 89-92 u	68	90	___
16224	True Value "Lawn Chief" Boxcar (027), 90 u	45	60	___
16225	Budweiser Vat Car, 90-91 u	61	105	___
16226	Union Pacific Boxcar "6226" (027), 90-91 u	15	19	___
16227	Santa Fe Boxcar (027), 91	13	17	___
16228	Union Pacific Auto Carrier, 92	26	33	___

			Exc	Mint
___	16229	Erie-Lackawanna Auto Carrier, 91 u	45	55
___	16232	Chessie System Boxcar, 92, 93 u, 94, 95 u	25	30
___	16233	MKT DD Boxcar, 92	20	29
___	16234	ACY Boxcar (SSS), 92	34	41
___	16235	Railway Express Agency Reefer, 92	19	23
___	16236	NYC Pacemaker Boxcar, 92 u	18	24
___	16237	Railway Express Agency Boxcar, 92 u	21	23
___	16238	NYNH&H Boxcar, 93-95	10	14
___	16239	Union Pacific Boxcar, 93-95	15	20
___	16241	Toys 'R' Us Boxcar, 92-93 u	35	45
___	16242	Grand Trunk Western Auto Carrier, 93	35	40
___	16243	Conrail Boxcar, 93	26	34
___	16244	Duluth, South Shore & Atlantic Boxcar, 93	20	24
___	16245	Contadina Boxcar, 93	16	20
___	16247	ACL Boxcar, 94	15	19
___	16248	Budweiser Boxcar, 93-94 u	52	70
___	16249	United Auto Workers Boxcar, 93 u		55
___	16250	Santa Fe Boxcar (O27), 93 u, 94	8	10
___	16251	Columbus & Greenville Boxcar, 94	8	15
___	16252	U.S. Navy Boxcar "6106888," 94-95		30
___	16253	Santa Fe Auto Carrier, 94	32	38
___	16255	Wabash DD Boxcar, 95	20	26
___	16256	Ford DD Boxcar, 94 u	30	34
___	16257	Crayola Boxcar, 94 u, 95	17	23
___	16258	Lehigh Valley Boxcar, 95	17	22
___	16259	Chrysler Mopar Boxcar, 97 u	33	43
___	16260	Chrysler Mopar Auto Carrier, 96 u	59	69
___	16261	Union Pacific DD Boxcar, 95	26	29
___	16263	ATSF Boxcar, 96-99		25
___	16264	Red Wing Shoes Boxcar, 95	26	32
___	16265	Georgia Power "Atlanta '96" Boxcar, 95 u	200	236
___	16266	Crayola Boxcar, 95	17	23
___	16267	Sears Zenith Boxcar, 95-96 u		55
___	16268	GM/AC Delco Boxcar, 95 u		51
___	16269	Lionel Lines Boxcar, 96		10
___	16272	Christmas Boxcar, 97		36
___	16273	Lionel Employee Christmas Boxcar, 97		55
___	16274	Marvin the Martian Boxcar, 97		60
___	16279	Dodge Motorsports Boxcar, 96 u	148	192
___	16280	Rawlings Little League Boxcar, 97	25	30
___	16281	MacGregor Little League Boxcar, 97	25	30
___	16282	Wisk Detergent Boxcar, 97	25	30
___	16284	Galveston Wharves Boxcar, 98		28
___	16285	Savannah State Docks Boxcar, 98		26
___	16291	Christmas Boxcar, 98		34
___	16292	Lionel Employee Christmas Boxcar, 98	309	369
___	16293	JCPenney Boxcar, 97		100
___	16294	Pedigree Boxcar, 97	148	168
___	16295	Kal Kan Boxcar, 97	154	175
___	16296	Whiskas Boxcar, 97	142	168
___	16297	Sheba Boxcar, 97	136	160
___	16298	Mobil Boxcar, 97		50
___	16300	Rock Island Flatcar with fences (O27), 87-88	8	10

		Exc	Mint
16301	Lionel Barrel Ramp Car, 87	14	19 ___
16303	PRR Flatcar with trailers, 87	26	33 ___
16304	RI Gondola with cable reels (O27), 87-88	5	9 ___
16305	Lehigh Valley Ore Car, 87	80	130 ___
16306	Santa Fe Barrel Ramp Car, 88	13	18 ___
16307	NKP Flatcar with trailers, 88	30	40 ___
16308	Burlington Northern Flatcar with trailer, 88-89	20	25 ___
16309	Wabash Gondola with canisters, 88-91	9	13 ___
16310	Mopar Express Gondola with canisters, 87-88 u	35	39 ___
16311	Mopar Express Flatcar with trailers, 87-88 u	117	162 ___
16313	PRR Gondola with cable reels (O27), 88 u, 89	5	10 ___
16314	Wabash Flatcar with trailers, 89	26	30 ___
16315	PRR Flatcar with fences (O27), 88 u, 89	7	9 ___
16317	PRR Barrel Ramp Car, 89	18	22 ___
16318	LL Depressed Center Flatcar with cable reels, 89	22	26 ___
16320	Great Northern Barrel Ramp Car, 90	13	19 ___
16321/22	Sealand TTUX Flatcar Set with trailers, 90	65	73 ___
16323	Lionel Lines Flatcar with trailers, 90	21	25 ___
16324	PRR Depressed Center Flatcar with cable reels, 90	16	20 ___
16325	Microracers Exhibition Ramp Car, 89 u	21	28 ___
16326	Santa Fe Depressed Center Flatcar with cable reels, 91	16	21 ___
16327	The Big Top Circus Gondola with canisters, 89 u	19	24 ___
16328	NKP Gondola with cable reels, 90-91	17	23 ___
16329	SP Flatcar with horses (O27), 90-91	19	24 ___
16330	MKT Flatcar with trailers, 91	25	30 ___
16332	LL Depressed Center Flatcar with transformer, 91	28	33 ___
16333	Frisco Bulkhead Flatcar with lumber, 91	17	22 ___
16334	C&NW Flatcar Set (16337, 16338) with trailers, 91	55	60 ___
16335	NYC Pacemaker Flatcar with trailer (SSS), 91	46	65 ___
16336	UP Gondola "6336" with canisters, 90-91 u	17	21 ___
16339	Mickey's World Tour Gondola with canisters (O27), 91, 92 u	17	21 ___
16341	NYC Depressed Center Flatcar with transformer, 92	29	32 ___
16342	CSX Gondola with coil covers, 92	18	23 ___
16343	Burlington Gondola with coil covers, 92	20	23 ___
16345/46	SP TTUX Flatcar Set with trailers, 92	55	65 ___
16347	Ontario Northland Bulkhead Flatcar with pulp load, 92	22	26 ___
16348	Erie Liquefied Petroleum Car, 92	23	25 ___
16349	Allis Chalmers Condenser Car, 92	28	35 ___
16350	CP Rail Bulkhead Flatcar with lumber, 91 u	20	29 ___
16351	Flatcar with U.S. Navy submarine, 92	27	39 ___
16352	U.S. Military Flatcar with cruise missile, 92	33	43 ___
16353	B&M Gondola with coil covers, 91 u	33	39 ___
16355	Burlington Gondola, 92, 93 u, 94-95	11	17 ___
16356	MKT Depressed Center Flatcar with cable reels, 92	17	21 ___
16357	L&N Flatcar with trailer, 92	24	31 ___
16358	L&N Gondola with coil covers, 92	17	21 ___
16359	Pacific Coast Gondola with coil covers (SSS), 92	33	38 ___
16360	N&W Maxi-Stack Flatcar Set (16361, 16362) with containers, 93	44	55 ___
16363	Southern TTUX Flatcar Set (16364, 16365) with trailers, 93	38	49 ___
16367	Clinchfield Gondola with coil covers, 93	18	21 ___
16368	MKT Liquid Oxygen Car, 93	21	22 ___
16369	Amtrak Flatcar with wheel load, 92 u	19	28 ___

	MODERN 1970-2023	Exc	Mint
___	16370	Amtrak Flatcar with rail load, 92 u	19	28
___	16371	BN I-Beam Flatcar with load, 92 u	23	30
___	16372	Southern I-Beam Flatcar with load, 92 u	24	34
___	16373	Erie-Lackawanna Flatcar with stakes, 93	19	23
___	16374	D&RGW Flatcar with trailer, 93	25	28
___	16375	NYC Bulkhead Flatcar, 93-95	21	25
___	16376	UP Flatcar with trailer, 93-95	31	37
___	16378	Toys 'R' Us Flatcar with trailer, 92-93 u	60	95
___	16379	NP Bulkhead Flatcar with pulp load, 93	16	23
___	16380	UP I-Beam Flatcar with load, 93	20	26
___	16381	CSX I-Beam Flatcar with load, 93	20	30
___	16382	Kansas City Southern Bulkhead Flatcar, 93	14	18
___	16383	Conrail Flatcar with trailer, 93	50	58
___	16384	Soo Line Gondola with cable reels, 93	14	19
___	16385	Soo Line Ore Car, 93	65	75
___	16386	SP Flatcar with lumber, 94	15	19
___	16387	KCS Gondola with coil covers, 94	13	16
___	16388	LV Gondola with canisters, 94	16	20
___	16389	PRR Flatcar with wheel load, 94	27	32
___	16390	Flatcar with water tank, 94	24	27
___	16391	Lionel Lines Gondola, 93 u		15
___	16392	Wabash Gondola with canisters (O27), 93 u, 94	7	9
___	16393	Wisconsin Central Bulkhead Flatcar, 94	13	19
___	16394	Vermont Central Bulkhead Flatcar, 94	20	30
___	16395	CP Flatcar with rail load, 94	19	29
___	16396	Alaska Bulkhead Flatcar, 94	17	22
___	16397	Milwaukee Road I-Beam Flatcar with load, 94	30	34
___	16398	C&O Flatcar with trailer, 94	80	85
___	16399	Western Pacific I-Beam Flatcar with load, 94	31	35
___	16400	PRR Hopper (O27), 88 u, 89	15	18
___	16402	Southern Quad Hopper with coal (SSS), 87	30	42
___	16406	CSX Quad Hopper with coal, 90	29	34
___	16407	B&M Covered Quad Hopper (SSS), 91	28	37
___	16408	UP Hopper "6408" (O27), 90-91 u	17	21
___	16410	MKT Hopper (O27), 92, 93 u	19	24
___	16411	L&N Quad Hopper with coal, 92	28	32
___	16412	C&NW Covered Quad Hopper, 94	16	21
___	16413	Clinchfield Quad Hopper with coal, 94	16	22
___	16414	CCC&StL Hopper (O27), 94	16	23
___	16416	D&RGW Covered Quad Hopper, 95	16	20
___	16417	Wabash Quad Hopper with coal, 95	19	21
___	16418	C&NW Hopper with coal (O27), 95	15	21
___	16419	Tennessee Central Hopper, 96		17
___	16420	WM Quad Hopper with coal (SSS), 95	30	34
___	16421	WM Quad Hopper with coal (SSS), 95	30	33
___	16422	WM Quad Hopper with coal (SSS), 95		33
___	16423	WM Quad Hopper with coal (SSS), 95		30
___	16424	WM Covered Quad Hopper (SSS), 95	34	39
___	16425	WM Covered Quad Hopper (SSS), 95	25	29
___	16426	WM Covered Quad Hopper (SSS), 95	24	27
___	16427	WM Covered Quad Hopper (SSS), 95	27	30
___	16429	WM Quad Hopper with coal, set of 2		70
___	16430	Georgia Power Quad Hopper "82947" with coal, 95 u		109

		Exc	Mint
16431	Lionel Corporation 2-bay Hopper "6456-1," 96		30 ___
16432	Lionel Corporation 2-bay Hopper "6456-2," 96		64 ___
16433	Lionel Corporation 2-bay Hopper "6456-3," 96		18 ___
16434	LV 2-bay Hopper "6456," "TLDX," 97		25 ___
16435	Virginian 2-bay Hopper "6456-1," 97		30 ___
16436	N&W 2-bay Hopper "6456-2," 97		33 ___
16437	C&O 2-bay Hopper "6456-3," 97		33 ___
16438	Frisco 4-bay Covered Hopper "87538," 98		34 ___
16439	Southern 4-bay Covered Hopper "77836," 98		34 ___
16440	Alaska 2-bay Hopper "7100," 98-99		35 ___
16441	New York Central 4-bay Hopper, 99		26 ___
16442	Bethlehem Gondola "6462" (SSS), 99		40 ___
16443	GN 2-bay Hopper "172364," 99-00		20 ___
16444	CNJ 2-bay Hopper "643," 00		20 ___
16445	Frisco 2-bay Hopper "93108," 00		20 ___
16446	Burlington 2-bay Hopper, 00		20 ___
16447	PRR Tuscan 2-bay Hopper, 00 u		30 ___
16448	PRR Gray 2-bay Hopper, 00 u		30 ___
16449	PRR Black 2-bay Hopper, 00 u		30 ___
16450	PRR Green 2-bay Hopper, 00 u		30 ___
16451	Lionel Mines 2-bay Hopper, 00 u		50 ___
16453	SP 2-bay Hopper "460604," 01		15 ___
16454	Bethlehem Steel Hopper "41025," 01		37 ___
16455	Pioneer Seed 2-bay Hopper, 00 u		50 ___
16456	B&O 2-bay Hopper, 01		20 ___
16459	LV 2-bay Hopper "51102," 01		23 ___
16460	Reading 2-bay Hopper "79636," 02		25 ___
16463	Rio Grande Icebreaker Tunnel Car "18936," 02		32 ___
16464	NYC Icebreaker Tunnel Car "X3200," 02		32 ___
16465	WP 2-bay Hopper "100340," 03		19 ___
16466	Pennsylvania Icebreaker Tunnel Car, 03		33 ___
16467	Naughty and Nice Hopper 2-pack, 02		60 ___
16468	ACL Wood-chip Hopper, 02		20 ___
16469	B&O Hopper "435351," 02		22 ___
16470	Naughty and Nice Ore Car 2-pack, 03		43 ___
16473	Rock Island Ore Car "99122," 03		18 ___
16474	Alaska Ore Car "16474," 04		21 ___
16475	Santa Fe Hopper "16475," 04		18 ___
16480	Lionelville Snow Transport Quad Hopper, 04		45 ___
16482	Norfolk Southern Hopper, traditional, 05		27 ___
16487	Alaska 2-bay Hopper, 05		35 ___
16489	BNSF Ore Car, traditional, 05		15 ___
16490	Sodor Mining Hopper, 05, 13		35 ___
16491	CNJ Hopper "60714," 06		30 ___
16492	C&NW Ore Car "114023," 06		30 ___
16493	Christmas Ice Breaker Car, 06		55 ___
16500	Rock Island Bobber Caboose, 87-88	9	13 ___
16501	Lehigh Valley SP-type Caboose, 87	19	24 ___
16503	NYC Transfer Caboose, 87	16	22 ___
16504	Southern N5c Caboose (SSS), 87	17	30 ___
16505	Wabash SP-type Caboose, 88-91	10	15 ___
16506	Santa Fe Bay Window Caboose, 88	18	28 ___
16507	Mopar Express SP-type Caboose, 87-88 u	42	54 ___

	MODERN 1970-2023	Exc	Mint
___	16508	Lionel Lines SP-type Caboose "6508," 89 u	13	17
___	16509	D&RGW SP-type Caboose (SSS), 89	19	24
___	16510	New Haven Bay Window Caboose, 89	25	30
___	16511	PRR Bobber Caboose, 88 u, 89	9	13
___	16513	Union Pacific SP-type Caboose, 89	14	21
___	16515	Lionel Lines SP-type Caboose, RailScope, 89	20	23
___	16516	Lehigh Valley SP-type Caboose, 90	15	26
___	16517	Atlantic Coast Line Bay Window Caboose, 90	21	26
___	16518	Chessie System Bay Window Caboose, 90	41	50
___	16519	Rock Island Transfer Caboose, 90	13	17
___	16520	Welcome to the Show Circus SP-type Caboose, 89 u	13	21
___	16521	PRR SP-type Caboose, 90-91	8	11
___	16522	Chills & Thrills Circus N5c Caboose, 90-91	10	15
___	16523	Alaska SP-type Caboose, 91	24	31
___	16524	Anheuser-Busch SP-type Caboose, 89-92 u	36	47
___	16525	D&H Bay Window Caboose (SSS), 91	30	39
___	16526	Kansas City Southern SP-type Caboose, 91	17	21
___	16528	UP SP-type Caboose "6528," 90-91 u	17	21
___	16529	Santa Fe SP-type Caboose "16829," 91	9	13
___	16530	Mickey's World Tour SP-type Caboose "16830," 91, 92 u	13	17
___	16531	Texas & Pacific SP-type Caboose, 92	18	23
___	16533	C&NW Bay Window Caboose, 92	22	30
___	16534	Delaware & Hudson SP-type Caboose, 92	14	19
___	16535	Erie-Lackawanna Bay Window Caboose, 91 u	42	50
___	16536	Chessie System SP-type Caboose, 92, 93 u, 94, 95 u		23
___	16537	MKT SP-type Caboose, 92, 93 u	17	21
___	16538	L&N Bay Window Caboose "1041," 92 u	29	33
___	16539	WP Steelside Caboose "539," smoke, SSS (std O), 92	50	55
___	16541	Montana Rail Link EV Caboose "10131" with smoke, 93	50	73
___	16543	NYC SP-type Caboose, 93-95		20
___	16544	Union Pacific SP-type Caboose, 93-95	22	26
___	16546	Clinchfield SP-type Caboose, 93	22	26
___	16547	Happy Holidays SP-type Caboose, 93-95	46	55
___	16548	Conrail SP-type Caboose, 93	15	20
___	16549	Soo Line Work Caboose, 93	18	26
___	16550	U.S. Navy Searchlight Caboose, 94-95	16	21
___	16551	Budweiser SP-type Caboose, 93-94 u	30	33
___	16552	Frisco Searchlight Caboose, 94	23	26
___	16553	United Auto Workers SP-type Caboose, 93 u		40
___	16554	GT Extended Vision Caboose "79052," smoke, 94	40	47
___	16555	C&O SP-type Caboose, 94	22	26
___	16557	Ford SP-type Caboose, 94 u	19	24
___	16558	Crayola SP-type Caboose, 94 u, 95	17	21
___	16559	Seaboard Center Cupola Caboose "5658," 95	23	24
___	16560	Chrysler Mopar Caboose, 94 u	24	26
___	16561	UP Center Cupola Caboose "25766," 95	27	31
___	16562	Reading Center Cupola Caboose, 95	25	29
___	16563	Lionel Lines SP-type Caboose, 95	22	26
___	16564	Western Maryland Center Cupola Caboose (SSS), 95	30	34
___	16565	Milwaukee Road Bay Window Caboose, 95	45	70
___	16566	U.S. Army SP-type Caboose "907," 95		28
___	16568	ATSF SP-type Caboose, 96-99		23
___	16571	Georgia Power SP-type Caboose "52789," 95 u		68

		Exc	Mint	
16575	Sears Zenith SP-type Caboose, 95		38	___
16577	U.S. Coast Guard Work Caboose, 96		26	___
16578	Lionel Lines SP-type Caboose, 95 u		20	___
16579	GM/AC Delco, SP-type Caboose, 95		35	___
16580	SP-type Caboose, 96-99		11	___
16581	UP Illuminated Caboose, 96		30	___
16586	SP Illuminated Caboose "6357," 97		42	___
16589	Zenith SP-type Caboose, 97	20	45	___
16590	Dodge Motorsports SP-type Caboose "6950," 96		58	___
16591	Little League Baseball SP-type Caboose "6397," 97		45	___
16593	Lionel Belt Line Caboose "6257," 98		32	___
16594	Caboose "6357," 98		29	___
16600	Illinois Central Coal Dump Car, 88	14	23	___
16601	Canadian National Searchlight Car, 88	19	24	___
16602	Erie-Lackawanna Coal Dump Car, 87	16	26	___
16603	Detroit Zoo Giraffe Car (027), 87	40	49	___
16604	NYC Log Dump Car, 87	15	27	___
16605	Bronx Zoo Giraffe Car (027), 88	39	44	___
16606	Southern Searchlight Car, 87	13	21	___
16607	Southern Coal Dump Car "16707" (SSS), 87	18	26	___
16608	Lehigh Valley Searchlight Car, 87	11	30	___
16609	Lehigh Valley Derrick Car, 87	22	30	___
16610	Track Maintenance Car, 87-88	15	25	___
16611	Santa Fe Log Dump Car, 88	15	23	___
16612	Soo Line Log Dump Car, 89	14	24	___
16613	MKT Coal Dump Car, 89	17	26	___
16614	Reading Cop and Hobo Car (027), 89	24	25	___
16615	Lionel Lines Extension Searchlight Car, 89	20	28	___
16616	D&RGW Searchlight Car (SSS), 89	22	30	___
16617	C&NW Boxcar with ETD, 89	23	34	___
16618	Santa Fe Track Maintenance Car, 89	11	19	___
16619	Wabash Coal Dump Car, 90	14	25	___
16620	C&O Track Maintenance Car, 90-91	16	19	___
16621	Alaska Log Dump Car, 90	24	31	___
16622	CSX Boxcar with ETD, 90-91	20	28	___
16623	MKT DD Boxcar with ETD, 91	16	23	___
16624	NH Cop and Hobo Car (027), 90-91	23	31	___
16625	NYC Extension Searchlight Car, 90	22	30	___
16626	CSX Searchlight Car, 90	18	26	___
16627	CSX Log Dump Car, 90	19	23	___
16628	Cop and Hobo Circus Gondola, 90-91	36	43	___
16629	Operating Circus Elephant Car (027), 90-91	38	50	___
16630	SP Operating Cowboy Car (027), 90-91	22	26	___
16631	RI Boxcar, steam RailSounds, 90	110	130	___
16632	BN Boxcar, diesel RailSounds, 90	82	98	___
16634	WM Coal Dump Car, 91	26	31	___
16636	D&RGW Log Dump Car, 91	19	25	___
16637	WP Extension Searchlight Car, 91	27	30	___
16638	Operating Circus Animal Car (027), 91	50	55	___
16639	B&O Boxcar, steam RailSounds, 91	100	120	___
16640	Rutland Boxcar, diesel RailSounds, 91	100	120	___
16641	Toys 'R' Us Giraffe Car (027), 90-91 u	48	68	___
16642	Mickey's World Tour Goofy Car (027), 91, 92 u	33	41	___

			Exc	Mint
____	**16644**	Amtrak Crane Car, 91, 92 u	36	42
____	**16645**	Amtrak Searchlight Caboose, 91	27	30
____	**16649**	Railway Express Agency Boxcar, steam RailSounds, 92	110	140
____	**16650**	NYC Pacemaker Boxcar, diesel RailSounds, 92	100	135
____	**16651**	Operating Circus Clown Car (O27), 92	24	30
____	**16652**	Radar Car, 92	25	29
____	**16653**	Western Pacific Crane Car (SSS), 92	44	60
____	**16655**	Steam Tender "1993," RailSounds, 93	115	140
____	**16656**	Burlington Log Dump Car, 92 u	18	25
____	**16657**	Lehigh Valley Coal Dump Car, 92 u	22	29
____	**16658**	Erie-Lackawanna Crane Car, 93	47	65
____	**16659**	Union Pacific Searchlight Car, 93-95	15	18
____	**16660**	Fire Car with ladders, 93-94	28	33
____	**16661**	Flatcar with boat, 93	20	22
____	**16662**	Bugs Bunny and Yosemite Sam Outlaw Car (O27), 93-94	25	34
____	**16663**	Missouri Pacific Searchlight Car, 93	16	19
____	**16664**	L&N Coal Dump Car, 93	22	25
____	**16665**	Maine Central Log Dump Car, 93	23	27
____	**16666**	Toxic Waste Car, 93-94	25	32
____	**16667**	Conrail Searchlight Car, 93	27	30
____	**16668**	Ontario Northland Log Dump Car, 93	20	24
____	**16669**	Soo Line Searchlight Car, 93	17	21
____	**16670**	TV Car, 93-94	12	22
____	**16673**	Lionel Lines Tender, whistle, 94-97	33	42
____	**16674**	Pinkerton Animated Gondola, 94	28	32
____	**16675**	Great Northern Log Dump Car, 94	21	25
____	**16676**	Burlington Coal Dump Car, 94	23	28
____	**16677**	NATO Flatcar with Royal Navy submarine, 94	34	44
____	**16678**	Rock Island Searchlight Car, 94	12	23
____	**16679**	U.S. Mail Operating Boxcar, 94	45	50
____	**16680**	Cherry Picker Car, 94	25	28
____	**16681**	Aquarium Car, 95	35	44
____	**16682**	Lionelville Farms Operating Stock Car (O27), 94	23	27
____	**16683**	Los Angeles Zoo Elephant Car (O27), 94	22	26
____	**16684**	U.S. Navy Crane Car, 94-95	35	40
____	**16685**	Erie Extension Searchlight Car, 95	30	34
____	**16686**	Mickey Mouse Animated Boxcar, 95	32	38
____	**16687**	U.S. Mail Operating Boxcar, 94	29	37
____	**16688**	Fire Car with ladders, 94	35	43
____	**16689**	Toxic Waste Car, 94	29	32
____	**16690**	Bugs Bunny and Yosemite Sam Outlaw Car (O27), 94	30	34
____	**16701**	Southern Tool Car (SSS), 87	43	55
____	**16702**	Amtrak Bunk Car, 91, 92 u	25	27
____	**16703**	NYC Tool Car, 92	24	31
____	**16704**	TV Car, 94	27	29
____	**16705**	Chesapeake & Ohio Cop and Hobo Car, 95	28	34
____	**16706**	Animal Transport Service Giraffe Car, 95	27	30
____	**16708**	C&NW Track Maintenance Car, 95	24	31
____	**16709**	New York Central Derrick Car, 95	22	28
____	**16710**	U.S. Army Operating Missile Car, 95	40	42
____	**16711**	Pennsylvania Searchlight Car, 95	27	31
____	**16712**	Pinkerton Animated Gondola, 95	34	39
____	**16715**	ATSF Log Dump Car, 96-99		24

		Exc	Mint	
16717	Jersey Central Crane Car, 96		41	___
16718	USMC Missile Launching Flatcar, 96	26	31	___
16719	Exploding Boxcar, 96		38	___
16720	Lionel Lines Searchlight Car "3650," 96-97		50	___
16724	Mickey and Friends Submarine Car, 96		39	___
16725	Rhino Transport Car, 97		31	___
16726	U.S. Army Fire Ladder Car, 96		43	___
16734	U.S. Coast Guard Searchlight Car, 96		30	___
16735	U.S. Coast Guard Flatcar with radar, 96	28	35	___
16736	U.S. Coast Guard Derrick Car, 96		34	___
16737	Road Runner and Wile E. Coyote Gondola "3444," 96		66	___
16738	Pepe LePew Boxcar "3370," 96		40	___
16739	Foghorn Leghorn Poultry Car "6434," 96		44	___
16740	Lionel Corporation Mail Car "3428," 96		37	___
16741	Union Pacific Illuminated Bunk Car, 97		25	___
16742	Trout Ranch Aquarium Car "3435," 96		32	___
16744	Port of Lionel City Searchlight Car, 97		30	___
16745	Port of Lionel City Flatcar with radar, 97		30	___
16746	Port of Lionel City Derrick Car, 97		30	___
16747	Breyer Animated Horse Car "6473," 97		34	___
16748	U.S. Forest Service Log-Dump Car "3361," 97		30	___
16749	Midget Mines Ore-Dump Car "3479," 97		36	___
16750	Lionel City Aquarium Car "3436," 97		32	___
16751	AIREX Sports Channel TV Car "3545," 97		25	___
16752	Marvin the Martian Missile Launching Flatcar "6655," 97	143	158	___
16754	Porky Pig and Instant Martians Flatcar "6805," 97	100	147	___
16755	Daffy Duck Animated Balloon Car "3470," 97	143	181	___
16760	Pluto and Cats Animated Gondola "3444," 97		55	___
16765	Bureau of Land Management Log Car "3351," 98		30	___
16766	Bureau of Land Management Ore Car "3479," 98		31	___
16767	New York Central Ice Docks Ice Car "6352," 98		47	___
16776	Holiday Boxcar, RailSounds, 98		68	___
16777	Animated Cola Car and Platform, 98		100	___
16782	Bethlehem Ore Dump Car "3479," 99	24	95	___
16783	Westside Lumber Log Dump Car "3351," 99		32	___
16784	Pratt's Hollow Seed Dump Car "3479," 99		36	___
16785	Happy Holidays Music Reefer "5700," 99		100	___
16789	Easter Operating Boxcar, 99		39	___
16790	UP Stock Car "3356," Crowsounds, 99		90	___
16791	New York City Lights Boxcar, 99		44	___
16792	Constellation Boxcar "9600," 99		37	___
16793	Animated Glow-in-the-Dark Alien Boxcar, 99		44	___
16794	Wicked Witch Halloween Boxcar, 99		46	___
16795	Elf Chasing Rudolph Gondola "6462," 99		55	___
16796	Snowman Loading Ice Car "6352," 99		55	___
16805	Budweiser Malt Nutrine Reefer "3285," 91-92 u	82	109	___
16806	Toys 'R' Us Boxcar, 92 u	21	26	___
16807	H.J. Heinz Reefer "301," 93	23	27	___
16808	Toys 'R' Us Boxcar, 93 u	28	30	___
16817	Ambassador 1-D Tank Car, 00 u		184	___
16818	Engineer Award Tank Car, 00 u		715	___
16819	JLC Award Tank Car, 00 u		760	___
16820	Ambassador Boxcar, 00 u	318	520	___

		Exc	Mint
16822	CSX Water Tower, 08		23
16824	O36 Command Control Switch, left hand (FasTrack), 09-14		110
16825	O36 Command Control Switch, right hand (FasTrack), 09-14		110
16826	O72 Command Control Switch, left hand (FasTrack), 09-14		120
16827	O72 Command Control Switch, right hand (FasTrack), 09-14		120
16828	O60 Command Control Switch, left hand (FasTrack), 09-14		120
16829	O60 Command Control Switch, right hand (FasTrack), 09-14		120
16830	O48 Command Control Switch, left hand (FasTrack), 09-14		120
16831	O48 Command Control Switch, right hand (FasTrack), 09-14		120
16832	O72 Command Control Wye Switch (FasTrack), 09-14		115
16834	FasTrack O48 Half-Curved Track, 09-23		7
16835	FasTrack O48 Quarter-Curved Track, 09-23		5
16836	Christmas Girder Bridge, 09		21
16837	Christmas Operating Billboard, 09		45
16841	Halloween Gateman, 09		80
16842	Big Moe Crane, 10		70
16843	City and Western Diorama, 10-11		15
16845	Bookstore, 09-10		60
16846	Burning Hobo Depot, 09		90
16847	Legacy Hotel, 10-11		70
16848	Creature Comforts Pet Store, sound, 09-10		80
16849	Rotary Dumper with coal conveyor, CC, 10		600
16850	Operating Wind Turbine, 3-pack, 09-11		225
16851	Sunoco Cylindrical Oil Tank, gray, 10-11		100
16852	Sunoco Cylindrical Oil Tank, yellow, 10-11		90
16853	Polar Express Diorama, 09-11, 13		18
16854	MTA LIRR Blinking Billboard, 09		30
16855	MTA LIRR Illuminated Station Platform, 09		37
16856	MTA LIRR Passenger Station, 09		60
16857	Thomas & Friends Diorama, 10-16, 20		18
16859	Grand Central Terminal, 09		1500
16861	50,000-gallon Water Tank, 09-11		150
16863	Santa's Christmas Wish Station, 09-11		125
16868	Straight O Gauge Tunnel, 09-17		55
16871	Winter Wonderland Diorama, 09-11		15
16872	Illuminated Christmas Station Platform, 09		35
16873	Bathtub Gondola Coal Load 3-pack, 10-19		20
16874	Coaling Station, 10-11		80
16880	Freight Platform, 10-12		30
16881	Barrel Shed, 10-11		30
16882	12" Covered Bridge, 10-18		60
16883	Neil's Guitar Shop, 10-11		60
16889	Coal Tipple Pack, 11-20		15
16891	Tank Car Accident, 10-11		130
16896	Flagpole with lights, 10-16		28
16897	75th Anniversary Gateman, 10		80
16903	CP Bulkhead Flatcar with pulp load (SSS), 94	22	25
16904	NYC Pacemaker Flatcar Set with trailers, 94	55	60
16907	Flatcar with farm tractors, 94	27	33
16908	U.S. Navy Flatcar "04039" with submarine, 94-95	39	46
16909	U.S. Navy Gondola "16556" with canisters, 94-95	16	22
16910	Missouri Pacific Flatcar with trailer, 94	22	27
16911	B&M Flatcar with trailer, 94	28	34

		Exc	Mint	
16912	CN Maxi-Stack Flatcar Set with containers, 94	70	75	___
16915	Lionel Lines Gondola (O27), 93-94 u	7	10	___
16916	Ford Flatcar with trailer, 94 u	38	45	___
16917	Crayola Gondola with crayons, 94 u, 95	8	9	___
16919	Chrysler Mopar Gondola with coil covers, 94-96	33	36	___
16922	Chesapeake & Ohio Flatcar with trailer, 95	25	31	___
16923	Intermodal Service Flatcar with wheel chocks, 95	15	22	___
16924	Lionel Corporation Flatcar "6424" with trailer, 96		24	___
16925	New York Central Flatcar with trailer, 95	65	85	___
16926	Frisco Flatcar with trailers, 95	24	31	___
16927	New York Central Flatcar with gondola, 95	17	22	___
16928	Soo Line Flatcar with dump bin (O27), 95	12	15	___
16929	BC Rail Gondola with cable reels, 95	21	25	___
16930	Santa Fe Flatcar with wheel load, 95	20	25	___
16932	Erie Flatcar with rail load, 95	17	22	___
16933	Lionel Lines Flatcar with autos, 95	23	25	___
16934	Pennsylvania Flatcar with Ertl road grader, 95	28	39	___
16935	UP Depressed Center Flatcar with Ertl bulldozer, 95	22	35	___
16936	Sealand Maxi-Stack Flatcar Set with containers, 95	61	85	___
16939	U.S. Navy Flatcar "04040" with boat, 95	25	30	___
16940	ATSF Flatcar with trailer, 96-99		40	___
16941	ATSF Flatcar with autos, 96-99		25	___
16943	Jersey Central Gondola, 96		18	___
16944	Georgia Power Flatcar "31438" with transformer, 95 u		50	___
16945	Georgia Power Flatcar "31950" with cable reels, 95 u		53	___
16946	C&O F9 Well Car "3840," 96		31	___
16951	Southern I-Beam Flatcar "9823" with load, 97		25	___
16952	U.S. Navy Flatcar with Ertl helicopter, 96		25	___
16953	NYC Flatcar with Red Wing Shoes trailer, 95 u	39	45	___
16954	NYC Flatcar "6424" with Ertl scraper, 96		30	___
16955	ATSF Flatcar with Ertl Challenger, 96		30	___
16956	Zenith Flatcar with trailer, 95 u	50	141	___
16957	Depressed Center Flatcar "6461" with Ertl Case tractor, 96		29	___
16958	Flatcar with Ertl New Holland loader, 96		26	___
16960	U.S. Coast Guard Flatcar with boat, 96		40	___
16961	GM/AC Delco Flatcar with trailer, 95		73	___
16963	Lionel Corporation Flatcar "6411," 96-97		34	___
16964	Lionel Corporation Gondola "6462," 97		22	___
16965	Scout Flatcar "6424" with stakes, 96-97		20	___
16967	Depressed Center Flatcar "6461" with transformer, 96		21	___
16968	Depressed Center Flatcar "6461" with Ertl Helicopter, 96	10	40	___
16969	Flatcar "6411" with Beechcraft Bonanza, 96		33	___
16970	LA County Flatcar "6424" with motorized powerboat, 96	11	20	___
16971	Port of Lionel City Flatcar with boat, 97		35	___
16972	P&LE Gondola "6462," 97		22	___
16975	Well Car Doublestack Set, 97		75	___
16978	MILW Flatcar "6424" with P&H shovel, 97		43	___
16980	Speedy Gonzales Missile Flatcar "6823," 97	30	56	___
16982	BC Rail Bulkhead Flatcar "9823" with lumber, 97		28	___
16983	PRR F9 Well Car "6983" with cable reels, 97		39	___
16986	Sears Zenith Bulkhead Flatcar, 96 u		45	___
16987	Musco Lighting Bulkhead Flatcar, 97 u		35	___
16997	Lionel Lines Recovery Crane Car, 99		50	___

	MODERN 1970-2023	Exc	Mint
___	**17002** Conrail 2-bay ACF Hopper (std O), 87	42	47
___	**17003** Du Pont 2-bay ACF Hopper (std O), 90	39	45
___	**17004** MKT 2-bay ACF Hopper (std O), 91	23	27
___	**17005** Cargill 2-bay ACF Hopper (std O), 92	26	37
___	**17006** Soo Line 2-bay ACF Hopper (std O, SSS), 93	31	36
___	**17007** GN 2-bay ACF Hopper "173872" (std O), 94	26	31
___	**17008** D&RGW 2-bay ACF Hopper "10009" (std O), 95		31
___	**17009** New York Central 2-bay ACF Hopper, 96		35
___	**17010** Govt. of Canada ACF 2-bay Covered Hopper "7000," 98	13	32
___	**17010** NP PS-1 Boxcar 6-pack, LionScale, 17		360
___	**17011** NP ACF 2-bay Covered Hopper "75052," 98		44
___	**17012** Govt. of Canada ACF 2-bay Covered Hopper "7001," 98	15	36
___	**17013** NYC Graffiti 2-bay Covered Hopper "7000," 99		55
___	**17014** Graffiti 2-bay Covered Hopper "7000" (std O), 99		45
___	**17015** Corning 2-bay Hopper "90409" (std O), 01		40
___	**17016** C&NW 2-bay Hopper "96644" (std O), 01		46
___	**17017** Chessie System 2-bay Hopper "605527" (std O), 02		32
___	**17018** Nickel Plate Road Offset Hopper "33074," 02		43
___	**17019** Santa Fe Offset Hopper "78299," 02		43
___	**17020** Frisco Offset Hopper "92092," 02		43
___	**17020** UP PS-1 Boxcar 6-pack, LionScale, 17		360
___	**17021** NYC Offset Hopper "867999," 02		43
___	**17022** Burlington 2-bay ACF Hopper "183925" (std O), 03		30
___	**17023** BNSF 2-bay Hopper "409038" (std O), 04		30
___	**17024** Reading Offset Hopper "81089" (std O), 03-04		43
___	**17025** C&O Offset Hopper "300027" (std O), 03-04		43
___	**17026** D&H Offset Hopper "7215" (std O), 03-04		41
___	**17027** IC Offset Hopper "92142" (std O), 03-04		49
___	**17028** GE PS-2 2-bay Covered Hopper "326" (std O), 03-04		35
___	**17029** CNJ PS-2 2-bay Covered Hopper "803" (std O), 03-04		35
___	**17030** MILW PS-2 2-bay Covered Hopper "99708" (std O), 03-04	18	43
___	**17030** Reading PS-1 Boxcar 6-pack, LionScale, 17		360
___	**17031** SP PS-2 2-bay Covered Hopper "401306" (std O), 03-04		38
___	**17038** Clinchfield PS-2 Covered Hopper, 05		70
___	**17039** Boston & Maine PS-2 2-bay Covered Hopper, 05		55
___	**17040** Norfolk & Western PS-2 2-bay Covered Hopper, 05		55
___	**17040** NYC PS-1 Boxcar 6-pack, LionScale, 17		360
___	**17041** Great Northern Offset Hopper, 05		60
___	**17042** Green Bay & Western Offset Hopper, 05		60
___	**17043** Baltimore & Ohio Offset Hopper, 05		60
___	**17044** DT&I PS-2 Covered Hopper (std O), 05-06	15	38
___	**17050** NYC 14-panel Hopper 6-pack, LionScale, 17		330
___	**17060** D&RGW 14-panel Hopper 6-pack, LionScale, 17		330
___	**17063** Santa Fe PS-2 2-bay Covered Hopper "82297" (std O), 06		55
___	**17064** MKT PS-2 2-bay Covered Hopper "1311" (std O), 06		55
___	**17065** Boraxo PS-2 2-bay Covered Hopper "31062" (std O), 06		55
___	**17066** PRR PS-2 2-bay Covered Hopper "256177" (std O), 06		55
___	**17067** Rock Island Offset Hopper "89500" with gravel (std O), 06		65
___	**17068** CNJ Offset Hopper "61261" (std O), 06		65
___	**17069** Maine Central Offset Hopper "3785" (std O), 06		65
___	**17070** P&LE Offset Hopper "4990" (std O), 06		65
___	**17070** Conrail 14-panel Hopper 6-pack, LionScale, 17		330
___	**17080** EL 14-panel Hopper 6-pack, LionScale, 17		330

		Exc	Mint	
17083	C&O Offset Hopper "47386" (std O), 05		40	
17090	Trailer Train 50' Flatcar 6-pack, 17		330	
17100	Chessie System 3-bay ACF Hopper	49	85	
17100	BN 50' Flatcar 6-pack, 17		330	
17101	Chessie System 3-bay ACF Hopper (std O), 88	37	45	
17102	Chessie System 3-bay ACF Hopper (std O), 88	35	41	
17103	Chessie System 3-bay ACF Hopper (std O), 88	31	34	
17104	Chessie System 3-bay ACF Hopper (std O), 88	38	46	
17105	Chessie System 3-bay ACF Hopper (std O), 88	39	46	
17107	Sinclair 3-bay ACF Hopper (std O), 89	40	48	
17108	Santa Fe 3-bay ACF Hopper (std O), 90	42	48	
17109	N&W 3-bay ACF Hopper (std O), 91	24	31	
17110	UP Hopper with coal (std O), 91	24	30	
17110	AT&SF 50' Flatcar 6-pack, 17		330	
17111	Reading Hopper with coal (std O), 91	23	28	
17112	Erie-Lackawanna 3-bay ACF Hopper (std O), 92	24	34	
17113	LV Hopper with coal (std O), 92-93	25	32	
17114	Peabody Hopper with coal (std O), 92-93	26	30	
17118	Archer Daniels Midland 3-bay ACF Hopper "60029" (std O), 93	28	35	
17120	CSX Hopper "295110" with coal (std O), 94	28	30	
17120	PRR 50' Flatcar 6-pack, 17		330	
17121	ICG Hopper "72867" with coal (std O), 94	26	33	
17122	RI 3-bay ACF Hopper "800200" (std O), 94	32	39	
17123	Cargill Covered Grain Hopper "844304" (std O), 95	26	37	
17124	Archer Daniels Midland 3-bay ACF Hopper "50224" (std O), 95	24	30	
17127	Delaware & Hudson 3-bay Hopper, 96	11	34	
17128	Chesapeake & Ohio 3-bay Hopper, 96		30	
17129	WM 3-bay Hopper "9300" with coal (std O), 97		34	
17130	ACFX ACF 4-bay Covered Hopper 6-pack, LionScale, 17		360	
17132	PRR 3-bay ACF Hopper "260815," 98		40	
17133	BNSF ACF 3-bay Covered Hopper "403698," 98	16	39	
17134	BNSF 3-bay Covered Hopper "403698" (std O), 01		38	
17135	BNSF ACF 3-bay Covered Hopper with ETD, 98	16	39	
17137	Cargill 3-bay Covered Hopper "1219" (std O), 99		45	
17138	Farmers Elevator 3-bay Covered Hopper (std O), 99		45	
17139	Grain Train 3-bay Hopper "BLMR 1025," 99-00	20	50	
17140	Virginian 3-bay Hopper 6-pack, "5260-5265," 99		230	
17140	GN ACF 4-bay Covered Hopper 6-pack, LionScale, 17		360	
17147	C&O 3-bay Hopper 6-pack, "156330-156335," 99		230	
17150	AT&SF ACF 4-bay Covered Hopper 6-pack, LionScale, 17		360	
17154	Alberta Cylindrical Hopper "628373" (std O), 01		40	
17155	Shell Cylindrical Hopper "3527" (std O), 01		40	
17156	ACF Pressureaide 3-bay Hopper "59267" (std O), 01		27	
17157	Wonder Bread "56670" 3-bay Hopper (std O), 01		45	
17158	Conrail Coal Hopper "487739" (std O), 01		42	
17159	N&W Coal Hopper "1776" (std O), 01		45	
17160	C&NW (UP) ACF 4-bay Covered Hopper 6-pack, LionScale, 17		360	
17163	C&O 3-bay Hopper (std O), 01		30	
17170	General Mills 3-bay Covered Hopper (std O), 00 u		60	
17170	PFE 57' Mechanical Reefer, 17		390	
17171	Lionel Lion Cylindrical Hopper (std O), 01		45	
17172	CP Rail Cylindrical Hopper "385206" (std O), 02		37	
17173	Govt. of Canada Cylindrical Hopper "111031" (std O), 02		33	

		Exc	Mint
17174	GN 3-bay Hopper "171250" (std O), 02		29
17175	IC PS-2CD 4427 Covered Hopper "57031" (std O), 02		40
17176	Cargill PS-2CD 4427 Covered Hopper "2514" (std O), 02		46
17177	PS-2CD 4427 Covered Hopper "2500" (std O), 02		40
17178	Santa Fe PS-2CD 4427 Covered Hopper "304774" (std O), 02		40
17179	Indianapolis Power & Light Coal Hopper "10074" (std O), 02		40
17180	Rock Island Coal Hopper "700665" (std O), 02		40
17180	SPFE 57' Mechanical Reefer 6-pack, LionScale, 17		390
17181	NYC 4-bay ACF Centerflow Hopper "892138" (std O), 03		45
17182	Sigco Hybrids 4-bay ACF Centerflow Hopper "1100" (std O), 03		46
17183	C&O Hopper "156341" (std O), 01		30
17184	Virginian Hopper "5271" (std O), 01		30
17185	LLCX Bathtub Gondola "877900" (std O), 01		36
17186	Cannonaide 4-bay ACF Centerflow Hopper "96169" (std O), 03		40
17187	Rio Grande 4-bay ACF Centerflow Hopper "15521" (std O), 03		40
17188	Govt. of Canada 3-bay Cylindrical Hopper (std O), 03		48
17189	Saskatchewan Grain 3-bay Cylindrical Hopper (std O), 03		48
17190	Soo/CP 3-bay ACF Hopper "119303" (std O), 03		37
17190	UPFE 57' Mechanical Reefer 6-pack, LionScale, 17		390
17191	BN PS-2CD 4427 Hopper "450669" (std O), 03-04		45
17192	Lehigh Valley PS-2CD 4427 Hopper "51118" (std O), 03-04		40
17193	Chessie System/WM PS-2CD Hopper "4673" (std O), 03-04		30
17194	MKT PS-2CD 4427 Hopper "1122" (std O), 03-04		40
17195	L&N 3-bay Hopper "240850" (std O), 04		40
17196	Firestone 4-bay Hopper "53240" (std O), 04		40
17197	Diamond Chemicals 4-bay Hopper "53286" (std O), 04		40
17198	Hercules 4-bay Hopper "50503" (std O), 04		40
17199	Conrail 4-bay Hopper "888367" (std O), 04		46
17200	Canadian Pacific Boxcar (std O), 89	26	32
17200	BNFE 57' Mechanical Reefer 6-pack, LionScale, 17		390
17201	Conrail Boxcar (std O), 87	33	38
17202	Santa Fe Boxcar (std O), diesel RailSounds, 90	80	85
17203	Cotton Belt DD Boxcar (std O), 91	33	38
17204	Missouri Pacific DD Boxcar (std O), 91	27	30
17207	C&IM DD Boxcar (std O), 92	36	42
17208	Union Pacific DD Boxcar (std O), 92	32	40
17209	B&O DD Boxcar "296000" (std O), 93	37	43
17210	Chicago & Illinois Midland Boxcar "16021" (std O), 92 u	30	39
17210	BN 100-Ton, 4-Bay Hopper 6-pack, 17		330
17211	Chicago & Illinois Midland Boxcar "16022" (std O), 92 u	30	39
17212	Chicago & Illinois Midland Boxcar "16023" (std O), 92 u	24	31
17213	Susquehanna Boxcar "501" (std O), 93	28	31
17214	Railbox Boxcar (std O), diesel RailSounds, 93	75	85
17216	PRR DD Boxcar "60155" (std O), 94	34	38
17217	New Haven State of Maine Boxcar "45003" (std O), 95	28	35
17218	BAR State of Maine Boxcar "2184" (std O), 95	23	36
17219	Tazmanian Devil 40th Birthday Boxcar (std O), 95	40	50
17220	Pennsylvania Boxcar (std O), 96		23
17220	CSX 100-Ton, 4-Bay Hopper 6-pack, 17		330
17221	NYC Boxcar (std O), 96	19	33
17222	Western Pacific Boxcar (std O), 96	28	34
17223	Milwaukee Road DD Boxcar (std O), 96		34
17224	Central of Georgia Boxcar "9464-197" (std O), 97	15	29

		Exc	Mint	
17225	Penn Central Boxcar "9464-297" (std O), 97	13	26	___
17226	Milwaukee Road Boxcar "9464-397" (std O), 97	13	27	___
17227	UP DD Boxcar "9200" (std O), 97		35	___
17230	NS 100-Ton, 4-Bay Hopper 6-pack, 17		330	___
17231	Wisconsin Central DD Boxcar "9200" with auto frames, 98		40	___
17232	SP/UP Merger DD Boxcar "9200," 98		33	___
17233	Western Pacific Boxcar "9464-198," 98		27	___
17234	Port Huron & Detroit Boxcar "9464-298," 98		33	___
17235	Boston & Maine Boxcar "9464-398," 98		41	___
17239	ATSF Texas Chief Boxcar "9464-1," 97		50	___
17240	ATSF Super Chief Boxcar "9464-2," 97		50	___
17240	UP 100-Ton, 4-Bay Hopper 6-pack, 17		330	___
17241	ATSF El Capitan Boxcar "9464-3," 97		50	___
17242	ATSF Grand Canyon Boxcar "9464-4," 97		60	___
17243	NP Boxcar "8722," 98		48	___
17244	Santa Fe Chief Boxcar, 98		37	___
17245	C&O Boxcar with Chessie kitten, 98		44	___
17246	NYC Pacemaker Rolling Stock 4-pack, 98		200	___
17247	NYC 9464 Boxcar "174940," 98		135	___
17248	NYC 9464 Boxcar "174945," 98	50	115	___
17249	NYC 9464 Boxcar "174949," 98		60	___
17250	UP Boxcar "507406" (std O), 99		45	___
17250	AT&SF Stockcar 6-pack, 17		360	___
17251	BNSF Boxcar "103277," 99		41	___
17252	NS Boxcar "564824" (std O), 99		41	___
17253	CSX Boxcar "141756" (std O), 99		35	___
17254	UP Boxcar "551967" (std O), 99		42	___
17255	Chevy DD Boxcar "9200" (std O), 99		38	___
17257	Atlantic Coast Line Boxcar "28809" (std O), 99		36	___
17258	D&H 9464 Boxcar "29055" std O, 99		41	___
17259	MKT 9464 Boxcar "1422" (std O), 99		34	___
17260	CP Rail 9464 Boxcar "286138" (std O), silver, 00		45	___
17260	PRR Stockcar 6-pack, 17		360	___
17261	CP Rail 9464 Boxcar "85154," green, 00	20	45	___
17262	CP Rail 9464 Boxcar "56776," red (std O), 00		48	___
17263	NYC Boxcar "45725" (std O), 00		46	___
17264	C&O Boxcar "6054" (std O), 00		44	___
17265	U.S. Army Boxcar (std O), 00		35	___
17266	Monon Boxcar "911" (std O), 00		45	___
17268	C&O 9464 Boxcar "12700" (std O), 01		44	___
17269	Western Maryland 9464 Boxcar "29140" (std O), 01		44	___
17270	B&O Time-Saver 9464 Boxcar "467439" (std O), 01		42	___
17270	Nickel Plate Road Stockcar 6-pack, 17		360	___
17271	The Rock Boxcar "300324" (std O), 01		37	___
17272	Railbox Boxcar "15150" (std O), 01		27	___
17273	DT&I DD Boxcar "26852" (std O), 01		44	___
17274	Soo Line DD Boxcar "177587" (std O), 01		42	___
17275	NYC PS-1 Boxcar "175008" (std O), 02		43	___
17276	Cotton Belt PS-1 Boxcar "75000" (std O), 02		44	___
17277	Rio Grande PS-1 Boxcar "69676" (std O), 02		40	___
17278	WP PS-1 Boxcar "1953" (std O), 02		44	___
17279	Ontario Northland Boxcar "7428" (std O), 02		40	___
17280	Santa Fe Boxcar "600194" with auto frames (std O), 02		45	___

| --- | --- | --- |
___ 17280	UP Stockcar 6-pack, 17		360
___ 17281	PRR DD Boxcar "83158" (std O), 04		42
___ 17282	UP DD Boxcar "160300" (std O), 04		42
___ 17283	GM&O DD Boxcar "9077" (std O), 04		41
___ 17284	Erie DD Boxcar "66000" (std O), 04		41
___ 17285	CSX Big Blue Boxcar "151296" (std O), 03		36
___ 17287	BAR Boxcar "5976" (std O), 03		35
___ 17288	NYC PS-1 Boxcar "175012" (std O), 03-04		38
___ 17289	GN PS-1 Boxcar "18485" (std O), 03	29	43
___ 17290	Seaboard PS-1 Boxcar "24452" (std O), 03-04		42
___ 17290	Portland Terminal Wood-chip Hopper 6-pack, 17		360
___ 17291	RI PS-1 Boxcar "21110" (std O), 03-04		42
___ 17292	B&M PS-1 Boxcar "76182" (std O), 04		34
___ 17293	IC PS-1 Boxcar "400666" (std O), 04		40
___ 17294	TP&W PS-1 Boxcar "5036" (std O), 04		36
___ 17295	Santa Fe PS-1 Boxcar "276749" (std O), 04		40
___ 17296	C&O PS-1 Boxcar (std O), 04		40
___ 17297	UP PS-1 Boxcar, 03		100
___ 17298	Southern PS-1 Boxcar w/box load (std O), 05-06	18	42
___ 17300	Canadian Pacific Reefer (std O), 89	28	33
___ 17300	Chessie System Wood-chip Hopper 6-pack, 17		360
___ 17301	Conrail Reefer (std O), 87	35	42
___ 17302	Santa Fe Reefer with ETD (std O), 90	27	41
___ 17303	C&O Reefer "7890" (std O), 93	23	30
___ 17304	Wabash Reefer "26269" (std O), 94	29	37
___ 17305	Pacific Fruit Express Reefer "459400" (std O), 94	27	40
___ 17306	Pacific Fruit Express Reefer "459401" (std O), 94	19	27
___ 17307	Tropicana Reefer "300" (std O), 95	44	65
___ 17308	Tropicana Reefer "301" (std O), 95	22	35
___ 17309	Tropicana Reefer "302" (std O), 95	21	29
___ 17310	Tropicana Reefer "303" (std O), 95	20	27
___ 17310	GM&O Wood-chip Hopper 6-pack, 17		360
___ 17311	REA Reefer (std O), 96	28	30
___ 17314	PFE Reefer "9800-198," 98		42
___ 17315	PFE Reefer "9800-298," 98		39
___ 17316	NP Reefer "98583," 98		50
___ 17317	PRR Reefer FGE "91904," 98		36
___ 17318	UP Reefer "170650" (std O), 99		47
___ 17319	PFE Reefer 6-pack (std O), 01	240	300
___ 17320	WM Wood-chip Hopper 6-pack, 17		360
___ 17331	Hood General American Milk Car "802" (std O), 02	38	100
___ 17332	Pfaudler General American Milk Car "501" (std O), 02		70
___ 17334	REA General American Milk Car "1741" (std O), 02	21	77
___ 17335	New Haven General American Milk Car "102" (std O), 02	25	73
___ 17336	PFE Steel-sided Reefer "17760" (std O), 03		45
___ 17337	CN Steel-sided Reefer "209712" (std O), 03		38
___ 17338	Merchants Dispatch Transit Steel Reefer "12322" (std O), 03		39
___ 17339	Burlington Steel-sided Reefer "74825" (std O), 03		45
___ 17340	White Bros. General American Milk Car "891" (std O), 03		44
___ 17341	Dairymen League General American Milk Car 779 (std O), 03		43
___ 17342	Miller Beer Steel-sided Reefer American Eagle (std O), 03 u	40	63
___ 17343	Miller Beer Steel-sided Reefer Lady and Moon (std O), 03 u	40	64
___ 17349	NYC General American Milk Car "6581" (std O), 03 u		42

		Exc	Mint
17350	Hood General American Milk Car "503" (std 0), 03 u		45 ___
17351	Santa Fe Steel-sided Reefer "3526" (std 0), 04		43 ___
17352	PFE Steel-sided Reefer "20043" (std 0), 04		41 ___
17353	Needham Packing Steel-sided Reefer "60507" (std 0), 04		44 ___
17354	Swift Steel-sided Reefer "15392" (std 0), 04		42 ___
17355	Hood Steel-sided Reefer "550" (std 0), 04	15	40 ___
17356	Nestle Nesquik Steel-sided Reefer (std 0), 04		44 ___
17357	Borden Steel-sided Reefer "522" (std 0), 04		47 ___
17358	Fairfield Farms Steel-sided Reefer (std 0), 04		44 ___
17360	Hood General American Milk Car "810" (std 0), 03	25	53 ___
17361	Hood General American Milk Car "811" (std 0), 03		43 ___
17362	Pfaudler General American Milk Car "502" (std 0), 03		47 ___
17363	Pfaudler General American Milk Car "503" (std 0), 03		40 ___
17364	REA General American Milk Car "1742" (std 0), 03		38 ___
17365	REA General American Milk Car "1743" (std 0), 03		44 ___
17366	NH General American Milk Car "103" (std 0), 03	25	50 ___
17367	NH General American Milk Car "104" (std 0), 03		47 ___
17368	White Brothers General American Milk Car "892" (std 0), 03		43 ___
17369	White Brothers General American Milk Car "893" (std 0), 03		47 ___
17370	Dairymen League General American Milk Car "780 (std 0), 03		47 ___
17371	Dairymen League Milk Car "781" (std 0), 03		47 ___
17372	NYC General American Milk Car "6582" (std 0), 03		47 ___
17373	NYC General American Milk Car "6583" (std 0), 03		40 ___
17374	Hood General American Milk Car "504" (std 0), 03	28	54 ___
17375	Hood General American Milk Car "505" (std 0), 03	25	54 ___
17377	Railway Express Operating Milk Car "302" (std 0), 05	121	173 ___
17378	Supplee General American Milk Car (std 0), 05		63 ___
17379	NP Steel-sided Reefer "91353" (std 0), 05	33	60 ___
17380	PFE Silver Steel-sided Reefer "45698" (std 0), 05		60 ___
17381	North Western Steel-sided Reefer "751" (std 0), 05		40 ___
17397	PFE Steel-sided Reefer "47767" (std 0), 05		45 ___
17398	A&P General American Milk Car "737" (std 0), 06		65 ___
17399	Bowman Dairy General American Milk Car "117" (std 0), 06		65 ___
17400	CP Rail Gondola with coal (std 0), 89	30	34 ___
17401	Conrail Gondola with coal (std 0), 87	24	26 ___
17402	Santa Fe Gondola with coal (std 0), 90	19	25 ___
17403	Chessie System Gondola "371629" with coil covers (std 0), 93	18	25 ___
17404	ICG Gondola "245998" with coil covers (std 0), 93	26	32 ___
17405	Reading Gondola "24876" with coil covers (std 0), 94	27	31 ___
17406	PRR Gondola "385405" with coil covers (std 0), 95	37	42 ___
17407	NKP Gondola with scrap load, 96		24 ___
17408	Cotton Belt Gondola "9820" with scrap load (std 0), 97		32 ___
17410	UP Gondola "903004" with scrap load (std 0), 99		30 ___
17412	Gondola, blue, online store, 98		20 ___
17413	Service Center Gondola with parts load (SSS), 00		24 ___
17414	Nickel Plate PS-5 Gondola "44801" (std 0), 01-02		40 ___
17415	Frisco PS-5 Gondola "61878" (std 0), 01-02		35 ___
17416	D&H Gondola "14011" with scrap load (std 0), 01		33 ___
17417	BN Rotary Bathtub Gondola 3-pack, 01		140 ___
17421	CSX Rotary Bathtub Gondola 3-pack, 01		135 ___
17425	Western Maryland PS-5 Gondola "354903" (std 0), 01-02		36 ___
17426	Maine Central PS-5 Gondola "1116" (std 0), 01-02		40 ___
17427	CSX Rotary Bathtub Gondola Add-on Unit (std 0), 02		47 ___

			Exc	Mint
___	17428	BN Rotary Bathtub Gondola Add-on Unit (std O), 02		42
___	17429	Conrail Rotary Bathtub Gondola 3-pack (std O), 02-03		115
___	17433	BNSF Rotary Bathtub Gondola 3-pack (std O), 02-03		145
___	17439	UP PS-5 Gondola "229606" (std O), 03		35
___	17440	Algoma Central PS-5 Gondola "801" (std O), 03		32
___	17441	Conrail Rotary Bathtub Gondola "507673" (std O), 03		39
___	17442	BNSF Rotary Bathtub Gondola "668330" (std O), 03		46
___	17443	NS Rotary Bathtub Gondola 3-pack (std O), 03		90
___	17447	UP Rotary Bathtub Gondola 3-pack (std O), 03		100
___	17457	GN PS-5 Gondola "72839" (std O), 03		35
___	17458	Reading PS-5 Gondola "33267" (std O), 03		35
___	17459	CP Rail PS-5 Gondola "338966" (std O), 04		35
___	17460	NYC PS-5 Gondola "749592" (std O), 04		40
___	17461	Pennsylvania PS-5 Gondola "374256" (std O), 04		36
___	17462	Santa Fe PS-5 Gondola "167340" (std O), 04		35
___	17463	NS Bathtub Gondola "10303" (std O), 04		40
___	17464	UP Bathtub Gondola "28100" (std O), 04		35
___	17465	CP Rail Bathtub Gondola 3-pack (std O), 04		105
___	17469	B&O/Chessie System PS-5 Drop-end Gondola (std O), 05-06	15	38
___	17470	CP Rail Bathtub Gondola, 05		50
___	17471	Burlington PS-5 Gondola with covers (std O), 05		44
___	17472	New Haven PS-5 Gondola with covers (std O), 05		53
___	17473	NYC PS-5 Gondola "502351" (std O), 06-07		65
___	17474	D&H PS-5 Gondola "13816" (std O), 06-07		65
___	17475	Koppers PS-5 Gondola "213" (std O), 06-07		65
___	17477	L&N PS-5 Gondola "170012" (std O), 06-07		46
___	17478	N&W PS-5 Gondola "275005" with containers (std O), 08		70
___	17479	LV PS-5 Gondola "33455" with containers (std O), 08		70
___	17480	RI PS-5 Gondola with coke containers (std O), 08-09		70
___	17488	UP Bathtub Gondola 3-pack (std O), 09		190
___	17500	CP Flatcar with logs (std O), 89	22	37
___	17501	Conrail Flatcar with stakes (std O), 87	37	45
___	17502	Santa Fe Flatcar with trailer (std O), 90	70	75
___	17503	NS Flatcar with trailer (std O), 92	55	65
___	17504	NS Flatcar with trailer (std O), 92	55	65
___	17505	NS Flatcar with trailer (std O), 92	50	55
___	17506	NS Flatcar with trailer (std O), 92	46	55
___	17507	NS Flatcar with trailer (std O), 92	50	55
___	17510	NP Flatcar "61200" with logs (std O), 94	28	35
___	17511	WM Flatcar with logs, set of 3 (std O), 95		145
___	17512	WM Flatcar with logs (std O), 95	35	41
___	17513	WM Flatcar with logs (std O), 95	43	50
___	17514	WM Flatcar with logs (std O), 95	39	45
___	17515	Norfolk Southern Flatcar with tractors (std O), 95	24	42
___	17516	T&P Flatcar "9823" with 2 Beechcraft Bonanzas (std O), 97		50
___	17517	WP Flatcar "9823" with Ertl Caterpillar frontloader (std O), 97		39
___	17518	PRR Flatcar "9823" with 2 Corgi Mack trucks (std O), 97	32	53
___	17522	Flatcar with Plymouth Prowler, 98		41
___	17527	Flatcar with 2 Dodge Vipers, 98		38
___	17529	ATSF Flatcar "90010" with Ford milk truck, 99		55
___	17533	MTTX Ford Flatcar with auto frames, 99		38
___	17534	Diamond T Flatcar with Mack trucks "9823," 99		55
___	17536	Route 66 Flatcar "9823-3" with 2 luxury coupes, 99		37

		Exc	Mint	
17537	Route 66 Flatcar "9823-4" with 2 touring coupes, 99		32	___
17538	NYC Flatcar with Ford tow truck, 99		43	___
17539	Flatcar "9823" with 2 Corvettes (std O), 99		70	___
17540	Flatcar "9823" with 2 Corvettes (std O), 99		70	___
17546	LL Recovery Flatcar "6424" with rail load, 99		50	___
17547	Lionel Lines Recovery Flatcar "6429" with machinery, 99		50	___
17548	Route 66 Flatcar "9823-6" with 2 luxury coupes, 99		42	___
17549	Route 66 Flatcar "9823-5" with station wagon and trailer, 99		42	___
17550	BN Center Beam Flatcar "6216" with lumber (std O), 99		39	___
17551	NYC Flatcar with NYC pickups "499," 99		49	___
17553	Trailer Train Flatcar "98102" with combine (std O), 99		125	___
17554	GN Flatcar "61042" with logs, 00		32	___
17555	Ford Mustang Flatcar with 2 cars (std O), 01		NRS	___
17556	Ford Mustang Flatcar with 2 cars (std O), 01		NRS	___
17557	Route 66 Flatcar "9823-7" with black sedans, 99-00		39	___
17558	Route 66 Flatcar "9823-8" with brown sedans, 99		39	___
17559	Route 66 Flatcar "9823-9" with 2 wagons (std O), 01		40	___
17560	Route 66 Flatcar "9823-10" with 2 sedans (std O), 01		40	___
17563	Santa Fe Flatcar "90011" with pickup trucks (std O), 01		49	___
17564	West Side Lumber Shay Log Car 3-pack #2 (std O), 01		95	___
17568	PRR Flatcar "470333" with pickup trucks (std O), 02		50	___
17571	UP Flatcar "909231" with pickup trucks (std O), 03		50	___
17572	Pioneer Seed Flatcar with pedal cars, 02 u		220	___
17573	WM PS-4 Flatcar "2631" (std O), 03		35	___
17574	Santa Fe PS-4 Flatcar "90081" (std O), 03		35	___
17575	NYC PS-4 Flatcar "506098" (std O), 03		40	___
17576	Ontario Northland PS-4 Flatcar "2020" (std O), 03		35	___
17577	B&O PS-4 Flatcar "8651" (std O), 04		35	___
17578	B&M PS-4 Flatcar "34007" (std O), 04		35	___
17579	Milwaukee Road PS-4 Flatcar "64073" (std O), 04		35	___
17580	UP PS-4 Flatcar "54603" (std O), 04		35	___
17581	GN Flatcar "X4168" with pickup trucks (std O), 04		42	___
17582	PRR PS-4 Flatcar "469617" with trailers (std O), 05		110	___
17583	GN PS-4 Flatcar with trailers, 05	43	90	___
17584	SP PS-4 Flatcar with trailers, 05		80	___
17585	C&O PS-4 Flatcar "81000" with trailers (std O), 05		80	___
17586	BN Husky Stack Car "63322" (std O), 05		80	___
17587	SP Husky Stack Car "513915" (std O), 05		80	___
17588	CSX Husky Stack Car "620350" (std O), 05		80	___
17589	TTX Trailer Train Husky Stack Car "456249" (std O), 05		65	___
17590	Penn Central PS-4 Flatcar w/stakes (std O), 05-06	15	38	___
17600	NYC Wood-sided Caboose (std O), 87 u	35	45	___
17601	Southern Wood-sided Caboose (std O), 88	35	44	___
17602	Conrail Wood-sided Caboose (std O), 87	65	75	___
17603	RI Wood-sided Caboose (std O), 88	19	34	___
17604	Lackawanna Wood-sided Caboose (std O), 88	42	53	___
17605	Reading Wood-sided Caboose (std O), 89	34	37	___
17606	NYC Steel-sided Caboose, smoke (std O), 90	49	65	___
17607	Reading Steel-sided Caboose, smoke (std O), 90	55	65	___
17608	C&O Steel-sided Caboose, smoke (std O), 91	46	55	___
17610	Wabash Steel-sided Caboose, smoke (std O), 91	39	55	___
17611	NYC Wood-sided Caboose "6003" (std O), 90 u	40	55	___
17612	NKP Steel-sided Caboose, smoke (FF 6), 92	60	65	___

			Exc	Mint
___	**17613**	Southern Steel-sided Caboose "7613," smoke (std O), 92	60	65
___	**17615**	NP Wood-sided Caboose, smoke (std O), 92	65	70
___	**17617**	D&RGW Steel-sided Caboose (std O), 95	43	63
___	**17618**	Frisco Wood-sided Caboose (std O), 95	65	75
___	**17620**	NP Wood-sided Caboose "1746," 98		70
___	**17623**	Farmrail Extended Vision Caboose, 99		74
___	**17624**	Conrail Extended Vision Caboose "6900," 99		43
___	**17625**	Burlington Northern Steel-sided Caboose "7606," 99		65
___	**17626**	Service Center Extended Vision Caboose (SSS), 00		29
___	**17627**	C&O Extended Vision Caboose, 01		65
___	**17628**	BNSF Extended Vision Caboose, 01		65
___	**17629**	Santa Fe Extended Vision Caboose, 01		80
___	**17630**	UP Extended Vision Caboose, 01		85
___	**17631**	Virginian Bay Window Caboose, 01		85
___	**17632**	CSX Bay Window Caboose, 01		75
___	**17633**	NYC Bay Window Caboose, 01		90
___	**17634**	Delaware & Hudson Bay Window Caboose, 01		75
___	**17635**	100th Anniversary Die-cast Gold Caboose, 00		345
___	**17636**	NYC Die-cast Caboose "18096," 00-01		100
___	**17637**	NYC "Quicker via Peoria" Die-cast Caboose, 00		135
___	**17638**	RI Extended Vision Caboose "17011" (std O), 02		55
___	**17639**	Chessie Extended Vision Caboose "3322" (std O), 02		55
___	**17640**	CP Extended Vision Caboose "434604" (std O), 02		57
___	**17641**	Soo Line Extended Vision Caboose "2" (std O), 02		55
___	**17642**	Conrail Bay Window Caboose "21023" (std O), 02		65
___	**17643**	NKP Bay Window Caboose "480" (std O), 02		60
___	**17644**	Erie Bay Window Caboose "C307," (std O), 02		55
___	**17645**	N&W Bay Window Caboose "C-6," (std O), 02		55
___	**17646**	UP Bay Window Caboose "24555," (std O), 02		65
___	**17647**	B&O Caboose "C-2820" (std O), 03-04		65
___	**17648**	Chessie System Caboose "C-2800" (std O), 03-04		75
___	**17649**	Lionel Lines Caboose "7649" (std O), 03-04		65
___	**17650**	Rio Grande Extended Vision Caboose "01500" (std O), 03		65
___	**17651**	BN Extended Vision Caboose "10531" (std O), 03-05		80
___	**17652**	NYC Bay Window Caboose "20200" (std O), 03		75
___	**17653**	SP Bay Window Caboose "1337" (std O), 03		65
___	**17654**	Alaska Extended Vision Caboose "989" (std O), 03		75
___	**17655**	WP Bay Window Caboose "448" (std O), 03-04		75
___	**17657**	Norman Rockwell Holiday Caboose, 03		30
___	**17658**	Burlington Extended Vision Caboose "13611" (std O), 04		70
___	**17659**	CN Extended Vision Caboose "79646" (std O), 04	33	85
___	**17660**	Seaboard Extended Vision Caboose "5700" (std O), 04		65
___	**17661**	C&NW Bay Window Caboose "10871" (std O), 04		65
___	**17662**	PC Bay Window Caboose "21001" (std O), 04		65
___	**17663**	Southern Bay Window Caboose "X546" (std O), 04		65
___	**17664**	B&O Caboose "C-2824" (std O), 03-04		65
___	**17665**	Chessie System Caboose "C-2802" (std O), 03-04		75
___	**17669**	NYC Bay Window Caboose, smoke, 05		85
___	**17670**	CP Rail Bay Window Caboose, smoke, 05		85
___	**17671**	BN Extended Vision Caboose, 05		85
___	**17672**	GN Extended Vision Caboose "X-106" (std O), 05		85
___	**17673**	Santa Fe Extended Vision Caboose, 05		85
___	**17674**	Reading Extended Vision Caboose "94119" (std O), 05		75

		Exc	Mint
17675	Rio Grande Extended Vision Caboose "01507" (std O), 06		90 ___
17676	NYC Bay Window Caboose "20300," 07		60 ___
17677	Erie-Lack. Bay Window Caboose "C359" (std O), 06		90 ___
17678	B&O I-12 Caboose "C2421" (std O), 06		90 ___
17679	Long Island Bay Window Caboose "C-62" (std O), 06		90 ___
17682	Reading Northeastern Caboose "92841" (std O), 06-07		85 ___
17683	Chessie System Northeastern Caboose "1893" (std O), 07		85 ___
17684	Conrail Northeastern Caboose "18873" (std O), 07		85 ___
17685	Jersey Central Northeastern Caboose "91533" (std O), 07		85 ___
17687	B&O/Chessie System Smoking Caboose (std O), 05-06	45	92 ___
17690	UP CA-4 Caboose "3826" (std O), 06	21	90 ___
17691	UP CA-4 Caboose "25103" (std O), 06		90 ___
17692	LL CA-4 B22 Caboose "7629" (std O), 06		90 ___
17693	Chessie Extended Vision Caboose "3285" (std O), 06		90 ___
17694	NS Extended Vision Caboose "555582" (std O), 06		90 ___
17695	Alaska I-12 Caboose "1001" (std O), 06		90 ___
17696	CP Bay Window Caboose "437266" (std O), 06		90 ___
17697	CN Extended Vision Caboose "78128" (std O), 06		90 ___
17699	UP CA-4 Caboose "25193" (std O), 07		90 ___
17700	UP ACF 40-ton Stock Car "47456" (std O), 01-02		85 ___
17701	Rio Grande ACF 40-ton Stock Car "39269" (std O), 01-02		60 ___
17702	CP ACF 40-ton Stock Car "277083" (std O), 01-02		75 ___
17703	NYC ACF 40-ton Stock Car "23334" (std O), 01-02		85 ___
17703	Crayola 2-bay Hopper, LionScale, 17-18		70 ___
17704	B&O ACF 40-ton Stock Car "110234" (std O), 02		40 ___
17705	CB&Q ACF 40-ton Stock Car "52886" (std O), 02		40 ___
17707	PRR ARF 40-ton Stock Car "128994" (std O), 03		35 ___
17708	CP Rail ACF 40-ton Stock Car "277313" (std O), 03	12	47 ___
17709	UP Stock Car "48154" (std O), 04		45 ___
17710	Great Northern Stock Car "56385" (std O), 04		40 ___
17711	C&O ACF 40-ton Stock Car "95237" (std O), 06		60 ___
17712	N&W ACF 40-ton Stock Car "33000" (std O), 06		60 ___
17713	MKT ACF 40-ton Stock Car "47150" (std O), 06		60 ___
17714	CN 40-ton Stock Car "172755" (std O), 06		60 ___
17715	MP 40-ton Stock Car "52428" (std O), 06		60 ___
17716	CGW 40-ton Stock Car "838," 08		60 ___
17717	UP 40-ton Stock Car "48217," 08		60 ___
17718	NS Heritage 3-bay Hopper 2-pack (std O), 12		160 ___
17719	C&BQ ACF Stock Car "52925" (std O), 09	30	70 ___
17720	UP ACF Stock Car (std O), 10		70 ___
17721	Postwar Scale Stock Car 2-pack, 10-11		140 ___
17724	CN Scale Steel-sided Reefer "210552," (std O), 11		80 ___
17725	NP Scale Steel-sided Reefer "98528," (std O), 11		80 ___
17726	IC Scale Steel-sided Reefer "16644," (std O), 11		80 ___
17727	Mopac/Wabash Scale Steel-sided Reefer "30790," (std O), 11		80 ___
17729	C&O Scale PS-1 Boxcar "2992" (std O), 12		70 ___
17730	Seaboard Scale Round-roof Boxcar "19293" (std O), 11		70 ___
17731	Pere Marquette Scale Boxcar "81805" (std O), 12		70 ___
17732	L&N Scale PS-1 Boxcar "4798" (std O) , 12		70 ___
17733	PRR Scale Round-roof Boxcar "78948" (std O), 11		70 ___
17734	PRR Scale Round-roof Boxcar "76644" (std O), 11		70 ___
17735	PRR Round-roof DD Boxcar "77851" (std O), 12		70 ___
17736	PRR Round-roof DD Boxcar "60156" (std O), 12		70 ___

___ 17737	N&W Scale Round-roof Boxcar "46494" (std O), 11		70
___ 17738	NP Round-roof DD Boxcar "39300" (std O), 12		70
___ 17739	DT&I Round-roof DD Boxcar "12250" (std O), 12		70
___ 17740	Alaska Scale Round-roof Boxcar "27781" (std O), 11		70
___ 17741	Santa Fe Scale Slogan Reefer 5-car Set (std O), 12		320
___ 17747	Santa Fe Scale Boxcar "39009" (std O), 12		70
___ 17748	Grave's Mortuary Supply Scale PS-1 Boxcar (std O), 12-13		70
___ 17749	Erie Scale PS-1 Boxcar "90300" (std O), 12		70
___ 17750	NYC Round-roof DD Boxcar "77147" (std O), 12		70
___ 17751	NKP Scale PS-1 Boxcar "6605" (std O), 12		70
___ 17752	Polar Round-roof Boxcar "1202" (std O), 12-13, 16-17		70
___ 17753	LV Scale PS-1 Boxcar "65124" (std O), 12		70
___ 17754	EL DD Boxcar "65000" (std O), 12		75
___ 17755	D&H DD Boxcar "25025" (std O), 12		75
___ 17756	CP Rail DD Boxcar "42630" (std O), 12		75
___ 17757	Milwaukee Road DD Boxcar "13441" (std O), 12		75
___ 17758	ATSF Map and Slogan Reefer 3-pack, 12		190
___ 17762	BN 57' Mechanical Reefer "9618" (std O), 12		85
___ 17763	NYC 57' Mechanical Reefer "6762" (std O), 12		85
___ 17764	ATSF 57' Mechanical Reefer "56244" (std O), 12		85
___ 17765	Virginian Round-roof DD Boxcar "3131" (std O), 13-14		80
___ 17766	NH Round-roof Boxcar "39303" (std O), 13		70
___ 17767	SP Round-roof DD Boxcar "166052" (std O), 13-14		80
___ 17768	Grave's Mortuary Supply Round-roof Boxcar (std O), 13		70
___ 17769	D&RGW PS-1 Boxcar "60046" (std O), 13		70
___ 17770	MILW PS-1 Boxcar "8777" (std O), 13		70
___ 17771	CNJ PS-1 Boxcar "23522" (std O), 13-14		80
___ 17772	Central of Georgia PS-1 Boxcar (std O), 13		70
___ 17773	D&M Round-roof Boxcar "3148" (std O), 13-14		80
___ 17774	D&M PS-1 Boxcar "2833" (std O), 13		70
___ 17775	NS Heritage 3-bay Hopper 3-pack (std O), 13-15		240
___ 17779	NS Heritage 3-bay Hopper 3-pack (std O), 13-15		240
___ 17783	NS Heritage 3-bay Hopper 3-pack (std O), 13-15		240
___ 17787	NS Heritage 3-bay Hopper 3-pack (std O), 13		240
___ 17791	NS Heritage 3-bay Hopper 3-pack (std O), 13		240
___ 17795	NS Heritage 3-bay Hopper 3-pack (std O), 13		240
___ 17800	Ontario Northland Ore Car "6126," 00		30
___ 17801	CN Ore Car "345165," 00		37
___ 17802	CP Ore Car "377249," 00		28
___ 17803	DMIR Ore Car "31456," 00		30
___ 17804	UP Ore Car "8023," 01		29
___ 17805	CP Rail Ore Car "377238," 01		29
___ 17806	UP Ore Car "27250," 03		30
___ 17807	BN Ore Car "95887," 02		28
___ 17900	Santa Fe Unibody Tank Car (std O), 90	37	46
___ 17901	Chevron Unibody Tank Car (std O), 90	26	32
___ 17902	NJ Zinc Unibody Tank Car (std O), 91	26	34
___ 17903	Conoco Unibody Tank Car (std O), 91	24	29
___ 17904	Texaco Unibody Tank Car (std O), 92	39	48
___ 17905	Archer Daniels Midland Unibody Tank Car (std O), 92	24	33
___ 17906	SCM Unibody Tank Car "78286" (std O), 93	47	55
___ 17908	Marathon Oil Unibody Tank Car (std O), 95	55	60
___ 17909	Hooker Chemicals Unibody Tank Car (std O), 96	25	55

		Exc	Mint
17910	Sunoco Unibody Tank Car "7900," 97		37 __
17913	J.M. Huber Tank Car, 98		29 __
17914	Englehard Tank Car, 98		36 __
17915	Gulf Unibody Tank Car "8438," 00		43 __
17916	Burlington Unibody Tank Car "130000," 00	24	38 __
17918	Southern Unibody Tank Car, 01		32 __
17919	Koppers Unibody Tank Car, 01		39 __
17924	Safety Kleen Unibody Tank Car "77603" (std O), 02		40 __
17925	Beefmaster Unibody Tank Car "120021" (std O), 02		38 __
17926	Cargill Unibody 1-D Tank Car "5836" (std O), 03		40 __
17927	Union Starch Unibody 1-D Tank Car "59137" (std O), 03		35 __
17928	Merck 1-D Tank Car "25421" (std O), 03		35 __
17929	Wyandotte Chemicals 1-D Tank Car "1325" (std O), 03		34 __
17930	CSX Unibody Tank Car "993369" (std O), 04		35 __
17931	UP Unibody Tank Car "6" (std O), 04		35 __
17932	CIBRO TankTrain Intermediate Car "26263" (std O), 04		35 __
17933	GATX TankTrain Intermediate Car 3-pack (std O), 04		100 __
17946	Candy Cane Unibody Tank Car (std O), 04		60 __
17947	Domino Sugar Unibody Tank Car (std O), 04		50 __
17948	Philadelphia Quartz 1-D Tank Car "806" (std O), 06		55 __
17949	Skelly Oil 1-D Tank Car "2293" (std O), 06		55 __
17950	ADM Unibody Tank Car "19020" (std O), 06		60 __
17951	Cerestar Unibody Tank Car "190177" (std O), 06		60 __
17959	Dow 1-D Tank Car "310101" (std O), 07		55 __
17960	Amaizo 1-D Tank Car "15440" (std O), 07		55 __
17962	Domino Sugar 1-D Tank Car "3008" (std O), 07		60 __
17966	Procor 1-D Tank Car "82607" (std O), 07		60 __
17971	Simonin 1-D Tank Car "9569" (std O), 07		60 __
17972	Union Starch 1-D Tank Car "724" (std O), 08		60 __
17973	UP 1-D Tank Car "907838" (std O), 08		60 __
17975	Cargill Foods Unibody Tank Car 3-pack (std O), 08-09		195 __
17976	Huber Unibody Tank Car 3-pack (std O), 08-09		195 __
17983	GATX TankTrain Intermediate Car 3-pack, 08		195 __
18000	PRR 0-6-0 Locomotive "8977," 89, 91	209	405 __
18001	Rock Island 4-8-4 Locomotive "5100," 87	305	315 __
18002	NYC 4-6-4 Locomotive "785," 87 u	365	421 __
18003	DL&W 4-8-4 Locomotive "1501," 88	187	285 __
18004	Reading 4-6-2 Locomotive "8004," 89	159	205 __
18005	NYC 4-6-4 Locomotive "5340," display case, 90	536	770 __
18006	Reading 4-8-4 Locomotive "2100," 89 u	408	528 __
18007	Southern Pacific 4-8-4 Locomotive "4410," 91	332	383 __
18008	Disneyland 35th Anniversary 4-4-0 Locomotive, display case, 90	266	315 __
18009	NYC 4-8-2 Locomotive "3000," 90 u, 91	373	561 __
18010	PRR 6-8-6 Steam Turbine Locomotive "6200," 91-92	900	1041 __
18010	L&NE AC-2 Covered Hopper 6-pack, 18		360 __
18011	Chessie System 4-8-4 Locomotive "2101," 91	402	527 __
18012	NYC 4-6-4 Locomotive "5340," 90	615	750 __
18013	Disneyland 35th Anniversary 4-4-0 Locomotive, 90	255	296 __
18014	Lionel Lines 2-6-4 Locomotive "8014," 91	145	190 __
18016	Northern Pacific 4-8-4 Locomotive "2626," 92	385	440 __
18018	Southern 2-8-2 Locomotive "4501," 92	523	650 __
18020	N&W AC-2 Covered Hopper 6-pack, 18		360 __
18021	Frisco 2-8-2 Mikado Locomotive, 93	530	640 __

			Exc	Mint
___	18022	Pere Marquette 2-8-4 Locomotive "1201," 93	550	650
___	18023	Western Maryland Shay Locomotive "6," 92	637	1350
___	18024	Sears T&P 4-8-2 Locomotive "907," display case, 92 u	750	790
___	18025	T&P 4-8-2 Locomotive "907," 92 u		640
___	18026	NYC 4-6-4 Dreyfuss Hudson Locomotive, 2-rail, 92 u		2350
___	18027	NYC 4-6-4 Dreyfuss Hudson Locomotive, 3-rail, 93 u		1450
___	18028	Smithsonian PRR 4-6-2 Locomotive "3768," 2-rail, 93 u		2150
___	18029	NYC 4-6-4 Dreyfuss Hudson Locomotive, 3-rail, 93 u	1900	2150
___	18030	Frisco 2-8-2 Locomotive "4100," 93 u	530	625
___	18030	Pere Marquette AC-2 Covered Hopper 6-pack, 18		360
___	18031	2-10-0 Bundesbahn BR-50 Locomotive, 2-rail, 93 u		1500
___	18034	Santa Fe 2-8-2 Locomotive "3158," 94	540	620
___	18035	2-10-0 Reichsbahn BR-50 Locomotive, 2-rail, 93 u		1500
___	18036	2-10-0 French BR-50 Locomotive, 2-rail, 93 u		1500
___	18040	N&W 4-8-4 Locomotive "612," 95	523	710
___	18040	WM AC-2 Covered Hopper 6-pack, 18		360
___	18041	WM AC-2 Covered Hopper "5125," 18		60
___	18042	Boston & Albany 4-6-4 Locomotive "618," 95		250
___	18043	Chesapeake & Ohio 4-6-4 Locomotive "490," 95	580	750
___	18044	Southern 4-6-2 Locomotive "1390," 96		242
___	18045	NYC 4-6-4 Commodore Vanderbilt Locomotive "777," 96	213	678
___	18046	Wabash 4-6-4 Locomotive "700," 96	190	375
___	18049	N&W Warhorse 4-8-4 Locomotive "600," 96		490
___	18050	JCPenney 4-6-2 Pacific Locomotive "2055," 96	235	245
___	18050	Continental Grain ACF 3-Bay Covered Hopper 6-pack, 18		360
___	18051	Continental Grain ACF 3-Bay Covered Hopper "46611," 18		60
___	18052	Pennsylvania Torpedo Locomotive "238E," 97		455
___	18053	LL 2-8-4 Berkshire Locomotive "726," 96-97	310	400
___	18054	NYC 0-4-0 Switcher "1665," black, 97		145
___	18055	Continental Grain ACF 3-Bay Covered Hopper "46615," 18		60
___	18056	NYC J1-e Hudson Locomotive "763E," Vanderbilt tender, 97	343	603
___	18057	PRR 6-8-6 Turbine Locomotive "671," 96-98	280	450
___	18058	NYC 4-6-4 Hudson Locomotive "773," 96-97	300	550
___	18060	PRR ACF 3-Bay Covered Hopper 6-pack, 18		360
___	18062	ATSF 4-6-4 Hudson Locomotive "3447," 97		680
___	18063	NYC 4-6-4 Commodore Vanderbilt Locomotive, 99	475	952
___	18064	NYC 4-8-2 Mohawk L-3A Locomotive "3005," tender, 98	275	450
___	18067	NYC Weathered Commodore Vanderbilt Scale Hudson, 97		840
___	18068	PRR S2 Steam Tender, 99	145	250
___	18070	Tenneco ACF 3-Bay Covered Hopper 6-pack, 18		360
___	18071	SP Daylight Locomotive "4449," 98		680
___	18072	Lionel Lines Torpedo Locomotive, tender, 98		360
___	18079	NYC 2-8-2 Mikado Locomotive "1967," 99		710
___	18080	D&RGW 2-8-2 Mikado Locomotive "1210," 99		720
___	18080	BN ACF 3-Bay Covered Hopper 6-pack, 18		360
___	18082	NYC 4-6-4 Hudson Locomotive "5404," 99		230
___	18083	C&O 4-6-4 Hudson Locomotive "305," 99		205
___	18084	Santa Fe 4-6-4 Hudson Locomotive "305," 99		225
___	18085	NH 4-6-2 Pacific Locomotive "1334," 99		275
___	18086	NYC 4-6-2 Pacific Locomotive "4929," 99		235
___	18087	Santa Fe 4-6-2 Pacific Locomotive "3448," 99		265
___	18088	SP 4-6-2 Pacific Locomotive "1407," 99		350
___	18089	CNJ 4-6-0 Camelback Locomotive "771," 99		405

MODERN 1970-2023		Exc	Mint
18090	Vesuvius Crucible PS-1 Boxcar 6-pack, 18		360 ___
18091	PRR 4-6-0 Camelback Locomotive "821," 99		405 ___
18092	SP 4-6-0 Camelback Locomotive "2283," 99	113	395 ___
18093	C&NW 4-6-0 Camelback Locomotive "3006," 99		285 ___
18094	B&O 4-4-2 E6 Atlantic Locomotive, CC, 99-00		345 ___
18095	PRR 4-4-2 E6 Atlantic Locomotive, CC, 99-00	275	455 ___
18096	ATSF 4-4-2 E6 Atlantic Locomotive, CC, 99-00		370 ___
18097	CNJ 4-6-0 Camelback Locomotive "770," 99		330 ___
18098	PRR 4-6-0 Camelback Locomotive "820," 99		355 ___
18099	SP 4-6-0 Camelback Locomotive "2282," 99		360 ___
18100	Santa Fe F3 Diesel A Unit "8100," powered, 91		300 ___
18100	EJ&E PS-1 Boxcar 6-pack, 18		360 ___
18101	Santa Fe F3 Diesel B Unit "8101," powered, 91		250 ___
18102	Santa Fe F3 Diesel A Unit "8102," unpowered, 91		200 ___
18103	Santa Fe F3 Diesel B Unit "8103," unpowered, 91 u	180	190 ___
18104	GN F3 Diesel A Unit "366A," powered, 92		500 ___
18105	GN F3 Diesel B Unit "370B," unpowered, 92		220 ___
18106	GN F3 Diesel A Unit "351C," unpowered, 92		260 ___
18107	D&RGW Alco PA1 Diesel ABA Set, 92	445	740 ___
18108	GN F3 Diesel B Unit "371B," 93	85	105 ___
18109	Erie Alco Diesel A Unit "725A," powered, 93		250 ___
18110	Erie Alco Diesel B Unit "725B," unpowered, 93		160 ___
18110	Monon PS-1 Boxcar 6-pack, 18		360 ___
18111	Erie Alco Diesel A Unit "736A," unpowered, 93		170 ___
18115	Santa Fe F3 Diesel B Unit, 93	90	115 ___
18116	Erie-Lackawanna Alco PA1 Diesel AA Set, 93	450	490 ___
18117	ATSF F3 Diesel A Unit, powered, 93		375 ___
18117/18	ATSF F3 Diesel AA Set "200," 93	330	510 ___
18118	ATSF F3 Diesel A Unit, unpowered, 93		200 ___
18119	UP Alco FA-2 Diesel A Unit powered, 94	150	300 ___
18119/20	UP Alco FA-2 Diesel AA Set, 94	200	350 ___
18120	UP Alco FA-2 Diesel A Unit, unpowered, 94		120 ___
18120	Rutland PS-1 Boxcar 6-pack, 18		360 ___
18121	Santa Fe F3 Diesel B Unit "200A," 94	75	95 ___
18122	Santa Fe F3 Diesel B Unit "200B," 95	140	150 ___
18123	ACL F3 Diesel A Unit "342," powered, 96		250 ___
18124	ACL F3 Diesel B Unit "342B," unpowered, 96		185 ___
18125	ACL F3 Diesel A Unit "343," unpowered, 96		190 ___
18128	Santa Fe F3 Diesel A Unit "2343," 96		435 ___
18129	Santa Fe F3 Diesel B Unit "2343C," 96		245 ___
18130	Santa Fe F3 Diesel AB Set, 96	198	600 ___
18130	NYC AAR 3-Bay Hopper 6-pack, 18		360 ___
18131	NP F3 Diesel AB Set, "2390A, 2390C," 97	323	480 ___
18132	NP F3 Diesel A Unit, powered		300 ___
18133	NP F3 Diesel B Unit, dummy		150 ___
18134	Santa Fe F3 Diesel A Unit "2343," dummy, 97		195 ___
18135	NYC F3 AA Diesel Set "2333," 99		650 ___
18135	NYC F3 Diesel AA Set "2333," 96-99	300	520 ___
18136	Santa Fe F3 Diesel B Unit "2343C," 97	135	240 ___
18138	Milwaukee Road F3 Diesel A Unit "75A," 98		400 ___
18139	Milwaukee Road F3 Diesel B Unit "2378B," 98		250 ___
18140	Milwaukee Road F3 Diesel AB Set, 98	380	600 ___
18140	Nickel Plate Road AAR 3-Bay Hopper 6-pack, 18		360 ___

	MODERN 1970-2023	Exc	Mint
___	18145 NP F3 Diesel A Unit "2390A," powered, 97	300	360
___	18146 NP F3 Diesel B Unit "2390C," 97		170
___	18147 NP F3 Diesel AB Set, 97	438	580
___	18149 UP Veranda Gas Turbine Locomotive "61," 98	860	900
___	18150 LG Everist AAR 3-Bay Hopper 6-pack, 18		360
___	18154 Deluxe Santa Fe FT Diesel AA Set, 98-00		375
___	18155 Deluxe Santa Fe FT Diesel A Unit, powered, 98-00		200
___	18156 Deluxe Santa Fe FT Diesel A Unit, unpowered, 98-00		160
___	18157 Santa Fe FT Diesel AA Set, 98-00		240
___	18158 Santa Fe FT Diesel A Unit, powered, 98-00		220
___	18159 Santa Fe FT Diesel A Unit, unpowered, 98-00		120
___	18160 NYC Deluxe FT Diesel AA Set, "1602"/"1603," 98-00		500
___	18160 UP AAR 3-Bay Hopper 6-pack, 18		360
___	18161 NYC Deluxe FT Diesel A Unit "1603," powered, 98-00		350
___	18162 NYC Deluxe FT Diesel A Unit "1602," unpowered, 98-00		120
___	18163 NYC FT Diesel AA Set, "1600, 2400," 98-00		300
___	18164 NYC FT Diesel A Unit "1600," powered, 98-00		200
___	18165 NYC FT Diesel A Unit "2400," unpowered, 98-00		110
___	18166 B&O FT Diesel AA Set, CC, 99-00		340
___	18167 B&O FT Diesel A Unit "8167," CC, 99-00		230
___	18168 B&O FT Diesel A Unit "8168," unpowered, 99-00		110
___	18169 B&O FT Diesel AA Set, traditional, 99-00		240
___	18170 B&O FT Diesel A Unit, traditional, 99-00		140
___	18171 B&O FT Diesel A Unit, unpowered, 99-00		90
___	18178 NYC F3 Diesel B Unit, unpowered, 99		275
___	18189 Army of Potomac Operating Stock Car, 99		45
___	18190 McNeil's Rangers Operating Stock Car "2," 99		45
___	18191 WP F3 Diesel AA Set, 98	153	570
___	18192 WP F3 Diesel A Unit, powered, 98		485
___	18193 WP F3 Diesel A Unit, unpowered, 98		495
___	18194 EL F3 Diesel AB Set, 99		450
___	18195 EL F3 Diesel A Unit "7091," powered, 99		300
___	18196 EL F3 B Unit, nonpowered, 99		150
___	18197 WP F3 Diesel B Unit "2355C," 99	88	255
___	18198 WP F3 Diesel B Unit "2345C" CC, 99		360
___	18200 Conrail SD40 Diesel "8200," 87	180	200
___	18201 Chessie System SD40 Diesel "8201," 88	245	340
___	18202 Erie-Lack. SD40 Diesel Unit "8459," dummy, 89 u	90	140
___	18203 CP Rail SD40 Diesel "8203," 89	195	250
___	18204 Chessie SD40 Diesel Unit "8204," dummy, 90 u	135	190
___	18205 Union Pacific Dash 8-40C Diesel "9100," 89	275	335
___	18206 Santa Fe Dash 8-40B Diesel "8206," 90	195	293
___	18207 Norfolk Southern Dash 8-40C Diesel "8689," 92	230	270
___	18208 BN SD40 Diesel Dummy Unit "8586," 91 u	115	165
___	18209 CP Rail SD40 Diesel Dummy Unit "8209," 92 u	135	165
___	18210 Illinois Central SD40 "6006," 93	220	250
___	18210 Northwestern Refrigerated Wood-sided Refrigerator Car 6-pack, 18		360
___	18211 Susquehanna Dash 8-40B Diesel "4002," 93	145	165
___	18212 Santa Fe Dash 8-40B Diesel Dummy Unit "8212," 93	155	180
___	18213 Norfolk Southern Dash 8-40C Diesel "8688," 94	225	240
___	18214 CSX Dash 8-40C Diesel "7500," 94	235	255
___	18215 CSX Dash 8-40C Diesel "7643," 94	240	260
___	18216 Conrail SD-60M Diesel "5500," 94	355	380

		Exc	Mint	
18217	Illinois Central SD40 Diesel "6007," 94	170	175	
18218	Susquehanna Dash 8-40B Diesel "4004," 94	205	225	
18219	C&NW Dash 8-40C Diesel "8501," 95	325	330	
18220	C&NW Dash 8-40C Diesel "8502," 95	215	315	
18220	PFE Wood-sided Refrigerator Car 6-pack, 18		360	
18221	D&RGW SD50 Diesel "5512," 95	455	520	
18222	D&RGW SD50 Diesel "5517," 95	280	325	
18223	Milwaukee Road SD40 Diesel "154," 95	375	380	
18224	Milwaukee Road SD40 Diesel "155," 95	190	265	
18226	GE Dash 9 Diesel, 97		295	
18228	SP Dash 9 Diesel "8228," gray with red nose, 97		340	
18229	SP SD40 Diesel "7333," 98	300	425	
18230	Swift Wood-sided Refrigerator Car 6-pack, 18		360	
18231	BNSF Dash 9 Diesel "739," 98		435	
18232	Soo Line SD60 Diesel "5500," 97		350	
18233	BNSF Dash 9 Diesel "745," 98		330	
18234	BNSF Dash 9 Diesel "740," CC, 98-99		405	
18235	BNSF Dash 9 Diesel 2-pack, "739, 740," 98		710	
18238	Conrail SD70 Diesel "4145," 99-00		300	
18239	SP SD40 Diesel "7340," 98		300	
18240	Conrail Dash 8-40B Diesel "5065" CC, 98		260	
18240	Rath Wood-sided Refrigerator Car 6-pack, 18		360	
18241	BN SD70 Diesel "9413," 99-00		345	
18245	PRR Alco PA1 Diesel AA Set, 99		495	
18246	PRR Alco PA1 Diesel A Unit "5750A," powered, 99		350	
18247	PRR Alco PA-1 A Unit, unpowered, 99		240	
18248	PRR Alco PB-1 Diesel "5750B," 99		215	
18249	Erie Alco PB-1 Diesel "850B," 00		250	
18250	BNSF SD70 Diesel "9870," 99-00		365	
18251	CSX SD60 Diesel "8701," 99-00		300	
18252	Amtrak Dash 9 Diesel, CC, 99		285	
18253	BNSF Dash 9 Diesel, CC, 99		305	
18254	ATSF Dash 9 Diesel, CC, 99		340	
18255	NS Dash 9 Diesel, CC, 99		315	
18256	Amtrak Dash 9 Diesel, traditional, 99		200	
18257	BNSF Dash 9 Diesel, traditional, 99		190	
18258	ATSF Dash 9 Diesel, traditional, 99		205	
18259	NS Dash 9 Diesel, traditional, 99		215	
18260	Conrail SD70 Diesel "4144," 99-00		280	
18261	BN SD60 Diesel "9412," 99-00		255	
18262	BNSF SD70 Diesel "9869," 99-00		250	
18263	CSX SD60 Diesel "8700," 99-00		255	
18264	Southern Pacific SD70M Diesel "8238," 99-00		245	
18265	Southern Pacific SD70M Diesel "9803," 99-00		340	
18266	Norfolk Southern SD60 Diesel "6552," CC, 01-02		400	
18268	Lionel Centennial SD90MAC Diesel, CC, 00		428	
18269	UP SD90MAC Diesel "8006," CC, 00		405	
18270	UP SD90MAC Diesel "8004," traditional, 00		330	
18271	CP SD90MAC Diesel "9129," CC, 00		440	
18272	CP SD90MAC Diesel "9127," traditional, 00		330	
18273	UP SD40 Diesel "8071," 99-00		330	
18274	Burlington U30C Diesel "891," CC, 01		370	
18276	Seaboard U30C Diesel "7274," CC, 01		325	
18278	UP U30C Diesel "2938," CC, 01		330	

| --- | --- | --- | --- |
____ 18280	Maersk SD70 Diesel, CC, 00		345
____ 18281	BNSF Dash 9-44CW Diesel "788," CC, 00		340
____ 18282	BNSF Dash 9-44CW Diesel "789," traditional, 00		225
____ 18283	CSX Dash 9-44CW Diesel "9019," CC, 00		340
____ 18284	CSX Dash 9-44CW Diesel "9020," traditional, 00		300
____ 18285	UP Dash 9-44C Diesel "9659," CC, 01		325
____ 18286	UP Dash 9-44CW Diesel "9717," CC, 01		355
____ 18287	CN Dash 9-44C Diesel "2529," CC, 01		460
____ 18288	Odyssey System SD70 Diesel, CC, 00 u		400
____ 18289	CN Dash 9-44C Diesel "2528," traditional, 01		220
____ 18290	Amtrak Dash 8-32BWH Diesel "509," CC, 01		325
____ 18291	BNSF Dash 8-32BWH Diesel "580," CC, 02		340
____ 18292	Chessie GE U30C Diesel "3312," CC, 02		340
____ 18293	Santa Fe U30C Diesel, CC, 03		395
____ 18294	Alaska SD70MAC Diesel "4005," CC, 01-02		435
____ 18295	Conrail SD80MAC Diesel "7200," CC, 02-03		365
____ 18296	CSX SD80MAC Diesel "801," CC, 02-03		405
____ 18297	NYC SD80MAC Diesel "9914," CC, 02-03		405
____ 18298	UP "Desert Victory" SD40-2 Diesel "3593," CC, 02-03		380
____ 18299	CP Rail SD40-2 Diesel "5420," CC, 02-03		375
____ 18300	PRR GG1 Electric Locomotive "8300," 87	285	335
____ 18301	Southern FM Train Master Diesel "8301," 88	150	204
____ 18302	GN EP-5 Electric Locomotive "8302" (FF 3), 88	170	260
____ 18303	Amtrak GG1 Electric Locomotive "8303," 89	275	338
____ 18304	Lackawanna MU Commuter Car Set, 91	278	435
____ 18305	Lackawanna MU Commuter Car Dummy Set, 92	230	255
____ 18306	PRR MU Commuter Car Set, 92	218	330
____ 18307	PRR FM Train Master Diesel "8699," 94	170	202
____ 18308	PRR GG1 Electric Locomotive "4866," 92	193	264
____ 18309	Reading FM Train Master Diesel "863," 93	173	212
____ 18310	PRR MU Commuter Car Dummy Set, 93	265	345
____ 18311	Disney EP-5 Electric Locomotive "8311," 94	303	412
____ 18313	Pennsylvania GG1 Electric Locomotive "4907," 96	103	280
____ 18314	PRR GG1 Electric Locomotive "2332," 5 gold stripes, 97	300	507
____ 18315	Virginian E33 Electric Locomotive "2329," 97		240
____ 18319	New Haven EP-5 Electric Locomotive, 99	200	365
____ 18321	CNJ Train Master Diesel "2341," 99		405
____ 18322	Lackawanna Train Master Diesel "2321," 99	150	465
____ 18323	Amtrak HHP-8 Diesel "656F," CC, 09		500
____ 18326	PRR Congressional GG1 Electric Locomotive, 00		600
____ 18327	Virginian FM Train Master Diesel "2331," 99-00		410
____ 18328	NH MU Commuter Car Set, CC, 00		385
____ 18329	NH MU Commuter Car "4082," powered, 00		240
____ 18330	NH MU Commuter Car "4083," unpowered, 00		140
____ 18331	Reading MU Commuter Car Set, CC, 00		460
____ 18332	Reading MU Commuter Car "9109," powered, 00		340
____ 18333	Reading MU Commuter Car "9110," unpowered		140
____ 18334	NH MU Commuter Car Set, unpowered, 01		180
____ 18335	NH MU Commuter Car "4084," unpowered, 01		90
____ 18336	NH MU Commuter Car "4085," unpowered, 01		90
____ 18337	Reading MU Commuter Car Set, unpowered, 01		200
____ 18338	Reading MU Commuter Car "9111," unpowered, 01		100
____ 18339	Reading MU Commuter Car "9112," unpowered, 01		100

		Exc	Mint	
18340	Train Master Demonstrator AA Set, CC, 00		650	___
18341	Train Master Demonstrator A Unit "TM-1," CC, 00		350	___
18342	Train Master Demonstrator A Unit "TM-2," CC, 00		350	___
18343	PRR GG1 Electric Locomotive "2332," CC, 01		610	___
18344	LIRR MU Commuter Car Set, CC, 01		470	___
18345	LIRR MU Commuter Car "1163," CC, 01		360	___
18346	LIRR MU Commuter Car "1163," unpowered, 01		120	___
18347	IC MU Commuter Car Set, CC, 01		470	___
18348	IC MU Commuter Car "1204," CC, 01		360	___
18349	IC MU Commuter Car "1204," unpowered, 01		120	___
18350	Archive No. 2350 NH EP-5 electric, 01		375	___
18351	NYC S1 Electric Locomotive, 03		400	___
18352	JCPenney SP MU Commuter Car, display case, 02		140	___
18353	Pennsylvania E33 Electric Locomotive "4403," CC, 02		280	___
18354	PRR GG1 Electric Locomotive "4918," tuscan, CC, 04		790	___
18355	PRR GG1 Electric Locomotive "4876," green, CC, 04		900	___
18356	Penn Central GG1 Electric Locomotive "4901," CC, 04		1050	___
18357	Amtrak Acela Power Unit "2026," CC, 04-05		530	___
18358	Amtrak Acela Power Unit "2029," unpowered, 04-05		270	___
18359	PRR GG1 Electric Locomotive "2360," CC, 04		430	___
18360	New York City R27 Subway Power Unit "8026," CC, 06-07		220	___
18361	New York City R27 Subway Power Unit "8027," unpowered, 04		120	___
18362	New York City R27 Subway Power Unit "8028," unpowered, 06-07		120	___
18363	New York City R27 Subway End Car "8029," unpowered, 06-07		120	___
18364	PRR BB1 Electric Locomotive Set "3900, 3901," CC, 05-07		530	___
18365	PRR BB1 Electric Locomotive "3900," CC, 05-07		370	___
18366	PRR BB1 Electric Locomotive "3901," unpowered, 05-07		160	___
18367	LIRR BB3 Electric Locomotive Set "328A, 329B," CC, 05		530	___
18368	LIRR BB3 Electric Locomotive "328 A," CC, 05		360	___
18369	LIRR BB3 Electric Locomotive "329B," unpowered, 05		160	___
18370	Postwar Virginian Train Master Diesel "2331," CC, 05-07		340	___
18371	PRR GG1 Electric "4912," Tuscan, 5 stripes, CC, 05-07		780	___
18372	PRR GG1 Electric "4925," green, 1 stripe, CC, 05-07		780	___
18373	NYC S2 Electric Locomotive "125," CC, 05-07		410	___
18374	PRR GG1 Electric Locomotive "4866," silver, CC, 06-08		900	___
18375	Lackawanna FM Train Master Diesel "850," CC, 06		400	___
18376	Lackawanna FM Train Master "851," nonpowered (std O), 06		130	___
18378	New York City R27 Subway Car 2-pack, 07		360	___
18379	New York City R27 Subway Car "8030," unpowered, 06-07		100	___
18380	New York City R27 Subway Car "8031," unpowered, 06-07		100	___
18381	PRR BB1 Electric Locomotive "4751," CC, 06		500	___
18383	Postwar GN EP-5 Electric "2358," CC, 06-08		740	___
18384	MILW EP-2 Electric Locomotive, CC, 07-08		950	___
18385	NYC H-16-44 Diesel "7001," 07-09		202	___
18386	NYC H-16-44 Diesel "7002," nonpowered (std O), 07-09		123	___
18388	CNJ Train Master Diesel "2341," CC, 08-09		500	___
18389	MILW EP-2 Electric Locomotive "E-1," CC, 07-08		950	___
18399	NH EF-4 Rectifier Locomotive "306," CC, 09		360	___
18400	Santa Fe Vulcan Rotary Snowplow "8400," 87	135	170	___
18401	Workmen Handcar, 87-88	30	37	___
18402	Lionel Lines Burro Crane, 88	65	87	___
18403	Santa Claus Handcar, 88	26	29	___

			Exc	Mint
___	18404	San Francisco Trolley "8404," 88	55	85
___	18405	Santa Fe Burro Crane, 89	70	83
___	18406	Track Maintenance Car, 89, 91	34	49
___	18407	Snoopy and Woodstock Handcar, 90-91	91	108
___	18408	Santa Claus Handcar, 89	26	35
___	18410	PRR Burro Crane, 90	100	115
___	18411	Canadian Pacific Fire Car, 90	70	98
___	18412	UP Fire Car, 91	70	100
___	18413	Charlie Brown and Lucy Handcar, 91	40	61
___	18416	Bugs Bunny and Daffy Duck Handcar, 92-93	123	174
___	18417	Section Gang Car, 93	65	80
___	18419	Lionelville Electric Trolley "8419," 94	75	90
___	18421	Sylvester and Tweety Handcar, 94	44	50
___	18422	Santa and Snowman Handcar, 94	32	37
___	18423	On-track Step Van, 95	23	28
___	18424	On-track Pickup Truck, 95	20	32
___	18425	Goofy and Pluto Handcar, 95	45	58
___	18426	Santa and Snowman Handcar, 95	25	30
___	18427	Tie-Jector Car "55," 97		60
___	18429	Workmen Handcar, 96	28	34
___	18430	Crew Car, 96		28
___	18431	Trolley Car, 96-97		46
___	18433	Mickey and Minnie Handcar, 96-97	48	87
___	18434	Porky and Petunia Handcar, 96		35
___	18436	Dodge Ram Track Inspection Vehicle, 97		39
___	18438	PRR High-rail Inspection Vehicle, 98		50
___	18439	Union Pacific High-rail Inspection Vehicle, 98		42
___	18440	NJ Transit High-rail Inspection Vehicle, 98		50
___	18444	Lionelville Fire Car (SSS), 98		150
___	18445	NYC Fire Car, 98		90
___	18446	Postwar "58" GN Rotary Snowplow, 99		181
___	18447	Executive Inspection Vehicle, 99		125
___	18452	Boston Trolley "3321," 99-00		65
___	18454	Executive Inspection Vehicle, blue, 00	48	118
___	18455	NYC Tie-Jector Car "X-2," 00-01		74
___	18456	Postwar "59" Minuteman Motorized Unit, 01-02		290
___	18457	Postwar "65" Handcar, 00-01		45
___	18458	Postwar "53" D&RGW Snowplow, 00		160
___	18459	Christmas Handcar, 01		35
___	18461	Track Cleaning Car, 02-03		90
___	18463	Hot Rod Inspection Vehicle, 01-02		100
___	18464	Postwar "54" Track Ballast Tamper, 02-03		170
___	18465	Postwar "50" Gang Car, 03		78
___	18466	UP Rotary Snow Plow, 01-02		150
___	18467	Train Robbery Handcar, 02		45
___	18468	CN Railroad Speeder, 03-04		49
___	18469	Chessie System Railroad Speeder, 03-04		49
___	18470	Postwar "52" Fire Car, 02		105
___	18471	UP GP20 Diesel "1977," 03		105
___	18473	Lehigh Valley GP38 Diesel "310," 03		160
___	18474	Postwar "41" U.S. Army Switcher, 03-04		145
___	18475	Toy Story Handcar, 03		55
___	18476	Mickey and Minnie Mouse Handcar, 03-04	30	60

		Exc	Mint	
18477	UP Burro Crane "MOW 10166," 03		95	___
18479	Postwar "45" USMC Mobile Missile Launcher, 03-04		125	___
18480	Hobo Motorized Handcar, 03-04		35	___
18481	Christmas Yuletide Trolley, 03		50	___
18482	New Haven Rail Bonder "16," 04		35	___
18483	C&O Ballast Tamper "48," 04		55	___
18484	NS Dodge Inspection Vehicle, 04-05		55	___
18485	NYC Gang Car, 04-05		100	___
18486	Donald and Daisy Duck Handcar, 04-05		63	___
18487	Postwar "56" M&StL Mine Transport Car, 04-05		230	___
18488	CP Rotary Snow Plow, 03-05		160	___
18489	Great Northern Rail Bonder "HR-73," 04		35	___
18490	UP Ballast Tamper, 04-05		150	___
18491	MOW Ballast Tamper "325," 04		44	___
18492	MOW Rail Bonder "58," 04		35	___
18493	Santa's Speeder, 05		60	___
18497	N&W Speeder "541005," traditional, 05		65	___
18498	New York Central Rotary Snowplow, 05		210	___
18500	Milwaukee Road GP9 Diesel "8500" (FF 2), 87	155	198	___
18501	WM NW2 Switcher "8501" (FF 4), 89	185	215	___
18502	LL 90th Anniversary GP9 Diesel "1900," 90	148	173	___
18503	Southern Pacific NW2 Switcher "8503," 90	250	280	___
18504	Frisco GP7 Diesel "504" (FF 5), 91	155	240	___
18505	NKP GP7 Diesel Set "400, 401" (FF 6)	295	365	___
18506	CN Budd RDC Set, "D202, D203"	180	261	___
18507	CN Budd RDC Baggage Car "D202," powered, 92	50	75	___
18508	CN Budd RDC Passenger Dummy Unit "D203," 92	125	150	___
18510	CN Budd RDC Passenger Dummy Unit "D200"	50	75	___
18511	CN Budd RDC Passenger Dummy Unit "D250"	50	75	___
18512	CN Budd RDC Dummy Set, "D200, D250," 93	125	195	___
18513	NYC GP7 Diesel "7420," 94	90	125	___
18514	Missouri Pacific GP7 Diesel "4124," 95	245	310	___
18515	Lionel Steel Vulcan Diesel "57" (SSS), 96		190	___
18516	Phantom III Locomotive, CC, 02		345	___
18517	Phantom IV Locomotive, CC, 08		390	___
18550	JCPenney MILW GP9 Diesel "8500," display case, 87 u	180	245	___
18551	JCPenney Susquehanna RS3 Diesel "8809," display case, 89 u	180	195	___
18552	JCPenney DM&IR SD18 Diesel "8813," display case, 90 u	170	195	___
18553	Sears UP GP9 Diesel "150," display case, 91 u	100	150	___
18554	JCPenney GM&O RS3 "721," display case, 92-93 u	160	180	___
18555	Sears C&IM SD9 Diesel "52," 92 u	165	190	___
18556	Sears Chicago & Illinois Midland Freight Car Set, 92 u	110	120	___
18557	Chessie System 4-8-4 Locomotive "2101," display case, export, 92 u		NRS	___
18558	JCPenney MKT GP9 Diesel "91," display case, 94 u	160	180	___
18562	SP GP9 Diesel "2380," 96		195	___
18563	NYC GP9 Diesel "2380," 96		230	___
18564	CP GP9 Diesel "2380," 97		265	___
18565	Milwaukee Road GP9 Diesel "2338," 97	93	220	___
18566	CR SD20 Diesel "8495" (SSS), 97		150	___
18567	PRR GP9 Diesel "2028," 97		225	___
18569	CB&Q GP9 Diesel "2380," 98		190	___
18570	B&M GP7 Diesel "2380," CC, 98		190	___

|---|---|---|---|
18571	B&M GP7 Diesel "2381," unpowered, 98		135
18572	B&M GP7 Diesel "2389," CC, 98		190
18573	Santa Fe GP9 Diesel "2380," 98	49	155
18574	Milwaukee Road GP20 Diesel "975," 98	110	270
18575	Custom Series GP9 Diesel "2398," 98		350
18576	SP GP9 Diesel B Unit "2385," nonpowered, 98		135
18577	NYC GP9 Diesel B Unit "2385," nonpowered, 98		145
18578	NYC Ballast Tamper "8578," 98		150
18579	MILW GP9 Diesel "2384," nonpowered, 99		135
18580	Pennsylvania GP9 Diesel B Unit "2027," 98		165
18582	Seaboard NW2 Switcher, 98	250	455
18583	AEC Switcher "57," 98	75	214
18585	Centennial SD40 Diesel, 99		450
18587	NKP Alco C420 Switcher "577," CC, 99-01	215	255
18588	D&H Alco C420 Switcher "412," CC, 99-01	250	275
18589	LV Alco C420 Switcher "409," CC, 99-01	255	300
18590	NKP Alco C420 Switcher "578," traditional, 99-01		170
18591	D&H Alco C420 Switcher "411," traditional, 99-01		215
18592	LV Alco C420 Switcher "410," traditional, 99-01		175
18594	Farmrail GP7 Diesel "8252," traditional, 99		155
18595	D&H RS-11 Diesel "5002," traditional, 99-00		160
18596	D&H Alco RS-11 Diesel "5001," CC, 99-01		370
18597	NYC RS-11 Diesel "8011," traditional, 99-00		160
18598	NYC Alco RS-11 Switcher "8010," CC, 99-01		380
18599	C&O GP38 Diesel "3855," 99-00		145
18600	ACL 4-4-2 Locomotive "8600," 87 u	65	75
18601	Great Northern 4-4-2 Locomotive "8601," 88	80	95
18602	PRR 4-4-2 Locomotive "8602," 87	75	85
18604	Wabash 4-4-2 Locomotive "8604," 88-91	65	75
18605	Mopar Express 4-4-2 Locomotive "1987," 87-88 u	75	120
18606	NYC 2-6-4 Locomotive "8606," 89	170	190
18607	Union Pacific 2-6-4 Locomotive "8607," 89	130	155
18608	D&RGW 2-6-4 Locomotive "8608" (SSS), 89	90	105
18609	Northern Pacific 2-6-4 Locomotive "8609," 90	170	195
18610	Rock Island 0-4-0 Locomotive "8610," 90	105	115
18611	Lionel Lines 2-6-4 Locomotive (SSS), 90	125	140
18612	C&NW 4-4-2 Locomotive "8612," 89	75	100
18613	NYC 4-4-2 Locomotive "8613," 89 u	75	95
18614	Circus Train 4-4-2 Locomotive "1989," 89 u	95	125
18615	GTW 4-4-2 Locomotive "8615," 90	70	85
18616	Northern Pacific 4-4-2 Locomotive "8616," 90 u	85	110
18617	Adolphus III 4-4-2 Locomotive, 89-92 u	100	125
18618	B&O 4-4-2 Atlantic Locomotive, 91	105	125
18620	Illinois Central 2-6-2 Locomotive "8620," 91	165	190
18622	Union Pacific 4-4-2 Locomotive "8622," 90-91 u	65	80
18623	Texas & Pacific 4-4-2 Locomotive "8623," 92	80	110
18625	Illinois Central 4-4-2 Locomotive "8625," 91 u	70	95
18626	Delaware & Hudson 2-6-2 Locomotive "8626," 92	105	115
18627	C&O 4-4-2 Locomotive "8627" or "8633," 92, 93 u, 94, 95 u	75	95
18628	MKT 4-4-2 Locomotive "8628," 92, 93 u	70	85
18630	C&NW 4-6-2 Locomotive "2903," 93	325	370
18632	NYC 4-4-2 Locomotive "8632," 93-95	75	95
18632	C&O 4-4-2 Locomotive "8632," 97-99	75	95

		Exc	Mint	
18633	C&O 4-4-2 Locomotive "8633," 94-95	65	85	___
18633	UP 4-4-2 Locomotive "8633," 93-95	65	85	___
18635	Santa Fe 2-6-4 Locomotive "8625," 93	135	155	___
18636	B&O 4-6-2 Locomotive "5300," 94	295	315	___
18637	United Auto Workers 4-4-2 Locomotive "8633," 93 u		90	___
18638	Norfolk & Western 2-6-4 Locomotive "638," 94	170	220	___
18639	Reading 4-6-2 Locomotive "639," 95	145	170	___
18640	Union Pacific 4-6-2 Locomotive "8640," 95	110	130	___
18641	Ford 4-4-2 Locomotive "8641," 94 u	65	85	___
18642	Lionel Lines 4-6-2 Locomotive, 95	110	130	___
18644	ATSF 4-4-2 Locomotive "8644," 96-99	75	90	___
18648	Sears Zenith 4-4-2 Locomotive "8632," 96 u		140	___
18649	Chevrolet 4-4-2 Locomotive "USA-1," 96 u		150	___
18650	LL 4-4-2 Locomotive "X-1110," 96-99	95	120	___
18653	B&A 4-6-2 Pacific Locomotive "2044," 97		140	___
18654	SP 4-6-2 Pacific Locomotive "2044," 97		140	___
18656	Bloomingdale's 4-4-2 Locomotive "8632," 96		112	___
18657	Sears Zenith 4-4-2 Locomotive "8632," 96		120	___
18658	LL Little League 4-4-2 Locomotive "X-1110," 97		90	___
18660	CN 4-6-2 Locomotive "2044," tender, 98		175	___
18661	N&W 4-6-2 Locomotive "2044," tender, 98		160	___
18662	Pennsylvania 0-4-0 Switcher, 98	165	230	___
18666	SP&S 4-6-2 Pacific Locomotive "2044," 97		200	___
18668	Bloomingdale's 4-4-2 Locomotive "8632," 97		130	___
18669	JCPenney IC 4-6-2 Pacific Locomotive "2099," 98		205	___
18670	D&H 4-4-2 Locomotive "1400," 98		80	___
18671	N&W 4-4-2 Locomotive "1201," 98		70	___
18673	N&W 0-4-0 Locomotive "203," 99		110	___
18676	Safari RR 0-4-0 Locomotive, 99		110	___
18678	Quaker Oats 4-4-2 Locomotive "8632," 98		162	___
18679	JCPenney T&P 4-6-2 Locomotive "2000," traditional, 99, 00 u		250	___
18680	LRRC Century Club 4-6-4 Hudson "2000," 00		200	___
18681	PRR 4-4-2 Locomotive "460," 99		75	___
18682	Santa Fe 4-4-2 Locomotive "524," traditional, 00-01		70	___
18683	Mickey's Holiday Express 4-4-2 Atlantic, 99		90	___
18684	LRRC Inside Track Special Edition 4-6-2 Pacific, 99		185	___
18685	NYC 4-4-2 Atlantic "8632," 99		100	___
18686	Tinsel Town Express 4-4-2 Atlantic "3766," 00-01		95	___
18689	NS Dash 8-40C Diesel "8689," 92		200	___
18690	Centennial Express 4-4-2 Atlantic "100," 00		90	___
18691	PRR -4-4-2 Atlantic "201," 00		70	___
18692	PRR 4-6-4 Hudson, 00		80	___
18693	Lionel Mines 4-6-4 Hudson "49," 00		80	___
18694	Whirlpool Limited 4-4-2 Atlantic "201," 00		75	___
18695	Mickey's Millennium Express 2000, 00		250	___
18696	ACL 4-6-4 Locomotive "1800," 01		120	___
18697	Santa Fe 4-6-4 Locomotive "3465," 01		100	___
18698	Wabash 4-4-2 Atlantic, 07		85	___
18699	Alaska 4-4-2 Locomotive "64," 01		105	___
18700	Rock Island 0-4-0T Locomotive "8700," 87-88	36	43	___
18701	Polar Express LionScale 3-Bay Covered Hopper, 18		65	___
18702	V&TRR 4-4-0 Locomotive "8702" (SSS), 88	160	195	___
18703	Merry Christmas LionScale 3-Bay Covered Hopper, 18		60	___

		Exc	Mint
18704	Lionel Lines 2-4-0 Locomotive, 89 u	36	43
18704	Halloween ELX 3-Bay Hopper, LionScale, 18		65
18705	Neptune 0-4-0T Locomotive "8705," 90-91	35	42
18706	Santa Fe 2-4-0 Locomotive "8706," 91	36	43
18707	Mickey's World Tour 2-4-0 Locomotive "8707," 91, 92 u	58	68
18709	Lionel Employee Learning Center 0-4-0T Locomotive, 92 u		140
18710	SP 2-4-0 Locomotive "2000," 93	30	38
18711	Southern 2-4-0 Locomotive "2000," 93	30	38
18712	Jersey Central 2-4-0 Locomotive "2000," 93	30	38
18713	Chessie System 2-4-0 Locomotive "1993," 94-95	30	38
18716	Lionelville Circus 4-4-0 Locomotive, 90-91	90	110
18718	LL 0-4-0 Dockside Switcher "8200," 97-98		40
18719	Thomas the Tank Engine "1," 97		158
18720	Union 4-4-0 General Locomotive "1865," 99		175
18721	Confederate 4-4-0 General Locomotive "1861," 99		175
18722	Percy the Tank Engine "6," 99		170
18723	Union Pacific 4-4-0 General Locomotive, 05		100
18725	World of Disney General Locomotive, 03		100
18728	Thomas the Tank Engine "1," 04-07		120
18730	Transylvania RR 4-4-0 Locomotive "13," traditional, 05		105
18731	PH-1 PowerHouse Transformer, 97	75	120
18732	North Pole Central 4-4-0 Locomotive "25," 06		110
18733	Percy the Tank Engine "6," 05-12		120
18734	James the Tank Engine "5," 06-12		120
18736	PRR 4-4-2 Atlantic "1645," 06-07		60
18738	North Pole Central 4-4-2 Atlantic "25," 08-09		90
18739	Great Western 4-4-0 General Locomotive, traditional, 07-09		80
18740	Walter E. Disney 4-4-0 General Locomotive, traditional, 06		90
18741	Thomas the Tank Engine, 08-13		120
18742	Nutcracker 4-4-0 General Locomotive, 08		140
18744	PRR 0-8-0 Locomotive "565," 08		125
18745	Hallow's Eve 4-6-0 Steam Locomotive, 11-12		190
18749	Rio Grande General Locomotive "346," 11-12		145
17850	SP 0-8-0 Locomotive w/Vanderbilt tender "4508," 12		140
18751	Santa Flyer 0-8-0 Locomotive, 11-13		120
18753	Route of the Reindeer RS3 Diesel, 11		190
18754	Polar Express 2-8-4 Berkshire Steam Locomotive, 11, 13		300
18755	C&O Berkshire Steam Locomotive "2751," TrainSounds, 11		290
18756	Coca-Cola 4-4-0 General Locomotive "125," 11-12		175
18765	PRR 2-8-4 Berkshire Locomotive "2331," 12-13		190
18769	Thomas, remote system, 12		140
18770	Christmas Thomas the Tank Engine "1," 13-15		90
18771	Percy, remote system, 13-16		140
18773	UP 0-8-0 Locomotive "4500," 12-13		105
18774	James, remote system, 13-16		140
18775	Diesel, remote system, 13-16		140
18776	Hershey's 0-8-0 Locomotive, 12-13		140
18778	GN 0-8-0 Locomotive w/Vanderbilt Tender "819," 12-13		130
18780	NYC 0-8-0 Locomotive "7794," 11-13		150
18783	Menard's C&NW 0-8-0 Locomotive "1009," 12 u		135
18784	Silver Bells 2-4-2 Columbia Locomotive, 13-15		110
18787	PRR 4-4-0 General Locomotive "1510," 94-95		125
18788	U.S. Military 4-4-0 General Locomotive, 13-14		300

		Exc	Mint	
18789	Peanuts LC 2-4-2 Columbia Locomotive "1031," 13-16		155	___
18790	Gingerbread Junction 0-6-0 Docksider "1226," 13-15		130	___
18791	PRR 0-8-0 LC Locomotive, 13-17		140	___
18799	Bethlehem Steel Switcher "44," 99		100	___
18800	Lehigh Valley GP9 Diesel "8800," 87	80	95	___
18801	Santa Fe U36B Diesel "8801," 87	100	120	___
18802	Southern GP9 Diesel "8802" (SSS), 87	100	115	___
18803	Santa Fe RS3 Diesel "8803," 88	90	105	___
18804	Soo Line RS3 Diesel "8804," 88	95	115	___
18805	Union Pacific RS3 Diesel "8805," 89	100	125	___
18806	New Haven SD18 Diesel "8806," 89	100	115	___
18807	Lehigh Valley RS3 Diesel "8807," 90	90	120	___
18808	ACL SD18 Diesel "8808," 90	85	105	___
18809	Susquehanna RS3 Diesel "8809," 89 u		130	___
18810	CSX SD18 Diesel "8810," 90	95	130	___
18811	Alaska SD9 Diesel "8811," 91	95	135	___
18812	Kansas City Southern GP38 Diesel "4000," 91	120	140	___
18813	DM&IR SD18 Diesel "8813," 90 u	90	145	___
18814	D&H RS3 Diesel "8814" (SSS), 91	90	120	___
18815	Amtrak RS3 Diesel "1815," 91, 92 u	100	130	___
18816	C&NW GP38-2 Diesel "4600," 92	105	135	___
18817	UP GP9 Diesel "150" (see 18553), 91 u		135	___
18818	LRRC GP38-2 Diesel, 92 u	100	117	___
18819	L&N GP38-2 Diesel "4136," 92	115	145	___
18820	WP GP9 Diesel "8820" (SSS), 92	120	140	___
18821	Clinchfield GP38-2 Diesel "6005," 93	125	150	___
18822	Gulf, Mobile & Ohio RS3 Diesel "721," 92-93 u		NRS	
18823	Chicago & Illinois Midland SD9 Diesel "52," 92 u		235	___
18824	Montana Rail Link SD9 Diesel "600," 93	185	230	___
18825	Soo Line GP38-2 Diesel "4000" (SSS), 93	120	145	___
18826	Conrail GP7 Diesel "5808," 93	100	120	___
18827	Happy Holidays RS3 Diesel "8827," 93	165	220	___
18830	Budweiser GP9 Diesel "1947," 93-94 u	125	165	___
18831	SP GP20 Diesel "4060," 94	105	120	___
18832	PRR RSD-4 Diesel "8446," 95	110	135	___
18833	Milwaukee Road RS3 Diesel "2487," 94	100	110	___
18834	C&O SD28 Diesel "8834," 94	110	140	___
18835	NYC RS3 Diesel "8223" (SSS), 94	135	195	___
18836	CN (Grand Trunk) GP38-2 Diesel "5800," 94	135	160	___
18837	Happy Holidays RS3 Diesel "8837," 94-95	150	190	___
18838	Seaboard RSC-3 Diesel "1538," 95	110	140	___
18840	U.S. Army GP7 Diesel "1821," 95	85	124	___
18841	Western Maryland GP20 Diesel "27" (SSS), 95	120	150	___
18842	JCPenney B&LE SD38 Diesel "868," 95 u	80	265	___
18843	Great Northern RS3 Diesel "197," 96		145	___
18844	Nacionales de Mexico GP38 Diesel, 96		150	___
18845	D&RGW RS3 Diesel "5204," 97		100	___
18846	Lionel Centennial Series GP9 Diesel, 98	265	426	___
18847	Santa Fe H-12-44 Switcher "602," 99	85	385	___
18848	PRR H-12-44 Switcher "9087," 99		420	___
18853	JCPenney Santa Fe GP9 Diesel "2370," 97 u		150	___
18854	UP GP9 Diesel Dummy Set, "2380, 2387," 97		450	___
18855	UP GP9 Diesel "2381," unpowered, 97		210	___

	MODERN 1970-2023	Exc	Mint
18856	NJ Transit GP38-2 Diesel "4303," 99		315
18857	Union Pacific GP9 Diesel "2397," 97		240
18858	Lionel Centennial GP20 Diesel, 98		450
18859	Phantom II Locomotive, 99		360
18860	Pratt's Hollow Collection I: Phantom, 98		400
18864	Southern Pacific GP9 Diesel B Unit, 98		140
18865	New York Central GP9 Diesel B Unit, 98		170
18866	Milwaukee Road GP7 Diesel "2383," 98		205
18868	NJ Transit GP38-2 Diesel "4300," 98 u		140
18870	Pennsylvania GP9 Diesel "2029," 98		180
18872	Wabash GP7 Diesel Set, "453, 454, 455," 99	213	560
18873	Wabash GP7 Diesel "454," unpowered, 99		125
18874	Wabash GP7 Diesel "455," CC, 99		260
18876	C&NW H-12-44 Switcher "1053," 99	125	319
18877	Union Pacific GP9 Diesel "2399," nonpowered, 99		175
18878	Alaska GP7 Diesel "1803," 99		115
18879	B&O GP9 Diesel "5616," 99		260
18881	Custom GP9 Diesel "5616," 99		350
18890	UP RS-3 Diesel "8805," 89		85
18892	Burlington GP9 Diesel "2328," 99	75	205
18893	Corvette GP7 Diesel, traditional, 99		230
18897	Christmas GP7 Diesel "1999," 99		200
18900	PRR Switcher "8900," 88 u, 89	26	34
18901	PRR Alco Diesel AA Set "8901, 8902," 88		320
18901/02	PRR Alco Diesel AA Set, 88	110	130
18902	PRR Alco Diesel FA-2 Unit, unpowered, 88		80
18903	Amtrak "Mopar Express," 99		500
18903/04	Amtrak Alco Diesel AA set, 88-89	90	130
18904	Amtrak Alco Diesel FA-2, unpowered, 88-89		80
18905	PRR 44-ton Switcher "9312," 92	80	116
18906	Erie-Lackawanna RS3 Diesel "8906," 91 u	70	90
18907	Rock Island 44-ton Switcher "371," 93	95	110
18908	NYC Alco Diesel AA Units "8908, 8909," 93	60	150
18908/09	NYC Alco Diesel AA Set, 93	105	115
18909	NYC Alco FA-2 Diesel "8909," unpowered, 93	50	80
18910	CSX Switcher "8910," 93	40	46
18911	UP Switcher "8911," 93	33	37
18912	Amtrak Switcher "8912," 93	37	43
18913	Santa Fe Alco Diesel A Unit "8913," 93-94	55	65
18915	WM Alco Diesel A Unit "8915," 93	65	80
18916	WM Alco Diesel A Unit "8916," dummy, 93	38	42
18917	Soo Line NW2 Switcher, 93	65	75
18918	B&M NW2 Switcher "8918," 93	75	90
18919	Santa Fe Alco Diesel A Unit "8919," dummy, 93-94	36	55
18920	Frisco NW2 Switcher "254," 94	70	75
18921	C&NW NW2 Switcher "1017," 94	60	80
18922	New Haven Alco Diesel A Unit "8922," 94	75	120
18923	New Haven Alco Diesel A Unit "8923," dummy, 94	50	55
18924	IC Switcher "8924," 94-95	37	44
18925	D&RGW Switcher "8925," 94-95	32	37
18926	Reading Switcher "8926," 94-95	31	39
18927	U.S. Navy NW2 Switcher "65-00637," 94-95	65	85
18928	C&NW NW2 Switcher Calf Unit, 95	50	55

		Exc	Mint	
18929	B&M NW2 Switcher Calf Unit, 95	44	48	___
18930	Crayola Switcher, 94 u, 95	27	30	___
18931	Chrysler Mopar NW2 Switcher "1818," 94 u	76	88	___
18932	Jersey Central NW2 Switcher "8932," 96		65	___
18933	Jersey Central NW2 Switcher Calf Unit "8933," 96		55	___
18934	Reading Alco Diesel AA Set, 95		220	___
18934/35	Reading Alco Diesel AA Set, 95	75	95	___
18935	Reading Alco FA-2 Diesel "8935," unpowered, 95		80	___
18936	Amtrak Alco Diesel A Unit "8936," 95		65	___
18937	Amtrak FA2 Alco Diesel, nonpowered, 95-97		50	___
18938	U.S. Navy NW2 Switcher Calf Unit, 95	55	65	___
18939	Union Pacific NW2 Switcher Set, 96		145	___
18940	UP NW2 Switcher, unpowered, 96		75	___
18943	Georgia Power NW2 Switcher "1960," 95 u		170	___
18945	MP NW2 Switcher, 96		168	___
18946	U.S. Coast Guard NW2 Switcher "8946," 96		80	___
18947	Port of Lionel City Alco FA2 Diesel "2030," 97		70	___
18948	Port of Lionel City Alco FB-2 Diesel "2030B," 97		45	___
18949	NYC NW2 Switcher, 97		170	___
18951	Erie NW2 Switcher "6220," 97		165	___
18952	ATSF Alco PA1 Diesel "2000," 97		345	___
18953	NYC Alco PA1 Diesel "2000," 97		260	___
18954	ATSF Alco FA2 Diesel "212," powered, 97-99		80	___
18955	NJ Transit NW2 Switcher "500," 96 u		110	___
18956	Dodge Motorsports NW2 Switcher "8956," 96 u		172	___
18959	New York Central NW2 Switcher "622," 97		475	___
18961	Erie Alco PA1 Diesel "850," 98		315	___
18965	Santa Fe Alco PB1 Diesel, 98	150	235	___
18966	New York Central Alco BP1 Diesel "2008," 98		250	___
18971	Alco Diesel A Unit, nonpowered, 98		60	___
18972	RI Alco FA Diesel AA Set, 98		180	___
18973	RI Alco FA2 Diesel "2031," powered, 98-99		165	___
18974	RI Alco FA2 Diesel Dummy Unit, 98-99		80	___
18975	Southern 44-ton Switcher "1955," 99		190	___
18978	C&O NW2 Switcher "624," 99-00		410	___
18979	Area 51 Groom Lake RR Alco FA-2 Diesel, 02		170	___
18981	Pennsylvania Railroad Speeder "16," 04		45	___
18982	Santa Fe Railroad Speeder "122," 04-05		65	___
18988	MP15 Diesel, K-Line, 06		140	___
18989	Bethlehem Steel Plymouth Switcher, traditional, K-Line, 06		100	___
18992	SP S2 Diesel Switcher "1440," CC, 08		410	___
18993	C&NW S2 Diesel Switcher "1031," CC, 08		410	___
18994	Lionel Lines FA Diesel, traditional, 08-09		90	___
19000	Blue Comet Diner, 87 u	60	75	___
19001	Southern Diner, 87 u	55	65	___
19002	Pennsylvania Diner, 88 u	29	41	___
19003	Milwaukee Road Diner, 88 u	29	44	___
19010	B&O Diner, 89 u	36	55	___
19011	Lionel Lines Baggage Car, 93	164	290	___
19015	Lionel Lines Passenger Coach, 91	108	163	___
19016	Lionel Lines Passenger Coach, 91	95	130	___
19017	Lionel Lines Passenger Coach, 91	88	110	___
19018	Lionel Lines Observation Car, 91	90	110	___

		Exc	Mint
MODERN 1970-2023			
___ **19019**	SP Baggage Car "9019," 93	120	153
___ **19023**	SP Passenger Coach "9023," 92	125	160
___ **19024**	SP Passenger Coach "9024," 92	85	100
___ **19025**	SP Passenger Coach "9025," 92	100	115
___ **19026**	SP Observation Car "9026," 92	85	100
___ **19038**	Adolphus Busch Observation Car, 92-93 u		85
___ **19039**	Pere Marquette Baggage Car, 93		75
___ **19040**	Pere Marquette Passenger Coach "1115," 93		75
___ **19041**	Pere Marquette Passenger Coach "1116," 93		75
___ **19042**	Pere Marquette Observation Car "36," 93		75
___ **19047**	Baltimore & Ohio Combination Car "9047," 96		55
___ **19048**	Baltimore & Ohio Passenger Coach "9048," 96		50
___ **19049**	Baltimore & Ohio Diner "9049," 96		42
___ **19050**	Baltimore & Ohio Observation Car "9050," 96		42
___ **19056**	NYC Heavyweight Baggage Car, 96		105
___ **19057**	NYC Willow Run Heavyweight Coach, 96		95
___ **19058**	NYC Willow Trail Heavyweight Coach, 96		90
___ **19059**	NYC Seneca Valley Heavyweight Observation Car, 96		100
___ **19060**	Pullman Heavyweight Set, 96		473
___ **19061**	Wabash Passenger Set, 97		235
___ **19062**	Wabash City of Columbia Coach "2361," 97		90
___ **19063**	Wabash City of Danville Coach "2362," 97		75
___ **19064**	Wabash REA Baggage Car "2360," 97		47
___ **19065**	Wabash Windy City Observation Car "2363," 97		90
___ **19066**	Commodore Vanderbilt Pullman Heavyweight 2-pack, 97		190
___ **19067**	Commodore Vanderbilt Willow River Pullman "2543," 97		115
___ **19068**	Commodore Vanderbilt Willow Valley Pullman "2544," 97		100
___ **19069**	Pullman Baby Madison Set "9500-02," 97		155
___ **19070**	Baby Madison Combination Car "9501," 97		40
___ **19071**	Laurel Gap Baby Madison Coach "9500," 97		34
___ **19072**	Laurel Summit Baby Madison Coach "9500," 97		40
___ **19073**	Catskill Valley Baby Madison Observation Car "9502," 97		34
___ **19074**	Legends of Lionel Madison Set, 97	65	385
___ **19075**	Mazzone Lionel Legends Coach "2621," 97		105
___ **19076**	Caruso Lionel Legends Coach "2624," 97		90
___ **19077**	Raphael Lionel Legends Coach "2652," 97		90
___ **19078**	Cowen Lionel Legends Observation Car "2600," 97		95
___ **19079**	NYC Heavyweight Passenger Car Set, 97		275
___ **19080**	NYC Heavyweight REA Baggage Car "2564," 97		100
___ **19081**	NYC Park Place Heavyweight Coach "2565," 97		100
___ **19082**	NYC Star Beam Heavyweight Coach "2566," 97		100
___ **19083**	NYC Hudson Valley Heavyweight Observation "2567," 97		100
___ **19085**	N&W Operating Hopper, 97		84
___ **19087**	C&O Heavyweight Passenger Car 4-pack, "2571-74," 97		290
___ **19088**	C&O Heavyweight Baggage Car "2571," 97		100
___ **19089**	C&O Heavyweight Sleeper Car "2572," 97		100
___ **19090**	C&O Heavyweight Diner "2573," 97		110
___ **19091**	C&O Heavyweight Observation Car "2574," 97		100
___ **19093**	Commodore Vanderbilt Heavyweight Sleeper Car 2-pack, 98		170
___ **19094**	Commodore Vanderbilt Niagara Falls Sleeper, 98		75
___ **19095**	Commodore Vanderbilt Highland Falls Sleeper, 98		75
___ **19096**	Legends of Lionel Madison Car 2-pack, 98		130
___ **19097**	Bonnano Lionel Legends Coach "2653," 98		80

	MODERN 1970-2023	Exc	Mint	
19098	Pagano Lionel Legends Coach "2654," 98		105	
19099	PRR Liberty Gap Baggage Car "2623," 99		80	
19100	Amtrak Baggage Car "9100," 89	125	165	
19101	Amtrak Combination Car "9101," 89	75	85	
19102	Amtrak Passenger Coach "9102," 89	75	85	
19103	Amtrak Vista Dome Car "9103," 89	70	90	
19104	Amtrak Diner "9104," 89	65	80	
19105	Amtrak Full Vista Dome Car "9105," 89 u	70	80	
19106	Amtrak Observation Car "9106," 89	75	90	
19107	SP Full Vista Dome Car, 90 u	70	88	
19108	N&W Full Vista Dome Car "576," 91 u	75	85	
19109	Santa Fe Baggage Car "3400," 91	168	263	
19110	Santa Fe Combination Car "3500," 91	70	108	
19111	Santa Fe Diner "601," 91	85	123	
19112	Santa Fe Passenger Coach, 91	90	135	
19113	Santa Fe Vista Dome Car, 91	100	135	
19116	Great Northern Baggage Car "1200," 92	135	165	
19117	Great Northern Combination Car "1240," 92	65	80	
19118	Great Northern Passenger Coach "1212," 92	75	95	
19119	Great Northern Vista Dome Car "1322," 92	75	95	
19120	Great Northern Observation Car "1192," 92	75	95	
19121	Union Pacific Vista Dome Car "9121," 92 u	90	100	
19122	D&RGW California Zephyr Baggage Car, 93	170	210	
19123	D&RGW California Zephyr Silver Bronco Vista Dome Car, 93	95	115	
19124	D&RGW California Zephyr Silver Colt Vista Dome Car, 93	95	115	
19125	D&RGW California Zephyr Silver Mustang Vista Dome Car, 93	100	125	
19126	D&RGW California Zephyr Silver Pony Vista Dome Car, 93	95	115	
19127	D&RGW California Zephyr Vista Dome Car, 93	85	100	
19128	Santa Fe Full Vista Dome Car "507," 92 u	143	163	
19129	IC Full Vista Dome Car "9129," 93	75	85	
19130	Lackawanna Passenger Cars, set of 4, 94	280	350	
19131	Lackawanna Baggage Car "2000" (see 19130)		150	
19132	Lackawanna Diner "469" (see 19130)		100	
19133	Lackawanna Passenger Coach "260" (see 19130)		100	
19134	Lackawanna Observation Car "789" (see 19130)		85	
19135	Lackawanna Combination Car "425," 94	85	100	
19136	Lackawanna Passenger Coach "211," 94	65	75	
19137	New York Central Roomette Car, 95	71	105	
19138	Santa Fe Roomette Car, 95	75	95	
19139	N&W Baggage Car "577," 95	150	200	
19140	N&W Combination Car "494," 95	60	80	
19141	N&W Diner "495," 95	105	135	
19142	N&W Passenger Coach "538," 95	75	95	
19143	N&W Passenger Coach "537," 95	75	95	
19144	N&W Observation Car "582," 95	80	95	
19145	C&O Combination Car "1403," 96		65	
19146	C&O Passenger Coach "1623," 96		60	
19147	C&O Passenger Coach "1803," 96		55	
19148	C&O Chessie Club Coach "1903," 96		55	
19149	C&O Coach/Diner "1950," 96		50	
19150	C&O Observation Car "2504," 96		55	
19151	Norfolk & Western Duplex Roomette car, 96		108	
19152	Union Pacific Duplex Roomette Car, 96		75	

| --- | --- | --- | --- |
___	**19153**	C&O Passenger Cars, set of 4, 96		340
___	**19154**	Atlantic Coast Line Passenger Car Set, 96		340
___	**19155**	ACL Combination Car "101," 96		90
___	**19156**	ACL Talladega Diner, 96		90
___	**19157**	ACL Moultrie Coach, 96		95
___	**19158**	ACL Observation Car "256," 96		90
___	**19159**	N&W Passenger Cars, set of 4, 95 u	300	385
___	**19160**	LL REA Baggage Car, 96		90
___	**19161**	LL Silver Mesa Coach, 96		80
___	**19162**	LL Silver Sky Vista Dome Car, 96		75
___	**19163**	LL Silver Rail Observation Car, 96		75
___	**19164**	C&O Passenger Car Add-on, 2-pack, 96		160
___	**19165**	ATSF Super Chief Set, 96		305
___	**19166**	NP Vista Dome Car Set, 97	113	323
___	**19167**	NP Pullman Coach "2571," 97		105
___	**19168**	NP Pullman Coach "2571," 97		105
___	**19169**	NP Pullman Coach "2570," 97		95
___	**19170**	NP Pullman Coach "2571," 97		100
___	**19171**	NYC Streamliner Car 4-pack, 97		290
___	**19172**	NYC Aluminum Passenger/Baggage Car "2570," 97		95
___	**19173**	NYC Manhattan Island Aluminum Passenger Diner, 97		100
___	**19174**	NYC Queensboro Bridge Aluminum Passenger Coach, 97		100
___	**19175**	NYC Windgate Brook Aluminum Observation Car, 97		90
___	**19176**	ATSF Indian Arrow Diner "2572," 97		90
___	**19177**	ATSF Grass Valley Coach "2573," 97		90
___	**19178**	ATSF Citrus Valley Coach "2574," 97		90
___	**19179**	ATSF Vista Heights Coach "2575," 97		90
___	**19180**	ATSF Surfliner Passenger Car 4-pack, 97		250
___	**19181**	GN Empire Builder Prairie View Full Vista Dome Car, 98	33	78
___	**19182**	GN Empire Builder River View Full Vista Dome Car, 98	38	93
___	**19183**	GN Empire Builder Vista Dome Car 2-pack, 98	75	163
___	**19184**	Milwaukee Road Passenger Car 4-pack, 99		390
___	**19185**	MILW Red River Valley Aluminum Passenger Coach "194," 99		125
___	**19186**	MILW Aluminum Coach/Diner "170," 99		110
___	**19187**	MILW Cedar Rapids Aluminum Observation Car "186 ," 99		120
___	**19188**	MILW Aluminum REA Passenger/Baggage Car "1336," 99		95
___	**19194**	KCS Aluminum Passenger Car 4-pack, 00		380
___	**19195**	KCS Aluminum Baggage Car "19195," 00-01		95
___	**19196**	KCS Aluminum Coach "Texarkana," 00-01		95
___	**19197**	KCS Aluminum Coach "Joplin," 00-01		95
___	**19198**	KCS Aluminum Observation "New Orleans," 00-01		95
___	**19200**	Tidewater Southern Boxcar, 87	14	21
___	**19201**	Lancaster & Chester Boxcar, 87	23	37
___	**19202**	PRR Boxcar, 87	22	30
___	**19203**	D&TS Boxcar, 87	11	18
___	**19204**	Milwaukee Road Boxcar (FF 2), 87	30	43
___	**19205**	Great Northern DD Boxcar (FF 3), 88	19	24
___	**19206**	Seaboard System Boxcar, 88	18	23
___	**19207**	CP Rail DD Boxcar, 88	17	22
___	**19208**	Southern DD Boxcar, 88	11	13
___	**19209**	Florida East Coast Boxcar, 88	15	19
___	**19210**	Soo Line Boxcar, 89	19	23
___	**19211**	Vermont Railway Boxcar, 89	18	21

MODERN 1970-2023		Exc	Mint	
19212	PRR Boxcar, 89	21	25	___
19213	SP&S DD Boxcar, 89	17	25	___
19214	Western Maryland Boxcar (FF 4), 89	23	27	___
19215	Union Pacific DD Boxcar, 90	17	21	___
19216	Santa Fe Boxcar, 90	17	22	___
19217	Burlington Boxcar, 90	16	21	___
19218	New Haven Boxcar, 90	16	20	___
19219	Lionel Lines 1900-1906 Boxcar, diesel RailSounds, 90	120	145	___
19220	Lionel Lines 1926-1934 Boxcar, 90	27	30	___
19221	Lionel Lines 1935-1937 Boxcar, 90	27	30	___
19222	Lionel Lines 1948-1950 Boxcar, 90	27	30	___
19223	Lionel Lines 1979-1989 Boxcar, 90	18	25	___
19228	Cotton Belt Boxcar, 91	16	22	___
19229	Frisco Boxcar, diesel RailSounds (FF 5), 91	75	90	___
19230	Frisco DD Boxcar (FF 5), 91	21	26	___
19231	TA&G DD Boxcar, 91	13	16	___
19232	Rock Island DD Boxcar, 91	17	20	___
19233	Southern Pacific Boxcar, 91	15	19	___
19234	NYC Boxcar, 91	60	65	___
19235	MKT Boxcar, 91	55	65	___
19236	NKP DD Boxcar (FF 6), 92	21	30	___
19237	C&IM Boxcar, 92	17	24	___
19238	Kansas City Southern Boxcar, 92	17	24	___
19239	Toronto, Hamilton & Buffalo DD Boxcar, 92	15	20	___
19240	Great Northern DD Boxcar, 92	17	23	___
19241	Mickey Mouse 60th Anniversary Hi-Cube Boxcar, 91 u	135	180	___
19242	Donald Duck 50th Anniversary Hi-Cube Boxcar, 91 u	143	152	___
19243	Clinchfield Boxcar "9790," 91 u	35	41	___
19244	L&N Boxcar "9791," 92	35	38	___
19245	Mickey's World Tour Hi-Cube Boxcar, 92 u	35	40	___
19246	Disney World 20th Anniversary Hi-Cube Boxcar, 92 u	33	40	___
19247	Postwar "6464" Series Boxcar Set I, 3 cars, 93	323	550	___
19248	Western Pacific Boxcar "6464," 93	75	95	___
19249	Great Northern Boxcar "6464," 93	75	95	___
19250	M&StL Boxcar "6464," 93	80	105	___
19251	Montana Rail Link DD Boxcar "10001," 93	21	34	___
19254	Erie Boxcar (FF 7), 93	21	25	___
19255	Erie DD Boxcar (FF 7), 93	22	26	___
19256	Goofy Hi-Cube Boxcar, 93	23	26	___
19257	Postwar "6464" Series Boxcar Set II, 3 cars, 94	73	116	___
19258	Rock Island Boxcar "6464," 94	25	34	___
19259	Western Pacific Boxcar "6464100," 94	33	46	___
19260	Western Pacific Boxcar "6464100," 94	35	49	___
19261	Perils of Mickey Hi-Cube Boxcar #1, 93	20	30	___
19262	Perils of Mickey Hi-Cube Boxcar #2, 93	20	28	___
19263	NYC DD Boxcar (SSS), 94	36	42	___
19264	Perils of Mickey Hi-Cube Boxcar #3, 94	28	31	___
19265	Mickey Mouse 65th Anniversary Hi-Cube Boxcar, 94	22	44	___
19266	Postwar "6464" Series Boxcar Set III, 3 cars, 95	66	98	___
19267	NYC Pacemaker Boxcar "6464125," 95	37	42	___
19268	Missouri Pacific Boxcar "6464150," 95	25	29	___
19269	Rock Island Boxcar "6464," 95	25	26	___
19270	Donald Duck 60th Anniversary Hi-Cube Boxcar, 95	30	34	___

|---|---|---|---|
____ 19271	Minnie Mouse Hi-Cube Boxcar, 95	21	43
____ 19272	Postwar "6464" Series Boxcar Set IV, 3 cars, 96	73	103
____ 19273	BAR State of Maine Boxcar "6464275," 96		35
____ 19274	SP Overnight Boxcar "6464225," 96		28
____ 19275	Pennsylvania Boxcar "6464," 96		44
____ 19276	Postwar "6464" Series Boxcar Set V, 3 cars, 96	56	103
____ 19277	Rutland Boxcar "6464-300," 96		26
____ 19278	B&O Boxcar "6464-325," 96		30
____ 19279	Central of Georgia Boxcar "6464-375," 96		29
____ 19280	Mickey's Wheat Hi-Cube Boxcar, 96		32
____ 19281	Mickey's Carrots Hi-Cube Boxcar, 96		40
____ 19282	Santa Fe "Super Chief" Boxcar "6464-196," 96		24
____ 19283	Erie Boxcar "6464-296," 96		22
____ 19284	Northern Pacific Boxcar "6464-396," 96	10	35
____ 19285	B&A State of Maine Boxcar "6464-275," 96	10	30
____ 19286	Tweety and Sylvester Boxcar, 96		46
____ 19287	NYC/PC Merger Boxcar "6464-125X" (SSS), 97	50	75
____ 19288	PRR/CR Merger Boxcar "6464-200X" (SSS), 97	43	56
____ 19289	Monon "Hoosier Line" Boxcar "6464," 97		27
____ 19290	Seaboard "Silver Meteor" Boxcar "6464," 97		24
____ 19291	GN Boxcar "6464-397," 97	14	33
____ 19292	Postwar "6464" Series Boxcar Set VI, 3 cars, 97	25	45
____ 19293	MKT Boxcar "6464-350," 97	28	32
____ 19294	B&O Boxcar "6464-400," 97	27	34
____ 19295	NH Boxcar "6464-425," 97	25	34
____ 19300	PRR Ore Car, 87	15	23
____ 19301	Milwaukee Road Ore Car, 87	19	26
____ 19302	Milwaukee Road Quad Hopper with coal (FF 2), 87	23	35
____ 19303	Lionel Lines Quad Hopper with coal, 87 u	20	31
____ 19304	GN Covered Quad Hopper (FF 3), 88	17	27
____ 19305	Chessie System Ore Car, 88	18	23
____ 19307	B&LE Ore Car with load, 89	19	25
____ 19308	GN Ore Car with load, 89	18	23
____ 19309	Seaboard Covered Quad Hopper, 89	16	19
____ 19310	L&C Quad Hopper with coal, 89	16	30
____ 19311	SP Covered Quad Hopper, 90	14	18
____ 19312	Reading Quad Hopper with coal, 90	21	36
____ 19313	B&O Ore Car with load, 90-91	20	25
____ 19315	Amtrak Ore Car with load, 91	22	30
____ 19316	Wabash Covered Quad Hopper, 91	18	23
____ 19317	Lehigh Valley Quad Hopper with coal, 91	47	55
____ 19318	NKP Quad Hopper with coal (FF 6), 92	29	32
____ 19319	Union Pacific Covered Quad Hopper, 92	19	23
____ 19320	PRR Ore Car with load, 92	21	30
____ 19321	B&LE Ore Car with load, 92	21	30
____ 19322	C&NW Ore Car with load, 93	27	34
____ 19323	Detroit & Mackinac Ore Car with load, 93	20	29
____ 19324	Erie Quad Hopper with coal (FF 7), 93	25	33
____ 19325	N&W 4-bay Hopper "6446-1" with coal, 97		65
____ 19326	N&W 4-bay Hopper "6446-2" with coal, 96		60
____ 19327	N&W 4-bay Hopper "6446-3" with coal, 96		60
____ 19328	N&W 4-bay Hopper "6446-4" with coal, 96		60
____ 19329	N&W 4-bay Hopper "6436" with coal, 97		55

		Exc	Mint	
19330	Cotton Belt 4-bay Hopper "64661" with coal, 98		45	___
19331	Cotton Belt 4-bay Hopper "64662" with coal, 98		45	___
19332	Cotton Belt 4-bay Hopper "64663" with coal, 98		45	___
19333	Cotton Belt 4-bay Hopper "64664" with coal, 98		45	___
19338	Cotton Belt 4-bay Hopper 2-pack, 99		120	___
19339	Cotton Belt 4-bay Hopper "64469," 99		60	___
19340	Cotton Belt 4-bay Hopper "64470," 99		60	___
19341	LV 2-bay Hopper "6456," 99		30	___
19344	D&RGW 3-bay Cylindrical Hopper "15990," 99-00		42	___
19345	CN 3-bay Cylindrical Hopper "370708," 99-00	35	98	___
19346	PRR 4-bay Hopper with coal "744433," 01		40	___
19347	LV 2-bay Hopper "643657," 01		40	___
19348	Duluth, Missabe & Iron Range Ore Car "28000," 03		25	___
19349	U.S. Steel Ore Car "19349," 03		29	___
19350	Postwar "6636" Alaska Quad Hopper, 03		34	___
19357	N&W Hopper "6446-25," Archive Collection, 07		50	___
19361	Twizzlers Quad Hopper, 10		55	___
19362	Coursers Christmas Hopper with gifts, 10		60	___
19364	Milk Duds Covered Hopper, 11		55	___
19365	Coca-Cola Quad Hopper, 10		60	___
19366	Santa's Little Hopper, 10-11		55	___
19367	ATSF Quad Hopper, 11		60	___
19368	Southern Offset Hopper "106723," (std O), 11		70	___
19369	Alaska Quad Hopper "20756," 12		60	___
19371	Burlington Northern I-Beam Car, 04		60	___
19374	NS Bathtub Gondola 2-pack (std O), 15		140	___
19377	DETX Bathtub Gondola 2-pack (std O), 15		140	___
19380	CSX Bathtub Gondola 2-pack (std O), 15		140	___
19383	UP PS-4 Flatcar "57125" (std O), 13		70	___
19384	ATSF PS-4 Flatcar "90088" (std O), 13		70	___
19385	CNJ PS-4 Flatcar "339" (std O), 13		70	___
19386	BN PS-4 Flatcar "613200" (std O), 13		70	___
19388	BN 89' Auto Carrier (std O), 13-14		110	___
19389	SP 89' Auto Carrier (std O), 13-14		110	___
19390	CP 89' Auto Carrier (std O), 13-14, 16		110	___
19391	Soo Line 89' Auto Carrier (std O), 13-14, 16		110	___
19393	BNSF Auto Carrier 2-pack (std O), 12		220	___
19394	UP Auto Carrier 2-pack (std O), 12		220	___
19395	Grand Trunk Auto Carrier 2-pack (std O), 12		220	___
19396	CSX Auto Carrier 2-pack (std O), 12		220	___
19397	CN Auto Carrier 2-pack (std O), 12		220	___
19398	Conrail Auto Carrier 2-pack (std O), 12		220	___
19400	Milwaukee Road Gondola with cable reels (FF 2), 87	21	33	___
19401	GN Gondola with coal (FF 3), 88	19	25	___
19402	GN Crane Car (FF 3), 88	47	65	___
19403	WM Gondola with coal (FF 4), 89	20	25	___
19404	Trailer Train Flatcar with WM trailers (FF 4), 89	29	33	___
19405	Southern Crane Car, 91	42	65	___
19406	West Point Mint Car, 91	38	50	___
19408	Frisco Gondola with coil covers (FF 5), 91	26	31	___
19409	Southern Flatcar with stakes, 91	18	22	___
19410	NYC Gondola with canisters, 91	47	55	___
19411	NKP Flatcar with Sears trailer (FF 6), 92	30	59	___

		Exc	Mint
19412	Frisco Crane Car, 92	49	65
19413	Frisco Flatcar with stakes, 92	16	21
19414	Union Pacific Flatcar with stakes (SSS), 92	19	26
19415	Erie Flatcar with trailer "7200" (FF 7), 93	28	39
19416	ICG TTUX Flatcar Set with trailers (SSS), 93	70	75
19419	Charlotte Mint Car, 93	25	32
19420	Lionel Lines Vat Car, 94	18	22
19421	Hirsch Brothers Vat Car, 95	16	21
19423	Circle L Racing Flatcar "6424" with stock cars, 96		27
19424	Edison Electric Depressed Center Flatcar "6461" with transformer, 97		31
19427	Evans Auto Loader "6414," 99		55
19428	Evans Boat Loader "6414," 99		70
19429	Culvert Gondola "6342," 98-99		48
19430	ATSF Flatcar "6411" with Beechcraft Bonanza, 98		47
19438	Christmas Gondola (std O), 98		42
19439	Flatcar with safes, 98		35
19440	Flatcar with FedEx trailer, 98		34
19441	Lobster Vat Car, 98		35
19442	Water Supply Flatcar with tank (SSS), 98		31
19444	Flatcar with VW Bug, 98		38
19445	Borden Milk Tank Car "520," 99		38
19446	Pittsburgh Paint Vat Car, 99		43
19447	Mama's Baked Beans Vat Car, 99		35
19448	Easter Gondola "6462" with candy, 99		27
19449	Liquified Gas Tank Car "6469," 99		31
19450	Barrel Ramp Car "6343," 99		31
19451	Wheel Car "6262," 99		32
19454	PRR Flatcar "6424" with gondola, 99		25
19455	Lionel Lines Flatcar "6430" with Cooper-Jarrett trailers, 99		60
19457	Lionel Lines Extension Searchlight Car, 99		40
19459	Valentine Gondola "6462" with candy, 99		50
19471	Mobil Flatcar with 2 trailers, 00 u		96
19472	Mobil Bulkhead Flatcar with tank, 00 u		68
19474	L&N Flatcar "6424" with trailer frames, 99		26
19476	Zoo Gondola "6462" with animals, 99-00		43
19477	Monday Night Football Flatcar with trailer, 01		30
19478	Culvert Gondola "6342," 99		45
19479	Borden Milk Car "521," 00		38
19480	Valentine's Vat Car "6475," 99-00		30
19481	Easter Vat Car, 99-00		38
19482	NYC Flatcar with trailer "6424," 00		50
19483	VW Beetle Flatcar, 00		48
19484	Flatcar "6264" with timber, 00		34
19485	PRR Culvert Gondola "347004," 01		41
19486	NYC Lumber Flatcar, 01		34
19487	Flatcar "6800" with airplane, 00		41
19489	Evans Auto Loader "500085," 00		50
19490	Postwar "6475" Libby's Vat Car, 01-02		36
19491	Christmas Vat Car, 01		30
19492	WM Skeleton Log Car 3-pack, 01		95
19496	Westside Lumber Skeleton Log Car 3-pack, 01		112
19500	Milwaukee Road Reefer (FF 2), 87	30	44

		Exc	Mint	
19502	C&NW Reefer, 87	30	33	___
19503	Bangor & Aroostook Reefer, 87	22	25	___
19504	Northern Pacific Reefer, 87	16	22	___
19505	Great Northern Reefer (FF 3), 88	29	35	___
19506	Thomas Newcomen Reefer, 88	18	23	___
19507	Thomas Edison Reefer, 88	21	27	___
19508	Leonardo da Vinci Reefer, 89	19	27	___
19509	Alexander Graham Bell Reefer, 89	17	20	___
19510	PRR Stock Car (FARR 5), 89 u	18	26	___
19511	WM Reefer (FF 4), 89	22	28	___
19512	Wright Brothers Reefer, 90	17	21	___
19513	Ben Franklin Reefer, 90	17	20	___
19515	Milwaukee Road Stock Car (FF 2), 90 u	31	43	___
19516	George Washington Reefer, 89 u, 91	14	19	___
19517	Civil War Reefer, 89 u, 91	14	19	___
19518	Man on the Moon Reefer, 89 u, 91	13	17	___
19519	Frisco Stock Car (FF 5), 91	26	31	___
19520	CSX Reefer, 91	18	23	___
19522	Guglielmo Marconi Reefer, 91	19	23	___
19523	Dr. Robert Goddard Reefer, 91	19	23	___
19524	Delaware & Hudson Reefer (SSS), 91	29	32	___
19525	Speedy Alka Seltzer Reefer, 91 u	31	32	___
19526	Jolly Green Giant Reefer, 91 u	21	33	___
19527	Nickel Plate Road Reefer (FF 6), 92	20	29	___
19528	Joshua L. Cowen Reefer, 92	23	28	___
19529	A.C. Gilbert Reefer, 92	18	23	___
19530	Rock Island Stock Car, 92 u	34	38	___
19531	Rice Krispies Reefer, 92 u	23	33	___
19532	Hormel Reefer "901," 92 u	18	24	___
19535	Erie Reefer (FF 7), 93	23	26	___
19536	Soo Line REA Reefer (SSS), 93	25	30	___
19537	Kellogg's Corn Flakes Refrigerator Car, 93 u		NRS	___
19538	Hormel Reefer "102," 94	22	25	___
19539	Heinz Reefer, 94	38	47	___
19540	Broken Arrow Ranch Stock Car "3356," 97		28	___
19552	Rutland Reefer "395" (std O), 00		32	___
19553	ATSF Stock Car "23003," 00		37	___
19554	Postwar Celebration Milk Car "36621," 00		125	___
19555	Swift Reefer "5839," red, 01		33	___
19556	Swift Reefer "1020," silver, 01		31	___
19557	Circus Stock Car "6376," 00		32	___
19558	Postwar "6556" MKT Stock Car, 02		126	___
19559	MKT Stock Car, girls set add-on, 02		95	___
19560	NP 2-door Stock Car "6356," Archive Collection, 02		33	___
19561	Norman Rockwell Holiday Reefer, 03		25	___
19562	Norman Rockwell Holiday Reefer, 03		25	___
19563	Norman Rockwell Holiday Reefer, 03		25	___
19564	Postwar "6672" Santa Fe Reefer, 03		35	___
19565	Burlington Reefer "6672," Archive Collection, 03		35	___
19567	Postwar "6572" Railway Express Agency Reefer, 05		45	___
19568	GN Reefer, Archive Collection, 05	18	45	___
19569	Pillsbury Reefer, traditional, 05		53	___
19570	Nestle Nesquik Reefer, traditional, 05		53	___

			Exc	Mint
___	19572	NYC Reefer "6672," Archive Collection, 06		45
___	19573	Postwar "6356" NYC Stock Car, 06-07		50
___	19574	GN Stock Car, 08		50
___	19575	REA Reefer "6721," 08-09		50
___	19576	Alaska Reefer, 08		50
___	19577	Krey's Reefer, 10-11		60
___	19578	Granny Smith Apples Wood-sided Reefer, 10-11		53
___	19585	NS Transparent Instruction Car, 10-11		75
___	19586	Alaska Husky Transport Car, 10-11		75
___	19587	Hershey's Chocolate Wood-sided Reefer, 10		75
___	19588	Santa's Wish Transparent Gift Car, 10		75
___	19589	Blood Transfusion Bunk Car, 10-11		60
___	19590	Wood-sided Reefer 2-pack, 10		110
___	19593	Hershey's Kisses Wood-sided Reefer, 11-15		60
___	19594	York Peppermint Patty Wood-sided Reefer, 10-11		55
___	19595	ATSF Warbonnet Refrigerator Car, 10-11	30	55
___	19599	Old Glory Reefers, set of 3, 89 u, 91	37	43
___	19600	Milwaukee Road 1-D Tank Car (FF 2), 87	30	45
___	19601	North American 1-D Tank Car (FF 4), 89	19	31
___	19602	Johnson 1-D Tank Car (FF 5), 91	24	30
___	19603	GATX 1-D Tank Car (FF 6), 92	32	41
___	19604	Goodyear 1-D Tank Car (SSS), 93	33	36
___	19605	Hudson's Bay 1-D Tank Car (SSS), 94	25	29
___	19607	Sunoco 1-D Tank Car "6315," 96	10	31
___	19608	Sunoco Aviation Services 1-D Tank Car "6315" (SSS), 97		38
___	19611	Gulf Oil 1-D Tank Car "6315," 98		33
___	19612	Gulf Oil 3-D Tank Car "6425," 98		30
___	19614	BASF 1-D Tank Car "UTLX 78252," 99-00		25
___	19615	Vulcan Chemicals 1-D Tank Car, 99-00		25
___	19621	Centennial 1-D Tank Car "6015-1," 99		55
___	19622	Centennial 1-D Tank Car "6015-2," 99		62
___	19623	Centennial 1-D Tank Car "6015-3," 99		62
___	19624	Centennial 1-D Tank Car "6015-4," 99		58
___	19625	Ethyl Tank Car "6236," 01		31
___	19626	Diamond Chemical Tank Car "19419," 01		29
___	19627	Shell 1-D Tank Car "1227," 01		37
___	19628	Lion Oil 1-D Tank Car "2256," 01		35
___	19634	General American 1-D Tank Car, 01		30
___	19635	U.S. Army 1-D Tank Car "10936," 01		31
___	19636	Hooker Chemicals 1-D Tank Car "6180," 01		36
___	19637	GATX TankTrain Intermediate Car "44589" (std O), 02		55
___	19638	CN TankTrain Intermediate Car "75571" (std O), 02		65
___	19639	GATX TankTrain Intermediate Car 3-pack (std O), 02		140
___	19644	Union Texas 1-D Tank Car "9922," 02		33
___	19645	Penn Salt 1-D Tank Car "4730," 02		33
___	19646	CN TankTrain Intermediate Car "75571" (std O), 03		45
___	19647	GATX TankTrain Intermediate Car "44589" (std O), 03		45
___	19649	Scrooge McDuck Mint Car, 05	90	207
___	19651	Santa Fe Tool Car, 87	30	35
___	19652	Jersey Central Bunk Car, 88	25	33
___	19653	Jersey Central Tool Car, 88	26	28
___	19654	Amtrak Bunk Car, 89	22	25
___	19655	Amtrak Tool Car, 90-91	23	30

		Exc	Mint	
19656	Milwaukee Road Bunk Car, smoke, 90	38	44	___
19657	Wabash Bunk Car, smoke, 91-92	36	42	___
19658	Norfolk & Western Tool Car, 91	24	29	___
19660	Mint Car, 98		40	___
19663	Pratt's Hollow Bunk Car "5717," 99		40	___
19664	Ambassador Award Bunk Car, bronze, 99 u	200	450	___
19665	Ambassador Engineer Bunk Car, silver, 99 u		610	___
19666	Ambassador Cowen Bunk Car, gold, 99 u		443	___
19667	Wellspring Gold Bullion Car, 99		58	___
19669	King Tut Museum Car "9660," 99		70	___
19670	NY Federal Reserve Bullion Car "6445," 00		44	___
19671	Lionel Model Shop Display Car "6445-01," 99-00		50	___
19672	Lionel Mines Mint Car, 00 u		250	___
19673	Wellspring Capital Management Mint Car, 99 u		220	___
19674	Lionel Lines Platinum Car, 00		43	___
19675	Lionel Model Shop Display "6445-2," 01		42	___
19676	Philadelphia Mint Car, 01		40	___
19677	Fort Knox Mint Car "6445," 00		50	___
19678	U.S. Army Bunk Car, 02		45	___
19679	St. Louis Federal Reserve Mint Car, 02		38	___
19681	Area 51 Alien Suspension Car, 02		47	___
19682	Alaska Klondike Mining Mint Car, 02		40	___
19683	Pony Express Mint Car, 02	13	50	___
19686	Chicago Federal Reserve Mint Car "6445," 03-04		45	___
19687	UP Bunk Car "3887," smoke, 03		40	___
19688	Postwar "6445" Fort Knox Mint Car, 02-03		39	___
19689	CIBRO TankTrain Intermediate Car 3-pack (std O), 03		100	___
19694	Pony Express Mint Car, 03		50	___
19696	U.S. Savings Bond Mint Car, 00		150	___
19697	U.S. Bureau of Engraving and Printing Mint Car "19697," 04		40	___
19698	San Francisco Federal Reserve Mint Car, 04		40	___
19700	Chessie System Extended Vision Caboose, 88	43	50	___
19701	Milwaukee Road N5c Caboose (FF 2), 88	50	65	___
19702	PRR N5c Caboose, 87	44	55	___
19703	GN Extended Vision Caboose (FF 3), 88	41	51	___
19704	WM Extended Vision Caboose, smoke (FF 4), 89	42	49	___
19705	CP Rail Extended Vision Caboose, smoke, 89	44	64	___
19706	UP Extended Vision Caboose "9706," smoke, 89	40	56	___
19707	SP Work Caboose with searchlight, smoke, 90	55	60	___
19708	Lionel Lines Bay Window Caboose, 90	43	46	___
19709	PRR Work Caboose, smoke, 89, 91	49	70	___
19710	Frisco Extended Vision Caboose, smoke (FF 5), 91	43	47	___
19711	NS Extended Vision Caboose, smoke, 92	47	65	___
19712	PRR N5c Caboose, 91	44	47	___
19714	NYC Work Caboose with searchlight, smoke, 92	70	110	___
19715	DM&IR Extended Vision Caboose "C-217," 92 u	50	60	___
19716	IC Extended Vision Caboose "9405," smoke, 93	105	135	___
19717	Susquehanna Bay Window Caboose "0121," 93	44	55	___
19718	C&IM Extended Vision Caboose "74," 92 u	38	45	___
19719	Erie Bay Window Caboose "C-300" (FF 7), 93	47	55	___
19720	Soo Line Extended Vision Caboose (SSS), 93	32	41	___
19721	GM&O Extended Vision Caboose "2956," 93 u	47	50	___
19723	Disney Extended Vision Caboose, 94	36	45	___

| --- | --- | --- | --- |
___	**19724**	JCPenney MKT Extended Vision Caboose "125," 94 u	38	43
___	**19726**	NYC Bay Window Caboose (SSS), 95	50	60
___	**19727**	Pennsylvania N5c Caboose "477938," 96		30
___	**19728**	N&W Bay Window Caboose, 96		70
___	**19732**	ATSF Bay Window Caboose "6517," 96		43
___	**19733**	New York Central Caboose "6357," 96		30
___	**19734**	Southern Pacific Caboose "6357," 96		26
___	**19736**	PRR N5c Caboose "6417," 97		27
___	**19737**	Lackawanna Searchlight Caboose "2420," 97		75
___	**19738**	Conrail N5c Caboose "6417" (SSS), 97		55
___	**19739**	NYC Wood-sided Caboose "6907," 97	20	60
___	**19740**	Virginian N5c Caboose "6427," 97 u		65
___	**19741**	Pennsylvania N5c Caboose "6417," 98		50
___	**19742**	Erie Bay Window Caboose "C301," Caboose Talk, 98		95
___	**19748**	SP&S Bay Window Caboose "6517," 97 u		50
___	**19749**	SP Bay Window Caboose "6517," 98		100
___	**19750**	Holiday Music Bay Window Caboose, 98		160
___	**19751**	PRR N5c Caboose "492418," 98		30
___	**19752**	NP Bay Window Caboose "407," 98		50
___	**19753**	UP Extended Vision Caboose "25641," 98		55
___	**19754**	NYC Caboose "20112," 98		55
___	**19755**	Centennial Porthole Caboose, 99		68
___	**19756**	Lionel Lines Bay Window Caboose, 99		50
___	**19758**	DL&W Work Caboose "6419," 99		55
___	**19759**	Corvette N5c Caboose, 99		60
___	**19772**	Lionel Visitor's Center Vat Car, 99 u		40
___	**19773**	Lionel Kids Club Barrel Ramp Car "6343," 96 u		48
___	**19778**	Case Cutlery Wood-sided Caboose "1889" (std O), 99 u		30
___	**19779**	SP Bay Window Caboose "1908," 99		65
___	**19780**	LV Porthole Caboose "641751," 99-00		43
___	**19781**	Vapor Records Holiday Porthole Caboose "6417," 99-00		62
___	**19782**	NYC Bay Window Caboose "21719," 00		65
___	**19783**	Ford Mustang Extended Vision Caboose, 01		50
___	**19785**	SP Bay Window Caboose "6517," 00		55
___	**19786**	PRR Extended Vision Caboose, 00 u		40
___	**19787**	PRR Porthole Caboose "477927," 01		40
___	**19790**	Postwar "6417" Lehigh Valley Caboose, 02		41
___	**19792**	Postwar "C301" Erie Bay Window Caboose, 03		45
___	**19796**	C&O Bay Window Caboose, 03		50
___	**19800**	Circle L Ranch Operating Cattle Car, 88	75	95
___	**19801**	Poultry Dispatch Chicken Car, 87	20	27
___	**19802**	Carnation Milk Car, 87	87	102
___	**19803**	Reading Ice Car, 87	38	44
___	**19804**	Wabash Operating Hopper, 87	25	34
___	**19805**	Santa Fe Operating Boxcar, 87	28	36
___	**19806**	PRR Operating Hopper, 88	28	32
___	**19807**	PRR Extended Vision Caboose, smoke, 88	39	53
___	**19808**	NYC Ice Car, 88	38	49
___	**19809**	Erie-Lackawanna Operating Boxcar, 88	27	35
___	**19810**	Bosco Milk Car, 88	80	89
___	**19811**	Monon Brakeman Car, 90	50	55
___	**19813**	Northern Pacific Ice Car, 89 u	41	46
___	**19815**	Delaware & Hudson Brakeman Car, 92	49	60

		Exc	Mint	
19816	Madison Hardware Operating Boxcar "190991," 91 u	90	105	___
19817	Virginian Ice Car, 94	31	35	___
19818	Dairymen's League Milk Car "788," 94	65	80	___
19819	Poultry Dispatch Car (SSS), 94	36	43	___
19820	Die-cast Tender, RailSounds II, 95-96		175	___
19821	UP Operating Boxcar, 95	27	36	___
19822	Pork Dispatch Car, 95	29	44	___
19823	Burlington Ice Car, 94 u, 95	39	49	___
19824	U.S. Army Target Launcher, 96		32	___
19825	Generator Car, 96		48	___
19827	NYC Operating Boxcar, 97		37	___
19828	C&NW Animated Stock Car "3356" and Stockyard, 96-97		100	___
19830	U.S. Mail Operating Boxcar "3428," 97		39	___
19831	GM Generator Car "3530," power pole and wire, 97		45	___
19832	Cola Ice Car "6352," 97		47	___
19833	Tender "2426RS," RailSounds II, 97		240	___
19834	LL 6-wheel Crane Car "2460," 97		60	___
19835	FedEx Animated Boxcar "3464X," 97		40	___
19837	Bucyrus 6-wheel Crane Car "2460," 99		49	___
19845	Aquarium Car "3435," CC, 98		151	___
19846	Animated Giraffe Car "3376C," 98		105	___
19850	Stock Car "33760," RailSounds, 00		130	___
19853	Firefighting Instruction Generator Car (SSS), 98		60	___
19854	Lionelville Fire Car (SSS), 98		55	___
19855	Christmas Aquarium Car, 98		60	___
19856	Mermaid Transport, 98		65	___
19857	NYC Firefighting Instruction Car "19853," 98-99		175	___
19858	Lionelville Operating Searchlight Car "19854," 99		65	___
19859	REA Boxcar "6267," steam RailSounds, 99		170	___
19860	Conrail Boxcar "169671," diesel RailSounds, 99		140	___
19864	Animated Ostrich Boxcar, 99		37	___
19867	Operating Poultry Dispatch Car "3434," 99		48	___
19868	Shark Aquarium Car "3435," 99		190	___
19869	Alien Aquarium Car "3435," 99		49	___
19877	ATSF Operating Barrel Car, 99		55	___
19878	Operating Helium Tank Flatcar "3362," 99		40	___
19880	Lionel Lines Extension Searchlight Car, 00		50	___
19882	Sanderson Farms Poultry Car "3434," 99		41	___
19883	LL Bucyrus Erie Crane Car "64608," 99		45	___
19884	Atlantis Travel Aquarium Car, 00 u		95	___
19885	N&W Operating Hopper Car, 00		31	___
19886	Seaboard Boxcar "16126," steam RailSounds, 00		140	___
19887	SP Boxcar "651663," diesel RailSounds, 00		140	___
19888	Christmas Music Boxcar, 01		65	___
19889	PRR Bay Window Caboose "477719," Crewtalk, 00		140	___
19890	Santa Fe Bay Window Caboose "999211," Crewtalk, 00		100	___
19894	Hood's Operating Milk Car with platform, 03-04		95	___
19895	3356 Santa Fe Horse Car with corral, 04		120	___
19896	USMC Missile Launch Sound Car "45," 03-04		165	___
19897	NYC Crane Car, TMCC, 04	159	263	___
19898	Nestle Nesquik Operating Milk Car with platform, 04		95	___
19899	Pennsylvania Crane Car "19899" CC, 03-05		260	___
19900	Toy Fair Boxcar, 87 u	65	80	___

			Exc	Mint
___	**19901**	"I Love Virginia" Boxcar, 87	25	35
___	**19902**	Toy Fair Boxcar, 88 u	55	80
___	**19903**	Christmas Boxcar, 87 u	22	34
___	**19904**	Christmas Boxcar, 88 u	32	43
___	**19905**	"I Love California" Boxcar, 88	20	24
___	**19906**	"I Love Pennsylvania" Boxcar, 89	26	32
___	**19907**	Toy Fair Boxcar, 89 u	38	55
___	**19908**	Christmas Boxcar, 89 u	30	39
___	**19909**	"I Love New Jersey" Boxcar, 90	19	25
___	**19910**	Christmas Boxcar, 90 u	35	38
___	**19911**	Toy Fair Boxcar, 90 u	75	95
___	**19912**	"I Love Ohio" Boxcar, 91	21	28
___	**19913**	Christmas Boxcar, 91	34	52
___	**19913**	Lionel Employee Christmas Boxcar, 91 u	150	200
___	**19914**	Toy Fair Boxcar, 91 u	38	50
___	**19915**	"I Love Texas" Boxcar, 92	35	60
___	**19916**	Lionel Employee Christmas Boxcar, 92 u	190	220
___	**19917**	Toy Fair Boxcar, 92 u	45	53
___	**19918**	Christmas Boxcar, 92 u	49	70
___	**19919**	"I Love Minnesota" Boxcar, 93	40	60
___	**19920**	Lionel Visitor's Center Boxcar, 92 u	16	28
___	**19921**	Lionel Employee Christmas Boxcar, 93 u	140	185
___	**19922**	Christmas Boxcar, 93	33	41
___	**19923**	Toy Fair Boxcar, 93 u	65	95
___	**19925**	Lionel Employee Learning Center Boxcar, 93 u	55	63
___	**19926**	"I Love Nevada" Boxcar, 94	21	26
___	**19927**	Lionel Visitor's Center Boxcar, 93 u	26	33
___	**19928**	Lionel Employee Christmas Boxcar, 94 u	205	230
___	**19929**	Christmas Boxcar, 94	30	40
___	**19931**	Toy Fair Boxcar, 94 u	49	65
___	**19932**	Lionel Visitor's Center Boxcar, 94 u	26	33
___	**19933**	"I Love Illinois" Boxcar, 95	21	27
___	**19934**	Lionel Visitor's Center Boxcar, 95 u	18	22
___	**19937**	Toy Fair Boxcar, 95 u	55	75
___	**19938**	Christmas Boxcar, 95	26	34
___	**19939**	Lionel Employee Christmas Boxcar, 95 u	100	128
___	**19941**	"I Love Colorado" Boxcar, 95	23	30
___	**19942**	"I Love Florida" Boxcar, 96	19	27
___	**19943**	"I Love Arizona" Boxcar, 96	20	25
___	**19944**	Lionel Visitor's Center Tank Car, 96 u		35
___	**19945**	Holiday Boxcar, 96		29
___	**19946**	Lionel Employee Christmas Boxcar, 96 u		195
___	**19947**	Lionel Toy Fair Boxcar, 96 u		200
___	**19948**	Visitor's Center Flatcar with trailer, 96 u		34
___	**19949**	"I Love NY" Boxcar, 97		50
___	**19950**	"I Love Montana" Boxcar, 97		30
___	**19951**	"I Love Massachusetts" Boxcar, 98		26
___	**19952**	"I Love Indiana" Boxcar, 98		31
___	**19955**	Lionel Visitor's Center Gondola with coil covers, 98 u		20
___	**19956**	Toy Fair Boxcar "777," 98 u		65
___	**19957**	Ambassador Caboose, 97 u		488
___	**19958**	Ambassador Caboose, silver (std O), 98 u		558
___	**19959**	Ambassador Caboose, gold (std O), 98 u	500	756

		Exc	Mint	
19964	U.S. JCI Senate Boxcar, 92 u	55	63	___
19968	"I Love Maine" Boxcar, 99		40	___
19969	"I Love Vermont" Boxcar, 99		40	___
19970	"I Love New Hampshire" Boxcar, 99		34	___
19971	"I Love Rhode Island" Boxcar, 99		34	___
19976	Lionel Employee Holiday Boxcar, 99 u		150	___
19977	Toy Fair Boxcar, 99 u		50	___
19981	Lionel Centennial Boxcar, 99		36	___
19982	Lionel Centennial Boxcar, 99		36	___
19983	Lionel Centennial Boxcar, 99		36	___
19984	Lionel Centennial Boxcar, 99		36	___
19985	"I Love Georgia" Boxcar, 99-00		45	___
19986	"I Love North Carolina" Boxcar, 99-00		40	___
19987	"I Love South Carolina" Boxcar, 99-00		40	___
19988	"I Love Tennessee" Boxcar, 99-00		55	___
19989	Toy Fair Boxcar, 00 u		55	___
19996	Toy Fair Boxcar, 01 u		50	___
19997	Lionel Employee Boxcar, 01 u		125	___
19998	Christmas Boxcar, 01		33	___
19999	Lionel Visitor's Center 4-bay Hopper, 02 u		153	___
20000	PRR Senator Coach 4-pack (std O), 13, 15		640	___
20005	SP Sunset Limited Coach 4-pack (std O), 13, 15		640	___
20010	UP City of Los Angeles Coach 4-pack (std O), 13, 15		640	___
20015	B&O Capitol Limited Coach 4-pack (std O), 13		640	___
20020	FEC City of Miami Coach 4-pack (std O), 13		640	___
20025	KCS Southern Belle Coach 4-pack (std O), 13		640	___
20030	MILW Olympian Coach 4-pack (std O), 13, 15		640	___
21029	World of Little Choo Choo Set, 94u, 95	36	43	___
21141	North Dakota State Quarter Gondola Bank, 07		60	___
21142	South Dakota State Quarter Hopper Bank, 07		60	___
21163	SuperStreets FasTrack Grade Crossing, 08-10		20	___
21164	SuperStreets 10" Transition to FasTrack, 08-10		9	___
21165	SuperStreets Transition to FasTrack, 2 pieces, 08-10		17	___
21168	City Traction Trolley Add-on, 08		75	___
21169	City Traction Speeder Add-on, 08		75	___
21170	NYC 15" Heavyweight Passenger Car 4-pack, 07		250	___
21175	NYC 15" Heavyweight Passenger Car 2-pack, 07		125	___
21198	ATSF Alco Diesel AA Set, horn, 08		200	___
21199	ATSF Midnight Chief Streamliner Car 4-pack, 08		200	___
21204	ATSF Midnight Chief Streamliner Car 2-pack, 08		100	___
21207	SP Diesel Work Train, 07		175	___
21212	NH Diesel Freight Set, 07		250	___
21217	Southern Diesel Executive Inspection Train, 07		175	___
21229	Ringling Bros. S2 Diesel Switcher, horn, 07		80	___
21230	Ringling Bros. Porter Locomotive, 07		105	___
21231	Ringling Bros. Streamliner Car 4-pack, 07		210	___
21234	Ringling Bros. Streamliner Car 2-pack, 07		105	___
21237	Ringling Bros. Flatcar with 3 wagons, 07		50	___
21238	Ringling Bros. Flatcar with 3 wagons, 07		50	___
21239	Ringling Bros. Flatcar with crates, 07		45	___
21240	Ringling Bros. Flatcar with front end loader and poles, 07		45	___
21252	Boy Flying Kite, 08		60	___
21253	Operating Bunk Car Yard Office, 07		80	___

		Exc	Mint
____ 21261	SuperStreets 2.5" Straight-to-Curve Connector, 08-10		9
____ 21265	Operating Voltmeter Car, 07		75
____ 21266	SuperStreets Intersection, 4 pieces, 08-10		40
____ 21267	PRR Boxcab Electric Locomotive, horn, 07		77
____ 21271	WP Operating Coal Dump Car with vehicle, 07		33
____ 21276	Congressional Diner, smoke, 07		110
____ 21277	Operating Flagman's Shanty, 08		70
____ 21279	Roach Wranglers Pest Control Van, 08		30
____ 21281	SuperStreets D21 Curve, 08-10		3
____ 21282	SuperStreets 2.5" Curve-to-Curve Connector, 4 pieces, 08-10		9
____ 21283	SuperStreets Tubular Track Grade Crossing, 08-10		18
____ 21284	SuperStreets 10" Tubular Transition, 08-10		8
____ 21285	SuperStreets 10" Tubular Transition, 2 pieces, 08-10		14
____ 21286	SuperStreets Intersection, 08-10		10
____ 21287	SuperStreets Y Roadway, 08-10		12
____ 21288	SuperStreets O Gauge Conversion Pins, 08-10		2
____ 21289	SuperStreets Connector Pins, 08-10		2
____ 21290	SuperStreets Hookup Wires, 2 pieces, 08-10		3
____ 21291	Dogbone Expander pack, 08-10		25
____ 21296	City Traction Classic Truck, 07		30
____ 21298	NYC 4-6-4 Hudson Locomotive "5279," CC, 07		500
____ 21316	PE RS3 Diesel "2815," CC, 07		350
____ 21324	Acrobats and Clowns Figures, 10 pieces, 08-10		12
____ 21325	Ringmaster Circus Figures, 5, with accessories, 08-10		12
____ 21326	PRR 15" Interurban Car 2-pack, 07		200
____ 21354	Fresh Never Frozen Fish Transport Car, 07		80
____ 21355	Dump Bin, 08-10		20
____ 21358	Special Addition Boxcar, Girl, 08-10		25
____ 21359	Special Addition Boxcar, Boy, 08-10		25
____ 21368	Passenger Coach Figures, 9 pieces, 08-10		11
____ 21369	Walking Figures, 8 pieces, 08-10		11
____ 21370	Sitting Figures, 6, with benches, 08-10		11
____ 21371	Standing Figures, 8 pieces, 08-10		11
____ 21372	Railroad Station Figures, 6, with accessories, 08-10		11
____ 21373	School Figures, 7, with accessories, 08-10		11
____ 21374	Service Station Figures, 5, with accessories, 08-10		11
____ 21375	Police Figures, 10, with dog, 08		20
____ 21376	Seated Passenger Figures, 40 pieces, 08		27
____ 21377	Mounted Police, 3, with horses, 08-10		11
____ 21378	Factory, 08-10		18
____ 21379	Police Station, 08-10		16
____ 21380	Colonial House, 08-10		16
____ 21381	Suburban Station, 08-10		16
____ 21382	School, 08-10		17
____ 21383	Suburban Ranch House, 08-10		15
____ 21384	Service Station with gas pumps, 08-10		17
____ 21385	Barn and Chicken Coop, 08-10		20
____ 21386	Firehouse, 08-10		17
____ 21387	Church, 08-10		15
____ 21388	Country L-shaped Ranch House, 08-10		16
____ 21389	Supermarket, 08-10		12
____ 21390	Diner, 08-10		15
____ 21394	Rotating Beacon, 08-09		31

		Exc	Mint
21396	Single Tunnel Portals, pair, 08-10		15
21397	SuperSnap 31" Remote Switch, left hand, 08-09		55
21398	SuperSnap 31" Remote Switch, right hand, 08-09		55
21399	SuperSnap 72" Remote Switch, left hand, 08-09		70
21400	SuperSnap 72" Remote Switch, right hand, 08-09		70
21412	NYC Plymouth Switcher Freight Set, 07		155
21430	SuperStreets D16 Curve, 08-10		2
21431	SuperStreets 10" Straight Track, 08-10		2
21432	SuperStreets D16 Curved Track, 8 pieces, 08-10		18
21433	SuperStreets 5" Straight Track, 4 pieces, 08-10		14
21434	SuperStreets 10" Straight Track, 8 pieces, 08-10		19
21435	World War II Seated Soldiers, 9, with benches, 08-09		20
21436	Rings and Things Circus Accessories, 08-09		10
21438	Remote Controller, 07-10		35
21442	City Figures, 7, with scooter, 08-10		11
21443	Factory Figures, 6, with accessories, 08-10		11
21444	Church Figures, 5, with accessories, 08-10		11
21445	Firefighting Figures, 11, with accessories, 08-10		20
21449	Operating Loading Platform with flatcar, 07-08		80
21450	Unloading Station with dump bins, 07		100
21451	Girder Bridge with stone piers, 07		40
21452	Graduated Trestle Set, 26 pieces, 07		50
21453	Elevated Trestle Set, 10 pieces, 07		40
21454	Double Tunnel Portals, 2 pieces, 08-10		20
21456	UPS Step Van, 07		30
21466	Ringling Bros. 15" Aluminum Advertising Car, 07		110
21469	Ringling Bros. Flatcar, white, with container, 07		45
21470	Ringling Bros. Flatcar, blue, with container, 07		45
21471	Ringling Bros. Flatcar with 2 trailers, 08-10		60
21472	Ringling Bros. Flatcar with 2 trailers, 08-10		60
21476	Strasburg Plymouth Diesel Switcher, 07		100
21494	WM RS3 Diesel "189," CC, 07		350
21529	Montana State Quarter Boxcar Bank, 08		45
21542	Washington State Quarter Tank Car Bank, 08		45
21543	Boyd Bros. Ford Classic Truck, 08		33
21549	Ringling Bros. Crew Bus, 08		33
21552	S.W.A.T. Team Step Van, 08		30
21560	Reading Flatcar with rail load, 07		25
21567	School Bus SuperStreets Set, 08		110
21568	Dirty Dogz Van SuperStreets Set, 08		100
21569	Angelo's Pizza Delivery Van, 08		30
21570	Flying Colors Painting Van, 08		30
21571	SuperStreets 10" Insulated Roadway, 2 pieces, 08-10		8
21572	SuperStreets 5" Straight School, 2 pieces, 08-10		8
21573	SuperStreets 5" Straight Stop Ahead, 2 pieces, 08-10		8
21574	SuperStreets 5" Straight Crosswalk, 2 pieces, 08-10		8
21575	SuperStreets 10" Crossing, 2 pieces, 08-10		10
21576	SuperStreets Skid Mark Roadway Pack, 08-10		13
21577	Snack-On Step Van, 08		30
21582	Keystone Coal Porter Locomotive, 08		100
21583	Keystone Coal Freight Car 4-pack, 08		100
21590	ATSF "Midnight Chief" 2-bay Hopper "162277," 08		25
21591	ATSF "Midnight Chief" Flatcar "94468" with trailer, 08		43

		Exc	Mint
21592	ATSF "Midnight Chief" Caboose, 08		25
21593	ATSF "Midnight Chief" Boxcar "621593," 08		35
21594	NYC Empire State Express 15" Aluminum Car 4-pack, 08-09		420
21599	SP Flatcar with wheel load, 07		35
21600	B&M RS3 Diesel "1538," CC, 08-09	113	350
21607	Jack Frost Hopper "327" with sugar load, 08		25
21609	Elephants and Giraffes, 2 pair, 08-10		13
21610	Lions and Tigers, 2 pair, 08-10		13
21611	Horses, 4 pieces, 08		13
21621	ATSF Operating Boxcar "22658," 08-09		90
21623	Rutland Operating Milk Car with platform, 08-10		150
21626	Rath Wood-sided Reefer "622," 09		45
21627	Greenlee Packing Wood-sided Reefer "3862," 10		45
21628	CNJ Reefer "1438," 08-09		35
21629	C&O Reefer "7783," 08-09		35
21630	UP Stock Car "42005," 09		45
21631	Reading Boxcar "107984," 08-09		35
21632	GN Boxcar "34285," 08-09		35
21633	RI "Route of the Rockets" Boxcar "21110," 09-10		40
21634	Tidewater Flying A 1-D Tank Car "1367," 09		40
21635	Southern Depressed Center Flatcar, 2 transformers, 09		43
21636	NS Flatcar with bulkheads and stakes, 08-09		35
21637	Ontario Northland Ribbed Hopper with coal, 09		40
21639	Pan Am Boxcar "32126," 08-09		55
21640	UP Modern Steel-sided Reefer "499030," 08-09		55
21641	Ringling Bros. Merchandise Flatcar, 08		50
21643	PRR Die-cast Gondola with covers, 09		73
21644	PRR 16-wheel Flatcar with transformer, 08-09		80
21646	DT&I Work Crane and Boom Car, 09		85
21649	City Traction Trolley with Ringling Bros. banner, 08-09		80
21651	Moo-Town Creamery Step Van, 08-09		38
21656	Quikrete Step Van, 08-09		42
21658	Ringling Bros. Vintage Truck, 08-09		42
21659	DT&I Flatcar "90059" with Ford trailer, 08-09		60
21662	Moo-Town Creamery Vending Machine, 08-09		13
21663	Moo-Town Creamery Bunk Car Ice Cream Shop, 08-09		115
21664	RI Operating Coal Dump Car with vehicle, 08-09		40
21665	Alaska Operating Log Dump Car with vehicle, 09		40
21667	Red River Lumber Boxcab Diesel with horn, 08-09		100
21668	CP Operating Hopper "9628," 08-09		45
21675	Mountain View Creamery Loading Depot, 08-10		130
21676	Beaver Creek Logging Die-cast Porter Locomotive, 08-09		120
21677	Ford Factory, 09		22
21679	Assured Comfort HVAC Van, 08-09		38
21680	Division of Prisons Bus SuperStreets Set, 08-09		150
21688	Ringling Bros. Heavyweight Coach 2-pack, 08-11		240
21691	Ringling Bros. Flatcar with 2 trailers, 08-10		60
21692	C&NW MP15 Diesel with Ringling Bros. banner, 08-09		140
21693	Southern MP15 Diesel Pair, powered and dummy, 10		200
21696	Ford Flatcar with 2 trucks, 08-09		53
21698	Lionel Van SuperStreets Set, 08-10		130
21701	Star Spangled GG1 Electric Locomotive "4837," 08-10		260
21702	Milwaukee Road Girder Bridge, 08-09	8	20

Number	Description	Exc	Mint	
21703	ATSF Black Mesa Aluminum Business Car, 09-10		160	___
21704	C&O Double Searchlight Car with vehicle, 08-09		50	___
21706	Chatham Police Van, 08-09		38	___
21707	NYC Aluminum Business Car, 09		160	___
21708	CN Operating Log Dump Car, 10		120	___
21709	PRR Girder Bridge, 08-09		15	___
21715	Ringling Bros. Stock Car, 08-09		60	___
21717	Pullman-Standard 1-D Tank Car, 08-09		35	___
21719	NYC Bay Window Caboose, 99		70	___
21720	Ringling Bros. Billboard Set #2, 08-09		10	___
21721	Warning Sign Pack, 12 pieces, 08-10		25	___
21730	Regulatory Sign Pack, 12 pieces, 08-10		25	___
21738	Railroad Crossing Sign Pack, 6 pieces, 08-10		21	___
21750	NKP Rolling Stock 4-pack, 98		160	___
21751	PRR Rolling Stock 4-pack, 98		145	___
21752	Conrail Unit Trailer Train, 98		285	___
21753	Service Station Fire Rescue Train, 98	505	590	___
21754	BNSF 3-bay Covered Hopper 2-pack (std O), 98	30	73	___
21755	4-bay Covered Hoppers 2-pack, 98		65	___
21756	Conrail Overstamped Boxcars 2-pack, 98		65	___
21757	UP Freight Car Set, 98	117	188	___
21758	Bethlehem Steel "44" (SSS), 99	113	375	___
21759	Canadian Pacific F3 Diesel Passenger Set, 99	413	930	___
21761	B&M Boxcar Set, 4-pack, 99		180	___
21763	New Haven Freight Set, 99		265	___
21766	ACL Passenger Car 2-pack, 99		385	___
21769	Centennial 1-D Tank Car Set, 4-pack, 99		239	___
21770	NYC Reefer Set, 4-pack, 99		225	___
21771	D&RGW Stock Car Set, 4-pack, 99		230	___
21774	Custom Series Consist I, 3-pack, 99		150	___
21775	Train Wreck Recovery Set, 99	95	220	___
21778	ATSF Train Master Diesel Freight Set, 99		950	___
21779	Seaboard Freight Car Set, 99	143	280	___
21780	NYC Aluminum Passenger Car 2-pack, 99		160	___
21781	Case Cutlery Freight Set, 99 u	700	1025	___
21782	PRR Congressional Set, 00		930	___
21783	Monday Night Football 2-pack, 01-02		50	___
21784	QVC PRR Coal Freight Steam Set, 00 u		360	___
21785	QVC Gold Mine Freight Steam Set, 00 u		300	___
21786	Santa Fe F3 Diesel ABBA Passenger Set, 00		1500	___
21787	Blue Comet Steam Passenger Set, 01-02		1525	___
21788	Postwar Missile Launch Freight Set, 02-03		350	___
21789	Norfolk Southern Piggyback Set, CC (SSS), 01		370	___
21790	CN TankTrain Dash 9 Diesel Freight Set, 02		630	___
21791	Freedom Train Diesel Passenger Set, RailSounds, 03		645	___
21792	C&O Coal Hopper 6-pack #2 (std O), 01		145	___
21793	Virginian Coal Hopper 6-pack #2 (std O), 01		160	___
21794	Pioneer Seed GP7 Diesel Freight Set, 01 u	630	925	___
21795	Case Farmall Freight Set, 01 u	540	750	___
21796	NJ Medical Steam Freight Set, 01 u		487	___
21797	SP Daylight Passenger Set, 01		670	___
21852	MILW PS-2CD Hopper 3-pack (std O), 06		155	___
21853	BNSF PS-2CD Hopper 3-pack (std O), 06		155	___

		Exc	Mint
21854	N&W PS-2CD Hopper 3-pack (std O), 06		155
21855	A&P Milk Car 3-pack, 06		150
21856	Bowman Dairy Milk Car 3-pack (std O), 06		150
21857	Western Dairy Milk Car 3-pack (std O), 06		150
21858	NP PS-4 Flatcar with trailers, 2-pack (std O), 06		170
21859	C&NW PS-4 Flatcar with trailers, 2-pack (std O), 06		170
21860	UP PS-4 Flatcar with trailers, 2-pack (std O), 06		170
21861	PRR PS-4 Flatcar with trailers (std O), 06		170
21863	ADM Unibody Tank Car 3-pack (std O), 06		135
21864	Cerestar Unibody Tank Car 3-pack (std O), 06		135
21865	Coe Rail Husky Stack Car 2-pack (std O), 06		170
21866	Santa Fe Husky Stack Car 2-pack (std O), 06		170
21872	C&O Offset Hopper 3-pack (std O), 05		130
21873	P&LE Offset Hopper 3-pack (std O), 06		145
21874	TTX Trailer Train 2-pack (std O), 06		170
21875	CSX Husky Stack Car 2-pack (std O), 06		170
21876	Disney Villain Hi-Cube Boxcar 3-pack, 05-06		135
21877	Domino Sugar 1-D Tank Car 3-pack (std O), 07		135
21878	Procor 1-D Tank Car 3-pack (std O), 07		135
21879	C&EI Offset Hopper 3-pack (std O), 07		145
21880	Erie Offset Hopper 3-pack (std O), 07		145
21881	Frisco Offset Hopper 3-pack (std O), 07-08		200
21882	Chessie System Offset Hopper 3-pack (std O), 07		145
21883	C&O 3-bay Hopper 2-pack (std O), 07-08		140
21884	Pennsylvania Power & Light 3-bay Hopper 2-pack (std O), 07		140
21885	Santa Fe 3-bay Hopper 2-pack (std O), 07		140
21886	C&NW 3-bay Hopper 2-pack (std O), 07-08		140
21888	IMC Canada Cylindrical Hopper 2-pack, 06		130
21893	Greenbrier Husky Stack Car 2-pack (std O), 07		170
21894	CSX Husky Stack Car 2-pack (std O), 07		170
21895	BN Husky Stack Car 2-pack (std O), 07		170
21896	Arizona & California Husky Stack Car 2-pack (std O), 07		170
21897	REA PS-4 Flatcar with trailers, 2-pack (std O), 07-08		170
21898	NYC PS-4 Flatcar with trailers, 2-pack (std O), 07-08		170
21899	Lackawanna PS-4 Flatcar with trailers, 2-pack (std O), 07		170
21900	Civil War Union Train Set, 99		375
21901	Civil War Confederate Train Set, 99		375
21902	MILW PS-4 Flatcar with trailers, 2-pack (std O), 07-08		170
21902	Construction Zone Set, 99 u		87
21904	UP PS-2 Covered Hopper 2-pack (std O), 07		120
21904	Safari Adventure Set, 99 u		90
21905	NYC Flyer Set, 99 u		100
21909	AGFA Film Steam Freight Set, 98 u		1413
21914	Lionel Lines Freight Set, 99		120
21916	Lionel Village Trolley, 99		75
21917	N&W Freight Set, 99		70
21918	PC PS-2 Covered Hopper 2-pack (std O), 07		120
21918	Thomas Circus Play Set, 00		100
21921	Imco PS-2 Covered Hopper 2-pack (std O), 07-08		120
21924	Holiday Trolley Set, 99		65
21925	Thomas the Tank Engine Island of Sodor Train Set, 99-00		150
21930	NYC PS-2 Covered Hopper 2-pack (std O), 07		120
21932	JCPenney NYC Freight Flyer Steam Set, 00 u		170

		Exc	Mint
21934	Custom Series Consist II, 3-pack, 99		140 ___
21936	Looney Tunes Train Set, 00 u		400 ___
21937	NYC Steel-sided Reefer 2-pack (std O), 07		130 ___
21939	Dubuque Steel-sided Reefer 2-pack (std O), 07-08		130 ___
21940	ADM Steel-sided Reefer 2-pack (std O), 07		130 ___
21941	National Car Steel-sided Reefer 2-pack (std O), 07		130 ___
21944	Celebrate a Lionel Christmas Steam Set, 00-01		165 ___
21945	Christmas Trolley Set, 00		100 ___
21948	NYC Freight Flyer Set, air whistle, 00		240 ___
21950	Maersk SD70 Diesel Maxi-Stack Set, 00	560	700 ___
21951	World War II Troop Train, 00		410 ___
21952	Lionel Lines Service Station Special Set, 00	125	294 ___
21953	Ford Mustang GP7 Diesel Set, CC, 01		345 ___
21955	D&RGW F3 Diesel AA Passenger Set, CC, 01	163	740 ___
21956	New York Central Freight Set, 99-00	152	355 ___
21969	Lionel Village Trolley Set, 00		85 ___
21970	SP RS3 Diesel Freight Set, horn, 00-01		110 ___
21971	Pennsylvania Flyer Steam Set, 00	75	195 ___
21972	Frisco GP7 Diesel Freight Set, horn, 00		150 ___
21973	ATSF Passenger Set, RailSounds, 00-01		375 ___
21974	ATSF Passenger Set, SignalSounds, 00-01	75	240 ___
21975	Burlington Steam Freight Set, SignalSounds, 00		275 ___
21976	Centennial Steam Freight Starter Set, 00	283	692 ___
21977	NYC Train Master Steam Freight Set, 99-00		620 ___
21978	ATSF Train Master Diesel Freight Set, 99-00		500 ___
21981	JCPenney NYC Flyer Set, 00 u		150 ___
21988	NYC Freight Set, RailSounds, 00		325 ___
21989	Burlington Steam Freight Set, RailSounds, 00		338 ___
21990	NYC Flyer Freight Set, RailSounds, 00		175 ___
21999	Whirlpool Steam Freight Set, 00 u	500	740 ___
22103	PRR A5 Scale Switcher "411," CC, 08-09		330 ___
22104	PRR Freight Car 3-pack, 08		135 ___
22105	NYC Empire State Express 4-6-4 Hudson "5429," CC, 08-09		420 ___
22113	NYC Empire State Express 15" Aluminum Car 2-pack, 08-10		210 ___
22116	Ringling Bros. Diesel Freight Set, 08-10		245 ___
22121	Ringling Bros. Freight Set, 08-10		390 ___
22126	Ringling Bros. Expansion Pack, 08-10		135 ___
22131	NH Streamliner Car 3-pack, 07		150 ___
22135	CB&Q S2 Diesel Switcher "9305," horn, 07		80 ___
22136	Erie S2 Diesel Switcher "522," horn, 07		80 ___
22137	Alaska MP15 Diesel "1552," horn, 07		100 ___
22138	Astoria Heat & Power Porter Locomotive "4," 07		100 ___
22139	LIRR Speeder, 08		50 ___
22140	CNJ Boxcab Diesel "1000," horn, 08		90 ___
22141	Lackawanna 15" Interurban Car 2-pack, 07		200 ___
22142	FEC Operating Dump Car, 07		70 ___
22143	B&A Operating Log Dump Car, 08-09		70 ___
22144	Alaska Operating Coal Dump Car with vehicle, 08		33 ___
22145	WM Operating Log Dump Car with vehicle, 08		33 ___
22146	PFE Operating Boxcar, 08		80 ___
22147	B&O Operating Hopper with coal, 08		35 ___
22148	GN Operating Hopper with coal, 08		35 ___
22149	Dairymen's League Operating Milk Car, green, with platform, 08		140 ___

		Exc	Mint
____ 22150	D&RGW Bunk Car, smoke, 08		65
____ 22151	Alaska Searchlight Car with vehicle, 08		45
____ 22152	NKP 2-bay Outside-braced Hopper "31299," 08		50
____ 22153	L&N 2-bay Offset Hopper "78660," 08		50
____ 22154	D&H 2-bay Rib Side Hopper "5737," 07		50
____ 22155	Erie-Lackawanna 2-bay Aluminum Hopper "21353," 08		60
____ 22156	ACF Demonstrator 2-bay Aluminum Hopper "44586," 07		60
____ 22157	GN Aluminum Tank Car "74787," 08		60
____ 22158	MILW Bulkhead Flatcar "967116" with wood, 08-09		43
____ 22159	BNSF Flatcar "585011" with trailer, 08		43
____ 22160	UP Flatcar "58059" with container, 08		43
____ 22161	Conrail Flatcar "705910" with NS container, 08		43
____ 22162	Foppiano Wine 3-D Tank Car "1112," 08		45
____ 22163	PRR Weed Control Car "6321226," 07		45
____ 22166	PRR Reefer "19492," 08		25
____ 22167	Seaboard Reefer "16622," 08		25
____ 22168	N&W Boxcar "645772," 08		25
____ 22169	ATSF Reefer "11744," 07		25
____ 22170	P&LE Reefer "22300," 07		25
____ 22171	B&O DD Boxcar "495289," 08		25
____ 22172	CB&Q Stock Car "52731," 08		25
____ 22174	Erie-Lack. Transfer Caboose, 07		25
____ 22176	PRR Caboose "478884," 07		25
____ 22177	L&N Caboose "100," 07		25
____ 22179	NYC Depressed Center Flatcar "66256" with 2 girders, 08		25
____ 22180	IC Depressed Center Flatcar with 2 transformers, 07		25
____ 22182	RI Gondola "180043" with coils, 08		25
____ 22184	B&O Covered Hopper "604321," 08		25
____ 22185	UP Covered Hopper "53186," 08		25
____ 22186	P&LE (NYC) Gondola "17243," 08-09		35
____ 22187	PRR 2-D Tank Car "6351815," 07		25
____ 22188	Deep Rock 3-D Tank Car "2152," 08		25
____ 22189	NP Java Diner, smoke, 08		110
____ 22190	C&O Operating Billboard, 08		65
____ 22191	Operating Passenger Station, 08-09		105
____ 22192	Hot Box Operating BBQ Shack, 07		80
____ 22193	Cold Drinks Vending Machine, 08		12
____ 22194	Water Tower with light, 08-09		20
____ 22199	City Traction Trolley Barn, 08-09		65
____ 22202	Loading Ramp, 08-10		20
____ 22203	Dairymen's League Operating Milk Car, white, with platform, 07		140
____ 22204	Snacks Vending Machine, 08		12
____ 22205	Soup and Sandwich Vending Machine, 08		12
____ 22206	PRR Crew Bus, 08		30
____ 22222	Ringling Bros. Speeder Chase Set, 08-10		92
____ 22225	Ringling Bros. Jomar Heavyweight Private Car, 08-11		120
____ 22226	Ringling Bros. 18" Caledonia Heavyweight Private Car, 08		100
____ 22227	Ringling Bros. 18" Advertising Car, 08		100
____ 22228	Ringling Bros. Flatcar with 3 wagons, 08		50
____ 22231	Ringling Bros. Flatcar with 3 wagons, 08		50
____ 22235	Ringling Bros. Flatcar with pole wagon and truck, 08		75
____ 22238	Ringling Bros. Work Caboose with calliope wagon, 08		40
____ 22240	Ringling Bros. Flatcar/Stock Car with wagon, 08		50

No.	Description	Exc	Mint
22243	Ringling Bros. Human Cannonball Car, 08		45
22244	Ringling Bros. Operating Searchlight Car with 3 spotlights, 08		60
22247	Ringling Bros. Stock Car "54," 08		50
22248	Ringling Bros. Stock Car "47," 08		50
22249	Ringling Bros. Dining Dept. Billboard Reefer, 08		80
22250	Ringling Bros. Dining Dept. Wood-sided Reefer, 08-09		90
22251	Ringling Bros. Dormitory Bunk Car "22," 08		75
22252	Ringling Bros. Operating Billboard, 08-09		75
22253	Ringling Bros. Vintage Billboard Set #1, 08		9
22255	Ringling Bros. Aluminum Coach "40010," 08-10		165
22257	Ringling Bros. Aluminum Shop Car "63002," 08-10		165
22258	Ringling Bros. 18" Aluminum Large Animal Car, 08-10		165
22259	Ringling Bros. Flatcar with trailer, 08		53
22260	Ringling Bros. Tractor Trailer, 08		30
22261	Idaho State Quarter Hopper Bank, 08		65
22262	Wyoming State Quarter Tank Car Bank, 08		50
22263	Utah State Quarter Boxcar Bank, 08		45
22264	SuperStreets Figure-8 Expander Pack, 08-10		35
22267	Mulligan Spring Water Step Van, 08		30
22270	Quikrete Classic Truck with 2 pallets, 08		33
22271	MILW EP-5 Electric Locomotive "E20," CC, 08-09		460
22272	MILW Olympian Hiawatha 18" Aluminum Car 4-pack, 08		480
22277	MILW Olympian Hiawatha 18" Aluminum Car 2-pack, 08		250
22280	Erie-Lackawanna RS3 Diesel "933," CC, 08-09		350
22281	Southern Train Master Diesel "6300," CC, 08-09		420
22282	Southern Bay Window Caboose "X270," 08-09		70
22283	UP S2 Diesel Switcher "1103" and Caboose "25384," 08		130
22286	GN Boxcab Electric Locomotive "5008-A," horn, 08		90
22287	North Shore Line 15" Interurban Car 2-pack, 08		230
22288	Commuter Train Station, 6 road name stickers, 09		25
22289	Ringling Bros. 18" Aluminum Passenger Car 2-pack, 08		270
22290	Erie Boxcar "86448" with graffiti, 08		46
22291	C&NW Stock Car "14303," 08		46
22292	Land o' Lakes Butter Billboard Reefer, 08		75
22293	PRR 4-bay Hopper "253776," 08		65
22294	Montana Rail Link 3-bay Aluminum Hopper "50049," 08		70
22295	Canada Wheat 4-bay Aluminum Hopper "606418," 08		73
22296	Eaglebrook Aluminum Tank Car "19039," 08		70
22297	Petri Wine 3-D Tank Car "904," 08-09		45
22298	Cotton Belt Offset Cupola Wood-sided Caboose "2230," 08		80
22299	MILW Bay Window Caboose "980502," 08-09		70
22300	Detroit, Toledo & Ironton Coil Car "1352," 08		60
22301	NYC Flatcar "506090" with freight kit, 08		35
22302	C&O Flatcar "80951" with freight kit, 08		35
22303	Extruded Aluminum I-Beam, 3 pieces, 08-09		6
22304	Rails, 12 pieces, 08-09		6
22305	Small Transformer Load, pair, 08-09		15
22306	Large Transformer Load, 08		19
22307	Forklifts, 3, with pallets, 08-09		27
22308	Loaders with crates, pair, 08-09		13
22309	Loaders with logs, pair, 08-09		13
22310	KBL Logistics Container 2-pack, 08		40
22312	Commemorative Quarter Extended Vision Caboose, 09		80

			Exc	Mint
___	22313	ATSF Boxcar "137460," 08		25
___	22314	Coastal King Seafood Wood-sided Reefer, 08		25
___	22315	Wisconsin & Southern "God Bless America" Boxcar, 09		43
___	22316	NP Depressed Center Flatcar "66130" with water tank, 08		25
___	22317	U.S. Air Force Hopper "55175" with ballast load, 08		25
___	22318	DM&IR Ore Car "29991," 08		25
___	22319	Celanese Chemicals 1-D Tank Car "12730," 08		25
___	22320	Baldwin Locomotives Works 1-D Tank Car "6809," 08		25
___	22321	B&O Operating Boxcar, 08		45
___	22322	PRR Operating Ballast Dump Car, 08		75
___	22323	FEMA Voltmeter Car, 08		75
___	22324	C&NW Cop and Robber Chase Gondola, 08-09		55
___	22325	White Milk Cans, 10 pieces, 08-10		8
___	22326	Twin Searchlight Tower, 08-10		33
___	22327	Tommy's Bunk Car Grill, 08-09		100
___	22328	Santa Fe Operating Freight Transfer Platform, 08-09		130
___	22329	Dual Track Signal Bridge, 08-10		45
___	22330	Stella's Heavyweight Diner, smoke, 08-09		140
___	22331	Coffee Vending Machine, 08		12
___	22332	Spring Water Vending Machine, 08		12
___	22333	Candy Vending Machine, 08		12
___	22334	Ford Plymouth Diesel Switcher and Ore Car 6-pack, 08		200
___	22335	NS Operating Paint Shop with boxcar, 08-09		140
___	22344	KBL Logistics ISO Tank, 08		19
___	22346	Tableau Circus Wagons, 08		13
___	22349	Forklift with 6 pallets, 08-09		23
___	22350	Twin Lamp Posts, 3 pieces, 08-09		22
___	22352	Lamp Posts, 4 pieces, 08-09		20
___	22354	Portable Spotlights, 3 pieces, 08-09		15
___	22356	High Tension Poles, 4 pieces, 08-09		8
___	22358	Rail Yard Signs, 12 pieces, 08-09		10
___	22360	Telephone Poles, 6 pieces, 08-09		7
___	22362	Girder Bridge, 08-09		8
___	22363	Stone Bridge Piers, pair, 08-10		27
___	22365	Heavyweight Coach 6-wheel Scale Trucks, pair, 08-09		25
___	22366	Aluminum Passenger Coach 4-wheel Scale Trucks, pair, 08-09		25
___	22367	Timken Scale Sprung Trucks, pair, 08-09		19
___	22368	Bettendorf Scale Sprung Trucks, pair, 08-09		19
___	22369	Scale Couplers, pair, 08-09		6
___	22379	SuperStreets Barricade, 2 pieces, 08-10		11
___	22387	Kiosk with 3 vending machines, 08-09		40
___	22391	Ford MP15 Diesel "10021," horn, 08		115
___	22392	Ford Farming Boxcar "1681," 08		30
___	22393	Ford Stampings DD Boxcar "101," 08		35
___	22394	Ford 2-bay Covered Hopper "1667," 08		30
___	22395	Ford Speeder "14," 08		65
___	22396	Ford Water Tower, 08		25
___	22397	Ford Rotating Sign Tower, 08		55
___	22398	Boyd Bros. and Ford Barn and Chicken Coop, 08		25
___	22399	Ford ISO Tank, 08-09		21
___	22402	PRR Streamlined K4 4-6-2 Pacific Locomotive, tender, 09-10		500
___	22408	Ringling Bros. Tractor Trailer #1, 08-09		35
___	22411	Tableau Wagon Set #2, 08-10		18

22412	PRR Operating Flagman's Shanty, 08-09		90 ___
22414	Linde Union Carbide Boxcar with aluminum tank, 08-09		70 ___
22415	Ringling Bros. Flatcar with circus wagon, 08		50 ___
22417	Ringling Bros. Flatcar with container, 09		55 ___
22420	PRR Broadway Limited Passenger Car 2-pack, 09-10		300 ___
22423	GN Aluminum Passenger Car 2-pack, 09-10		360 ___
22426	Ford Gondola "13447" with coils, 08-09		43 ___
22427	Ford Operating Billboard, 08-09		75 ___
22428	Ford Tin Sign Replica 4-pack, 08-09		17 ___
22433	PRR Broadway Limited Passenger Car 4-pack, 09-10		600 ___
22438	Mail Crane, 08-10		30 ___
22439	Milwaukee Road Aluminum Passenger Car 2-pack, 09-11		360 ___
22447	Wabash Die-cast 2-bay Ribbed Hopper "37751," 08-09		60 ___
22449	UP Crew Bus, 08-09		38 ___
22450	Seaboard Die-cast Hopper with gravel, 10		80 ___
22454	Oklahoma State Quarter Die-cast Hopper Bank, 08-09		75 ___
22455	New Mexico State Quarter Die-cast Gondola Bank, 08-09		74 ___
22456	Arizona State Quarter Tank Car Bank, 08-09		55 ___
22457	Alaska State Quarter Boxcar Bank, 09		55 ___
22458	Hawaii State Quarter Die-cast Hopper Bank, 09		75 ___
22459	Southern Aluminum Passenger Car 2-pack #1, 09		300 ___
22460	Southern Aluminum Passenger Car 2-pack #2, 09		300 ___
22461	Scale Skeleton Log Car 4-pack, 08-09		160 ___
22467	Railroad Water Tower, 08-09		23 ___
22468	Fast Eddie's Used Car Lot with 2 die-cast vehicles, 08-09		50 ___
22469	Cola Illuminated Vending Machine, 08-09		13 ___
22470	SuperStreets Guard Rails, 08-10		20 ___
22472	Ringling Bros. Tin Sign Replica 4-pack, 08-09		17 ___
22477	Lionel Tin Sign Replica 4-pack, 08-09		15 ___
22482	Vintage Tin Sign Replica 4-pack, 08-09		15 ___
22487	Scooter Gang with scooters, 09-10		13 ___
22492	Airport Revolving Searchlight, 10		40 ___
22493	Ringling Bros. Lighted Clown Wood-sided Reefer, 09		75 ___
22494	Ford Flatcar with 2 Thunderbird convertibles, 09		53 ___
22496	Vita O Flavored Water Vending Machine, 09		13 ___
22497	Top Pop Soda Illuminated Vending Machine, 09		13 ___
22498	Ringling Bros. Flatcar with 3 circus wagons, 09-10		55 ___
22500	Defense Dept. Flatcar with 2 jeeps and soldier, 09		50 ___
22501	C&NW Railroad Van, CC, 09-10		100 ___
22502	Ringling Bros. Flatcar with 3 circus wagons, 09-10		55 ___
22504	Ford Water Tower with vintage Ford logo, 09-10		25 ___
22505	Sparkling Springs Beverage Truck, 09		45 ___
22506	SuperStreets Fishtail Roadway, 09		25 ___
22507	Ringling Bros. Flatcar with boxcar and ticket wagon, 09		60 ___
22509	Pallet Pack with banded loads, 09		20 ___
22510	Lionel Step Van, CC, 09-10		100 ___
22511	BNSF Flatcar with helicopter, 09		50 ___
22513	Ringling Bros. Heavyweight Advertising Car, 09		120 ___
22514	NYC Girder Bridge, 09-10		15 ___
22515	Milwaukee Road/REA Scale Boxcar "6436," 09		55 ___
22516	BNSF MP15 Diesel "3704" with horn, 09		120 ___
22517	Quick Lane Ford Motorcraft Auto Parts Van, 09-10		42 ___
22518	Lionel Tank Container Leasing ISO Tank, 09-10		23 ___

		Exc	Mint
___ 22519	Roma Wine Wood-sided Billboard Reefer, 09-10		70
___ 22520	WWII Soldiers in Action, 10 pieces, 09-10		20
___ 22521	1959 Ford Billboard Set, 09		10
___ 22523	American Flyer Vintage Truck, 09		38
___ 22524	Ford Coil Car "749772," 09		73
___ 22525	Vermont Railway Operating Boxcar "177," 09		50
___ 22526	Crabby Matt's Smoking Heavyweight Diner, 09		150
___ 22527	Toledo, Peoria & Western Boxcar "5067," 09-10		55
___ 22528	GN Stock Car "55973," 09-10		55
___ 22529	U.S. Army 1-D Tank Car "11278," 09		35
___ 22530	Milwaukee Road Aluminum Coach "627," 09-11		180
___ 22531	Southern Girder Bridge, 09		15
___ 22532	Montana Rail Link 1-D Tank Car "100017," 09		35
___ 22533	GN Aluminum Coach "1377," 09-10		180
___ 22534	SuperStreets D16 Curve Guard Rails, 09-10		20
___ 22536	SuperStreets D21 Curve Guard Rails, 09-10		22
___ 22538	Ford Modern Aluminum Tank Car "30166," 09		90
___ 22539	BNSF Flatcar "922267" with Ford trailer, 09-10		60
___ 22542	PRR Flatcar "480227" with freight kit, 09		40
___ 22543	Biodiesel 2-D Tank Car "1544," 09		40
___ 22544	Ringling Bros. Wood-sided Gondola with equipment, 09		63
___ 22548	Kiosk #2 with 3 illuminated vending machines, 09		40
___ 22553	Convenience Mart, 09-10		25
___ 22554	Auto Parts Store, 09-10		20
___ 22555	Ringling Bros. Tractor with Gold Tour container, 09-10		55
___ 22558	PRR Flatcar "469301" with milk containers, 09		50
___ 22559	UP Gondola "229794" with freight kit, 09-10		80
___ 22560	CB&Q Wood-sided Gondola "85150" with spools, 09-10		60
___ 22561	Gondola Scrap Load, 09		9
___ 22562	Operation Lifesaver Boxcar with flashing LEDs, 09		65
___ 22563	Ringling Bros. Handcar and Trailer Set, 10-11		70
___ 22566	SuperStreets 2.5" Straight Roadway, 4 pieces, 10		12
___ 22568	Generators, 2 pieces, 09		9
___ 22570	Large transformer, 09		22
___ 22571	Cage Wagon Set, 09-10		18
___ 22573	Display Base, 09		20
___ 22574	Ringling Bros. Flatcar "39" with trailer, 09		60
___ 22577	Biodiesel Storage Tank with 2 figures, 09-10		40
___ 22578	Ringling Bros. Heavyweight Coach "70," 09		120
___ 22579	Circus Horses, 4 pieces, 09-10		15
___ 22580	Bollards and Chains, 09-10		20
___ 22582	Pipe Stack Load, 09		30
___ 22583	KBL Operating Wind Turbine, 09-10		75
___ 22584	KBL Die-cast 16-wheel Flatcar "34807," 09		85
___ 22587	Old Reading Flatcar Foot Bridge with stone piers, 09-10		50
___ 22590	Roadside Fender Bender, 09-10		75
___ 22592	SuperStreets D16 Turn Roadways, left and right, 10		35
___ 22595	SuperStreets D21 Turn Roadways, left and right, 10		39
___ 22598	SuperStreets Adjustable Straight Kit, 09-10		20
___ 22600	Wire Spool Load, 6 pieces, 09		20
___ 22610	Napa Valley Wine Train Alco FA Diesel AA Set, 10		230
___ 22611	Napa Valley Wine Train Alco FA Diesel "71," powered, 10		150
___ 22612	Napa Valley Wine Train Alco FA Diesel "72," unpowered, 10		80

		Exc	Mint	
22613	Napa Valley Wine Train 15" Passenger Car 4-pack, 10		450	___
22614	Napa Valley Wine Train Heavyweight Observation "1018," 10		110	___
22615	Napa Valley Wine Train Heavyweight Observation "1011," 10		110	___
22616	Napa Valley Wine Train Heavyweight Diner "1090," 10		115	___
22617	Napa Valley Wine Train Heavyweight Diner "1015," 10		115	___
22618	Signal Oil Co. 1-D Tank Car, 10		40	___
22619	PRR Paoli MU Commuter Train 2-pack, 10		290	___
22622	PRR Paoli Motorized Combine, 10		200	___
22623	PRR Commuter Train Station, 10		35	___
22624	NH Die-cast Plymouth Switcher with snowplow, 10		160	___
22625	Ringling Bros. 18" Aluminum Generator Car, 10-11		180	___
22627	Ringling Bros. Lighted Clown Wood-sided Reefer, 10-11		90	___
22628	Ringling Bros. 18" Aluminum Advertising Car, 10-11		180	___
22629	Ringling Bros. Stock Car, 10-11		60	___
22630	Ringling Bros. Tractor and Trailer, 10-11		35	___
22633	Ringling Bros. 18" Aluminum Coach, 10-11		180	___
22634	Ringling Bros. 18" Heavyweight Advertising Car, 10-11		146	___
22635	Ringling Bros. Operating Dual Searchlight Car, 10-11		60	___
22637	Quikrete Step Van, 10		48	___
22638	PRR Crew Bus, 10		45	___
22639	B&O Boxcab Diesel "195," 10		100	___
22640	Central of Georgia Boxcar "5823," 10		45	___
22641	New Haven Boxcar "36438," 10		45	___
22642	Ringling Bros. Operating Large Animal Feed Car, 10-11		150	___
22643	Ford MP15 Diesel "10022," 10-11		135	___
22644	Ford Motorcraft 48' Aluminum Tank Car, 10-11		95	___
22645	Ringling Bros. Operating Tent Pole Dump Car, 10-11		130	___
22646	Ford Speeder, 10-11		75	___
22647	Rock Island Gondola "180044," 10		35	___
22648	PRR Gondola "353381," 10		35	___
22651	Central Vermont Operating Milk Car with platform, 10		175	___
22653	Starlite Diner with parking lot, 10		200	___
22654	Ringling Bros. Flatcar with 3 circus wagons, 10-11		60	___
22656	Ringling Bros. Flatcar with 3 circus wagons, 10-11		60	___
22658	Operating Flagman's Shanty, 10		100	___
22659	Union 76 1-D Tank Car "6322," 10		40	___
22660	Moose Pond Creamery Operating Loading Depot, 10		140	___
22661	WM 2-Bay Covered Hopper "5051," 10		35	___
22662	PRR Reefer "19494," 10		45	___
22663	New Haven Illuminated Caboose, 10		40	___
22667	Acme Scrap Platform Crane, 10		60	___
22670	ATSF Operating Boxcar, 10		140	___
22671	Smoking Southern Bay Window Caboose, 10		90	___
22672	Ringling Bros. 18" Sarasota Observation Car, 10-11		146	___
22673	Ford Water Tower with light, 10		27	___
22674	MILW 21" Aluminum Passenger Car 2-pack, 10-11		400	___
22679	Ringling Bros. Operating Billboard, 10-11		100	___
22902	Quonset Hut, 98-99	30	45	___
22907	Die-cast Girder Bridge, 98-01		10	___
22910	Gilbert Tractor Trailer, 98		20	___
22914	PowerHouse Lockon, 98-01		24	___
22915	Municipal Building, 98-99		28	___
22916	190-watt Power Accessory System, 98		425	___

			Exc	Mint
	22918	Locomotive Backshop, 98	300	460
	22919	ElectroCouplers Kit for GP9 Diesel, 98-00		20
	22922	Intermodal Crane, 98		195
	22931	Die-cast Cantilever Signal Bridge, 98-06		35
	22934	Walkout Cantilever Signal, 98-03		42
	22936	Coaling Tower, 3 pieces, 98		85
	22940	Mast Signal, 98-00		37
	22942	Accessories Box, 98-01		20
	22944	Automatic Operating Semaphore, 98-03, 08	17	35
	22945	Block Target Signal, 98-00		39
	22946	Automatic Crossing Gate and Signal, 98-99		45
	22947	Auto Crossing Gate, 98-00		36
	22948	Gooseneck Street Lamps, set of 2, 98-00		30
	22949	Highway Lights, set of 4, 98-99		20
	22950	Classic Street Lamps, set of 3, 98-02		20
	22951	Dwarf Signal, 98-00		24
	22952	Classic Billboards, set of 3, 98-00		15
	22953	Linex Gasoline Tall Oil Tank, 98-99		6
	22954	Linex Gasoline Wide Oil Tank, 98-99		6
	22955	ElectroCouplers Kit for J Class and B&A tenders, 98-00		20
	22956	ElectroCouplers Kit for NW2 Switcher, 98		20
	22957	ElectroCouplers Kit for F3 Diesel, 98-01		20
	22958	ElectroCouplers Kit for Dash 9 Diesel, 98-01		20
	22959	ElectroCoupler Conversion Kit for Atlantic Locomotive, 98-01		13
	22960	Trainmaster Command Basic Upgrade Kit, 98-01		34
	22961	Standard GP9 Diesel B Unit Upgrade Kit, 98-01		30
	22962	Deluxe GP9 Diesel B Unit Upgrade Kit, black trucks, 98-01		44
	22963	RailSounds Upgrade Kit, steam RailSounds, 98-01		55
	22964	RailSounds Upgrade Kit, diesel RailSounds, 98-01		55
	22965	Culvert Loader, CC, 98-01	160	255
	22966	Figure-8 Add-on Track Pack (027), 98-16	10	17
	22967	Double Loop Add-on Track Pack (027), 98-16		62
	22968	Double Loop Track Pack (027), 98-03		65
	22969	Deluxe Complete Track Pack (O), 98-16		120
	22972	Bascule Bridge, 98-99		337
	22973	Lionel Corporation Tractor and Trailer, 98		15
	22975	Culvert Unloader, CC, 99-00		225
	22979	GP9 Diesel B-Unit Deluxe Upgrade Kit, silver trucks, 98-01		34
	22980	TMCC SC-2 Switch Controller, 99-16		130
	22982	Postwar ZW Controller and Transformer Set, 98		265
	22983	180-watt PowerHouse Power Supply, 99-18		125
	22990	Flatcar with Route 66 autos, 4-pack, 99		37
	22991	Christmas Tree and Blue Comet Train, 99-00		60
	22993	Route 66 Sinclair Dino Cafe, 99-00		210
	22997	Oil Drum Loader, 99-00		100
	22998	Triple Action Magnetic Crane, 99		220
	22999	Sound Dispatching Station, 99-00		90
	23000	NYC Dreyfuss Hudson Operating Base, 2-rail, 92 u		190
	23001	NYC Dreyfuss Hudson Operating Base, 3-rail, 93 u		190
	23002	NYC Hudson Operating Base, 92 u, 93-94		190
	23003	PRR B-6 Switcher Operating Base, 92 u, 93-94		190
	23004	NP 4-8-4 Operating Base, 92 u, 93-94		190
	23005	Reading T-1 Operating Base, 92 u, 93-94		190

		Exc	Mint	
23006	Chessie System T-1 Operating Base, 92 u, 93-94		190	___
23007	SP Daylight Operating Base, 92 u, 93-94		190	___
23008	NYC L-3 Mohawk Operating Base, 92 u, 93-94		190	___
23009	PRR S2 Turbine Locomotive Operating Base, 92 u, 93-94		190	___
23010	31" Remote Switch, left hand (O), 95-99	30	37	___
23011	31" Remote Switch, right hand (O), 95-99	20	30	___
23012	F3 Diesel ABA Operating Base, 92 u, 93-94		190	___
24018	PRR Boxcar, 05		25	___
24101	Mainline Color Position Signal, 04-08		25	___
24102	Industrial Water Tower, 03		55	___
24103	Double Floodlight Tower, 09		42	___
24104	Hobo Tower, 03-05		70	___
24105	Track Gang, 03-06		70	___
24106	Exploding Ammunition Dump, 02		25	___
24107	Missile Firing Range Set, 02		60	___
24108	World War II Pylon, 03		80	___
24109	Santa Fe Railroad Tugboat, 03		125	___
24110	Pennsylvania Railroad Tugboat, 03		118	___
24111	Swing Bridge, 03		215	___
24112	Oil Field with bubble tubes, 03		44	___
24113	Lionelville Ford Auto Dealership, 03		225	___
24114	AMC/ARC Gantry Crane, CC, 03		195	___
24115	AMC/ARC Log Loader, CC, 03, 06-07		140	___
24117	Illuminated Covered Bridge, 02-23		100	___
24119	Big Bay Lighthouse, 04-05		170	___
24122	Lionelville People Pack, 03, 08-09, 15-17		27	___
24123	Passenger Station People Pack, 03, 08-09, 15-20		27	___
24124	Carnival People Pack, 03, 08-20	5	27	___
24130	TMCC 135/180 PowerMaster, 04-12		79	___
24131	Dumbo Pylon, 03		70	___
24134	Bethlehem Steel Gantry Crane, 02		200	___
24135	Lionel Lighthouse, 02-03		100	___
24137	Mr. Spiff and Puddles, 03, 08		34	___
24138	Playtime Playground, 03, 08		50	___
24139	Duck Shooting Gallery, 03		110	___
24140	Charles Bowdish Homestead, 03		60	___
24147	Lionel Sawmill, 03		90	___
24148	Coal Tipple Coal Pack, 02, 08-10, 13-20		15	___
24149	NYC Hobo Hotel, 02		42	___
24151	Hobo Campfire, 03		25	___
24152	Conveyor Lumber Loader, 03		65	___
24153	Railroad Control Tower, 03, 08-10	30	63	___
24154	Maiden Rescue, 03		35	___
24155	Blinking Light Billboard, 04-10		21	___
24156	Lionelville Street Lamps, 4-pack, 04-23		35	___
24159	Illuminated Station Platform, 04-08		32	___
24160	Rub-a-Dub-Dub, 04		42	___
24161	Test O' Strength, 04-06		70	___
24164	Summer Vacation, 04-05		80	___
24168	Tire Swing, 04-05		70	___
24170	Rover's Revenge, 04-05		70	___
24171	Campbell's Soup Water Tower, 04		45	___
24172	Balancing Man, 04-05		70	___

		Exc	Mint
___ 24173	Derrick Platform, 03-05		60
___ 24174	Icing Station, 04-06		100
___ 24176	Irene's Diner, 06-07		65
___ 24177	Hot Air Balloon Ride, 04, 06		95
___ 24179	Scrambler Amusement Ride, 04-07		165
___ 24180	Choo Choo Barn Lionelville Zoo, 04-05		105
___ 24182	Lionelville Firehouse, 04		100
___ 24183	Lionelville Gas Station, 04-09		115
___ 24187	Classic Billboard Set: 3 stands and 5 inserts, 04-08		10
___ 24190	Station Platform, 05-09		17
___ 24191	Park People Pack, 04-18		27
___ 24192	Park Benches People Pack, 04-09		23
___ 24193	Railroad Yard People Pack, 04-08, 14-18	10	19
___ 24194	Civil Servants People Pack, 04-18		27
___ 24196	Farm People Pack, 04-09		23
___ 24197	City Accessory Pack, 04-17		27
___ 24200	Lionel FasTrack Book, 07-10, 13-15		35
___ 24201	UPS Centennial Operating Billboard Signmen, 07		100
___ 24203	Polar Express Original Figures, 4 pieces, 08-23		30
___ 24204	Christmas Tractor Trailer with trees, 08		25
___ 24205	Classic Billboard Set, 08-10		20
___ 24206	MOW Gantry Crane, 08		280
___ 24212	Lionel Art Blinking Billboard, 08-09		23
___ 24213	Universal Lockon, 12-16		4
___ 24214	Postwar "395" Floodlight Tower, 08		75
___ 24215	MTA Metro-North Passenger Station, 07		53
___ 24218	Sunoco Elevated Tank, 08-09		75
___ 24219	PRR Plastic Girder Bridge, 08		18
___ 24220	ATSF Girder Bridge, 08-09		18
___ 24221	UP Die-cast Girder Bridge, 08		30
___ 24222	UPS Die-cast Girder Bridge, 08		30
___ 24223	Santa's Sleigh Pylon, 08		150
___ 24224	Postwar "38" Water Tower, 08-09		150
___ 24226	Christmas Toy Store, 08		52
___ 24227	Halloween Animated Billboard, 08-09		54
___ 24228	Christmas Operating Billboard, 08		38
___ 24229	Pennsylvania Water Tower, 08-09		23
___ 24230	Maiden Rescue, 08		60
___ 24232	Burning Switch Tower, 08		80
___ 24233	Exploding Ammunition Dump, 08		36
___ 24234	Missile Firing Range, 08		43
___ 24235	UPS Water Tower, 08		80
___ 24236	Wimpy's All-Star Burger Stand, 08		97
___ 24238	Sunoco Oil Derrick, 08		90
___ 24240	MTA Metro-North Blinking Billboard, 07		21
___ 24242	Postwar "352" Icing Station, 08		100
___ 24243	Rosie's Roadside Diner, 08		85
___ 24244	Commuter People, 08, 13-18		27
___ 24245	MTA Metro-North Illuminated Station Platform, 07		32
___ 24248	Manual Crossing Gate, 08-23		20
___ 24250	Mainline Gooseneck Lamps, pair, 08-09		32
___ 24251	Polar Express Caribou Pack, 08-23		30
___ 24252	Polar Express Wolves and Rabbits Figures, 08-23		30

		Exc	Mint
MODERN 1970-2023			
24264	Halloween People, 08-12		23 ___
24265	Trick or Treat People, 08-13		23 ___
24270	Operating Forklift Platform, 08-09		280 ___
24272	Train Orders Building, 08		80 ___
24273	Christmas Water Tower, 08-10		23 ___
24274	Christmas Girder Bridge, 08		18 ___
24279	PowerMaster Bridge, 08-13		55 ___
24283	NYC Girder Bridge, 09-10		21 ___
24284	Halloween Girder Bridge, 09-11		21 ___
24285	CP Rail Girder Bridge, 08-09		30 ___
24286	Polar Express Girder Bridge, 09-14		21 ___
24287	ATSF Blinking Light Water Tower, 09		30 ___
24288	NYC Blinking Light Water Tower, 09		30 ___
24293	Legacy Module Garage, 08-09		50 ___
24294	AEC Nuclear Reactor, 09-10		325 ___
24295	Cowen's Corner Hobby Shop, 09		420 ___
24296	Engine House, 09-12, 14		70 ___
24298	Franklin Mutual Bank, 08		60 ___
24299	Main Street Ice Cream Parlor, 08		37 ___
24500	D&RGW Alco PA Diesel AA Set, 04		530 ___
24503	D&RGW Alco PB Diesel, 04		150 ___
24504	Santa Fe E6 Diesel AA Set, CC, 03		530 ___
24507	Milwaukee Road E6 Diesel AA Set, CC, 03		530 ___
24511	Burlington FT Diesel AA Set, RailSounds, 03		225 ___
24516	Santa Fe F3 Diesel B Unit, 03		235 ___
24517	NYC F3 Diesel B Unit "2404," powered, CC, 03		250 ___
24518	WP F3 Diesel B Unit, 03		275 ___
24519	B&O F3 Diesel B Unit, 03		270 ___
24520	Alaska F3 Diesel AA Set, 03		650 ___
24521	Alaska F3 Diesel B Unit, nonpowered, 03		200 ___
24522	Alaska F3 Diesel B Unit "1519," powered, CC, 03		300 ___
24528	Postwar "2379T" Rio Grande F3 Diesel A Unit, nonpowered, 04		175 ___
24529	Santa Fe F3 Diesel AA Set, CC, 04		690 ___
24532	Santa Fe F3 Diesel B Unit "18A," nonpowered, 04		150 ___
24533	Santa Fe F3 Diesel B Unit "18B," 04		200 ___
24534	Erie-Lackawanna F3 Diesel ABA Set, CC, 05		900 ___
24538	Erie-Lackawanna F3 Diesel B Unit "8042," powered, CC, 05		225 ___
24544	NYC FA2 Diesel AA Set, CC, 05		600 ___
24547	NYC FB2 Diesel B Unit "3330" (std O), 05		150 ___
24548	CN FPA-4 Diesel AA Set, CC, 05		600 ___
24551	CN FPB-4 Diesel B Unit "6865" (std O), 05		150 ___
24552	UP F3 Diesel ABA Set, CC, 05		680 ___
24556	UP F3 Diesel B Unit "900C," powered, CC, 05		285 ___
24562	Santa Fe F3 Diesel B Unit, powered, 04-05	100	300 ___
24563	PRR F3 Diesel B Unit, powered, 04-05		195 ___
24566	Napa Valley Wine Train FPA-4 A Unit "71," powered, 05		400 ___
24567	Napa Valley Wine Train FPA-4 B Unit "72," nonpowered, 05		100 ___
24570	Santa Fe FT Diesel B Unit, nonpowered, 05		85 ___
24571	Postwar "2383" ATSF F3 Diesel A Unit, powered, 05		400 ___
24572	Postwar "2383" ATSF F3 Diesel A Unit, nonpowered, 05		100 ___
24573	Postwar "2383C" Santa Fe F3 Diesel B Unit, nonpowered, 05		180 ___
24574	UP E7 Diesel AA Set, CC, 06		700 ___
24577	UP E7 Diesel B Unit "990," nonpowered (std O), 06		150 ___

			Exc	Mint
___	24578	UP E7 Diesel B Unit "988," powered, 06		300
___	24579	NYC E7 Diesel AA Set, CC, 06		700
___	24582	NYC E7 Diesel B Unit "4105," nonpowered (std O), 06		150
___	24583	NYC E7 Diesel B Unit "4104," powered, 06		300
___	24584	Pennsylvania F7 Diesel ABA Set, CC, 06		900
___	24588	Pennsylvania F7 Diesel B Unit "9643B," powered, 06-07		300
___	24589	Santa Fe F7 Diesel ABA Set, CC, 06-07		900
___	24593	Santa Fe F7 Diesel B Unit "332B," powered, 06-07		300
___	24594	PRR F7 Diesel Breakdown B Unit, RailSounds, 06-07		160
___	24595	Santa Fe F7 Diesel Breakdown B Unit, RailSounds, 06-07		270
___	24596	UP E7 Diesel Breakdown B Unit, RailSounds, 06		270
___	24597	NYC E7 Diesel Breakdown B Unit, RailSounds, 06		270
___	25002	P&LE Boxcar "20982," 05	20	25
___	25003	WP Boxcar, orange with silver feather, 05		30
___	25008	Holiday Boxcar, 06		50
___	25009	Santa Fe Hi-Cube Boxcar "14064," 06		30
___	25010	NP Boxcar "48189," 06		30
___	25011	Angela Trotta Thomas "Santa's Break" Boxcar, 06		50
___	25014	PRR Boxcar, silver, 10		30
___	25016	ATSF Boxcar, 10		35
___	25022	NYC Boxcar, 06		35
___	25024	GM&O Boxcar, 07		30
___	25025	Reading Boxcar "106502," 07-08		35
___	25026	RI Hi-Cube Boxcar, 07-08		35
___	25030	Billboard Boxcar with catalog art, 06		20
___	25033	Holiday Boxcar, 07		50
___	25034	Angela Trotta Thomas "Santa's Workshop" Boxcar, 07		50
___	25035	Disney Holiday Boxcar, 06		50
___	25041	UPS Centennial Boxcar #1, 06		60
___	25042	UPS Centennial Boxcar #2, 07		60
___	25043	Macy's Parade Boxcar, 06		40
___	25047	It's a Wonderful Life Bedford Falls Boxcar, 07 u		75
___	25048	It's a Wonderful Life Happy Holidays Boxcar, 07 u		75
___	25050	British Columbia Hi-Cube Boxcar "8008," 08		35
___	25051	Seaboard Boxcar, 08		35
___	25052	Disney Holiday Boxcar, 07		75
___	25053	NYC DD Boxcar "75500," 08		55
___	25054	Angela Trotta Thomas "Christmas Memories" Boxcar, 08		55
___	25057	PRR Boxcar "19751," 08		20
___	25058	Santa Fe Boxcar, 10		30
___	25059	Democrat 2008 Election Boxcar, 08		50
___	25060	Republican 2008 Election Boxcar, 08		50
___	25061	Holiday Boxcar, 08		55
___	25063	Conrail Boxcar "25063," 09		40
___	25064	CP Rail Hi-Cube Boxcar, 09-10	18	40
___	25065	Disney Holiday Boxcar, 08		40
___	25066	Holiday Boxcar, 09		65
___	25067	Angela Trotta Thomas "General Delivery" Boxcar, 09		65
___	25068	D&H Boxcar, 08 u		60
___	25077	Milwaukee Road Boxcar "8484" 09-10	13	40
___	25083	Wizard of Oz Boxcar, 1, 09		50
___	25084	Wizard of Oz Boxcar, 2, 09		50
___	25087	Wabash Boxcar "6439," 10-11		40

		Exc	Mint
25088	Georgia Power Boxcar, 10		40
25093	Seaboard Boxcar, 10		30
25095	Texas Special Boxcar, 10		100
25096	CN Boxcar, 10		45
25103	Chessie "Steam Special" Madison Car 2-pack, 05		100
25106	Pennsylvania Madison Car 4-pack, 05		210
25111	Pennsylvania Madison Car 2-pack, 05		120
25114	Lionel Lines Passenger Car 3-pack, 05		120
25118	Lionel Lines Passenger Car 2-pack, 05		80
25121	Southern Streamliner Car 4-pack, 05		210
25126	Southern Streamliner Car 2-pack, 05-06		120
25134	Polar Express Add-on Diner, 05-17		70
25135	Polar Express Add-on Baggage Car, 05-17		70
25142	NYC Combination Car, "5018," 05		40
25143	NYC Coach, "3807," 05		45
25144	NYC Observation, "4152," 05		40
25148	B&O Madison Car 4-pack, 06-07		220
25153	B&O Madison Car 2-pack, 06-07		125
25156	California Zephyr Streamliner Car 4-pack (std O), 06-07		220
25161	California Zephyr Streamliner Car 2-pack, 06-07		125
25164	UP Madison Car 4-pack, 06-07		220
25169	UP Madison Car 2-pack, 06-07		125
25176	B&O Baggage Car, TrainSounds, 06-07		160
25177	UP Baggage Car, TrainSounds, 06-07		160
25178	California Zephyr Streamliner Baggage Car, TrainSounds, 06-07		160
25186	Polar Express Hot Chocolate Car Add-on, 06-14, 16-17		70
25187	GN Streamliner Car 4-pack, 07		220
25188	GN Streamliner Car 2-pack, 07		125
25189	GN Streamliner Baggage Car, TrainSounds, 07		160
25196	North Pole Central Vista Dome Car, 07-08		45
25197	North Pole Central Baggage Car, 07-10		45
25198	PRR Vista Dome Car "4058," 07-08		45
25199	PRR Baggage Car "9359," 07-09		45
25307	B&M Operating Boxcar, 07		55
25404	FEC Champion Aluminum Passenger Car 2-pack, 04-05		290
25407	FEC Champion Aluminum Diner, StationSounds, 04-05		290
25408	Santa Fe El Capitan Aluminum Passenger Car 2-pack, 05		290
25411	Santa Fe El Capitan Aluminum Diner, StationSounds, 05		290
25412	B&O Columbian Aluminum Passenger Car 2-pack, 05		275
25415	B&O Columbian Aluminum Diner, StationSounds, 05		290
25416	SP Daylight Aluminum Passenger Car 2-pack, 04-05		290
25419	SP Daylight Aluminum Diner, StationSounds, 04-05		290
25420	PRR Trail Blazer Aluminum Passenger Car 2-pack, 04-05		290
25423	PRR Trail Blazer Aluminum Diner, StationSounds, 04-05		290
25433	UP City of Denver Aluminum Passenger Car 4-pack (std O), 05		1000
25438	UP Aluminum Passenger Car 2-pack, 05		250
25441	UP City of Denver 18" Aluminum Diner, StationSounds, 05		290
25442	REA Baggage Car, 05		60
25443	Santa Fe Super Chief Vista Dome "Regal Pass," 05		60
25444	Santa Fe Super Chief Coach "Indian Falls," 05		60
24445	Santa Fe Super Chief Observation "Vista Valley," 05		60
25446	Santa Fe Super Chief Streamliner Car 2-pack, 05		150
25447	Santa Fe Super Chief Vista Dome "Royal Gorge," 05		70

			Mint
____	25448	Santa Fe Super Chief Coach "Indian Arrow," 05	70
____	25450	PRR Congressional Aluminum Car 4-pack (std O), 06-07	580
____	25455	PRR Congressional Aluminum Car 2-pack (std O), 06-07	300
____	25458	PRR Congressional Diner, StationSounds (std O), 06-07	300
____	25473	NYC Commodore Vanderbilt Aluminum Car 2-pack (std O), 06	300
____	25476	NYC Commodore Vanderbilt Diner, StationSounds (std O), 06	300
____	25496	Texas Special 21" Streamliner Diner, StationSounds (std O), 07	300
____	25503	Santa Fe Heavyweight Passenger Car 4-pack (std O), 07-09	495
____	25504	Santa Fe Heavyweight Passenger Car 2-pack (std O), 07-09	265
____	25505	Santa Fe Heavyweight Diner, StationSounds (std O), 07-09	295
____	25506	SP Heavyweight Passenger Car 4-pack (std O), 07	495
____	25507	SP Heavyweight Passenger Car 2-pack (std O), 07-08	265
____	25508	SP Heavyweight Diner, StationSounds (std O), 07-08	295
____	25512	Texas Special Streamliner Car 2-pack (std O), 07	300
____	25514	Best Friend of Charleston Coach, 08	125
____	25515	MILW Heavyweight Passenger Car 4-pack (std O), 07	495
____	25516	MILW Heavyweight Passenger Car 2-pack (std O), 07	265
____	25517	MILW Heavyweight Diner, StationSounds (std O), 07-08	295
____	25518	PRR Heavyweight Passenger Car 4-pack (std O), 07	495
____	25519	PRR Heavyweight Passenger Car 2-pack (std O), 07	265
____	25520	PRR Heavyweight Diner, StationSounds (std O), 07-08	295
____	25521	B&O Heavyweight Passenger Car 4-pack (std O), 07	495
____	25522	B&O Heavyweight Passenger Car 2-pack (std O), 07	265
____	25523	B&O Heavyweight Diner, StationSounds (std O), 07-08	295
____	25559	Phantom IV Passenger Car 4-pack, 08	380
____	25574	UP Streamlined Diner, StationSounds (std O), 08	325
____	25575	Polar Express Heavyweight Car 2-pack, 09	400
____	25576	Polar Express Scale Observation Car, 14, 16	210
____	25578	Polar Express Heavyweight Add-on Coach, 09	200
____	25582	New York City Transit R30 Subway 2-pack, 10	400
____	25586	Polar Express Heavyweight Baggage Car, 10, 12-14	210
____	25587	Polar Express Abandoned Toy Car, 10, 13	200
____	25595	New York City Transit R16 Subway 2-pack, 10	400
____	25598	Polar Express Heavyweight Combination Car, 12-14	210
____	25600	Postwar Scale CP 18" Aluminum Passenger Car 4-pack , 11	640
____	25605	Postwar Scale CP 18" Aluminum Passenger Car 2-pack , 11	320
____	25608	ATSF Super Chief 18" Aluminum Passenger Cars 4-pack, 11	640
____	25613	ATSF Super Chief 18" Aluminum Passenger Cars 2-pack, 11	320
____	25616	UP 18" Passenger Car 2-pack (std O), 11	320
____	25619	PRR "Lindbergh Special" Passenger Car 2-pack, 11	280
____	25622	Milwaukee Road 18" Passenger Car 4-pack, 11	640
____	25623	Milwaukee Road 18" Passenger Car 2-pack, 11	320
____	25630	Polar Express Scale Heavyweight Diner, 12-14, 16	210
____	25631	Lionel Funeral Set Add-on 2-pack (std O), 13	300
____	25635	PRR Red Arrow Heavyweight Coach 3-pack (std O), 13	430
____	25639	PRR Red Arrow Heavyweight Diner (std O), 13	150
____	25646	ATSF Scout Heavyweight Coach 4-pack (std O), 12-14	550
____	25651	ATSF Scout Heavyweight Coach 2-pack (std O), 12-14	280
____	25654	Southern Crescent Limited Heavyweight Passenger Car 2-pack, 12	550
____	25655	Blue Comet Heavyweight Passenger Car 2-pack, 12-13	550
____	25656	Alton Limited Heavyweight Passenger Car 2-pack, 12-14	550
____	25665	Amtrak Acela Passenger Car 2-pack, 12	500
____	25713	NYC 20th Century Limited Heavyweight 4-pack (std O), 12-14	550

		Exc	Mint	
25714	NYC 20th Century Limited Van Twiller Combo Car (std O), 12		140	___
25715	NYC 20th Century Limited Schuyler Mansion Sleeper Car (std O), 12		140	___
25716	NYC 20th Century Limited Macomb House Sleeper Car (std O), 12		140	___
25717	NYC 20th Century Limited Catskill Valley Observation (std O), 12		140	___
25718	NYC 20th Century Limited Heavyweight Car 2-pack, 12-14		280	___
25719	NYC 20th Century Limited Baggage Car "4857" (std O), 12		140	___
25720	NYC 20th Century Limited Poplar Highlands Sleeper (std O), 12		140	___
25721	NYC 20th Century Limited Heavyweight Diner "655" (std O), 12		280	___
25722	D&RGW California Zephyr 18" Aluminum Car 4-pack, 12		640	___
25727	WP California Zephyr 18" Aluminum Passenger Car 2-pack, 12		320	___
25731	CB&Q California Zephyr 18" Aluminum Car 2-pack, 12		320	___
25757	Texas Special Passenger Car 2-pack, 13-14		400	___
25760	PRR Passenger Car 2-pack, 13-14		400	___
25773	SAL Round-roof Boxcar "19297" (std O), 14		80	___
25790	NYC 20th Century Limited Heavyweight Diner (std O), 12		140	___
25795	Polar Express 10th Anniversary Scale Coach, 14		215	___
25795	Polar Express Gold Coach, 17		200	___
25796	Polar Express 10th Anniversary Scale Observation Car, 14, 16		215	___
25922	NS Caboose, 13-14	10	25	___
25923	Interstate 1-D Tank Car, 13-14	12	30	___
25930	John Adams Presidential Boxcar, 13, 15-16		70	___
25931	Andrew Johnson Presidential Boxcar, 13, 15-16		70	___
25932	Calvin Coolidge Presidential Boxcar, 13, 15-16		70	___
25933	Harry S. Truman Presidential Boxcar, 13, 15-16		70	___
25934	Santa Fe Reefer 3-pack, 14-17		145	___
25938	PRR Freight Expansion 3-pack, 13		155	___
25942	Western Freight Expansion 3-pack, 13-16		155	___
25946	SP Hi-Cube Boxcar "128132," 13-15		50	___
25947	North Pole Express Jack Frost Reefer, 13		43	___
25958	Gingerbread Dough Vat Car, 13-14		60	___
25959	Gingerbread 3-D Tank Car, 13		55	___
25960	Christmas Tree Transparent Boxcar, 13-14		75	___
25961	Thanksgiving on Parade Boxcar, 13		60	___
25962	Thanksgiving Poultry Car, 13		70	___
25963	A Christmas Story 30th Anniversary Boxcar, 13-14		65	___
25964	Silver Bell Casting Co. Ore Car, 13		55	___
25965	Polar Express 10th Anniversary Boxcar, 13		65	___
25972	MILW Scale Round-roof Boxcar (std O), 15	35	61	___
25973	Seaboard Round-roof Boxcar "19297" (std O), 14		80	___
25977	A Christmas Story Leg Lamp Mint Car, 13		80	___
26000	C&O Flatcar with pipes, 01		20	___
26001	BP Flatcar "6424" with trailers, 01 u		150	___
26002	Monopoly Pennsylvania Ave. Flatcar w/Airplane, 00 u		60	___
26003	Lackawanna Flatcar with NH trailer, 01		60	___
26004	Conrail Flatcar "71693" with trailer, 01		50	___
26005	Nickel Plate Flatcar with trailer, 01		55	___
26006	Southern Flatcar "50126" with trailer, 01		50	___
26007	NW Flatcar "203029" with trailer, 01		50	___
26008	Farmall Flatcar, 01 u		100	___
26011	B&M Bulkhead Flatcar, 01 u	20	30	___
26013	CN Flatcar with Zamboni ice resurfacing machine, 01		48	___
26014	JCPenney Flatcar, 01 u		145	___
26016	Soo Line Flatcar with trucks, 01 u		120	___

		Exc	Mint
26017	Soo Line Flatcar with trailer, 01 u		120
26018	Soo Line Flatcar with trailer, 01 u		120
26019	Alaska Gondola "13801," 02		30
26020	Postwar "3830" Flatcar with submarine, 02		46
26021	CN Flatcar with trailer, 02		44
26022	PFE Flatcar with trailer, 02		32
26023	Postwar "6816" Flatcar with bulldozer, 02		65
26024	Postwar "6817" Flatcar with scraper, 02		65
26025	Postwar "6407" Flatcar with rocket, 02		42
26026	Postwar "6413" Flatcar with Mercury capsules, 02		95
26027	Flatcar "6425" with U.S. Army boat, 02		30
26028	Conrail Well Car "768121," 02		40
26030	NYC Flatcar "601172" with stakes and bulkheads, 02		22
26033	NYC Gondola "6462," 01		30
26035	LL Flatcar with traffic helicopter, 01		50
26039	Lions Flatcar with 2 Zamboni ice resurfacing machines, 02		39
26042	B&O Gondola "601272" with canisters, 03		19
26043	Seaboard Flatcar "48109" with trailer, 03		30
26044	NYC Flatcar "506089" with trailers, 03		35
26045	Postwar "2411" Flatcar with pipes, 03		40
26046	Postwar "6561" Flatcar with cable reels, 03		30
26047	Postwar "2461" Flatcar with transformer, 03		25
26048	Postwar "6801" Flatcar with boat, 02		29
26049	Speedboat Willie Flatcar with boat, 03		29
26053	PRR Gondola with canisters, 04-05		20
26055	C&O Flatcar "475227" w/Trailer Train Truck, 03		50
26056	Southern Bulkhead Flatcar "50125," 02		19
26057	SP Flatcar "599365" w/Tractors, 02		37
26058	SP Flatcar "599366" w/Trailer Frames, 02		35
26060	Postwar "6467" Flatcar w/Bulkheads, 03		42
26061	Lionelville Tree Transport Gondola, 03		40
26062	NYC Gondola "26062" with cable reels, 03		19
26063	Pennsylvania Bulkhead Flatcar "26063," 03		19
26064	Rock Island Flatcar "90088" with trailer, 04		34
26065	REA Flatcar with trailers "TLCX2," 04		35
26066	Great Northern Bulkhead Flatcar "26066," 04		20
26067	Southern Gondola "60141" with cable reels, 04		20
26070	Nestle Nesquik Flatcar "26070" with trailer, 03		70
26077	LL Flatcar "6424" with autos, girls set add-on, 03		44
26078	LL Flatcar "6801" with boat, boys set add-on, 03		40
26080	NJ Medical School Flatcar with handcar, 03		80
26082	Frisco Auto Carrier, 2-tier, 04		20
26085	New York Auto Carrier, 2-tier, 05		27
26086	Alaska Flatcar with bulkheads, 05		25
26087	Rock Island Gondola with canisters, traditional, 05		27
26089	LRRC Western Union Telegraph Gondola w/Handcar, 10		70
26090	Elvis Presley Flatcar w/Billboards, 05		45
26091	Elvis Flatcar with tractor and trailer, traditional, 05		60
26092	WC Gondola "54214" w/Canisters, 04		50
26093	Hobby Town USA Gondola w/Canisters, 04 u		45
26094	UP Screened Auto Carrier, 04		55
26095	CSX Screened Auto Carrier, 04		55
26096	BNSF Screened Auto Carrier, 04		55

		Exc	Mint	
26097	ATSF Screened Auto Carrier "89474" (std O), 04	26	45	___
26099	PRR Auto Carrier "500423," 3-tier, 07		30	___
26100	PRR 1-D Tank Car, 00		27	___
26101	Len-Oil 1-D Tank Car "6015," 00		34	___
26102	AEC Glow-in-Dark 1-D Tank Car, 00		58	___
26103	GATX Tank Train 1-D Tank Car "44588," 00		34	___
26107	BP Petroleum 3-D Tank Car, 00 u		105	___
26108	Lionel Visitor's Center Reefer "206482," 00 u		38	___
26109	NYC (P&LE) 1-D Tank Car, 00		42	___
26110	SP 3-D Tank Car "6415," 00-01		15	___
26111	Frisco Tank Car, 00		29	___
26112	Gulf Oil Tank Car, 00		40	___
26113	U.S. Army 1-D Tank Car, 00		35	___
26114	Service Station 1-D Tank Car (SSS), 00		32	___
26115	Lionel Centennial Tank Car, 00 u		90	___
26116	Pepe LePew 1-D Tank Car, 00 u		85	___
26118	NYC Tank Car "101900," 01		23	___
26119	Protex 3-D Tank Car "1054," 00		29	___
26120	KCS Tank Car "1229," 00		32	___
26122	Pioneer Seed Tank Car, 00 u		60	___
26123	Santa Fe Stock Car "23002," 01		35	___
26124	C&O 1-D Tank Car "X1019," 01		30	___
26125	Winter Wonderland Clear Tank Car with confetti, 00		50	___
26126	Cheerios Boxcar, 98		70	___
26127	Wellspring Capital Management Tank Car with confetti, 00 u	110	233	___
26131	Santa Fe 1-D Tank Car "335268," 02		22	___
26132	UP 1-D Tank Car "69015," 02		40	___
26133	Tootsie Roll 1-D Tank Car "26133," 02		40	___
26135	Whirlpool 1-D Tank Car, 01 u		60	___
26136	Southern 1-D Tank Car "8790011," 03		20	___
26137	Jack Frost 1-D Tank Car "106," 03		32	___
26138	Nestle Nesquik 1-D Tank Car "26138," 03		40	___
26139	Lionel Lines Stock Car "26139" with horses, 03		39	___
26141	Whirlpool 1-D Tank Car, 03 u		97	___
26143	Airco 1-D Tank Car "1137," 03		45	___
26144	Chessie System 1-D Tank Car "2233," 02		22	___
26145	Do It Best 1-D Tank Car, 03 u		82	___
26146	Valspar 1-D Tank Car, 03 u		95	___
26147	Diamond Chemicals 1-D Tank Car "6315," Archive Collection, 02		33	___
26149	Egg Nog 1-D Tank Car, 03		43	___
26150	Alaska 3-D Tank Car "26150," 03		23	___
26151	NP Wood-sided Reefer "26151," 03	13	29	___
26152	Morton Salt 1-D Tank Car "26152," 04		40	___
26153	Pillsbury 1-D Tank Car "26153," 04		40	___
26154	NYC 3-D Tank Car "26154," 04		25	___
26155	Pennsylvania 1-D Tank Car "26155," 04		20	___
26156	North Western Wood-sided Reefer "15356," 04		20	___
26157	Ballyhoo Brothers Circus Stock Car "26157," 04		35	___
26158	Campbell's Soup 1-D Tank Car, 04		35	___
26164	LL 1-D Tank Car "6315," girls set add-on, 03		43	___
26167	New Haven 1-D Tank Car, traditional, 05		27	___
26168	Conrail 3-D Tank Car, traditional, 05		27	___
26169	Santa Fe Wood-sided Reefer, traditional, 05		27	___

			Exc	Mint
	MODERN 1970-2023			
___	26170	Atlanta States Gas 1-D Tank Car, 05	20	25
___	26171	Alaska 1-D Tank Car, 05		30
___	26176	Tidmouth Milk 1-D Tank Car, 05		35
___	26179	GN 3-D Tank Car, 06	15	35
___	26180	DM&IR 1-D Tank Car "S15," 06		30
___	26181	NYC Wood-sided Reefer, 06		30
___	26193	UP 1-D Tank Car, 07		20
___	26194	Hooker Chemical 1-D Tank Car, 06		45
___	26195	PRR 3-D Tank Car "2280," 06		20
___	26196	Candy Cane 1-D Tank Car, 06		60
___	26197	D&H 1-D Tank Car "55," 07-08		35
___	26198	D&RGW 3-D Tank Car, 07		30
___	26199	WP PFE Wood-sided Reefer "55327," 07		30
___	26200	NKP Boxcar "18211," 98		35
___	26201	Operation Lifesaver Boxcar, 98		29
___	26203	D&H Boxcar "1829," 98		25
___	26204	Alaska Boxcar "10806," 98-99		35
___	26205	Rocky & Bullwinkle Boxcar, 99		36
___	26206	Curious George Boxcar, 99		40
___	26208	Vapor Records Boxcar #2, 98		60
___	26214	Celebrate the Century Stamp Boxcar, 98 u		97
___	26215	AEC Glow-in-the-Dark Boxcar, 98		105
___	26216	Cheerios Boxcar, 98 u		83
___	26218	Quaker Oats Boxcar, 98 u		464
___	26219	Ace Hardware Boxcar, 98 u		NRS
___	26220	Smuckers Boxcar, 98 u		96
___	26222	Penn Central Boxcar "125962," 99		31
___	26223	FEC Boxcar "5027," 99		31
___	26224	D&H Boxcar, 99		24
___	26228	Vapor Records Holiday Boxcar, 99 u		130
___	26230	AEC Glow-in-the-Dark Boxcar #2, 99		59
___	26232	Martin Guitar Lumber Boxcar "9823," 99		50
___	26234	NYC Boxcar, 99		29
___	26235	Valentine Boxcar, 99		40
___	26236	Aircraft Boxcar, 99		28
___	26237	Boy Scout Boxcar, 99		85
___	26238	Detroit Historical Museum Boxcar, 99		29
___	26239	M.A.D.D. Boxcar, 99		19
___	26240	RailBox Boxcar, 99-00		24
___	26241	Norfolk & Western Boxcar, 99-00		17
___	26242	D.A.R.E. Boxcar, 99		30
___	26243	Christmas Boxcar, 99		35
___	26244	Woody Woodpecker Boxcar, 99		43
___	26247	Lionel Lines Boxcar, 99		38
___	26253	Acme Explosives Boxcar, 99 u		NRS
___	26254	Keebler Boxcar, 99 u		NRS
___	26255	NYC Boxcar "200495," 99 u		30
___	26256	Salvation Army Charity Boxcar, 99		29
___	26257	Wheaties Boxcar, 99		86
___	26264	Lionel Station Boxcar, 99		44
___	26265	NYC Pacemaker Boxcar, 00		30
___	26271	AEC Glow-in-the-Dark Boxcar, 99		62
___	26272	Christmas Boxcar, 00		42

		Exc	Mint	
26275	Boy Scout Boxcar, 00		55	___
26276	C&O Boxcar "23296," 99-00		23	___
26277	UP Boxcar "491050," 00		20	___
26278	Cap'n Crunch Christmas Boxcar, 99		698	___
26280	Tinsel Town Express Boxcar, music, 00		50	___
26284	Toy Fair Preview Boxcar, 99 u		725	___
26285	NYC Pacemaker Boxcar, 00		40	___
26288	AEC Glow-in-Dark Boxcar, 99		55	___
26290	SP Boxcar, 00		20	___
26291	Pennsylvania Boxcar "47158," 00		20	___
26292	Frisco Boxcar "22015," 00		20	___
26293	Burlington Boxcar, 00		30	___
26294	Centennial Express Boxcar, 00		NRS	___
26295	Trainmaster Boxcar, 99 u		55	___
26296	Service Station Boxcar Set (SSS), 00		105	___
26298	Taz Bobbing Boxcar, 00		70	___
26300	UPS Flatcar with trailers, 04		50	___
26301	UPS Flatcar with airplane, traditional, 05		53	___
26302	Troublesome Truck #1, 05		35	___
26303	Troublesome Truck #2, 05		35	___
26305	SP Auto Carrier, 2-tier, 06		30	___
26306	D&RGW Gondola "56135" with canisters, 06		30	___
26307	Chessie System Bulkhead Flatcar, 06		30	___
26308	Hard Rock Cafe Flatcar with billboards, 06		55	___
26309	Alaska Depressed Center Flatcar with cable reels, 06		50	___
26310	CGW Flatcar "3707" with trailer, 06		55	___
26311	Santa Fe Flatcar with pickups, 06		60	___
26317	AEC Gondola with toxic waste containers		30	___
26318	AEC Gondola with toxic waste containers		30	___
26327	NYC Gondola w/Canisters	10	15	___
26330	Gondola with trees and presents, 06		60	___
26331	Lionel Lines Bulkhead Flatcar, 07		30	___
26332	CP Rail Gondola "337061" with canisters, 07		30	___
26335	Domino Sugar Flatcar with trailer, 07-08		60	___
26355	Kasey Kahne Auto Loader w/2 Autos, 07	25	80	___
26357	CSX Flatcar "600514" with pipes , 07-08		50	___
26366	REA Flatcar with trailers, 07		60	___
26367	Santa's Egg Nog Flatcar with container, 07		60	___
26368	Gondola with trees and presents, 07		60	___
26378	Conrail Auto Carrier "786414," 2-tier, 08		35	___
26379	PRR Gondola with cable reels, 08-09		35	___
26380	NYC Bulkhead Flatcar, 08		35	___
26389	ATSF Flatcar "108477" with 2 pickups, 08		60	___
26390	ATSF Flatcar with bulkheads, 09-10		40	___
26391	NYC Gondola "263910" with containers, 09		40	___
26392	BNSF Auto Carrier, 09		40	___
26400	C&NW Hopper, 07-08		35	___
26401	NP Ore Car "78540," 08		35	___
26410	Chessie System Hopper "47806," 08		35	___
26411	Lionel Lines Ore Car "2026," 08-09		35	___
26412	Chessie System 4-bay Hopper "60573," 08		35	___
26418	B&M Hopper, 09		40	___
26421	PRR Ore Car, 11		40	___

			Exc	Mint
___	26422	White Pass Ice Breaker Car, 09		50
___	26423	Soo Line Ore Car, 10		40
___	26424	LV Hopper, 11		30
___	26425	UP Hopper, 11		40
___	26429	PRR Hopper, 11		40
___	26430	CP Hopper w/Coal, 11		60
___	26431	CN ACF 2-Bay Hopper "370088," 10-11		40
___	26435	B&M Ice Breaker Hopper, 11		50
___	26437	CSX Hopper, 11		40
___	26439	Central of Georgia Hopper, 11-12		40
___	26443	M&StL Ore Car "6700," 11		40
___	26445	Polar Hopper with presents, 11-14		60
___	26446	Thomas & Friends Troublesome Trucks Christmas 2-pack, 11-15		70
___	26448	U.S. Army Gondola with reels, 11		40
___	26449	CN Hi-Cube Boxcar "799346," 13		55
___	26451	DM&IR Ore Car "28003," 13		43
___	26452	PRR Hopper "153935," 13		43
___	26457	PRR Ore Car, 12		40
___	26467	Central of Georgia 2-Bay Grain Hopper, 13-14	12	30
___	26473	Lackawanna NS Heritage 2-bay Hopper, 13		55
___	26474	NYC NS Heritage Quad Hopper, 13		55
___	26477	Monopoly Electric Company Hopper, 13		65
___	26481	Boy Scouts of America Christmas Gondola, 13		65
___	26488	Hershey's Ice Breakers Hopper, 13		66
___	26489	Hershey's Chistmas Bells Boxcar, 13		65
___	26491	Pennsylvania Power & Light Gondola with canisters, 13		43
___	26492	Area 51 3-D Tank Car, 13		43
___	26493	Monopoly Water Works 3-D Tank Car, 13		65
___	26494	PRR Truss Rod Gondola with vats, 13		60
___	26495	C&NW Poultry Car, 13		60
___	26496	Lionelville Aquarium Co. Fish Food Vat Car, 13-16		65
___	26497	Bethlehem Steel Depressed Flatcar with reels, 13		43
___	26499	CN Hi-Cube Boxcar "799346," 14		55
___	26502	UP Bay Window Caboose "6517," 97		47
___	26503	ATSF High-Cupola Caboose "7606R," 97		85
___	26504	Mobil Oil Square Window Caboose "6257," 97 u		37
___	26505	Rescue Unit Caboose, 98		50
___	26506	N&W Square Window Caboose "562748," 98		15
___	26507	D&H Square Window Caboose "35707," 98		20
___	26508	Alaska Square Window Caboose "1081," 98		28
___	26509	ATSF Square Window Caboose, 98	15	20
___	26511	Quaker Oats Square Window Caboose, 98 u		52
___	26513	NYC Emergency Caboose "26505," 99		47
___	26515	Lionel Lines Bobber Caboose, 99		10
___	26516	Safari Bobber Caboose, 99 u		10
___	26519	Christmas Work Caboose "6496," 99		41
___	26520	Bethlehem Steel Work Caboose "6130" (SSS), 99		55
___	26523	Keebler Cheezit Square Window Caboose, 99 u		NRS
___	26524	NYC Square Window Caboose "295," 99 u		20
___	26526	Santa Fe Square Window Caboose "999471," 01		30
___	26527	Christmas Work Caboose with presents, 02		27
___	26528	PRR Square Window Caboose "6257," 99		21
___	26530	LL Square Window Caboose "6257," 99		22

		Exc	Mint
26532	NYC Square Window Caboose "296," 00		20 ___
26533	SP Square Window Caboose, 00		20 ___
26534	PRR Square Window Caboose "6257," 00		20 ___
26535	Frisco Square Window Caboose "1700," 00		20 ___
26536	Centennial Express Square Window Caboose, 00		NRS ___
26537	Lionel Mines Square Window Caboose, 00 u		45 ___
26539	Whirlpool Square Window Caboose, 00 u		NRS ___
26542	ACL Square Window Caboose "069," 01		31 ___
26543	GN Square Window Caboose "X66," 00-01		28 ___
26544	Alaska Square Window Caboose "1084," 01		25 ___
26545	Snap-On Square Window Caboose, 00 u		NRS ___
26548	Pioneer Seed Square Window Caboose, 00 u		NRS ___
26549	PRR Square Window Caboose "4977947," 01		20 ___
26550	NYC Square Window Caboose "19293," 01		20 ___
26551	Chessie System Center Cupola Caboose, 01		25 ___
26552	Santa Fe Square Window Caboose "999472," 01		25 ___
26553	C&O Center Cupola Caboose "A918," 01		30 ___
26554	Monopoly Short Line Square Window Caboose, 00 u		65 ___
26556	NH Center Cupola Caboose, 01		35 ___
26557	Farmall Square Window Caboose, 01 u		NRS ___
26559	N&W Center Cupola Caboose "518408," 01		20 ___
26560	B&M Square Window Caboose, 01 u		20 ___
26564	Soo Line Center Cupola Caboose, 01 u		20 ___
26565	Lionel Employee Square Window Caboose, 01 u		165 ___
26566	WP Square Window Caboose "731," 02		25 ___
26568	NKP Square Window Caboose "1155," 02		25 ___
26569	Southern Square Window Caboose "252," 02		25 ___
26570	B&O Square Window Caboose "295," 02		25 ___
26572	Lionel 20th Century Square Window Caboose, 00 u		25 ___
26580	Wabash Square Window Caboose "2805," 03		22 ___
26581	C&O Square Window Caboose "C-1831," 03		20 ___
26582	L&N Square Window Caboose "318," 03		20 ___
26583	PRR Square Window Caboose "477814," 03		25 ___
26584	World of Disney Caboose, 03		40 ___
26589	PRR Square Window Caboose "982234," 03-05	15	20 ___
26590	Southern Square Window Caboose "X250," 04		50 ___
26591	Indiana RR Caboose "2001," 01		79 ___
26592	GN Caboose "X-242," 03-04		30 ___
26593	Erie Square Window Caboose "C-101," 03	25	40 ___
26594	Ontario Northland Work Caboose "26594," 03		25 ___
26595	UP Caboose "26595," 03		18 ___
26596	NYC Caboose "17716," 04		25 ___
26597	Great Northern Caboose "X295," 04		25 ___
26598	UP Caboose "26598," 04		25 ___
26599	DM&IR Work Caboose "26599," 04		25 ___
26600	American Fire and Rescue Water Tank Car, 09-11		55 ___
26603	LV Depressed Flatcar with reels, 09		40 ___
26604	Halloween Spooky Grave Gondola, 09		58 ___
26609	NYC Gondola with Pacemaker canisters		40 ___
26612	Christmas Gifts Gondola, 09		60 ___
26614	Tupelo Dairy Farms Milk Car, 10-11		60 ___
26616	UP Bulkhead Flatcar with pipes, 10		40 ___
26617	B&O Depressed Center Flatcar with generator, 10		40 ___

		Exc	Mint
___	26629	PRR Flatcar w/Generators, 10		35
___	26630	Soo Flatcar w/Menards trailer, 10		40
___	26631	CP Flatcar w/Log, 11		65
___	26632	CN Boat Loader, 10-11		65
___	26633	CP Flatcar w/Generators, 10-11		35
___	26634	Texas Special Flatcar w/Navajo trailers, 10		40
___	26635	US Army Flatcar w/Helicopter, 11		23
___	26636	Postwar "6830" Flatcar w/Submarine, 10 u		120
___	26637	Postwar "6640" Missile Launching Car, 10 u		65
___	26638	Pennsylvania Power & Light Flatcar w/Reels, 11		40
___	26639	Cities Service 3-Tier Auto Carrier, 11-12		40
___	26640	CN Maple Syrup Barrel Ramp Car, 11-12		40
___	26641	Coca-Cola Flatcar with trailer, 11		78
___	26642	CN Jet Snowblower, 11-12		65
___	26643	D&RGW Jet Snowblower, 11-13		65
___	26644	BNSF Flatcar with generator, 11		40
___	26645	BNSF Flatcar with trailer, 11		40
___	26646	Pennsylvania Power & Light Flatcar with transformer, 11-12		40
___	26647	IC Bulkhead Flatcar with pipes, 11		40
___	26649	Erie-Lack. Gondola with canisters, 11		40
___	26650	M&StL Flatcar with pipes, 11		40
___	26651	ATSF Scout Heavyweight Passenger Car 2-pack (std O), 12		280
___	26652	NYC Gondola with canisters, 11		40
___	26653	PC Flatcar with generator, 11		35
___	26654	Boy Scouts Flatcar with Pinewood Derby Kit, 11-13	33	75
___	26660	Coca-Cola Vat Car, 11-16		75
___	26661	Reindeer Feed Barrel Ramp Car, 09		60
___	26665	Hershey's Special Dark Flatcar with trailer, 11		60
___	26666	Boy Scouts Flatcar with trailer, 11		70
___	26667	Flatcar with Santa's sleigh, 12		70
___	26668	Strasburg Flatcar with wheels, 11		55
___	26669	U.S. Navy Flatcar with Shark submarine, 12-13		60
___	26673	B&M Flatcar with Milk Tank, 12	33	60
___	26674	AT&SF Barrel Ramp Car, 10-11	10	20
___	26675	Monopoly Auto Loader, 12		80
___	26676	Heinz Baked Beans Vat Car, 12		60
___	26677	LIRR Gondola with canisters, 12		40
___	26679	ATSF Gondola with reels, 12-13		55
___	26683	Christmas Track Maintenance Car, 12-13		67
___	26684	Georgia Power Flatcar w/Generator, 12		45
___	26685	Flatcar with Santa's plane, 12		55
___	26686	Hershey's Cocoa Vat Car, 12-13		63
___	26687	Lone Ranger Gondola with gunpowder vats, 12-14		65
___	26691	UP Flatcar w/Trailers, 12-13	39	66
___	26692	UP Gondola w/Coil Covers, 12-13	28	40
___	26693	Hershey's Krackel Piggyback Flatcar with trailer, 12-13		78
___	26694	Carnegie Science Center Flatcar with submarine, 13	50	73
___	26695	NJ Transit Flatcar "9907" w/Trailer, 12	36	55
___	26696	NJ Transit Gondola "9412" w/Wood ties, 12	40	75
___	26699	PRR Flatcar with wheel load, 12-14		55
___	26706	Lighted Christmas Boxcar, 00		47
___	26707	Lionel Steel Operating Welding Flatcar "1108," 00		90
___	26708	ABC Monday Night Football TV Car, 01		50

		Exc	Mint
26709	Postwar "6511" Flatcar w/Psychedelic submarine, 99		32 ___
26710	Southern Stock Car, Carsounds, 99		95 ___
26712	Churchill Downs Horse Car "6473," 99-00		38 ___
26713	Shay Log Car 3-pack, 99		105 ___
26714	Westside Lumber Flatcar with logs (std O), 99		45 ___
26715	Westside Lumber Flatcar with logs (std O), 99		45 ___
26716	Westside Lumber Flatcar with logs (std O), 99		45 ___
26717	Orion Star Boxcar 9600, 00		30 ___
26718	Christmas Boxcar, RailSounds, 00		160 ___
26719	Bobbing Ghost Halloween Boxcar, 00		46 ___
26721	Lionel Lines Coal Dump Car "3379," 00		31 ___
26722	Lionel Lines Log Dump Car "3351," 00		31 ___
26723	Lion Chasing Trainer Gondola "3444," 00		49 ___
26724	Veterans Day Boxcar, 00		70 ___
26725	NYC Jumping Hobo Boxcar "88160," 00		38 ___
26726	T. Rex Bobbing Boxcar, 00		41 ___
26727	San Francisco City Lights Boxcar, 00		50 ___
26736	Lionel Birthday Boxcar, 02 u		40 ___
26737	Operating Santa Gondola "6462," 00 u		65 ___
26738	Lionel Mines Animated Gondola, 00 u		90 ___
26739	Santa and Snowman Boxcar, 00		46 ___
26740	Reindeer Car, 00		43 ___
26741	Operating Santa Boxcar, 00		50 ___
26743	Christmas Reindeer Car, 01		55 ___
26745	Traveling Aquarium Car "506," 01		70 ___
26746	Bobbing Vampire Boxcar, 01		46 ___
26747	Halloween Bats Aquarium Car, 01		75 ___
26748	T&P Operating Hopper Car "9699," 01		38 ___
26749	Alaska Log Dump Car, 01		29 ___
26751	Chessie Coal Dump Car, 01		27 ___
26752	Christmas Aquarium Car, 01		55 ___
26753	Christmas Operating Dump Car, 01		43 ___
26757	Operating Barrel Car "35621," 00		55 ___
26758	AEC Nuclear Gondola "719766," 01		95 ___
26759	Postwar "3459" Coal Dump Car, 02		60 ___
26760	Postwar "3461" Log Dump Car, 02		60 ___
26761	AEC Security Caboose 3535, 01		64 ___
26762	Postwar "3665" Minuteman Car, 01		55 ___
26763	Postwar "6448" Exploding Boxcar, 01		40 ___
26764	Bethlehem Steel Operating Welding Car, 01		75 ___
26765	Postwar "3370" Sheriff and Outlaw Car, 01-02	40	49 ___
26766	Priority Mail Operating Boxcar, 01-02		32 ___
26768	Postwar "6520" Searchlight Car, 02		49 ___
26769	Santa Fe Crane Car "199793," CC, 03		255 ___
26770	Wabash Brakeman Car "3424," 01		70 ___
26773	Chessie Searchlight Car, 01		20 ___
26774	Santa Fe Log Dump Car, 01		25 ___
26775	U.S. Army Searchlight Car, 00		50 ___
26776	U.S. Army Operating Boxcar "26413," 00		55 ___
26777	U.S. Flag Boxcar, 01 u		250 ___
26779	Burlington Operating Hopper "189312," 02		40 ___
26780	Postwar "3376" Bronx Zoo Giraffe Car, 02	25	36 ___
26781	Postwar "3540" Operating Radar Car, 02		35 ___

MODERN 1970-2023

		Exc	Mint
26782	Lenny the Lion Bobbing Head Car, 02		38
26784	Stingray Express Aquarium Car, 02		35
26785	Flatcar with powerboat, 02		31
26786	Lionelville Operating Parade Car, 02		40
26787	Erie Jumping Hobo Boxcar, 01-02		43
26788	Christmas Music Boxcar, 02		46
26789	Kiss Kringle Chase Gondola, 02		35
26790	Lighted Christmas Boxcar, 02		34
26791	UP Animated Gondola, 02	40	50
26792	REA Operating Boxcar "6299," 03		39
26793	Alaska Extension Searchlight Car, 01		44
26794	Postwar "6352" PFE Ice Car, 01-02		85
26795	NYC Stock Car "3121," Cattle Sounds, 02		50
26796	Lionel Farms Poultry Dispatch Car, 01		55
26797	GN Log Dump Car "60011," 02		48
26798	Bethlehem Steel Coal Dump Car "26798," 02		70
26801	Jumping Bart Simpson Boxcar, 04		44
26802	Simpsons Animated Gondola, 04		46
26803	Santa Fe Derrick Car "26803," 04		25
26804	NYC Coal Dump Car "26804," 04		36
26805	Pennsylvania Log Dump Car "26805," 04		24
26806	Pillsbury Operating Boxcar "3428," Archive Collection, 04		40
26807	Blue Chip Line Motorized Animated Gondola, 04		40
26808	Egg Nog Barrel Car, 04		55
26809	Santa's Extension Searchlight Car, 04		42
26810	NYC Operating Searchlight Car, 05		33
26811	Pennsylvania Coal Dump Car, 05		33
26812	Santa Fe Log Dump Car, 05		33
26813	Lionel Lines Derrick Car, 05		33
26814	NYC Walking Brakeman Car "174226," 05		40
26815	PRR "Workin' on the Railroad" Boxcar "24255," 05		42
26816	REA Boxcar, steam TrainSounds, 05		105
26817	Alaska Boxcar, diesel TrainSounds, 05		145
26818	Christmas Music Boxcar, 05		63
26819	Holiday Animated Gondola, 05		55
26820	Penguin Transport Aquarium Car, 05		60
26821	NP Moe & Joe Lumber Flatcar, 05		75
26824	Elvis Presley Searchlight Car, 04		40
26825	GN Log Dump Car, 04		35
26826	Alaska Searchlight Car, 05		40
26827	UPS Operating Boxcar "9237," Archive Collection, 05		62
26828	Tornado Chaser Radar Tracking Car, 05		63
26829	UPS Holiday Operating Boxcar, 05		59
26832	Lionel Lines Tender, TrainSounds, 07-08		105
26833	Wellspring Radar Car, 04	40	75
26834	PFE Ice Car "20042" (std O), 05-06		63
26835	MOW Track Cleaning Car, 05		140
26836	Halloween Boxcar, SpookySounds, 05		105
26841	PRR Log Dump Car, 05		27
26842	NYC Coal Dump Car, 05		27
26843	Christmas Flatcar w/Handcar, 06		60
26844	Christmas Reindeer Transport Car, 06		30
26845	Southern Derrick Car, 06		35

		Exc	Mint
26846	GN Coal Dump Car, 06		38 ___
26847	C&O Coal Dump Car, 06-07		80 ___
26848	Lionel Lines Moe & Joe Flatcar, 06		80 ___
26849	SP Log Dump Car, 06-07		80 ___
26850	D&RGW Searchlight Car, 06		75 ___
26851	WM Log Dump Car, 06		35 ___
26852	Postwar "3562-25" Santa Fe Barrel Car, 06		75 ___
26853	SeaWorld Aquarium Car, 06		75 ___
26854	UP Walking Brakeman Car, 06-07		75 ___
26855	Halloween Animated Gondola, 06		65 ___
26856	Christmas Chase Gondola, 06		65 ___
26857	Alien Radar Tracking Car, 06		65 ___
26858	Christmas Music Boxcar, 06		65 ___
26859	Christmas Parade Boxcar, 06		75 ___
26860	B&O Boxcar "466035," steam TrainSounds (std O), 06-07		75 ___
26861	Santa Fe Boxcar, diesel TrainSounds (std O), 06-07		110 ___
26862	Hard Rock Cafe Boxcar, 06		35 ___
26863	Railway Express Operating Milk Car with platform, 06		140 ___
26864	Domino Sugar Operating Boxcar, 06-07		40 ___
26865	CP Animated Caboose, 06-07	35	80 ___
26867	Boxcar, AlienSounds, 06-07		110 ___
26868	U.S. Steel Operating Welding Car, 06		75 ___
26869	REA Jumping Hobo Boxcar, 06-07		70 ___
26870	Christmas Dump Car with presents, 06		80 ___
26871	PRR Tender, steam TrainSounds (std O), 06		105 ___
26872	U.S. Army Security Car, 06		75 ___
26876	Missile Firing Trail Car, 06		75 ___
26877	U.S. Army Missile Launch Car, 06-07		190 ___
26881	Neiman Marcus Holiday Musical Boxcar, 05		90 ___
26882	NYC Animated Caboose "17719," 06		120 ___
26883	Weyerhaeuser Timber Co. Log Dump Car "117," 06		25 ___
26884	Hammacher Schlemmer Music Boxcar, 08		45 ___
26885	WC Log Dump Car, 06		50 ___
26886	Lionel Lines Log Dump Car, 06		50 ___
26887	Postwar "6470" Exploding Target Car, 06		120 ___
26888	Weyerhaeuser Timber Co. Log Dump Car "115," 06	11	40 ___
26889	Weyerhaeuser Timber Co. Log Dump Car "116," 06		40 ___
26891	PRR Coal Dump Car, 05		30 ___
26897	Great Western Flatcar with handcar, 07		65 ___
26898	NYC Log Dump Car, 05		25 ___
26905	Bethlehem Steel Gondola "6462" with canisters, 98		29 ___
26906	SP Flatcar "9823" with Corgi '57 Chevy, 98		40 ___
26908	TTUX Flatcar "6300" with Apple trailers, 98		70 ___
26913	East St. Louis Gondola "9820," 98		29 ___
26920	Union Pacific Die-cast Ore Car "64861," 97		70 ___
26921	Union Pacific Die-cast Ore Car "64862," 97		55 ___
26922	Union Pacific Die-cast Ore Car "64863," 97		65 ___
26923	Union Pacific Die-cast Ore Car "64864," 97		55 ___
26924	Union Pacific Die-cast Ore Car "64865," 97		55 ___
26925	Union Pacific Die-cast Ore Car "64866," 97		60 ___
26926	Union Pacific Die-cast Ore Car, 98		55 ___
26927	Union Pacific Die-cast Ore Car, 98		55 ___
26928	Union Pacific Die-cast Ore Car, 98		55 ___

			Exc	Mint
___	26929	Union Pacific Die-cast Ore Car, 98		40
___	26936	Die-cast Tank Car 4-pack, 98		335
___	26937	Die-cast Hopper 4-pack, 98		325
___	26938	NYC Reefer, 99		80
___	26940	Rio Grande Stock Car "37710," 99		80
___	26946	D&H Semi-Scale Hopper "9642"		85
___	26947	Gulf Die-cast Tank Car, 98		120
___	26948	P&LE Die-cast Hopper, 98		65
___	26949	NP Flatcar with trailer "6424-2017," 98		47
___	26950	NP Flatcar with trailer "6424-2016," 98		47
___	26951	TTX Flatcar "475185" with PRR trailer, 98		55
___	26952	J.B. Hunt Flatcar with trailer, 98		40
___	26953	J.B. Hunt Flatcar with trailer, 98		40
___	26954	J.B. Hunt Flatcar with trailer, 98		40
___	26955	J.B. Hunt Flatcar with trailer, 98		40
___	26956	C&O Gondola (O27), 98-99		15
___	26957	Delaware & Hudson Flatcar with stakes, 98		20
___	26971	Lionel Steel 16-wheel Depressed Center Flatcar, 98		135
___	26972	Pony Express Animated Gondola, 98		36
___	26973	Getty Die-cast Tank Car 3-pack, 98		270
___	26974	Getty Die-cast 1-D Tank Car "4003," 98		80
___	26975	Getty Die-cast 1-D Tank Car "4004," 98	45	125
___	26976	Getty Die-cast 1-D Tank Car "4005," 98		80
___	26977	Sinclair Die-cast Tank Car 3-pack, 98		275
___	26978	Sinclair Tank Car UTLX "64026," 98		105
___	26979	Sinclair Tank Car UTLX "64027," 98		85
___	26980	Sinclair Tank UTLX "64028," 98		90
___	26981	Gulf Die-cast Tank Car 2-pack, 99		165
___	26985	B&O Die-cast Hopper 2-pack, 99		160
___	26987	Chessie System (B&O) Die-cast 4-bay Hopper "235154," 99		90
___	26991	Lionelville Ladder Fire Car, 99		47
___	26992	NYC Reefer, 99		75
___	26993	NYC Reefer, 99		85
___	26994	NYC Reefer, 99		135
___	26995	Rio Grande Stock Car "37714," 99		80
___	26996	Rio Grande Stock Car "37715," 99		80
___	26997	Rio Grande Stock Car "37716," 99		80
___	27000	C&EI Offset Hopper "97393" (std O), 07		65
___	27001	Erie Offset Hopper "28001" (std O), 07		65
___	27002	Frisco Offset Hopper "92399" (std O), 07		65
___	27003	Chessie System Offset Hopper "234355" (std O), 07		65
___	27016	UP PS-2 Covered Hopper "1312" (std O), 07-08		60
___	27019	Imco PS-2 Covered Hopper "41001" (std O), 07-08		60
___	27022	PC PS-2 Covered Hopper "74217" (std O), 07		60
___	27025	NYC PS-2 Covered Hopper "883180" (std O), 07		60
___	27026	NYC PS-2 Covered Hopper "883181" (std O), 07		60
___	27027	NYC PS-2 Covered Hopper "883182" (std O), 07		60
___	27028	C&O Offset Hopper "27028" (std O), 07		65
___	27029	ATSF Offset Hopper 3-pack (std O), 08-09		200
___	27030	Monon Offset Hopper 3-pack (std O), 08-09		200
___	27031	MoPac Offset Hopper 3-pack (std O), 08-09		200
___	27032	NYC Offset Hopper 3-pack (std O), 08-09		200
___	27033	Chessie System PS-2 Hopper 3-pack (std O), 08-09		180

		Exc	Mint
27034	Nickel Plate Road PS-2 Hopper 3-pack (std O), 08-09		180 ___
27053	CB&Q ACF 2-bay Covered Hopper "183925" (std O), 08-09		55 ___
27059	Bakelite Plastics PS-2 Hopper "61445" (std O), 10-11		70 ___
27061	Clinchfield Freight Car 2-pack (std O), 10		150 ___
27064	PRR Flatcar with PRR piggyback trailers (std O), 12		98 ___
27065	SP Flatcar with SP piggyback trailers (std O), 12		98 ___
27066	IC Flatcar with IC piggyback trailers (std O), 12		98 ___
27067	C&O Flatcar with REA piggyback trailers (std O), 12		98 ___
27068	ATSF Flatcar with Santa Fe piggyback trailers (std O), 12		98 ___
27069	Conrail PS-2 Hopper "878330" (std O), 12-13		70 ___
27070	N&W Scale Offset Hopper "279850" (std O), 12		70 ___
27071	CSX 4-Bay Covered Hopper "256300" (std O), 12		90 ___
27072	C&NW Scale PS-1 Boxcar "7" (std O), 12-13		70 ___
27073	PRR Scale Offset Hopper 3-pack (std O), 12		200 ___
27077	L&N Scale Offset Hopper "88494" (std O), 12-13		70 ___
27078	Frisco Scale 3-Bay Open Hopper "88299" (std O), 12-14		75 ___
27079	NYC Boxcar, 09		30 ___
27080	Lionel Vision Boxcar, 14-15		60 ___
27081	BN PS-2 Hopper "424796" (std O), 12-13		70 ___
27082	Grand Trunk 4-Bay Covered Hopper "38111" (std O), 12		90 ___
27083	RI PS-2 Hopper "500751" (std O), 12-13		70 ___
27084	Seaboard 8000-gallon 1-D Tank Car "27084" (std O), 12		70 ___
27085	Wabash PS-2 Hopper "30425" (std O), 12-13		70 ___
27086	Grand Trunk 60' Boxcar "383575" (std O), 12, 14		85 ___
27087	CN 60' Boxcar "799424" (std O), 12, 14		85 ___
27088	MKT PS-5 Gondola "12447" (std O), 12-13		65 ___
27089	LIRR PS-5 Gondola "6053" (std O), 12		65 ___
27090	NP 8000-gallon 1-D Tank Car "27090" (std O), 12		70 ___
27091	WM Scale 3-Bay Open Hopper "85125" (std O), 12		80 ___
27092	CSX Heritage 60' Boxcar "176740" (std O), 12		85 ___
27093	Boy Scouts PS-2 Hopper "2013" (std O), 13		70 ___
27094	BNSF PS-2 Hopper 2-pack (std O), 13-14		130 ___
27095	KCS PS-2 Hopper 2-pack (std O), 13		130 ___
27096	C&NW PS-2 Hopper 2-pack (std O), 13		130 ___
27099	North Pole Central PS-1 Boxcar "125025" (std O), 13		70 ___
27100	C&NW PS-2CD 4427 Hopper "450669" (std O), 04		40 ___
27101	Morton Salt PS-2CD 4427 Hopper "504" (std O), 04		43 ___
27102	Pillsbury PS-2CD 4427 Hopper "3980" (std O), 04		42 ___
27103	Soo Line PS-2CD 4427 Hopper "70207" (std O), 04		49 ___
27104	Wabash Cylindrical Hopper "33007" (std O), 03		43 ___
27105	PC Cylindrical Hopper "884312" (std O), 03		42 ___
27113	Govt. of Canada Cylindrical Hopper, 04-05		60 ___
27114	Canadian National Cylindrical Hopper, 04-05		60 ___
27115	D&H 3-bay ACF Hopper "3454" (std O), 05-06		65 ___
27116	NYC 3-bay ACF Hopper "886270" (std O), 05-06		65 ___
27117	DM&IR 3-bay ACF Hopper "5017" (std O), 05		65 ___
27118	WP 3-bay ACF Hopper "11774" (std O), 05-06		65 ___
27119	Firestone 3-Bay ACF Hopper (std O), 05	35	45 ___
27129	N&W 3-bay ACF Hopper "10717" (std O), 06		70 ___
27130	PRR 3-bay ACF Hopper "180658" (std O), 06		70 ___
27131	Conrail 3-bay ACF Hopper "473877" (std O), 06		70 ___
27132	UP 3-bay ACF Hopper "18137" (std O), 06		70 ___
27133	MILW PS-2CD Hopper "98606" (std O), 06		70 ___

| --- | --- | --- | --- |
___ 27134	BNSF PS-2CD Hopper "414367" (std O), 06		70
___ 27135	N&W PS-2CD Hopper "71573" (std O), 06		70
___ 27142	CP Rail 3-bay Hopper, 06		48
___ 27146	CP Soo 3-bay Hopper, 06		48
___ 27165	C&O 3-bay Hopper "86912" (std O), 07		70
___ 27166	Pennsylvania Power & Light 3-bay Hopper "347" (std O), 07		70
___ 27167	Santa Fe 3-bay Hopper "178558" (std O), 07-08		70
___ 27168	C&NW 3-bay Hopper "135000" (std O), 07		70
___ 27169	CN Cylindrical Hopper "370708" (std O), 06		65
___ 27172	IMC Canada Cylindrical Hopper "45726" (std O), 06		65
___ 27177	Union Starch Cylindrical Hopper 3-pack (std O), 08		210
___ 27186	PRR Cylindrical Hopper 3-pack (std O), 08		210
___ 27187	TH&B Cylindrical Hopper 3-pack (std O), 08		210
___ 27188	KCS 3-bay Covered Hopper 3-pack, 08		225
___ 27189	BNSF 3-bay Aluminum Covered Hopper 3-pack, 08		225
___ 27190	C&NW PS-2CD Covered Hopper 3-pack (std O), 08		225
___ 27191	RI PS-2CD Covered Hopper 3-pack, 08		225
___ 27192	NP PS-2CD Covered Hopper 3-pack (std O), 08		225
___ 27203	NYC DD Boxcar "75509" (std O), 05		63
___ 27204	Grand Trunk Western DD Boxcar "596377" (std O), 05		63
___ 27205	D&RGW DD Boxcar "63798" (std O), 05		40
___ 27206	UP PS 60' Boxcar "960342" (std O), 08		75
___ 27207	IC PS 60' Boxcar "44295" (std O), 08		75
___ 27208	ATSF PS 60' Boxcar "37287" (std O), 08		75
___ 27209	D&RGW PS 60' Boxcar "63835" (std O), 08		75
___ 27210	PRR PS-1 Boxcar "47009" (std O), 05		60
___ 27211	MKT PS-1 Boxcar "948" (std O), 05		60
___ 27212	Rutland PS-1 Boxcar "358" (std O), 05		60
___ 27213	N&W DD Boxcar, 05		35
___ 27214	Chessie System PS-1 Boxcar "23770" (std O), 06		60
___ 27215	Rock Island PS-1 Boxcar "57607" (std O), 06		60
___ 27216	Erie-Lack. PS-1 Boxcar "84433" (std O), 06		60
___ 27217	Frisco PS-1 Boxcar "17826" (std O), 06		19
___ 27218	Santa Fe DD Boxcar "9870" (std O), 06-07		70
___ 27219	GN DD Boxcar "35449" (std O), 06-07		70
___ 27220	L&N DD Boxcar "41237" (std O), 06-07		70
___ 27221	CB&Q DD Boxcar "48500" (std O), 06-07		70
___ 27224	CGW PS-1 Boxcar "5180" (std O), 06		60
___ 27225	WP PS-1 Boxcar "19528" (std O), 06		60
___ 27226	NH PS-1 Boxcar "32196" (std O), 06		60
___ 27227	UP PS-1 Boxcar "100306" (std O), 06		60
___ 27228	UP DD Boxcar "454400" (std O), 07		70
___ 27229	Nickel Plate Road DD Boxcar "87100" (std O), 08		70
___ 27230	LV DD Boxcar "8505" (std O), 08	21	70
___ 27231	GN USRA Double-sheathed Boxcar (std O), 07		65
___ 27232	UP USRA Double-sheathed Boxcar (std O), 07		65
___ 27233	Cotton Belt USRA Double-sheathed Boxcar (std O), 07		65
___ 27234	C&NW USRA Double-sheathed Boxcar (std O), 07		65
___ 27235	Railbox Boxcar "10011" (std O), 07		55
___ 27236	D&RGW DD Boxcar "63799" (std O), 07		35
___ 27237	MP USRA Double-sheathed Boxcar (std O), 07		65
___ 27238	Nickel Plate DD Boxcar "87101" (std O), 07		35
___ 27239	SP DD Boxcar "232852" with auto rack (std O), 08		75

	Exc	Mint
27240 Pere Marquette DD Boxcar with auto rack (std O), 08		75 ___
27241 C&O PS-1 Boxcar "18719," 08		60 ___
27242 LV PS-1 Boxcar "62080," 08		60 ___
27243 SP PS-1 Boxcar "128131," 08		60 ___
27244 GN PS-1 Boxcar "39404," 08	36	60 ___
27246 SP Double-sheathed Boxcar "133" (std O), 08		70 ___
27247 MP Double-sheathed Boxcar "45111" (std O), 08		70 ___
27249 GN Express Boxcar "2500" (std O), 08		65 ___
27250 CN Express Boxcar "11061" (std O), 08-09		65 ___
27251 WP Express Boxcar "220116," 08-09		65 ___
27254 Western Pacific UP Heritage Boxcar (std O), 09-11, 13		85 ___
27259 PRR ACF Stock Car "128988" (std O), 10		70 ___
27260 ATSF Tool Car "190021" (std O), 09-10		80 ___
27261 D&RGW Double-sheathed Boxcar "3282," 09		80 ___
27263 Polar Railroad PS-1 Boxcar, 09		70 ___
27264 C&O Double-sheathed Boxcar "3502," 10		80 ___
27265 Virginian PS-1 Boxcar "63300" (std O), 10		70 ___
27266 PRR Express Boxcar "504141" (std O), 10		70 ___
27267 SP UP Heritage 60' Boxcar "699" (std O), 10		85 ___
27268 NYC DD Boxcar "47100" (std O), 10		70 ___
27270 B&O PS-1 Boxcar 2-pack (std O), 10-11		140 ___
27273 Ann Arbor PS-1 Boxcar "1314" (std O), 11		70 ___
27274 Polar Railroad Double-sheathed Boxcar "1201," 10		70 ___
27275 SP Overnight PS-1 Boxcar "97938" (std O), 10		70 ___
27276 NKP Double-sheathed Boxcar "10580" (std O), 10-11		70 ___
27277 WP Scale PS-1 Boxcar "1925" (std O), 11		70 ___
27278 Cryo-Trans Trans-Mechanical Reefer (std O), 10		95 ___
27282 UP DD Boxcar "163100" (std O), 10		70 ___
27283 Postwar Scale Boxcar 2-pack, 10		140 ___
27286 Postwar Scale 6464 Boxcar 2-pack #2, 11-13		140 ___
27287 LV Boxcar and Caboose Set (std O), 10-11		160 ___
27289 Jersey Central Boxcar and Caboose Set (std O), 10-11		160 ___
27291 PRR Double-sheathed Boxcar "539335" (std O), 10-11		70 ___
27294 ATSF 57' Mechanical Reefer "3006" (std O), 10		85 ___
27296 Cryo-Trans 57' Mechanical Reefer (std O), 11		85 ___
27299 WM Steel-sided Reefer (std O), 11		80 ___
27300 Western Dairy General American Milk Car (std O), 06		65 ___
27305 GN Steel-sided Reefer "70290" (std O), 06		65 ___
27306 Santa Fe Steel-sided Reefer "3494" (std O), 06		42 ___
27307 Pepper Packing Steel-sided Reefer "2330" (std O), 06		65 ___
27327 BNSF Mechanical Reefer "798870" (std O), 07		70 ___
27328 SP Fruit Express Reefer "456465" (std O), 07-09		70 ___
27329 UP Fruit Express Reefer "55962" (std O), 07		70 ___
27330 Great Northern WFE Reefer "8873" (std O), 07-08		70 ___
27331 Alderney Dairy General American Milk Car (std O), 07		65 ___
27332 Freeport General American Milk Car (std O), 07		65 ___
27345 Milwaukee Road 40' Steel-sided Reefer "531" (std O), 12	54	80 ___
27349 ADM Steel-sided Reefer "7019" (std O), 07		65 ___
27350 National Car Steel-sided Reefer "2430" (std O), 07		48 ___
27355 NYC Steel-sided Reefer "2570" (std O), 07-08		65 ___
27358 Dubuque Steel-sided Reefer "63648" (std O), 07		65 ___
27361 PFE Wood-sided Reefer "97680" (std O), 06		65 ___
27364 Erie URTX Steel-sided Reefer (std O), 11		80 ___

		Exc	Mint
___ 27365	Sheffield Farms Milk Car 2-pack (std O), 08		140
___ 27368	CNJ 40' Steel-sided Reefer "1443" (std O), 12		80
___ 27369	Borden's Milk Car 2-pack (std O), 08		140
___ 27372	PFE Steel-sided Reefer 3-pack (std O), 08		210
___ 27373	MILW Reefer 3-pack (std O), 08-09		225
___ 27374	Alaska Reefer 3-pack (std O), 08-09		225
___ 27375	NP Reefer 3-pack (std O), 08-09		225
___ 27394	Detroit, Toledo & Ironton Steel-sided Reefer (std O), 09-10		80
___ 27395	Amtrak ExpressTrak Baggage Car, 10		75
___ 27396	C&NW UP Heritage Mechanical Reefer (std O), 10		85
___ 27409	ATSF Water Tank Car "100844" (std O), 09-10		70
___ 27410	30,000-gallon Ethanol Tank Car 3-pack, sound, 09		270
___ 27411	30,000-gallon Ethanol Tank Car 3-pack, 09		210
___ 27412	GATX TankTrain Car "53782" (std O), 10		70
___ 27418	PRR NS Heritage Unibody Tank Car (std O), 10		70
___ 27419	Pennsylvania Power & Light 3-bay Open Hopper, 08		80
___ 27421	MoPac UP Heritage Cylindrical Hopper (std O), 09-11		80
___ 27422	N&W 3-bay Open Hopper "1776" (std O), 09		80
___ 27424	Penn Central PS-2 Hopper "440774" (std O), 10-11		80
___ 27425	Saskatchewan Cylindrical Hopper "397015" (std O), 09		80
___ 27426	Stourbridge Lion Anthracite Coal Car 2-pack, 09-10		130
___ 27429	MKT UP Heritage PS2-CD Hopper (std O), 09		80
___ 27431	CSX B&O Quad Hopper, 11		50
___ 27432	UP 3-bay Open Hopper "78123" (std O), 10		80
___ 27433	Conrail NS Heritage Cylindrical Hopper (std O), 10-11		80
___ 27434	D&RGW UP Heritage PS2-CD Hopper (std O), 10		80
___ 27435	Polar Railroad Tank Car, 09		70
___ 27436	Alberta Cylindrical Hopper "396363" (std O), 10		80
___ 27438	Virginian NS Heritage 3-bay Open Hopper (std O), 10		80
___ 27439	NS Heritage Unibody Tank Car "14098" (std O), 10		70
___ 27440	BN Cylindrical Hopper "458456" (std O), 10		80
___ 27441	D&M PS-2 Hopper "6133" (std O), 11		70
___ 27445	N&W NS Heritage PS-2CD Hopper (std O), 10		80
___ 27446	Southern NS Heritage Cylindrical Hopper (std O), 10		80
___ 27448	PRR NS Heritage 3-Bay Open Hopper (std O), 11		80
___ 27449	UP Boy Scouts 100th Anniversary Cylindrical Hopper (std O), 11		80
___ 27450	NW NS Heritage 3-Bay Open Hopper (std O), 11		80
___ 27451	Conrail NS Heritage Unibody 1-D Tank Car (std O), 11		80
___ 27452	PRR NS Heritage PS-1 Boxcar "45540" (std O), 11		70
___ 27453	NS Heritage PS-1 Boxcar "67850" (std O), 11		70
___ 27454	CP Cylindrical Hopper (std O), 11	48	77
___ 27455	Amtrak 57' Mechanical Reefer (std O), 11		85
___ 27456	Soo Line PS2 Covered Hopper "70702" (std O), 11		70
___ 27457	NS 3-Bay Open Hopper "148028" (std O), 11		80
___ 27458	UP Mechanical Reefer "457244" (std O), 11		85
___ 27459	WP DD Boxcar "19404" (std O), 11		70
___ 27460	M&StL Double-sheathed Boxcar "26002" (std O), 11		70
___ 27461	UP ACF 4-Bay Covered Hopper "91341" (std O), 11		85
___ 27462	Chessie ACF 4-Bay Covered Hopper "601878" (std O), 11		85
___ 27463	PRR ACF 3-Bay Covered Hopper "259900" (std O), 11-12		80
___ 27464	BNSF ACF 3-Bay Covered Hopper "453403" (std O), 11		80
___ 27465	CSX 89' Auto Rack Car "604540" (std O), 12-13		150
___ 27466	UP 89' Auto Rack Car (std O), 12-13		150

		Exc	Mint	
27467	ATSF 89' Auto Rack Car (std O), 12-13		150	___
27468	Grand Truck 89' Auto Rack Car (std O), 12-13		150	___
27469	Frisco Cylindrical Hopper "81021" (std O), 11		80	___
27470	MKT Scale 1-D Tank Car (std O), 11		70	___
27471	DT&I 3-Bay Hopper "2070" (std O), 11		80	___
27472	CP Scale 1-D Tank Car "9943" (std O), 11		70	___
27473	Conrail 89' Auto Rack Car "456249" (std O), 12		150	___
27474	SP Cylindrical Hopper "491020" (std O), 11		80	___
27475	Lionelville & Western Scale 1-D Tank Car "2747" (std O), 11		80	___
27476	U.S. Army Scale 1-D Tank Car (std O), 11		70	___
27477	D&RGW 3-Bay Hopper "14901" (std O), 11		80	___
27478	NYC 3-Bay Hopper "922158" (std O), 11		80	___
27479	BN Scale 3-Bay Open Hopper "516400" (std O), 12		80	___
27480	NKP Scale Offset Hopper "33060" (std O), 12		70	___
27481	W&LE Scale Offset Hopper "62240" (std O), 12		70	___
27482	CP Scale Offset Hopper '354000" (std O), 12	33	69	___
27483	SP Unibody 1-D Tank Car "67200" (std O), 12		70	___
27484	D&H Unibody 1-D Tank Car "59" (std O), 12		70	___
27485	KCS Unibody 1-D Tank Car '996" (std O), 12		70	___
27488	Clinchfield CSX Heritage 3-Bay Open Hopper (std O), 12		80	___
27489	Chessie System CSX Heritage 3-Bay Open Hopper (std O), 12		80	___
27490	ATSF 3-Bay Covered Hopper "314000" (std O), 12-13		85	___
27491	GN 3-Bay Covered Hopper "171400" (std O), 12		85	___
27492	CN 89' Auto Rack Car "710833" (std O), 12		150	___
27493	CN PS-4 Flatcar with piggyback trailers (std O), 12		98	___
27494	CN PS-4 Flatcar with piggyback trailers (std O), 12		98	___
27495	CN PS-4 Flatcar with piggyback trailers (std O), 12		98	___
27496	Polar PS-2 Covered Hopper "124" (std O), 12, 14		70	___
27497	UP Offset Hopper "74556" (std O), 12		80	___
27498	DM&I 8000-gallon 1-D Tank Car "S19" (std O), 12		70	___
27499	Monon Scale PS-1 Boxcar "916" (std O), 12		70	___
27510	WP PS-4 Flatcar "2001" (std O), 05-06		53	___
27511	P&LE PS-4 Flatcar "1154" (std O), 05-06		35	___
27512	Reading PS-4 Flatcar "9314" (std O), 05		53	___
27513	UP 40' Flatcar "51219" (std O), 06		55	___
27514	CP 40' Flatcar "307401" (std O), 06		55	___
27515	Pennsylvania 40' Flatcar "473567" (std O), 06		55	___
27516	N&W 40' Flatcar "32900" (std O), 06		55	___
27517	NP PS-4 Flatcar "62829" with trailers (std O), 06		85	___
27518	C&NW PS-4 Flatcar "44503" with trailers (std O), 06		85	___
27519	UP PS-4 Flatcar "53007" with trailers (std O), 06		85	___
27520	Coe Rail Husky Stack Car "5540" (std O), 06		85	___
27521	Santa Fe Husky Stack Car "254220" (std O), 06		85	___
27535	UP PS-4 Flatcar "53008" with trailers (std O), 07		65	___
27536	UP PS-4 Flatcar "53009" with trailers (std O), 08		65	___
27537	UP Flatcar with wood load, 06		39	___
27541	NYC 40' Flatcar "496299" with load (std O), 07		63	___
27542	NH 40' Flatcar "17808" with load (std O), 07-08		70	___
27543	ATSF 40' Flatcar "191549" with load (std O), 07-08		70	___
27544	GT 40' Flatcar "64301" with load (std O), 07-08		70	___
27545	REA PS-4 Flatcar "81003" with trailers (std O), 07-08		85	___
27546	Greenbrier Husky Stack Car "1993" (std O), 07		85	___
27552	Arizona & California Husky Stack Car (std O), 07		85	___

		Exc	Mint
___ 27562	NYC PS-4 Flatcar "506075" with trailers (std O), 07-08		85
___ 27563	Lackawanna PS-4 Flatcar "16540" with trailers (std O), 07		85
___ 27564	MILW PS-4 Flatcar with trailers "64074" (std O), 07-08		85
___ 27583	UP 40' Flatcar "59292" with load (std O), 08		70
___ 27584	Reading Flatcar with covered load (std O), 08-09		70
___ 27585	B&M 40' Flatcar "33773" with stakes (std O), 08-09		65
___ 27586	Cass Scenic Skeleton Log Car 3-pack, 07		170
___ 27587	Birch Valley Lumber Skeleton Log Car 3-pack, 07		170
___ 27594	Wabash PS-4 Flatcar with stakes (std O), 08-09		65
___ 27600	RI Bay Window Caboose "17070" (std O), 07		90
___ 27601	MILW Extended Vision Caboose "992300" (std O), 07		90
___ 27602	C&O Wood-side Caboose "90332" (std O), 07		90
___ 27603	MP UP Heritage Ca-4 Caboose "2891" (std O), 08		95
___ 27604	UP Caboose "3881" (std O), 08		90
___ 27605	Pere Marquette Northeastern Caboose "A986" (std O), 08		90
___ 27606	LL Northeastern Caboose "4679" (std O), 08		90
___ 27607	Monongahela NS Heritage Caboose (std O), 12		95
___ 27608	WM Caboose "1863" (std O), 08		85
___ 27609	B&O Caboose "C-2445" (std O), 07		90
___ 27612	WP Bay Window Caboose "446" (std O), 08		90
___ 27615	NYC Bay Window Caboose "20383" (std O), 07		90
___ 27617	D&H Bay Window Caboose "35725" (std O), 08		90
___ 27618	MKT UP Heritage CA-4 Caboose "8891" (std O), 08		95
___ 27619	WP UP Heritage CA-4 Caboose "3891" (std O), 08		95
___ 27623	N&W Northeastern Caboose "500837" (std O), 09		90
___ 27624	D&RGW UP Heritage CA-4 Caboose (std O), 09		95
___ 27625	C&NW UP Heritage CA-4 Caboose (std O), 09		95
___ 27626	SP UP Heritage CA-4 Caboose (std O), 09		95
___ 27628	Wabash Northeastern Caboose "02222" (std O), 09-10		90
___ 27629	C&O Northeastern Caboose (std O), 10		90
___ 27630	Virginian NS Heritage CA-4 Caboose (std O), 10		95
___ 27631	NS Heritage CA-4 Caboose (std O), 10		95
___ 27633	UP CA-3 Caboose (std O), 10		95
___ 27634	ATSF Extended Vision Caboose (std O), 10		85
___ 27635	B&O I-12 Caboose (std O), 10		85
___ 27636	NKP Northeastern Caboose (std O), 10-11		85
___ 27638	Southern NS Heritage CA-4 Caboose (std O), 10-11		95
___ 27639	N&W NS Heritage CA-4 Caboose (std O), 10		95
___ 27640	Clinchfield Northeastern CA-3 Caboose, 10-11		90
___ 27642	Virginian Scale Caboose with smoke, 10-13		90
___ 27645	UP Boy Scouts 100th Anniversary CA-3 Caboose (std O), 11		95
___ 27648	PRR NS Heritage CA-3 Caboose (std O), 11		95
___ 27649	Baldwin Locomotive Works I-12 Caboose "6000" (std O), 12-13		85
___ 27650	CSX Heritage Scale Bay Window Caboose "2510" (std O), 12		90
___ 27651	B&O CSX Heritage I-12 Caboose (std O), 11		90
___ 27652	CSX Heritage Chessie System Scale Caboose (std O), 12		90
___ 27653	Family Lines CSX Heritage CA-4 Caboose (std O), 11		90
___ 27654	CSX/Clinchfield Scale Bay-Window Caboose (std O), 12		90
___ 27655	WM CSX Heritage Extended Vision Caboose (std O), 11		90
___ 27656	Polar Express I-12 Caboose, 11		85
___ 27657	Central of Georgia NE Caboose "X 17" (std O), 10		90
___ 27658	Pennsylvania Power & Light Work Caboose (std O), 11		80
___ 27659	Bethlehem Steel Work Caboose (std O), 11		80

		Exc	Mint
27660	UP George Bush Extended Vision Caboose (std O), 11		90 ___
27661	KCS Extended Vision Caboose (std O), 11		90 ___
27662	GTW Northeastern Caboose (std O), 11		90 ___
27663	IC Extended Vision Caboose (std O), 11		90 ___
27664	Lionel & Western Northeastern Caboose (std O), 11-12		90 ___
27665	BN Bicentennial Extended Vision Caboose (std O), 11		90 ___
27666	NH Scale Northeastern Caboose "C-666" (std O), 12		90 ___
27667	UP Scale CA-4 Caboose "3857" (std O), 12-13		95 ___
27668	UP Scale CA-3 Caboose "3779" (std O), 12-13		95 ___
27669	PC Scale Northeastern Caboose "18420" with smoke (std O), 12-13		90 ___
27670	CP Scale Northeastern Caboose "400501" (std O), 12-13		90 ___
27671	West Side Lumber Scale Work Caboose "8" (std O), 12		80 ___
27672	Weyerhaeuser Timber Scale Work Caboose "12" (std O), 12-13		80 ___
27673	NYC Scale Northeastern Caboose "20090" (std O), 12		90 ___
27674	Elk River Lumber Work Caboose "6" (std O), 12, 14		80 ___
27676	CN Wood-Sided Caboose (std O), 12		90 ___
27677	UP Work Caboose "907306" (std O), 12		80 ___
27678	ATSF Wood-Sided Caboose "1790" (std O), 12		85 ___
27679	NP Wood-Sided Caboose "1282" (std O), 12		85 ___
27680	GN Wood-Sided Caboose "X499" (std O), 12		85 ___
27681	Southern NS Heritage Caboose (std O), 12		95 ___
27682	Conrail NS Heritage Caboose (std O), 12		95 ___
27683	Erie NS Heritage Caboose (std O), 12, 14-15		95 ___
27684	Illinois Terminal NS Heritage Caboose (std O), 12, 14-15		95 ___
27685	Central of Georgia NS Heritage Caboose (std O), 12		95 ___
27686	LV NS Heritage Caboose (std O), 12		95 ___
27687	Reading NS Heritage Caboose (std O), 13-15		95 ___
27688	NYC NS Heritage Caboose (std O), 13		95 ___
27689	Wabash NS Heritage Caboose (std O), 13-15		95 ___
27690	Virginian NS Heritage Caboose (std O), 13		95 ___
27691	PRR NS Heritage Caboose (std O), 12		95 ___
27692	N&W NS Heritage Caboose (std O), 12		95 ___
27693	CNJ NS Heritage Caboose (std O), 13-14		95 ___
27694	NS Heritage Caboose (std O), 12		95 ___
27695	DL&W NS Heritage Caboose (std O), 13-15		95 ___
27696	Savannah & Atlanta NS Heritage Caboose (std O), 13-15		95 ___
27697	Nickel Plate Road NS Heritage Caboose (std O), 12		95 ___
27698	Interstate NS Heritage Caboose (std O), 12		95 ___
27699	PC NS Heritage Caboose (std O), 13		95 ___
27702	Maersk Husky Stack Car 2-pack (std O), 09		225 ___
27705	ATSF Wedge Plow Flatcar "191369" (std O), 09		90 ___
27706	ATSF Idler Flatcar "191852" with load (std O), 09		75 ___
27707	UP Husky Stack Car 2-pack (std O), 09-10		225 ___
27710	No. 6464 Variation Boxcar 2-pack #2, 09		110 ___
27767	Santa Fe Passenger 4-pack, 11-12		240 ___
27771	Postwar "6572" REA Reefer, 11-13		60 ___
27772	Santa Fe Baggage Car and Diner 2-pack, 11-12		120 ___
27775	Postwar "2414" Santa Fe Blue-stripe Coach, 11-13		60 ___
27776	No. 6464 Variation Boxcar 2-pack #3, 11		105 ___
27779	Postwar Archive UP Caboose "8561," 11-12		48 ___
27791	Archive 6464-50 M&StL Boxcar, 12		55 ___
27792	Archive Pastel Freight Car 3-pack, 12		170 ___
27800	B&M Gondola with coke containers, 09-11		80 ___

		Exc	Mint
____ 27816	D&RGW Flatcar "22177" with pipes, 09-10		80
____ 27820	Wabash PS-4 Flatcar with piggyback trailers (std O), 09-10		98
____ 27824	MILW 40' Flatcar with metal pipes (std O), 10		80
____ 27825	West Side Lumber Skeleton Log Car, 11		70
____ 27826	CP Skeleton Log Car 2-pack (std O), 10		133
____ 27827	UP Bathtub Gondola "28081" (std O), 10		65
____ 27828	CN Bathtub Gondola "193140" (std O), 10		65
____ 27829	WM Skeleton Log Car 2-pack, 10		133
____ 27834	Pere Marquette PS-5 Gondola "18400," 11		70
____ 27835	P. Bunyan Lumber Skeleton Log Car, 11-12		70
____ 27836	Elk River Lumber Skeleton Log Car "11203" (std O), 11		70
____ 27837	B&M PS-4 Flatcar with bulkheads (std O), 10-11		80
____ 27838	PRR PS-4 Flatcar with bulkheads (std O), 10		80
____ 27840	Polar Railroad PS-4 Flatcar with trailers, 10		98
____ 27841	CSX Bathtub Gondola 2-pack (std O), 11		130
____ 27842	UP Scale Flatcar with bulkheads "15775" (std O), 11		70
____ 27843	WP Scale PS-5 Gondola "6774" (std O), 11		70
____ 27844	BNSF Bathtub Gondola 3-pack (std O), 10		200
____ 27848	Virginian NS Heritage 60' Boxcar (std O), 11		85
____ 27849	Southern NS Heritage 60' Boxcar (std O), 11		85
____ 27850	CSX 60' Boxcar "196911" (std O), 11		85
____ 27851	BNSF Bathtub Gondola 2-pack, 11		130
____ 27854	B&O Double-sheathed Boxcar "196500" (std O), 11		70
____ 27855	NYC 60' DD Boxcar "53423" (std O), 11		85
____ 27856	KCS PS-1 Boxcar "18741" (std O), 11		70
____ 27857	PRR DD Boxcar "81919" (std O), 11, 14		75
____ 27858	MP DD Boxcar "90103" (std O), 11		70
____ 27860	Sugar Creek Lumber Skeleton Log Car "1749" (std O), 11		70
____ 27863	Merrill & Ring Lumber Skeleton Log Car, 11-12		70
____ 27868	NS Bathtub Gondola 2-pack (std O), 11		130
____ 27871	NS 60' Boxcar "499646" (std O), 11		85
____ 27872	Polar Hot Cocoa Milk Car, 11, 13		70
____ 27873	Polar Reindeer Stock Car, 11, 13		70
____ 27874	Grove's Mortuary Double-sheathed Boxcar (std O), 11		70
____ 27875	NYC DD Boxcar "45395" (std O), 11		70
____ 27876	State of Maine PS-1 Boxcar "5141" (std O), 11		70
____ 27877	NH DD Boxcar "40510" (std O), 11		70
____ 27882	Southern ACF 40-ton Stock Car "45655" (std O), 11		70
____ 27883	T&P ACF 40-ton Stock Car "24042" (std O), 11		70
____ 27884	RI ACF 40-ton Stock Car "77601" (std O), 11		70
____ 27885	ATSF ACF 40-ton Stock Car "60390" (std O), 11		70
____ 27886	GN PS-1 Boxcar "11310" (std O), 11		70
____ 27887	D&RGW PS-5 Gondola "56316" with covers (std O), 11		65
____ 27888	LIRR 40' Flatcar with wheels (std O), 11		70
____ 27889	Erie 40' Flatcar "6361" with wheels (std O), 11		70
____ 27890	L&N 40' Flatcar "22269" with wheels (std O), 11		70
____ 27891	NKP Heritage PS-4 Flatcar with trailers (std O), 11		98
____ 27892	Conrail PS-5 Gondola "612690" with covers (std O), 11		65
____ 27893	GTW PS-1 Boxcar "516650" (std O), 11		70
____ 27894	C&O PS-5 Gondola "362600" with covers (std O), 11		65
____ 27895	ATSF PS-4 Bulkhead Flatcar "90085" (std O), 11		80
____ 27896	CP 40' Flatcar with pipe load (std O), 11		80
____ 27899	UP Scale PS-1 Boxcar "196889" (std O), 12		70

		Exc	Mint	
27903	Sager Place Observation Car, 09		65	___
27912	Postwar "2445" Elizabeth Coach, 08		60	___
27917	Postwar "2550" Baggage-Mail RDC, nonpowered, 13-14		83	___
27928	UP Boy Scouts 100th Anniversary PS-1 Boxcar (std O), 11		70	___
27929	Postwar Nos. 2484/2485 UP Passenger Car 2-pack, 12-13		120	___
27935	Postwar "6820" Aerial Missile Transport Car, 13		60	___
27941	Postwar "3854" Merchandise Car, 12	25	75	___
27946	Postwar "6050-25" Christmas Savings Boxcar, 13-14		55	___
27947	Postwar "6473-25" Reindeer Transport Car, 13		60	___
27948	Postwar "6464-25" Great Northern Christmas Boxcar, 13		60	___
27949	Postwar "3854-25" PRR Christmas Merchandise Car, 13-14		75	___
27953	Reading PS-2 Hopper 2-pack (std O), 13-14		140	___
27962	L&N PS-2 Hopper 2-pack (std O), 13-14		140	___
27965	P&WV Offset Hopper 3-pack (std O), 13-15		210	___
27969	N&W Offset Hopper 3-pack (std O), 13-15		210	___
27973	C&O Offset Hopper 3-pack (std O), 13-15		210	___
27977	GN Offset Hopper 3-pack (std O), 13-15	90	210	___
27981	PRR USRA Double-sheathed Boxcar (std O), 13		70	___
27982	SP USRA Double-sheathed Boxcar (std O), 13-14		80	___
27983	UP USRA Double-sheathed Boxcar (std O), 13-14		70	___
27984	Procor 30,000-gallon 1-D Tank Car 3-pack (std O), 13		240	___
27988	UTLX 30,000-gallon 1-D Tank Car 3-pack (std O), 13	255	400	___
27992	ADM 30,000-gallon 1-D Tank Car 3-pack (std O), 13		240	___
27996	ACFX 30,000-gallon 1-D Tank Car 3-pack (std O), 13		240	___
28000	C&NW 4-6-4 Hudson Locomotive "3005," 99		205	___
28004	B&O 4-4-2 E6 Atlantic Locomotive, traditional, 99-00		410	___
28005	PRR 4-4-2 E6 Atlantic Locomotive, 99-00		345	___
28006	ATSF 4-4-2 E6 Atlantic Locomotive, traditional, 99-00		285	___
28007	NYC 4-6-4 Hudson Locomotive "5406," 99		380	___
28008	C&O 4-6-4 Hudson Locomotive "306," 99		345	___
28009	Santa Fe 4-6-4 Hudson Locomotive "3463," 99		330	___
28011	C&O 2-6-6-6 Allegheny Locomotive "1601," 99		1800	___
28012	4-6-4 Commodore Vanderbilt Locomotive, red, 00 u		1700	___
28013	NH 4-6-2 Pacific Locomotive "1335," 99		325	___
28014	NYC 4-6-2 Pacific Locomotive "4930," 99		305	___
28015	Santa Fe Pacific 4-6-2 Pacific Locomotive "3449," 99		340	___
28016	Southern 4-6-2 Pacific Locomotive "1407," 99		345	___
28017	Case Cutlery 4-6-2 Pacific Locomotive, 99 u		313	___
28018	Reading 4-6-0 Camelback Locomotive "571," CC, 01		495	___
28020	Lionel Lines 4-6-2 Pacific Locomotive "3344," 99		250	___
28022	West Side Lumber Shay Locomotive "800," 99		810	___
28023	PRR K4 4-6-2 Pacific Locomotive "3755," CC, 99		375	___
28024	4-6-4 Commodore Vanderbilt Locomotive, blue, 00 u		1663	___
28025	PRR K4 4-6-2 Pacific Locomotive, traditional, 99		330	___
28026	LL 4-6-2 Pacific Locomotive, CC, 99		325	___
28027	NYC 4-6-4 Hudson Locomotive "5413," 00		590	___
28028	Virginian 2-6-6-6 Allegheny Locomotive "1601," 99		1318	___
28029	UP 4-8-8-4 Big Boy Locomotive "4006," 99-00		1500	___
28030	NYC 4-6-4 Hudson Locomotive "5450," gray, CC, 00		315	___
28032	B&O 4-6-2 Pacific Locomotive, CC, 00		315	___
28033	B&O 4-6-2 Pacific Locomotive, traditional, 00		195	___
28034	UP 4-6-2 Pacific Locomotive, CC, 00		310	___
28035	UP 4-6-2 Pacific Locomotive, traditional, 00		210	___

		Exc	Mint
28036	SP 2-8-0 Consolidation Locomotive "2685," CC, 00-01		270
28037	SP 2-8-0 Consolidation Locomotive "2686," traditional, 00-01		295
28038	UP 2-8-0 Consolidation Locomotive "324," CC, 00-01		315
28039	UP 2-8-0 Consolidation Locomotive "326," traditional, 00-01		240
28044	NYC 4-6-4 Hudson Locomotive, 04		250
28051	B&O 2-8-8-4 EM-1 Articulated Locomotive "7617," 00		970
28052	N&W 2-6-6-4 Class A Locomotive "1218," 00		870
28055	GN 4-6-4 Hudson Locomotive "1725," traditional, 00-01		170
28057	Southern 4-8-2 Mountain Locomotive "1491," CC, 00		690
28058	NH 4-8-2 Mountain Locomotive "3310," CC, 00		670
28059	WP 4-8-2 Mountain Locomotive "179," CC, 00		630
28062	LL Gold-plated 700E J-1E 4-6-4 Hudson, display case, 00		1050
28063	PRR T-1 4-4-4-4 Duplex Locomotive "5511," CC, 00	450	910
28064	UP Challenger Coal Tender "3985," CC, 00 u	1350	1800
28065	NYC Hudson 4-6-4 Locomotive "5412," RailSounds, 00		290
28066	B&O President Polk 4-6-2 Locomotive, CC, 01		750
28067	Erie 4-6-2 Locomotive "2934," CC, 01		570
28068	D&RGW 4-6-4 Hudson Locomotive, traditional, 01 u		300
28070	SP Daylight 4-4-2 Atlantic Locomotive "3000," CC, 01		425
28071	NP 4-4-2 Atlantic Locomotive "604," CC, 01		415
28072	NYC 4-6-4 Hudson J3a Locomotive "5444," CC, 01		790
28074	NP 2-8-4 Berkshire Locomotive "759," CC, 01	150	640
28075	C&O 2-6-6-2 Locomotive "1521," CC, 01		930
28076	NKP 2-6-6-2 Locomotive "921," CC, 01		960
28077	UP 4-6-6-4 Challenger Locomotive "3983," CC, 01		680
28078	PRR 2-10-4 J1a Locomotive "6496," CC, 01		880
28079	C&O 2-10-4 Class T Locomotive "3004," CC, 01		882
28080	NYC 0-8-0 Locomotive "7745," CC, 01-02		540
28081	C&O 0-8-0 Locomotive "75," CC, 01-02		520
28084	NYC Dreyfuss Hudson 4-6-4 Locomotive "5452," CC, 01-02		790
28085	N&W 2-8-8-2 Y6b Class Locomotive "2200," CC, 03		1207
28086	PRR H9 Consolidation Locomotive "1111," CC, 01		480
28087	UP Auxiliary Tender, yellow, CC, 01		210
28088	N&W Auxiliary Water Tender, CC, 01-02		200
28089	PRR 4-4-4-4 T-1 Duplex Locomotive "5511," 2-rail, 00		1150
28090	UP Challenger Oil Tender "3977," 2-rail, 00 u		1800
28098	NYC 4-6-0 Ten-Wheeler Locomotive "1916," CC, 01-02		520
28099	UP Challenger Oil Tender "3977," CC, 00 u		1700
28200	D&H U30C Diesel "702," CC (SSS), 02		375
28201	UP SD90MAC Diesel "8049," 03		345
28202	Conrail SD80MAC Diesel "7203," 03		325
28203	CSX SD80MAC Diesel "803," 03		325
28204	NS SD80MAC Diesel "7201," 03		345
28205	Chessie System SD9 Diesel "1833," CC, 03		230
28207	Erie-Lackawanna U33C Diesel "3304," CC, 02		355
28208	BN U33C Diesel "5734," CC, 02		355
28211	CP SD90MAC Diesel "9107," 03		300
28213	Amtrak GE Dash 8 Diesel "516," CC, 02		300
28214	BNSF GE Dash 8 Diesel "582," CC, 02		325
28215	B&O GP30 Diesel "6939," CC, 02		315
28216	Reading GP30 Diesel "5518," CC, 02		315
28217	Rio Grande GP30 Diesel "3013," CC, 02		315
28218	Lehigh Valley Alco C420 Switcher "407," CC, 04		325

		Exc	Mint
28219	Seaboard Alco C420 Switcher "136," CC, 04		300
28220	CSX SD60 Diesel "3329," 05		250
28222	Santa Fe Dash 9 Diesel "605" CC, 05		250
28223	BNSF SD70MAC Diesel "9433," CC, 05		250
28224	Jersey Central SD40-2 Diesel "3067," CC, 04		350
28225	SPSF SD40T-2 Diesel "8521," CC, 04-05		430
28226	NS SD80MAC Diesel "7204," CC, 04-05		430
28227	UP SD70MAC Diesel "4979," CC, 04		375
28228	C&NW Dash 9-44CW Diesel "8669," CC, 03		350
28229	SP Dash 9-44CW Diesel "8132," CC, 03		350
28230	Amtrak Dash 8 Diesel "505," CC, 04		295
28235	Great Northern U33C Diesel "2543," CC, 05		455
28237	Reading U30C Diesel "6301," CC, 05		455
28239	Union Pacific SD70 Diesel, TMCC, 04		360
28241	C&NW U30C Diesel "935," CC, 06		455
28242	SP U33C Diesel "8773," CC, 06		475
28243	LIRR Alco C420 Hi-nose Switcher "206," CC, 06		420
28244	N&W Alco C420 Hi-nose Switcher "417," CC, 06-07		420
28245	Chessie System SD40T-2 Diesel "7617," RailSounds, 06		265
28246	Chessie System SD40T-2 Diesel "7618," nonpowered (std O), 06		168
28247	Rio Grande SD40T-2 Diesel "5348," RailSounds, 06		265
28248	Rio Grande SD40T-2 Diesel "5349," nonpowered (std O), 06		160
28250	N&W C420 Hi-nose Switcher "416," nonpowered (std O), 06-07		160
28251	LIRR Alco C420 Hi-nose Switcher "206," nonpowered (std O), 06		160
28252	SP U33C Diesel "8774," nonpowered (std O), 06		160
28253	C&NW U30C Diesel "936," nonpowered (std O), 06		160
28255	UP SD40T-2 Diesel "4551," traditional, CC, 07-08		265
28256	UP SD40T-2 Diesel "4596," nonpowered (std O), 07		170
28257	NS SD40-2 Diesel "3340," CC, 06		430
28258	NS SD40-2 Diesel "3341," nonpowered (std O), 06		450
28259	CN SD40-2 Diesel "5383," CC, 06		430
28260	CN SD40-2 Diesel "5384," nonpowered (std O), 06		170
28261	UP (MP) SD70ACe Diesel "1982," CC, 07		450
28262	UP (WP) SD70ACe Diesel "1983," CC, 07		450
28263	UP (MKT) SD70ACe Diesel "1988," CC, 07		450
28264	UP "Building America" SD70ACe Diesel "8348," CC, 07		450
28265	MILW U30C Diesel "5657," CC, 07		455
28266	MILW U30C Diesel "5657," nonpowered (std O), 07-08		170
28267	Conrail U30C Diesel "6837," CC, 07		455
28268	Conrail U30C Diesel "6838," nonpowered (std O), 07-08		170
28269	ATSF Dash 8-40BW Diesel "562," CC, 08		500
28270	ATSF Dash 8-40CW Diesel "563," nonpowered, 08		220
28272	"I Love USA" SD60 Diesel "1776," traditional, 06	80	250
28279	UP SD70ACe Diesel "1989," CC, 07		450
28280	UP (C&NW) SD70ACe Diesel "1995," CC, 07		450
28281	UP (SP) SD70ACe Diesel "1996," CC, 07		450
28283	UP "Building America" SD70AC3 Diesel, nonpowered (std O), 07		170
28284	Ferromex SD70ACe Diesel "4011," CC, 08		495
28287	KCS SD70ACe Diesel "4050," CC, 08		495
28292	Chessie System U30C Diesel "3312," CC, 02		300
28293	Santa Fe U28CG Diesel "354," CC, 02		375
28295	Conrail LionMaster SD80MAC Diesel, nonpowered, 08		200
28296	UP AC6000 Diesel "7526," CC, 08		660

			Exc	Mint
___	**28297**	SP GP9 Diesel "446," CC, 10		390
___	**28298**	CSX AC6000 Diesel "608," CC, 08		660
___	**28299**	CSX AC6000 Diesel "609," nonpowered, 08		370
___	**28300**	NS Dash 9 Diesel "9607," nonpowered, 08		220
___	**28302**	BNSF SD70ACe Diesel "9380," CC, 08		495
___	**28305**	CSX AC6000 Diesel "610," nonpowered, RailSounds, 08		430
___	**28306**	GE ES44AC Evolution Hybrid Diesel "2010," CC, 09-10	698	1698
___	**28307**	Wabash Train Master Diesel "550," CC, 09-10		495
___	**28311**	UP DD35A Diesel "70," CC, 11		600
___	**28312**	BN SD60 Diesel "8301," CC, 09		800
___	**28314**	UP 3GS21B Genset Switcher "2701," CC, 10		675
___	**28316**	PRR NS Heritage SD70ACe Diesel "1854," CC, 10		500
___	**28318**	Conrail NS Heritage SD70ACe Diesel "1209," CC, 10		500
___	**28320**	CP Evolution Hybrid Diesel, 10		1320
___	**28323**	NS Genset Switcher, CC, 11		800
___	**28327**	UP AC6000 Diesel "7050," CC, 10		700
___	**28328**	UPAC6000 Diesel "7055," nonpowered, CC, 10		350
___	**28330**	UP SD70ACe Diesel "8444," CC, 10		500
___	**28331**	CSX AC6000 Diesel "618," CC, 10		700
___	**28333**	Virginian NS Heritage SD70ACe Diesel, CC, 10		500
___	**28334**	NS Heritage SD70ACe Diesel "1982," CC, 10		500
___	**28338**	PRR NS Heritage SD70ACe Diesel, CC, 11		500
___	**28339**	ATSF AC6000 Diesel "9876," CC, 10		550
___	**28340**	WP GP7 Diesel "705," CC, 10		450
___	**28343**	Amtrak Dash 9 Diesel "519," CC, 10		500
___	**28344**	Southern NS Heritage SD70ACe Diesel, CC, 10		500
___	**28345**	N&W NS Heritage SD70ACe Diesel "247," CC, 10		500
___	**28347**	UP Boy Scouts 100th Anniversary ES44AC Diesel, CC, 11		875
___	**28350**	BNSF ES44AC Diesel, CC, 11		850
___	**28351**	KCS ES44AC Diesel "4655," CC, 11		850
___	**28353**	Erie GP7 Diesel, CC, 11		450
___	**28354**	CSX Genset Switcher "1303," CC, 11		800
___	**28355**	BNSF Genset Switcher "1249," CC, 11		800
___	**28356**	CSX SD60 Diesel, CC, 11		500
___	**28357**	CSX SD60 Diesel, CC, 11		500
___	**28358**	Soo Line SD60 Diesel, CC, 11		500
___	**28359**	Soo Line SD60 Diesel, CC, 11		500
___	**28360**	WP GP7 Diesel "707," CC, 11		450
___	**28361**	WM GP7 Diesel "21," CC, 11		450
___	**28362**	WM GP7 Diesel "23," CC, 11		450
___	**28363**	BN SD60 Diesel "8302," CC, 11		500
___	**28364**	BNSF Dash-9 Diesel "4081," CC, 11		500
___	**28365**	BNSF Dash-9 Diesel "5121," CC, 11		500
___	**28366**	CN Dash-9 Diesel "2643," CC, 11		500
___	**28367**	CN Dash-9 Diesel "2692," CC, 11		500
___	**28368**	Amtrak Dash-9 Diesel, CC, 11		500
___	**28369**	NYC DD35A Diesel "9950," CC, 11		600
___	**28370**	UP DD35 Diesel "84," CC, 12		600
___	**28371**	UP DD35A Diesel "72," CC, 11		600
___	**28372**	NYC DD35A Diesel "9955," CC, 11		600
___	**28373**	C&NW UP Heritage SD70ACe Diesel, CC, 11		500
___	**28374**	SP UP Heritage SD70ACe Diesel, CC, 11		500
___	**28375**	Katy UP Heritage SD70ACe Diesel, CC, 11		500

		Exc	Mint
28376	MoPac UP Heritage SD70ACe Diesel, CC, 11		500
28377	Rio Grande UP Heritage SD70ACe Diesel, CC, 11		500
28378	WP UP Heritage SD70ACe Diesel, CC, 11		500
28380	NYC DD35A Diesel, nonpowered, 11		440
28381	ATSF GP30 Diesel, CC, 11		500
28382	U.S. Army Genset Switcher, CC, 11		800
28383	Conrail Genset Switcher, CC, 11		800
28384	CN Genset Switcher "7990," CC, 11-12		800
28385	ATSF GP30 Diesel "1214," CC, 11		500
28386	ATSF GP30 Diesel "2710," 11		380
28387	ATSF GP30 Diesel "2715," nonpowered, 11		240
28388	ICG GP30 Diesel "2268," CC, 11		500
28389	ICG GP30 Diesel "2271," CC, 11		500
28390	UP DD35 Diesel "79," nonpowered, 12		440
28394	ICG GP30 Diesel "2277," 11		380
28395	ICG GP30 Diesel "2279," nonpowered, 11		240
28396	UP ES44AC Diesel "7454," CC, 11		850
28397	UP ES44AC Diesel "7459," CC, 11		850
28398	BNSF ES44AC Diesel "6436," CC, 11		850
28399	KCS ES44AC Diesel "4682," CC, 11		850
28400	Amtrak Rail Bonder, 05		65
28403	Pennsylvania Ballast Tamper, traditional, 05-06		105
28404	Maintenance Car, 05		105
28405	Picatinny Arsenal Switcher, CC, 05		290
28406	CSX Rail Bonder "92794," traditional, 05		65
28407	UP Speeder, 05		65
28408	CNJ Speeder "MW840," traditional, 06		70
28409	Conrail Rail Bonder "X409," traditional, 06		70
28411	U.S. Army Missile Launcher Locomotive, 06-07		300
28412	Santa's Speeder, 06		70
28413	Milwaukee Road Snowplow "X903," traditional, 06		210
28414	Lionel Lines Burro Crane, traditional, 06		160
28415	Third Avenue Trolley "1651," traditional, 06		70
28416	Hobo Handcar, traditional, 06		70
28417	Christmas Rotary Snowplow, 06		180
28418	Christmas Trolley, 06		70
28419	Lionel Lines Speeder, 07-08		70
28420	D&RGW Handcar, 07-08		70
28421	Fort Collins Trolley, 07		73
28422	PRR Burro Crane, 07-08		160
28423	Alaska Rotary Snowplow, 06-07		220
28424	Postwar "51" Navy Switcher, 07		210
28425	Polar Express Elf Handcar, 06-23		120
28427	Christmas Snowplow, 08-10		210
28428	Halloween Handcar, 07		70
28430	Wellspring Capital Management Trolley, 06	50	85
28432	Bethlehem Steel Switcher, traditional, 07		210
28434	Christmas Trolley, 07		70
28438	Portland Birney Trolley, 08-09		65
28440	PRR Inspection Vehicle, 08-09		170
28441	Transylvania Trolley, 08	60	72
28442	Postwar "50" Gang Car, 08		120
28444	NH Handcar, 08-09		75

		Exc	Mint
____ 28445	AEC Burro Crane Car		100
____ 28446	Silver Bell Trolley, 09		90
____ 28447	4850TM Factory Trackmobile, CC, 10		300
____ 28448	CSX 4850TM Trackmobile, CC, 10		300
____ 28449	UP 4850TM Trackmobile, CC, 10		300
____ 28450	CP Rail Trackmobile, CC, 11		300
____ 28451	Christmas Track Cleaning Car, 10-13		150
____ 28452	MOW Early Era Inspection Vehicle, 10		130
____ 28453	PRR Early Era Inspection Vehicle, 10		130
____ 28454	CP Early Era Inspection Vehicle, 10		130
____ 28455	NYC Trackmobile, CC, 11-13		300
____ 28456	Coca-Cola Trolley, 10		90
____ 28457	B&M Rotary Snowplow "8457," 11		250
____ 28466	U.S. Army Trackmobile, CC, 11		300
____ 28467	PRR Trackmobile, CC, 11		300
____ 28468	Amtrak Trackmobile, CC, 11		300
____ 28469	BNSF Trackmobile, CC, 11		300
____ 28470	NYC Early Era Inspection Vehicle , 11		130
____ 28471	ATSF Early Era Inspection Vehicle, CC, 11		130
____ 28472	Southern Early Era Inspection Vehicle, 11		130
____ 28473	GN Early Era Inspection Vehicle, CC, 11		130
____ 28474	North Pole Central Elf Handcar, 11		80
____ 28475	UP Early Era Insprection Vehicle, 11		130
____ 28476	IC Early Era Inspection Vehicle, 11		130
____ 28478	Frisco Early Era Inspection Vehicle, CC, 11		130
____ 28479	Christmas Early Era Inspection Vehicle, 11		130
____ 28480	Grand Trunk Early Era Inspection Vehicle, CC, 11		130
____ 28500	Mopac GP20 Diesel "2274," 99-00		205
____ 28501	ATSF GP9 Diesel "2924," traditional, 99		200
____ 28502	ATSF GP9 Diesel "2925," CC, 99-00		255
____ 28503	ACL GP7 Diesel, CC, 00		245
____ 28504	ACL GP7 Diesel, traditional, 00		170
____ 28505	Monon Alco C420 Switcher "505," CC, 00-01		230
____ 28506	Monon Alco C420 Switcher "506," traditional, 00-01		170
____ 28507	NH Alco C420 Switcher "2556," CC, 00-01		275
____ 28508	NH Alco C420 Switcher "2557," traditional, 00-01		290
____ 28509	FEC GP7 Diesel Set, 99		560
____ 28514	B&O GP9 Diesel "6590," 00		85
____ 28515	Lionel Service Station Alco C420 Switcher, CC, 00		205
____ 28516	Lehigh & Hudson River Alco C420 Diesel, 00		160
____ 28517	C&NW GP7 Diesel "1518," CC, 00-01		275
____ 28518	PRR EP-5 Electric Locomotive "2352," CC, 00		410
____ 28519	NP GP9 Diesel "2349," CC, 01	98	270
____ 28521	SP Alco RS-11 Switcher "5725," CC, 01-02		280
____ 28522	MP Alco RS-11 Switcher "4611," CC, 01-02		305
____ 28523	Soo SD40-2 Diesel "6622," CC, 01		375
____ 28524	Chessie SD40-2 Diesel "7616," CC, 01		355
____ 28527	AEC GP9 Diesel "2001," CC, 01		400
____ 28528	NH Alco RS-11 Diesel "1406," 01-02	150	300
____ 28529	Norfolk Southern GP9 Diesel, CC, 02		200
____ 28530	NP Alco S4 Diesel "722," CC, 02		285
____ 28531	Santa Fe Alco S2 Switcher "2337," CC, 02		285
____ 28532	LV Alco S2 Switcher "150," CC, 02		280

		Exc	Mint
28533	Seaboard Air Line Alco S4 Diesel "1489," CC, 02		290
28536	Rock Island GP7 Diesel "1274," CC, 02-03		230
28538	WP Alco S2 Switcher "553," CC, 03		340
28539	B&O Alco S2 Switcher "9045," CC, 03	125	320
28540	UP SD40T-2 Diesel "4455," CC, 03		390
28541	SP SD40T-2 Diesel "8239," CC, 03		400
28542	Rio Grande SD40T-2 Diesel "5350," CC, 03		400
28543	Ontario Northland RS-3 Diesel "1308," 03		80
28544	PRR Alco RS-11 Switcher "8618," CC, 04		350
28545	NP Alco RS-11 Switcher "900," CC, 03		325
28547	SP SD40T-2 Diesel "8232," CC, 04		400
28548	Chessie System Alco S-4 Diesel "9009,"CC, 05		400
28553	PRR Alco RS-11 Switcher "8620," traditional, 07-08	90	285
28554	PRR Alco RS-11 Diesel "8621," nonpowered, 07-08		170
28555	Alaska GP38-2 Diesel "2001," CC, 06		400
28556	Alaska GP38-2 Diesel "2002," nonpowered (std O), 06		160
28557	CP GP30 Diesel "5000," CC, 06-07		400
28558	CP GP30 Diesel "5001," nonpowered (std O), 06-07		150
28559	Chessie System GP30 Diesel "3044," CC, 06-07		400
28560	Chessie System GP30 "3045," nonpowered (std O), 06-07		150
28561	NYC GP7 Diesel "5628," CC, 07-08		340
28562	NYC GP7 Diesel "5629," nonpowered (std O), 07		170
28563	GN GP7 Diesel "626," CC, 07	138	400
28564	GN GP7 Diesel "627," nonpowered (std O), 07		170
28565	RI GP7 Diesel "1265," CC, 07		400
28566	RI GP7 Diesel "1266," nonpowered (std O), 07		170
28567	UP GP7 Diesel "105," CC, 07		400
28568	UP GP7 Diesel "106," nonpowered (std O), 07		170
28570	D&RGW GP7 Diesel "5101," CC, 08		440
28573	PRR GP7 Diesel "8512," CC, 08		440
28578	D&H GP38-2 Diesel "7307," CC, 08		440
28587	PRR GP7 Diesel "8510," CC, 10		450
28592	N&W GP7 Diesel "2446," CC, 09		500
28594	White Pass & Yukon NW2 Diesel Switcher, traditional, 09-10	100	300
28595	ATSF SD40 Diesel "5004," CC, 09		380
28596	Erie GP7 Diesel "1210," CC, 11		450
28598	ATSF GP7 Diesel "2791," CC, 10		450
28599	Erie GP9 Diesel "1261," CC, 10		390
28601	Winter Wonderland 4-4-2 Atlantic Locomotive "34," 02		85
28602	PRR 4-4-2 Atlantic Locomotive, 01-02		90
28603	NYC 4-4-2 Atlantic Locomotive, 01-02		90
28604	ATSF 4-6-4 Hudson Locomotive "3458," 02		150
28606	Monopoly 4-4-2 Atlantic Locomotive, 00 u		200
28611	ATSF 4-6-4 Hudson Locomotive "3459," 02		100
28612	WP 4-4-2 Atlantic Locomotive, traditional, 02		80
28613	Reading 0-6-0 Dockside Switcher "1251," traditional, 04		100
28615	B&O 4-6-4 Hudson Locomotive, traditional, 02		225
28616	Nickel Plate 2-8-4 Berkshire Locomotive, traditional, 02		190
28617	Southern 2-8-4 Berkshire Locomotive, traditional, 02		235
28624	Santa Fe 0-6-0 Dockside Switcher "2174," traditional, 04		175
28625	Wabash 4-4-2 Atlantic Locomotive "8625," traditional, 03		85
28626	PRR 4-6-4 Hudson Locomotive "626," traditional, 03		175
28627	C&O 2-8-4 Berkshire Locomotive "2755," traditional, 03		200

		Exc	Mint
___ 28628	L&N 2-8-4 Berkshire Locomotive "1970," traditional, 03	150	200
___ 28633	JCPenney B&O 2-8-4 Berkshire Locomotive, 07		135
___ 28636	D&RGW 4-4-2 Atlantic Locomotive "8636," traditional, 04		95
___ 28637	UP 4-6-4 Hudson Locomotive "673," traditional, 04		160
___ 28638	GN 2-8-4 Berkshire Locomotive "3414," traditional, 04		200
___ 28639	NYC 2-8-4 Berkshire Locomotive "9401," traditional, 04		200
___ 28646	North Pole Central 2-8-4 Berkshire "1900," traditional, 04		315
___ 28649	Polar Express 2-8-4 Berkshire Locomotive, 03,àí10		120
___ 28650	NYC 0-6-0 Dockside Switcher "X-8688," traditional, 05		80
___ 28651	Bethlehem Steel 0-6-0 Dockside Switcher "72," traditional, 05		80
___ 28652	LL 4-4-2 Locomotive "8652," traditional, 05		105
___ 28655	Erie 2-8-4 Berkshire Locomotive "3338," traditional, 05		240
___ 28656	PRR 2-8-4 Berkshire Locomotive "56," traditional, 05		240
___ 28660	North Pole Central 0-6-0 Dockside Switcher "25," traditional, 05		105
___ 28661	Santa Fe 0-4-0 Locomotive "2300" traditional, 05		160
___ 28662	C&O 0-4-0 Locomotive "39," traditional, 05		160
___ 28663	Nieman Marcus 4-4-2 Atlantic Locomotive, traditional, 06 u		125
___ 28665	LRRC Western Union 2-8-4 Berkshire Locomotive "665," 10 u		200
___ 28667	Elvis "He Dared to Rock" 2-8-4 Berkshire Locomotive, 04		200
___ 28669	Copper Range 0-6-0 Locomotive "194," 05		155
___ 28671	ATSF 2-8-4 Berkshire Locomotive "4193," 06-07		225
___ 28674	C&O 0-6-0 Dockside Switcher "67," traditional, 06-07		110
___ 28675	SP 0-6-0 Dockside Switcher "675," traditional, 06-07		110
___ 28676	U.S. Steel 0-6-0 Dockside Switcher "76," traditional, 06-07		110
___ 28677	WM 4-4-2 Atlantic Locomotive "103," traditional, 06		110
___ 28678	Rio Grande 0-4-0 Locomotive "55," traditional, 06-07		170
___ 28679	U.S. Army Transportation Corps 0-4-0 Locomotive "40," traditional, 06		170
___ 28680	Reading 0-4-0 Locomotive "1152," traditional, 06		170
___ 28681	Virginian 2-8-4 Berkshire Locomotive "509," traditional, 06		260
___ 28683	B&O 2-8-2 Mikado Locomotive "1520," TrainSounds, 06-07		260
___ 28684	UP 2-8-2 Mikado Locomotive "2498," TrainSounds, 06-07		260
___ 28693	B&O 4-4-2 Atlantic Locomotive "28," traditional, 05		105
___ 28694	NYC 4-4-2 Atlantic Locomotive "8637," traditional, 06		100
___ 28695	Halloween 0-6-0 Dockside Switcher "X-131," traditional, 06-07		85
___ 28699	Holiday 2-8-2 Mikado Locomotive "25," red, RailSounds, 08		260
___ 28700	CB&Q 0-8-0 Locomotive "543," RailSounds, 05		650
___ 28701	NP 0-8-0 Locomotive "1178," RailSounds, 05		650
___ 28702	Boston & Albany 0-8-0 Locomotive "53," RailSounds, 05		650
___ 28704	PRR 4-4-2 Atlantic Locomotive "68," CC, 05		550
___ 28706	PRR Reading Seashore 4-4-2 Atlantic "6064," CC, 05		550
___ 28742	B&O 4-6-0 Camelback Locomotive "1630," CC, 03		335
___ 28743	B&O 4-6-0 Camelback Locomotive "1632," traditional, 03		300
___ 28744	D&H 4-6-0 Camelback Locomotive "548," CC, 03		325
___ 28745	D&H 4-6-0 Camelback Locomotive "555," traditional, 03		300
___ 28746	Erie 4-6-0 Camelback Locomotive "860," CC, 03		375
___ 28747	Erie 4-6-0 Camelback Locomotive "878," traditional, 03		300
___ 28748	Jersey Central 4-6-0 Camelback Locomotive "772," CC, 03		300
___ 28749	Jersey Central 4-6-0 Camelback Locomotive "773," traditional, 03		300
___ 28750	Lackawanna 4-6-0 Camelback Locomotive "690," CC, 03		375
___ 28751	Lackawanna 4-6-0 Camelback Locomotive "1031," traditional, 03		300
___ 28752	LIRR 4-6-0 Camelback Locomotive "126," CC, 03		300
___ 28753	LIRR 4-6-0 Camelback Locomotive "127," traditional, 03		300

		Exc	Mint
28754	NYO&W 4-6-0 Camelback Locomotive "249," CC, 03		300 ___
28755	NYO&W 4-6-0 Camelback "253" Locomotive, traditional, 03		300 ___
28756	PRR Reading Seashore 4-6-0 Camelback "6000," CC, 03		325 ___
28757	PRR Reading Seashore 4-6-0 Camelback "6001," 03		300 ___
28758	Susquehanna 4-6-0 Camelback Locomotive "30," CC, 03		365 ___
28759	Susquehanna 4-6-0 Camelback Locomotive "36," traditional, 03		300 ___
28800	N&W GP7 Diesel "507," 99-00		80 ___
28801	Lionel Lines 44-ton Switcher, 99		135 ___
28806	Jersey Central FM H16-44 Diesel "1516," CC, 01		335 ___
28811	Santa Fe FM H16-44 Diesel "3003," CC, 01		290 ___
28813	Milwaukee Road FM H16-44 Diesel "406," CC, 01		315 ___
28815	B&O GP30 Diesel "6935," CC, 02		295 ___
28817	Reading GP30 Diesel "5513," CC, 02		310 ___
28819	Rio Grande GP30 Diesel "3013," CC, 02		310 ___
28821	GT GP7 Diesel "4438," 01		100 ___
28822	Southern RS3 Diesel "2127," 01		70 ___
28823	Virginian Electric Locomotive "234," 01		122 ___
28826	Pioneer Seed GP7 Diesel "2001," traditional, 00 u		NRS ___
28827	Chessie GP38 Diesel, traditional, 01		100 ___
28830	Soo Line GP9 Diesel, traditional, 01 u	95	270 ___
28831	Conrail U36B Diesel "2971," traditional, 02		100 ___
28832	Santa Fe RS3 Diesel "2099," traditional, 02		70 ___
28836	NYC FM H-16-44 Diesel "7000," CC, 02		330 ___
28837	NH FM H-16-44 Diesel "591," CC, 02		325 ___
28838	UP FM H-16-44 Diesel "1340," CC, 02		325 ___
28839	Alaska GP 30 Diesel "2000," CC, 04		315 ___
28840	Burlington GP30 Diesel "945," CC, 03		325 ___
28841	Seaboard GP30 Diesel "1315," CC, 03		220 ___
28842	C&O GP9 Diesel, horn, 04		160 ___
28843	Southern GP38 Diesel, horn, 04		140 ___
28845	Amtrak RS3 Diesel "106," 03		70 ___
28846	Western Pacific U36B Diesel "3067," traditional, 04		100 ___
28847	DM & IR GP38 Diesel "203," traditional, 04		170 ___
28848	JCPenney Santa Fe GP38 Diesel, 04		125 ___
28849	Western Maryland GP7 Diesel, horn, 04		185 ___
28850	NYC GP30 Diesel "6115" CC, 04		360 ___
28851	Pennsylvania RS3 Diesel, 04		75 ___
28852	CSX U36B Diesel "1976," traditional, 05		140 ___
28853	Santa Fe GP38 Diesel "2371," traditional, 05		210 ___
28855	B&O/Chessie System GP30 Diesel "6945," CC, 05-06	225	425 ___
28857	Alaska GP9 Diesel, 05		125 ___
28859	Pennsylvania GP30 Diesel "2206," nonpowered, 06		160 ___
28860	UP GP30 Diesel "844," CC, 06		360 ___
28861	UP GP30 Diesel "845," nonpowered (std O), 06		150 ___
28862	CSX GP30 Diesel "4249," CC, 06		400 ___
28863	CSX GP30 Diesel "4250," nonpowered (std O), 06		150 ___
28864	UP RS3 Diesel "1195," traditional, 06		85 ___
28865	GN GP9 Diesel "688," traditional, 06		160 ___
28866	NYC GP20 Diesel "6110," traditional, 06		140 ___
28868	ATSF GP38 Diesel		140 ___
28873	NYC RS3 Diesel "8226," traditional, 06		85 ___
28874	UP GP9 Diesel "178," traditional, 06-07		210 ___
28875	Santa Fe GP20 "1107," traditional, 06		140 ___

|---|---|---|---|
28876	GN FT Diesel "418," traditional, 07-08		245
28879	UPS Centennial GP38 Diesel, traditional, 06		210
28881	Conrail GP20 Diesel "2107," traditional, 07		140
28882	Alaska RS3 Diesel "1079," traditional, 07		85
28883	Thomas & Friends Diesel, 07-13		120
28884	PRR GP38 Diesel "2389," traditional, 08-09		210
28886	RI RS3 Diesel "492," traditional, 08		95
28887	Southern RS3 Diesel "2028," traditional, 08		95
28890	CN GP9 Diesel "4573," traditional, 08		210
28897	Seaboard U36B Diesel "1762,"traditional, 08		140
28900	Iron 'Arry and Iron Bert 2-pack, 08-09		240
28905	ATSF FT Diesel "160," nonpowered, 09-10		120
29000	PRR Caleb Strong Madison Coach "2622," 99		80
29001	PRR Villa Royal Madison Coach "2621," 99		80
29002	PRR Philadelphia Madison Coach "2624," 99	30	80
29003	PRR Madison Car 4-pack, 98		220
29004	NYC Heavyweight Passenger Car 2-pack, 99		170
29007	NYC Pullman Passenger Car 2-pack, 98 u		143
29008	NYC Heavyweight Diner "383," 98		95
29009	NYC Van Twiller Heavyweight Combination Car, 98		95
29010	C&O Heavyweight Passenger Car 2-pack, 99		150
29039	Lionel Lines Recovery Combination Car "9501," 99	65	85
29041	Alaska Streamliner Car 4-pack, 99-00	59	230
29042	Alaska Streamliner Baggage Car "6310," 99-00		50
29043	Alaska Streamliner Coach "5408," 99-00		65
29044	Alaska Streamliner Vista Dome Car "7014," 99-00		65
29046	B&O Streamliner Car 4-pack, 99-00		165
29047	B&O Streamliner Baggage Car, 99-00		35
29048	B&O Streamliner Coach, 99-00		50
29049	B&O Streamliner Vista Dome Car, 99-00		50
29050	B&O Streamliner Observation Car, 99-00		40
29051	ATSF Streamliner Car 4-pack, 99-00		200
29052	ATSF Streamliner Baggage Car, 99-00		40
29053	ATSF Streamliner Coach, 99-00		60
29054	ATSF Streamliner Vista Dome Car, 99-00		60
29055	ATSF Streamliner Observation Car, 99-00		40
29056	NYC Streamliner Car 4-pack, 99-00		180
29057	NYC Streamliner Baggage Car, 99-00		40
29058	NYC Streamliner Coach, 99-00		50
29059	NYC Streamliner Vista Dome Car, 99-00		50
29060	NYC Streamliner Observation Car, 99-00		45
29061	PRR Madison Passenger Car 4-pack, 99-00		190
29062	PRR Indian Point Madison Baggage Car, 99-00		50
29063	PRR Christopher Columbus Madison Coach, 99-00		50
29064	PRR Andrew Jackson Madison Coach, 99-00		50
29065	PRR Broussard Madison Observation Car, 99-00		50
29066	CNJ Madison Passenger Car 4-pack, 99-00		210
29067	CNJ Madison Baggage Car "420," 99-00		50
29068	CNJ Beachcomber Madison Coach, 99-00		50
29069	CNJ Echo Lake Madison Coach, 99-00		50
29070	CNJ Madison Observation Car "1178," 99-00		50
29071	NYC Baby Madison Car 4-pack, 00	78	203

		Exc	Mint
29072	NYC Baby Madison Baggage Car "1001," 00		50 ___
29073	NYC Baby Madison Coach "1005," 00		50 ___
29074	NYC Baby Madison Coach "1006," 00		50 ___
29075	NYC Detroit Baby Madison Observation Car "1019," 00		40 ___
29076	Southern Baby Madison Car 4-pack, 00		155 ___
29077	Southern Delaware Madison Baggage Car "702," 00		30 ___
29078	Southern North Carolina Madison Coach "800," 00		50 ___
29079	Southern Maryland Madison Coach "801," 00		50 ___
29080	Southern Madison Observation Car "1100," 00		40 ___
29081	ATSF Baby Madison Car 4-pack, 00		160 ___
29082	ATSF Baby Madison Baggage Car "1765," 00		30 ___
29083	ATSF Baby Madison Coach "3040," 00		50 ___
29084	ATSF Baby Madison Coach "1535," 00		50 ___
29085	ATSF Baby Madison Observation Car "10," 00		45 ___
29086	Madison Car 3-pack, 99		280 ___
29090	Lionel Liontech Madison Car "2656," 99		75 ___
29091	Lawrence Cowen Lionel Legends Madison Coach "2657," 99-00		75 ___
29105	PRR Trail Blazer Aluminum Passenger Car 4-pack, 04-05		550 ___
29108	Searchlight Car, 00		30 ___
29110	B&O Columbian Aluminum Passenger Car 4-pack, 04		425 ___
29115	SP Daylight Aluminum Passenger Car 4-pack, 04-05		550 ___
29122	EL F3 Diesel Passenger Set, 99		840 ___
29123	Erie-Lack. Aluminum Coach/Baggage Car "203," 99		100 ___
29124	Erie-Lack. Aluminum Coach/Diner "770," 99		100 ___
29125	Erie-Lack. Eleanor Lord Aluminum Coach, 99		100 ___
29126	Erie-Lack. Tavern Lounge Aluminum Observation Car "789," 99		125 ___
29127	ACL Aluminum Baggage Car "152," 99		100 ___
29128	ACL North Hampton Aluminum Coach, 99		100 ___
29129	Texas Special Passenger Car 4-pack, 99	650	700 ___
29130	Texas Special Edward Burleson Aluminum Coach "1200," 99	58	125 ___
29131	Texas Special David G. Burnett Aluminum Coach "1201," 99	58	125 ___
29132	Texas Special J. Pinckney Henderson Aluminum Coach "1202," 99	38	122 ___
29133	Texas Special Stephen F. Austin Aluminum Observation Car "1203," 99	50	118 ___
29135	California Zephyr Silver Poplar Aluminum Vista Dome Car, 99		150 ___
29136	California Zephyr Silver Palm Aluminum Vista Dome Car, 99		150 ___
29137	California Zephyr Silver Tavern Aluminum Vista Dome Car, 99		150 ___
29138	California Zephyr Silver Planet Aluminum Vista Dome Car, 99		150 ___
29139	Kughn Lionel Legends Madison Car "2655," 99		113 ___
29140	NYC Castleton Bridge Aluminum Sleeper Car, 99		120 ___
29141	NYC Martin Van Buren Aluminum Combination Car, 99		120 ___
29142	CP Skyline Aluminum Vista Dome Car "596," 99		125 ___
29143	CP Banff Park Aluminum Observation Car, 99		125 ___
29144	Santa Fe El Capitan Aluminum Passenger Car 4-pack, 04		400 ___
29149	CB&Q California Zephyr Aluminum Passenger Car 2-pack, 03		300 ___
29152	Santa Fe Super Chief Aluminum Passenger Car 2-pack, 03		190 ___
29155	D&H Aluminum Passenger Car 2-pack, 03		190 ___
29158	Southern Aluminum Passenger Car 2-pack, 03		205 ___
29165	Amtrak Superliner Passenger Car 2-pack, Phase IV, 04		195 ___
29168	Amtrak Superliner Diner, StationSounds, Phase IV, 04		200 ___
29169	Alaska Superliner Passenger Car 2-pack, 04		200 ___
29172	Alaska Superliner Diner, StationSounds, 04		200 ___
29182	N&W Powhatan Arrow Aluminum Car 4-pack (std O), 05		550 ___
29187	N&W Powhatan Arrow Aluminum Car 2-pack (std O), 05		290 ___

		Exc	Mint
29190	N&W Powhatan Arrow Aluminum Diner, StationSounds, 05		290
29191	MILW Hiawatha Passenger Car 4-pack, 06		370
29192	MILW Hiawatha Combination Car "153," 06		95
29193	MILW Hiawatha Coach "437," 06		95
29194	MILW Hiawatha Coach "438," 06		95
29195	MILW Hiawatha Observation "Miller," 06		95
29196	MILW Hiawatha Passenger Car 2-pack, 06		190
29197	MILW Hiawatha Baggage Car "1305," 06		95
29198	MILW Hiawatha Coach "439," 06		95
29199	MILW Hiawatha Diner, StationSounds, 06		190
29202	Santa Fe Map Boxcar "6464," 97 u		53
29203	Maine Central Boxcar "6464-597," 97 u	10	35
29205	Mickey Mouse Hi-Cube Boxcar "9555," 97		70
29206	Vapor Records Boxcar #1, 97		90
29209	Postwar "6464" Boxcar Series VII, 3 cars, 98	23	97
29210	GN Boxcar "6464-450," 98		33
29211	B&M Boxcar "6464-475," 98		27
29212	Timken Boxcar "6464-500," 98		28
29213	ATSF Grand Canyon Route 6464 Boxcar "6464-198," 98		26
29214	Southern 6464 Boxcar "6464-298," 98	32	86
29215	Canadian Pacific 6464 Boxcar "6464-398," 98	9	28
29217	1997 Toy Fair Airex Boxcar, 97		78
29218	Vapor Records Boxcar "6464-496," 97 u	20	49
29220	Lionel Centennial Series Hi-Cube Boxcar Set, 4 cars, 97		235
29221	Centennial Series Hi-Cube Boxcar "9697-1," 97		65
29222	Centennial Series Hi-Cube Boxcar "9697-2," 97		72
29223	Centennial Series Hi-Cube Boxcar "9697-3," 97		65
29224	Centennial Series Hi-Cube Boxcar "9697-4," 97		62
29225	H.O.R.D.E. Music Festival Boxcar, 97	48	70
29229	Vapor Records Holiday Car, 98		160
29231	Halloween Animated Boxcar, 98		42
29233	Conrail PC Overstamped Boxcar "6464-598," 98		38
29234	Conrail Erie Overstamped Boxcar "6464-698," 98		32
29235	NYC Boxcar "6464-510," 99		47
29236	MKT Boxcar "6464-515," 99		40
29237	M&StL Boxcar "6464-525," 99	13	35
29247	Green Mainline Classic Street Lamps, 3-pack, 08-23		40
29250	Phoebe Snow Boxcar "6464-199," 99		41
29251	BN Boxcar "6464-299," 99	13	36
29252	CP Boxcar "6464-399," 99	13	37
29253	B&M Boxcar "76032," 99		50
29254	B&M Boxcar "76033," 99		50
29255	B&M Boxcar "76034," 99		50
29256	B&M Boxcar "76035," 99		50
29257	Southern Boxcar "9464-199," 99		38
29258	Reading Boxcar "9464-299," 99		36
29259	NP Bicentennial Boxcar "9464-399," 99		34
29265	Maine Central Boxcar "8661," 99	10	36
29266	Frisco Boxcar "8722," 99	15	38
29267	No. 6464 Boxcar 3-pack, Series VIII, 99	38	86
29268	Rio Grande Boxcar "63067," 99		40
29271	Lionel Cola Tractor and Trailer, 98		12
29279	Conrail Jersey Central Overstamped Boxcar "6464-28X," 99		40

No.	Description	Exc	Mint	
29280	Conrail LV Overstamped Boxcar "6464-31X," 99		41	
29281	Conrail Overstamped Boxcar 2-pack, 99		70	
29282	Postwar "6464" Boxcar 3-pack, 99	43	125	
29283	NYC Boxcar, 99		55	
29284	GN Boxcar, 99	14	39	
29285	Seaboard Boxcar, 99		36	
29286	Overstamped Boxcar 2-pack, 99		65	
29287	NH PC Overstamped Boxcar "6464-29X," 99	18	34	
29288	Conrail Reading Overstamped Boxcar "6464-32X," 99		38	
29289	Postwar "6464" Series IX, 3 cars, 99-00	35	85	
29290	D&RGW Boxcar "6464-650," 00		41	
29291	ATSF Boxcar "6464-700," 00		38	
29292	NH Boxcar "6464-725," 00		39	
29293	NH Boxcar "6464-425," 99		95	
29294	Hellgate Bridge Boxcar "1900-2000," 99 u		38	
29295	PRR "Don't Stand Me Still" Boxcar "24018," 99-00		65	
29296	PRR "Merchandise" Boxcar "29296," 99-00		65	
29297	PRR "No Damage" Boxcar "47158," 99-00		65	
29298	Lionel Boxcar "6464-2000," 00		46	
29300	50th Anniversary Clear Shell Aquarium Car, 10		85	
29301	Postwar "3662" Transparent Milk Car with platform, 11, 13		155	
29302	Christmas Music Reefer, 10		75	
29303	North Pole Central Crane Car, 10-11		65	
29305	UP Chisholm Trail Stock Car, Cattle Sounds, 11, 13		200	
29306	PRR Hi-Cube Lighted Garland Boxcar, 10-11		70	
29309	GN Pullman-Standard Diesel Freight Set, CC, 13		830	
29310	Marine Science Deep Sea Exhibition Aquarium Car, 11		75	
29311	Strasburg Derrick Car, 11		45	
29312	Santa's Operating Boxcar, 11-12		75	
29314	SP DD Boxcar "214051" (std O), 13-14		75	
29317	CN DD Boxcar "551334" (std O), 13-14	40	80	
29318	NJ Transit Gondola "9422" w/Ballast Load, 12-13		35	
29319	NJ Transit BW Caboose "905," 12-13	70	90	
29320	CNJ DD Boxcar "25031" (std O), 13-14	40	75	
29320	UP Walking Brakeman Car "454400," 12	52	70	
29321	Ice Skating Aquarium Car, 12		80	
29322	Koi Aquarium Car, 13-14		80	
29323	UP DD Boxcar "500019" (std O), 13-14		75	
29324	Walking Zombie Brakeman Car, 12		80	
29326	NP "Pig Palace" Operating Stock Car "84144," 12		200	
29327	Bethlehem Steel Operating Hopper "2025," 12		60	
29328	Beatles "Nothing is Real" Aquarium Car, 12-13		85	
29329	Peanuts Halloween Aquarium Car, 12-13		85	
29333	ATSF 89' Auto Carrier 2-pack (std O), 13-14, 16		220	
29338	BN 89' Auto Carrier 2-pack (std O), 13-14		220	
29344	C&NW DD Boxcar "57766" (std O), 13		75	
29345	ATSF 89' Auto Carrier (std O), 13-14		110	
29346	Soo Line 89' Auto Carrier 2-pack (std O), 13-16		220	
29349	SP 89' Auto Carrier 2-pack (std O), 13-16		220	
29364	NYC Water Level Steam Freight Set, CC, 12-13		1600	
29365	N&W Pocahontas Steam Passenger Set, CC, 12		1950	
29366	SP TankSet Diesel Set, CC, 12		850	
29372	BNSF 89' Auto Carrier "300267" (std O), 13		110	

		Exc	Mint
____	**29373** CN 89' Auto Carrier "710771" (std O), 13, 16		110
____	**29376** Conrail 89' Auto Carrier "964444" (std O), 13		110
____	**29377** CP 89' Auto Carrier 2-pack (std O), 13-14, 16		220
____	**29380** CSX 89' Auto Carrier "604544" (std O), 13		110
____	**29381** GTW 89' Auto Carrier "50450" (std O), 14-15		110
____	**29382** UP 89' Auto Carrier "604545" (std O), 13		110
____	**29384** DL&W USRA Double-sheathed Boxcar "44153" (std O), 13		70
____	**29385** ATSF USRA Double-sheathed Boxcar "39012" (std O), 13		70
____	**29386** PRR PS-4 Flatcar with stakes "469614" (std O), 13		70
____	**29387** GN PS-4 Flatcar with stakes "629387" (std O), 13		70
____	**29400** Bethlehem Steel Slag Car 3-pack (std O), 03		185
____	**29404** Bethlehem Steel Hot Metal Car 3-pack (std O), 03		210
____	**29408** PRR Coil Car, 01		40
____	**29411** Sherwin-Williams Vat Car, 02		35
____	**29412** Tabasco Brand Vat Car, 02		36
____	**29413** Airex Boat Loader Car "29413," 02		42
____	**29414** PRR Evans Auto Loader "480123," 01		56
____	**29415** WM Skeleton Log Car 3-pack #2 (std O), 02		90
____	**29419** West Side Lumber Skeleton Log Car 3-pack #2 (std O), 02		90
____	**29423** Wellspring Capital Management Happy Holidays Vat Car, 03 u		255
____	**29424** Meadow River Lumber Skeleton Log Car 3-pack (std O), 03		90
____	**29429** Campbell's Soup Vat Car "29429," 03		38
____	**29430** Meadow River Lumber Skeleton Log Car 3-pack #2 (std O), 03		90
____	**29434** Weyerhauser Skeleton Log Car 3-pack, 05		108
____	**29438** Trailer Train Flatcar with 2 UP trailers, 03		60
____	**29439** Postwar "6414" Evans Auto Loader, 02		43
____	**29441** UP Flatcar "53471" with grader, 02		43
____	**29442** CSX Flatcar "600513" with backhoe, 02		43
____	**29449** Weyerhaeuser Timber Skeleton Log Car 3-pack #2 (std O), 03		90
____	**29453** Elk River Lumber Skeleton Log Car 3-pack #2 (std O), 03		90
____	**29457** NS Flatcar "157590" with Caterpillar loader, 03		42
____	**29458** BNSF Flatcar "922268" with Caterpillar truck, 03		44
____	**29459** Water Barrel Car "1878," Archive Collection, 03		40
____	**29460** LL Flatcar "3460" with trailers, Archive Collection, 03		39
____	**29461** Postwar "6500" Flatcar with red-and-white airplane, 03		32
____	**29462** Postwar "6500" Flatcar with white-and-red airplane, 03		31
____	**29463** Postwar "6414" Evans Auto Loader, 03		30
____	**29464** U.S. Army Vat Car "29464," 04		35
____	**29465** U.S. Steel Slag Car 3-pack (std O), 04-05		160
____	**29469** U.S. Steel Hot Metal Car 3-pack (std O), 04-05		190
____	**29473** Youngstown Sheet & Tube Slag Car 3-pack (std O), 03		150
____	**29477** Youngstown Sheet & Tube Hot Metal Car 3-pack (std O), 03		170
____	**29481** Cass Scenic Railroad Skeleton Log Car 3-pack (std O), 03		80
____	**29487** Boat-loader with 4 boats, 04		65
____	**29488** Cass Scenic Railroad Skeleton Log Car 3-pack #2 (std O), 04		90
____	**29492** Pickering Lumber Skeleton Log Car 3-pack #1 (std O), 04		100
____	**29496** Pickering Lumber Skeleton Log Car 3-pack #2 (std O), 04		90
____	**29602** Celanese Chemicals 1-D Tank Car, 05		45
____	**29603** Comet 1-D Tank Car, traditional, 05		53
____	**29604** Meadow Brook Molasses 1-D Tank Car, traditional, 05		53
____	**29606** Elvis Presley Gold Record Transport Car, 04		120
____	**29607** Las Vegas Mint Car, traditional, 05		58
____	**29609** Alien Suspension Car, 06		60

MODERN 1970-2023		Exc	Mint
29610	Dixie Honey 1-D Tank Car, 06		60 ___
29611	Sunoco 1-D Tank Car, 06	30	63 ___
29612	Las Vegas Poker Chip Car, 06		40 ___
29613	Postwar "6463" Rocket Fuel 2-D Tank Car, 06		75 ___
29614	Postwar "6315" Gulf Chemical Tank Car, 06		48 ___
29617	Cities Service Tank Car, 06-07		48 ___
29618	Hooker Chemicals 3-D Tank Car, 07		60 ___
29619	Grave's Formaldehyde 1-D Tank Car, 07		60 ___
29622	Fort Knox Mint Car, lilac, Archive Collection, 07		60 ___
29624	Monopoly Mint Car with money, 08		65 ___
29626	"Case Closed" Mint Car with shredded documents, 08		109 ___
29628	Poinsettia Mint Car, 09		70 ___
29629	AEC Glow-in-the-Dark Tank Car, 09-10		65 ___
29633	Christmas Ornament Lighted Mint Car, 10		70 ___
29634	Federal Reserve Bailout Mint Car, 10		70 ___
29635	Monopoly "Go To Jail" Mint Car, 10		70 ___
29636	Vampire Transport Mint Car, 10-11		70 ___
29637	Candy Cane 2-D Tank Car, 10-11		55 ___
29638	Fort Knox Mint Car, 10-11	40	65 ___
29640	Coca-Cola Tank Car, 10		65 ___
29642	Jolly Rancher 1-D Tank Car, 11		55 ___
29643	Hershey's Syrup 1-D Tank Car, 11		58 ___
29644	ATSF 1-D Tank Car, 11		55 ___
29645	Atlantic City Casino Mint Car, 11		70 ___
29646	Alaska Oil 2-D Tank Car, 11		50 ___
29647	Gingerbread Man Mint Car, 11		70 ___
29648	Kansas City Federal Reserve Mint Car, 11		70 ___
29649	Lionel SP Smoke Pellets Mint Car, 12-13		70 ___
29650	Cleveland Federal Reserve Mint Car, 11		70 ___
29651	Richmond Federal Reserve Mint Car, 12		70 ___
29654	Boston Federal Reserve Mint Car, 13		70 ___
29655	PRR 16-wheel Flatcar with girders "469846," 12		75 ___
29656	ATSF 16-wheel Flatcar with transformer "90096," 12		75 ___
29671	Smoke Pellet Mint Car #2, 13-15		70 ___
29694	Hershey's Mint Car, 14	64	95 ___
29695	Trailer Set Maxi-Stack Pair "48," 13		120 ___
29697	Santa's Flatcar with submarine, 13		70 ___
29698	Tree Topper Star Transport Car, 13-14		80 ___
29699	Silver and Gold Christmas Mint Car, 13-14		70 ___
29703	Postwar "6427-500" Girl's PRR Porthole Caboose, 01		45 ___
29704	Postwar "6427" Boy's Set PRR Porthole Caboose, 02		50 ___
29705	PRR Porthole Caboose "477951" (std O), 04		40 ___
29706	Postwar "6437" PRR Porthole Caboose, 04		40 ___
29707	NIckel Plate BW Caboose "408" (std O), 04		80 ___
29708	C&O Bay Window Caboose "8315," 04		45 ___
29709	PRR Porthole Caboose "477938," 04		40 ___
29710	Postwar "6657" D&RGW Caboose, 04-05		33 ___
29711	ATSF Bay Window Caboose, 04-05		60 ___
29712	Postwar "2420" Searchlight Caboose, 04		50 ___
29713	Postwar "6437" PRR Porthole Caboose, 05		20 ___
29714	Postwar "6557" Lionel Lines Smoking Caboose, 05-07		120 ___
29715	PRR Porthole Caboose "477953," 05		45 ___
29716	UP EV Caboose "25462," 04		40 ___

		Exc	Mint
____ 29717	NS EV Caboose "555533," 05	40	50
____ 29718	Postwar "6419-100" N&W Work Caboose, 05-06		48
____ 29719	ATSF Porthole Caboose "6427," Archive Collection, 05-06		48
____ 29720	PRR Porthole Caboose "477861," 06		45
____ 29721	PRR Work Caboose "491064," 06		50
____ 29722	Postwar "6517" LL BW Caboose w.Strobe light, 06		49
____ 29723	LL Porthole Caboose "64273" Archive Collection, 06-08	27	50
____ 29724	Postwar "6517" LL BW Caboose, 06-07		50
____ 29725	CP EV Caboose "43615," 06		50
____ 29726	Virginian Porthole Caboose "6427-60," Archive, 06-07		50
____ 29727	"I Love U.S.A." Bay Window Caboose "1985," 06		60
____ 29728	UP Smoking EV Caboose, 07		60
____ 29729	Bethlehem Steel Searchlight Caboose, 06		90
____ 29730	Postwar "6427-3" LL Porthole Caboose, 07		45
____ 29732	PRR Porthole Caboose "477871," 08		45
____ 29733	White Pass & Yukon EV Caboose, 09-10		90
____ 29734	PRR NS Heritage CA-4 Caboose (std O), 09-10		95
____ 29735	Conrail NS Heritage CA-4 Caboose (std O), 10		95
____ 29736	NYC Smoking NE Caboose "20883," 09-10		55
____ 29737	ATSF Bay Window Caboose, traditional, 10-11		70
____ 29738	Postwar "6517" Transparent Smoking BW Caboose, 10-11		80
____ 29739	B&M Transfer Caboose, 10-11		50
____ 29761	GATX TankTrain A-End "44570," 12		100
____ 29762	GATX TankTrain Intermediate Car "44559," 12		80
____ 29763	GATX TankTrain Intermediate Car "44580," 12		80
____ 29764	GATX TankTrain B-End "44575," 12		100
____ 29765	GATX TankSet Add-on 3-pack (std O), 12		240
____ 29766	GATX TankTrain Intermediate Car "44598," 12		80
____ 29767	GATX TankTrain Intermediate Car "44581," 12		80
____ 29768	GATX TankTrain Intermediate Car "44578," 12		80
____ 29769	NYC/Michigan Central Double-sheathed Boxcar "51071," 12-13		100
____ 29770	B&M Offset Hopper "7168," 12-13		40
____ 29771	CN TankSet 2-pack (std O), 12		160
____ 29772	CN TankTrain Intermediate Car "75565," 12		80
____ 29773	CN TankTrain Intermediate Car "75561," 12		80
____ 29774	GATX TankSet 2-pack (std O), 12		160
____ 29775	GATX TankTrain Intermediate Car "57009," 12		80
____ 29776	GATX TankTrain Intermediate Car "48671," 12		80
____ 29777	CIBRO TankSet 2-pack (std O), 12		160
____ 29778	CIBRO TankTrain Intermediate Car "26251," 12		80
____ 29779	CIBRO TankTrain Intermediate Car "26255," 12		80
____ 29780	NYC 1-D Tank Car, 12-13		90
____ 29781	NYC Smoking Wood-sided Caboose, 12-13		200
____ 29786	Bethlehem Steel PS-2 3-bay Hopper (std O), 13		80
____ 29787	PRR PS-2 3-bay Hopper (std O), 13		80
____ 29788	PRR Porthole Caboose "477939," 13-17		35
____ 27789	Penn Salt Chemicals 3-D Tank Car "4727," 13-17		35
____ 29790	PRR Boxcar "539339," 13-17		36
____ 29791	Wizard of Oz Anniversary Boxcar, 13-15		70
____ 29792	Angela Trotta Thomas "Toyland Express" Boxcar, 13		65
____ 29793	"Where the Wild Things Are" Boxcar, 13-15		70
____ 29800	MOW Crane Car, TMCC, 04		250

| --- | --- | --- | --- |
29801	ATSF Operating Barrel Ramp Car, 04-05		89 ___
29802	Postwar "3530" EMD Generator Car, 04-05		89 ___
29803	Postwar "3444" Erie Animated Gondola, 04-05		89 ___
29804	UP Crane Car "JPX 250," CC, 05		320 ___
29805	Conrail Crane Car "50202," CC, 05		320 ___
29806	Weyerhaeuser Log Dump Car, 05		75 ___
29807	DM&IR Coal Dump Car, 05		75 ___
29808	Candy Cane Dump Car, 05		55 ___
29809	Santa's Delivery Service Dump Car w/Presents, 05		60 ___
29810	Operating Egg Nog Car with platform, 05		140 ___
29811	NYC Merchant's Despatch Transit Hot Box Reefer, 05	85	110 ___
29812	Santa Fe Hot Box Reefer "20699," 05		90 ___
29813	Santa Fe Boom Car "19144," Crane Sounds, 05		270 ___
29814	Pennsylvania Boom Car "491063," Crane Sounds, 05		210 ___
29815	NYC Boom Car "X923," Crane Sounds, 05		210 ___
29816	MOW Boom Car "X-816," Crane Sounds, 05		210 ___
29817	UP Boom Car "909438," Crane Sounds, 05		210 ___
29818	Conrail Boom Car, Crane Sounds, 05		210 ___
29820	Postwar "3356" Operating Horse Car and Corral, 05		75 ___
29821	Postwar "2460" Lionel Lines Crane Car, gray cab, 05		43 ___
29822	Postwar "773W" NYC Tender, whistle, 05		48 ___
29823	Postwar "3484" Pennsylvania Operating Boxcar, 05		38 ___
29824	Postwar "3662" Operating Milk Car and Platform, 05		59 ___
29825	Postwar "3434" Poultry Dispatch Car, 05		60 ___
29826	Postwar "3530" Generator Car and Light Pole, 05		48 ___
29827	Postwar "3419" Helicopter Launching Car, 06		49 ___
29828	Postwar "3666" Minuteman Car with cannon, 06		85 ___
29829	Postwar "6905" Radioactive Waste Car, 06		85 ___
29830	PFE Hot Box Reefer "5890" (std O), 06		105 ___
29831	Swift Hot Box Reefer "15342" (std O), 06		150 ___
29832	Chessie System Crane Car "940504," CC, 06		320 ___
29833	Chessie System Boom Car "940561," CC, 06		210 ___
29834	LL Bay Window Caboose "834," TrainSounds (std O), 06-07		110 ___
29835	SP Bay Window Caboose "4667," TrainSounds (std O), 06-07		160 ___
29838	Postwar "3666" Cannon Firing Boxcar, 05		149 ___
29839	Postwar "6512" Cherry Picker Car, 06		63 ___
29841	PRR Ballast Dump Car, 06		28 ___
29842	REA Express Hot Box Refrigerator Car w/Smoke, 06-07		125 ___
29843	Postwar "3356" ATSF Horse Car and Corral, 06-07		110 ___
29844	Postwar "3512" Fireman and Ladder Car, 06-08		50 ___
29845	Postwar "6812" Track Maintenance Car, 06-08		50 ___
29846	Postwar "6650" Operating Missile Launching Car, 06-08		30 ___
29847	Postwar "3419" Helicopter Launching Car, 06-07		60 ___
29648	Postwar "3540" Operating Radar Car, 06-07		50 ___
29849	Lionel Lines Crane Car, silver cab, 05-06		60 ___
29850	N&W J Class Tender, air whistle, 06-07		73 ___
29851	NYC Operating Crane Car "X-15," CC, 06		180 ___
29852	NYC Boom Car w/Sounds, 06		220 ___
29853	Postwar "6651" Big John Cannon Car, 08		75 ___
29854	Satellite Launching Car, 07		70 ___
29855	Lionel Lines Operating Milk Car with platform, 07		140 ___
29856	Monon Operating Boxcar, 06-07		65 ___
29857	Lionel Lines Boom Car, 06-07		55 ___

		Exc	Mint
___ 29858	CP Rail Crane Car "414475," CC, 07		320
___ 29859	CP Rail Boom Car "412567," CC, 07		210
___ 29865	Southern Operating Barrel Car, 07-08		75
___ 29866	Pirates Aquarium Car, 07		75
___ 29867	NYC Jet Snow Blower "X27207," 07		120
___ 29868	Alaska Jet Snow Blower, 07		120
___ 29869	Bethlehem Steel Crane Car, 06		60
___ 29870	MOW Jet Snow Blower "MWX-16," 07		120
___ 29871	Postwar "3359" Twin Bin Dump Car, 07		40
___ 29872	Postwar "3494-275" State of Maine Operating Boxcar, 07		55
___ 29873	Postwar "3361" LL Log Dump Car, 07		40
___ 29874	Peanuts Halloween Aquarium Car, 12		85
___ 29877	Southern Crane Car "D76," CC, 08		350
___ 29878	Southern Boom Car "T-193," CC, 08		230
___ 29882	Witches Operating Brew Car, 08		150
___ 29883	C&NW Operating Crane Car, CC, 10 u		340
___ 29884	CNJ Twin Dump Car, 08		85
___ 29885	BN Crane Car "S-104," CC, 10		340
___ 29886	BN Boom Car "S-1040," CC, 10		220
___ 29888	Postwar "3494-625" Soo Line Operating Boxcar, 08		70
___ 29891	ATSF Operating Crane Car, CC, 09-10		340
___ 29892	ATSF Boom Car, CC, 09-10		220
___ 29893	PRR Operating Stock Car "129893," RailSounds, 09		150
___ 29894	Christmas Chase Gondola, 09		65
___ 29895	Christmas Operating Snow Globe Car, 10		75
___ 29897	CSX Chessie System Research Car "3440," 11		65
___ 29900	"I Love Wisconsin" Boxcar, 01		35
___ 29901	"I Love Kentucky" Boxcar, 01		30
___ 29902	"I Love Iowa" Boxcar, 01		31
___ 29903	"I Love Missouri" Boxcar, 01		31
___ 29904	2002 Toy Fair Boxcar, 02		22
___ 29905	2002 Lionel Employee Christmas Boxcar, 02		80
___ 29906	"I Love Connecticut" Boxcar, 02		33
___ 29907	"I Love West Virginia" Boxcar, 02		33
___ 29908	"I Love Delaware" Boxcar, 02		33
___ 29909	"I Love Maryland" Boxcar, 02		65
___ 29910	Toy Fair Centennial Boxcar, 03		40
___ 29911	2003 Lionel Employee Christmas Boxcar, 03 u		90
___ 29912	"I Love Alabama" Boxcar, 03		30
___ 29913	"I Love Mississippi" Boxcar, 03		35
___ 29914	"I Love Louisiana" Boxcar, 03		35
___ 29915	"I Love Arkansas" Boxcar, 03		30
___ 29918	2003 Toy Fair Boxcar, 03 u		48
___ 29919	2004 Toy Fair Boxcar, 04 u		37
___ 29920	"I Love North Dakota" Boxcar, 03		35
___ 29921	"I Love South Dakota" Boxcar, 03		40
___ 29922	"I Love Nebraska" Boxcar, 03		30
___ 29923	"I Love Kansas" Boxcar, 03		30
___ 29924	2004 Lionel Employee Christmas Boxcar, 04 u		110
___ 29925	Toy Fair Polar Express Boxcar, 05 u		250
___ 29926	2005 Lionel Employee Christmas Boxcar, 05 u		90
___ 29927	"I Love Washington" Boxcar, 05		45
___ 29928	"I Love Oregon" Boxcar, 05		40

		Exc	Mint	
29929	"I Love Idaho" Boxcar, 05		45	___
29930	"I Love Utah" Boxcar, 05		45	___
29931	LRRC Season's Greetings Boxcar, 05 u		40	___
29932	"I Love Oklahoma" Boxcar, 06		45	___
29933	"I Love New Mexico" Boxcar, 06		45	___
29934	"I Love Hawaii" Boxcar, 06		45	___
29935	"I Love Alaska" Boxcar, 06		45	___
29936	"I Love Wyoming" Boxcar, 06		45	___
29937	2006 Toy Fair Boxcar, 06		38	___
29938	2006 Lionel Employee Christmas Boxcar, 06 u		25	___
29939	LRRC Anniversary Boxcar, 06 u		26	___
29941	LRRC 2006 Christmas Boxcar, 06 u		40	___
29942	Santa Fe Railroad Art Boxcar, 06		50	___
29943	Texas Special Railroad Art Boxcar, 06		50	___
29944	1957 Lionel Art Boxcar, 06	10	50	___
29945	1947 Lionel Art Boxcar, 06		50	___
29946	LRRC 2007 Christmas Boxcar, 07 u		40	___
29947	LRRC 2007 Commemorative Boxcar, 07 u		42	___
29949	2007 Lionel Employee Christmas Boxcar, 07 u		60	___
29950	1948 Lionel Art Boxcar, 08		50	___
29951	1954 Lionel Art Boxcar, 08	18	50	___
29952	GN Art Boxcar, 08		50	___
29953	SP Art Boxcar, 08		50	___
29954	2007 Lionel Dealer Christmas Boxcar, 07 u		50	___
29955	2008 Lionel Dealer Appreciation Boxcar, 08 u		70	___
29956	2008 Lionel Employee Christmas Boxcar, 08 u		60	___
29957	LRRC 2008 Christmas Boxcar, 08 u		42	___
29958	2009 Lionel Dealer Appreciation Boxcar, 09 u		40	___
29959	1952 Lionel Art Boxcar, 09	15	58	___
29960	Rock Island Art Boxcar, 09-10		58	___
29961	Meet the Beatles Boxcar 2-pack, 10-14		130	___
29962	Meet the Beatles Boxcar, 10-14		65	___
29963	The Beatles' Second Album Boxcar, 10-14		65	___
29964	2009 Lionel Employee Christmas Boxcar, 09 u		25	___
29965	Lionel Art Boxcar 2-pack, 10-11		116	___
29966	Lionel Art Boxcar, 12	45	55	___
29967	Lionel Santa Fe Art Boxcar, 10-11		35	___
29968	Beatles "A Hard Day's Night" Boxcar, 11-14		65	___
29969	Beatles "Something New" Boxcar, 11-14		65	___
29970	2010 Lionel Employee Christmas Boxcar, 10 u		25	___
29971	2011 Lionel Employee Christmas Boxcar, 11 u		25	___
29972	2012 Lionel Employee Christmas Boxcar, 12 u		25	___
29973	NYC Pacemaker Boxcar "175005," 10-11		60	___
29974	SP Boxcar "128133," 11		60	___
29975	Holiday Boxcar, 11		60	___
29976	Holiday Boxcar, 12-13		65	___
29977	2011 LRRC Holiday Boxcar, 11 u		60	___
29978	Railroad Museum of Pennsylvania Boxcar, 12		65	___
29979	Angela Trotta Thomas "Christmas Morning" Boxcar, 12-13		60	___
29980	Elvis Presley 35th Anniversary Boxcar, 12		70	___
29982	CV Milk Car "575" (std O), 16		80	___
29985	B&M Milk Car "1903" (std O), 16		80	___
29989	PFE Steel-sided Refrigerator Car 3-pack (std O), 14-15		240	___

			Exc	Mint
___	29990	PFE Steel-sided Refrigerator Car "8383" (std O), 14-15		80
___	29991	PFE Steel-sided Refrigerator Car "8171" (std O), 14-15		80
___	29992	PFE Steel-sided Refrigerator Car "8080" (std O), 14-15		80
___	29994	U.S. Army Boxcar, 13-15		70
___	29995	U.S. Navy Boxcar, 13-15		70
___	29996	U.S. Marines Boxcar, 13-15		70
___	29997	U.S. Air Force Boxcar, 13-15		70
___	29998	U.S. National Guard Boxcar, 13-16		70
___	29999	U.S. Coast Guard Boxcar, 13-16		70
___	30000	PRR Keystone Super Freight Steam Train, TMCC, 05		450
___	30001	Santa Fe El Capitan Passenger Set, TrainSounds, 05-10	150	370
___	30002	Neil Young's Greendale Diesel Freight Set, 04		420
___	30003	Pennsylvania Flyer Operating Freight Expansion Pack, 05		99
___	30004	Pennsylvania Flyer Passenger Expansion Pack, 05-08		120
___	30005	Disney Passenger Train, 05		190
___	30007	NYC Flyer Operating Freight Expansion Pack, 05		99
___	30008	NYC Flyer Passenger Expansion Pack, 05-08		120
___	30011	Holiday Expansion Pack, 05		100
___	30012	Thomas the Tank Engine Expansion Pack, 05-13, 16		150
___	30016	NYC Flyer Steam Freight Set, 06-08		290
___	30018	Pennsylvania Flyer Steam Freight Set, 06-07	100	240
___	30020	North Pole Central Christmas Steam Train, 06-07		208
___	30021	Cascade Range Steam Logging Train, 06-08		190
___	30022	Southwest Diesel Freight Set, TrainSounds, 06	80	295
___	30024	UP Fast Freight Steam Set, TrainSounds, 06-07		340
___	30025	Chesapeake Super Freight Steam Set, TMCC, 06-07	238	488
___	30026	CP Diesel Freight Set, TMCC, 06		540
___	30034	Great Western Train Set with Lincoln Logs, 07-09	115	315
___	30035	Sodor Freight Expansion Pack, 06-09		120
___	30036	Great Western Expansion Pack, 07-08		120
___	30037	Pennsylvania Flyer Operating Freight Expansion Pack, 06-08		120
___	30038	NYC Flyer Operating Freight Expansion Pack, 06-08		120
___	30039	North Pole Central Passenger Expansion Pack, 06-11		110
___	30040	North Pole Central Freight Expansion Pack, 06-11		110
___	30041	Southwest Diesel Freight Expansion Pack, 06		110
___	30042	Cascade Range Expansion Pack, 06		110
___	30044	NYC Empire Builder Steam Freight Set, TMCC, 06		2800
___	30045	Alaska Steam Work Train, 07-09		270
___	30046	Alaska Work Train Expansion Pack, 07-08		110
___	30047	Northwest Special Diesel Freight Set, TrainSounds, 07-08		295
___	30048	Northwest Special Freight Expansion Pack, 07-08		110
___	30049	D&RGW Fast Freight Set, TrainSounds, 08-09		320
___	30050	Pennsylvania Super Freight Set, CC, 08		450
___	30051	UP Diesel Freight Set, TMCC, 07		500
___	30056	Halloween Steam Freight Set, 07-10		225
___	30061	UPS Centennial Stream Freight Set, 07-08	100	230
___	30063	It's a Wonderful Life Christmas Steam Freight Set, 07 u		225
___	30064	Pennsylvania Speeder Set, traditional, K-Line, 06		75
___	30065	Best Friend of Charleston Locomotive, 07		425
___	30066/67	C&O Empire Builder Steam Freight Set, CC, 07-09		2700
___	30068	North Pole Central Christmas Freight Set, 08		220
___	30069	Thomas & Friends Passenger Train, 08-12		170
___	30070	Lionel Lines 4-4-2 Steam Freight Set, 07		300

		Exc	Mint	
30076	Disney Christmas Train, 07		400	___
30081	UP Merger Special GP38 Freight Set, 08		300	___
30082	UP Heritage Freight Car 3-pack, 08		100	___
30084	British Great Western Shakespeare Express Train, 08		300	___
30085	MTA Metro-North M-7 Commuter Car Set, 07-08		280	___
30087	Alien Spaceship Recovery Freight Set, 08-09		230	___
30088	John Bull Passenger Train, 08		430	___
30089	Pennsylvania Flyer Freight Set, 08-10		200	___
30091	ATSF Steam Freight Set, 08-09		270	___
30094	Chicago & North Western Passenger Set, 08		150	___
30096	Pennsylvania Keystone Special Steam Freight Set, 09		260	___
30103	NYC 0-8-0 Steam Freight Set, 09-10	167	291	___
30108	American Fire and Rescue GP20 Freight Set, 09-10		400	___
30109	Nutcracker Route Christmas Train Set, 10-11		270	___
30111	Pullman Passenger Expansion Pack, 09-16		155	___
30112	Eastern Freight Expansion Pack, 09-17		155	___
30114	MTA LIRR M-7 Commuter Set, 09		320	___
30116	Lone Ranger Wild West Freight Set, 09-13		400	___
30118	A Christmas Story Steam Freight Set, 09-12		330	___
30120	Menards C&NW Steam Passenger Set, 09		250	___
30121	ATSF Baby Madison Car 3-pack, 10-11		190	___
30122	Wizard of Oz Steam Freight Set, 10-12		310	___
30123	Boy Scouts of America Steam Freight Set, 10		310	___
30124	Thunder Valley Quarry Steam Freight Set, 10-11		300	___
30125	Rio Grande Ski Train, TrainSounds, 10-11		340	___
30126	Pennsylvania Flyer Steam Freight Set, 10		230	___
30127	Scout Steam Freight Set, 10-12		200	___
30128	Western Freight Expansion Pack, 10-12		138	___
30131	Chessie System Merger Diesel Freight Set, 10		300	___
30133	Strasburg Steam Passenger Set, 10-13		330	___
30135	Scout Freight Expansion Pack, 11-15		115	___
30136	Thunder Valley Quarry Freight Car Add-on 2-pack, 10-11		110	___
30138	Chessie System Merger Freight Car Add-on 2-pack, 10-11		120	___
30139	Santa Fe Flyer Steam Freight Set, 10		270	___
30141	Sodor Tank and Wagon Expansion Pack, 10-16		150	___
30142	Texas Special Freight Set, TrainSounds, 10-11		700	___
30144	Operation Eagle Justice Diesel Freight Set, 10-11	138	500	___
30145	Maple Leaf Diesel Freight Set, 10-11		550	___
30146	Menards Soo Line Freight Set, 10	175	275	___
30147	MTA Long Island M-7 Commuter Set, 11		320	___
30149	Bass Pro Shops North Pole Central Christmas Set, 08 u		220	___
30153	CSX Diesel Freight Set, 11		330	___
30154	BNSF Diesel Freight Set, 11		340	___
30155	M&StL Diesel Freight Set, 11-12		230	___
30156	NYC Flyer Freight Set, TrainSounds, 11		300	___
30157	M&StL Flatcar and Erie-Lack. Gondola 2-pack, 11-15		110	___
30158	Norfolk Southern GP38 Diesel Freight Train Set, 11		320	___
30159	Wabash Blue Bird Passenger Set, 11-12		360	___
30161	Boy Scouts Steam Freight Set, 11-13		320	___
30162	Thomas & Friends Christmas Set, 13-15		200	___
30164	Santa's Flyer Steam Freight Set, 11-13		250	___
30165	Candy Cane Transit Commuter 2-pack, 11-13		180	___
30166	Coca-Cola 125th Anniversary Steam Set, 11-12		350	___

	MODERN 1970-2023	Exc	Mint
___ 30167	SP Merger Steam Freight Train Set , 12		400
___ 30168	Rio Grande General Set, TrainSounds, 11-12		300
___ 30169	NJ Transit Train Set, 11		350
___ 30170	Sodor Freight 3-pack, 11-13		100
___ 30171	GG1 Electric Freight Train Set, 11-13		550
___ 30173	Santa Fe Flyer Freight Set, 11-12		270
___ 30174	Pennsylvania Flyer Freight Set, 11-13	80	290
___ 30176	Wegmans Steam Freight Train Set, 11 u		300
___ 30177	Menards Milwaukee Road Steam Freight Set, 11 u		175
___ 30178	ATSF Super Chief Diesel Passenger Train Set, 12-13		400
___ 30179	RI Rocket Diesel Freight Train Set, 12-13		400
___ 30180	Horseshoe Curve Steam Freight Train Set, 12-13		440
___ 30181	CP Diesel Passenger Set, RailSounds, 13, 15		450
___ 30183	Scout Remote Steam Freight Set, 13, 15		220
___ 30184	Polar Express Steam Freight Set, 13		420
___ 30185	NJ Transit Diesel MOW Train Set, 12-13		350
___ 30186	KCS Southern Belle Diesel Freight Train Set, 12-13		350
___ 30187	Titanic Centennial Diesel Freight Train Set, 12-13		450
___ 30188	UP Flyer Steam Freight Train Set, 12-13		330
___ 30189	LIRR Diesel Passenger Train Set, 12-13		330
___ 30190	Thomas & Friends Set, LionChief, 12-16		200
___ 30191	Sodor Work Set 3-pack, 12-15		100
___ 30193	Peanuts Christmas Steam Freight Set, 12-15		370
___ 30194	North Pole Express Steam Freight Set, 12-13		290
___ 30195	Grand Central Express Diesel Passenger Train Set, 12-14		440
___ 30196	Hershey's Steam Freight Train Set, 12-13		312
___ 30200	NYC Flyer Steam Freight Train Set, 12-13		350
___ 30205	Silver Bells Christmas Steam Freight Set, 13-14		240
___ 30206	Area 51 RS3 Diesel Freight Set, 13		250
___ 30207	Santa Fe RS3 Diesel Freight Set, 13		200
___ 30210	CP Rail Grain Diesel Freight Set, 13		390
___ 30211	BNSF Maxi Stack Diesel Freight Set, 13		440
___ 30213	Northeast NS Heritage Diesel Freight Set, 13		410
___ 30214	Peanuts Halloween Steam Freight Set, 13, 15-16		320
___ 30217	SP Black Widow Diesel Freight Set, 13, 15		460
___ 30218	Polar Express Steam Passenger Set, 13-16		400
___ 30218	Polar Express LC Passenger Set w/Personalized Tender, 18		440
___ 30219	Gingerbread Junction Steam Freight Set, 13-14		290
___ 30220	Polar Express 10th Anniversary Passenger Set, 13-16		500
___ 30221	Diesel Remote Control Set, 13-16		200
___ 30222	Percy Remote Control Set, 13-15		200
___ 30223	James Remote Control Set, 13-15		200
___ 30224	Pennsylvania Limited Steam Passenger Set, 13		340
___ 30225	Medal of Honor Train, 13		430
___ 30226	NS Diesel Freight Set, RailSounds, 13		410
___ 30228	Chattanooga Express Steam Passenger Set, 13		250
___ 30233	Pennsylvania Flyer Remote Steam Freight Set, 13-17		280
___ 31569	Western & Atlantic Passenger Car 2-pack, 08		100
___ 31700	Postwar Girls Freight Set, 01	350	570
___ 31701	Postwar Boys Freight Set, 02	138	345
___ 31704	Alton Limited Steam Passenger Set, 02		870
___ 31705	50th Anniversary Hudson Passenger Set, 02		910
___ 31706	UP Burro Crane Set, 02		210

No.	Description	Exc	Mint
31707	C&O Diesel Freight Set, 03		280
31708	Postwar "1805" Marines Missile Launch Train, 03	175	400
31710	BN Diesel Coal Train, RailSounds, 03	345	745
31711	Postwar "1563W" Wabash Diesel Freight Set, RailSounds, 03	200	570
31712	UP Alco PA Diesel Passenger Set, RailSounds, 03	475	1495
31713	Southern Crescent Steam Passenger Set, RailSounds, 03		1195
31714	Amtrak Acela Diesel Passenger Set, RailSounds, 04-05	850	2000
31715	Fire Rescue Steam Freight Set, 02		300
31716	Fire Rescue Steam Freight Set, 03		280
31717	CP Rail Snow Removal Train, 03	90	255
31718	SP "Oil Can" Tank Train Freight Set, 03		1600
31719	Western Maryland Fireball Diesel Freight Set, 04	193	363
31720	FEC Champion Diesel Passenger Set, RailSounds, 04	275	900
31721	Postwar "13138" Majestic Electric Freight Set, RailSounds, 04		580
31724	Nabisco 3-car Passenger Set, 03		110
31727	Postwar "2291W" Rio Grande Diesel Freight Set, RailSounds, 04	267	640
31728	Elvis "He Dared to Rock" Steam Freight Set, 04		325
31730	Norman Rockwell Boxcar 4-pack, 05		95
31733	Jones & Laughlin Steel Slag Train, 05		250
31734	Chessie Steam Special Passenger Set, TMCC, 05		405
31735	Chessie Diesel Freight Set, TMCC, 05-06		670
31736	CP Diesel Grain Train, TMCC, 05	457	813
31737	Napa Valley Diesel Wine Train, CC, 05		1000
31739	Postwar "13150" Hudson Steam Freight Set, Super O, 05		940
31740	Postwar "2519W" Virginian Diesel Freight Set, TMCC, 05-07	292	620
31742	Postwar "2544W" ATSF Super Chief Passenger Set, 05		700
31746	GN Mountain Mover Steam Freight Set, 12-13		430
31747	Pennsylvania Electric Ballast Train, TMCC, 06	205	550
31748	Santa Fe U28CG Diesel Freight Set (std 0), TMCC, 06-07		770
31749	Pennsylvania Diesel Coal Train, TMCC, 06		770
31750	NYC Hotbox Reefer Steam Freight Set, TMCC, 06-07		530
31751	New York City Transit Authority R27 Subway Train, CC, 07		700
31752	B&O Diesel Freight Set, TMCC, 06-07		740
31753	GN Diesel Freight Set, TMCC, 06-08	163	740
31754	Postwar "2545WS" N&W Space Freight Set, TMCC, 06-07	250	957
31755	Texas Special Diesel Passenger Set, CC, 07-08		1340
31757	Postwar "2289WS" Berkshire Freight Set, CC, 07	225	750
31758	Postwar "2270W" Jersey Central Diesel Passenger Car Set, CC, 08		750
31760	CSX SD40-2 Diesel Husky Stack Car Set, CC, 07-08		770
31765	Postwar "11268" C&O Diesel Freight Set, 08		580
31767	Bethlehem Steel Rolling Stock Set, K-Line, 06		100
31768	B&O Rolling Stock Set, K-Line, 06		100
31772	Conrail LionMaster Diesel Freight Set, CC, 08-09		535
31773	NS Dash 9 Diesel TankTrain Set, CC, 08		785
31774	AEC Burro Crane Set, traditional, 09-11		260
31775	Postwar "1562" Burlington GP Passenger Set, 08		470
31776	Postwar "2219W" Lackawanna Train Master Freight Set, 08		415
31777	Postwar "2124W" GG1 Passenger Set, 08		452
31778	Postwar "1484WS" Steam Passenger Set, 08		610
31779	Amtrak HHP-8 Amfleet Passenger Set, CC, 09		500
31782	ATSF Crane Car and Boom Car, CC (std 0), 09-10		560

		Exc	Mint
___ 31783	BNSF Ice Cold Express Diesel Freight Set, CC, 10		1000
___ 31784	No. 1593 UP Work Train Set, 09	80	470
___ 31787	CN SD70M-2 Diesel Coal Train, CC, 09		800
___ 31790	PRR GG1 Passenger Set, 10		500
___ 31791	NYC LionMaster Diesel Freight Set, CC, 10		700
___ 31793	White Pass & Yukon Freight Car Add-on 3-pack, 10-11, 13		195
___ 31794	New York City Transit R30 Subway 4-pack, 10	375	700
___ 31795	Pere Marquette Freight Car 3-pack (std O), 10-11		210
___ 31796	Feather Route Freight Car 3-pack (std O), 10-11		210
___ 31797	New York City Transit R16 Subway Set, CC, 10	1050	1460
___ 31799	GN Empire Steam Freight Express Set, 10		430
___ 31901	Christmas Steam Freight Set, 02		145
___ 31902	PRR K4 Freight Set, 01-02		580
___ 31904	C&O Steam Freight Set, RailSounds, 01		400
___ 31905	NH Diesel Freight Set, CC, 01		660
___ 31907	PRR Atlantic Freight Set, 01 u		400
___ 31908	Reading Hobo Express Freight Set, 01 u		365
___ 31909	Santa Fe Shell Tank Car Freight Set, 01 u		320
___ 31910	Soo Line Diesel Freight Set, 01 u		365
___ 31911	Snap-On Anniversary Steam Freight Set, 00 u	113	615
___ 31913	PRR Flyer Steam Freight Set, 01		126
___ 31914	NYC Flyer Steam Freight Set, RailSounds, 01-02		170
___ 31915	Chessie GP38 Diesel Freight Set, 01-02	70	155
___ 31916	Santa Fe Steam Freight Set, 01		300
___ 31918	C&O Steam Freight Set, SignalSounds, 01		315
___ 31919	T&P Steam Passenger Set, RailSounds, 01		210
___ 31920	L.L. Bean Freight Set, 01 u		270
___ 31922	Snap-On Tool Diesel Freight Set, 01 u	90	356
___ 31923	PRR Flyer Freight Set, 01 u		130
___ 31924	Union Pacific RS3 Diesel Freight Set, 02		95
___ 31926	Area 51 FA Diesel Freight Set, 02		160
___ 31928	Great Train Robbery Set, 02	70	180
___ 31931	Ballyhoo Brothers Circus Train, 02		190
___ 31932	NYC Limited Passenger Set, RailSounds, 02		285
___ 31933	Santa Fe Steam Freight Set, RailSounds, 02		320
___ 31934	Lionel 20th Century Express Steam Freight Set, 00 u		285
___ 31936	Pennsylvania Flyer Steam Freight Set, 03-05		158
___ 31938	Southern Diesel Freight Set, 03-04	75	160
___ 31939	Great Train Robbery Steam Freight Set, 03		185
___ 31940	NYC Flyer Steam Freight Set, RailSounds, 03		225
___ 31941	Winter Wonderland Railroad Christmas Train, 03		150
___ 31942	Norman Rockwell Christmas Train, 03		330
___ 31944	NYC Limited Diesel Passenger Set, RailSounds, 03		250
___ 31945	Santa Fe Steam Super Freight Set, RailSounds, 03		350
___ 31946	Disney Christmas Steam Train, 04-05		310
___ 31947	World of Disney Steam Freight Set, 03		215
___ 31950	Kraft Holiday UP RS3 Diesel Freight Set, 02 u	35	149
___ 31952	Great Northern Glacier Route Diesel Freight Set, 03-04		110
___ 31953	"Riding the Rails" Hobo Train Set, 03-04		225
___ 31956	Thomas the Tank Engine Set, 04-07	88	195
___ 31958	Santa Fe Flyer Steam Freight Set, RailSounds, 04		205
___ 31960	Polar Express Steam Passenger Set, 04-13	175	420
___ 31961	Bloomingdale's Pennsylvania Flyer Steam Freight Set, 02 u		160

		Exc	Mint
31962	Nickel Plate Road Super Freight Set, RailSounds, 04		350 ___
31963	Southern Pacific Overnight Steam Freight Set, 04		340 ___
31966	Holiday Tradition Steam Freight Set, 04-05		210 ___
31969	NYC Flyer Steam Freight Set, RailSounds, 04		205 ___
31976	Yukon Special Diesel Freight Set, 05		225 ___
31977	New York Central Flyer Steam Freight Set, 05		250 ___
31985	Santa Fe Steam Fast Freight Set, TrainSounds, 05		320 ___
31987	Mickey's Holiday Express Train, 04		280 ___
31989	UP Overland Freight Express Set, 04		880 ___
31990	Copper Range Steam Freight Mine Set, 05		175 ___
31993	NS Black Diamond Diesel Freight Set, TMCC, 05		500 ___
32900	DC Billboard, 99		24 ___
32902	Construction Zone Signs, set of 6, 99-19		10 ___
32904	Hellgate Bridge, 99	235	415 ___
32905	Irvington Factory, 99-00		295 ___
32910	Rotary Coal Tipple with bathtub gondola, 02		442 ___
32919	Animated Maiden Rescue, 99		65 ___
32920	Animated Pylon with airplane, 99	50	130 ___
32921	Electric Coaling Station, 99-01		125 ___
32922	Highway Barrels, set of 6, 99-23		10 ___
32923	Accessory Transformer, 99-03, 06-16		46 ___
32929	Icing Station with Santa, 99		90 ___
32930	Power Supply Set w/ ZW controller and 2 supplies, 99-02, 06-09	240	425 ___
32933	Christmas Stocking Hanger Set, 4-piece, 99-00		50 ___
32934	Stocking Hanger, gondola, 99-00		15 ___
32935	Stocking Hanger, boxcar, 99-00		15 ___
32960	Hindenburger Cafe, 99		210 ___
32961	Route 66 UFO Cafe, 99		200 ___
32987	Hobo Campfire, 99-00	25	45 ___
32988	Postwar "192" Railroad Control Tower, 99-00		75 ___
32989	Postwar "464" Sawmill, 99-00		75 ___
32990	Linex Oil Derrick, 99-00		55 ___
32991	WLLC Radio Station, 99		75 ___
32996	Postwar "362" Barrel Loader, 00		125 ___
32997	Aluminum Rico Station, 00		300 ___
32998	Hobby Shop, 99-00		300 ___
32999	Hellgate Bridge, 99-00		400 ___
33000	GP9 Diesel "3000," RailScope video camera system, 88-90	130	175 ___
33002	RailScope Television Monitor, 88-90	53	78 ___
34102	Amtrak Shelter, 04-08		25 ___
34108	Lionelville Suburban House, 03		20 ___
34109	Lionelville Large Suburban House, 03		15 ___
34110	Lionelville Estate House, 03		30 ___
34111	Lionelville Deluxe Fieldstone House, 03		17 ___
34112	Lionelville Fieldstone House, 03		17 ___
34113	Lionelville Large Suburban House, 03		17 ___
34114	Late Illuminated Station and Terrace, red trim, 03		475 ___
34117	Early Illuminated Station and Terrace, green trim, 03		475 ___
34120	TMCC Direct Lockon, 04-23		60 ___
34121	Lionelville Bungalow, 04		20 ___
34122	Lionelville Bungalow with garage, 04		20 ___
34123	Lionelville Bungalow with addition, 04		20 ___

		Exc	Mint
34124	Lionelville Anastasia's Bakery, 04		20
34125	Lionelville Cotton's Candy, 04		20
34126	Lionelville Market, 04		20
34127	Lionelville O'Grady's Tavern, 04		22
34128	Lionelville Pharmacy, 04		15
34129	Lionelville Kiddie City Toy Store, 04		20
34130	Lionelville Jim's 5&10, 04		25
34131	Lionelville Al's Hardware, 04		30
34144	Santa Fe Scrap Yard, 05-06		80
34145	New Haven Scrap Yard, 06		100
34149	Sly Fox and the Hunter, 05-07		80
34150	Reading Room, 05-06		70
34158	Ring Toss Midway Game, 05-06		20
34159	Camel Race Midway Game, 05-06		20
34162	Operating Oil Pump, 04-09		53
34163	Speeder Shed, 04-06		30
34164	Nutcracker Operating Gateman, 05-08		80
34190	Carousel, 04-06		165
34191	Hobo Depot, 04-05		70
34192	Operating Lumberjacks, 04-06		60
34193	UPS Animated Billboard, 04		30
34194	UPS Package Station, 05		120
34195	UPS People Pack, 06-09, 11		27
34210	TMCC Direct Lockon, 09		52
34359	2011 Lionel Dealer Appreciation Boxcar, 11 u		40
34360	2012 Lionel Dealer Appreciation Boxcar, 12 u		40
34500	Rio Grande FT Diesel "5484," traditional, 06		245
34501	Southern FT Diesel "4102," traditional, 06		400
34504	B&O F3 Diesel A Unit "2368," nonpowered, 06-07		200
34505	B&O E7 Diesel AA Set, CC, 07		700
34508	PRR E7 Diesel AA Set, CC, 07		700
34509	PRR E7 Diesel B Unit, nonpowered (std O), 07		170
34510	PRR E7 Diesel B Unit, powered, CC, 07		300
34511	NYC F7 Diesel ABA Set, CC, 07-08		900
34512	NYC F7 Diesel B Unit "2439," powered, CC, 07-08		300
34513	WP F7 Diesel ABA Set, CC, 07-08		900
34514	WP F7 Diesel B Unit "918C," powered, CC, 07-08		300
34515	NYC F7 Diesel Breakdown B Unit "2440," RailSounds, 07		270
34518	PRR E7 Diesel Breakdown B Unit, RailSounds, 07		270
34519	NYC Sharknose RF-16 Diesel AA Set, CC, 07-08		630
34520	NYC Sharknose B Unit "3818," nonpowered (std O), 07-08		160
34521	Santa Fe F3 Diesel A Unit "17," traditional, 07		265
34522	Santa Fe F3 Diesel B Unit "17," nonpowered (std O), 07		150
34544	ATSF F3 Diesel B Unit, CC, 08		270
34545	D&RGW F3 Diesel B Unit, CC, 08		270
34546	Southern F3 Diesel B Unit, CC, 08		270
34547	Texas Special F3 Diesel B Unit, CC, 08		270
34559	Archive New Haven F3 Diesel AA Set, 10		500
34564	SP Alco PA Diesel AA Set, CC, 10-11		750
34567	SP Alco PB B Unit, CC, 10-11		400
34568	ATSF Alco PA AA Diesel Set, CC, 11		750
34569	ATSF Alco PB Diesel, CC, 11		400
34570	B&O FA Diesel AA Set, CC, 10		650

		Exc	Mint
34573	Postwar Scale ATSF F3 AA Diesel Set, CC, 11		700
34576	Postwar Scale NYC F3 AA Diesel Set, CC, 11		700
34579	Postwar Scale ATSF F3 B Unit, CC, 11		380
34580	Postwar Scale NYC F3 B Unit, CC, 11		380
34581	Postwar "2331" Virginian Train Master Diesel, CC, 10		495
34582	Postwar "2373" CP F3 Diesel AA Set, CC, 10		673
34585	Postwar "2375" CP F3 B Unit, CC, 10		350
34586	Postwar "2378" MILW F3 Diesel AB Set, CC, 10		700
34589	Postwar "2377" MILW F3 A, powered, CC, 10		425
34594	UP Alco PA AA Diesel Set, CC, 11		750
34597	UP Alco PB Diesel, CC, 11		400
34600	SP GP30 Diesel "5010," CC, 11		500
34601	SP GP30 Diesel "5012," CC, 11		500
34602	SP GP30 Diesel "5014," 11		380
34603	SP GP30 Diesel "5017," nonpowered, 11		240
34604	Conrail GP30 Diesel "2178," CC, 11		500
34605	Conrail GP30 Diesel "2180," CC, 11		500
34606	Conrail GP30 Diesel "2182," 11		380
34607	Conrail GP30 Diesel "2185," nonpowered, 11		240
34608	Lionelville & Western GP30 Diesel "1100," CC, 11		450
34609	Lionelville & Western GP30 Diesel "1103," CC, 11		450
34610	Lionelville & Western GP30 Diesel "1107," 11		330
34611	Lionelville & Western GP30 Diesel "1112," nonpowered, 11		190
34612	NS SD70M-2 Diesel "2658," CC, 11		550
34613	NS SD70M-2 Diesel "2663," CC, 11		550
34614	CN SD70M-2 Diesel "8020," CC, 11		550
34615	CN SD70M-2 Diesel "8024," CC, 11		550
34616	FEC SD70M-2 Diesel "101," CC, 11		550
34617	FEC SD70M-2 Diesel "103," CC, 11		550
34618	George Bush SD70ACe Diesel "4141," CC, 11		550
34619	NH SD70ACe Diesel "8696," CC, 11		550
34620	NH SD70ACe Diesel "8699," CC, 11		550
34623	Texas Special SD70ACe Diesel "6340," CC, 11		550
34624	Texas Special SD70ACe Diesel "6344," CC, 11		550
34625	NP F3 AA Diesel Set, CC, 11		700
34628	NP F3 Diesel B Unit "6005C," CC, 11		380
34629	NP F3 Diesel B Unit "6006C," nonpowered, 11		240
34630	Frisco F3 AA Diesel Set, CC, 11		700
34633	Frisco F3 Diesel B Unit, CC, 11		380
34634	Frisco F3 Diesel B Unit, nonpowered, 11		260
34635	ATSF F3 AA Diesel Set, CC, 11		700
34638	ATSF F3 Diesel B Unit, CC, 11		380
34639	ATSF F3 Diesel B Unit, nonpowered, 11		240
34640	GTW F3 AA Diesel Set, CC, 11		700
34643	GTW F3 Diesel B Unit, CC, 11		380
34644	GTW F3 Diesel B Unit, nonpowered, 11		260
34645	CN F3 AA Diesel Set, CC, 11		700
34648	CN F3 Diesel B Unit, CC, 11		380
34649	CN F3 Diesel B Unit, nonpowered, 11		260
34650	MILW DD35A Diesel "1535," CC, 11		600
34651	MILW DD35A Diesel "1537," nonpowered, 11		440
34662	RI GP9 Diesel "1331," CC, 12-13		480
34663	RI GP9 Diesel "1327," CC, 12-13		480

		Exc	Mint
34664	GN GP9 Diesel "688," CC, 12-13		480
34665	GN GP9 Diesel "695," CC, 12-13		480
34666	L&N GP9 Diesel "504," CC, 12-13		480
34667	L&N GP9 Diesel "525," CC, 12-13		480
34668	CN GP90 Diesel "4463," CC, 12		480
34669	CN GP90 Diesel "4455," CC, 12		480
34670	C&O GP9 Diesel "6240," CC, 12-13		480
34671	C&O GP9 Diesel "6243," CC, 12		480
34672	PRR Baldwin Centipede Diesel AA, CC, 12-13		2200
34673	UP Baldwin Centipede Diesel AA, CC, 12		2200
34676	PRR Baldwin Centipede Diesel "5821," CC, 12-14		1100
34677	Seaboard Baldwin Centipede Diesel "4503," CC, 12-14		1100
34680	NdeM Baldwin Centipede Diesel "6402," CC, 12-14		1100
34681	UP GP9 Diesel "256," CC, 12		480
34682	UP GP9 Diesel "261," CC, 12		480
34683	PRR Baldwin Centipede Diesel AA, CC, 12-13		2200
34686	Baldwin Demonstrator Centipede AA, CC, 12		2200
34689	WM F7 AA Diesel Set, CC, 12-13		730
34692	WM F7 B Unit "410," CC, 12-13		400
34693	WM F7 B Unit, 12-13		250
34694	L&N F7 AA Diesel Set, CC, 12		730
34697	L&N F7 B Unit "900," CC, 12-13		400
34698	L&N F7 B Unit, 12-13		250
34701	PRR Baldwin RF-16 Diesel AA Set, CC, 12-14		730
34704	PRR Baldwin RF-16 Diesel B Unit, CC, 12-14		400
34705	PRR Baldwin RF-16 Diesel B Unit, nonpowered, 12-14		250
34731	NH Alco RS-11 Diesel "1413," nonpowered, 12		240
34732	LV Alco RS-11 Diesel "7640," CC, 12		480
34733	LV Alco RS-11 Diesel "7642," CC, 12		480
34734	LV Alco RS-11 Diesel "7643," nonpowered, 12		240
34735	ATSF GP9 Diesel "726," CC, 12		480
34736	ATSF GP9 Diesel "741," CC, 12		480
34737	NP GP9 Diesel "202," CC, 12		480
34738	NP GP9 Diesel "317," CC, 12-13		480
34739	RI GP9 Diesel "1325," nonpowered, 12		240
34740	GN GP9 Diesel "668," nonpowered, 12		240
34741	L&N GP9 Diesel "531," nonpowered, 12		240
34742	CN GP90 Diesel "4527," nonpowered, 12		240
34743	C&O GP9 Diesel "6249," nonpowered, 12		240
34744	UP GP9 Diesel "268," nonpowered, 12		240
34745	Monon Alco C-420 Diesel "509," CC, 12-13		530
34746	Monon Alco C-420 Diesel "512," CC, 12-13		530
34747	Monon Alco C-420 Diesel "514," nonpowered, 12-13		260
34748	LV Alco C-420 Diesel "404," CC, 12		530
34749	LV Alco C-420 Diesel "412," CC, 12		530
34750	LV Alco C-420 Diesel "414," nonpowered, 12		260
34754	Alaska Alco C-420 Diesel "1210," CC, 12		530
34755	Alaska Alco C-420 Diesel "1214," CC, 12		530
34756	Alaska Alco C-420 Diesel "1217," nonpowered, 12		260
34757	Seaboard Alco C-420 Diesel "127,," CC, 12-13		530
34758	Seaboard Alco C-420 Diesel "129," CC, 12-13		530
34759	Seaboard Alco C-420 Diesel "134," nonpowered, 12-13		260
34760	NKP Alco C-420 Diesel "578," CC, 12-13		530

		Exc	Mint
34761	NKP Alco C-420 Diesel "575," CC, 12-13		530
34762	NKP Alco C-420 Diesel "572," nonpowered, 12-13		260
34763	CNJ Scale NW2 Diesel Switcher "1060," CC, 12		470
34764	CNJ Scale NW2 Diesel Switcher "106," CC, 12		470
34765	KCS Scale NW2 Diesel Switcher "1221," CC, 12		470
34766	KCS Scale NW2 Diesel Switcher "1224," CC, 12		470
34767	L&N Scale NW2 Diesel Switcher "2203," CC, 12		470
34768	L&N Scale NW2 Diesel Switcher "2206," CC, 12		470
34769	MKT Scale NW2 Diesel Switcher "8," CC, 12		470
34770	MKT Scale NW2 Diesel Switcher "12," CC, 12		470
34771	Reading Scale NW2 Diesel Switcher "102," CC, 12		470
34772	Reading Scale NW2 Diesel Switcher "104," CC, 12		470
34773	PRR Scale NW2 Diesel Switcher "9163," CC, 12		470
34774	PRR Scale NW2 Diesel Switcher "9171,"" CC, 12		470
34775	N&W SD40-2 Diesel "6106," nonpowered, 12-13		240
34776	N&W SD40-2 Diesel "6121," CC, 12-13		530
34777	N&W SD40-2 Diesel "6109," CC, 12-14		530
34778	CSX SD40-2 Diesel "8023," nonpowered, 12-13		240
34779	CSX SD40-2 Diesel "8028," CC, 12-13		530
34780	CSX SD40-2 Diesel "8033," CC, 12-13		530
34781	BN SD40-2 Diesel "7140," nonpowered, 12-13		240
34782	BN SD40-2 Diesel "7153," CC, 12-13		530
34783	BN SD40-2 Diesel "7162," CC, 12-13		530
34784	Frisco SD40-2 Diesel "957," CC, 12-13		530
34785	Frisco SD40-2 Diesel "950," nonpowered, 12-13		240
34786	Frisco SD40-2 Diesel "952," CC, 12-13		530
34787	C&NW SD40-2 Diesel "6816," nonpowered, 12-13		240
34788	C&NW SD40-2 Diesel "6820," CC, 12-13		530
34789	C&NW SD40-2 Diesel "6832," CC, 12-13		530
34790	MKT SD40-2 Diesel "602," nonpowered, 12-13		240
34791	MKT SD40-2 Diesel "609," CC, 12-13		530
34792	MKT SD40-2 Diesel "620," CC, 12-13		530
35100	NYC Vista Dome Car "7012," 07-09		45
35101	NYC Baggage Car "5028," 07		40
35102	Santa Fe El Capitan Streamliner Diner, 07		65
35124	Alton Limited Madison Passenger Car 4-pack, 08-10		240
35128	ATSF El Capitan Baggage Car "2103," 08		70
35129	ATSF El Capitan Vista Dome Car "3153," 08		70
35130	Polar Express Disappearing Hobo Car, 08-14, 16-17		75
35133	MTA Metro-North M-7 Commuter Add-on 2-pack, 07-08		85
35134	North Pole Central Vista Dome Car, 08		45
35135	North Pole Central Diner, 08-10		45
35136	Alaska Heavyweight Passenger Car 4-pack, 08		240
35137	Alaska Baggage Car w/TrainSounds, 08		200
35138	Alton Limited Baggage Car w/TrainSounds, 08		200
35144	Alton Limited Heavyweight Coach "Webster Groves," 08		60
35145	Alton Limited Heavyweight Combination Car "Missouri," 08		60
35146	Alton Limited Heavyweight Diner "Bloomington," 08		60
35147	Alton Limited Heavyweight Observation "Chicago," 08		60
35167	PRR Diner "2044," 10		52
35168	PRR Coach "4046," 09		52
35173	North Pole Central Blitzen Coach, 09		45
35174	MTA LIRR M-7 Add-on 2-pack, 09		98

			Exc	Mint
	MODERN 1970-2023			
___	35184	Western & Atlantic Baggage Car, 09		60
___	35185	Great Western Passenger Car 2-pack, 09		100
___	35193	PRR Streamliner 4-pack, 10-11		250
___	35200	Strasburg Observation Car, 10		60
___	35202	Rio Grande Ski Train Vista Dome "California," 10-11		80
___	35203	Rio Grande Ski Train Baggage Car "1230," 10-11		75
___	35204	Rio Grande Ski Train Observation "Kansas," 10-11		75
___	35205	D&RGW Pikes Peak Add-on Coach, 10-11		70
___	35211	Strasburg Passenger Car Add-on 2-pack, 10		100
___	35214	Rio Grande Winter Park Diner, 11		70
___	35219	Hallow's Eve Express Passenger Car 2-pack, 11		120
___	35229	Hogwarts Express Dementors Coach, 11-15		60
___	35239	NJ Transit 2-pack Passenger Car Add-on, 11-14		100
___	35247	Grand Central Express Passenger Car 2-pack, 12-13		140
___	35250	North Pole Coach 2-pack, 12-13		120
___	35256	Hallow's Eve Express Passenger Car 2-pack #2, 12		120
___	35257	ATSF Vista Dome, 12		70
___	35258	ATSF Baggage Car, 12-13		70
___	35259	LIRR Passenger Car 2-pack, 12-15		110
___	35281	ATSF Super Chief Diner "1495," 13		70
___	35282	LIRR Jamaica Coach, 13-15		60
___	35283	CP Baggage Car and Diner 2-pack, 13		130
___	35286	Peanuts Coach 3-pack, 13		165
___	35290	Polar Express Passenger Car Add-on 2-pack, 13-14, 16		150
___	35293	Angela Trotta Thomas "Toyland Express" Boxcar, 13		45
___	35294	Polar Express Snow Tower, 13-14		28
___	35295	Christmas Billboard Set, 13-14, 16		13
___	35403	NYC 20th Century Limited 18" Aluminum Passenger Car 4-pack (std O), 08		625
___	35408	NYC 20th Century Limited 18" Aluminum Passenger Car 2-pack (std O), 08		325
___	35411	NYC 20th Century Limited Diner, StationSounds (std O), 08		325
___	35412	Lenny Dean Passenger Coach, 08		100
___	35413	LL Streamliner Car 2-pack, 08		270
___	35415	UP 18" Streamliner Car 4-pack (std O), 08		625
___	35423	UP 18" Streamliner Car 2-pack (std O), 08		325
___	35430	Amtrak Coach		45
___	35431	Amtrak Coach		45
___	35432	Amtrak Coach		45
___	35433	Amfleet Phase IVB Coach 2-pack (std O), 10		140
___	35445	SP Shasta Daylight 18" Passenger Car 4-pack (std O), 11		640
___	35446	SP Shasta Daylight 18" Passenger Car 2-pack (std O), 11		320
___	35454	Amfleet Cab Control End Car (std O), 10		250
___	35473	Amfleet Capstone Coach 3-pack (std O), 10		180
___	35481	NYC Add-on Passenger Car "M-498," 11		120
___	35490	Alaska Budd RDC Combination Car "702," nonpowered, 11		130
___	35497	RI Budd RDC Combination Car "751," nonpowered, 11		130
___	35498	RI Budd RDC Coach "750," nonpowered, 11		130
___	35499	Alaska Budd RDC Coach "712," nonpowered, 11		130
___	36000	Route 66 Flatcar with 2 red sedans, 98		44
___	36001	Route 66 Flatcar with 2 wagons, 98		42
___	36002	Pratt's Hollow Passenger Car 4-pack, 98		445
___	36006	Uranium Flatcar "6508," 99		60

		Exc	Mint	
36016	Flatcar with propellers, 98		45	___
36020	Flatcar "TT-6424" with auto frames, 99		32	___
36021	Alaska Flatcar "6424" with airplane, 99		44	___
36024	J.B. Hunt Flatcar "64245" with trailer, 99		44	___
36025	J.B. Hunt Flatcar "64246" with trailer, 99		50	___
36026	Flatcar with J.B. Hunt trailers 2-pack, 99		85	___
36027	Tredegar Iron Works Flatcar with cannon, 99		45	___
36028	Heavy Artillery Flatcar with cannon, 99		45	___
36029	SP Auto Carrier "516712," 99		44	___
36030	Troublesome Truck #1, 99		35	___
36031	Troublesome Truck #2, 99		35	___
36032	Christmas Gondola "6462" with presents, 99		35	___
36036	C&O Gondola, 99		20	___
36038	Construction Zone Gondola, 99 u	11	20	___
36040	Bethlehem Flatcar with block (SSS), 99		75	___
36041	Bethlehem Ore Car (SSS), 99		40	___
36043	Custom Consist Flatcar with pickup truck, 99		40	___
36044	Custom Consist Flatcar with dragster, 99		40	___
36045	Flatcar with dragster, 04		30	___
36046	Flatcar with custom truck, 04		30	___
36047	Construction Zone Gondola, 99 u	11	20	___
36048	Construction Zone Gondola, 99 u	11	20	___
36051	NYC Flatcar w/Bulkhead, 04	8	20	___
36054	Archaeological Expedition Gondola with eggs, 00 u		55	___
36055	Flatcar with dragster, 01 u		30	___
36056	Flatcar with roadster, 01 u		30	___
36059	"Season's Greetings" Gondola, 99 u		50	___
36062	NYC 6462 Gondola, 99-00		22	___
36063	Conrail Gondola "604768," 99-00		20	___
36064	Billboard Flatcar "6424," 00		41	___
36065	Wabash Flatcar "25536" with trailer, 00		35	___
36066	Christmas Gondola with presents, 00		32	___
36067	King Auto Sales Flatcar "6424" with pink Cadillac, 00		40	___
36068	Pine Peak Tree Transport Gondola, 00	38	55	___
36079	Service Station Ltd. Flatcar with trailer, 00		34	___
36082	D&H Flatcar "16533" w/Whirlpool trailer, 00	27	45	___
36083	Santa Fe Gondola "168998," 01		17	___
36084	Grand Trunk Western Coil Car, 00		32	___
36085	FEC Coil Car, 00		29	___
36086	SP Flatcar with trailer, 01	34	35	___
36087	Flatcar "6424" with wooden whistle, 01		25	___
36088	Allis Chalmers Condenser Car "6519," 00		43	___
36089	Frisco Flatcar with airplane, 00		35	___
36090	TT Flatcar "6424" with Pepsi truck, 01		44	___
36091	Maersk Flatcar "250129" with die-cast tractors, 00		55	___
36092	Maersk Flatcar "250130" with die-cast frames, 00		55	___
36093	Soo TT Auto Carrier "906760," 00		49	___
36094	PC F9 Well Car "768122," 01		41	___
36095	Christmas Chase Gondola, 01		37	___
36098	PRR Gondola "385186," 01		20	___
36099	NYC Flatcar with stakes and bulkheads, 01		25	___
36104	Area 51 3-D Tank Car, 07		60	___
36105	Skelly Oil 1-D Tank Car, 08		55	___

			Exc	Mint
___	36107	WC Wood-sided Refrigerator Car, 08		35
___	36108	Candy Cane 1-D Tank Car, 07		60
___	36109	Alaska 3-D Tank Car, 07		40
___	36110	CP 1-D Tank Car, 07		30
___	36111	D&RGW 1-D Tank Car, 07		24
___	36112	NP 3-D Tank Car, 08		35
___	36113	IC 1-D Tank Car, 08		35
___	36114	ART Wood-sided Reefer, 08		35
___	36117	Lionel Lines 2-D Tank Car, 08		50
___	36118	NYC Pastel Stock Car "63561," 08-09		55
___	36128	Texas & Pacific 3-D Tank Car, 09		40
___	36129	British Columbia 1-D Tank Car, 09		38
___	36130	Jiminy Cricket 1-D Tank Car, 09		70
___	36131	Lackawanna Wood-sided Reefer "7000," 09-10		40
___	36132	Southern 1-D Tank Car, 08		35
___	36145	Philadelphia Quartz 3-D Tank Car "606," 10		40
___	36146	Cities Service 1-D Tank Car "11800," 10		40
___	36149	Strasburg Wood-sided Reefer "105," 10		55
___	36151	Grave's Blood Bank Tank Car, 10		50
___	36156	Pennsylvania Power & Light 1-D Tank Car, 10		40
___	36162	Diamond Chemicals 3-D Tank Car, 11		40
___	36163	Celanese 2-D Tank Car, 11-12		40
___	36166	Polar Express Reefer, 11-12		55
___	36169	Coca-Cola 3-D Tank Car, 11		55
___	36170	Partridge in a Pear Tree Reefer, 11-13		55
___	36172	Bubble Yum 1-D Tank Car, 11		55
___	36173	Santa's Flyer Hot Cocoa 3-D Tank Car, 11		40
___	36176	C&O 1-D Tank Car, 13		43
___	36177	WP 3-D Tank Car, 12		40
___	36178	Frisco 2-D Tank Car, 12-13		40
___	36182	Eggnog Unibody 1-D Tank Car, 12		70
___	36191	GN Waffle-sided Boxcar, 13		43
___	36195	PRR Flatcar with patrol helicopter , 13		60
___	36200	Quaker Life Cereal Boxcar, 00		500
___	36203	Whirlpool Boxcar, 00 u		150
___	36205	eBay Boxcar, 00		275
___	36206	REA Boxcar, 01		25
___	36207	Vapor Records Christmas Boxcar, 01		80
___	36208	Father's Day Boxcar, 00		35
___	36210	Burlington Hi-Cube Boxcar "19825," 01		40
___	36211	NP Hi-Cube Boxcar "659999," 01	18	40
___	36212	Lionel Employee Christmas Boxcar, 00 u		410
___	36213	Vapor Records Christmas Boxcar, 00		50
___	36214	GN Boxcar (Lionel Service Station), 00 u	49	55
___	36215	Train Station 25th Anniversary Boxcar, 00 u		48
___	36218	Snap-On Boxcar, 00 u		150
___	36219	UP Boxcar "183518," 02		78
___	36220	Pioneer Seed Boxcar, 00 u		NRS
___	36221	PRR Boxcar "569356," 01		20
___	36222	NYC Boxcar "162440," 01		20
___	36223	Chessie System Boxcar, 01		20
___	36224	Santa Fe Boxcar "16263," 01		20
___	36225	C&O Boxcar "250549," 01		20

		Exc	Mint
36226	E-Hobbies Boxcar, 01 u		219 ___
36227	Monopoly Community Chest Boxcar, 00 u		50 ___
36228	Lionel Visitor Center Boxcar, 01 u		34 ___
36229	Island Trains 20th Anniversary Boxcar, 01 u		29 ___
36232	Farmall McCormick Boxcar, 01 u		275 ___
36236	TM Books "I Love Lionel" Boxcar "7474-1," 01 u		43 ___
36238	Snap-On Tool Team ASE Racing Boxcar, 01 u		NRS ___
36239	L.L. Bean Boxcar, 01 u		150 ___
36240	Do It Best Boxcar, 01 u		100 ___
36242	Erie-Lackawanna Boxcar "73113," 02		24 ___
36243	Christmas Boxcar "2002," 02		31 ___
36244	Teddy Bear Centennial Boxcar, 02		36 ___
36245	Lionel 20th Century Boxcar "1900-1925," 00 u		30 ___
36246	Lionel 20th Century Boxcar "1926-1950," 00 u		30 ___
36247	Lionel 20th Century Boxcar "1951-1975," 00 u		30 ___
36248	Lionel 20th Century Boxcar "1976-2000," 00 u		30 ___
36250	NYC Early Bird Boxcar, 04		20 ___
36253	Christmas Boxcar (O), 03		32 ___
36254	Goofy Hi-Cube Boxcar, 03		37 ___
36255	Donald Duck Hi-Cube Boxcar, 03		40 ___
36256	GN Boxcar "6341," 03		23 ___
36261	PRR Boxcar, 03-05		15 ___
36262	Southern Central of Georgia Boxcar, 03,àí04		20 ___
36264	Santa Fe Boxcar "600196," 02		18 ___
36265	Angela Trotta Thomas "Window Wishing" Boxcar, 02		38 ___
36267	Mickey Mouse Hi-Cube Boxcar, 03		50 ___
36270	Angela Trotta Thomas "Home for the Holidays" Boxcar, 02-03		30 ___
36272	New Haven Boxcar "6501," 04		20 ___
36273	Railbox Hi-Cube Boxcar "15000," 04		21 ___
36275	Christmas Boxcar, 04		35 ___
36276	Angela Trotta Thomas "Tis the Season" Boxcar, 04		34 ___
36277	Pluto Hi-Cube Boxcar, 04-05		50 ___
36278	Winnie the Pooh Hi-Cube Boxcar, 04-05		50 ___
36281	B&O Boxcar, 04		35 ___
36291	Simpsons Boxcar, 04-05		44 ___
36294	UP Hi-Cube Boxcar, traditional, 05		27 ___
36295	CN Boxcar, traditional, 05		27 ___
36296	2005 Holiday Boxcar, 05		48 ___
36297	Angela Trotta Thomas "Christmas Eve" Boxcar, 05		48 ___
36299	Hammacher Schlemmer Music Boxcar, 04		65 ___
36305	eBay Boxcar, 00 u		120 ___
36339	Caterpillar Caboose	22	50 ___
36500	Western Pacific Caboose "36500," 04		23 ___
36501	D&RGW Caboose "36501," 04		22 ___
36502	Reading Caboose "36502," 04		25 ___
36515	North Pole Central Lines Caboose "36515," 04		36 ___
36519	Lionel Lines Caboose, 04		22 ___
36520	Santa Fe Caboose "36520," 04		22 ___
36525	CSX Work Caboose, lighted, 05		35 ___
36526	Pennsylvania Work Caboose, traditional, 05		27 ___
36527	Santa Fe Work Caboose, traditional, 05		28 ___
36528	Chesapeake & Ohio Work Caboose, traditional, 05		40 ___

		Exc	Mint
36529	North Pole Central Work Caboose w/Presents, traditional, 05		38
36530	Pennsylvania Caboose, traditional, 05		33
36531	Erie Caboose "C150," traditional, 05		33
36532	SP Caboose "1097," traditional, 05		48
36533	Reading Caboose "92803," traditional, 05		33
36534	NYC Center Cupola Caboose, traditional, 05		40
36535	LL Center Cupola Caboose, traditional, 05		28
36536	Southern Center Cupola Caboose, traditional, 05		40
36539	Elvis Presley Caboose, 04		40
36541	Copper Range Caboose, 05		28
36542	NYC Caboose, 05		28
36543	ATSF Square-Window Caboose, 05		40
36544	Alaska Caboose, 05		35
36547	Bethlehem Steel Transfer Caboose, traditional, 05		38
36548	Transylvania RR Work Caboose, traditional, 05		45
36550	Halloween Transfer Caboose, traditional, 06-07		45
36551	Christmas Caboose, 06		45
36552	U.S. Steel Work Caboose, traditional, 06-07		45
36553	NYC Caboose, 08		20
36554	SP Work Caboose, traditional, 06		45
36555	Pennsylvania Transfer Caboose, 06		45
36556	Lionel Lines Work Caboose, 06-07		30
36557	Rio Grande Work Caboose, traditional, 06		29
36558	Virginian Center Cupola Caboose "316," traditional, 06		45
36559	WM Center Cupola Caboose "1863," traditional, 06		45
36560	C&O Center Cupola Caboose "90876," traditional, 06		45
36562	Army Transportation Work Caboose, traditional, 06		45
36563	Reading Work Caboose, traditional, 06		45
36565	UP SP-type Caboose, traditional, 06		48
36566	NYC SP-type Caboose, traditional, 06		48
36567	GN SP-type Caboose, traditional, 06		48
36571	PRR Caboose, 08		20
36580	B&O Center Cupola Caboose "C2047," traditional, 05		40
36582	C&O Caboose, 05		22
36583	Holiday Caboose, 07		50
36587	SP Caboose "1121," 07-09		40
36589	PRR Work Caboose, 07		40
36590	UP Work Caboose, 07		45
36591	Southern Caboose "X99," 08		45
36592	Santa Fe Caboose "999471," 06		48
36593	NYC Caboose, 06		48
36601	UP Caboose, 06		48
36602	UPS Centennial Caboose, 06		45
36604	Pennsylvania Caboose, 06		25
36607	K-Line Caboose, 06		40
36611	Conrail Caboose "19674," 07		40
36612	Alaska Caboose "1080," 07		40
36613	NYC Caboose, 07		30
36618	It's a Wonderful Life Caboose, 07		
36621	Marriott Caboose, 07		75
36622	C&O Caboose "C-1838," 08-09		40
36623	ATSF Caboose, 07-09		40
36624	Lionel Lines Caboose, 08-09		40

No.	Description	Exc	Mint	
36625	B&M Caboose, 08		50	__
36626	Erie Caboose "C101," 08-09		45	__
36632	PRR Center Cupola Caboose, 08	8	20	__
36634	Holiday Porthole Caboose, green, 08		50	__
36646	Monopoly Caboose, 10		48	__
36647	Strasburg Caboose, 10		48	__
36648	Wizard of Oz Caboose, 09		50	__
36649	Pennsylvania Power & Light Work Caboose, 10		45	__
36657	Western & Atlantic Caboose, 10-11		48	__
36659	PRR Illuminated Porthole Caboose, 11		35	__
36668	CSX Illuminated Square Window Caboose, 10		35	__
36672	NS Caboose, 11		25	__
36674	Polar RR Caboose "C-1225," 11-12		53	__
36690	UP Overland Freight Caboose, 12		25	__
36701	Baldwin Locomotive Works Operating Welding Car "36701," 02		68	__
36702	Bosco Operating Milk Car with platform, 02		115	__
36703	Circus Horse Car with corral, 06		132	__
36704	Animated Reindeer Stock Car and Corral, 02		145	__
36718	AEC Security Caboose, 02		45	__
36719	Lionel Lion Bobbing Head Car, 02		20	__
36720	Aladdin Aquarium Car, 03		40	__
36721	101 Dalmatians Animated Gondola, 03		45	__
36722	Peter Pan Bobbing Head Boxcar, 03		45	__
36726	Santa Fe Searchlight Car "36726," 03		50	__
36727	Weyerhaeuser Moe & Joe Flatcar, 03		65	__
36728	SP Walking Brakeman Boxcar 163143," 03		42	__
36729	Lionel Lines Animated Caboose, 04-05	60	68	__
36730	U.S. Army Missile Launch Sound Car "44," 03		175	__
36731	Motorized Aquarium Car "3435," 03		83	__
36732	C&NW Jumping Hobo Car, 03		41	__
36733	Christmas Music Boxcar, 03		45	__
36734	Santa Fe Operating Searchlight Car "20611," 02		25	__
36735	WP Ice Car "7045," 02		55	__
36736	D&RGW Stock Car "39268," RailSounds, 04		45	__
36738	T&P Poultry Dispatch Car "36738," 02		50	__
36739	Postwar "3461" Lionel Lines Log Dump Car, 03		50	__
36740	Postwar "3469" Lionel Lines Coal Dump Car, 03		49	__
36743	Santa Claus Bobbing Head Boxcar, 03		40	__
36744	Little Mermaid Aquarium Car, 03		55	__
36745	Toy Story Animated Gondola, 03		70	__
36753	LFD Firecar with ladder, 02		60	__
36757	Southern Searchlight Car "51422," 03-04		40	__
36758	Patriotic Lighted Boxcar, 02		60	__
36760	B&O Sentinel Brakeman Car "3424," Archive Collection, 02		65	__
36761	Wellspring Capital Management Lighted Boxcar, 02 u		220	__
36764	West Side Lumber Log Dump Car "36764," 03		55	__
36765	Alaska Coal Dump Car "401," 03		50	__
36766	Erie Chase Gondola, 03		50	__
36767	Santa's Radar Tracking Car, 03		40	__
36769	Fourth of July Lighted Boxcar, 03		70	__
36770	American Refrigerator Transit Ice Car "23701," 04		42	__
36771	CN Barrel Car "74208," 04		48	__
36772	Spokane, Portland & Seattle Log Dump Car "36772," 04		46	__

		Mint
36773	Jersey Central Coal Dump Car "92926," 04	45
36774	PRR Moe & Joe Lumber Flatcar, 04	50
36775	Santa Fe Animated Caboose "999010," 05	75
36776	Santa Fe Walking Brakeman Car "19938," 04	43
36778	C&O Searchlight Car "216614," 04	30
36780	Sea-Monkeys Motorized Aquarium Car, 04	45
36781	Finding Nemo Aquarium Car, 04	50
36782	Goofy and Pete Jumping Boxcar, 05	70
36783	Disney Operating Boxcar, 04-05	65
36784	Monsters Inc. Bobbing Head Boxcar, 04	40
36786	Postwar "3494-150" MP Operating Boxcar, 03	40
36787	MOW Remote Control Searchlight Car, 04	45
36788	Lionel Lines Tender, TrainSounds, 04	75
36789	Railbox Boxcar, TrainSounds, 04-05	105
36790	Christmas Music Boxcar, 04	70
36791	Kinzua Pine Mills Operating Log Dump Car, 96	40
36793	Pennsylvania Derrick Car, 03	22
36794	NYC Log Dump Car, 03	25
36795	Southern Coal Dump Car, 03	25
36796	GN Searchlight Car, 03	24
36797	"Operation Iraqi Freedom" Minuteman Car, 03	45
36803	Santa Animated Caboose, 06	75
36804	Candy Cane Dump Car, 06	80
36805	Reindeer Jumping Boxcar, 06	70
36809	NYC Derrick Car, 07-08	35
36810	PRR Searchlight Car, 07	35
36811	UP Dump Coal Dump Car, 07	35
36812	British Columbia Log Dump Car, 07-08	35
36813	State of Maine Brakeman Car, 08	80
36814	D&RGW Animated Caboose "01415," 07-09	80
36815	Santa Fe Moe & Joe Flatcar, 07-08	80
36816	Virginian Coal Dump Car, 08	80
36818	U.S. Steel Searchlight Car, 07-08	75
36821	"Naughty or Nice" Dump Car, 07	80
36823	Halloween SpookySmoke Boxcar, 07	115
36824	Alien Smoking Boxcar, 07	110
36825	Lionel Lines Boom w/Crane, 07	35
36826	Home Depot/Tony Stewart Searchlight Car, 07	30
36829	Alien Radioactive Car, 07	70
36830	Trick or Treat Aquarium Car, 07	75
36831	MOW Welding Car, 07-08	75
36833	Christmas Music Boxcar, 07	65
36834	Santa Fe Transparent Instruction Car, 07-08	65
36838	Lionel Power Co. Voltmeter Car, K-Line, 06	75
36839	Operating Milk Car with platform, K-Line, 06	140
36841	Visitor Center 15th Anniversary Lighted Boxcar, 06	70
36847	Polar Express Tender, TrainSounds, 08-14	130
36848	Candy Cane Dump Car, 07	80
36849	Tell-Tale Reindeer Car, 07	53
36850	Santa and Snowman Boxcar, 07	75
36851	Generator Car with Christmas tree, 07	75
36853	U.S. Army Exploding Boxcar, 08	60
36855	GW Horse Car and Corral, 08	160

|---|---|---|---|
36856	W&ARR Sheriff and Outlaw Car, 08		75
36857	Bobbing Ghost Boxcar, 08		65
36859	Lionel Lines Aquarium Car, 08		80
36861	PRR Poultry Dispatch Car, 08-09		80
36863	Alien Security Car, 08		80
36864	Bethlehem Steel Searchlight Car, 08		40
36866	WP Coal Dump Car "52369," 08		40
36868	NH Barrel Ramp Car, 08		40
36869	Bobbing Santa Boxcar, 08		65
36870	Postwar "6812" Track Maintenance Car, 08		65
36874	PRR Searchlight Car, 09		35
36875	Polar Express Coach, sound, 08-14, 16		132
36878	NYC Track Cleaning Car, 08		150
36879	REA Ice Car "1221," 08		65
36880	Koi Fish Aquarium Car, 10		75
36881	Christmas Music Boxcar, 08		70
36887	Great Western Animated Gondola, 08-09		65
36888	Casper Aquarium Car, 09-10		90
36889	PRR Barrel Ramp Car, 09-10		46
36893	UP Transparent Instruction Car "195220," 09-10		75
36896	Christmas Music Boxcar, 09		80
36897	Pennsylvania Power & Light Coal Dump Car, 09-10		46
36898	Wisconsin Central Log Dump Car, 09		46
36900	Depressed Center Flatcar with backshop load, 99		115
36913	Allied Chemical 1-D Tank Car 2-pack, 00		150
36914	Allied Chemical 1-D Tank Car "68075," die-cast, white, 00		90
36915	Allied Chemical 1-D Tank Car "68076," die-cast, white, 00		90
36916	Allied Chemical 1-D Tank Car 2-pack, 00		175
36917	Allied Chemical 1-D Tank Car "65124," die-cast, black, 00		95
36918	Allied Chemical 1-D Tank Car "65125," die-cast, black, 00		90
36919	Maersk Maxi-Stack Car, 00		33
36927	B&O DC Hopper 6-pack, "435040-45," 01		520
36935	Maersk Maxi-Stack Car 2-pack, "250131-32," 00		135
36937	SP Maxi-Stack Car "513957," 02		65
36998	Gingerbread Man Gateman, 12-13		80
37001	No. 3444 Erie Animated Gondola, 09		70
37002	Operating Plutonium Car 2-pack, 10-11		140
37003	PRR Jet Snow Blower "491252" 09-10		138
37004	Area 51 Searchlight Car, 09		46
37006	Lionel Flatcar with operating LCD billboard, 09		180
37009	Smoking Mount St. Helens Boxcar, 10-11		125
37010	Pennsylvania Power & Light Searchlight Car, 10		46
37011	B&M Operating Milk Car with platform, 10		155
37012	GN Jumping Hobo Boxcar, 10		75
37015	Jack-o-Lantern Flatcar, 11-13		75
37016	Radioactive Plutonium Flatcar, 11		70
37017	Plutonium Boom Car, 11		70
37022	ATSF Blinking Billboard, 12		25
37032	Postwar "3562" Operating Barrel Car, 11		75
37033	Casper Animated Gondola , 11		70
37035	Santa's Operating Snow Globe Car, 11		75
37036	Halloween Operating Globe Car, 11		78
37038	Halloween Searchlight Car, 12-13		45

			Exc	Mint
___	**37039**	Minuteman Searchlight Car, 11		45
___	**37040**	UP Derrick Car, 11-12		46
___	**37041**	Pennsylvania Power & Light Coal Dump Car, 11		80
___	**37042**	IC Coal Dump Car, 11		46
___	**37043**	Seaboard Log Dump Car, 11		46
___	**37044**	CP Rail Log Dump Car, 11, 13		80
___	**37045**	Beatles Yellow Submarine Aquarium Car, 11		85
___	**37047**	Santa's Flyer Animated Gondola, 11		55
___	**37053**	EL Derrick Car, 12		45
___	**37054**	CSX Coal Dump Car, 12		46
___	**37055**	SP Log Dump Car, 12		46
___	**37056**	Zombie Aquarium Car, 12		80
___	**37057**	Bethlehem Steel Culvert Car, 12		65
___	**37058**	Ghost Globe Halloween Car, 12-15		80
___	**37059**	Christmas Snow Globe Car, 12		85
___	**37060**	LIRR Derrick Car, 13-14		50
___	**37061**	UP Railroad Speeder, CC, 12-14		150
___	**37062**	NS Railroad Speeder, CC, 12-14		150
___	**37063**	PRR Railroad Speeder, CC, 12-14, 16		150
___	**37064**	CSX Railroad Speeder, CC, 12-14		150
___	**37065**	BNSF Railroad Speeder, CC, 12-14		150
___	**37066**	MOW Railroad Speeder, CC, 12-14		150
___	**37067**	NYC Railroad Speeder, CC, 12-14		150
___	**37068**	CN Railroad Speeder, CC, 12-14		150
___	**37069**	Strasburg RR Crane Car, 12		65
___	**37070**	Gingerbread Man and Santa Animated Gondola, 12		55
___	**37071**	MOW Searchlight Car, 12		46
___	**37073**	U.S. Marine Corps Cannon Car, 12		75
___	**37075**	Boy Scouts of America Crane Car, 13		75
___	**37076**	Bethlehem Steel Coal Dump Car, 13		50
___	**37078**	RI Searchlight Car, 13		50
___	**37079**	Santa Fe Derrick Car, 13		50
___	**37081**	Peanuts Pumpkin Jack-O-Lantern Car, 13		85
___	**37082**	Peanuts Animated Trick or Treat Chase Gondola, 14-16		75
___	**37083**	Strasburg Coal Dump Car, 13		50
___	**37084**	PRR Cop and Hobo Animated Gondola, 13		65
___	**37085**	BN Log Dump Car, 13		50
___	**37086**	Lionelville Aquarium Co. Aquarium Car, 13		80
___	**37087**	NH Walking Brakeman Car, 13-14		75
___	**37089**	Santa's List Snow Globe Car, 13		90
___	**37090**	Polar Express Searchlight Car, 13		60
___	**37094**	Wizard of Oz Aquarium Car, 13-15		85
___	**37095**	North Pole Sleigh Repair Welding Car, 13		85
___	**37097**	Where the Wild Things Are Aquarium Car, 13-15		85
___	**37099**	North Pole Central EV Caboose "2510" (std O), 13		95
___	**37100**	Barrel Loader Building, 12-14		43
___	**37101**	Smiley Water Tower, 12-14		23
___	**37102**	Watchman Shanty, 12-14		30
___	**37103**	FasTrack O31 Curved Track, 13-23		6
___	**37110**	FasTrack Terminal, LionChief, 14-23		10
___	**37112**	Helicopter 2-pack, 13-20		35
___	**37115**	Pedestrian Walkover, green, 16-18		55
___	**37120**	Railroad Crossing Signs, 13-20		10

		Exc	Mint	
37121	Christmas Station Platform, 13		25	___
37122	Santa Fe Blinking Billboard, 13		25	___
37123	Weyerhaeuser Timber Operating Sawmill, 12-13		140	___
37124	West Side Lumber Operating Sawmill, 12-13		140	___
37125	Legacy Writable Utility Mobile, 12-16, 20		20	___
37127	Angela Trotta Thomas Gallery, 12		75	___
37129	Boy Scouts of America Girder Bridge, 13		23	___
37130	Boy Scouts of America Covered Bridge, 13		60	___
37139	Tis the Season Accessories, 12-13		310	___
37140	All Aboard Accessories, 12-13		65	___
37141	Rail Yard Accessories, 12-13		277	___
37142	Welcome Home Accessories, 12-13		154	___
37146	Legacy PowerMaster, 12-23		130	___
37147	CAB-1L/Base-1L Command Set, 12-16, 18-20		250	___
37149	FasTrack Modular Layout Straight Section Kit, 13		200	___
37150	FasTrack Modular Layout Template, 13-16		30	___
37151	Red Christmas Classic Street Lamps, 3-pack, 14-23		40	___
37152	Operating Coaling Station, 13-14		180	___
37153	FasTrack Modular Layout 45-Degree Reversible Corner Kit, 13		225	___
37154	FasTrack Modular Layout 45-Degree Corner Kit, 13		225	___
37155	CAB-1L Remote Controller, 12-16, 20-23		165	___
37156	Base-1L, 12-16		125	___
37158	Hershey's Water Tower, 13		30	___
37159	Peanuts Figure Pack, 13-15		30	___
37160	Strasburg Girder Bridge, 13		21	___
37161	Container 4-pack, 13		40	___
37162	Lionelville Water Tower, 13		25	___
37163	LIRR Girder Bridge, 13		21	___
37164	NS Girder Bridge, 13		21	___
37165	CP Water Tower, 13		25	___
37166	Crossing Shanty, 13-14, 16		25	___
37167	Freight Platform, 13		30	___
37169	Peanuts Psychiatric Booth, 13-16		40	___
37172	Gooseneck Lamps, 2-pack, 13-23	13	35	___
37173	Globe Lamp 3-pack, 13-14, 16-19		25	___
37174	Black Classic Street Lamps, 3-pack, 13-23		40	___
37176	Santa Fe Shanty, 13		25	___
37183	Polar Express 10th Anniversary Snowman and Kids, 13-17		37	___
37184	Christmas Half Covered Bridge, 13		43	___
37185	Christmas Railroad Signs, 13-14, 16-18		10	___
37187	Kris Kringle's Kloseout Shop, 13		50	___
37191	36-watt Power Supply, LionChief, 14		36	___
37195	Grand Central Terminal 100th Anniversary, 13-15		280	___
37196	Christmas Extension Bridge, 13, 16-18		15	___
37197	North Pole Central Girder Bridge, 13-17		30	___
37530	Santa Animated Caboose, 11		80	___
37807	Station Platform, 10-15		23	___
37808	Sunoco Spherical Oil Tank, 10-11		100	___
37810	Curved O Gauge Tunnel, 11-17		65	___
37813	Christmas Tractor and Trailer with trees, 10		27	___
37814	Christmas Crossing Shanty, 10-14		30	___
37816	Rockville Bridge, 11-12		700	___
37820	Lionel Auto Loader Cars 4-pack, 12-13, 16-17		25	___

		Exc	Mint
37821	Smoke Fluid Loader, 11		250
37826	Classic Travel Billboard Set, 11-14		13
37827	Coca-Cola Covered Bridge, 11		45
37828	Vintage Boy Scouts Figure Pack, 11-14		30
37829	Polar Express Station Platform, 11-18		40
37831	NJ Transit Blinking Light Water Tower, 11-12		30
37834	Lionel Boat 4-pack, 11-20		25
37836	Monopoly Auto 4-pack, 12		25
37837	Polar Express Straight Tunnel, 12-14		80
37840	Santa Fe Diorama, 12-17		15
37841	Premium Smoke Fluid, 12-16		7
37842	CN Tractor with piggyback trailer, 12, 15		90
37846	PRR Tractor Trailer, 12		90
37847	SP Tractor Trailer, 12		90
37848	IC Tractor Trailer, 12		90
37849	ATSF Tractor Trailer, 12		90
37850	REA Tractor Trailer, 12		90
37851	Scale Telephone Poles, 6-pack, 12-23		40
37852	Christmas People Pack, 12-14, 16-18		20
37853	Alien Billboard, 13, 15		13
37854	Classic Christmas Billboard , 12		11
37855	Lionel Airplane 2-pack, 12-20		37
37900	Silver Truss Bridge, 11		70
37901	Lehigh Valley Tugboat, 10		270
37902	Illuminated Barge, 10		180
37903	Cell Tower, 10-23		85
37904	Boy Scouts Billboard Set, 10		13
37907	Christmas Street Lamps with wreaths, 10-14		30
37909	North Pole Central Jet Snowblower, 11-14		138
37910	Operating Lighthouse, 10		180
37911	D&RGW Blinking Light Water Tower, 10-11		30
37912	Lighted Coaling Tower, 10-15		180
37913	Hopper Shed, 10-15		35
37914	Illuminated Work House, 10-18		40
37916	Beige Brick Suburban House, 10		80
37917	Red Brick Suburban House, 10		80
37919	Operating Sawmill, 10		130
37920	Bascule Bridge, 10		350
37921	ZW-L Transformer, 11-23	392	1000
37922	Coca-Cola Blinking Light Billboard, 10-11		28
37923	Coca-Cola Blinking Light Water Tower, 11		28
37928	Passenger Station, sounds, 11		90
37929	Coca-Cola Diner, 11, 13		75
37930	Rotary Aircraft Beacon, 11-12		81
37933	MG Switch Tower, 11-13		300
37935	Operating Track Gang, 11		100
37939	Assorted Telephone Poles, 6-pack, 11-23		45
37940	PRR Hobo Hotel, 12		150
37941	House Under Construction, 11		90
37942	Christmas Hobo Hotel, 12-13		150
37944	Weathered 50,000-gallon Water Tank, 11-12		170
37946	House Under Construction #2, 12-13		90
37947	GW-180 180-watt Transformer, 12-23		360

		Exc	Mint
37948	Boy Scouts Flagpole with lights, 11		30
37951	Postwar "342" Culvert Loader, 11		165
37952	Postwar "345" Culvert Unloader, 11		190
37953	Jacobs Pharmacy, 11		50
37954	Halloween Station Platform, 11-13		35
37955	Sodor Station Platform, 11-15		35
37957	Deluxe Holiday House, 11		85
37958	SP Scrap Yard, 11-14		110
37959	Midway Basketball Shot Game, 11-13		21
37960	Burning Switch Tower, 11-13		100
37961	NYC Scrap Yard, 11-13		110
37962	NJ Transit Station Platform, 11		37
37964	Archive Operating Freight Terminal, 11-14		150
37965	Christmas Operating Freight Terminal, 11-17		150
37966	Lionel Cylindrical Oil Tank, 11-17		100
37967	Boy Scouts Troop Cabin, 12-13		80
37971	Bethlehem Steel Culvert Loader, 11		165
37972	Bethlehem Steel Culvert Unloader, 11		190
37973	Coca-Cola Station Platform, 12		37
37975	PFE Operating Freight Terminal, 11-16		150
37977	Hooker Tank Car Accident, 11-17		130
37978	Deluxe Suburban House, 11-13		80
37979	Rotary Coal Tipple, 12		540
37980	Operating Coal Conveyor, 12		90
37984	Santa's Repair Work House, 12-14		40
37985	Operating Wind Turbine, 12-15		75
37986	NJ Transit Blinking Billboard, 12-13		28
37989	Sodor Train Shed, 12-16		60
37993	Snoopy and the Red Baron Animated Pylon, 12		160
37994	Deluxe Holiday House #2, 12-14		120
37995	Illuminated Scale Telephone Poles, 6-pack, 12-23		55
37996	Postwar 192 Control Tower, 12		70
37997	Christmas Lawn Figure Pack, 12-14, 16-18		20
37998	Halloween Haunted Passenger Station, 12-13, 15		75
38004	Virginian 4-6-0 Ten-Wheeler Locomotive "203," CC, 01-02		570
38005	Long Island 4-6-0 Ten-Wheeler "138," CC, 01-02		570
38007	UP Auxiliary tender, black, CC, 01		200
38008	UP Auxiliary tender, gray, CC, 01		205
38009	D&RGW 4-6-6-4 Challenger Locomotive "3803," CC, 01		1550
38010	Clinchfield 4-6-6-4 Challenger Locomotive "673," CC, 01		1400
38012	Wheeling & Lake Erie 2-6-6-2 Locomotive "8005," CC, 01		610
38013	D&H 4-6-6-4 Challenger Locomotive "1527," CC, 01		720
38014	D&RGW 4-6-6-4 Challenger Locomotive "3800," CC, 01		710
38015	NYC 4-6-4 Hudson Locomotive "773," CC, 01		900
38016	Southern 0-8-0 Yard Goat "6536," CC, 01-02, 05		530
38017	CN 2-6-0 Mogul Locomotive "86," CC, 03, 05		600
38018	Wabash 2-6-0 Mogul Locomotive "826," CC, 03		485
38019	B&M 2-6-0 Mogul Locomotive "1455," CC, 03, 05		600
38020	PRR 4-4-4-4 T1 Duplex Locomotive "5514," 02-03		630
38021	WP 4-6-6-4 Challenger Locomotive "402," CC, 02		650
38022	WM 4-6-6-4 Challenger Locomotive "1206," CC, 02		690
38023	UP 4-6-6-4 Challenger Locomotive "3976," CC, 02		620
38024	PRR 6-4-4-6 S-1 Duplex Locomotive "6100," TMCC, 03		1000

		Exc	Mint
38025	PRR 4-6-2 K4 Pacific Locomotive "1361," CC, 02		950
38026	N&W 4-8-4 J Class Northern Locomotive "606," CC, 02		1450
38027	Meadow River Lumber Heisler Geared Locomotive "6," CC, 03		880
38028	PRR 6-8-6 S2 Steam Turbine Locomotive, 01		650
38029	UP 4-12-2 Locomotive "9000," CC, 03		633
38030	Santa Fe 2-8-8-2 Locomotive "1795," CC, 03		920
38031	SP 2-8-8-4 AC-9 Locomotive "3809," CC, 04		1100
38032	Virginian 2-8-8-2 Locomotive "741," CC, 03		928
38036	Long Island 2-8-0 Consolidation Locomotive, 01		500
38037	PRR Reading Seashore 2-8-0 Consolidation "6072," CC, 01		495
38038	D&RGW Auxiliary Water Tender, 01		230
38039	Clinchfield Auxiliary Water Tender, 01		220
38040	LV 4-6-0 Camelback Locomotive, 01		405
38042	C&NW 4-6-0 Ten-Wheeler Locomotive "361," CC, 02		450
38043	Frisco 4-6-0 Ten-Wheeler Locomotive "719," CC, 02		525
38044	PRR 4-6-2 K4 Pacific Locomotive "5385," CC, 02		920
38045	NYC Hudson J-3a 4-6-4 Locomotive "5418," CC, 03		495
38046	GN 0-8-0 Locomotive "815," CC, 02	225	530
38047	N&W 0-8-0 Locomotive "266," CC, 02		550
38048	NPR 0-8-0 Locomotive "303," CC, 02		530
38049	N&W 2-6-6-4 Locomotive "1234," CC, 02		690
38050	Nickel Plate 2-8-4 Berkshire Locomotive "779," CC, 03		925
38051	Erie 2-8-4 Berkshire Locomotive "3315," CC, 03		810
38052	Pere Marquette 2-8-4 Berkshire Locomotive "1225," CC, 03		1000
38053	NYC 4-8-2 Mohawk L-2a Locomotive "2793," CC, 03		915
38055	Santa Fe 4-8-4 Northern Locomotive "3751" CC, 04		1100
38056	PRR 4-8-2 Mountain M1a Locomotive "6759," CC, 03		850
38057	Weyerhaeuser Shay Locomotive, CC, 03		1000
38058	C&O 2-8-8-2 H7 Locomotive "1580," CC, 04		1200
38060	UP 2-8-8-2 H7 Locomotive "3590," CC, 04		1200
38061	Cass Scenic Heisler Geared Locomotive "6," CC, 03		940
38062	Lionel Lines 4-6-2 Pacific Locomotive "8062," CC, 02-03		275
38065	UP 2-8-8-2 Mallet Locomotive "3672," CC, 02		1002
38066	Elk River Shay Locomotive, CC, 03		1000
38067	MILW 4-6-2 Pacific Locomotive "6316," CC, 03		300
38068	WM 4-6-2 Pacific Locomotive "204," CC, 03		300
38069	Erie 4-6-4 Hudson Locomotive, whistle, 05		150
38070	C&O 4-6-2 Pacific Locomotive "489," CC, 04		300
38071	SP Cab Forward AC-12 Locomotive "4294," CC, 05		1550
38075	UP 4-8-8-4 Big Boy Locomotive "4024," LionMaster, 03		800
38076	C&O 2-8-4 Berkshire Locomotive "2699," CC, 04		860
38077	Virginian 2-8-4 Berkshire Locomotive "508," CC, 04		1000
38079	SP 4-8-4 Northern GS-2 Locomotive "4410" CC, 04		980
38080	WP 4-8-4 Northern GS-64 Locomotive "485" CC, 04		1000
38081	C&O 2-6-6-6 Allegheny Locomotive "1650," CC, 05-07		1700
38082	Pennsylvania 2-8-8-2 Y3 Locomotive "374," CC, 04		1000
38083	N&W 2-8-8-2 Y3 Locomotive "2009," CC, 04		910
38085	NYC 4-6-4 Hudson J-3a Locomotive "5422," CC, 03		495
38086	B&A 4-6-4 Hudson Locomotive "607," CC, 03		495
38087	Nickel Plate 2-8-4 Berkshire Locomotive, RailSounds, 05		190
38088	NYC 2-6-0 Mogul Locomotive "1924," CC, 03, 05		600
38089	Pennsylvania 4-6-2 Pacific Locomotive "3678," CC, 04		300
38090	Clinchfield 4-6-6-4 Challenger Locomotive "672" CC, 04		640

No.	Description	Exc	Mint
38091	NP 4-6-6-4 Challenger Locomotive "5121" CC, 04		660 ___
38092	Pickering Lumber Heisler Locomotive "5," CC, 04		1000 ___
38093	UP 4-6-6-4 Challenger Locomotive "3980," CC, 04		700 ___
38094	MILW Hiawatha 4-4-2 Atlantic Locomotive, CC, 06		950 ___
38095	N&W 4-8-4 J Class Locomotive "611," CC, 05-06		1250 ___
38100	Texas Special F3 Diesel AB Set, 99	860	930 ___
38103	Texas Special F3 Diesel "2245," 99	435	510 ___
38104	CP F3 A Unit "2373," powered, 99		400 ___
38105	CP F3 A Unit "2373," nonpowered, 99		100 ___
38106	NYC F3 A Unit "2333," powered, 99		400 ___
38107	NYC F3 A Unit "2333," nonpowered, 99		250 ___
38114	ATSF FT Diesel B Unit, 99-00		170 ___
38115	NYC FT Diesel B Unit "2403," nonpowered, 99-00		130 ___
38116	B&O FT Diesel B Unit, 99-00		130 ___
38144	C&O F3 Diesel AA Set "7019, 7021," 00		700 ___
38147	GN Alco FA2 AA Diesel Set, CC, 02		405 ___
38150	Platinum Ghost "2333," 99	198	495 ___
38153	"Spirit of the Century" F3 Diesel AA Set, 99		800 ___
38160	Pennsylvania Alco FB2 Diesel, 02		125 ___
38161	MKT Alco FB2 Diesel, 02		125 ___
38162	Burlington FT Diesel B Unit, 01		NRS ___
38167	Burlington FT Diesel AA Set, 01		225 ___
38176	Pennsylvania Alco FA2 AA Diesel Set, CC, 02		405 ___
38182	MKT Alco FA2 AA Diesel Set, CC, 02		360 ___
38188	Southern F3 Diesel ABA Set, 00		557 ___
38194	GN Alco FB2 Diesel, 02		125 ___
38195	Santa Fe FT Diesel A Unit "170," 00		125 ___
38196	Santa Fe FT Diesel A Unit "171," 00		175 ___
38197	SP F3 Diesel ABA Set, 00		640 ___
38202	Wild West Handcar, 10		75 ___
38203	Holly Jolly Trolley 2-car Set, 10		160 ___
38204	ATSF FT B Unit, nonpowered, 10		120 ___
38210	PRR Alco Diesel AA Set, CC, 10		400 ___
38213	Rio Grande Ski Train FT A Unit "541," powered, 10-11		200 ___
38214	Rio Grande Ski Train FT B Unit, nonpowered, 11		120 ___
38215	ATSF FT Diesel "165," RailSounds, 10-11		280 ___
38216	Rio Grande Ski Train FT A Unit, nonpowered, 11		120 ___
38219	Texan FT B Unit Diesel, nonpowered, 11-14	25	120 ___
38221	CNJ Alco AA Diesel Set, 11		300 ___
38224	Alaska Alco AA Diesel Set, 11		300 ___
38234	Classic PRR GG1 Electric Locomotive "4866," 12		330 ___
38235	Classic PC GG1 Electric Locomotive "4840," 12		330 ___
38240	Elf Gang Car, 12		120 ___
38241	MOW Gang Car, 12-13		120 ___
38248	NS GP38 Diesel "1030," 13-14	180	300 ___
38252	CP GE U36B Diesel, "4245," 13	155	200 ___
38300	Postwar "2331" Virginian Train Master Diesel, 08	190	230 ___
38303	Postwar "2340" GG1 Electric Locomotive, 08		280 ___
38305	Postwar "2338" Milwaukee Road GP7 Diesel, 08		220 ___
38308	Postwar 2146WS Berkshire Passenger Set, 12		460 ___
38310	"2185W" NYC F3 Diesel Freight Set, 09		600 ___
38311	"2276W" B&O RDC Commuter Set, 09		470 ___
38312	"2343" Santa Fe F3 Diesel AA Set, 09		500 ___

		Exc	Mint
38313	B&O Budd RDC 2-pack, 09		350
38323	Postwar "2348" M&StL GP9 Diesel, CC, 10		390
38324	Postwar 2507W NH F3 Diesel Freight Set, 10		600
38328	Postwar 1623W NP GP9 Diesel Freight Set, 10		750
38329	Postwar 2261W Freight Hauler Set, 10		610
38334	Postwar 11288 Orbitor Diesel Freight Set, 10		500
38338	Postwar 2129WS Berkshire Freight Set, 12		550
38339	Postwar 2505W Virginian Rectifier Freight Set, 10		470
38340	Postwar 1587S Girl's Steam Freight Set, 10		580
38342	Postwar 1619W Santa Fe Freight Set, 10-11	125	470
38348	Postwar "2339" Transparent Wabash GP7 Diesel, 11		290
38349	Postwar 12885-500 C&O GP7 Freight Set, 11-12		600
38351	Postwar Archive UP GP7 Diesel, 11		290
38353	Postwar X-628 Promotional Navy Diesel Freight Set, 12-14		600
38354	Postwar 1464W UP Anniversary Diesel Passenger Set, 12-14	230	480
38357	Postwar 221 U.S. Marine Corps Alco Diesel A Unit, 12-14		300
38358	Postwar 2239 IC F3 Freight Set, 12-14		600
38365	Archive ATSF Black Bonnet F3 AA Diesel Set, 12-14		500
38368	Archive NYC Red Lightning F3 AA Diesel Set, 12-14		500
38371	Postwar 2031 RI Alco Diesel AA Set, 12-13		400
38374	Postwar 221 U.S. Marine Corps Alco Diesel B Unit, 12-14		120
38377	Postwar 2363T F3 A Unit, nonpowered, 12-14		170
38379	Archive ATSF Black Bonnet F3 B Unit, 12-14		170
38380	Archive NYC Red Lightning F3 B Unit, 12-14		170
38386	Postwar "2367" Wabash F3 Diesel AB Units, 12-14		500
38388	Postwar "2367" Wabash F3 A Unit, nonpowered, 12-14		170
38389	Postwar "2362" UP F3 Diesel AA Set, 14		460
38392	Postwar "2362" F3 Diesel B Unit, nonpowered, 14		170
38393	PRR Round-roof Boxcar "76648" (std O), 14		80
38401	NYC M-497 Jet-Powered Rail Car, 10		600
38402	Amtrak HHP-8 Electric Locomotive, RailSounds, 10		400
38403	B&O CSX Heritage AC6000 Diesel "6607," CC, 11		550
38404	B&O CSX Heritage AC6000 Diesel "7812," CC, 11		550
38405	Chessie System CSX Heritage AC6000 Diesel, CC, 11-14		550
38406	Chessie System CSX Heritage AC6000 Diesel, CC, 11-14		550
38407	WM CSX Heritage AC6000 Diesel "2652," CC, 11		550
38408	WM CSX Heritage AC6000 Diesel "2659," CC, 11		550
38409	Clinchfield CSX Heritage AC6000 Diesel, CC, 11-13	188	550
38410	Clinchfield CSX Heritage AC6000 Diesel, CC, 11-14		550
38411	Family Lines CSX Heritage AC6000 Diesel "4825," CC, 11		550
38412	Family Lines CSX Heritage AC6000 Diesel "4837," CC, 11		550
38413	CSX Heritage AC6000 Diesel "607," CC, 11-13		550
38414	CSX Heritage AC6000 Diesel "654," CC, 11-13		550
38415	PRR U28C Diesel "6531," CC, 11-12		530
38416	PRR U28C Diesel "6534," CC, 11-12		530
38417	BN Bicentennial U30C Diesel "1776," CC, 11		530
38418	BN Bicentennial U30C Diesel "1777," CC, 11		530
38419	UP U30C Diesel '2918," CC, 11-12		530
38420	UP U30C Diesel '2897," CC, 11-12		530
38421	NP U33C Diesel "3305," CC, 11-12		530
38422	NP U33C Diesel "3307," CC, 11-12		530
38423	Southern U30C Diesel "3801," CC, 11-12		530
38424	Southern U30C Diesel "3804," CC, 11-12		530

38425	RI Budd RDC Jet Car, 11		330 ___
38426	Central of Georgia GP7 Diesel "126," CC, 11		450 ___
38427	Central of Georgia GP7 Diesel "128," CC, 11		450 ___
38428	Alaska Budd RDC Coach, 11		300 ___
38429	NYC Budd RDC M-497 Jet Car, 11		330 ___
38432	MKT H16-44 Diesel "1591," CC, 11		500 ___
38433	MKT H16-44 Diesel "1731," CC, 11		500 ___
38434	MKT H16-44 Diesel "1732," 11		380 ___
38435	MKT H16-44 Diesel "1733," nonpowered, 11		240 ___
38436	LIRR H-16-44 Diesel "1501," CC, 11		500 ___
38437	LIRR H-16-44 Diesel "1504," CC, 11		500 ___
38438	LIRR H-16-44 Diesel "1507," 11		380 ___
38439	LIRR H-16-44 Diesel "1509," nonpowered, 11		240 ___
38440	UP H-16-44 Diesel "1341," CC, 11		500 ___
38441	UP H-16-44 Diesel "1342," CC, 11		500 ___
38442	UP H-16-44 Diesel "1343," 11		380 ___
38443	UP H-16-44 Diesel "1344," nonpowered, 11		240 ___
38444	PRR H16-44 Diesel "8807," CC, 11		500 ___
38445	PRR H16-44 Diesel "8810," CC, 11		500 ___
38446	PRR H16-44 Diesel "8812," 11		380 ___
38447	PRR H16-44 Diesel "8815," nonpowered, 11		240 ___
38452	PC Alco RS-11 Diesel "7605," CC, 12		480 ___
38453	PC Alco RS-11 Diesel "7608," CC, 12		480 ___
38454	PRR Alco RS-11 Diesel "9622," CC, 12		480 ___
38455	PC Alco RS-11 Diesel "7625," nonpowered, 12		240 ___
38456	N&W Alco RS-11 Diesel "308," CC, 12-13		480 ___
38457	N&W Alco RS-11 Diesel "318," CC, 12		480 ___
38458	PRR Alco RS-11 Diesel "8631," CC, 12		480 ___
38459	N&W Alco RS-11 Diesel "330," nonpowered, 12		240 ___
38460	NKP Alco RS-11 Diesel "855," CC, 12		480 ___
38461	NKP Alco RS-11 Diesel "859," CC, 12		480 ___
38462	PRR Alco RS-11 Diesel "8639," nonpowered, 12		240 ___
38463	NKP Alco RS-11 Diesel "863," nonpowered, 12		240 ___
38464	Alaska Alco RS-11 Diesel "3602," CC, 12		480 ___
38465	Alaska Alco RS-11 Diesel "3604," CC, 12		480 ___
38466	NH Alco RS-11 Diesel "1403," CC, 12		480 ___
38467	Alaska Alco RS-11 Diesel "3607," nonpowered, 12		240 ___
38468	Seaboard Alco RS-11 Diesel "101," CC, 12-13		480 ___
38469	Seaboard Alco RS-11 Diesel "102," CC, 12		480 ___
38470	NH Alco RS-11 Diesel "1405," CC, 12		480 ___
38471	Seaboard Alco RS-11 Diesel "104," nonpowered, 12		240 ___
38472	C&O Alco S2 Diesel Switcher "5001," CC, 11		470 ___
38473	C&O Alco S2 Diesel Switcher "5505," CC, 11		480 ___
38474	C&O Alco S2 Diesel Switcher "5020," 11		360 ___
38475	C&O Alco S2 Diesel Switcher "5027," nonpowered, 11		220 ___
38476	CN Alco S2 Diesel Switcher "7946," CC, 11		480 ___
38477	CN Alco S2 Diesel Switcher "7949," CC, 11		480 ___
38478	CN Alco S2 Diesel Switcher "7951," 11		360 ___
38479	CN Alco S2 Diesel Switcher "7954," 11		360 ___
38480	NYC Alco S2 Diesel Switcher "8504," CC, 11		480 ___
38481	NYC Alco S2 Diesel Switcher "8507," CC, 11		480 ___
38482	NYC Alco S2 Diesel Switcher "8514," 11		360 ___
38483	NYC Alco S2 Diesel Switcher "8521," nonpowered, 11		220 ___

		Exc	Mint
38484	Southern Alco S2 Diesel Switcher "2209," CC, 11		480
38485	Southern Alco S2 Diesel Switcher "2211," CC, 11		480
38486	Southern Alco S2 Diesel Switcher "2215," 11		360
38487	Southern Alco S2 Diesel Switcher "2218," nonpowered, 11		220
38488	Mopac Alco S2 Diesel Switcher "9108," CC, 11		480
38489	Mopac Alco S2 Diesel Switcher "9113," CC, 11		480
38490	Mopac Alco S2 Diesel Switcher "9116," 11		360
38491	Mopac Alco S2 Diesel Switcher "9131," nonpowered, 11		220
38493	ATSF Early Era Inspection Vehicle, CC, 12		150
38494	CP DD35 Diesel "9864," CC, 12		600
38495	CP DD35 Diesel "9868," nonpowered, 12		440
38496	SP DD35A Diesel "9903," CC, 11		600
38497	SP DD35A Diesel "9914," nonpowered , 11		440
38498	PRR DD35A Diesel "2380," CC, 11		600
38499	PRR DD35A Diesel "2383," nonpowered, 11		440
38505	CSX GP-38 Diesel, 11		140
38521	PRR GG1 Electric "4839," 11		330
38522	Amtrak GG1 Electric "926," 11		330
38524	NYC GP35 Diesel "6131," CC, 12		500
38525	NYC GP35 Diesel "6138," CC, 12		500
38526	NYC GP35 Diesel "6147," nonpowered, 12		260
38527	UP GP35 Diesel "742," CC, 12		500
38528	UP GP35 Diesel "753," CC, 12		500
38529	UP GP35 Diesel "760," nonpowered, 12		260
38530	SP GP35 Diesel "7465," CC, 12		500
38531	SP GP35 Diesel "7474," CC, 12		500
38532	SP GP35 Diesel "7481," nonpowered, 12		260
38533	CP GP35 Diesel "5014," CC, 12		500
38534	CP GP35 Diesel "5018," CC, 12		500
38535	CP GP35 Diesel "5023," nonpowered, 12		260
38536	PRR GP35 Diesel "2297," CC, 12		500
38537	PRR GP35 Diesel "2302," CC, 12		500
38538	PRR GP35 Diesel "2305," nonpowered, 12		260
38539	N&W Alco RS-11 Diesel "308," CC, 12		480
38539	Conrail GP35 Diesel "2297," CC, 12		500
38540	Conrail GP35 Diesel "2302," CC, 12		500
38541	Conrail GP35 Diesel "2305," nonpowered, 12		260
38542	Milwaukee Road GP35 Diesel "361," CC, 12		500
38543	Milwaukee Road GP35 Diesel "363," CC, 12		500
38544	Milwaukee Road GP35 Diesel "366," nonpowered, 12		260
38545	Pacific Harbor Line Genset Switcher "31," CC, 11		800
38546	KCS Genset Switcher "1404," CC, 11-12		800
38547	Santa Fe Genset Switcher "9910," CC, 11		800
38548	EL GP35 Diesel "2555," CC, 12		500
38549	EL GP35 Diesel "2558," CC, 12		500
38550	EL GP35 Diesel "2561," nonpowered, 12		260
38558	D&H Baldwin RF-16 Diesel AA Set, CC, 12		730
38561	D&H Baldwin RF-16 Diesel B Unit, CC, 12		400
38562	D&H Baldwin RF-16 Diesel B Unit, nonpowered, 12		250
38563	B&O Baldwin RF-16 Diesel AA Set, CC, 12-14		730
38566	B&O Baldwin RF-16 Diesel B Unit, CC, 12-14		400
38567	B&O Baldwin RF-16 Diesel B Unit, nonpowered, 12-14		250
38568	NYC Baldwin RF-16 Diesel AA Set "3806-3808," CC, 12-14		730

		Exc	Mint	
38571	NYC Baldwin RF-16 Diesel B Unit, CC, 12-14		400	___
38572	NYC Baldwin RF-16 Diesel B Unit, nonpowered, 12-14		250	___
38573	SP Baldwin RF-16 Diesel AA Set, CC, 12-14		730	___
38576	SP Baldwin RF-16 Diesel B Unit, CC, 12-14		400	___
38577	SP Baldwin RF-16 Diesel B Unit, nonpowered, 12-14		250	___
38579	ATSF GP9 Diesel "744," nonpowered, 12		240	___
38580	NP GP9 Diesel "324," nonpowered, 12		240	___
38581	CSX SD80MAC Diesel "809," CC, 12-13		530	___
38582	CSX SD80MAC Diesel '812," CC, 12		530	___
38583	CSX SD80MAC Diesel "804," nonpowered, 12		260	___
38584	NS SD80MAC Diesel "7207," CC, 12		530	___
38585	NS SD80MAC Diesel "7203," CC, 12		530	___
38586	NS SD80MAC Diesel "7209," nonpowered, 12		260	___
38587	Conrail SD80MAC Diesel "4126," CC, 12		530	___
38588	Conrail SD80MAC Diesel "4129," CC, 12		530	___
38589	Conrail SD80MAC Diesel "4103," nonpowered, 12		260	___
38593	UP NW2 Diesel Switcher Locomotive "1028," CC, 12		470	___
38594	UP NW2 Diesel Switcher Locomotive "1043," CC, 12		470	___
38595	CB&Q Scale NW2 Diesel Switcher "9227," CC, 12		470	___
38596	CB&Q Scale NW2 Diesel Switcher '9245," CC, 12		470	___
38597	CB&Q F3 AA Diesel Set "9962A-9962C," CC, 12-13		730	___
38600	UP 0-6-0 Dockside Switcher "87," traditional, 07-09		110	___
38601	Lionel Lines 0-6-0 Dockside Switcher, traditional, 07-09		110	___
38605	PRR 0-4-0 Locomotive "94," traditional, 07		170	___
38606	SP 0-4-0 Locomotive "71," traditional, 07-08		170	___
38607	Southern 2-8-4 Berkshire "2718," RailSounds, 07-08		175	___
38608	LL 2-8-2 Mikado Locomotive "57," RailSounds, 07	95	251	___
38609	NYC 2-8-2 Mikado Locomotive "1843," CC, 07		370	___
38610	NKP 2-8-4 Berkshire Locomotive "779," CC, 07-08		370	___
38619	Santa Fe 4-6-2 Pacific "2037," traditional, K-Line, 06		260	___
38620	B&O Porter Locomotive "16," traditional, K-Line, 06		100	___
38621	4-6-2 Pacific Locomotive, traditional, K-Line, 06		260	___
38626	Holiday 2-8-2 Mikado Locomotive "25," green, RailSounds, 08		260	___
38627	GN 4-4-2 Atlantic Locomotive "1702," traditional, 08-09		110	___
38630	U.S. Army 0-6-0 Dockside Switcher "486," traditional, 08-09		110	___
38634	NYC 4-6-4 Hudson Locomotive "5417," TrainSounds, 07		200	___
38635	C&O 4-6-4 Hudson Locomotive "309," TrainSounds, 08		200	___
38636	ATSF 4-6-4 Hudson Locomotive "3459," TrainSounds, 07		200	___
38637	LL 4-6-4 Hudson Locomotive "5242," TrainSounds, 08		200	___
38638	UP 4-6-2 Pacific Locomotive "2888," RailSounds, 08		300	___
38639	Erie 4-6-2 Pacific Locomotive "2939," RailSounds, 08		300	___
38640	Southern 4-6-2 Pacific Locomotive "1317,"" RailSounds, 08		300	___
38641	B&M 4-6-2 Pacific Locomotive "3713," RailSounds, 08		300	___
38642	PRR 4-6-2 Pacific Locomotive "5385," RailSounds, 08		300	___
38643	Alaska Mikado 2-8-2 Locomotive "701," CC, 08-09		280	___
38644	T&P Mikado 2-8-2 Locomotive "810," CC, 08-09		400	___
38649	Christmas 4-6-4 Hudson Locomotive, traditional, 08		210	___
38651	Lionel Lines 0-8-0 Locomotive "100," traditional, 08-09		120	___
38654	Bethlehem Steel 0-4-0 Locomotive, traditional, 08-09		170	___
38657	Alton Limited Pacific 4-6-2 Locomotive "659," traditional, 08		300	___
38658	W&ARR 4-4-0 General "1892," TrainSounds, 08-09		165	___
38664	LL 4-4-2 Atlantic Locomotive "1058" traditional, 08-09		110	___

	MODERN 1970-2023	Exc	Mint
___ 38671	Santa Flyer 4-6-0 Locomotive, 09		200
___ 38677	Strasburg 0-6-0 Dockside Switcher "1252," 10		130
___ 38678	Monopoly Hudson Locomotive, TrainSounds, 10		240
___ 38679	ATSF 0-4-0 Switcher "1387," 10-11		190
___ 38684	Pennsylvania Power & Light Docksider Switcher, 10		110
___ 38687	Western & Atlantic 0-4-0 Locomotive "1897,", 10-11		190
___ 38689	AT&SF 0-8-0 Steam Locomotive "8689," 10-11	140	255
___ 38691	North Pole Central Santa Flyer "2," 10-11		190
___ 38692	Angela Trotta Thomas Signature Express, 10-11		190
___ 38700	CB&Q F3 B Unit "9962B," CC, 12-13		400
___ 38701	CB&Q F3 B Unit, 12-13		250
___ 38702	D&RGW F3 AA Diesel Set "5531-5533," CC, 12-14		730
___ 38705	D&RGW F3 B Unit "5532," CC, 12-14		400
___ 38706	D&RGW F3 B Unit, 12-14		250
___ 38707	WP F3 AB Diesel Set "803A-803B," CC, 12-14		730
___ 38710	WP F3 A Unit, nonpowered, 12-14		380
___ 38711	WP F3 B Unit "803C," CC, 12-14		400
___ 38712	Wabash F7 AA Diesel Set "1102A-1102C," CC, 12-13		730
___ 38715	Wabash F7 B Unit "1102B," CC, 12-13		400
___ 38716	Wabash F7 B Unit, 12-13		250
___ 38717	Milwaukee Road F7 AA Diesel Set, CC, 12		730
___ 38720	Milwaukee Road F7 B Unit "109B," CC, 12		400
___ 38721	Milwaukee Road F7 B Unit, 12		250
___ 38722	Grand Trunk SD80MAC Diesel "9085," CC, 12		530
___ 38723	Grand Trunk SD80MAC Diesel "9088," CC, 12		530
___ 38724	Grand Trunk SD80MAC Diesel "9079," nonpowered, 12		260
___ 38725	CB&Q SD80MAC Diesel "9654," CC, 12		530
___ 38726	CB&Q SD80MAC Diesel "9651," CC, 12		530
___ 38727	CB&Q SD80MAC Diesel "9660," nonpowered, 12		260
___ 38728	PRR SD80MAC Diesel "9942," CC, 12		530
___ 38729	PRR SD80MAC Diesel "9945," CC, 12		530
___ 38730	PRR SD80MAC Diesel "9947," nonpowered, 12-13		260
___ 38731	Polar SD80MAC Diesel, CC, 12		530
___ 38732	CB&Q BNSF Heritage SD70ACe Diesel "1848," CC, 12-13		530
___ 38733	CB&Q BNSF Heritage SD70ACe Diesel "1852," CC, 12-13		530
___ 38734	CB&Q BNSF Heritage SD70ACe Diesel "1856," nonpowered, 12-13		260
___ 38735	ATSF BNSF Heritage SD70ACe Diesel "1996," CC, 12-13		530
___ 38736	ATSF BNSF Heritage SD70ACe Diesel "1997," CC, 12-13		530
___ 38737	ATSF BNSF Heritage SD70ACe "1999," nonpowered, 12-13		260
___ 38738	Frisco BNSF Heritage SD70ACe Diesel "1876," CC, 12-13		530
___ 38739	Frisco BNSF Heritage SD70ACe Diesel "1896," CC, 12-14		530
___ 38740	Frisco BNSF Heritage SD70ACe "1916," nonpowered, 12-13		260
___ 38741	BN BNSF Heritage SD70ACe Diesel "1970," CC, 12-13		530
___ 38742	BN BNSF Heritage SD70ACe Diesel "1975," CC, 12-13		530
___ 38743	BN BNSF Heritage SD70ACe "1980," nonpowered, 12-13		260
___ 38744	GN BNSF Heritage SD70ACe Diesel "1889," CC, 12-13		530
___ 38745	GN BNSF Heritage SD70ACe Diesel "1891," CC, 12-13		530
___ 38746	GN BNSF Heritage SD70ACe "1893," nonpowered, 12-13		260
___ 38747	NP BNSF Heritage SD70ACe Diesel "1870," CC, 12-13		530
___ 38748	NP BNSF Heritage SD70ACe Diesel "1872," CC, 12-13		530
___ 38749	NP BNSF Heritage SD70ACe "1875," nonpowered, 12-13		260
___ 38750	EMD Demonstrator SD70ACe Diesel "2012," CC, 12-13		530
___ 38751	CNJ F3 AA Diesel Set, CC, 13-14		730

		Exc	Mint
38752	Vision Centipede AA Pilot Diesels, CC, 13		2200 ___
38754	C&NW F7 AA Diesel Set, CC, 13-14		730 ___
38757	SP F7 AA Diesel Set, CC, 13-14		730 ___
38760	CNJ F3 B Unit, CC, 13-14		400 ___
38761	CNJ F3 B Unit, 13-14		250 ___
38762	C&NW F7 B Unit "410," CC, 13-14		400 ___
38763	C&NW F7 B Unit, 13-14		250 ___
38764	SP F7 B Unit "8219," CC, 13		400 ___
38765	SP F7 B Unit, 13		250 ___
38768	N&W GP35 Diesel "1306," CC, 13-14		500 ___
38769	N&W GP35 Diesel "1308," nonpowered, 13-14		260 ___
38770	RI GP35 Diesel "307," CC, 13-14		500 ___
38771	RI GP35 Diesel "309," CC, 13-14		500 ___
38772	RI GP35 Diesel "323," nonpowered, 13-14		260 ___
38773	WP GP35 Diesel "3002," CC, 13-14		500 ___
38774	WP GP35 Diesel "3009," CC, 13-14		500 ___
38775	WP GP35 Diesel "3014," nonpowered, 13-14		260 ___
38778	C&NW RS3 Diesel "1621," LionChief, 14-16		330 ___
38779	NYC RS3 Diesel "8244," LionChief, 14-16		330 ___
38782	C&BQ GP35 Diesel "990," CC, 13		500 ___
38783	C&BQ GP35 Diesel "996," nonpowered, 13		500 ___
38784	CN GP35 Diesel "4000," CC, 13		500 ___
38785	CN GP35 Diesel "4005," CC, 13		500 ___
38786	CN GP35 Diesel "4001," nonpowered, 13		260 ___
38787	D&RGW GP35 Diesel "3031," CC, 13		500 ___
38788	D&RGW GP35 Diesel "3034," CC, 13		500 ___
38789	D&RGW GP35 Diesel "3038," nonpowered, 13		260 ___
38790	DT&I GP35 Diesel "351," CC, 13		500 ___
38791	DT&I GP35 Diesel "353," CC, 13	470	900 ___
38792	DT&I GP35 Diesel "355," nonpowered, 13		260 ___
38794	GN GP35 Diesel "3018," CC, 13-14		500 ___
38795	GN GP35 Diesel "3036," nonpowered, 13-14		260 ___
38796	Chessie System GP35 Diesel "1125," CC, 13		500 ___
38797	Chessie System GP35 Diesel "1128," CC, 13		500 ___
38798	Chessie System GP35 Diesel "1113," nonpowered, 13		260 ___
38799	N&W GP35 Diesel "1302," CC, 13-14		500 ___
38800	B&M Early Era Inspection Vehicle, CC, 12		150 ___
38801	KCS Trackmobile, CC, 12-13		300 ___
38802	North Pole Central Trackmobile, CC, 12		300 ___
38803	MOW Trackmobile, CC, 12		300 ___
38804	LIRR Trackmobile, CC, 12		300 ___
38805	Conrail Trackmobile, CC, 12		300 ___
38806	NS Trackmobile, CC, 12		300 ___
38807	NP Trackmobile, CC, 12-13		300 ___
38808	Chessie System Trackmobile, CC, 12		300 ___
38809	CN Trackmobile, CC, 12		300 ___
38810	PRR Early Era Inspection Vehicle, CC, 12		150 ___
38811	D&RGW Early Era Inspection Vehicle, CC, 12		150 ___
38812	SP Early Era Inspection Vehicle, CC, 12-13		150 ___
38813	C&O Early Era Inspection Vehicle, CC, 12-13		150 ___
38814	Milwaukee Road Early Era Inspection Vehicle, CC, 12		150 ___
38815	Transylvania Early Era Inspection Vehicle, CC, 12		150 ___
38816	PRR RS3 Diesel "5620," LionChief, 14-16		330 ___

		Exc	Mint
38819	D&RGW RS3 Diesel "5202," LionChief, 14-16		330
38821	AT&SF GP7 Diesel "2656," LionChief, 14-15		330
38824	NP GP7 Diesel "563," LionChief, 14-15		330
38825	UP GP7 Diesel "121," LionChief, 14-15		330
38827	CB&Q GP7 Diesel "1596," LionChief, 14-15		330
38848	Christmas Pioneer Zephyr Set, CC, 13-14		1100
38853	Santa and Mrs. Claus Handcar, 13		90
38855	GN GP35 Diesel "2519," CC, 13-14		500
38856	CB&Q Mark Twain Zephyr, CC, 13-14		1100
38860	CB&Q Pioneer Zephyr, CC, 13-14		1100
38864	Lionel Lines Zephyr, CC, 13-14		1100
38865	L&N GP35 Diesel "1105," CC, 13		500
38866	L&N GP35 Diesel "1109," CC, 13		500
38867	L&N GP35 Diesel "1114," nonpowered, 13		260
38868	C&BQ GP35 Diesel "978," CC, 13		500
38874	B&O GP9 Diesel "6448," CC, 13-14		480
38875	B&O GP9 Diesel "6456," CC, 13-14		480
38876	B&O GP9 Diesel "6461," nonpowered, 13-14		240
38877	B&M GP9 Diesel "1705," CC, 13		480
38878	B&M GP9 Diesel "1714," CC, 13		480
38879	B&M GP9 Diesel "1722," nonpowered, 13		240
38883	C&NW GP9 Diesel "701," CC, 13		480
38884	C&NW GP9 Diesel "704," CC, 13		480
38885	C&NW GP9 Diesel "712," nonpowered, 13		240
38886	Erie GP9 Diesel "1260," CC, 13		480
38887	Erie GP9 Diesel "1263," CC, 13		480
38888	Erie GP9 Diesel "1265," nonpowered, 13		240
38889	Nickel Plate Road GP9 Diesel "514," CC, 13		480
38890	Nickel Plate Road GP9 Diesel "452," CC, 13		480
38891	Nickel Plate Road GP9 Diesel "457," nonpowered, 13		240
38892	SP GP9 Diesel "3411," CC, 13		480
38893	SP GP9 Diesel "3415," CC, 13		480
38894	SP GP9 Diesel "3419," nonpowered, 13		240
38895	Wabash GP9 Diesel "484," CC, 13		480
38896	Wabash GP9 Diesel "488," CC, 13		480
38897	Wabash GP9 Diesel "491," nonpowered, 13		240
38918	Chessie System SD40-2 Diesel "7609," CC, 13		530
38919	Chessie System SD40-2 Diesel "7611," CC, 13		530
38920	Chessie System SD40-2 Diesel "7614," nonpowered, 13		240
38921	SP SD40T-2 Diesel Locomotive "8322," CC, 13		530
38922	SP SD40T-2 Diesel Locomotive "8326," CC, 13		530
38923	SP SD40T-2 Diesel, nonpowered, 13		260
38924	B&O SD40-2 Diesel "7602," CC, 13		530
38925	B&O SD40-2 Diesel "7607," CC, 13		530
38926	B&O SD40-2 Diesel "7611," nonpowered, 13		240
38933	Conrail SD40-2 Diesel "6424," CC, 13		530
38934	Conrail SD40-2 Diesel "6437," CC, 13		530
38935	Conrail SD40-2 Diesel "6468," nonpowered, 13		240
38936	UP SD40-2 Diesel "2929," CC, 13		530
38937	UP SD40-2 Diesel "2932," CC, 13		530
38938	UP SD40-2 Diesel "2947," nonpowered, 13		240
38939	NS SD40-2 Diesel "3355," CC, 13		530
38940	NS SD40-2 Diesel "3365," CC, 13		530

		Exc	Mint
38941	NS SD40-2 Diesel "3379," nonpowered, 13		240 ___
38942	Central of Georgia NS Heritage ES44AC Diesel, CC, 12		550 ___
38943	Central of Georgia NS Heritage ES44AC Diesel, CC, 12		550 ___
38944	Central of Georgia NS Heritage ES44AC Diesel, nonpowered, 12		280 ___
38945	Conrail NS Heritage ES44AC Diesel, CC, 12		550 ___
38946	Conrail NS Heritage ES44AC Diesel, CC, 12		550 ___
38947	Conrail NS Heritage ES44AC Diesel, nonpowered, 12		280 ___
38948	Interstate NS Heritage ES44AC Diesel "8105," CC, 12		550 ___
38949	Interstate NS Heritage ES44AC Diesel, CC, 12		550 ___
38950	Interstate NS Heritage ES44AC Diesel, nonpowered, 12		280 ___
38951	LV NS Heritage ES44AC Diesel, CC, 12		550 ___
38952	LV NS Heritage ES44AC Diesel, CC, 12		550 ___
38953	LV NS Heritage ES44AC Diesel, nonpowered, 12		280 ___
38954	Nickel Plate Road NS Heritage ES44AC Diesel, CC, 12		550 ___
38955	Nickel Plate Road NS Heritage ES44AC Diesel, CC, 12		550 ___
38956	Nickel Plate Road NS Heritage ES44AC Diesel, nonpowered, 12		280 ___
38957	N&W NS Heritage ES44AC Diesel, CC, 12		550 ___
38958	N&W NS Heritage ES44AC Diesel, CC, 12		550 ___
38959	N&W NS Heritage ES44AC Diesel, nonpowered, 12		280 ___
38960	PRR NS Heritage ES44AC Diesel, CC, 12		550 ___
38961	PRR NS Heritage ES44AC Diesel, CC, 12		550 ___
38962	PRR NS Heritage ES44AC Diesel, nonpowered, 12		280 ___
38963	Southern NS Heritage ES44AC Diesel, CC, 12		550 ___
38964	Southern NS Heritage ES44AC Diesel, CC, 12		550 ___
38965	Southern NS Heritage ES44AC Diesel, nonpowered, 12		280 ___
38966	NS Heritage ES44AC Diesel, CC, 12		550 ___
38967	NS Heritage ES44AC Diesel, CC, 12		550 ___
38968	NS Heritage ES44AC Diesel, nonpowered, 12		280 ___
38969	North Pole Central GP35 Diesel "2525," CC, 13		500 ___
38970	North Pole Central GP35 Diesel "2512," CC, 13		500 ___
38971	North Pole Central GP35 Diesel "2513," nonpowered, 13		260 ___
38972	Reading GP35 Diesel "3625," CC, 13		500 ___
38973	Reading GP35 Diesel "3630," CC, 13		500 ___
38974	Reading GP35 Diesel "3633," nonpowered, 13		260 ___
38975	AT&SF GP35 Diesel "3312," CC, 13		500 ___
38976	AT&SF GP35 Diesel "3318," CC, 13		500 ___
38977	AT&SF GP35 Diesel "3329," nonpowered, 13		260 ___
38978	Alaska GP35 Diesel "2501," CC, 13		500 ___
38979	Alaska GP35 Diesel "2503," CC, 13		500 ___
38980	Alaska GP35 Diesel "2502," nonpowered, 13		260 ___
38981	B&O GP35 Diesel "2506," CC, 13-14		500 ___
38982	B&O GP35 Diesel "2511," CC, 13-14		500 ___
38983	B&O GP35 Diesel "2517," nonpowered, 13-14		260 ___
38984	C&O GP35 Diesel "3515," CC, 13-14		500 ___
38985	C&O GP35 Diesel "3521," CC, 13-14		500 ___
38986	C&O GP35 Diesel "3526," nonpowered, 13-14		260 ___
38987	MP GP35 Diesel "603," CC, 13		500 ___
38988	MP GP35 Diesel "607," CC, 13		500 ___
38989	MP GP35 Diesel "611," nonpowered, 13		260 ___

		Exc	Mint
___ 38990	GM&O GP35 Diesel "603," CC, 13-14		500
___ 38991	GM&O GP35 Diesel "607," CC, 13-14		500
___ 38992	GM&O GP35 Diesel "611," nonpowered, 13-14		260
___ 38993	WM GP35 Diesel "3576," CC, 13		500
___ 38994	WM GP35 Diesel "3578," CC, 13		500
___ 38995	WM GP35 Diesel "3580," nonpowered, 13		260
___ 38996	CSX GP35 Diesel "4355," CC, 13		500
___ 38997	CSX GP35 Diesel "4363," CC, 13		500
___ 38998	CSX GP35 Diesel "4390," nonpowered, 13		260
___ 38999	NS GP35 Diesel "2916," CC, 13		500
___ 39008	PRR Heavyweight Passenger Car 4-pack, 00		225
___ 39009	PRR Indian Rock Heavyweight Combination Car, 00		50
___ 39010	PRR Andrew Carnegie Heavyweight Passenger Coach, 00		60
___ 39011	PRR Solomon P. Chase Heavyweight Passenger Coach, 00		60
___ 39012	PRR Skyline View Heavyweight Observation Car, 00		50
___ 39013	B&O Heavyweight Passenger Car 4-pack, 00		400
___ 39014	B&O Harper‚Äôs Ferry Heavyweight Combination Car, 00		50
___ 39015	B&O Youngstown Heavyweight Passenger Coach, 00		50
___ 39016	B&O New Castle Heavyweight Passenger Coach, 00		50
___ 39017	B&O Chicago Heavyweight Observation Car, 00		50
___ 39028	LL Heavyweight Passenger Car 3-pack, 00		195
___ 39029	LL Irvington Heavyweight Coach "2625," 00		60
___ 39030	LL Madison Heavyweight Coach "2627," 00		60
___ 39031	LL Manhattan Heavyweight Coach "2628," 00		60
___ 39032	UP Madison Passenger Car 4-pack, 00		275
___ 39038	SP Madison Baggage Car "6015," 01		100
___ 39039	SP Madison Coach Car "1978," 01		100
___ 39040	SP Madison Coach "1975," 01		75
___ 39041	SP Madison Observation Car "2951," 01		100
___ 39042	N&W Heavyweight Passenger Car 4-pack, 00		325
___ 39047	B&O Heavyweight Passenger Car 2-pack, 01		160
___ 39050	PRR Heavyweight Passenger Car 2-pack, 01		215
___ 39053	Alaska Streamliner Car 2-pack, 01		90
___ 39056	NYC Streamliner Car 2-pack, 01		75
___ 39059	Santa Fe Streamliner Car 2-pack, 01		100
___ 39062	B&O Streamliner Car 2-pack, 01		75
___ 39065	PRR Streamliner Car 4-pack, 01	63	165
___ 39082	Blue Comet Heavyweight Passenger Car 2-pack, 02		325
___ 39085	Freedom Train Heavyweight Passenger Car 3-pack, 03		260
___ 39092	PRR Streamliner Car 2-pack, 01		70
___ 39099	Alton Limited Heavyweight Passenger Car 2-pack, 03		230
___ 39100	William Penn Congressional Coach, 00		115
___ 39101	Molly Pitcher Congressional Coach, 00		100
___ 39102	Betsy Ross Congressional Vista Dome Car, 00		100
___ 39103	Alexander Hamilton Congressional Observation Car, 00		100
___ 39104	Phoebe Snow Car, StationSounds, 99		255
___ 39105	Milwaukee Road Hiawatha Car, StationSounds, 99		235
___ 39106	CP Aluminum Passenger Car 2-pack, 00		185
___ 39107	CP Blair Manor Aluminum Passenger Coach "2553," 00		115
___ 39108	CP Craig Manor Aluminum Passenger Coach "2554," 00		110
___ 39109	"Spirit of the Century" Aluminum Passenger Car 4-pack, 99		520
___ 39110	"Spirit of the Century" Full Vista Dome Car, 99-00		100
___ 39111	"Spirit of the Century" Full Vista Dome Car, 99-00		100

| --- | --- | --- | --- |
39112	"Spirit of the Century" Full Vista Dome Car, 99-00		100
39113	"Spirit of the Century" Skytop Observation Car, 99-00		100
39118	Texas Special Garland Coach "1203," w/StationSounds, 99-00		220
39119	Southern Aluminum Passenger Car 4-pack, 00		335
39120	Southern Grand Junction Passenger/Baggage Car, 00		280
39121	Southern Charlottesville Aluminum Passenger Coach "812," 00		90
39122	Southern Roanoke Aluminum Passenger Coach "814," 00		250
39123	Southern Memphis Aluminum Observation Car "1152," 00		90
39124	Amtrak Superliner Aluminum Passenger Car 4-pack, 02		405
39129	Santa Fe Superliner Aluminum Passenger Car 4-pack, 02		305
39141	RI Aluminum Passenger Car 4-pack, 01		400
39146	UP Aluminum Passenger Car 4-pack, 01		285
39151	CP Aluminum Passenger Car 2-pack, 01		315
39154	PRR Congressional Aluminum Passenger Car 2-pack, 02		195
39155	PRR Congressional Baggage Car, 02		105
39156	PRR Robert Morris Congressional Coach, 02		100
39157	Southern Aluminum Passenger Car 2-pack, 01		290
39160	KCS Aluminum Passenger Car 2-pack, 01	170	260
39163	Erie-Lackawanna Aluminum Passenger Car 2-pack, 01		230
39166	Texas Special Aluminum Passenger Car 2-pack, 01	300	430
39169	ACL Aluminum Passenger Car 4-pack, 01		360
39170	ACL Aluminum Baggage Car "1634," 01		90
39171	ACL Aluminum Coach "1090," 01		90
39172	ACL Aluminum Coach "1111," 01		90
39173	ACL Aluminum Observation "1115," 01		90
39179	NP Aluminum Passenger Car 2-pack, 02	118	298
39182	WP Aluminum Passenger Car 2-pack, 02		280
39185	Rio Grande Aluminum Passenger Car 2-pack, 02		290
39194	UP Aluminum Passenger Car 2-pack, 02		220
39197	CP Aluminum Passenger Coach, StationSounds, 02		225
39198	PRR Aluminum Passenger Coach, StationSounds, 02		210
39200	Hellgate Bridge Boxcar #2 "1900-2000," 00 u		55
39202	Lionel Centennial Boxcar "1900-2000," 00		46
39203	Postwar "6464" Series X, 3 cars, 01	38	105
39204	New Haven Boxcar "6464-725," 01		44
39205	Alaska Boxcar "6464-825," 01		55
39206	NYC Boxcar "6464-900," 01		40
39207	UP Boxcar "508500," red, 00	23	55
39208	UP Boxcar "903658," silver, 00		42
39209	UP Boxcar "500200," yellow, 00		40
39210	Postwar "6530" Fire Fighting Car, 00		37
39211	Postwar "6464" Boxcar 3-pack #2, 00	28	88
39212	Postwar "6464" SP&S Boxcar, 00		30
39213	Postwar "6464" Wabash Boxcar, 00		30
39214	Postwar "6464" Kansas, Oklahoma & Gulf Boxcar, 00		30
39216	PRR DD Boxcar "47211," 01		46
39220	B&LE Heavyweight Boxcar "82101," 01		41
39221	L&N Heavyweight Boxcar "109829," 01		41
39222	Conrail Heavyweight Boxcar "269198," 01		44
39223	Postwar "6464" Archive Boxcar Set, 3-pack, 02		125
39224	Postwar "6464" Monon Boxcar, 02		45
39225	Postwar "6464" Tidewater Southern Boxcar, 02		40
39226	Postwar "6464" SP Boxcar, 02		45

		Exc	Mint
39227	Postwar "6468" Automobile Boxcar 3-pack, 01		95
39228	Postwar "6468" B&O DD Boxcar, Blue, 01		30
39229	Postwar "6468" B&O DD Boxcar, Tuscan, 01		40
39230	Postwar "6468" NH DD Boxcar, 01		30
39236	WP Boxcar "6464-250," 01		55
39238	Elvis Boxcar, 03		36
39239	P&LE Boxcar "22300," 02		35
39240	Pennsylvania Boxcar "118747," 02		32
39241	PC Boxcar "252455," 02		28
39242	Postwar "6464" Boxcar 3-pack #1, Archive Collection, 03-04	50	105
39243	Soo Line Boxcar, Archive Collection, 03-04		35
39244	D&RGW Cookie Box Boxcar, Archive Collection, 03-04		35
39245	Duluth, South Shore & Atlantic Boxcar, Archive, 03-04		30
39246	Century Club PRR Sharknose Diesel Boxcar, 00		50
39247	NYC DD Boxcar "6468," 02-03		32
39248	Lackawanna DD Boxcar w/Hobo, 03		45
39249	LRRC 2003 Christmas Boxcar, 03 u		40
39250	Campbell Kids Centennial Boxcar, 03-04		40
39252	Lenny Dean 60th Anniversary Boxcar, 04		38
39253	No. 6464 Boxcar 3-pack #2, Archive Collection, 04		100
39254	Detroit & Mackinac Boxcar, Archive Collection, 04		35
39255	NS Boxcar, Archive Collection, 04		35
39256	L&N Boxcar, Archive Collection, 04		35
39257	WP Boxcar "6464-100," boys set add-on, 03		50
39258	Elvis Presley "All Shook Up" Boxcar, 03-04		40
39259	Buick Centennial Boxcar, 03		40
39260	New Haven Boxcar, 04		40
39262	Elvis Presley "Elvis Has Left the Building" Boxcar, 04		38
39263	M&StL Boxcar, Postwar Celebration Series, 05		35
39267	No. 6464 Boxcar 3-pack #3, Archive Collection, 05		100
39271	State of Maine Boxcar, 04		35
39273	No. 6464 Boxcar 3-pack #4, Archive Collection, 06		100
39274	NP Boxcar, Archive Collection, 06		35
39275	US Air Force Boxcar, Archive Collection, 06		35
39276	Lilly Paper Cup Boxcar, Archive Collection, 06		35
39281	Florida State University Boxcar, 07	32	50
39282	Purdue University Boxcar, 08		50
39283	University of Virginia Boxcar, 08		50
39284	Penn State University Boxcar, 06-07		45
39285	U.S. Military Academy at West Point Boxcar, 08		50
39286	University of Illinois Boxcar, 06-07		45
39287	University of Alabama Boxcar, 06-07		45
39289	University of Oklahoma Boxcar, 06-08		50
39290	Postwar "6464" Boxcar 2-pack, rare variations, 08		100
39291	University of Michigan Boxcar, 06-07		45
39292	Monopoly Boxcar 3-pack, 08		135
39296	UPS Centennial Boxcar #3, 08-09		55
39297	Macy's Parade Boxcar, 07		55
39298	Monopoly Boxcar 3-pack #2, 08		145
39299	Lenny Dean Commemorative Boxcar, 08		50
39300	Postwar "6464-1" WP Boxcar, red lettering, 08		70
39301	Postwar "6464-300" Rutland Boxcar, 08		80
39302	University of Maryland Boxcar, 08		50

		Exc	Mint
39303	Villanova University Boxcar, 08		50 ___
39304	Auburn University Boxcar, 08		50 ___
39305	Monopoly Virginia Ave. Boxcar, 08		50 ___
39306	Monopoly Connecticut Ave. Boxcar, 08		50 ___
39307	Monopoly Marvin Gardens Boxcar, 08		50 ___
39308	CP Rail "6565" Boxcar "58700," 08-10		55 ___
39309	Macy‚Äôs Parade Boxcar, 08		50 ___
39310	Monopoly Boxcar 3-pack #3, 09-10		170 ___
39316	New Haven Automobile Boxcar, 09-10		60 ___
39317	Wizard of Oz Boxcar #1, 09-10		60 ___
39318	Wizard of Oz Boxcar #2, 09-10		60 ___
39319	Boy Scouts "Scout Law" Add-on Boxcar, 10		60 ___
39321	Lionel Art Boxcar 2-pack, 10		116 ___
39325	Macy Parade Boxcar, 09		45 ___
39326	UPS Centennial Boxcar #4, 10-11		60 ___
39328	Monopoly Boxcar 3-pack #4, 10-11		220 ___
39332	Holiday Boxcar, 10		60 ___
39334	Coca-Cola Christmas Boxcar, 10		70 ___
39335	Thomas Kinkade Boxcar, 10, 12		60 ___
39336	Angela Trotta Thomas "My Turn Yet, Dad?" Boxcar, 10		60 ___
39337	George Washington Presidential Boxcar, 11-12		60 ___
39338	Abraham Lincoln Presidential Boxcar, 11-12		60 ___
39339	Theodore Roosevelt Presidential Boxcar, 11-12		60 ___
39340	Thomas Jefferson Presidential Boxcar, 11-12		60 ___
39341	2010 Lionel Dealer Appreciation Boxcar, 10 u		40 ___
39342	Strasburg Boxcar, 11		55 ___
39343	New Jersey Central Boxcar, 10		45 ___
39344	Monopoly Boxcar 3-pack #5, 11-12		165 ___
39345	Monopoly Tennessee Avenue Boxcar, 11		55 ___
39346	Monopoly Atlantic Avenue Boxcar, 11		55 ___
39347	Monopoly Illinois Avenue Boxcar, 11		55 ___
39348	Lionel NASCAR Collectables Boxcar, 11-12		60 ___
39350	Thomas Kinkade "All Aboard for Christmas" Boxcar, 12-13		60 ___
39351	Peanuts Thanksgiving Boxcar, 12		70 ___
39354	Monopoly North Carolina Avenue Boxcar, 12		70 ___
39358	Boy Scouts "Prepared For Life" Boxcar, 12		60 ___
39359	Thanksgiving Boxcar, 12		60 ___
39360	Boy Scouts Cub Scout Boxcar, 12-13		60 ___
39361	Coca-Cola Polar Bear Boxcar, 14		70 ___
39362	Thomas Kinkade "Emerald City" Boxcar, 12-15		75 ___
39363	Peanuts Halloween Boxcar, 12		65 ___
39364	2013 Lionel Employee Christmas Boxcar, 13		60 ___
39372	Southern Hi-Cube Boxcar, 13-14	12	30 ___
39376	Monopoly Boxcar 2-pack, States and Vermont Avenues, 13-15		140 ___
39379	Monopoly Boxcar 2-pack, Med. and St. James Ave, 13-15		140 ___
39383	Prewar "2719" Boxcar, 13		65 ___
39385	U.S. Navy 1-D Tank Car, 13-15		70 ___
39386	U.S. Marines 1-D Tank Car, 13-15		70 ___
39387	U.S. Air Force 1-D Tank Car, 13-15		70 ___
39388	U.S. National Guard 1-D Tank Car, 13-16		70 ___
39389	U.S. Coast Guard 1-D Tank Car, 13-16		70 ___
39391	U.S. Army Flatcar, 13-16		70 ___
39392	U.S. Navy Flatcar, 13-16		70 ___

	Cat. No.	Description	Exc	Mint
___	39393	U.S. Marines Flatcar, 13-16		70
___	39394	U.S. Air Force Flatcar, 13-16		70
___	39395	U.S. National Guard Flatcar, 13-16		70
___	39396	U.S. Coast Guard Flatcar, 13-16		70
___	39398	Santa's Flyer Reefer, 13		43
___	39399	U.S. Army 1-D Tank Car, 13-15		70
___	39400	Republic Steel Slag Car 3-pack (std O), 04		100
___	39404	Republic Steel Hot Metal Car 3-pack (std O), 04		130
___	39411	Jones & Laughline Hot Metal Car 3-pack (std O), 05		190
___	39423	Postwar "3460" LL Flatcar with trailers, 05		45
___	39424	U.S. Steel 16-wheel Flatcar with girders, 05		70
___	39425	Hood Flatcar with milk container, traditional, 05		55
___	39426	Nestle Nesquik Flatcar with milk container, traditional, 05		55
___	39428	Bethlehem Steel Slag Car #4 (std O), 05		60
___	39429	Bethlehem Steel Hot Metal Car #8 (std O), 05		70
___	39430	Youngstown Sheet & Tube Slag Car #7 (std O), 05		60
___	39431	Youngstown Sheet & Tube Hot Metal Car #11 (std O), 05		70
___	39435	Postwar "6477" Flatcar with pipes, 06		50
___	39436	Postwar "6262" Wheel Car, 06		50
___	39437	Supplee Flatcar with milk container, 06		60
___	39439	6827 Flatcar with P&H power shovel, 04		50
___	39440	6828 Flatcar with P&H truck crane, 04		50
___	39443	U.S. Steel Slag Car 3-pack #2 (std O), 06		170
___	39447	Postwar "6561" LL Cable Reel Car, Archive Collection, 06-07		55
___	39450	Postwar "6414" Evans Auto Loader, Archive Collection, 06		70
___	39452	White Bros. Flatcar with milk container, 07		60
___	39457	Postwar "6175" Flatcar with rocket, 08		55
___	39458	Postwar "6844" Flatcar with missiles, 08		55
___	39463	Postwar "6430" Flatcar with trailers, 08		55
___	39468	Allis-Chalmers Car "52369," 08-09		60
___	39469	Christmas Egg Nog Barrel Car, 08		50
___	39470	UP Well Car "14712," 08		65
___	39471	Postwar "6264" Flatcar, 08		60
___	39472	ATSF Culvert Gondola, 08		60
___	39473	Play-Doh Vat Car, 08		55
___	39475	UPS Flatcar with trailer, 08		65
___	39476	Bethlehem Steel 16-wheel Flatcar, 08		75
___	39477	Christmas Flatcar with reindeer trailers, 08		60
___	39478	Postwar "6475" Pickles Vat Car, 08		55
___	39479	Postwar "6404" Flatcar with brown automobile, 08		50
___	39480	Western & Atlantic Cannon Flatcar, 09		60
___	39482	CSX WM Track Maintenance Car "6812", 11		65
___	39483	CSX P&LE Gondola "69812", 11		65
___	39484	Cocoa Marsh Vat Car, 10-12		60
___	39486	Deep Sea Challenger Submarine Car, 11		60
___	39487	BN I-Beam Flatcar "870798," 11		60
___	39488	Reese Vat Car, 10		60
___	39490	Western & Atlantic Cannonball Flatcar, 10		55
___	39497	Christmas Reindeer Stock Car, 10-11		60
___	39498	CNJ Gondola with culvert pipes, 11		55
___	39499	Alaska Oil Barrel Ramp Car, 11		50
___	39502	Monongahela NS Heritage ES44AC Diesel, nonpowered, 13		280
___	39530	PRR 1955 Pickup Truck, CC, 13		180

		Exc	Mint
39531	UP 1955 Pickup Truck, CC, 13		180 ___
39532	ATSF 1955 Pickup Truck, CC, 13-14		180 ___
39533	CP 1955 Pickup Truck, CC, 13-14		180 ___
39534	D&RGW 1955 Pickup Truck, CC, 13		180 ___
39535	GN 1955 Pickup Truck, CC, 13		180 ___
39536	MKT 1955 Pickup Truck, CC, 13-14		180 ___
39537	NYC 1955 Pickup Truck, CC, 13		180 ___
39538	Nickel Plate Road 1955 Pickup Truck, CC, 13		180 ___
39539	NP 1955 Pickup Truck, CC, 13-14		180 ___
39540	Southern 1955 Pickup Truck, CC, 13		180 ___
39541	SP 1955 Pickup Truck, CC, 13-14		180 ___
39542	Weyerhaueser 1955 Pickup Truck, CC, 13-14		180 ___
39543	Texas Special F3 B Unit, 13-14		230 ___
39544	Texas Special F3 B Unit, CC, 13-14		380 ___
39547	PRR F3 B Unit, 13-14		230 ___
39548	PRR F3 B Unit, CC, 13-14		380 ___
39554	NS GP35 Diesel "3918," CC, 13		500 ___
39555	NS GP35 Diesel "2915," nonpowered, 13		260 ___
39556	CP GP35 Diesel "5004," CC, 13-14		500 ___
39557	CP GP35 Diesel "5007," CC, 13-14		500 ___
39558	CP GP35 Diesel "5009," nonpowered, 13-14		260 ___
39562	BN GP35 Diesel "2533," CC, 13-14		500 ___
39563	BN GP35 Diesel "2509," CC, 13-14		500 ___
39564	BN GP35 Diesel "2523," nonpowered, 13-14		260 ___
39565	ATSF Dash-9 Diesel "612," CC, 13		530 ___
39566	ATSF Dash-9 Diesel "623," CC, 13		530 ___
39567	ATSF Dash-9 Diesel "631," nonpowered, 13		260 ___
39568	BC Rail Dash-9 Diesel "4641," CC, 13		530 ___
39569	BC Rail Dash-9 Diesel "4647," CC, 13		530 ___
39570	BC Rail Dash-9 Diesel "4652," nonpowered, 13		260 ___
39571	BNSF Dash-9 Diesel "4023," CC, 13		530 ___
39572	BNSF Dash-9 Diesel "4037," CC, 13		530 ___
39573	BNSF Dash-9 Diesel "4046," nonpowered, 13		260 ___
39574	C&NW Dash-9 Diesel "8605," CC, 13		530 ___
39575	C&NW Dash-9 Diesel "8610," CC, 13		530 ___
39576	C&NW Dash-9 Diesel "8622," nonpowered, 13		260 ___
39577	SP Dash-9 Diesel "8112," CC, 13		530 ___
39578	SP Dash-9 Diesel "8123," CC, 13		530 ___
39579	SP Dash-9 Diesel "8129," nonpowered, 13		260 ___
39580	UP Dash-9 Diesel "9599," CC, 13		530 ___
39581	UP Dash-9 Diesel "9714," CC, 13		530 ___
39582	UP Dash-9 Diesel "9717," nonpowered, 13		260 ___
39583	CSX Dash-9 Diesel "9036," CC, 13		530 ___
39584	CSX Dash-9 Diesel "9048," CC, 13		530 ___
39585	CSX Dash-9 Diesel "9051," nonpowered, 13		260 ___
39586	NS Dash-9 Diesel "9310," CC, 13		530 ___
39587	NS Dash-9 Diesel "9322," CC, 13		530 ___
39588	NS Dash-9 Diesel "9334," nonpowered, 13		260 ___
39589	CN Dash-9 Diesel "2534," CC, 13		530 ___
39590	CN Dash-9 Diesel "2547," CC, 13		530 ___
39591	CN Dash-9 Diesel "2570," nonpowered, 13		260 ___
39592	CNJ NS Heritage SD70ACe Diesel "1071," CC, 13		530 ___
39593	CNJ NS Heritage SD70ACe Diesel "1831," CC, 13		530 ___

		Exc	Mint
___ 39594	CNJ NS Heritage SD70ACe Diesel "1834," nonpowered, 13		260
___ 39595	DL&W NS Heritage SD70ACe Diesel "1074," CC, 13		530
___ 39596	DL&W NS Heritage SD70ACe Diesel "1853," CC, 13		530
___ 39597	DL&W NS Heritage SD70ACe Diesel "1856," nonpowered, 13		260
___ 39598	Monongahela NS Heritage ES44AC Diesel "8025," CC, 12		550
___ 39599	Monongahela NS Heritage ES44AC Diesel "1901," CC, 12		550
___ 39600	PRR E8 AA Diesel Set, CC, 13		930
___ 39603	B&O E9 AA Diesel Set, CC, 13		930
___ 39606	FEC E9 AA Diesel Set, CC, 13		930
___ 39609	SP E9 AA Diesel Set, CC, 13		930
___ 39612	UP E9 AA Diesel Set, CC, 13		930
___ 39615	CB&Q E9 AA Diesel Set, CC, 13		930
___ 39618	MILW E9 AA Diesel Set, CC, 13		930
___ 39621	KCS E9 AA Diesel Set, CC, 13		930
___ 39624	Erie NS Heritage SD70ACe Diesel "1068," CC, 13		530
___ 39625	Erie NS Heritage SD70ACe Diesel "1832," CC, 13		530
___ 39626	Erie NS Heritage SD70ACe Diesel "1835," nonpowered, 13		260
___ 39627	Illinois Terminal NS Heritage SD70ACe Diesel "1072," CC, 13		530
___ 39628	Illinois Terminal NS Heritage SD70ACe Diesel "1896," CC, 13		530
___ 39629	Illinois Terminal NS Heritage SD70ACe "1899," dummy, 13		260
___ 39630	NYC NS Heritage SD70ACe Diesel "1066," CC, 13		530
___ 39631	NYC NS Heritage SD70ACe Diesel "1831," CC, 13		530
___ 39632	NYC NS Heritage SD70ACe Diesel "1834," nonpowered, 13		260
___ 39633	Reading NS Heritage SD70ACe Diesel "1067," CC, 13		530
___ 39634	Reading NS Heritage SD70ACe Diesel "1833," CC, 13		530
___ 39635	Reading NS Heritage SD70ACe Diesel "1836," nonpowered, 13		260
___ 39636	Savannah & Atlanta NS Heritage SD70ACe Diesel "1065," CC, 13		530
___ 39637	Savannah & Atlanta NS Heritage SD70ACe Diesel "1915," CC, 13		530
___ 39638	Savannah & Atlanta NS Heritage SD70ACe "1918," dummy, 13		260
___ 39639	Virginian NS Heritage SD70ACe Diesel "1069," CC, 13		530
___ 39640	Virginian NS Heritage SD70ACe Diesel "1907," CC, 13		530
___ 39641	Virginian NS Heritage SD70ACe Diesel "1910," nonpowered, 13		260
___ 39642	Wabash NS Heritage SD70ACe Diesel "1070," CC, 13		530
___ 39643	Wabash NS Heritage SD70ACe Diesel "1877," CC, 13		530
___ 39644	Wabash NS Heritage SD70ACe Diesel "1880," nonpowered, 13		260
___ 39645	PC NS Heritage SD70ACe Diesel "1073," CC, 13		530
___ 39646	PC NS Heritage SD70ACe Diesel "1968," CC, 13		530
___ 39647	PC NS Heritage SD70ACe Diesel "1971," nonpowered, 13		260
___ 39680	Wizard of Oz 4-4-2 Atlantic Locomotive, 09		150
___ 51000	MILW Hiawatha Streamlined Steam Passenger Set, 88		700
___ 51008	CB&Q Pioneer Zephyr Diesel Passenger Set, RailSounds, 04	350	863
___ 51009	Prewar "269E" Steam Freight Set, TrainSounds, 06		630
___ 51010	Prewar "246E" Steam Passenger Set, TrainSounds, 07-08		630
___ 51012	Christmas Tinplate Freight Set, 08		675
___ 51014	Prewar "291W" Red Comet Passenger Car Set, 08	410	675
___ 51220	NYC Imperial Castle Passenger Coach, 93 u		500
___ 51221	NYC Niagara County Passenger Coach, 93 u		500
___ 51222	NYC Cascade Glory Passenger Coach, 93 u		500
___ 51223	NYC City of Detroit Passenger Coach, 93 u		500
___ 51224	NYC Imperial Falls Passenger Coach, 93 u		500
___ 51225	NYC Westchester County Passenger Coach, 93 u		500
___ 51226	NYC Cascade Grotto Passenger Coach, 93 u		500
___ 51227	NYC City of Indianapolis Passenger Coach, 93 u		500

		Exc	Mint
51228	NYC Manhattan Island Observation Car, 93 u		500
51229	NYC Diner "680," 93 u		500
51230	NYC Baggage Car "5017," 93 u		500
51231	NYC Century Club Passenger Coach, 93 u		500
51232	NYC Thousand Islands Observation Car, 93 u		500
51233	NYC Diner "684," 93 u		500
51234	NYC Baggage Car "5020," 93 u		500
51235	NYC Century Tavern Passenger Coach, 93 u		500
51236	NYC City of Toledo Passenger Coach, 93 u		500
51237	NYC Imperial Mansion Passenger Coach, 93 u		500
51238	NYC Imperial Palace Passenger Coach, 93 u		500
51239	NYC Cascade Spirit Passenger Coach, 93 u		500
51240	NYC Diner "681," 93 u		500
51241	NYC City of Chicago Passenger Coach, 93 u		500
51242	NYC Imperial Garden Passenger Coach, 93 u		500
51243	NYC Imperial Fountain Passenger Coach, 93 u		500
51244	NYC Cascade Valley Passenger Coach, 93 u		500
51245	NYC Diner "685," 93 u		500
51300	Shell Semi-Scale 1-D Tank Car "8124," 91	50	135
51301	Lackawanna Semi-Scale Reefer "7000," 92	119	161
51401	PRR Semi-Scale Boxcar "100800," 91	84	128
51402	C&O Semi-Scale Stock Car "95250," 92	98	138
51422	Southern Searchlight Car, 91-92	15	36
51501	B&O Semi-Scale Hopper "532000," 91	78	108
51502	LL Steel Die-cast Ore Car "6486-3" (SSS), 96		80
51503	LL Steel Die-cast Ore Car "6486-1" (SSS), 96		80
51504	LL Steel Die-cast Ore Car "6486-2" (SSS), 96		70
51600	NYC Depressed Center Flatcar with transformer "6418," 96		105
51701	NYC Semi-Scale Caboose "19400," 91	84	123
51702	PRR N-8 Caboose "478039," 91-92	300	385
52038	Southern Hopper "360794" w/Coal (std O), 94 u	36	46
52040	GTW Flatcar w/Tractor and trailer, 94 u	42	51
52044	Mogen David Wine Vat Car, 95 u	21	30
52053	TTOS Carail Convention Boxcar, 94 u	50	55
52054	Carail Boxcar, 94 u		300
52066	Trainmaster Tractor and Trailer, 94 u	80	125
52068	Toy Train Parade Contadina Boxcar "16245," 94	15	28
52069	Carail Tractor and Trailer, 94 u		75
52070	Knoebel Boxcar #1, 95 u		92
52075	United Auto Workers Boxcar, 95 u		90
52082	Steamtown Lackawanna Boxcar, 95 u		90
52096	Snow Village Boxcar "9756," 95 u	55	85
52126	MILW Boxcar "21027" with CTT Logo, 97 u		50
52132	Knoebel Boxcar #2, 99 u		95
52133	Knoebel Boxcar #3, 98 u		108
52134	Knoebel Boxcar #4, 00 u		100
52136A	Christmas Special Tractor and Trailer, 97 u		100
52136B	Frisco Special Tractor and Trailer, 98 u		100
52137	Red Wing Shoes Boot Oil Tank Car, 98		65
52141	Zep Manufacturing Boxcar, 96	81	127
52158	Monopoly Mint Car "M-0539," 98		340
52159	Monopoly Depressed Center Flatcar with transformer, 98		95
52160	Monopoly Water Works Tank Car, 98		105

	MODERN 1970-2023	Exc	Mint
___	52161 Monopoly SP-type Caboose "M-1006," 98		55
___	52168 Carail Flatcar with Trailer "17455," 99 u		120
___	52169 Zep Manufacturing Flatcar with trailer "62734," 99 u		90
___	52181 Monopoly Set #2, 4-pack, 99		295
___	52182 Monopoly Railroads Boxcar "M0636," 99 u		78
___	52183 Monopoly Jail Car "M-1131," 99		75
___	52184 Monopoly Free Parking Flatcar with 2 autos, 99		60
___	52185 Monopoly Chance Gondola "M-0893," 99		50
___	52187 Madison Hardware Flatcar with 2 trailers, 99		98
___	52188 Carail Aquarium with 2 autos, 25th Anniversary, 99		95
___	52189 Monopoly 4-6-4 Hudson Locomotive, 99	300	555
___	52200 TTOS SW SP Overnight Merchandise Service Boxcar, 00 u		40
___	52207 Lionel Lines SD40 Diesel, traditional, 00		600
___	52208 Lionel Lines Extended Vision Caboose, 00 u		200
___	52218 Monopoly 4-4-2 Steam Freight Set, 00 u		394
___	52219 Monopoly 4-6-4 Hudson Locomotive, bronze, 00 u		530
___	52224A SP Flatcar with Navajo tractor and trailer, 01		25
___	52224B SP Flatcar with Trailer Flatcar Service tractor and trailer, 01		25
___	52225 Monopoly 4-6-4 Hudson Locomotive, pewter, 01 u		495
___	52231 British Columbia 1-D Tank Car, 00 u		65
___	52249 Knoebel's Amusement Park 75th Anniversary Boxcar, 01 u		100
___	52262 Plasticville Boxcar, 01 u		120
___	52282 Western Pacific Feather Boxcar, red, 03		365
___	52315/20 PRR FM Diesel and Caboose, 04 u		440
___	52330 B&O Museum Fundraiser Boxcar, 03 u		100
___	52334 TTOS Smokey Bear 60th Anniversary 1-D Tank Car, 04 u		80
___	52335 TTOS Smokey Bear 60th Anniversary Boxcar, 04 u		70
___	52371 NYC Flatcar with tanker trailer, 05 u		150
___	52435 Georgia Power Caboose, 08 u		26
___	52447 LCCA NH Alco Diesel and Passenger Cars, 09 u		100
___	52452 Grzybowski Trains 30th Anniversary Boxcar, 07 u		39
___	52495 LCCA UP Water Tower, 08 u		30
___	52597 U.S. Navy Flatcar w/trailer, "832011," 11		60
___	55452 Norscot Caterpillar Steam Freight Set, 08 u	270	325
___	58032 CTT 30th Anniversary Boxcar "69013," 17 u		50
___	58213 LCCA B&M GP7 Diesel, 15 u		250
___	58253 LCCA Lionel 115th Anniversary Trailer, 15 u		25
___	58255 LCCA Lionelville Transit Tractor, 15 u		25
___	58262 U.S. Coast Guard Flatcar w/trailer "832011," 11 u		60
___	58267 LCCA KCS Inspection Truck, 16 u		125
___	58269 LCCA Tacoma Pickup Truck, 17 u		75
___	58270 LCCA NP Pickup Truck, 17 u		75
___	58504 Lionel Flatcar w/Madison Hardware Trailer, 15 u		120
___	58510 TCA Frisco Flatcar w/trailer "100011," 11 u		75
___	58513 LCCA Reading Blue Coal 2-bay Hopper w/ETD, 12 u		75
___	58515 LCCA NS Vulcan Switcher, 12 u		50
___	58517 NLOE LIRR Alco Diesels, 13 u		300
___	58522 TCA Los Alamos Mint Car, 16 u		75
___	58526 TCA Cumbres & Toltec Boxcar, 16 u		75
___	58527 LCCA Vulcan Switcher, 13 u		80
___	58528 LCCA Reading Vulcan Switcher, 14 u		80
___	58539 LCCA Texas Special Bay-Window Caboose, 13 u		95
___	58545 LCCA Vulcan Switcher, Gold, 12 u		75

58550	LCCA Texas Special Unibody Tank Car, 13 u		90 ___
58585	LCCA Wabash Auto Loader, 14 u		125 ___
58586	LCCA South Shore Trolley, 14 u		95 ___
58598	TCA Philly Pretzel Boxcar, 14 u		80 ___
58599	LCCA UP Cylindrical Hopper, 11 u		150 ___
59002	LCCA TVRM Boxcar, 13 u		150 ___
59015	LCCA Conway Scenic RR Boxcar, 15 u		200 ___
62162	Postwar "262" Automatic Crossing Gate and Signal, 99-14		60 ___
62180	Railroad Signs, set of 14, 99-04, 08-23		10 ___
62181	Telephone Pole Set, 10-pack, 99-04, 08-23		15 ___
62283	Die-cast Illuminated Bumpers, 99-17		27 ___
62709	Rico Station Kit, 99-00		46 ___
62716	Short Extension Bridge, 99-03, 07-23		15 ___
62900	Lockon, 99-13		3 ___
62901	Ives Track Clips, 12 pieces (O27), 99-10, 13-16		5 ___
62905	Lockon with wires, 99-10, 13-14		7 ___
62909	Smoke Fluid, 99-12		7 ___
62927	Lubrication/Maintenance Set, 99-23		25 ___
62985	The Lionel Train Book, 99-03		12 ___
65014	Half Curved Track (O27), 99-16		1 ___
65019	Half Straight Track (O27), 99-16		1 ___
65020	90-degree Crossover (O27), 99-16		11 ___
65021	27" Manual Switch, left hand (O27), 99-16		17 ___
65022	27" Manual Switch, right hand (O27), 99-16		18 ___
65023	45-degree Crossover (O27), 99-16		11 ___
65024	35" Straight Track (O27), 99-16		5 ___
65033	27" Diameter Curved Track (O27), 99-16		2 ___
65038	9" Straight Track (O27), 99-16		2 ___
65041	Insulator Pins, dozen (O27), 99-04, 06, 13-14		3 ___
65042	Steel Pins, dozen (O27), 99-04, 06-09, 13-14		3 ___
65049	42" Diameter Curved Track (O27), 99-16		3 ___
65113	54" Diameter Curved Track (O27), 99-16		3 ___
65121	27" Path Remote Switch, left hand (O27), 99-14		43 ___
65122	27" Path Remote Switch, right hand (O27), 99-14		43 ___
65149	Uncoupling Track (O27), 99-14		12 ___
65165	72" Path Remote Switch, right hand (O), 99-14		125 ___
65166	72" Path Remote Switch, left hand (O), 99-14		125 ___
65167	42" Remote Switch, right hand (O27), 99-14		25 ___
65168	42" Remote Switch, left hand (O27), 99-14		25 ___
65500	10" Straight Track (O), 99-16		2 ___
65501	31" Diameter Curved Track (O), 99-16		2 ___
65504	Half Curved Track (O), 99-16		2 ___
65505	Half Straight Track (O), 99-16		2 ___
65514	Half Curved Track (O27), 99-03		3 ___
65523	40" Straight Track (O), 99-16		7 ___
65530	Remote Control Track (O), 99-16		38 ___
65540	90-degree Crossover (O), 99-14		16 ___
65543	Insulator Pins, dozen (O), 99-16		3 ___
65545	45-degree Crossover (O), 99-14		27 ___
65551	Steel Pins, dozen (O), 99-16		3 ___
65554	54" Diameter Curved Track (O), 99-16		4 ___
65572	72" Diameter Curved Track (O), 99-16		5 ___
65824	NLOE LIRR Hopper w/Coal load, 17u		95 ___

			Exc	Mint
___	68677	Frisco Flatcar w/trailer "832013," 98 u		45
___	71998	LCCA Amtrak Refrigerator Car (Std O), 10 u		45
___	81000	BNSF Waffle-sided Boxcar "496464," 14-15		50
___	81001	SP&S Flatcar with bulkheads, 14-16		50
___	81002	UP 3-D Tank Car, 14-15		50
___	81003	CP Bilevel Auto Carrier, 14-16		50
___	81004	B&O Depressed-Center Flatcar with transformer, 14-15		50
___	81005	Maine Central 2-bay Hopper "1005," 14-16		50
___	81006	PRR Hi-Cube Boxcar "31010," 14-16		50
___	81007	Seaboard Waffle-sided Boxcar "25335," 14-16		50
___	81008	Central of Georgia Boxcar "5818," 14-17		50
___	81009	Southern 2-D Tank Car "951005," 14-16		50
___	81010	FEC Gondola "6121" with reels, 14-16		50
___	81011	PFE Reefer "33280," 14-16		50
___	81012	T&P 1-D Tank Car , 14-16		50
___	81013	Frisco Boxcar "700117," 14-16		50
___	81014	D&RGW Ore Car "31101," 14-15		50
___	81015	B&M Reefer "1878," 14-16		50
___	81016	Coaling Station, 14, 16-20		110
___	81017	Barrel Loading Building, 14-18		43
___	81018	Shell Vat Car, 17		80
___	81019	Short Tunnel, 14-16-17		45
___	81021	B&M Paul Revere GP9 Diesel Freight Set, 14-15		500
___	81023	Jersey Central Yard Boss 0-4-0 Steam Freight Set, 14-15		500
___	81024	Christmas Train Set, 02-04		150
___	81025	Lackawanna Pocono Berkshire Steam Freight Set, 14-15		480
___	81027	Thomas the Tank Engine Set, 01-04		120
___	81028	Pere Marquette GP38 Diesel Freight Set, 14-15		430
___	81029	C&NW Windy City GP38 Diesel Freight Set, 14-15		400
___	81030	UP Gold Coast Flyer Steam Freight Set, 14-15		455
___	81031	Dinosaur Diesel Freight Set, LionChief, 14-16		175
___	81038	MILW 2-8-2 Heavy Mikado Locomotive "8693" CC, 15	588	1300
___	81063	Classic Automatic Gateman, 14-23		130
___	81064	Construction Zone Signs #2, 14-19		10
___	81066	Milwaukee Road Double-sheathed Boxcar "8775" (std O), 14	33	83
___	81067	Monopoly Aquarium Car, 14-15		85
___	81073	Monopoly Boxcar 2-pack, Ventnor and Indiana Avenues, 14-15		135
___	81076	Pennsylvania Salt 8,000-gallon 1-D Tank Car "4724" (std O), 14		73
___	81077	Pere Marquette 8,000-gallon 1-D Tank Car "71710" (std O), 14		73
___	81078	NYC 8,000-gallon 1-D Tank Car "107898" (std O), 14		73
___	81079	NKP 8,000-gallon 1-D Tank Car "50277" (std O), 14		73
___	81080	BN 8,000-gallon 1-D Tank Car "977100" (std O), 14		73
___	81081	Alaska Steel-sided Reefer "10806" (std O), 14		80
___	81090	NS Hi-Cube Boxcar 2-pack (std O), 14-15		190
___	81093	2013 Lionel Dealer Appreciation Boxcar, 13 u		40
___	81094	Conrail "Big Blue" High-Cube Boxcar Diesel Freight Set, CC, 14		970
___	81095	Conrail Hi-Cube Boxcar 2-pack (std O), 14-16		190
___	81101	Polar Express 10th Anniversary Steam Passenger Set, 14-15		430
___	81113	SP 50' DD Boxcar "214051" (std O), 14-15		75
___	81122	Christmas Inspection Truck, 15		180
___	81134	BN SD70MAC Diesel "9424," CC, 14		550
___	81135	BN SD70MAC Diesel "9431," CC, 14		550
___	81137	BNSF SD70MAC Diesel "9858," CC, 14		550

		Exc	Mint
81138	BNSF SD70MAC Diesel "9860," CC, 14		550 ___
81141	Conrail SD70MAC Diesel "4138," CC, 14		550 ___
81142	PFE Steel-sided Reefers 3-pack (std O), 14		300 ___
81144	CSX SD70MAC Diesel "781," CC, 14		550 ___
81147	KCS SD7CMAC Diesel "3950," CC, 14		550 ___
81148	KCS SD7CMAC Diesel "3953," CC, 14		550 ___
81151	Alaska SD7CMAC Diesel "4002," CC, 14		550 ___
81152	Alaska SD7CMAC Diesel "4005," CC, 14		550 ___
81153	CSX SD70MAC Diesel "778," CC, 14		550 ___
81154	UP ES44AC Diesel "7361," CC, 14		550 ___
81155	UP ES44AC Diesel "7388," CC, 14		550 ___
81160	CSX ES44AC Diesel "937," CC, 14		550 ___
81161	CSX ES44AC Diesel "944," CC, 14		550 ___
81169	Iowa Interstate ES44AC Diesel "504," CC, 14		550 ___
81170	Iowa Interstate ES44AC Diesel "507," CC, 14		550 ___
81171	Ferromex ES44AC Diesel "4617," CC, 14		550 ___
81172	Ferromex ES44AC Diesel "4626," CC, 14		550 ___
81176	CN ES44AC Diesel "2812," CC, 14		550 ___
81177	CN ES44AC Diesel "2818," CC, 14		550 ___
81179	2-8-2 Heavy Mikado Pilot Locomotive, CC, 14		1300 ___
81180	2-8-2 Heavy Mikado Locomotive, CC, 15		1300 ___
81181	Southern 2-8-2 Heavy Mikado Locomotive "4866," CC, 15		1300 ___
81182	L&N 2-8-2 Heavy Mikado Locomotive "1757," CC, 14		1300 ___
81183	MP 2-8-2 Heavy Mikado Locomotive "1496," CC, 14		1300 ___
81184	P&WV 2-8-2 Heavy Mikado Locomotive "1152," CC, 14		1300 ___
81185	CNJ 2-8-2 Heavy Mikado Locomotive "845," CC, 14		1300 ___
81186	Frisco 2-8-2 Heavy Mikado Locomotive "4126," CC, 14		1300 ___
81187	C&IM 2-8-2 Heavy Mikado Locomotive "551," CC, 14		1300 ___
81188	NYC 2-8-2 Heavy Mikado Locomotive "9506," CC, 14		1300 ___
81189	CB&Q 2-8-2 Heavy Mikado Locomotive "5509," CC, 15		1300 ___
81190	WP 2-8-2 Heavy Mikado Locomotive "334," CC, 15		1300 ___
81191	Erie 2-8-2 Heavy Mikado Locomotive "3207," CC, 15		1300 ___
81192	GN 2-8-2 Heavy Mikado Locomotive "3148," CC, 14		1300 ___
81193	Wheeling & Lake Erie 2-8-2 Heavy Mikado "6012," CC, 15		1300 ___
81194	NKP 2-8-2 Heavy Mikado Locomotive "689," CC, 15		1300 ___
81195	PRR Boxcar, 14-15		70 ___
81196	Timken Boxcar, 14-15		70 ___
81197	Santa Fe Boxcar, 14-15		70 ___
81198	GN Boxcar, 14-16		70 ___
81199	PRR 1-D Tank Car, 14-15		70 ___
81200	Timken 1-D Tank Car, 14-16		70 ___
81201	GN 1-D Tank Car, 14-16		70 ___
81202	Santa Fe 1-D Tank Car, 14-15		70 ___
81203	PRR Flatcar, 14-15		70 ___
81204	Santa Fe Flatcar, 14-16		70 ___
81205	Timken Flatcar, 14-16		70 ___
81206	GN Flatcar, 14-16		70 ___
81207	CP H-24-66 Train Master Diesel "8900," CC, 14		550 ___
81208	CP H-24-66 Train Master Diesel "8903," CC, 14		550 ___
81209	CNJ H-24-66 Train Master Diesel "2401," CC, 14		550 ___
81210	CNJ H-24-66 Train Master Diesel "2406," CC, 14		550 ___
81211	Reading H-24-66 Train Master Diesel "801," CC, 14		550 ___
81212	Reading H-24-66 Train Master Diesel "804," CC, 14		550 ___

		Exc	Mint
___ 81213	SP H-24-66 Train Master Diesel "4803," CC, 14		550
___ 81214	SP H-24-66 Train Master Diesel "4809," CC, 14		550
___ 81215	Southern H-24-66 Train Master Diesel "6300," CC, 14		550
___ 81216	Southern H-24-66 Train Master Diesel "6303," CC, 14		550
___ 81217	N&W H-24-66 Train Master Diesel "151," CC, 14		550
___ 81218	N&W H-24-66 Train Master Diesel "164," CC, 14		550
___ 81219	Santa Fe E8 Diesel AA Set "84/85," CC, 14		930
___ 81222	PC E8 Diesel AA Set "4289/4325," CC, 14		930
___ 81225	RI E8 Diesel AA Set "647/648," CC, 14		930
___ 81228	C&O E8 Diesel AA Set "4027/4028," CC, 14		930
___ 81231	Erie E8 Diesel AA Set "822/823," CC, 14		930
___ 81234	MKT E8 Diesel AA Set "131/132," CC, 14		930
___ 81237	SAL E8 Diesel AA Set "3051/3055," CC, 14		930
___ 81240	Wabash E8 Diesel AA Set "1007/1011," CC, 14		930
___ 81243	Pilot M1a 4-8-2 Locomotive, CC, 14		1500
___ 81245	PRR M1a 4-8-2 Locomotive "6671," CC, 14		1500
___ 81246	PRR M1a 4-8-2 Locomotive "6764," CC, 14		1500
___ 81247	PRR M1a Coal Hauler Twin-hopper Steam Freight Set, CC, 14		1800
___ 81248	10" Girder Bridge Track, 14-23		25
___ 81249	Christmas Girder Bridge Track, 14, 16-18		25
___ 81250	FasTrack O-96 Curve, 14-23		8
___ 81251	FasTrack O-31 Manual Switch, right-hand, 14-23		55
___ 81252	FasTrack O-31 Manual Switch, left-hand, 14-23		55
___ 81253	FasTrack O-31 Remote Switch, right-hand, 14-23		130
___ 81254	FasTrack O-31 Remote Switch, left-hand, 14-23		130
___ 81256	Personalized Birthday Message Boxcar, 14-15		85
___ 81257	Amtrak Water Tower, 14-18		35
___ 81259	PRR Broadway Limited Steam Passenger Set, 14		370
___ 81261	NYC Early Bird Special Steam Freight Set, 16-17		380
___ 81262	UP Steam Freight Set, LionChief, 15		400
___ 81263	CNJ Diesel Passenger Set, LionChief, 14-16		390
___ 81264	Western Union Telegraph Steam Freight Set, 14-16		390
___ 81266	Amtrak FT Diesel Passenger Set, LionChief, 14-15		460
___ 81269	PRR Allegheny Hauler Steam Freight Set, 16-17		420
___ 81270	Bethlehem Steel Steam Work Train, LionChief, 15		340
___ 81279	Albert Hall European Steam Passenger Set, LionChief, 14-15		430
___ 81280	Victorian Christmas Steam Passenger Set, 14		400
___ 81284	Frosty the Snowman Steam Freight Set, LionChief, 14-16		320
___ 81286	Lionel Junction "Little Steam" Freight Set, 14-15		175
___ 81287	Lionel Junction UP Steam Freight Set, 14-15		175
___ 81288	Pet Shop Diesel Freight Set, 14-16		175
___ 81290	Thomas Kinkade Holiday Covered Bridge, 14		70
___ 81292	Valley Central 1-D Tank Car "45003," 14-17		45
___ 81294	LCS FasTrack IR Sensor Track, 13-23		100
___ 81295	AT&SF 2-8-2 Locomotive "3158," LionChief, 14-16		430
___ 81296	GN 2-8-2 Locomotive "3123," LionChief, 14-15		430
___ 81297	PRR 2-8-2 Locomotive "9633," LionChief, 14-15		430
___ 81299	Chessie System 2-8-2 Locomotive "2103," LionChief, 14-15		430
___ 81301	NYC 4-6-4 Locomotive "5421," LionChief, 14-15		430
___ 81302	C&O 4-6-4 Locomotive "308," LionChief, 14-17		430
___ 81303	UP 4-6-4 Locomotive "674," LionChief, 14-17		430
___ 81304	CN 4-6-4 Locomotive "5702," LionChief, 14-17		430
___ 81307	B&O 4-6-2 Locomotive "5307," LionChief, 14-17		430

81308	CP 4-6-2 Locomotive "2469," LionChief, 14-17		430 ___
81309	SP 4-6-2 Locomotive "3106," LionChief, 14-17		430 ___
81311	Alaska 4-6-2 Locomotive "652," LionChief, 14-17		430 ___
81313	FasTrack Power Lockon, 15-23		25 ___
81314	FasTrack Power Block Lockon, 15-23		44 ___
81315	Coaling Station, 15-17, 19-20		160 ___
81316	Personalized Christmas Message Boxcar, 15		80 ___
81317	FasTrack Accessory Activator Track Pack, 15-23		27 ___
81325	LCS WiFi Module, 13-16, 18-20		180 ___
81326	LCS Serial Converter #2, 14-23		70 ___
81331	Iron Arry Locomotive with Remote, LionChief, 14-15		140 ___
81332	Iron Bert Locomotive with Remote, LionChief, 14-15		140 ___
81373	Candy Cane Flatcar with bulkheads, 15		60 ___
81395	Thomas Kinkade Christmas Passenger Set, LionChief, 14-15		380 ___
81419	Alien Ooze 1-D Tank Car, 14-15		65 ___
81420	PRR Truss-rod Gondola with tarp, 14-16		65 ___
81422	NS Water Tower, 14		31 ___
81423	Sodor Coal and Scrap Cars 2-pack, 14-16		70 ___
81424	Sodor Crane Car and Work Caboose 2-pack, 14		70 ___
81425	Frosty the Snowman Passenger Station, 14		65 ___
81426	Frosty the Snowman Animated Gondola, 14		75 ___
81427	Frosty the Snowman Aquarium Car, 14		85 ___
81428	Frosty the Snowman Boxcar, 14		65 ___
81430	Lionelville Shanty, 14		22 ___
81432	PRR Girder Bridge, 14-15		21 ___
81433	PRR Crossing Shanty, 14		22 ___
81434	Pennsylvania Station Platform, 14-15		23 ___
81435	N&W NS Heritage Quad Hopper with coal, 14-15		60 ___
81436	Intermodal Container 4-pack, 14		43 ___
81437	York Peppermint Patty Vat Car, 14-15		70 ___
81439	Halloween Pumpkinheads Handcar, 14-16		90 ___
81440	Western Union Handcar, 14-16		100 ___
81441	North Pole Central Snowplow, CC , 16-18, 20		280 ___
81442	PRR Rotary Snowplow "1442," CC, 16, 18		280 ___
81443	D&RGW Rotary Snowplow "443," CC, 16, 18		280 ___
81444	PRR Tie-Jector, CC, 14-16		200 ___
81445	MOW Tie-Jector, CC, 14-16		200 ___
81446	Santa Fe Tie-Jector, CC, 14-16, 18		200 ___
81447	NS Tie-Jector, CC, 14-16		200 ___
81448	Amtrak Tie-Jector, CC, 14-16, 18		200 ___
81449	Zombie Motorized Trolley, 14		100 ___
81450	Polar Express Trolley, 14		110 ___
81451	St. Louis Motorized Trolley, 14		100 ___
81452	Neil Young Texas Special F3 AA Diesels, CC, 13-14		650 ___
81453	Neil Young PRR F3 AA Diesels, CC, 13-14		650 ___
81462	PRR Broadway Limited Add-on Baggage Car, 14-17		70 ___
81463	CNJ Water Tower, 14-17		31 ___
81464	CNJ Montclair Add-on Passenger Car, 14-16		60 ___
81465	SP Flatcar with piggyback trailers, 14-16		75 ___
81466	BN Maxi-Stack Pair, 14		140 ___
81469	GN Bilevel Stock Car "65385," 14-17		65 ___
81470	DC Comics Batman Phantom Train, 16-17		400 ___
81475	DC Comics Batman M7 Subway Set, LionChief, 14-15		370 ___

		Exc	Mint
____ 81479	Batman Add-on M7 Subway Car 2-pack, 14-15		140
____ 81480	John Deere RS-3 Diesel Freight Set, LionChief, 14-16	128	325
____ 81486	NYC Patrol Flatcar with helicopter, 14-15		65
____ 81487	Ronald Reagan Presidential Boxcar, 14-15		70
____ 81488	Andrew Jackson Presidential Boxcar, 14-16, 18		70
____ 81489	Warren G. Harding Presidential Boxcar, 14-16, 18, 20		75
____ 81490	Dwight D. Eisenhower Presidential Boxcar, 14-16		70
____ 81491	Jersey Central Coal Dump Car, 14-15		65
____ 81492	Strasburg RR Searchlight Car, 14		50
____ 81493	U.S.A.F. Missile Carrying Car, 15-16		65
____ 81494	Santa's Sleigh Rocket Fuel Tank Car, 16		65
____ 81495	40-watt Power Supply, 15-18		65
____ 81496	2014 Lionel Dealer Appreciation Boxcar, 14 u		40
____ 81497	2015 Lionel Dealer Appreciation Boxcar, 15 u		40
____ 81499	LCS Power Supply with DB9 cable, 13-16, 18-20		37
____ 81500	LCS PDI Sensor Track 1' Cable, 13-23		15
____ 81501	LCS PDI Sensor Track 3' Cable, 13-22		16
____ 81502	LCS PDI Sensor Track 10' Cable, 13-23		20
____ 81503	LCS PDI Sensor Track 20' Cable, 13-22		20
____ 81504	Ann Arbor FA-2 Diesel AA Set "53/53A," CC, 14		750
____ 81507	B&O FA-2 Diesel AA Set "817/827," CC, 14-15		750
____ 81510	Erie FA-2 Diesel AA Set "736A/736D," CC, 14-15		750
____ 81513	MKT FA-2 Diesel AA Set "331A/331C," CC, 14		750
____ 81516	NYC FA-2 Diesel AA Set "1075/1078," CC, 14-15		750
____ 81519	PRR FA-2 Diesel AA Set "9608/9609," CC, 14-15		750
____ 81522	Ann Arbor FB2 Diesel "53B", CC, 14	80	450
____ 81523	B&O FB2 Diesel "817B," CC, 14-15		450
____ 81524	Erie FB2 Diesel "736B," CC, 14-15		450
____ 81525	MKT FB2 Diesel "331B," CC, 14		450
____ 81526	NYC FB2 Diesel "3327," CC, 14-15		450
____ 81527	PRR FB2 Diesel "9608B," CC, 14		450
____ 81528	Ann Arbor FB2 Diesel, nonpowered, 14		350
____ 81529	B&O FB2 Diesel, nonpowered, 14-15		350
____ 81530	Erie FB2 Diesel, nonpowered, 14-15		350
____ 81531	MKT FB2 Diesel, nonpowered, 14		350
____ 81532	NYC FB2 Diesel, nonpowered, 14-15		350
____ 81533	PRR FB2 Diesel, nonpowered, 14-15		350
____ 81534	Christmas Toys Stock Car, 14		70
____ 81545	Operation Eagle Missile Launcher Car, CC, 15		350
____ 81546	Operation Eagle Sound Car, CC, 15		240
____ 81568	4th of July Parade Boxcar, 14-16		80
____ 81596	Weathered UP 4-12-2 Locomotive "9000," CC, 13		1400
____ 81597	Weathered B&O RF-16 Sharknose AA Diesels "855-857," CC, 13		830
____ 81600	Weathered PRR RF-16 Sharknose AA Diesels "2020A-2021A," CC, 13		830
____ 81603	72-watt Power Supply, LionChief, 14-23		60
____ 81605	Santa Fe PS-1 Boxcar 5-pack (std O), 14		380
____ 81615	UP 1-D Tank Car, 14		45
____ 81617	Pet Shop 1-D Tank Car, 14-16		45
____ 81619	Reading PS-1 Boxcar "109448" (std O), 14		80
____ 81620	Zombie Figure Pack, 14-15		23
____ 81621	John Deere Billboard Set, 15		25
____ 81622	John Deere Water Tower, 15		40

		Exc	Mint
81625	Amtrak Add-on Baggage Car, 14-16		85 ___
81626	Barrel Shed, 14-16, 18-20		40 ___
81627	Christmas Hopper Shed, 14, 16-17		45 ___
81628	Grain Elevator, 15		80 ___
81629	Lumber Shed Kit, 14-23		35 ___
81635	Water Tower, 14		35 ___
81639	LCS Accessory Switch Controller #2, 14-23		130 ___
81640	LCS Block Power Controller #2, 14-23		130 ___
81641	LCS Accessory Motor Controller, 17-23		130 ___
81644	Chessie System Baby Madison Passenger Car 3-pack, 14-16		270 ___
81649	SP Baby Madison Passenger Car 3-pack, 14-16		270 ___
81654	Philadelphia Energy Solutions 1-D Tank Car "0765," 15-18		60 ___
81662	FasTrack O-31 Quarter Curved Track, 14-23		5 ___
81668	Philadelphia Energy Solutions 1-D Tank Car "0771," 15-16, 18		60 ___
81680	Dinosaur 1-D Tank Car, 14-16		45 ___
81686	PRR GL-a 2-bay Hopper 3-pack (std O), 14		220 ___
81687	LV GL-a 2-bay Hopper 2-pack (std O), 14-15		146 ___
81688	CB&Q GL-a 2-bay Hopper 3-pack (std O), 14-16		220 ___
81689	C&O GL-a 2-bay Hopper 3-pack (std O), 14-16		220 ___
81693	Aerial Target Launcher, 15-16		90 ___
81699	Polar Express Scale Twin Hopper, 15		80 ___
81703	Santa Fe Hi-Cube Boxcar 2-pack (std O), 14-16		190 ___
81704	Grand Trunk Hi-Cube Boxcar 2-pack (std O), 14-16		190 ___
81705	Milwaukee Road Hi-Cube Boxcar 2-pack (std O), 14-16		190 ___
81706	Frisco Hi-Cube Boxcar 2-pack (std O), 14-16		190 ___
81707	NYC Hi-Cube Boxcar 2-pack (std O), 14-16		190 ___
81708	Santa Fe Hi-Cube Boxcar "36715" (std O), 14-15		95 ___
81710	Milwaukee Road Hi-Cube Boxcar "4980" (std O), 14-15		95 ___
81711	Frisco Hi-Cube Boxcar "9125" (std O), 14-15		95 ___
81712	NYC Hi-Cube Boxcar "67282" (std O), 14-15		95 ___
81723	Postwar "3413" Mercury Capsule Launcher Car, 15		80 ___
81725	UP Operating Merchandise Car, 14-15		68 ___
81726	REA Operating Merchandise Car, 14-15		80 ___
81729	Great Western Passenger Car Add-on 2-pack, 14		130 ___
81733	Christmas Boxcar, 14		65 ___
81734	FasTrack Oval Track and Power Pack, 14-17		200 ___
81735	FasTrack Figure-8 Track and Power Pack, 14-17		250 ___
81736	Classic Lionel Catalogs Billboard Pack, 14-15		13 ___
81737	Passenger Station, 14-15		60 ___
81738	Lionel Auto Loader Cars 4-pack, 14-15, 17		25 ___
81739	Santa Fe Baby Madison Passenger Car 3-pack, 14-16		270 ___
81744	CP Baby Madison Passenger Car 3-pack, 14-16		270 ___
81749	Pullman Baby Madison Passenger Car 3-pack, 14-16		270 ___
81754	NYC Baby Madison Passenger Car 3-pack, 14-16		270 ___
81759	NYC Coach/Diner 2-pack, 14-16		180 ___
81760	NYC Coach/Baggage Car 2-pack, 14-16		180 ___
81763	Pullman Baby Madison Passenger Car 3-pack, 14-16		180 ___
81764	Pullman Coach/Baggage Car 2-pack, 14, 16		180 ___
81768	Chessie System Coach/Diner 2-pack, 14-16		180 ___
81769	Chessie System Coach/Baggage Car 2-pack, 14-16		180 ___
81773	SP Coach/Diner 2-pack, 14-16		180 ___
81774	SP Coach/Baggage Car 2-pack, 14-16		180 ___
81778	Santa Fe Coach/Diner 2-pack, 14-16		180 ___

		Exc	Mint
81779	Santa Fe Coach/Baggage Car 2-pack, 14-16		180
81783	CP Coach/Diner 2-pack, 14-16		180
81784	CP Coach/Baggage Car 2-pack, 14-16		180
81789	NH GL-a 2-bay Hopper 2-pack (std O), 14-16		146
81793	Berwind GL-a 2-bay Hopper 3-pack (std O), 14-15		220
81800	Southern 18" Aluminum Observation/Coach, 2-pack (std O), 14		320
81801	Southern 18" Combination/Vista Dome Car, 2-pack (std O), 14		320
81806	PRR N5b Caboose "477814" (std O), 14		95
81807	Conrail N5b Caboose "22882" (std O), 14-15		95
81808	PC N5b Caboose "22802" (std O), 14-16		95
81809	LIRR N5b Caboose "2" (std O), 14-15		95
81810	Lionel Lines N5b Caboose "1402" (std O), 14-16		95
81811	Polar Express N5b Caboose, 16		95
81812	RI 18" Aluminum Observation/Coach Car, 2-pack (std O), 14		320
81813	RI 18" Aluminum Combination/Vista Dome Car, 2-pack (std O), 14		320
81818	C&O 18" Aluminum Observation/Coach Car, 2-pack (std O), 14		320
81819	C&O 18" Aluminum Combination/Dome Car, 2-pack (std O), 14		320
81824	P&WV GL-a 2-bay Hopper 2-pack (std O), 14-16		146
81827	PC Round-roof Boxcar "100104" (std O), 14		80
81828	GN Round-roof Boxcar "5885" (std O), 14		80
81829	WP Round-roof Boxcar "10211" (std O), 14		80
81830	MKT 18" Aluminum Observation/Coach Car, 2-pack (std O), 14		320
81831	MKT 18" Aluminum Baggage/Diner Car, 2-pack (std O), 14		320
81836	Erie Double-sheathed Boxcar "71107" (std O), 14-15		80
81837	Frisco Double-sheathed Boxcar "128528" (std O), 14-15		80
81838	CNJ Double-sheathed Boxcar "14014" (std O), 14-15		80
81839	Pacific Fright Express Steel-sided Reefer (std O), 14		80
81840	UP Ca-4 Caboose with smoke "3880" (std O), 14		90
81841	UP MOW Caboose "903224" (std O), 14		90
81842	Wabash 18" Dome-Observation/Coach Car, 2-pack (std O), 14		320
81843	Wabash 18" Aluminum Combination/Dome, 2-pack (std O), 14		320
81858	PRR GL-a 2-bay Hopper 3-pack (std O), 14		220
81862	FasTrack O-31 Curved Track 4-pack, 14-23		25
81866	RI 18" Aluminum Baggage/Diner Car, 2-pack (std O), 14		320
81869	C&O 18" Aluminum Baggage/Diner Car, 2-pack (std O), 14		320
81871	Loggers Figure Pack, 16-23		30
81872	Wabash 18" Aluminum Baggage/Diner Car, 2-pack (std O), 14		320
81875	MKT 18" Aluminum Combination/Dome Car, 2-pack (std O), 14		320
81878	Southern 18" Aluminum Baggage/Diner Car, 2-pack (std O), 14		320
81881	SP Crane Car, CC, 14-16		500
81882	DT&I Crane Car, CC, 14-16		500
81883	CSX Crane Car, CC, 14-16		500
81884	Bethlehem Steel Crane Car, CC, 14		500
81885	MOW Crane Car, CC, 14-16		500
81886	SP Boom Car, RailSounds, CC, 14-16		240
81887	DT&I Boom Car, RailSounds, CC, 14-16		240
81888	CSX Boom Car, RailSounds, CC, 14-16		240
81889	MOW Boom Car, RailSounds, CC, 14-16		240
81890	Bethlehem Steel Boom Car, RailSounds, CC, 14		240
81891	BNSF 52' Gondola "523300" with 3-piece covers (std O), 14		80
81892	Bethlehem Steel 52' Gondola "303022" with covers (std O), 14		80
81893	GTW 52' Gondola "145391" with 3-piece covers (std O), 14		80
81894	CSX 52' Gondola "709190" with 3-piece covers (std O), 14		80

No.	Description	Exc	Mint	
81895	North Pole Central 52' Gondola "128925" w/covers (std O), 14		80	___
81896	NYC PS-5 Flatcar "506266" with piggyback trailers (std O), 14		100	___
81897	MILW PS-5 Flatcar "64660" with piggyback trailers (std O), 14	43	108	___
81898	Lionel PS-5 Flatcar with piggyback trailers (std O), 14		100	___
81899	CP PS-5 Flatcar "301000" with piggyback trailers (std O), 14		100	___
81900	UP PS-5 Flatcar "258255" with piggyback trailers (std O), 14		100	___
81901	NYC Tractor and Piggyback Trailer, 14, 17		90	___
81902	Milwaukee Road Tractor and Piggyback Trailer, 14		90	___
81903	Lionel Tractor and Piggyback Trailer, 14		90	___
81904	CP Tractor and Piggyback Trailer, 14-15, 17		90	___
81905	UP Tractor and Piggyback Trailer, 14		90	___
81908	PFE Steel-sided Reefers 3-pack (std O), 14		240	___
81912	New York Yankees Boxcar, 14		70	___
81913	St. Louis Cardinals Boxcar, 14		70	___
81914	Oakland Athletics Boxcar, 14		70	___
81915	San Francisco Giants Boxcar, 14		70	___
81916	Boston Red Sox Boxcar, 14		70	___
81917	Los Angeles Dodgers Boxcar, 14		70	___
81918	Cincinnati Reds Boxcar, 14		70	___
81919	San Diego Padres Boxcar, 14		70	___
81920	Detroit Tigers Boxcar, 14		70	___
81921	Atlanta Braves Boxcar, 14		70	___
81922	Baltimore Orioles Boxcar, 14		70	___
81923	Minnesota Twins Boxcar, 14		70	___
81924	Chicago White Sox Boxcar, 14		70	___
81925	Chicago Cubs Boxcar, 14		70	___
81926	Philadelphia Phillies Boxcar, 14		70	___
81927	Cleveland Indians Boxcar, 14		70	___
81928	New York Mets Boxcar, 14		70	___
81929	Toronto Blue Jays Boxcar, 14		70	___
81930	Miami Marlins Boxcar, 14		70	___
81931	Angels Baseball Boxcar, 14		70	___
81932	Pittsburgh Pirates Boxcar, 14		70	___
81933	Texas Rangers Boxcar, 14		70	___
81934	Milwaukee Brewers Boxcar, 14		70	___
81935	Houston Astros Boxcar, 14		70	___
81936	Colorado Rockies Boxcar, 14		70	___
81937	Tampa Bay Rays Boxcar, 14		70	___
81938	Seattle Mariners Boxcar, 14		70	___
81939	Washington Nationals Boxcar, 14		70	___
81940	Arizona Diamondbacks Boxcar, 14		70	___
81941	Kansas City Royals Boxcar, 14		70	___
81944	Rotary Beacon, yellow, 14-16, 18-19		85	___
81945	Polar Express Scale Coach, 14		210	___
81946	FasTrack O-36 Remote Switch, right-hand, 14-23		130	___
81947	FasTrack O-36 Remote Switch, left-hand, 14-23		130	___
81948	FasTrack O-48 Remote Switch, right-hand, 14-23		140	___
81949	FasTrack O-48 Remote Switch, left-hand, 14-23		140	___
81950	FasTrack O-60 Remote Switch, right-hand, 14-23		140	___
81951	FasTrack O-60 Remote Switch, left-hand, 14-23		140	___
81952	FasTrack O-72 Remote Switch, right-hand, 14-23	45	130	___
81953	FasTrack O-72 Remote Switch, left-hand, 14-23		140	___
81954	FasTrack O-72 Remote Switch, wye, 14-23		140	___

		Exc	Mint
___ 81968	Halloween Pacific Fright Express Caboose (std O), 14		90
___ 81969	PRR 18" Aluminum Parlor/Coach Car, 2-pack (std O), 14-15		320
___ 81972	B&O 18" Aluminum Baggage/Sleeper Car, 2-pack (std O), 14		320
___ 81975	SP 18" Aluminum Sleeper/Coach Car, 2-pack (std O), 14-15		320
___ 81978	UP 18" Aluminum Sleeper/Coach Car, 2-pack (std O), 14-15		320
___ 81981	KCS 18" Aluminum Sleeper/Coach Car, 2-pack (std O), 14		320
___ 81984	Postwar "1887" Christmas Flatcar with reindeer, 14		70
___ 81985	Postwar "6428" Christmas Mail Car, 14		60
___ 81986	Christmas Wish 1-D Tank Car, 14		60
___ 81987	Angela Trotta Thomas "Santa's Letter" Boxcar, 14		65
___ 81988	Angela Trotta Thomas Christmas Billboard Pack, 14		15
___ 81990	Christmas Gondola with reindeer feed vats, 14		65
___ 81992	Santa Claus Bobbing Head Boxcar, 14		65
___ 81993	North Pole Central Santa Finder Searchlight Car, 14		55
___ 81999	PRR Gondola with Christmas gifts and trees, 14		65
___ 82000	PRR Christmas Crane Car, 14		75
___ 82001	Merry & Bright Hot Cocoa Car, 14		70
___ 82002	Old St. Nick Operating Billboard, 14, 16		60
___ 82003	Christmas Blinking Water Tower, 14		35
___ 82005	Christmas Wreath Clock Tower, 14, 16-17		43
___ 82008	Bungalow House, 15-17		80
___ 82009	Suburban House, 15-16		80
___ 82010	Joe's Bait & Tackle Shop, 15-16		65
___ 82011	Keystone Cafe, 15-16		80
___ 82012	Single Floodlight Tower, 15-23		80
___ 82013	Double Floodlight Tower, 15-23		90
___ 82014	Postwar "192" Control Tower, 15-16		100
___ 82015	Wind Turbine, 15-18		80
___ 82016	Oil Pump, 15-23		120
___ 82017	Lionel Art Operating Billboard, 15-20		70
___ 82018	Track Gang, 15-16		100
___ 82020	Burning Switch Tower, 15-17		130
___ 82021	Bascule Bridge, 15		450
___ 82022	Lionel Steel Gantry Crane, CC, 15-19		400
___ 82023	Operating Sawmill, CC, 15-17		350
___ 82024	Postwar "164" Log Loader, 15		340
___ 82026	Postwar "497" Coaling Station, 15-17		300
___ 82028	Postwar "352" Icing Station, 15-17		150
___ 82029	Culvert Loader, CC, 15-20		300
___ 82030	Culvert Unloader, CC, 15-20		300
___ 82033	MOW Trackside Crane, CC, 16-17, 19		600
___ 82034	Loading Station, 16		350
___ 82035	Work House, crane sounds, 16-19		150
___ 82036	Luxury Diner, 15-17		80
___ 82038	8" Female Pigtail Power Cable, 16-23		11
___ 82039	36" Male Pigtail Power Cable, 16-23		12
___ 82043	Plug-n-Play 6" 3-position Power Cable Extension, 16-23		18
___ 82045	Plug-n-Play 6" 6-position Power Cable Extension, 16-23		22
___ 82046	36" Power Tap Cable, 16-23		18
___ 82047	Lionel Lines Log Dump Car, 15-16		65
___ 82048	ATSF Ice Car, 15-17		75
___ 82049	Santa's Work Shoppe Log Dump Car, 16		65
___ 82050	Santa's Work Shoppe Sawmill, 16-20		240

		Exc	Mint
82051	North Pole Central Icing Station, 16-17		150 ___
82052	PFE Ice Car, 15-17		75 ___
82053	North Pole Central Icing Car, 16-17		75 ___
82054	Weyerhaeuser Log Dump Car, 15-17		65 ___
82055	Bethlehem Steel Trackside Crane, CC, 16-19		600 ___
82056	Operating Freight Station, 18-19		110 ___
82064	Halloween Operating Billboard , 15-19		80 ___
82066	PRR Log Dump Car, 15		65 ___
82067	Lionel Lines Coal Dump Car, 15-17		65 ___
82068	NS Coal Dump Car, 15		65 ___
82069	Conrail Coal Dump Car, 15-17		65 ___
82072	Philadelphia Quartz Hopper "755," 15-18		50 ___
82073	CN Ore Car, 15-17		50 ___
82074	SP 1-D Tank Car, 15-17		50 ___
82075	NYC Waffle-sided Boxcar, 15-17		50 ___
82076	Chessie System Gondola with containers, 16-18		50 ___
82077	D&H Hi-Cube Boxcar, 16		50 ___
82078	NP 1-D Tank Car, 16		50 ___
82079	UP Wood-sided Reefer, 16		50 ___
82080	C&NW 3-D Tank Car , 16-18		50 ___
82081	CSX Auto Carrier, 16-18		50 ___
82082	NS Flatcar with pipes, 16-18		50 ___
82083	Central of Georgia Gondola with cable reels, 16		50 ___
82084	Virginian Boxcar, 16-18		50 ___
82085	ATSF Waffle-sided Boxcar, 16-17		50 ___
82086	MKT Reefer, 16		50 ___
82087	WP Depressed Flatcar with generator, 16-18		50 ___
82088	Log Pack, 16-20		10 ___
82091	PRR Tie Work Car "82091," 14-16		75 ___
82092	MOW Tie Work Car "77," 14-16		75 ___
82093	AT&SF Tie Work Car "82093," 14-16		75 ___
82094	NS Tie Work Car "51," 14-16		75 ___
82095	Amtrak Tie Work Car "67," 14-16		75 ___
82096	Lionel Steel Culvert Gondola, 15-16		65 ___
82097	Bucyrus-Erie Gantry Crane, CC, 15-19		400 ___
82098	Bucyrus-Erie Culvert Gondola, 15		65 ___
82099	Zombie Apocalypse Survivors GP38 Freight Set, LionChief, 15		415 ___
82100	Polar Express Hero Boy's Home, 16-17		90 ___
82101	Postwar "6512" Mercury Capsule Astronaut Car, 15-16		80 ___
82102	Lumberjacks, 15-16		65 ___
82103	Playground Swing, 15-16		75 ___
82104	Playground Playtime, 15-16		100 ___
82105	Tire Swing, 15-16		100 ___
82106	Pony Ride, 15-17		75 ___
82107	Tug-of-War, 15-17		65 ___
82108	Hobo Campfire, 15		100 ___
82110	Extended Truss Bridge, 15-23		330 ___
82111	Lionel Industrial Coal 2-bay Hopper "28111," 15-17		60 ___
82112	B&M Alco S2 Diesel Switcher "1260," CC, 15		650 ___
82113	B&M Alco S2 Diesel Switcher "1263," CC, 15		650 ___
82114	CB&Q Alco S2 Diesel Switcher "9306," CC, 15		650 ___
82115	CB&Q Alco S2 Diesel Switcher "9308," CC, 15		650 ___
82116	CP Alco S2 Diesel Switcher "7020," CC, 15		650 ___

		Exc	Mint
___ 82117	CP Alco S2 Diesel Switcher "7024," CC, 15		650
___ 82118	GM&O Alco S2 Diesel Switcher "1001," CC, 15		650
___ 82119	GM&O Alco S2 Diesel Switcher "1007," CC, 15		650
___ 82120	GN Alco S2 Diesel Switcher "2," CC, 15		650
___ 82121	GN Alco S2 Diesel Switcher "5," CC, 15		650
___ 82122	PRR Alco S2 Diesel Switcher "5648," CC, 15		650
___ 82123	PRR Alco S2 Diesel Switcher "5652," CC, 15		650
___ 82124	South Buffalo Alco S2 Diesel Switcher "102," CC, 15		650
___ 82125	South Buffalo Alco S2 Diesel Switcher "104," CC, 15		650
___ 82126	UP Alco S2 Diesel Switcher "1111," CC, 15		650
___ 82127	UP Alco S2 Diesel Switcher "1138," CC, 15		650
___ 82128	C&O GP30 Diesel Locomotive "3011," CC, 15		650
___ 82129	C&O GP30 Diesel Locomotive "3018," CC, 15		650
___ 82130	EMD Demonstrator GP30 Diesel Locomotive "1962," CC, 15		650
___ 82131	TP&W GP30 Diesel Locomotive "700," CC, 15		650
___ 82132	PC GP30 Diesel Locomotive "2202," CC, 15		650
___ 82133	PC GP30 Diesel Locomotive "2246," CC, 15		650
___ 82134	GM&O GP30 Diesel Locomotive "501," CC, 15		650
___ 82135	GM&O GP30 Diesel Locomotive "521," CC, 15		650
___ 82136	N&W GP30 Diesel Locomotive "522," black, CC, 15		650
___ 82137	N&W GP30 Diesel Locomotive "542," blue, CC, 15		650
___ 82138	MILW GP30 Diesel Locomotive "344," CC, 15		650
___ 82139	MILW GP30 Diesel Locomotive "350," CC, 15		650
___ 82140	Southern GP30 Diesel Locomotive "2594," CC, 15		650
___ 82141	Southern GP30 Diesel Locomotive "2601," CC, 15		650
___ 82142	UP GP30 Diesel Locomotive "803," CC, 15		650
___ 82143	UP GP30 Diesel Locomotive "830," CC, 15		650
___ 82146	Soo Line PS-1 Boxcar "45025," 15		80
___ 82147	N&W PS-1 Boxcar "44292," 15		80
___ 82148	GB&W PS-1 Boxcar "777,", 15		80
___ 82150	Duluth, South Shore & Atlantic PS-1 Boxcar "15091," 15		80
___ 82163	B&O NW2 Diesel Locomotive "9555," LionChief, 15-16		300
___ 82164	BN NW2 Diesel Locomotive "546," LionChief, 15-16		300
___ 82165	CB&Q NW2 Diesel Locomotive "9412A," LionChief, 15-16		300
___ 82166	Southern NW2 Diesel Locomotive "2401A," LionChief, 15-16		300
___ 82171	BNSF GP20 Diesel Locomotive "2050," LionChief, 15-17		340
___ 82172	NYC GP20 Diesel Locomotive "2102," LionChief, 15-17		340
___ 82173	NS GP20 Diesel Locomotive "10," LionChief, 15-17		340
___ 82174	NYS&W GP20 Diesel Locomotive "1800," LionChief, 15-17		340
___ 82175	Virginian Rectifier Locomotive "135," LionChief, 15-17		340
___ 82176	N&W Rectifier Locomotive "235," LionChief, 15-17		340
___ 82177	NH Rectifier Locomotive "306," LionChief, 15-17		340
___ 82178	Conrail Rectifier Locomotive "4605," LionChief, 15-17		340
___ 82179	PRR Rectifier Locomotive "4466," LionChief, 15-17		340
___ 82184	PRR B6sb 0-4-0 Locomotive "1670," CC, 15		700
___ 82185	D&RGW Bicentennial Gondola with canisters, 16		50
___ 82186	Patriot Chemicals 1-D Tank Car "2015", 15, 18		60
___ 82187	Bethlehem Steel Water Tower, 15		35
___ 82188	Metro-North M7 Subway Set, LionChief, 15		350
___ 82192	MTA LIRR M7 Set, LionChief, 18-19		400
___ 82196	Metro-North Add-on 2-pack, 15		130
___ 82199	MTA LIRR Add-on Passenger 2-pack, 18		175
___ 82202	UP Big Boy Commemorative CA-4 Caboose, 15		95

		Exc	Mint
82203	Remote Control Box, 15-22		30 ___
82205	BNSF Golden Swoosh ES44AC Diesel Locomotive "7695," CC, 15		650 ___
82206	N&W 2-6-6-4 Locomotive "1218," CC, 16		1000 ___
82207	Iowa Interstate/Rock Island ES44AC Diesel "513," CC, 15		650 ___
82208	N&W 2-6-6-4 Locomotive "1212," CC, 16		1000 ___
82209	NS ES44AC Diesel Locomotive "8056," CC, 15		650 ___
82210	NS ES44AC Diesel Locomotive "8065," CC, 15		650 ___
82213	KCS ES44AC Diesel Locomotive 4696," CC, 15		650 ___
82214	KCS ES44AC Diesel Locomotive "4685," CC, 15		650 ___
82215	AT&SF ES44AC Diesel Locomotive "440," CC, 15		650 ___
82216	AT&SF ES44AC Diesel Locomotive "444," CC, 15		650 ___
82218	FEC ES44AC Diesel Locomotive "802," CC, 15		650 ___
82219	FEC ES44AC Diesel Locomotive "804," CC, 15		650 ___
82220	SP Alco PA AA Diesel Locomotive Set "6006, 6015," CC, 15		1000 ___
82223	D&RGW Alco PA AA Diesel Locomotive "6001, 6003," CC, 15		1000 ___
82226	LV Alco PA AA Diesel Locomotive Set "601, 602," CC, 15		1000 ___
82229	MP Alco PA AA Diesel Locomotive Set "8018, 8018," CC, 15		1000 ___
82232	NKP Alco PA AA Diesel Locomotive Set "190, 189," CC, 15		1000 ___
82235	PRR Alco PA AA Diesel Locomotive Set "5070A, 5071A," CC, 15		1000 ___
82238	Southern Alco PA AA Diesel Locomotive Set "6900, 6901," CC, 15		1000 ___
82241	Wabash Alco PA AA Diesel Locomotive Set "1020, 1020A," CC, 15		1000 ___
82244	SP Alco PB Diesel Locomotive, CC, 15		530 ___
82245	B&O 2-6-6-4 Locomotive "7620," CC, 16		1000 ___
82246	D&RGW Alco PB Diesel Locomotive, CC, 15		530 ___
82247	AT&SF 2-6-6-4 Locomotive "1798," CC, 16		1000 ___
82248	LV Alco PB Diesel Locomotive, CC, 15		530 ___
82249	Bethlehem Steel Boom Car, 15		55 ___
82250	MP Alco PB Diesel Locomotive, CC, 15		530 ___
82251	Zombie Animated Gondola, 15		75 ___
82252	Nickel Plate Road Alco PB Diesel Locomotive, CC, 15		530 ___
82253	John Deere 1-D Tank Car, 15		65 ___
82254	PRR Alco PB Diesel Locomotive, CC, 15		530 ___
82256	Southern Alco PB Diesel Locomotive, CC, 15		530 ___
82258	Wabash Alco PB Diesel Locomotive, CC, 15		530 ___
82260	PC 50' DD Boxcar "267210" (std O), 16-17		80 ___
82261	Frisco 50' DD Boxcar "7002" (std O), 16-17		80 ___
82263	PRR Scrapyard, 16-17		130 ___
82265	MOW Welding Car, 15-16		80 ___
82266	CN 4-6-0 Steam Locomotive "1158," CC, 15		900 ___
82267	C&NW 4-6-0 Steam Locomotive "1385," CC, 15		900 ___
82268	Frisco 4-6-0 Steam Locomotive "633," CC, 15		900 ___
82269	NP 4-6-0 Steam Locomotive "1382," CC, 15		900 ___
82270	SP 4-6-0 Steam Locomotive "2353," CC, 15		900 ___
82271	NYC 4-6-0 Steam Locomotive "1258," CC, 15		900 ___
82272	NH 4-6-0 Steam Locomotive "816," CC, 15		900 ___
82273	ACL 4-6-0 Steam Locomotive "1031," CC, 15		900 ___
82274	Chessie SD40 Diesel Locomotive "7500," CC, 15		650 ___
82275	Chessie SD40 Diesel Locomotive "7593," CC, 15		650 ___
82276	BN SD40 Diesel Locomotive "6314," CC, 15		650 ___
82277	BN SD40 Diesel Locomotive "6320," CC, 15		650 ___
82278	GT SD40 Diesel Locomotive "5922," CC, 15		650 ___
82279	GT SD40 Diesel Locomotive "5927," CC, 15		650 ___
82280	MP SD40 Diesel Locomotive "3007," CC, 15		650 ___

		Exc	Mint
82281	MP SD40 Diesel Locomotive "3014," CC, 15		650
82282	Conrail SD40 Diesel Locomotive "6308," CC, 15		650
82283	Conrail SD40 Diesel Locomotive "6350," CC, 15		650
82284	Conrail SD40 Diesel Locomotive "6300," CC, 15		650
82285	SP SD40 Diesel Locomotive "8402," CC, 15		650
82286	SP SD40 Diesel Locomotive "8451," CC, 15		650
82287	SP Daylight SD40 Diesel Locomotive "7342," CC, 15		650
82288	Clinchfield SD40 Diesel Locomotive "3000," CC, 15		650
82289	Clinchfield SD40 Diesel Locomotive "3006," CC, 15		650
82290	AT&SF FT AA Diesel Locomotive Set, LionChief, 15-17		500
82293	ACL FT AA Diesel Locomotive Set, LionChief, 15-17		500
82296	Erie FT AA Diesel Locomotive Set, LionChief, 15-17		500
82299	D&RGW FT AA Diesel Locomotive Set, LionChief, 15-17		500
82302	AT&SF FT B Unit, LionChief, 15-17		280
82303	ACL FT B Unit, LionChief, 15-17		280
82304	Erie FT B Unit, LionChief, 15-17		280
82305	D&RGW FT B Unit, LionChief, 15-17		280
82307	PRR B6sb 0-4-0 Locomotive "5244," CC, 15		700
82308	PRR B6sb 0-4-0 Locomotive "3233," CC, 15		700
82309	PRR-Reading Seashore Lines B6sb 0-4-0 "6096," CC, 15		700
82310	LIRR B6sb 0-4-0 Locomotive "2015," CC, 15		700
82311	Polar RR B6sb 0-4-0 Locomotive "2515," CC, 15		700
82312	UP ACF 40-ton Stock Car "48133," 15		80
82313	GN ACF 40-ton Stock Car "55989," 15		80
82314	MILW ACF 40-ton Stock Car "104954," 15		80
82315	NP ACF 40-ton Stock Car "84161," 15		80
82316	NKP ACF 40-ton Stock Car "42040," 15		80
82324	Chessie Diesel Freight Set, LionChief, 15		400
82330	U.S.A.F. Minuteman Missile Launcher Car, CC, 15		350
82331	U.S.A.F. Missile Launch Sound Car, CC, 15		240
82333	Illuminated Hopper Shed, 15-23		45
82334	Ulysses S. Grant Presidential Boxcar, 15		70
82335	Franklin D. Roosevelt Presidential Boxcar, 15		70
82340	N&W Y6b 2-8-8-2 Steam Locomotive "2171," CC, 15		2000
82341	N&W Y6b 2-8-8-2 Steam Locomotive "2175," CC, 15		2000
82342	N&W Y6b 2-8-8-2 Steam Locomotive "2195," CC, 15		2000
82343	Lionel Steel Welding Car, 15		80
82344	WM Wood Chip Hopper "2945," 15-16		65
82349	Friday the 13th Jason Voorhees Boxcar, 16		85
82394	UP Auxiliary Water Tender "907853," CC, 15		380
82395	UP Auxiliary Water Tender "907856," CC, 15		380
82396	UP Commemorative Auxiliary Water Tender "809," CC, 15		380
82410	Virginian 2-bay Hopper "13168," 16-17		60
82411	N&W 2-bay Hopper "113733," 15-17		60
82412	Reading Birney Trolley, 15, 18		100
82413	Lionel Transit Birney Trolley, 15		100
82414	CNJ 4-6-0 Camelback Locomotive "777," LionChief, 15-16		440
82415	DL&W 4-6-0 Camelback Locomotive "1035," LionChief, 15-17		440
82416	LV 4-6-0 Camelback Locomotive "1602," LionChief, 15-17		440
82417	Philadelphia & Reading 4-6-0 Camelback Locomotive "675," LC, 15-17		440
82418	Erie 4-6-0 Camelback Locomotive "861," LionChief, 15-17		440
82419	UP 8-door Hi-Cube Boxcar, 16		100
82420	SP 8-door Hi-Cube Boxcar, 16		100

		Exc	Mint
82421	B&O 8-door Hi-Cube Boxcar, 16		100 ___
82422	PRR 8-door Hi-Cube Boxcar, 16		100 ___
82423	C&NW 8-door Hi-Cube Boxcar, 16		100 ___
82424	Chessie 8-door Hi-Cube Boxcar, 16		100 ___
82425	PC 8-door Hi-Cube Boxcar, 16		100 ___
82426	RI 8-door Hi-Cube Boxcar, 16		100 ___
82427	Patriot U36B Diesel Freight Set, LionChief, 15-17		360 ___
82436	Pennsylvania Keystone GP38 Diesel Freight Set, LionChief, 15		450 ___
82442	Five-Star General Old-Time Steam Set, LionChief, 17-18		400 ___
82447	Sheriff & Outlaw Car, 17		80 ___
82453	Amtrak F40PH Diesel Phase II "200," CC, 16		550 ___
82454	Amtrak F40PH Diesel Phase II "207," CC, 16		550 ___
82455	Amtrak F40PH Diesel Phase III "364," CC, 16		550 ___
82456	Amtrak F40PH Diesel Phase III "388," CC, 16		550 ___
82460	CSX F40PH Diesel "9998," CC, 16		550 ___
82461	CSX F40PH Diesel "9999," CC, 16		550 ___
82473	N&W Early Era Inspection Vehicle, CC, 15		200 ___
82474	BN Early Era Inspection Vehicle, CC, 15		200 ___
82475	Bethlehem Steel Early Era Inspection Vehicle, CC, 15		200 ___
82476	NH Early Era Inspection Vehicle, CC, 15		200 ___
82477	Virginian Early Era Inspection Vehicle, CC, 15		200 ___
82478	Reading Early Era Inspection Vehicle, CC, 15		200 ___
82486	Weathered Virginian USRA Y-3 2-8-8-2 Locomotive "737," CC, 14		1450 ___
82487	Weathered AT&SF USRA Y-3 2-8-8-2 Locomotive "1797," CC, 14		1450 ___
82488	Weathered N&W USRA Y-3 2-8-8-2 Locomotive "2029," CC, 14		1450 ___
82489	MILW Olympian 18" Aluminum Passenger Car 2-pack, 14-15		320 ___
82494	Turbo Missile Launch Flatcar, 15		60 ___
82495	D&RGW Scrapyard, 16-19		130 ___
82498	Polar Express Mail Car, 16-17		70 ___
82500	Polar Express Covered Bridge, 15		70 ___
82501	Providence & Worcester 89' Auto Carrier "190091," 15-16		110 ___
82502	C&NW 89' Auto Carrier "962255," 15-16		110 ___
82503	Chessie 89' Auto Carrier "255798," 15-16		110 ___
82504	TFM 89' Auto Carrier "987408," 15-16		110 ___
82505	BNSF 89' Auto Carrier "212878," 15-16		110 ___
82506	UP 89' Auto Carrier "992579," 15-16		110 ___
82508	NYC Milk Car "6589" (std O), 16		80 ___
82510	Polar Express Aquarium Car, 16		85 ___
82512	Polar Express Work Caboose with presents, 15		85 ___
82514	Polar Express Reindeer Stock Car, 15		90 ___
82518	Moon Pie Boxcar, 15		85 ___
82528	NYC Empire State Express Steam Passenger Set, CC, 15		1950 ___
82534	NYC J3a 4-6-4 Hudson Locomotive "5429," tender, 15		1500 ___
82535	NYC J3a 4-6-4 Hudson Locomotive "5426," tender, 15		1500 ___
82536	NYC J3a 4-6-4 Hudson Locomotive "5429," tender, 15		1500 ___
82537	NYC J3a 4-6-4 Hudson Locomotive "5426," tender, 15		1500 ___
82543	Postwar "943" Exploding Ammunition Dump, 15-16, 18-20		50 ___
82544	Missile Firing Range, 15-16, 19		65 ___
82545	Santa's Helper Steam Freight Set, 16-17		238 ___
82550	Wabash 21" Streamlined Passenger Car 4-pack, 15		600 ___
82555	Wabash 21" Streamlined Passenger Car 2-pack, 15		300 ___
82558	Southern 21" Streamlined Passenger Car 4-pack, 15		600 ___
82563	Southern 21" Streamlined Passenger Car 2-pack, 15		300 ___

			Mint
___	82566	RI 21" Streamlined Passenger Car 4-pack, 15	600
___	82571	RI 21" Streamlined Passenger Car 2-pack, 15	300
___	82574	Texas Special 21" Streamlined Passenger Car 4-pack, 15	600
___	82579	Texas Special 21" Streamlined Passenger Car 2-pack, 15	300
___	82582	C&O 21" Streamlined Passenger Car 4-pack, 15	600
___	82587	C&O 21" Streamlined Passenger Car 2-pack, 15	300
___	82590	Amtrak 21" Passenger Car 4-pack, 16	600
___	82595	Amtrak 21" Passenger Car 2-pack, 16	300
___	82598	NYC Empire State Passenger Car Add-on 2-pack, 15	300
___	82611	PRR GL-a 2-bay Hopper 3-pack, 15	220
___	82621	Buffalo Creek Flour PS-1 Boxcar "2366," 15	80
___	82622	U.S. Army PS-1 Boxcar "26875," 15	80
___	82623	West India Fruit & Steamship Co. PS-1 Boxcar "321," 15	80
___	82624	Linde Air Products PS-1 Boxcar "3019," 15	80
___	82625	Air Reduction Products PS-1 Boxcar "100," 15	80
___	82629	PRR N5b Caboose "478883," 15-16	95
___	82630	PRR N5b Caboose with trainphone antenna, 15-16	95
___	82631	B&M N5b Caboose "C-16," 15-16	95
___	82639	MILW Milk Car "370" (std O), 16, 20, 23	100
___	82640	UTLX 30,000-Gallon 1-D Tank Car 3-pack, 15	250
___	82644	Philadelphia Energy Solutions 1-D Tank Car 3-pack, 15	250
___	82648	Midwest Ethanol Transport 1-D Tank Car 3-pack, 15	250
___	82652	Global Ethanol Transport 1-D Tank Car 3-pack, 15	250
___	82656	Conrail 60' Boxcar "216010," 15-17	90
___	82657	WM 60' Boxcar "38020," 15-17	90
___	82658	BN 60' Boxcar "355145," 15-17	90
___	82659	RI 60' Boxcar "33825," 15-17	90
___	82660	N&W 60' Boxcar "600949," 15-17	90
___	82661	P&LE PS-5 Gondola and PS-4 Flatcar, 15-16	175
___	82664	B&LE PS-5 Gondola and PS-4 Flatcar, 15-16	175
___	82667	DT&I PS-5 Gondola and PS-4 Flatcar, 15-16	175
___	82670	Conrail PS-5 Gondola and PS-4 Flatcar, 15-16	175
___	82674	UP Bathtub Gondola 2-pack, 15	140
___	82677	Strasburg 3-D Tank Car, 16	656
___	82678	Angela Trotta Thomas Christmas Boxcar, 16	85
___	82683	Batman and Flash Justice League Boxcar 2-pack, 15-16	170
___	82684	Superman and Green Lantern Justice League Boxcar 2-pack, 15-16	170
___	82685	New York Giants Cooperstown Boxcar, 15	85
___	82686	Washington Senators Cooperstown Boxcar, 15	85
___	82687	Detroit Tigers Cooperstown Boxcar, 15	85
___	82688	Pittsburgh Pirates Cooperstown Boxcar, 15	85
___	82689	Operation Eagle Missile Carrying Car, 15-17	65
___	82690	Coca-Cola Anniversary Bottle Boxcar, 15	90
___	82691	Christmas Boxcar, 15	75
___	82693	Santa's Helper Crane, 15	85
___	82694	UP LionMaster 4-6-6-4 Challenger Locomotive "3985," CC, 15	1000
___	82695	UP LionMaster 4-6-6-4 Challenger Locomotive "3977," CC, 15	1000
___	82696	UP LionMaster 4-6-6-4 Challenger Locomotive "3989," CC, 15	1000
___	82697	D&RGW LionMaster 4-6-6-4 Challenger "3803," CC, 15	1000
___	82698	WM LionMaster 4-6-6-4 Challenger Locomotive "1201," CC, 15	1000
___	82699	Angela Trotta Thomas Lionelville Christmas Boxcar, 15	75
___	82701	Escaping Snowmen Handcar, 15	90

		Exc	Mint
82702	Ontario Northland PS-4 Flatcar with covered load, 15		90
82703	BN PS-4 Flatcar with covered load, 15		90
82704	D&RGW PS-4 Flatcar with covered load, 15		90
82705	Reading PS-4 Flatcar with covered load, 15		90
82706	Southern PS-4 Flatcar with covered load, 15		90
82708	Christmas Gingerbread Shanty, 16-19		40
82709	PRR Silver & Gold Ore Car 2-pack, 16-17		130
82710	PRR Ice Breaker Tunnel Car, 16-17		65
82711	Santa's Favorites Transparent Gift Car, 16		85
82713	Christmas Music Boxcar, 15		80
82716	Mickey's Holiday to Remember Freight Set, 16		400
82717	W. E. Disney Girder Bridge, 16-18		33
82718	Disney Villains Hi-Cube Boxcar 2-pack, 16-19		160
82721	Dumbo 75th Anniversary Boxcar, 16-17		85
82726	Postwar Alco FA Diesel Green Passenger Set, 17-19		550
82728	LCS Switch Throw Monitor, 17-23		110
82734	New York Yankees Cooperstown Boxcar, 15	41	85
82735	Polar Express Conductor Gateman, 18-23		130
82736	North Pole Central Water Tower, 15		40
82737	Coca-Cola Santa Boxcar, 15		85
82739	North Pole Central Boxcar, 16-18		80
82740	Winter Wonderland Aquarium Car, 15		95
82741	Christmas Tinsel Vat Car, 16		70
82742	Candy Mountain Christmas Quad Hopper, 16-17		65
82743	Santa's Reindeer Station Platform, 15		50
82744	Santa Claus Automatic Gateman, 16-17		100
82745	Christmas Cocoa Barrel Shed, 15		50
82746	Christmas Floodlight Tower, 16		75
82747	Christmas Red Arch Under Bridge, 16		30
82748	Silver Bell Casting Co. Hopper, 15		70
82749	PRR GG1 Electric "4935," CC, 16		1400
82751	PRR GG1 Electric "4913," CC, 16		1400
82752	PRR GG1 Electric "4877," CC, 16		1400
82754	PC GG1 Electric "4828," CC, 16		1400
82755	Amtrak GG1 Electric "926," CC, 16		1400
82757	CP SD90MAC Diesel "9116," CC, 16		650
82758	CP SD90MAC Diesel "9130," CC, 16		650
82759	NS SD90MAC Diesel "7230," CC, 16		650
82760	NS SD90MAC Diesel "7245," CC, 16		650
82761	UP SD90MAC Diesel "8130," CC, 16		650
82762	UP SD90MAC Diesel "8133," CC, 16		650
82763	UP SD90MAC Diesel "8025," CC, 16		650
82764	UP SD90MAC Diesel "8055," CC, 16		650
82765	Indiana SD90MAC Diesel "9003," CC, 16		650
82766	Indiana SD90MAC Diesel "9006," CC, 16		650
82767	C&O 2-6-6-6 Locomotive "1601," CC, 16		2200
82768	C&O 2-6-6-6 Locomotive "1604," CC, 16		2200
82769	C&O 2-6-6-6 Locomotive "1608," CC, 16		2200
82770	Virginian 2-6-6-6 Locomotive "906," CC, 16		2200
82825	CP GP38 Diesel Locomotive "3019," 16-17		340
82826	CSX GP38 Diesel Locomotive "2145," 16-17		340
82827	SP GP38 Diesel Locomotive "4846," 16-18		340
82828	UP GP38 Diesel Locomotive "905," 16-17		340

		Exc	Mint
____ 82840	AT&SF PS-4 Flatcar with trailer (std O), 16		110
____ 82841	E-L PS-4 Flatcar with trailer (std O), 16		110
____ 82842	GN PS-4 Flatcar with trailer (std O), 16		110
____ 82843	WM PS-4 Flatcar with trailer (std O), 16		110
____ 82844	PRR PS-4 Flatcar with trailer (std O), 16		110
____ 82845	B&O Truck with 40' trailer, 16		90
____ 82846	MILW Truck with 40' trailer, 16-17		90
____ 82847	MKT Truck with 40' trailer, 16-17		90
____ 82848	Logging Disconnect with load, 16		65
____ 82849	Logging Disconnect with load 2-pack, 16		125
____ 82850	MILW 40' Flatcar with lumber (std O), 16-17		90
____ 82851	NP 40' Flatcar with lumber (std O), 16-17		90
____ 82852	Meadow River 40' Flatcar with lumber (std O), 16-17		90
____ 82853	Pickering 40' Flatcar with lumber (std O), 16-17		90
____ 82854	PRR 40' Flatcar with lumber (std O), 16		90
____ 82855	ADM Unibody Tank Car "190516" (std O), 16		75
____ 82856	GATX Unibody Tank Car "4415" (std O), 16		75
____ 82857	AFPX Unibody Tank Car "413303" (std O), 16		75
____ 82858	Shell Unibody Tank Car "82858" (std O), 16		85
____ 82859	Engelhard Unibody Tank Car "24586" (std O), 16		75
____ 82860	PC PS-5 Gondola "557065" (std O), 16		90
____ 82861	E-L PS-5 Gondola "14552" (std O), 16		90
____ 82862	Frisco PS-5 Gondola "61442" (std O), 16		90
____ 82863	CB&Q PS-5 Gondola "82050" (std O), 16		90
____ 82864	NYC PS-5 Gondola "712603" (std O), 16		90
____ 82865	PRR N5b Caboose "5017" (std O), 16		90
____ 82866	PRR N5b Caboose "477746" (std O), 16		90
____ 82867	PRR N5b Caboose "477625" (std O), 16		90
____ 82868	NH N5 Caboose "C-507" (std O), 16		90
____ 82869	IR Sensor Track O Gauge Tubular Compatible, 17-23		100
____ 82870	Loading Ramp, 16-20		25
____ 82872	Loader/Unloader Workers Figure Pack, 16-20		30
____ 82873	Loggers Cabin, sound, 16		140
____ 82874	Early Intermodal Work House, sound, 16-19		130
____ 82877	Thomas Kinkade Polar Express Boxcar, 16		85
____ 82878	Smithsonian Boxcar, 16		85
____ 82879	Coca-Cola Christmas Boxcar, 16-17		85
____ 82883	Legacy 360-watt PowerMaster, 16-23		240
____ 82884	Wabash 21" Streamlined Dining Car, StationSounds, 15		300
____ 82885	Southern 21" Streamlined Dining Car, StationSounds, 15		300
____ 82886	RI 21" Streamlined Dining Car, StationSounds, 15		300
____ 82887	Texas Special 21" Streamlined Dining Car, StationSounds, 15		300
____ 82888	C&O 21" Streamlined Dining Car, StationSounds, 15		300
____ 82889	Amtrak 21" Diner, StationSounds, 16		300
____ 82890	NYC Empire State Express Diner, StationSounds, 15		300
____ 82906	Pluto Walking Brakeman Car, 16-18		100
____ 82908	Mickey's Christmas Shanty, 16-18		50
____ 82913	Winnie the Pooh Boxcar, 16-17		85
____ 82914	Disney Aquarium Car, 16-18		85
____ 82917	Disney Station Platform, 17-19		55
____ 82918	36" Power Cable Extension (3-pin, M/F), 17-23		14
____ 82921	Evil Queen Hi-Cube Boxcar, 17-19		80
____ 82922	Scar Hi-Cube Boxcar, 17-19		80

		Exc	Mint
82925	Scrooge McDuck Mint Car, 17-18		80 ___
82942	James Monroe Presidential Boxcar, 16, 18		70 ___
82943	John F. Kennedy Presidential Boxcar, 16		70 ___
82944	Herbert Hoover Presidential Boxcar, 16		70 ___
82945	James Madison Presidential Boxcar, 16		70 ___
82947	Wonder Woman/Green Arrow Boxcar 2-pack, 16		170 ___
82950	Aquaman/Martian Manhunter Boxcar 2-pack, 16		170 ___
82953	Joker/Lex Luthor Boxcar 2-pack, 16		170 ___
82954	Lionel Christmas Boxcar, 16		65 ___
82958	Christmas Floodlight, 17-18		75 ___
82960	NYC 2-8-2 Steam Locomotive "1548," 16-18		430 ___
82961	UP 2-8-2 Steam Locomotive "2537," 16-18		430 ___
82962	Southern 2-8-2 Steam Locomotive "4501," 16-18		430 ___
82963	Rio Grande 2-8-2 Steam Locomotive "1208," 16-18		430 ___
82964	MILW 4-6-4 Steam Locomotive "125," 16-18		430 ___
82965	AT&SF 4-6-4 Steam Locomotive "3450," 16-18		430 ___
82966	DL&W 4-6-4 Steam Locomotive "1151," 16-18		430 ___
82967	CB&Q 4-6-4 Steam Locomotive "3007," 16-18		430 ___
82968	LL 4-6-2 Steam Locomotive "462," 16-17		430 ___
82969	WM 4-6-2 Steam Locomotive "202," 16-18		430 ___
82970	Reading & Northern 4-6-2 Locomotive "425," 16-17		450 ___
82971	C&NW 4-6-2 Steam Locomotive "600," 16-18		300 ___
82972	Lionel Junction PRR Diesel Freight Set, 16-17		175 ___
82973	PRR A5 0-4-0 Locomotive "3891," 16-18		450 ___
82974	SP A5 0-4-0 Locomotive "1040," 16-18		450 ___
82975	B&O A5 0-4-0 Locomotive "317," 16-18		450 ___
82976	Bethlehem Steel A5 0-4-0 Locomotive "140," LionChief, 16-18		450 ___
82982	Christmas Express Steam Freight Set, LionChief, 17-18		320 ___
82984	NYC RS-3 Diesel Freight Set, 16-17		260 ___
82992	115th Anniversary Boxcar, 16		90 ___
82993	Weathered UP Y-3 2-8-8-2 Steam Engine, 3595, CC, 15		1450 ___
82994	Weathered C&O H-7 2-8-8-2 Steam Engine, 1578, CC, 15		1450 ___
82995	Weathered UP Y-3 2-8-8-2 Steam Engine, 3671, CC, 15		1450 ___
82996	Weathered PRR Y-3 2-8-8-2 Steam Engine, 376, CC, 15		1450 ___
83002	PRR Broadway Limited 21" Diner 2-pack, StationSounds, 16		450 ___
83003	PC 21" StationSounds Diner "4552," 16		300 ___
83006	UP 21" Excursion Diner, StationSounds, 16		300 ___
83007	PRR Broadway Limited 21" Passenger Car 2-pack, 16		300 ___
83010	PC 21" Passenger Car 2-pack, 16		300 ___
83019	UP 21" Excursion Passenger Car 2-pack, 16		300 ___
83022	PRR Broadway Limited 21" Passenger Car 4-pack, 16		600 ___
83027	PC 21" Passenger Car 4-pack, 16		600 ___
83042	UP 21" Excursion Passenger Car 4-pack, 16		675 ___
83063	AT&SF Super Chief Boxcar "143093," 16-19		50 ___
83071	LC Universal Remote, 16-23		55 ___
83072	PRR "Keystone Special" Steam Freight Set, LionChief, 17-20		300 ___
83080	Rio Grande 0-4-0 Switcher Freight Set, 16-17		300 ___
83092	Steel City Switcher Freight Set, CC, 16		1300 ___
83102	SP 21" Passenger Car 4-pack, 16		600 ___
83107	SP 21" Passenger Car 2-pack, 16		300 ___
83110	SP 21" Diner "290," StationSounds, 16		300 ___
83111	American Freedom Train 21" Passenger Car 4-pack, 16-17		675 ___
83116	American Freedom Train 21" Passenger Car 2-pack, 16-17		300 ___

		MODERN 1970-2023	Exc	Mint
___	83119	American Freedom Train 21" Crew Car, 16-17		300
___	83120	CSX Office Car Special 21" Passenger Car 4-pack, 16-17		600
___	83125	CSX Office Car Special 21" Passenger Car 2-pack, 16-17		300
___	83128	CSX Office Car Special 21" Diner, StationSounds, 16-17		300
___	83147	Lighted Yard Tower, 16		60
___	83148	Christmas Express Boxcar, 16-17		53
___	83157	Smithsonian Air & Space Boxcar 2-pack, 16		170
___	83162	Nightmare on Elm Street Boxcar, 16		85
___	83163	Thomas Kinkade Christmas Boxcar, 16-17		85
___	83164	Frosty the Snowman 1-D Tank Car, 16-17		60
___	83165	PRR GG1 Electric "4899," CC, 16		1400
___	83166	PRR GG1 Electric "4800," CC, 16		1400
___	83167	Conrail Bicentennial GG1 Electric "4800," CC, 16		1400
___	83168	Iron Workers Figure Pack, 16-23		30
___	83169	NYC Flatcar with piggyback trailers, 16-19		75
___	83170	Steel Mill Structure, sound, 16-19		130
___	83171	MOW Workers Figure Pack, 16-22		30
___	83172	MOW Work Structure, sound, 16-19		130
___	83173	Single Signal Bridge, 16-23		90
___	83174	Double Signal Bridge, 16-23		120
___	83175	Christmas Music Boxcar, 16		80
___	83176	Lionel Lines Christmas Caboose, 16-17		75
___	83177	Angela Trotta Thomas Caboose, 16-17		80
___	83178	Coca-Cola Caboose, 16		75
___	83179	Conrail Caboose "23878," 16-19		75
___	83180	PRR Caboose "477100," 16-17		7
___	83181	AT&SF Caboose "999316," 16-17		75
___	83182	ACL Caboose "0634," 16-19		75
___	83183	Erie Caboose "C226," 16-19		75
___	83184	UP Caboose "25214," 16-18		75
___	83185	Polar Express Elves Figure Set, 16-23		33
___	83186	NYC Caboose "21777," 16-18		75
___	83190	Moon Pie 1-D Tank Car, 16-17		75
___	83191	Snow Transport Christmas 1-D Tank Car, 16, 19		85
___	83192	Smithsonian Dinosaur Aquarium Car, 16-17		85
___	83193	SP GS-4 4-8-4 Locomotive "4449," CC, 16		1700
___	83194	SP GS-4 4-8-4 Locomotive "4449," CC, 16		1700
___	83195	SP GS-4 4-8-4 Locomotive "4443," CC, 16		1700
___	83196	SP GS-4 4-8-4 Locomotive "4444," CC, 16		1700
___	83197	American Freedom Train GS-4 4-8-4 Locomotive, CC, 16		1700
___	83198	Reading T1 4-8-4 Locomotive "2100," CC, 16		1700
___	83199	Reading T1 4-8-4 Locomotive "2119," CC, 16		1700
___	83200	Reading T1 4-8-4 Locomotive "2102," CC, 16		1700
___	83201	Reading T1 4-8-4 Locomotive "2124," CC, 16		1700
___	83202	American Freedom Train T1 4-8-4 Locomotive, CC, 16		1700
___	83203	Chessie T1 4-8-4 Locomotive "2101," CC, 16		1700
___	83204	B&O 0-8-0 Locomotive "1695," CC, 16		900
___	83205	GTW 0-8-0 Locomotive "8380," CC, 16		900
___	83206	Indiana Harbor Belt 0-8-0 Locomotive "312," CC, 16		900
___	83208	Wabash 0-8-0 Locomotive "1526," CC, 16		900
___	83209	Terminal Railroad 0-8-0 Locomotive, CC, 16		900
___	83214	North Pole Central 4-6-2 Locomotive "1225," 16-17		430
___	83215	Transformer 2-pack, 16-19		15

		Exc	Mint
83223	Steel I-Beam 12-pack, 16-20		15 ___
83230	Amtrak Metal Girder Bridge, 16-20		43 ___
83231	Polar Express Metal Girder Bridge, 16-17		43 ___
83232	Bethlehem Steel Metal Girder Bridge, 16-19		40 ___
83233	CSX Metal Girder Bridge, 16-19		37 ___
83234	John Deere Plastic Girder Bridge, 16-19		33 ___
83238	John Deere Flatcar with spreaders, 16-17		80 ___
83239	Polar Express Bells Mint Car, 16-17		80 ___
83240	Shell Operating Oil Derrick, 16		120 ___
83241	Shell Oil Storage Tank with Light, 16		85 ___
83242	Shell 1-D Tank Car, 16		75 ___
83243	Shell 3-D Tank Car, 16-17		75 ___
83244	Shell Elevated Oil Tank, 17		100 ___
83246	Shell Boxcar, 16		85 ___
83247	Shell Billboard Pack, 16-17		25 ___
83248	"It's a Boy" Boxcar, 16		90 ___
83249	Polar Express Combination Car, 16-17		70 ___
83250	"It's a Girl" Boxcar, 16		90 ___
83251	Poultry Dispatch Sweep Car, 16-18		120 ___
83252	Gold Medal Milk Car with platform, 17-19		180 ___
83253	D&RGW Searchlight Car, 16-17		63 ___
83254	Western Union Animated Gondola, 16-18		70 ___
83256	GN Horse Transport , 16		80 ___
83257	Bobbing Werewolf Boxcar, 16-17		75 ___
83258	CP Boom Car, 16		63 ___
83266	Lionel Junction Santa Fe Steam Freight Set, 16		175 ___
83275	Sugar Cookie Scented Smoke Fluid, 17-23		9 ___
83276	Peppermint Scented Smoke Fluid, 17-23		9 ___
83277	Pine Scented Smoke Fluid, 17-23		9 ___
83278	Hot Chocolate Scented Smoke Fluid, 17-23		9 ___
83279	Wood Stove Scented Smoke Fluid, 17-23		9 ___
83280	Unscented Smoke Fluid, 17-23		9 ___
83284	Peekaboo Reindeer Operating Boxcar, 16-17		75 ___
83286	John Deere Steam Freight Set, 16-17		400 ___
83291	Christmas Half-covered Bridge, 16-19		70 ___
83292	Christmas Cookies & Candies Store, 16-17		85 ___
83304	North Pole Elves Work Shanty, 16		40 ___
83305	Illuminated Winter Covered Bridge, 16-23		100 ___
83308	North Pole Central Tank Car "122416," 16-17		75 ___
83311	Santa's Favorites Egg Nog Reefer, 16-18		65 ___
83312	Santa's Cookies Vat Car, 16-17		70 ___
83313	Reindeer Express Agency Flatcar with trailer, 16-17		70 ___
83315	Christmas Toys Stock Car, 16-18		70 ___
83316	Santa's Sleigh Aquarium Car, 16-18		80 ___
83317	BNSF 65' Mill Gondola "518357" (std O), 17		80 ___
83318	C&NW 65' Mill Gondola "342036" (std O), 17		80 ___
83319	CSX 65' Mill Gondola "491600" (std O), 17		80 ___
83320	NS 65' Mill Gondola "195015" (std O), 17		80 ___
83321	SP 65' Mill Gondola "365117" (std O), 17		80 ___
83322	UP 65' Mill Gondola "96257" (std O), 17		80 ___
83340	Boxcar Children Boxcar, 16		85 ___
83347	ACL USRA Double-sheathed Boxcar, 16		85 ___
83348	B&M USRA Double-sheathed Boxcar, 16		85 ___

		Exc	Mint
83349	RI USRA Double-sheathed Boxcar, 16		85
83350	Northwestern Pacific USRA Double-sheathed Boxcar, 16		85
83351	Wabash USRA Double-sheathed Boxcar, 16		85
83352	Polar Express USRA Double-sheathed Boxcar, 16		95
83353	D&RGW Flatcar with snowplow (std O), 16		95
83354	NYC Flatcar with snowplow (std O), 16		95
83355	UP Flatcar with snowplow (std O), 16		95
83356	MOW Flatcar with Snowplow (std O), 16		95
83357	Reading NE-style Caboose "92882" (std O), 16		90
83358	Reading NE-style Caboose "92902" (std O), 16		90
83359	Reading & Northern NE-style Caboose "92884" (std O), 16		90
83360	C&O NE-style Caboose "90352" (std O), 16		90
83361	N&W NE-style Caboose "500830" (std O), 16		90
83362	WM NE-style Caboose "1887" (std O), 16		90
83368	EL SD45 Diesel Locomotive "3607," CC, 16		650
83369	EL SD45 Diesel Locomotive "3618," CC, 16		650
83370	EL Bicentennial SD45 Diesel Locomotive "3632," CC, 16		650
83371	GN "Hustle Muscle" SD45 Diesel Locomotive "400," CC, 16		650
83372	GN SD45 Diesel Locomotive "402," CC, 16		650
83373	GN SD45 Diesel Locomotive "407," CC, 16		650
83374	PC SD45 Diesel Locomotive "6235," CC, 16		650
83375	PC SD45 Diesel Locomotive "6237," CC, 16		650
83376	Southern SD45 Diesel Locomotive "3137," CC, 16		650
83377	Southern SD45 Diesel Locomotive "3156," CC, 16		650
83378	SP SD45 Diesel Locomotive "8801," CC, 16		650
83379	SP SD45 Diesel Locomotive "8820," CC, 16		650
83380	UP SD45 Diesel Locomotive "1," CC, 16		650
83381	UP SD45 Diesel Locomotive "21," CC, 16		650
83382	AT&SF NW2 Diesel Locomotive "2405," CC, 16		500
83383	B&M NW2 Diesel Locomotive "1200," CC, 16		500
83384	B&O NW2 Diesel Locomotive "9527," CC, 16		500
83385	CSX NW2 Diesel Locomotive "9565," CC, 16		500
83387	NYO&W NW2 Diesel Locomotive "116," CC, 16	305	500
83388	PRR NW2 Diesel Locomotive "9171," CC, 16		500
83389	Philadelphia, Bethlehem & New England NW2 Diesel "27," CC, 16		500
83390	SP NW2 Diesel Locomotive "1423," CC, 16		500
83391	SP&S NW2 Diesel Locomotive "41," CC, 16		500
83392	Union NW2 Diesel Locomotive "555," CC, 16		500
83393	UP NW2 Diesel Locomotive "1011," CC, 16		500
83395	AC&Y H16-44 Diesel "201," CC, 16		550
83396	AC&Y H16-44 Diesel "202," CC, 16		550
83397	AT&SF H16-44 Diesel "2801," CC, 16		550
83398	AT&SF H16-44 Diesel "2807," CC, 16		550
83399	B&O H16-44 Diesel "6705," CC, 16		550
83400	B&O H16-44 Diesel "6708," CC, 16		550
83401	MILW H16-44 Diesel "402," CC, 16		550
83402	MILW H16-44 Diesel "404," CC, 16		550
83403	DL&W H16-44 Diesel "931," CC, 16		550
83404	DL&W H16-44 Diesel "934," CC, 16		550
83405	Southern H16-44 Diesel "6547," CC, 16		550
83406	Southern H16-44 Diesel "6550," CC, 16		550
83426	Johnstown Birney Trolley, 16		100
83434	Polar Express Passenger Station, 16-17		90

		Exc	Mint
83435	World War II Pylon, 17		160 ___
83437	Polar Express Conductor Announcement Car, 16-17, 19		110 ___
83438	Miller Coors Operating Billboard, 17		80 ___
83440	Rico Station Kit, 16-23		60 ___
83442	Large Suburban House, 17-18		95 ___
83443	Deluxe Bungalow House, 17-18		95 ___
83444	Illuminated Station Platform, 16-17		43 ___
83445	Smithsonian Old St. Nick Boxcar, 16-18		85 ___
83455	Polar Express Operating Billboard, 16-17		85 ___
83462	Bethlehem Steel Slag Car 3-pack, 16		240 ___
83466	U.S. Steel Slag Car 3-pack (std O), 16		240 ___
83470	Slag Car 3-pack (std O), 16		240 ___
83474	Weathered Slag Car 3-pack (std O), 16		240 ___
83478	Bethlehem Steel Hot Metal Car 2-pack, 16		200 ___
83481	U.S. Steel Hot Metal Car 2-pack (std O), 16		200 ___
83484	Hot Metal Car 2-pack (std O), 16		200 ___
83487	Weathered Hot Metal Car 2-pack (std O), 16		200 ___
83490	Lighted Coaling Tower, 16, 18		180 ___
83491	Boston Red Sox Cooperstown Boxcar, 16		85 ___
83492	St. Louis Cardinals Cooperstown Boxcar, 16		85 ___
83493	Philadelphia Phillies Cooperstown Boxcar, 16		85 ___
83494	Baltimore Orioles Cooperstown Boxcar, 16		85 ___
83496	Station Platform, 16-18, 21-23		40 ___
83497	National Train Day Boxcar, 16-17		85 ___
83503	Thomas with remote, 16-18		120 ___
83504	Birthday Thomas with remote, 16-18		120 ___
83510	Thomas Passenger Set, LionChief, 16-23		250 ___
83511	Thomas, Sodor Locomotive, LionelChief, 18-23		160 ___
83512	Thomas & Friends Christmas Freight Set, 16-17		200 ___
83518	PRR Boxcar "83518" (std O), 16		100 ___
83519	REA SensorCar Steel Reefer "7844" (std O), 16, 19		130 ___
83520	North Pole Central Flatcar with snowplow, 16		95 ___
83527	AT&SF PS-1 Boxcar "142501," sound (std O), 16		130 ___
83528	BAR PS-1 Boxcar "5149," sound (std O), 16		130 ___
83529	B&O PS-1 Boxcar "467931," sound (std O), 16		130 ___
83530	BN PS-1 Boxcar "132909," sound (std O), 16		130 ___
83531	C&NW PS-1 Boxcar "5," sound (std O), 16		130 ___
83532	NYC PS-1 Boxcar "175001," sound (std O), 16		130 ___
83533	PRR PS-1 Boxcar "47005," sound (std O), 16		130 ___
83534	UP PS-1 Boxcar "196883," sound (std O), 16		130 ___
83535	PRR GL-a 2-bay Hopper 3-pack #1 (std O), 16		220 ___
83539	PRR GL-a 2-bay Hopper 3-pack #2 (std O), 16		220 ___
83544	PRR N5b Caboose "477797" (std O), 16		95 ___
83545	PFE Reefer 3-pack (std O), 16		170 ___
83549	AT&SF Reefer 3-pack (std O), 16		300 ___
83553	Heisler Log Train Set, CC, 16		1450 ___
83555	Red Logging Disconnect Caboose "1" (std O), 16		40 ___
83556	Brown Logging Disconnect Caboose "6" (std O), 16		40 ___
83557	Logging Disconnect Boxcar (std O), 16		40 ___
83558	Logging Disconnect Flatcar (std O), 16		35 ___
83559	Logging Disconnect Gondola (std O), 16		40 ___
83560	Logging Disconnect Tank Car (std O), 16		40 ___
83561	ATSF Express 50' DD Boxcar "1342" (std O), 16-17		80 ___

		Exc	Mint
___ 83562	CNJ PS-1 Express Boxcar "22487" (std O), 16-17		80
___ 83563	C&EI PS-1 Express Boxcar "2" (std O), 16-17		80
___ 83564	GN PS-1 Express Boxcar "2538" (std O), 16-17		80
___ 83565	KCS PS-1 Express Boxcar "400" (std O), 16-17		80
___ 83566	SP PS-1 Express Boxcar "5712" (std O), 16-17		80
___ 83567	T&P PS-1 Express Boxcar "1721" (std O), 16-17		80
___ 83568	C&S Grain-door PS-1 Boxcar "1650" (std O), 16-17		80
___ 83569	CP Grain-door PS-1 Boxcar "260293" (std O), 16-17		80
___ 83570	GN Grain-door PS-1 Boxcar "18119" (std O), 16-17		80
___ 83571	CGW Grain-door PS-1 Boxcar "5450" (std O), 16-17		80
___ 83572	IC Grain-door PS-1 Boxcar "19000" (std O), 16-17		80
___ 83573	MKT Grain-door PS-1 Boxcar "92463" (std O), 16-17		80
___ 83574	UP CA-4 Caboose "3824" (std O), 16		90
___ 83575	UP CA-4 Caboose "25121" (std O), 16		90
___ 83576	B&O Milk Car "847" (std O), 16-17, 20		90
___ 83577	Supplee Milk Car "7" (std O), 16-17, 20		90
___ 83578	Hood Milk Car "807" (std O), 16-17, 20		90
___ 83579	Rutland Milk Car "351" (std O), 16-17, 20		90
___ 83580	BAR State of Maine 40' Trailer, 2-pack, 16-17		65
___ 83581	C&NW 40' Trailer, 2-pack, 16-17		65
___ 83582	PFE 40' Trailer, 2-pack, 16-17		65
___ 83583	PC 40' Trailer, 2-pack, 16-17		65
___ 83584	SP 40' Trailer, 2-pack, 16-17		65
___ 83585	UP 40' Trailer, 2-pack, 16-17		65
___ 83586	PRR Broadway Limited 21" Passenger Car 2-pack #2 (std O), 16		300
___ 83589	American Freedom Train Add-On 2-pack #2, 16-17		300
___ 83592	American Freedom Train Add-On 2-pack #3, 16-17		300
___ 83595	Conrail Office Car Special Diesel Passenger Set, CC, 17		1250
___ 83601	Conrail Office Car Special Add-on 2-pack, 17		310
___ 83604	Conrail Office Car Special 21" Dome Car "55," StationSounds , 17		320
___ 83605	Presidents 2-8-2 Mikado Locomotive "1789," 16-17		430
___ 83606	Halloween 2-8-2 Mikado Locomotive "1031," 16-17		430
___ 83607	USRA2-8-2 Mikado Locomotive "4500," 16-18		430
___ 83608	B&O 2-8-2 Mikado Locomotive "4500," 16-17		430
___ 83609	C&O 2-8-2 Mikado Locomotive "1067," 16-17		430
___ 83610	MKT 2-8-2 Mikado Locomotive "851," 16-17		430
___ 83611	NYC Empire State Express 21" Coach 4-pack #2, 17		620
___ 83616	NYC Empire State Express 21" Combine/Observation Car 2-pack #2, 17		310
___ 83617	NYC Empire State Express Martin Van Buren Combine, 19		155
___ 83618	NYC Empire State Express Franklin Roosevelt Observation, 19		155
___ 83619	NYC Empire State Express 21" Diner #2, StationSounds, 17		310
___ 83620	Hogwarts Express Passenger Set, 16-17		400
___ 83624	UP Sherman Hill Scout RS-3 Freight Set, 16-17		500
___ 83633	Alaska Gold Mint Car, 17		70
___ 83634	Keystone Smoke Fluid Loader, 16-20		350
___ 83635	North American Smoke Fluid Loader, 16-19		350
___ 83637	Mets-Phillies Mascot Aquarium Car, 16		85
___ 83644	Macy's Dry Goods Boxcar, 15 u		100
___ 83645	Polar Express Boxcar 2-pack, 16-18		170
___ 83648	New York Yankees Subway Set, 16		390
___ 83653	Scale Passenger Car Figures, 24-pack, 16-23		33
___ 83655	Hamm's Heritage Beer Wood-sided Reefer, 16-17		80

No.	Description	Exc	Mint
83656	Coors Heritage Beer Wood-sided Reefer, 16-17		80 ___
83657	Miller Heritage Beer Wood-sided Reefer, 16-17		80 ___
83658	Lionelville School Kit, 16-17		60 ___
83659	PRR Keystone Special Steam Freight Set, 16-17		280 ___
83688	Trackside Railroad Details Pack, 16-23		33 ___
83689	Angela Trotta Thomas Christmas Covered Bridge, 17-20		70 ___
83690	Company Row House, blue, 16-17		60 ___
83691	Company Row House, yellow, 16-17		60 ___
83692	Company Row House, white, 16-17		60 ___
83693	Company Row House, red, 16-17		60 ___
83694	Toymaker Limited Trolley Set, 18		200 ___
83696	NYC "Pacemaker" Lionel Junction Diesel Freight Set, 17		175 ___
83701	Alaska Gold Mine 0-4-0 Steam Freight Set, LionChief, 17		320 ___
83716	BNSF RS-3 Diesel Scout Freight Set, LionChief, 17		280 ___
83733	Lighted Aquarius Hi-Cube Boxcar, 17		90 ___
83734	Lighted Pegasus Hi-Cube Boxcar, 17		90 ___
83745	Lionelville Hospital Kit, 17-18		80 ___
83751	Illuminated Yard Tower, 18-19, 22-23		65 ___
83752	W&A Horse Car and Corral, 17-18		180 ___
83762	Personalized Christmas Boxcar, 16		90 ___
83763	Personalized Holiday Boxcar, 16		90 ___
83764	Happy Birthday Boxcar, 16		90 ___
83765	Anniversary Boxcar, 16-17		90 ___
83766	Personalized Polar Express Baggage Car, 16-18		95 ___
83779	Pearl Harbor 75th Anniversary Boxcar, 16-17		85 ___
83783	Rosie the Riveter Boxcar, 17		85 ___
83784	Heavies and Little Friends Boxcar, 17		85 ___
83785	Doolittle Raid Boxcar, 16-17		85 ___
83786	D-Day Boxcar, 17		85 ___
83788	Uncle Sam "Enlist Now" Boxcar, 16-17		85 ___
83790	Mickey Mouse Happy Holidays Boxcar, 17		85 ___
83791	Donald Duck Happy Holidays Boxcar, 17		85 ___
83792	Goofy Happy Holidays Boxcar, 17		85 ___
83794	75th Anniversary of Bambi Boxcar, 17		80 ___
83795	50th Anniversary of The Jungle Book Boxcar, 17		80 ___
83796	100th Anniversary Moon Pie Boxcar, 17		85 ___
83800	Happy Thanksgiving Boxcar, 17		80 ___
83801	Happy Hanukkah Boxcar, 17		80 ___
83802	Disney Happy Halloween Boxcar, 17		85 ___
83913	Personalized Halloween Boxcar, 17		95 ___
83918	Smithsonian Boxcar, John Bull, 17		85 ___
83923	Angela Trotta Thomas Santa's Cookies Boxcar, 17		85 ___
83924	Caddyshack Boxcar, 17		80 ___
83925	Frosty the Snowman Boxcar, 17		85 ___
83926	Personalized Polar Express Boxcar, 17-20		95 ___
83927	Lionel Smoke Fluid 1-D Tank Car, 17		75 ___
83928	Lionel Paint 1-D Tank Car, 17		75 ___
83929	Lionel Hydraulic Oil 1-D Tank Car, 17		75 ___
83938	Harry Potter Hogwarts House Gryffindor Boxcar, 17		80 ___
83939	Harry Potter Hogwarts House Ravenclaw Boxcar, 17		80 ___
83940	Harry Potter Hogwarts House Hufflepuff Boxcar, 17		80 ___
83941	Harry Potter Hogwarts House Slytherin Boxcar, 17		80 ___
83943	Polar Express Boxcar, 17-18		85 ___

		Exc	Mint
___ 83944	John Deere Boxcar, 17		85
___ 83945	Richard Nixon Presidential Boxcar, 17		70
___ 83946	Jimmy Carter Presidential Boxcar, 17, 19		70
___ 83947	Woodrow Wilson Presidential Boxcar, 17, 19-20		75
___ 83948	William Howard Taft Presidential Boxcar, 17, 19-20		75
___ 83950	Personalized "It's A Boy" Boxcar, 17-23		100
___ 83951	Personalized "It's A Girl" Boxcar, 17-23		100
___ 83952	Minnie Mouse Happy Holidays Boxcar, 17		85
___ 83959	Macy's Parade 90th Anniversary Boxcar, 16 u		30
___ 83964	Mickey Mouse Christmas Express Steam Freight Set, 17-18		420
___ 83972	Harry Potter Hogwarts Steam Passenger Set, LionChief, 17-19		420
___ 83974	CSX Diesel Intermodal Set, LionChief, 17-18		460
___ 83979	Mickey & Friends Express Steam Freight Set, LC, 17-20		370
___ 83984	Pennsylvania Flyer 0-8-0 Freight Set, LionChief, 17-20		300
___ 83994	C&NW Boxcar, 17		100
___ 84000	DETX Rotary Gondola 4-pack (std O), 16-17, 20-23		310
___ 84005	CSX Rotary Gondola 4-pack (std O), 16-17, 20-22		310
___ 84010	UP Rotary Gondola 4-pack (std O), 16-17, 20-22		310
___ 84015	NS Rotary Gondola 4-pack (std O), 16-17, 20-22		310
___ 84020	PPLX Rotary Gondola 4-pack (std O), 16-17, 20-23		310
___ 84025	PPLX Rotary Gondola 2-pack (std O), 16-17, 20-23		155
___ 84028	BNSF Rotary Gondola 4-pack (std O), 16-17, 20-22		310
___ 84033	BNSF Rotary Gondola 2-pack (std O), 16-17, 20-23		155
___ 84045	BN 21" Passenger Car 4-pack, 17		620
___ 84050	BN 21" Coach 2-pack, 17		310
___ 84053	BN 21" Diner, StationSounds, 17		310
___ 84063	Weathered N&W Y6B 2-8-8-2 Locomotive "2186," CC, 16		2200
___ 84064	MILW 4-8-4 Northern Locomotive "261," CC, 17		1700
___ 84065	MILW 4-8-4 Northern Locomotive "265," CC, 17		1700
___ 84066	MILW 4-8-4 Northern Locomotive "262," CC, 17		1700
___ 84067	MILW 4-8-4 Northern Locomotive "260 Hiawatha," CC, 17		1700
___ 84068	DL&W 4-8-4 Northern Locomotive "1661," CC, 17		1700
___ 84069	B&M 2-6-0 Mogul Locomotive "1397," CC, 16		700
___ 84070	CV 2-6-0 Mogul Locomotive "397," CC, 16		700
___ 84071	DL&W 2-6-0 Mogul Locomotive "565," CC, 16		700
___ 84072	Everett 2-6-0 Mogul Locomotive "11," CC, 16		700
___ 84073	GT 2-6-0 Mogul Locomotive "713," CC, 16		700
___ 84074	Rutland 2-6-0 Mogul Locomotive "145," CC, 16		700
___ 84075	ACL E8 Diesel AA Set "544, 545," CC, 17		1000
___ 84078	BN E8 Diesel AA Set "9935, 9940," CC, 17		1000
___ 84081	Conrail E8 Diesel AA Set "4020, 4021," CC, 17		1000
___ 84084	EMD Demonstrator E8 Diesel A Unit "950," CC, 17		650
___ 84085	L&N E8 Diesel AA Set "796, 797," CC, 17		1000
___ 84088	NYC E8 Diesel AA Set "4036, 4037," CC, 17		1000
___ 84091	PRR E8 Diesel AA Set "5763, 5764," CC, 17		1000
___ 84094	Arkansas & Missouri SD70ACe Diesel Locomotive "70," CC, 16		650
___ 84095	Arkansas & Missouri SD70ACe Diesel Locomotive "71," CC, 16		650
___ 84096	BNSF SD70ACe Diesel Locomotive "9372," CC, 16		650
___ 84097	BNSF SD70ACe Diesel Locomotive "9385," CC, 16		650
___ 84098	CN SD70ACe Diesel Locomotive "8100," CC, 16		650
___ 84099	CN SD70ACe Diesel Locomotive "8102," CC, 16		650
___ 84100	CSX SD70ACe Diesel Locomotive "4837," CC, 16		650
___ 84101	CSX SD70ACe Diesel Locomotive "4843," CC, 16		650

		Exc	Mint
84102	EMDX SD70ACe Diesel Locomotive "72," CC, 16		650
84103	EMDX SD70ACe Diesel Locomotive "73," CC, 16		650
84104	Montana Rail Link SD70ACe Diesel Locomotive "4309" CC, 16		650
84105	Montana Rail Link SD70ACe Diesel Locomotive "4312" CC, 16		650
84106	UP SD70ACe Diesel Locomotive "8360," CC, 16		650
84107	UP SD70ACe Diesel Locomotive "8415," CC, 16		650
84108	GN GP7 Diesel "601," 16-18		330
84109	L&N GP7 Diesel "405," 16-18		330
84110	Reading GP7 Diesel "619," 16-18		330
84111	WP GP7 Diesel "707," 16-18		330
84112	Cotton Belt 50' DD Boxcar "47509" (std O), 16-17		80
84113	D&RGW 50' DD Boxcar "63689" (std O), 16-17		80
84114	Seaboard 50' DD Boxcar "10090" (std O), 16-17		80
84115	PRR K4s 4-6-2 Pacific Locomotive "5385," CC, 16		1300
84116	PRR K4s 4-6-2 Pacific Locomotive "5432," CC, 16		1300
84117	Burlington Refrigerator Express 40' Steel Reefer (std O), 17		85
84118	BAR 40' Steel Reefer "7342" (std O), 17		85
84119	BN 40' Steel Reefer "70609" (std O), 17		85
84120	Eastern States ERDX 40' Steel Reefer "10060" (std O), 17		85
84121	National Car Co. 40' Steel Reefer "2430" (std O), 17		85
84122	FGE 40' Steel Reefer "41475" (std O), 17		85
84123	B&M PS-2CD Covered Hopper "5717" (std O), 17		90
84124	L&N PS-2CD Covered Hopper "37399" (std O), 17		90
84125	MILW PS-2CD Covered Hopper "98333" (std O), 17		90
84126	NP PS-2CD Covered Hopper "75675" (std O), 17		90
84127	AT&SF PS-2CD Covered Hopper "304713" (std O), 17		90
84128	TLDX Demonstrator PS-2CD Covered Hopper "91" (std O), 17, 19		90
84129	AT&SF Wide Vision Caboose "999705" (std O), 17		95
84130	BN Freedom Train Wide Vision Caboose "12618" (std O), 17		95
84131	BNSF Wide Vision Caboose "12584" (std O), 17		95
84132	CSX Wide Vision Caboose "903180" (std O), 17		95
84133	D&H Wide-Vision Caboose "35712," 18		100
84134	GN Wide-Vision Caboose "X-109," 18		100
84135	C&O Northeast Caboose "A918" (std O), 17		90
84137	Conrail Northeast Caboose "18866" (std O), 17		90
84138	Pere Marquette Northeast Caboose "A909" (std O), 17		90
84139	WM Northeast Caboose circle herald "1874" (std O), 17		90
84140	WM Northeast Caboose circus herald "1882" (std O), 17		90
84141	WM USRA 2-bay Hopper 3-pack #1 (std O), 17		220
84145	WM USRA 2-bay Hopper 3-pack #2 (std O), 17		220
84149	Reading USRA 2-bay Hopper 3-pack (std O), 17		220
84153	B&O 1905 2-bay Hopper 3-pack (std O), 17		220
84157	Bethlehem Steel 1905 2-bay Hopper 3-pack (std O), 17		220
84161	Logging Disconnect Stock Car, 17		40
84163	Logging Disconnect Christmas 4-pack (std O), 17		160
84165	Logging Disconnect Dinner Train 4-pack (std O), 17, 19		160
84166	Logging Disconnect, 1-pair, brown (std O), 17, 19		65
84167	Logging Disconnect, 2-pair, brown (std O), 17		125
84187	B&O 18" Heavyweight Coach 2-pack #1, 18		400
84190	B&O 18" Heavyweight Coach 2-pack #2, 18		400
84193	Reading, Blue Mountain & Northern 18" Heavyweight Coach 2-pack #1, 18		400
84196	Reading, Blue Mountain & Northern 18" Heavyweight Coach 2-pack #2, 18		400

			Exc	Mint
___	84199	MILW 18" Heavyweight Coach 2-pack #1, 18		400
___	84202	MILW 18" Heavyweight Coach 2-pack #2, 18		400
___	84205	Nickel Plate Road 18" Heavyweight Coach 2-pack #1, 18		400
___	84208	Nickel Plate Road 18" Heavyweight Coach 2-pack #2, 18		400
___	84211	TH&B 18" Heavyweight Coach 2-pack #1, 18		400
___	84214	TH&B 18" Heavyweight Coach 2-pack #1, 18		400
___	84217	Wabash 18" Heavyweight Coach 2-pack #1, 18		400
___	84220	Wabash 18" Heavyweight Coach 2-pack #2, 18		400
___	84226	American Freedom Train Add-On 2-pack #4, 17		300
___	84229	Conrail 21" Theater Inspection Car "9", 17		340
___	84230	NS 21" Theater Inspection Car Buena Vista, 17		340
___	84231	CSX 21" Theater Inspection Car Alabama, 17		340
___	84232	UP 21" Theater Inspection Car Fox River, 17		340
___	84237	Cass Scenic RR 3-Truck Shay Locomotive "6," CC, 17		1500
___	84238	Elk River Lumber Co. 3-Truck Shay Locomotive "20," CC, 17		1500
___	84239	WM 3-Truck Shay Locomotive "6," CC, 17		1500
___	84240	West Side Lumber Co. 3-Truck Shay Locomotive "3," CC, 17		1500
___	84248	SP AC-9 2-8-8-4 Locomotive "3800," CC, 17		2000
___	84249	SP AC-9 2-8-8-4 Locomotive "3805," CC, 17		2000
___	84250	SP AC-9 Daylight 2-8-8-4 Locomotive "3811," CC, 17		2000
___	84251	AT&SF 2-8-4 Berkshire Locomotive "4103," 17-18		450
___	84252	Nickel Plate Road 2-8-4 Berkshire Locomotive "767," 17-18		450
___	84253	Pere Marquette 2-8-4 Berkshire Locomotive "1223," 17-18		450
___	84254	IC 2-8-4 Berkshire Locomotive "8006," 17-18		450
___	84255	Lionel Lines 2-8-4 Berkshire Locomotive "726," 17-18		450
___	84256	AT&SF SD40 Diesel "5006," CC, 17		650
___	84257	AT&SF SD40 Diesel "5018," CC, 17		650
___	84258	UP SD40 Diesel "4057," CC, 17		650
___	84259	UP SD40 Diesel "4062," CC, 17		650
___	84260	CSX SD40 Diesel "4614," CC, 17		650
___	84261	CSX SD40 Diesel "4621," CC, 17		650
___	84262	PRR SD40 Diesel "6041," CC, 17		650
___	84263	PRR SD40 Diesel "6089," CC, 17		650
___	84264	Southern SD40 Diesel "3170," CC, 17		650
___	84265	Southern SD40 Diesel "3200," CC, 17		650
___	84267	SP SD40R Diesel "7372," CC, 17		650
___	84268	WM SD40 Diesel "7547," CC, 17		650
___	84269	WM SD40 Diesel "7549," CC, 17		650
___	84270	B&O EMD Torpedo GP9 Diesel "3414," CC, 18		550
___	84271	B&O EMD Torpedo GP9 Diesel "3419," CC, 18		550
___	84272	C&NW EMD Torpedo GP9 Diesel "1725," CC, 18		550
___	84273	C&NW EMD Torpedo GP9 Diesel "1730," CC, 18		550
___	84274	MILW EMD Torpedo GP9 Diesel "202," CC, 18		550
___	84275	MILW EMD Torpedo GP9 Diesel "208," CC, 18		550
___	84276	Nickel Plate Road EMD Torpedo GP9 Diesel "482," CC, 18		550
___	84277	Nickel Plate Road EMD Torpedo GP9 Diesel "484," CC, 18		550
___	84278	TH&B EMD Torpedo GP9 Diesel "402," CC, 18		550
___	84279	TH&B EMD Torpedo GP9 Diesel "403," CC, 18		550
___	84280	Wabash EMD Torpedo GP9 Diesel "484," CC, 18		550
___	84281	Wabash EMD Torpedo GP9 Diesel "486," CC, 18		550
___	84282	BN GE U33C Diesel "5716," CC, 18		580
___	84283	BN GE U33C Diesel "5723," CC, 18		580
___	84284	D&H GE U33C Diesel "757," CC, 18		580

		Exc	Mint
84285	D&H GE U33C Diesel "762," CC, 18		580 ___
84286	Guilford D&H GE U33C Diesel "650," CC, 18		580 ___
84287	Guilford D&H GE U33C Diesel "654," CC, 18		580 ___
84288	GN GE U33C Diesel "2530," CC, 18		580 ___
84289	GN GE U33C Diesel "2541," CC, 18		580 ___
84290	IC GE U33C Diesel "5052," CC, 18		580 ___
84291	IC GE U33C Diesel "5054," CC, 18		580 ___
84292	PC GE U33C Diesel "6547," CC, 18		580 ___
84293	PC GE U33C Diesel "6561," CC, 18		580 ___
84294	Sacramento Trolley, 17-18		100 ___
84295	Connecticut Trolley, 17-18		100 ___
84296	SP Salad Bowl Express Diesel Freight Set, CC, 17		900 ___
84297	Logging Disconnect Steel Tank Car (std O), 17		40 ___
84303	Bucking Feed and Tack, 17		85 ___
84304	CB&Q Gondola with covers, 17		55 ___
84306	Illuminated John Deere Flagpole, 17-18		60 ___
84307	Lionel Illuminated Flagpole, 17-18, 22-23		45 ___
84308	Gray Half-Covered Bridge, 17		60 ___
84309	PRR Blinking Water Tower, 17-18		45 ___
84310	Modular Train Car Repair Facility, 16-17		110 ___
84312	Alaska RR Gondola with canisters, 17, 19		55 ___
84314	BNSF ACF Covered Hopper "405850," 18		60 ___
84315	Branchline Water Tank Kit, 16-23		40 ___
84317	Passenger Station, 17		80 ___
84318	Illuminated Station Platform, 17-23		55 ___
84327	Santa Fe Operating Billboard, 17		70 ___
84328	Polar Express Steam Passenger Set, LionChief, 17-19		420 ___
84328P	Polar Express Steam Passenger Set w/Personalized Tender, 19-20		420 ___
84330	Witches Brew 1-D Tank Car, 17-18		70 ___
84332	Halloween Boxcar, SpookySounds, 17-18		80 ___
84333	Strasburg RR Gondola with vats, 17, 19		65 ___
84334	Strasburg Half-covered Bridge, 17-18		60 ___
84335	PRR Culvert Gondola "374200," 17, 19		65 ___
84336	UP Log Car, 17		65 ___
84337	MKT Wood-chip Hopper, 17		65 ___
84338	CSX Wood-chip Hopper, 17-18		65 ___
84339	SP Jumping Hobo Boxcar, 17		80 ___
84340	Santa and Snowman Operating Boxcar, 17-18		90 ___
84341	Tell-Tale Reindeer Car, 17		80 ___
84366	PRR Wood-chip Hopper, 17-19		65 ___
84367	Christmas Pylon, 17		160 ___
84369	NYC Welding Car "X939," 17		80 ___
84370	Polar Express Hopper with silver, 17-18		70 ___
84371	Mickey's Holiday Hopper with presents, 17-18		70 ___
84372	Christmas Station Platform, 17-18		43 ___
84373	Special Trolley Announcement Track, 18-23		60 ___
84374	Christmas Music Boxcar, 17		80 ___
84375	Christmas Boxcar, 17		65 ___
84376	Angela Trotta Thomas Express Aquarium Car, 17-18		85 ___
84377	Christmas Peppermint 1-D Tank Car, 17-18		60 ___
84378	Santa's Choice Milk Car with platform, 17-18		180 ___
84380	Reading & Northern Auxiliary Tender "425-A," CC, 18		300 ___

		Exc	Mint
___ 84383	Elevated Oil Tank, 17-18		95
___ 84388	Gray 10" Girder Bridge, 17-23		25
___ 84400	BN "Pulling for Freedom" SD60M Diesel "1991," CC, 17		650
___ 84401	BN SD60M Diesel "9200," CC, 17		650
___ 84402	BN SD60M Diesel "9225," CC, 17		650
___ 84403	Soo Line SD60M Diesel "6058," CC, 17		650
___ 84404	Soo Line SD60M Diesel "6061," CC, 17		650
___ 84405	Conrail SD60M Diesel "5504," CC, 17		650
___ 84406	Conrail SD60M Diesel "5510," CC, 17		650
___ 84407	CSX SD60M Diesel "8783," CC, 17		650
___ 84408	CSX SD60M Diesel "8784," CC, 17		650
___ 84409	NS SD60M Diesel "6808," CC, 17		760
___ 84410	NS SD60M Diesel "6815," CC, 17		650
___ 84411	UP SD60M Diesel "6165," CC, 17		650
___ 84412	UP SD60M Diesel "6187," CC, 17		650
___ 84413	B&O FA A-A Diesel Set, "814, 815," 17-18		500
___ 84416	GN FA A-A Diesel Set, "278A, 278B," 17-18		500
___ 84419	NH FA A-A Diesel Set, "417, 418," 17-18		500
___ 84422	UP FA A-A Diesel Set, "1616, 1617," 17-18		500
___ 84433	Polar Express 40' Scale Reefer "122517," 17		90
___ 84434	NS 30,000-gallon 1-D Tank Car 3-pack (std O), 16		250
___ 84438	NS 30,000-gallon 1-D Tank Car "362785" (std O), 16		80
___ 84439	UTLX 30,000-gallon 1-D Tank Car 3-pack (std O), 16		250
___ 84443	PESX 30,000-gallon 1-D Tank Car 3-pack (std O), 16, 19		250
___ 84447	TILX 30,000-gallon 1-D Tank Car 3-pack (std O), 16, 19		250
___ 84451	PRR Flatcar 6-pack, 17		120
___ 84452	AT&SF Flatcar 6-pack, 17-18		120
___ 84453	UP Flatcar 6-pack, 17-18		120
___ 84454	Trailer Train Flatcar 6-pack, 17		120
___ 84455	Assorted Flatcar 6-pack, 17-18		120
___ 84456	B&O Gondola 6-pack, 17-18		120
___ 84457	UP Gondola 6-pack, 17-18		120
___ 84458	East Assorted Gondola 6-pack, 17		120
___ 84459	Midwest Assorted Gondola 6-pack, 17		120
___ 84460	West Assorted Gondola 6-pack, 17-18		120
___ 84462	2-Rail Conversion Kit, 50-ton Scale Trucks, 16-23		20
___ 84463	2-Rail Conversion Kit, 70-ton Scale Trucks, 16-23		20
___ 84465	B&O 2-8-2 Light Mikado Locomotive "4500," CC, 17		1300
___ 84466	GTW 2-8-2 Light Mikado Locomotive "3734," CC, 17		1300
___ 84467	Maine Central 2-8-2 Light Mikado Locomotive "624," CC, 17		1300
___ 84468	NYC 2-8-2 Light Mikado Locomotive "5187," CC, 17		1300
___ 84469	PRR 2-8-2 Light Mikado Locomotive "9630," CC, 17		1300
___ 84470	Southern 2-8-2 Light Mikado Locomotive "4758," CC, 17		1300
___ 84471	UP 2-8-2 Light Mikado Locomotive "2537," CC, 17		1300
___ 84472	AT&SF 2-8-2 Mikado Locomotive, Brass Hybrid "3222," CC, 17		1300
___ 84480	John Deere Covered Bridge, 17-18		70
___ 84481	John Deere General Store, 17-18		85
___ 84482	John Deere Gondola with hay bales, 17-18		75
___ 84483	John Deere Grain Vat Car, 17		75
___ 84485	Disney Covered Bridge, 17-18		70
___ 84486	MILW NW2 Diesel Locomotive "1649," CC, 16		500
___ 84487	Donald Duck Holiday 1-D Tank Car, 17		70
___ 84489	Polar Express Covered Bridge, 17-18		70

		Exc	Mint
84490	NS First Responders Diesel Freight Set, LionChief, 17-18		450 ___
84496	Shell Service Station, 17		150 ___
84498	NS Fire Rescue Car, 17-18		75 ___
84499	Mickey Mouse & Friends Industrial Water Tower, 17-20		100 ___
84500	NS Unibody 1-D Tank Car "490112," 17-18		75 ___
84507	New York Central & Hudson River S2 Electric "3207," CC, 17		800 ___
84508	NYC S2 Electric "113," CC, 17		800 ___
84509	NYC S2 Electric "115," CC, 17		800 ___
84510	PC S2 Electric "4710," CC, 17		800 ___
84511	NYC "Lightning Stripe" S2 Electric "101," CC, 17		800 ___
84512	S2 Electric Scale Tinplate Freight Set, CC, 17		1000 ___
84525	Uptown Apartment Building, 17		100 ___
84526	Leuzure Marble Co. Warehouse, 17		110 ___
84529	NS Veterans Wide Vision Caboose "6920" (std O), 17-18		95 ___
84530	NS First Responders W-V Caboose "9-1-1" (std O), 17-18		95 ___
84532	Nickel Plate Road 2-8-2 Light Mikado Locomotive "587," CC, 17		1300 ___
84538	NS 65' Mill Gondola "195029" (std O), 17		80 ___
84539	NS 65' Mill Gondola "195065" (std O), 17		80 ___
84553	Logging Disconnect Reindeer Train 4-pack A, 17		160 ___
84554	Logging Disconnect Reindeer Train 4-pack B, 17		160 ___
84555	Logging Disconnect Santa Claus Observation (std O), 17		45 ___
84562	BN "Pulling for Freedom" SD60M Diesel "1991," LionChief, 17		500 ___
84563	BN SD60M Diesel "9215," LionChief, 17		500 ___
84564	Soo Line SD60M Diesel "6060," LionChief, 17		500 ___
84565	Conrail SD60M Diesel "5509," LionChief, 17		500 ___
84566	CSX SD60M Diesel "8757," LionChief, 17		500 ___
84567	NS SD60M Diesel "6810," LionChief, 17		500 ___
84568	UP SD60M Diesel "6170," LionChief, 17		500 ___
84570	First Responders EMT Boxcar, 17-22		100 ___
84571	First Responders Personalized Police Boxcar, 17-23		100 ___
84572	First Responders Fire Fighter Boxcar, 17-22		100 ___
84573	Happy Birthday Boxcar, 17		90 ___
84574	Personalized 2017 Merry Christmas Boxcar, 17		90 ___
84575	U.S. Army Boxcar, 17-23		100 ___
84576	U.S. Marine Boxcar, 17-23		100 ___
84577	U.S. Air Force Boxcar, 17-23		100 ___
84578	U.S. Navy Boxcar, 17-23		100 ___
84579	U.S. Coast Guard Boxcar, 17-22		100 ___
84580	From The Home Front Boxcar, blue, 17-22		100 ___
84581	From The Home Front Boxcar, green, 17-22		100 ___
84582	BNSF 65' Mill Gondola "518375" (std O), 17		80 ___
84583	BNSF 65' Mill Gondola "518392" (std O), 17		80 ___
84584	C&NW 65' Mill Gondola "342045" (std O), 17		80 ___
84585	C&NW 65' Mill Gondola "342049" (std O), 17		80 ___
84586	CSX 65' Mill Gondola "491616" (std O), 17		80 ___
84587	CSX 65' Mill Gondola "491638" (std O), 17		80 ___
84590	SP 65' Mill Gondola "365136" (std O), 17		80 ___
84591	SP 65' Mill Gondola "365142" (std O), 17		80 ___
84592	UP 65' Mill Gondola "96267" (std O), 17		80 ___
84593	UP 65' Mill Gondola "96281" (std O), 17		80 ___
84599	Bucking Feed & Tack Building, 18-20		85 ___
84600	Polar Express Combination Car, 18-23		85 ___
84601	Polar Express Letters to Santa Mail Car, 18-23		85 ___

			Exc	Mint
___	84602	Polar Express Disappearing Hobo Car, 18-23		90
___	84603	Polar Express Hot Chocolate Car, 18-19, 22-23		85
___	84604	Polar Express Diner, 18-23		85
___	84605	Polar Express Baggage Car, 18-23		85
___	84605P	Personalized Polar Express Baggage Car, 19-20		95
___	84608	Smithsonian Boxcar, Southern "1401," 17		85
___	84611	Lionel BlueTooth Radio Tower, 17		100
___	84616	Wonder Woman Boxcar, 17		80
___	84621	17 National Lionel Train Day Boxcar, 17		85
___	84622	D&RGW EMD SD40T-2 Diesel "5401," CC, 17		600
___	84623	D&RGW EMD SD40T-2 Diesel "5405," CC, 17		600
___	84624	KCS EMD SD40T-2 Diesel "6102," CC, 17		600
___	84625	KCS EMD SD40T-2 Diesel "6110," CC, 17		600
___	84626	Lancaster & Chester EMD SD40T-2 Diesel "6002," CC, 17		600
___	84627	GECX EMD SD40T-2 Diesel "8661," CC, 17		600
___	84628	GECX EMD SD40T-2 Diesel "8678," CC, 17		600
___	84629	Ohio Central EMD SD40T-2 Diesel "4026," CC, 17		600
___	84630	Ohio Central EMD SD40T-2 Diesel "4027," CC, 17		600
___	84631	RJ Corman EMD SD40T-2 Diesel "5361," CC, 17		600
___	84632	RJ Corman EMD SD40T-2 Diesel "5409," CC, 17		600
___	84633	SP EMD SD40T-2 Diesel "8532," CC, 17		600
___	84634	SP EMD SD40T-2 Diesel "8548," CC, 17		600
___	84635	UP EMD SD40T-2 Diesel "8593," CC, 17		600
___	84636	UP EMD SD40T-2 Diesel "8715," CC, 17		600
___	84637	Cotton Belt EMD SD40T-2 Diesel "9389," Bicentennial, CC, 17		600
___	84638	ACL EMD E6 A-A Diesel Set "500-501," CC, 17		1000
___	84641	AT&SF EMD E6 A-A Diesel Set "12-13," CC, 17		1000
___	84644	C&NW EMD E6 A-A Diesel Set "5005A-5005B," CC, 17		1000
___	84647	FEC EMD E3 A-A Diesel Set "1001-1002," CC, 17		1000
___	84650	IC EMD E6 A-A Diesel Set "4003-4004," CC, 17		1000
___	84653	KCS EMD E3 A-A Diesel Set "2-3," CC, 17		1000
___	84656	L&N EMD E6 A-A Diesel Set "754-755," CC, 17		1000
___	84659	MILW EMD E6 A-A Diesel Set "15A-15B," CC, 17		1000
___	84662	UP EMD E6 A-A Diesel Set "996-997," CC, 17		1000
___	84666	Battle for Guadalcanal Boxcar, 17		85
___	84667	Battle of the Bulge Boxcar, 17		85
___	84668	Silent Service Boxcar, 17		85
___	84669	Desert Storm Boxcar, 18, 20		90
___	84670	Korean War Boxcar, 18, 20		85
___	84671	Vietnam War Boxcar, 18, 20		85
___	84672	Memorial Day Boxcar, 18, 20		90
___	84674	ATSF 2-8-2 Mikado Locomotive, Brass Hybrid, Painted, Unlettered, CC, 17		1300
___	84675	ATSF 2-8-2 Mikado, Brass Hybrid, Unpainted, CC, 17		1300
___	84676	Peanuts Hilltop Boxcar, 18		90
___	84677	Peanuts Meadow Boxcar, 18		90
___	84678	Peanuts Winter Boxcar, 18		90
___	84679	ATSF 4-6-2 Pacific "1369," LionChief Plus, 17-18		450
___	84680	CNJ 4-6-2 Pacific Locomotive "832," LionChief Plus, 17-18		450
___	84681	Alton 4-6-2 Pacific "5299," LionChief Plus, 17-18		450
___	84682	Southern 4-6-2 Pacific "1401," LionChief Plus, 17-18		450
___	84683	MILW 4-6-2 Pacific Locomotive "810," LionChief Plus, 17-18		450
___	84685	Polar Express Scale 2-8-4 Berkshire Locomotive "1225," CC, 17		1500

		Exc	Mint
84686	Nickel Plate Road 2-8-4 Berkshire Locomotive "759," CC, 17	1500	___
84687	Nickel Plate Road 2-8-4 Berkshire Locomotive "765," CC, 17	1500	___
84688	Nickel Plate Road 2-8-4 Berkshire Locomotive "767," CC, 17	1500	___
84689	Southern 2-8-4 Berkshire Locomotive "2716," CC, 17	1500	___
84690	W&LE 2-8-4 Berkshire Locomotive "6401," CC, 17	1500	___
84691	American Railroads 2-8-4 Berkshire Locomotive "759," CC, 17	1500	___
84692	RF&P 2-8-4 Berkshire Locomotive "752," CC, 17	1500	___
84693	Pere Marquette 2-8-4 Berkshire Locomotive "1225," CC, 17	1500	___
84694	Pere Marquette 2-8-4 Berkshire Locomotive "1223," CC, 17	1500	___
84695	L&N 2-8-4 Berkshire Locomotive "1992," CC, 17	1500	___
84696	D&H Alco RS-3 Diesel "4121," LionChief Plus, 17-18	350	___
84697	AT&SF Alco RS-3 Diesel "2099," LionChief Plus, 17-18	350	___
84698	Peabody Coal Short Line RS-3 "101," LionChief Plus, 17-19	350	___
84699	B&M Alco RS-3 Diesel "1536," LionChief Plus, 17-18	350	___
84700	Hot Wheels Diesel Freight Set, LionChief, 17-19	400	___
84705	Hot Wheels 50th Anniversary Auto Rack, 17-18	85	___
84706	Hot Wheels 50th Anniversary Auto Loader, 17-18	90	___
84707	Hot Wheels 50th Anniversary Flatcar w/Trailers, 17-18	85	___
84708	Hot Wheels Auto Rack, 18	85	___
84709	NH RS-3 Diesel Freight Set, LionChief, 18	300	___
84719	AT&SF Super Chief Diesel Passenger Set, LionChief, 18-22	500	___
84724	AT&SF Add-on Baggage Car "1386," 18-23	100	___
84725	AT&SF Add-on Vista Dome Car "500," 18-23	100	___
84726	SP Rising Sun 0-8-0 Steam Freight Set, LionChief, 17-18	320	___
84732	BNSF Tier 4 Modern Freight Set, LionChief, 18-20	400	___
84737	Construction Railroad Diesel Freight Set, LionChief, 18-19	350	___
84747	2018 Christmas Boxcar, 18	65	___
84748	Christmas Music Boxcar #18, 18	80	___
84754	Anheuser-Busch Clydesdale Old-Time Freight Set, 18-19	420	___
84760	Daisy Duck 1-D Tank Car, 18-20	75	___
84761	Chip 'n' Dale Chasing Gondola, 18-20	80	___
84762	SP Daylight 1-D Tank Car, 17-19	60	___
84763	Disney Villains Ursula Hi-Cube Boxcar, 18, 20	80	___
84764	Disney Villains Queen of Hearts Hi-Cube Boxcar, 18, 20	80	___
84765	Angela Trotta Thomas Christmas Passenger Car 2-pack, 18, 20	300	___
84766	Gondola w/Construction Signs, 18-19	65	___
84767	Harry Potter Dementors Coach w/Sound, 18-23	95	___
84768	Moe & Joe Lumber Flatcar, 18-19	90	___
84769	Wile E. Coyote & Road Runner Ambush Shack, 18-19	120	___
84770	Peabody Coal Hopper 6-pack, 18-20	150	___
84771	PRR Hopper 6-pack, 18-19	150	___
84772	N&W Hopper 6-pack, 18-20	150	___
84773	UP Hopper 6-pack, 18-20	150	___
84774	NS Hopper 6-pack, 18-20	150	___
84775	DM&IR Ore Car 6-pack, 18-19	150	___
84776	C&NW Ore Car 6-pack, 18-20	150	___
84777	GN Ore Car 6-pack, 18-20	150	___
84778	MILW Ore Car 6-pack, 18-19	150	___
84779	B&LE Ore Car 6-pack, 18-20	150	___
84780	U.S. Caboose, 18	75	___
84781	ELX Halloween Caboose, 18-20	75	___
84782	Presidential Caboose, 18-20	75	___
84784	John Deere Harvest Dump Car, 18-19	80	___

			Exc	Mint
___	84785	Naughty or Nice Ore Car 2-pack, 18		80
___	84786	Christmas Essentials Barrel Car, 18-19		70
___	84787	Santa Freight Lines Steam Set, LionChief, 18-19		300
___	84792	House Under Construction, 18-19		100
___	84794	Budweiser Bar & Grille, 18		90
___	84795	Deluxe Christmas House, 18, 20		130
___	84797	Christmas Industrial Water Tower, 18, 20		85
___	84798	Hunting Rabbit Car, 18-19		85
___	84799	Marvin the Martian Earth Stomper Flatcar, 18-19		95
___	84801	Justice League Boxcar, 17		85
___	84802	Gilbson Wine 1-D Tank Car "66719," 17		75
___	84803	Tidewater 1-D Tank Car "1367," 17		75
___	84804	A.E. Staley 1-D Tank Car "704," 17		75
___	84805	Mid-Continent Petroleum 1-D Tank Car "1018," 17		75
___	84806	Shell 1-D Tank Car "662," 17		75
___	84807	John Deere 1-D Tank Car "236," 17		75
___	84810	Polar Express 1-D Tank Car "122518," 17		75
___	84811	Polar Express Scale Baggage Car, 17		200
___	84812	Polar Express Scale Combine, 17		200
___	84813	Polar Express Scale Coach, 17		200
___	84814	Polar Express Scale Diner, 17		200
___	84815	Polar Express Scale Observation, 17		200
___	84816	PRR 1930 Broadway Limited Steam Passenger Set, CC, 17		2000
___	84821	PRR Heavyweight Combine Liberty Hill, 17-18		200
___	84822	PRR Heavyweight Sleeper Cent Fawn, 17-18		200
___	84823	PRR Heavyweight Sleeper Central Park, 17-18		200
___	84824	PRR Heavyweight Sleeper Lafayette Square, 17-18		200
___	84825	PRR Heavyweight Diner "4498," 17-18		200
___	84826	PRR Heavyweight Observation Colonel Lindbergh, 17-18		200
___	84827	PRR Heavyweight Observation Washington Circle, 17-18		200
___	84828	BNSF 66' Mill Gondola "518726," w/Graffiti, 17		80
___	84829	BNSF 66' Mill Gondola "518770," 17		80
___	84830	BNSF 66' Mill Gondola "518795," 17		80
___	84831	GNTX Railgon 66' Mill Gondola "290146," w/Graffiti, 17		80
___	84832	GNTX Railgon 66' Mill Gondola "290087," 17		80
___	84833	GNTX Railgon 66' Mill Gondola "290102,", 17		80
___	84834	Atlantic & Western 66' Mill Gondola "400704," w/Graffiti, 17		80
___	84835	Atlantic & Western 66' Mill Gondola "400664," 17		80
___	84836	Atlantic & Western 66' Mill Gondola "400675," 17		80
___	84837	Arkansas & Oklahoma 66' Mill Gondola "35018," w/Graffiti, 17		80
___	84838	Arkansas & Oklahoma 66' Mill Gondola "35007," 17		80
___	84839	Arkansas & Oklahoma 66' Mill Gondola "35055," 17		80
___	84840	Steelton & Highspire 66' Mill Gondola "125," w/Graffiti, 17		80
___	84841	Steelton & Highspire 66' Mill Gondola "117," 17		80
___	84842	Steelton & Highspire 66' Mill Gondola "118," 17		80
___	84843	Demonstrator GE AC6000 Diesel "6000," CC, 17		650
___	84844	Demonstrator GE AC6000 Diesel "6001," CC, 17		650
___	84845	Demonstrator GE AC6000 Diesel "6002," CC, 17		650
___	84846	CSX GE AC6000 Diesel "691," CC, 17		650
___	84847	CSX GE AC6000 Diesel "5014," CC, 17		650
___	84848	CSX CSX GE AC6000 Diesel "Diversity 5000," CC, 17		650
___	84849	CSX CSX GE AC6000 Diesel "Diversity 5001," CC, 17		650
___	84850	SP GE AC6000 Diesel "601," CC, 17		650

		Exc	Mint
84851	SP GE AC6000 Diesel "602," CC, 17		650 ___
84852	UP GE AC6000 Diesel "7566," CC, 17		650 ___
84853	UP GE AC6000 Diesel "7579," CC, 17		650 ___
84854	TTX Husky Double-Stack Car "56210," w/Trailers, 17		130 ___
84855	TTX Husky Double-Stack Car "56289," w/Trailers, 17		130 ___
84856	TTX Husky Double-Stack Car "56368," w/Trailers, 17		130 ___
84857	TTX Husky Double-Stack Car "56150," w/Trailers, 17		130 ___
84858	TTX Husky Double-Stack Car "56168," w/Trailers, 17		130 ___
84859	TTX Husky Double-Stack Car "56174," w/Trailers, 17		130 ___
84860	BNSF Husky Double-Stack Car "203003," w/Trailers, 17		130 ___
84861	BNSF Husky Double-Stack Car "203015," w/Trailers, 17		130 ___
84862	BNSF Husky Double-Stack Car "203032," w/Trailers, 17		130 ___
84863	ARZC Husky Double-Stack Car "100000," w/Trailers, 17		130 ___
84864	ARZC Husky Double-Stack Car "100002," w/Trailers, 17		130 ___
84865	ARZC Husky Double-Stack Car "100005," w/Trailers, 17		130 ___
84866	Southwind Husky Double-Stack Car "5003," w/Trailers, 17		130 ___
84867	Southwind Husky Double-Stack Car "5005," w/Trailers, 17		130 ___
84868	Southwind Husky Double-Stack Car "5008," w/Trailers, 17		130 ___
84869	Hot Wheels Boxcar, 18		85 ___
84870	NP 50'Flatcar" 65110" w/NPT 40' Trailer, 17		120 ___
84871	NP 50' Flatcar" 65126" w/NPT 40' Trailer, 17		120 ___
84872	PRR 50' Flatcar "469615" w/PRRZ 40' Trailer, 17		120 ___
84873	PRR 50' Flatcar "469675" w/PRRZ 40' Trailer, 17		120 ___
84874	Trailer Train 50' Flatcar "475227" w/SOUZ 40' Trailer, 17		120 ___
84875	Trailer Train 50' Flatcar "475274" w/SOUZ 40' Trailer, 17		120 ___
84876	UP 50' Flatcar "53017" w/UPZ 40' Trailer, 17		120 ___
84877	UP 50' Flatcar "53022" w/UPZ 40' Trailer, 17		120 ___
84878	Wabash 50' Flatcar "25535" w/WABZ 40' Trailer, 17		120 ___
84879	Wabash 50' Flatcar "25549" w/WABZ 40' Trailer, 17		120 ___
84880	D&RGW 50' Flatcar "21032" w/RGMW 40' Trailer, 17		120 ___
84881	D&RGW 50' Flatcar "21036" w/RGMW 40' Trailer, 17		120 ___
84882	C&O 40' Trailer 2-pack, 17		65 ___
84883	GM&O 40' Trailer 2-pack, 17		65 ___
84884	L&N 40' Trailer 2-pack, 17		65 ___
84885	SAL 40' Trailer 2-pack, 17		65 ___
84886	Frisco 40' Trailer 2-pack, 17		65 ___
84887	WP 40' Trailer 2-pack, 17		65 ___
84888	PRR X31 Boxcar "78401," w/Circle Keystone, 17		120 ___
84889	PRR X31 Boxcar "78498," w/Circle Keystone, 17		80 ___
84890	PRR X31 Boxcar "68408," w/Shadow Keystone, 17		80 ___
84891	PRR X31 Boxcar "77061," w/Shadow Keystone, 17		80 ___
84892	PRR X31 Boxcar "76803," w/Plain Keystone, 17		80 ___
84893	PRR X31 Boxcar "77734," w/Plain Keystone, 17		80 ___
84894	PRR X31 Boxcar "497310," w/Stores, 17		80 ___
84895	PRR X31 Boxcar "497329," w/Stores, 17		80 ___
84896	N&W X31 Boxcar "46146," 17		80 ___
84897	N&W X31 Boxcar "46340," 17		80 ___
84898	Personalized Man's Best Friend Boxcar, 18-23		100 ___
84899	Personalized World's Best Cat Boxcar, 18-22		100 ___
84904	BNSF Scale Autorack, Orange "965375," 18		120 ___
84905	BNSF Scale Autorack, Orange "965530," 18		120 ___
84906	Ferromex Scale Autorack "705473," 18		120 ___
84907	Ferromex Scale Autorack "953615," 18		120 ___

		Exc	Mint
___ 84908	Southern Scale Autorack "159162," 18		120
___ 84909	Southern Scale Autorack "159166," 18		120
___ 84910	CSX Scale Autorack "156256," 18		120
___ 84911	CSX Scale Autorack "973924," 18		120
___ 84912	NS Scale Autorack "983818," 18		120
___ 84913	NS Scale Autorack "992879," 18		120
___ 84914	MKT Scale Autorack "254176," 18		120
___ 84915	MKT Scale Autorack "942194," 18		120
___ 84916	Union Tank Car Cylindrical Covered Hopper "44072," 18-19		90
___ 84917	Union Tank Car Cylindrical Covered Hopper "44094," 18-19		90
___ 84918	Davis Industries Cylindrical Covered Hopper "1002," 18-19		90
___ 84919	Davis Industries Cylindrical Covered Hopper "1003," 18-19		90
___ 84920	Conrail Cylindrical Covered Hopper "884244," 18-19		90
___ 84921	Conrail Cylindrical Covered Hopper "884270," 18-19		90
___ 84922	CSX Cylindrical Covered Hopper "225370," 18-19		90
___ 84923	CSX Cylindrical Covered Hopper "225382," 18-19		90
___ 84924	Wilkes-Barre Mining Cylindrical Covered Hopper "104," 18		90
___ 84925	Wilkes-Barre Mining Cylindrical Covered Hopper "106," 18		90
___ 84926	SP Cylindrical Covered Hopper "1002," 18		90
___ 84927	SP Cylindrical Covered Hopper "1027," 18		90
___ 84928	John Quincy Adams Presidential Boxcar, 18		70
___ 84929	James K. Polk Presidential Boxcar, 18		70
___ 84930	Benjamin Harrison Presidential Boxcar, 18		70
___ 84934	NYC 4-6-4 Hudson "5425," LionChief Plus, 17-18		450
___ 84935	B&A 4-6-4 Hudson Locomotive "616," LionChief Plus, 17-18		450
___ 84936	Nickel Plate 4-6-4 Hudson "170," LionChief Plus, 17-18		450
___ 84937	GN 4-6-4 Hudson Locomotive "171," LionChief Plus, 17-18		450
___ 84938	AT&SF EMD GP38 Diesel "3441," LionChief Plus, 17-18		350
___ 84939	NS First Responders GP38 "5642," LionChief Plus, 17-18		350
___ 84940	Seaboard System GP38 Diesel "543," LionChief Plus, 17-18		350
___ 84941	FEC EMD GP38 Diesel "506," LionChief Plus, 17-18		350
___ 84942	PRR 4-4-2 Atlantic Locomotive "460," CC, 17		800
___ 84943	PRR 4-4-2 Atlantic Locomotive "68," CC, 17		800
___ 84944	PRR 4-4-2 Atlantic Locomotive "1163," CC, 17		800
___ 84945	PRSL 4-4-2 Atlantic Locomotive "6009," CC, 17		800
___ 84946	LIRR 4-4-2 Atlantic Locomotive "1611," CC, 17		800
___ 84947	GN 4-4-2 Atlantic Locomotive "1707," CC, 17		800
___ 84948	PRR 2-8-0 Consolidation Locomotive "1288," CC, 18		750
___ 84949	PRSL 2-8-0 Consolidation Locomotive "8072," CC, 18		750
___ 84950	LIRR 2-8-0 Consolidation Locomotive "109," CC, 18		750
___ 84951	Bellefonte Central 2-8-0 Consolidation Locomotive "21," CC, 18		750
___ 84952	PRR 2-8-0 Consolidation Locomotive "3529," Weathered, CC, 18		750
___ 84953	Pennsylvania Coal Hauler Steam Freight Set, CC, 18		1100
___ 84964	Angela Trotta Thomas 4-6-4 Hudson, LionChief Plus, 18		450
___ 84965	Rio Grande A5 0-4-0 Locomotive "62," LionChief Plus, 18		480
___ 84966	NYC A5 0-4-0 Locomotive "1662," LionChief Plus, 18		480
___ 84967	PRR A5 0-4-0 Locomotive "577," LionChief Plus, 18		480
___ 84968	UP A5 0-4-0 Locomotive "218," LionChief Plus, 18		480
___ 84985	LIRR B60 Baggage Car "7715," 17-18		160
___ 84986	LIRR B60 Baggage Car "7724," 17-18		160
___ 84987	PRR B60 Baggage Car, Clerestory "7918," 17-18		160
___ 84988	PRR B60 Baggage Car, Clerestory "7941," 17-18		160
___ 84989	PRR B60 Baggage Car, Round Roof "7919," 17-18		160

84990	PRR B60 Baggage Car, Round Roof "7938," 17-18		160 ___
84991	PRR B60 Baggage Car, Round Roof, Messenger "9352," 17-18		160 ___
84992	PRR B60 Baggage Car, Round Roof, Messenger "9379," 17-18		160 ___
84993	PRR B60 Baggage Car, Round Roof, 1960s "9356," 17-18		160 ___
84994	PRR B60 Baggage Car, Round Roof, 1960s "9384," 17-18		160 ___
84995	PRSL Baggage Car "5437," 17-18		160 ___
84996	PRSL B60 Baggage Car "6403," 17-18		160 ___
84997	LIRR 18" Heavyweight Passenger Coach 2-pack, #1, 17-18		400 ___
85000	LIRR 18" Heavyweight Passenger Coach 2-pack, #2, 17-18		400 ___
85003	PRSL 18" Heavyweight Passenger Coach 2-pack, #1, 17-18		400 ___
85006	PRSL 18" Heavyweight Passenger Coach 2-pack, #2, 17-18		400 ___
85009	PRR 18" Heavyweight Passenger Coach 2-pack, #1, 17-18		400 ___
85012	PRR 18" Heavyweight Passenger Coach 2-pack, #2, 17-18		400 ___
85015	ACL/PRR Champion Passenger Car 4-pack, 17-18		620 ___
85016	ACL/PRR Champion Passenger Car 2-pack, 17-18		310 ___
85017	ACL Champion 21" Diner, w/StationSounds, 17-18		310 ___
85018	ACL EMD SW7 Diesel "648," CC, 18		500 ___
85019	BN EMD SW7 Diesel "111," CC, 18		500 ___
85020	Conemaugh & Black Lick EMD SW7 Diesel "106," CC, 18		500 ___
85021	Chessie System EMD SW7 Diesel "5224," CC, 18		500 ___
85022	LV EMD SW7 Diesel "222," CC, 18		500 ___
85023	MEC EMD SW7 Diesel "331," CC, 18		500 ___
85024	NYC EMD SW7 Diesel "8853," CC, 18		500 ___
85025	Frisco EMD SW7 Diesel "303," CC, 18		500 ___
85026	Southern EMD SW7 Diesel "1100," CC, 18		500 ___
85027	UP EMD SW7 Diesel "1808," CC, 18		500 ___
85028	AT&SF EMD SD45 Diesel "5305," CC, 18		600 ___
85029	AT&SF EMD SD45 Diesel "5319," CC, 18		600 ___
85030	B&P EMD SD45 Diesel "453," CC, 18		600 ___
85031	B&P EMD SD45 Diesel "455," CC, 18		600 ___
85032	C&NW EMD SD45 Diesel "6485," CC, 18		600 ___
85033	C&NW EMD SD45 Diesel "6568," CC, 18		600 ___
85034	Montana Rail Link EMD SD45 Diesel "320," CC, 18		600 ___
85035	Montana Rail Link EMD SD45 Diesel "331," CC, 18		600 ___
85036	MPI EMD SD45 Diesel "9009," CC, 18		600 ___
85037	MPI EMD SD45 Diesel "9011," CC, 18		600 ___
85038	N&W EMD SD45 Diesel "1776," CC, 18		600 ___
85039	N&W EMD SD45 Diesel "1790," CC, 18		600 ___
85040	NYS&W EMD SD45 Diesel "3612," CC, 18		600 ___
85041	NYS&W EMD SD45 Diesel "3614," CC, 18		600 ___
85042	WC EMD SD45 Diesel "6525," CC, 18		600 ___
85043	WC EMD SD45 Diesel "6580," CC, 18		600 ___
85046	BNSF EMD SD70ACe Diesel "9214," CC, 18		600 ___
85047	BNSF EMD SD70ACe Diesel "9287," CC, 18		600 ___
85048	CN EMD SD70ACe Diesel "8101," CC, 18		600 ___
85049	CN EMD SD70ACe Diesel "8103," CC, 18		600 ___
85050	CSX EMD SD70ACe Diesel "4849," CC, 18		600 ___
85051	Demonstrator EMD SD70ACe Diesel "1201," CC, 18		600 ___
85052	Demonstrator EMD SD70ACe Diesel "1202," CC, 18		600 ___
85053	KCS EMD SD70ACe Diesel "4156," CC, 18		600 ___
85054	KCS EMD SD70ACe Diesel "4164," CC, 18		600 ___
85055	NS EMD SD70ACe Diesel "1030," CC, 18		600 ___

		Exc	Mint
____ 85056	NS EMD SD70ACe Diesel "1111," CC, 18		600
____ 85057	UP EMD SD70ACe Diesel "8650," CC, 18		600
____ 85058	UP EMD SD70ACe Diesel "8665," CC, 18		600
____ 85059	MKT EMD NW2 Diesel "7," LionChief Plus, 18		320
____ 85060	PRR EMD NW2 Diesel "9172," LionChief Plus, 18		320
____ 85061	Nickel Plate Road EMD NW2 Diesel "13," LionChief Plus, 18		320
____ 85062	UP EMD NW2 Diesel "1037," LionChief Plus, 18		320
____ 85063	MILW EMD NW2 Diesel "1649," LionChief Plus, 18		320
____ 85065	Hot Wheels 50th Anniversary Boxcar, 17-18		85
____ 85066	TTX Husky Double-Stack Car "56210," w/EOT Device, 17		150
____ 85067	TTX Husky Double-Stack Car "56180," w/EOT Device, 17		150
____ 85068	BNSF Husky Double-Stack Car "203054," w/EOT Device, 17		150
____ 85069	ARZC Husky Double-Stack Car "100008," w/EOT Device, 17		150
____ 85070	Southwind Husky Double-Stack Car "5009," w/EOT Device, 17		150
____ 85071	AT&SF Wide-Vision Caboose w/Camera "999718," 18		125
____ 85072	BN Wide-Vision Caboose w/Camera "12345," 18		125
____ 85073	Chessie System Wide-Vision Caboose w/Camera "903118," 18		125
____ 85074	CSX Wide-Vision Caboose w/Camera "903282," 18		125
____ 85075	Reading Wide-Vision Caboose w/Camera "94116," 18		125
____ 85076	UP Wide-Vision Caboose w/Camera "13605," 18		125
____ 85077	NS Wide-Vision Caboose w/Camera "555059," 18		125
____ 85078	PRR Wide-Vision Caboose w/Camera "477900," 18		125
____ 85079	DODX Wide-Vision Caboose "902," 18		100
____ 85080	Montana Rail Link Wide-Vision Caboose "1005," 18		100
____ 85081	UTLX 30,000-Gallon 1-D Tank Car "212189" w/ FreightSounds, 18		150
____ 85082	GATX 30,000-Gallon 1-D Tank Car "36323" w/ FreightSounds, 18		150
____ 85083	Philadelphia Energy Solutions 1-D Tank Car "0756" w/ Sounds, 18		150
____ 85084	TILX 30,000-Gallon 1-D Tank Car "254088" w/ FreightSounds, 18		150
____ 85085	ADM 30,000-Gallon 1-D Tank Car "29248" w/ FreightSounds, 18		150
____ 85086	Cargill 30,000-Gallon 1-D Tank Car "7964" w/ FreightSounds, 18		150
____ 85087	UTLX 30,000-Gallon 1-D Tank Car "212187" w/EOT Device, 18		150
____ 85088	GATX 30,000-Gallon 1-D Tank Car "36328" w/EOT Device, 18		120
____ 85089	ADM 30,000-Gallon 1-D Tank Car "29252" w/EOT Device, 18		120
____ 85090	Cargill 30,000-Gallon 1-D Tank Car "7968" w/EOT Device, 18		120
____ 85091	ACFX 30,000-Gallon 1-D Tank Car "89990" w/EOT Device, 18		120
____ 85092	Procor 30,000-Gallon 1-D Tank Car "43579" w/EOT Device, 18		120
____ 85093	American Potash PS-2 Covered Hopper "31259," 17		75
____ 85094	American Potash PS-2 Covered Hopper "31275," 17		75
____ 85095	Bucyrus Erie PS-2 Covered Hopper "1114," 17		75
____ 85096	Bucyrus Erie PS-2 Covered Hopper "1118," 17		75
____ 85097	Georgia Marble PS-2 Covered Hopper "31340," 17		75
____ 85098	Georgia Marble PS-2 Covered Hopper "31341," 17		75
____ 85099	Ready Mixed Concrete PS-2 Covered Hopper "331," 17		75
____ 85100	Ready Mixed Concrete PS-2 Covered Hopper "340," 17		75
____ 85101	Linde PS-2 Covered Hopper "209," 17		75
____ 85102	Linde PS-2 Covered Hopper "211," 17		75
____ 85103	U.S. Borax PS-2 Covered Hopper "31064," 17		75
____ 85104	U.S. Borax PS-2 Covered Hopper "31066," 17		75
____ 85105	Tank Train 2-Pack with EOT Device, #1, 17		200

		Exc	Mint
85108	Tank Train 2-Pack with EOT Device, #2, 17		200 ___
85111	Tank Train 2-Pack with EOT Device, #3, 17		200 ___
85114	GATX Tank Train 2-Pack with EOT Device, 17		200 ___
85117	CN Tank Train 2-Pack with EOT Device, 17		200 ___
85120	Cibro Tank Train 2-Pack with EOT Device, 17		200 ___
85126	Tank Train Car #1, 17		90 ___
85127	Tank Train Car #2, 17		90 ___
85128	Tank Train Car #3, 17		90 ___
85129	Tank Train Car #4, 17		90 ___
85130	Tank Train Car #5, 17		90 ___
85131	Tank Train Car #6, 17		90 ___
85132	Tank Train Car #1, 17		90 ___
85133	Tank Train Car #2, 17		90 ___
85134	Tank Train Car #3, 17		90 ___
85135	Tank Train Car #4, 17		90 ___
85136	Tank Train Car #5, 17		90 ___
85137	Tank Train Car #6, 17		90 ___
85138	Tank Train Car #1, 17		90 ___
85139	Tank Train Car #2, 17		90 ___
85140	Tank Train Car #3, 17		90 ___
85141	Tank Train Car #4, 17		90 ___
85142	Tank Train Car #5, 17		90 ___
85143	Tank Train Car #6, 17		90 ___
85144	GATX Tank Train Car #1, 17		90 ___
85145	GATX Tank Train Car #2, 17		90 ___
85146	GATX Tank Train Car #3, 17		90 ___
85147	GATX Tank Train Car #4, 17		90 ___
85148	GATX Tank Train Car #5, 17		90 ___
85149	GATX Tank Train Car #6, 17		90 ___
85150	CN Tank Train Car #1, 17		90 ___
85151	CN Tank Train Car #2, 17		90 ___
85152	CN Tank Train Car #3, 17		90 ___
85153	CN Tank Train Car #4, 17		90 ___
85154	CN Tank Train Car #5, 17		90 ___
85155	CN Tank Train Car #6, 17		90 ___
85156	Cibro Tank Train Car #1, 17		90 ___
85157	Cibro Tank Train Car #2, 17		90 ___
85158	Cibro Tank Train Car #3, 17		90 ___
85159	Cibro Tank Train Car #4, 17		90 ___
85160	Cibro Tank Train Car #5, 17		90 ___
85161	Cibro Tank Train Car #6, 17		90 ___
85168	Tacoma Rail EMD SD70ACe Diesel "7001," CC, 18		600 ___
85169	Tacoma Rail EMD SD70ACe Diesel "7002," CC, 18		600 ___
85170	Atlanta & West Point USRA 4-6-2 Pacific "290," CC, 18		1400 ___
85171	B&O USRA 4-6-2 Pacific Locomotive 5300, CC, 18		1400 ___
85172	Reading & Northern USRA 4-6-2 Pacific "425," CC, 18		1400 ___
85173	NP USRA 4-6-2 Pacific Locomotive "2256," CC, 18		1400 ___
85174	Southern USRA 4-6-2 Pacific Locomotive "1372," CC, 18		1400 ___
85175	Halloween USRA 4-6-2 Pacific Locomotive "1031," CC, 18		1400 ___
85176	C&O USRA 2-6-6-2 Locomotive "1522," CC, 18		1600 ___
85177	W&LE USRA 2-6-6-2 Locomotive "8007," CC, 18		1600 ___
85178	B&O USRA 2-6-6-2 Locomotive "7555," CC, 18		1600 ___
85179	Buffalo, Rochester & Pittsburgh USRA 2-6-6-2 "755," CC, 18		1600 ___

		Exc	Mint
___ 85180	GN USRA 2-6-6-2 Locomotive "1855," CC, 18		1600
___ 85181	MEC USRA 2-6-6-2 Locomotive "1205," CC, 18		1600
___ 85182	NYC USRA 2-6-6-2 Locomotive "1400," CC, 18		1600
___ 85183	SP USRA 2-6-6-2 Locomotive "3932," CC, 18		1600
___ 85184	WM USRA 2-6-6-2 Locomotive "960," CC, 18		1600
___ 85185	Renz Hobby Shop, 17		300
___ 85186	AT&SF EMD F3 A-A Diesel Set, CC, 17		850
___ 85189	AT&SF Powered EMD F3 B Diesel, CC, 17		450
___ 85190	At&SF SuperBass EMD F3 B Diesel, CC, 17		300
___ 85191	GN EMD F3 A-A Diesel Set, CC, 17		850
___ 85194	GN Powered EMD F3 B Diesel, CC, 17		450
___ 85195	GN SuperBass EMD F3 B Diesel, CC, 17		300
___ 85196	T&P EMD F7 A-A Diesel Set, CC, 17		850
___ 85199	T&P Powered EMD F7 B Diesel, CC, 17		450
___ 85200	T&P SuperBass EMD F3 B Diesel, CC, 17		300
___ 85201	NYO&W EMD F3 A-A Diesel Set, CC, 17		850
___ 85204	NYO&W Powered EMD F3 B Diesel, CC, 17		450
___ 85205	NYO&W SuperBass EMD F3 B Diesel, CC, 17		300
___ 85206	PRR EMD F7 A-A Diesel Set, CC, 17		850
___ 85209	PRR Powered EMD F7 B Diesel, CC, 17		450
___ 85210	PRR SuperBass EMD F7 B Diesel, CC, 17		300
___ 85211	Reading EMD F3 A-A Diesel Set, CC, 17		850
___ 85214	Reading Powered EMD F3 B Diesel, CC, 17		450
___ 85215	ReadingSuperBass EMD F3 B Diesel, CC, 17		300
___ 85216	Conrail EMD F7 A-A Diesel Set "1792-1730," CC, 17		850
___ 85219	Conrail Powered EMD F7 B Diesel "3861," CC, 17		450
___ 85220	Conrail SuperBass EMD F7 B Diesel "3872," CC, 17		300
___ 85222	CSX Maxi-Stack "85222," 17		75
___ 85223	BNSF Maxi-Stack "237342," 17-C55718		75
___ 85226	180-Watt PowerHouse Power Supply, 10-amp, 19-23		230
___ 85227	GN Oriental Ltd Heavyweight Baggage/Coach, 17-18		400
___ 85230	GN Oriental Ltd Heavyweight Sleeper/Coach, 17-18		400
___ 85233	GN Oriental Ltd Heavyweight Sleeper/Diner, 17-18		400
___ 85236	GN Oriental Ltd Heavyweight Sleeper/Observation, 17-18		400
___ 85241	Mystery Machine FT Diesel Freight Set, Lionchief, 18-20		430
___ 85246	Anheuser-Busch Vintage Refrigerator Car, 18-20		80
___ 85247	Budweiser Clydesdale Vintage Refrigerator Car, 18-19		80
___ 85248	Budweiser Vintage Refrigerator Car, 18-20		80
___ 85253	End of the Line Express Diesel Freight Set, LionChief, 18-20		330
___ 85258	AT&SF FT Ranger Diesel Freight Set, LionChief, 18		430
___ 85263	Tomb of the Unknown Soldier Walking Brakeman Car, 18		100
___ 85264	Harry Potter Hogwarts Add-on Coach, 18-23		90
___ 85269	Scooby Doo Sam Witches Cafe, 18-20		100
___ 85270	Hot Wheels Checkered Flagpole, 18		45
___ 85271	Polar Express Flagpole, 18-23		45
___ 85274	PRR Gla Hopper 3-pack #1, 18		225
___ 85278	PRR Gla Hopper 3-pack #2, 18		225
___ 85282	PRR Coal Goes To War Gla Hopper 3-pack #3, 18		225
___ 85286	Berwind Gla Hopper 3-pack, 18		225
___ 85290	PRR MOW PRR Gla Hopper 3-pack #4, 18		225
___ 85294	Lionelville Hobby Shop, 18		300
___ 85295	LCS CSM2, 18-23		120
___ 85296	Layout Control System IRV2, 18-20		100

		Exc	Mint
85297	PRR N5 Caboose "477819," 18		100 ___
85298	PRR N5 Caboose "478884," 18		100 ___
85299	Reading & Northern N5 Caboose "477514," 18		100 ___
85300	PRSL N5 Caboose "202," 18		100 ___
85301	RJ Corman N5 Caboose, 18		100 ___
85309	Flight Night Halloween Pylon, 18-19		150 ___
85310	Witches Brew Storage Tank, 18-19		85 ___
85311	Warehouse Kit, 18-19		60 ___
85312	Office Building Kit, 19		80 ___
85314	Hometown Brewery Kit, 19		70 ___
85315	UP EMD SD70ACe Diesel "1943," CC, 18		600 ___
85316	UP Wide-Vision Caboose, Spirit of Union Pacific "1943," 18		100 ___
85317	UP Spirit of the Union Pacific Boxcar, 18		85 ___
85318	Personalized Happy Birthday Boxcar, 18		90 ___
85319	Personalized 18 Merry Christmas Boxcar, 18		90 ___
85320	Personalized Happy Anniversary Boxcar, 18-19		90 ___
85321	John Deere Flatcar w/Tractor Load, 18		80 ___
85322	Personalized 18 Halloween Boxcar, 18		90 ___
85323	Scooby Doo Boxcar, 18		85 ___
85324	Thomas & Friends Christmas Freight Set, LionChief, 18-23		250 ___
85326	NYC Vision Baggage Car "9152," 18		330 ___
85327	NYC Baggage Car 2-pack #1, 18		350 ___
85330	NYC Baggage Car 2-pack #2, 18		350 ___
85333	NYC Baggage/Combine 2-pack, 18		400 ___
85336	NYC 18" Heavyweight Baggage Car 2-pack, 18		350 ___
85339	SP Scale RPO Passenger Car "5124," 18		160 ___
85340	L&N Scale RPO Passenger Car "1099," 18		160 ___
85341	LIRR Scale RPO Passenger Car "737," 18		160 ___
85342	MILW Scale RPO Passenger Car "2105," 18		160 ___
85343	NYC Scale RPO Passenger Car "4819," 18		160 ___
85344	PRR Scale RPO Passenger Car "5265," 18		160 ___
85345	PRR Scale RPO Passenger Car "5269," 18		160 ___
85346	PC Scale RPO Passenger Car "5267," 18		160 ___
85347	UP Scale RPO Passenger Car "2060," 18		160 ___
85348	MILW 18" Columbian Passenger Car 2-pack #A, 18		400 ___
85351	MILW 18" Columbian Passenger Car 2-pack #B, 18		400 ___
85354	MILW 18" Columbian Passenger Car 2-pack #C, 18		400 ___
85357	MILW 18" Columbian Passenger Car 2-pack #D, 18		400 ___
85360	UP Challenger 21" Passenger Car 4-pack, 18		700 ___
85361	UP Challenger 21" Passenger Car 2-pack, 18		350 ___
85362	UP Challenger 21" Diner w/StationSounds, 18		330 ___
85367	L&N Hummingbird 21" Passenger Car 4-pack, 18		700 ___
85368	L&N Hummingbird 21" Passenger Car 2-pack, 18		350 ___
85369	L&N Hummingbird 21" Diner w/StationSounds, 18		330
85370	Reading & Northern 18" Excursion and Business Car 2-pack #A, 18		400 ___
85373	Reading & Northern 18" Excursion and Business Car 2-pack #B, 18		400 ___
85376	Reading & Northern 21" Dome Car w/StationSounds, 18		350 ___
85377	MOW Disconnect Work Car 4-pack, 18		160 ___
85378	PRR Disconnect Work Car 4-pack, 18		160 ___
85379	AT&SF Disconnect Work Car 4-pack, 18		160 ___
85380	UP Disconnect Work Car 4-pack, 18		160 ___

		Exc	Mint
___ 85381	NYC Disconnect Work Car 4-pack, 18		160
___ 85382	D&RGW Disconnect Work Car 4-pack, 18		160
___ 85383	Layout Control System IRV2 Sensor Add-on, 18-20		30
___ 85384	Orange 10" Straight FasTrack 4-pack, 18-20		25
___ 85386	Pennsylvania Lines 2-8-0 Consolidation "7109," CC, 18		750
___ 85387	Western Allegheny 2-8-0 Consolidation "85," CC, 18		750
___ 85389	FasTrack White 10" Straight, 4-pack, 18-23		28
___ 85390	FasTrack White O-36 Curve, 4-pack, 18-23		28
___ 85391	White PEP Activation Track, 18-20		25
___ 85392	White 10" Terminal FasTrack, 18-20		10
___ 85400	Polar Express Skiing Hobo Observation w/Snowy Roof, 19-20		90
___ 85401	UP LED Flag Boxcar, Yellow and Gray "1862," 18		120
___ 85402	UP LED Flag Boxcar, C&NW Heritage "1995," 18		120
___ 85403	UP LED Flag Boxcar, MKT Heritage "1988," 18		120
___ 85404	UP LED Flag Boxcar, MP Heritage "1982," 18		120
___ 85405	UP LED Flag Boxcar, D&RGW Heritage "1989," 18		120
___ 85406	UP LED Flag Boxcar, SP Heritage "1996," 18		120
___ 85407	UP LED Flag Boxcar, WP Heritage "1983," 18		120
___ 85408	UP LED Flag Boxcar, Spirit of Union Pacific "1943," 18		120
___ 85409	UP LED Flag Boxcar, Steam Program "4-8-8-4," 18		120
___ 85410	Polar Express Hero Boy's Home, 18-23		130
___ 85411	Pylon with World War II Planes, 18		145
___ 85412	Santa's Sleigh Pylon, 18		135
___ 99000	Keebler Elf Express Steam Freight Set, 99 u	775	1196
___ 99001	Mickey Holiday Express Freight Set, 99 u	163	180
___ 99002	Looney Tunes Square Window Caboose, 99 u		65
___ 99006	Keebler Bulkhead Flatcar, 99 u		200
___ 99007	Smuckers Fudge 1-D Tank Car, 99 u		90
___ 99008	Mickey's Merry Christmas Boxcar, 99 u		55
___ 99009	Mickey's Holiday Express Square Window Caboose, 99 u		45
___ 99013	Case Cutlery Tank Car "1889," 00 u		70
___ 99014	Case Cutlery Gondola "1889," 00 u		70
___ 99015	Case Cutlery Boxcar "1889," 00 u		70
___ 99018	Case Cutlery Rolling Stock 3-pack, 00 u	140	215
___ 1823010	Thomas' Best Buddies LionChief Set: Percy, 18-19		200
___ 1823011	Percy, Sodor Locomotive, LionChief, 18-19		120
___ 1823020	Thomas' Best Buddies LionChief Set: James, 18-19		200
___ 1823021	James, Sodor Locomotive, LionChief, 18-19		120
___ 1823030	Sodor Railway Troublemaker Diesel LionChief Set, 18-19		200
___ 1823031	Thomas & Friends Sodor Diesel, LionChief, 18-19, 23		160
___ 1823040	Thomas Kinkade Christmas LionChief Steam Freight Set, 18, 20		400
___ 1823050	Mickey Mouse Celebration LionChief Steam Freight Set, 18		400
___ 1830010	Polar Express Snowman & Children People Pack, 19-23		30
___ 1831010	N&W Brass Hybrid USRA 4-8-2 K2 Locomotive "118," CC, 18		1400
___ 1831020	N&W Brass Hybrid USRA 4-8-2 K2 Locomotive "123," CC, 18		1400
___ 1831030	N&W Brass Hybrid USRA 4-8-2 K2 Locomotive "116," CC, 18		1400
___ 1831040	N&W Brass Hybrid USRA 4-8-2 K2 Locomotive "125," CC, 18		1400
___ 1831050	N&W Brass Hybrid USRA 4-8-2 K2 Locomotive "9999," CC, 18		1400
___ 1831060	PRR 4-6-2 Pacific K4 w/Long-haul Tender "5453," CC, 18		1300
___ 1904010	58" x 86" Lionel Train Table, 19-23		1000
___ 1908010	LCS CSM2 DZ-2500 Breakout Board, 18-23		30
___ 1908080	Improved CW80 Transformer, 19-23		170
___ 1918210	Anheuser-Busch Malt Tonics Woodside Refrigerator Car, 19		80

MODERN 1970-2023		Exc	Mint
1922010	UP Sherman Hill 4-8-8-4 Freight Set, LionChief Plus 2.0, 19		1600 ___
1922020	Nickel Plate 2-8-4 Steam Freight Set, LionChief Plus 2.0, 19, 22		880 ___
1922030	Warren G. Harding Funeral Steam Passenger Train, CC, 18		2000 ___
1922040	AT&SF Gold Bonnet Streamlined Passenger Set, CC, 19		1000 ___
1922050	NYC Pacemaker Steam Passenger Set, CC, 19		2000 ___
1922060	BNSF Diesel Freight Oil Train Set, CC, 19		1000 ___
1922070	Pennsylvania Limited 2-8-4 Steam Passenger Set, 19, 22		880 ___
1922080	Lionel GE Bi-Polar Electric State Set, CC, 19		1800 ___
1922090	Erie Mining Diesel Ore Set, CC, 19		900 ___
1923020	NYC Flyer 0-8-0 Steam Freight Set, LionChief ,", 18-19		350 ___
1923030	Polar Express 15th Anniversary Steam Passenger Set, LC, 19		450 ___
1923040	UP Flyer 0-8-0 Steam Freight Set, LionChief, 19-22		370 ___
1923050	NS Tier 4 GE ET44C4 Diesel Freight Set, LionChief, 19-20		400 ___
1923070	Blue Comet Steam Passenger Set, LionChief, 19-20		370 ___
1923080	Promontory Summit 150th Anniversary Steam Set, 19		550 ___
1923090	LV GE U36B Diesel Freight Set, LionChief, 19-20		330 ___
1923100	U.S. Steam 0-8-0 Steam Freight Set, LionChief, 19-20		400 ___
1923110	UP America Proud GP38 Diesel Freight Set, LionChief, 19-20		400 ___
1923130	Polar Express Trolley Set, 19		200 ___
1923140	Disney Christmas Steam Freight Set, LionChief, 19-23		400 ___
1923150	Winter Wonderland Steam Freight Set, LionChief, 19-22		400 ___
1925001	FasTrack Screws, 100-pack, 19-20		10 ___
1926011	CSX 86' 4-Door Hi-Cube Boxcar (Boxcar Logo) "181032," 18		100 ___
1926012	CSX 86' 4-Door Hi-Cube Boxcar (Boxcar Logo) "181056," 18		100 ___
1926013	CSX 86' 4-Door Hi-Cube Boxcar "181053," 18		100 ___
1926014	CSX 86' 4-Door Hi-Cube Boxcar "180455," 18		100 ___
1926021	DT&I 86' 4-Door Hi-Cube Boxcar, Green "26341," 18		100 ___
1926022	DT&I 86' 4-Door Hi-Cube Boxcar, Purple/Pink "26888," 18		100 ___
1926023	DT&I 86' 4-Door Hi-Cube Boxcar, Blue "26443," 18		100 ___
1926024	DT&I 86' 4-Door Hi-Cube Boxcar, Blue w/Graffiti "26834," 18		100 ___
1926031	N&W 86' 4-Door Hi-Cube Boxcar "355155," 18		100 ___
1926032	N&W 86' 4-Door Hi-Cube Boxcar "355197," 18		100 ___
1926041	Southern 86' 4-Door Hi-Cube Boxcar "42954," 18		100 ___
1926042	Southern 86' 4-Door Hi-Cube Boxcar "42995," 18		100 ___
1926051	UP 86' 4-Door Hi-Cube Boxcar "980421," 18		100 ___
1926052	UP 86' 4-Door Hi-Cube Boxcar "980434," 18		100 ___
1926053	UP 86' 4-Door Hi-Cube Boxcar w/Graffiti "980455," 18		100 ___
1926061	Wabash 86' 4-Door Hi-Cube Boxcar "55023," 18		100 ___
1926062	Wabash 86' 4-Door Hi-Cube Boxcar "55055," 18		100 ___
1926070	ART Refrigerator Car w/FreightSounds "31823," 18		150 ___
1926080	FGE Refrigerator Car w/FreightSounds "38947," 18		150 ___
1926090	GN Refrigerator Car w/FreightSounds "68112," 18		150 ___
1926100	NYC (MDT) Refrigerator Car w/FreightSounds "19091," 18		150 ___
1926110	PFE Refrigerator Car w/FreightSounds "5860," 18		150 ___
1926120	AT&SF Refrigerator Car w/FreightSounds "3526," 18		150 ___
1926131	PRR Bunk Car "498393," 18		100 ___
1926132	PRR Bunk Car "498396," 18		100 ___
1926133	PRR Bunk Car "498398," 18		100 ___
1926141	AT&SF Bunk Car "196752," 18		100 ___
1926142	AT&SF Bunk Car "196754," 18		100 ___
1926143	AT&SF Bunk Car "196459," 18		100 ___
1926151	NYC Bunk Car "x19075," 18		100 ___

		Exc	Mint
___ 1926152	NYC Bunk Car "x19076," 18		100
___ 1926153	NYC Bunk Car "x19078," 18		100
___ 1926161	D&RGW Bunk Car "x2380," 18		100
___ 1926162	D&RGW Bunk Car "x2384," 18		100
___ 1926163	D&RGW Bunk Car "x2387," 18		100
___ 1926171	UP Bunk Car "906115," 18		100
___ 1926172	UP Bunk Car "906118," 18		100
___ 1926173	UP Bunk Car "906121," 18		100
___ 1926181	MOW Bunk Car "99832," 18		100
___ 1926182	MOW Bunk Car "99835," 18		100
___ 1926183	MOW Bunk Car "99837," 18		100
___ 1926190	PRR Kitchen Car w/Sounds "492774," 18		150
___ 1926200	AT&SF Kitchen Car w/Sounds "194200," 18		150
___ 1926210	NYC Kitchen Car w/Sounds "x22483," 18		150
___ 1926220	D&RGW Kitchen Car w/Sounds "x4013," 18		150
___ 1926230	UP Kitchen Car w/Sounds "903675," 18		150
___ 1926240	MOW Kitchen Car w/Sounds "99402," 18		150
___ 1926250	PRR Tool Car "493551," 18		90
___ 1926260	AT&SF Tool Car "190455," 18		90
___ 1926270	NYC Tool Car "x13568," 18		90
___ 1926280	D&RGW Tool Car "x4510," 18		90
___ 1926290	UP Tool Car "915129," 18		90
___ 1926300	MOW Tool Car "99500," 18		90
___ 1926311	Chessie 52-foot Coil Gondola "305005," 18		90
___ 1926312	Chessie 52-foot Coil Gondola "305012," 18		90
___ 1926321	C&SS 52-foot Coil Gondola "3859," 18		90
___ 1926322	C&SS 52-foot Coil Gondola "3862," 18		90
___ 1926331	DT&I 52-foot Coil Gondola "9326," 18		90
___ 1926332	DT&I 52-foot Coil Gondola "9372," 18		90
___ 1926341	EJ&E 52-foot Coil Gondola "4144," 18		90
___ 1926342	EJ&E 52-foot Coil Gondola "4156," 18		90
___ 1926351	P&LE 52-foot Coil Gondola "50062," 18		90
___ 1926352	P&LE 52-foot Coil Gondola "50086," 18		90
___ 1926361	Union RR 52-foot Coil Gondola "3021," 18		90
___ 1926362	Union RR 52-foot Coil Gondola "3163," 18		90
___ 1926370	Polar Express 52-foot Coil Gondola "122519" w/Presents, 18		95
___ 1926381	ACL 50-foot Bulkhead Flatcar "78310," 19		100
___ 1926382	ACL 50-foot Bulkhead Flatcar "78348," 19		100
___ 1926391	B&O 50-foot Bulkhead Flatcar "8831," 19		100
___ 1926392	B&O 50-foot Bulkhead Flatcar "8844," 19		100
___ 1926401	D&RGW 50-foot Bulkhead Flatcar "22392," 19		100
___ 1926402	D&RGW 50-foot Bulkhead Flatcar "22420," 19		100
___ 1926411	MKT 50-foot Bulkhead Flatcar "13912," 19		100
___ 1926412	MKT 50-foot Bulkhead Flatcar "13941," 19		100
___ 1926421	SAL 50-foot Bulkhead Flatcar "48102,", 19		100
___ 1926422	SAL 50-foot Bulkhead Flatcar "48124," 19		100
___ 1926431	Frisco 50-foot Bulkhead Flatcar "4052,", 19		100
___ 1926432	Frisco 50-foot Bulkhead Flatcar "4058," 19		100
___ 1926441	ATSF Grand Canyon Line 50-foot DD Boxcar "10206," 18		80
___ 1926442	AT&SF Scout 50-foot Double-Door Boxcar "10295," 18		80
___ 1926443	AT&SF El Capitan 50-foot Double-Door Boxcar "10350," 18		80
___ 1926444	AT&SF Super Chief 50-foot Double-Door Boxcar "10410," 18		80
___ 1926445	AT&SF Chief 50-foot Double-Door Boxcar "10456," 18		80

		Exc	Mint
1926451	KCS 50-foot Double-Door Boxcar "20825," 18		80
1926452	KCS 50-foot Double-Door Boxcar "20856," 18		80
1926461	Monon 50-foot Double-Door Boxcar "1423," 18		80
1926462	Monon 50-foot Double-Door Boxcar "1426," 18		80
1926471	T&P 50-foot Double-Door Boxcar "70707," 18		80
1926472	T&P 50-foot Double-Door Boxcar "70735," 18		80
1926480	ELX Halloween 50-foot Double-Door Boxcar "103119," 18		80
1926491	UP CA-4 Caboose "3830," 18		100
1926492	UP CA-4 Caboose "3830," 18		100
1926493	UP CA-4 Caboose "3859," 18		100
1926501	Bartlett Grain PS-2CD 4427-cu-ft Covered Hopper "5509," 19		100
1926502	Bartlett Grain PS-2CD 4427-cu-ft Covered Hopper "5511," 19		100
1926511	BN PS-2CD 4427-cu-ft Covered Hopper "439397," 19		100
1926512	BN PS-2CD 4427-cu-ft Covered Hopper "450621," 19		100
1926521	Cargill PS-2CD 4427-cu-ft Covered Hopper "2819," 19		100
1926522	Cargill PS-2CD 4427-cu-ft Covered Hopper "2853," 19		100
1926531	Conrail PS-2CD 4427-cu-ft Covered Hopper "886283," 19		100
1926532	Conrail PS-2CD 4427-cu-ft Covered Hopper "886304," 19		100
1926540	Ely Thomas Logging Cars 2-pack A, 19		150
1926550	Ely Thomas Logging Cars 2-pack B, 19		150
1926560	Long Bell Logging Cars 2-pack A, 19		150
1926570	Long Bell Logging Cars 2-pack B, 19		150
1926580	NY&P Logging Cars 2-pack A, 19		150
1926590	NY&P Logging Cars 2-pack B, 19		150
1926600	Unlettered Logging Cars 2-pack A, 19		150
1926610	Unlettered Logging Cars 2-pack B, 19		150
1926620	B&O Sentinel PS-1 Boxcar "466024" w/FreightSounds, 19		135
1926630	GN PS-1 Boxcar "39412" w/FreightSounds, 19		135
1926640	PRR PS-1 Boxcar "24267" w/FreightSounds, 19		135
1926650	D&RGW Cookie Box PS-1 Boxcar "60034" w/FreightSounds, 19		135
1926660	Southern PS-1 Boxcar "330434" w/FreightSounds, 19		135
1926670	SP Overnight PS-1 Boxcar "97945" w/FreightSounds, 19		135
1926680	NYS&W PS-1 Boxcar "501" w/FreightSounds, 19		135
1926690	WP PS-1 Boxcar "19531" w/FreightSounds, 19		135
1926701	B&M 40-foot Flatcar "33700" w/Sherman Tank Load, 19		130
1926702	B&M 40-foot Flatcar "33745" w/Sherman Tank Load, 19		130
1926711	NYC 40-foot Flatcar "496250" w/Sherman Tank Load, 19		130
1926712	NYC 40-foot Flatcar "496271" w/Sherman Tank Load, 19		130
1926721	PRR 40-foot Flatcar "925148" w/Sherman Tank Load, 19		130
1926722	PRR 40-foot Flatcar "925164" w/Sherman Tank Load, 19		130
1926731	SP 40-foot Flatcar "140014" w/Sherman Tank Load, 19		130
1926732	SP 40-foot Flatcar "140125" w/Sherman Tank Load, 19		130
1926741	UP 40-foot Flatcar "51125" w/Sherman Tank Load, 19		130
1926742	UP 40-foot Flatcar "51196" w/Sherman Tank Load, 19		130
1926751	US Army 40-foot Flatcar "35351" w/Sherman Tank Load, 19		130
1926752	US Army 40-foot Flatcar "35359" w/Sherman Tank Load, 19		130
1926760	CTCX 30,000-gallon 1-D Tank Car 3-pack, 19		250
1926770	GATX 30,000-gallon 1-D Tank Car 3-pack, 19		250
1926780	SCMX 30,000-gallon 1-D Tank Car 3-pack, 19		250
1926790	TILX (Black) 30,000-gallon 1-D Tank Car 3-pack, 19		250
1926800	TILX (White) 30,000-gallon 1-D Tank Car 3-pack, 19		250
1926810	VMSX 30,000-gallon 1-D Tank Car 3-pack, 19		250
1926820	Polar Express 15th Anniversary Boxcar w/FreightSounds, 19		145

		Exc	Mint
1926830	C&NW NE Caboose "10808", 19		100
1926840	Conrail (RDG patch) NE Caboose "19730," 19		100
1926850	D&H NE Caboose "35802," 19		100
1926860	L&HR NE Caboose "17," 19		100
1926870	LV NE Caboose "95003," 19		100
1926880	Halloween (ELX) NE Caboose "1313," 19		100
1926890	Alaska RR EV Caboose "1086" w/CupolaCam, 19		130
1926900	C&O EV Caboose "3160" w/CupolaCam, 19		130
1926910	Conrail EV Caboose "22137" w/CupolaCam, 19		130
1926920	D&RGW EV Caboose "01510" w/CupolaCam, 19		130
1926930	Milwaukee Road EV Caboose "992303" w/CupolaCam, 19		130
1926940	MKT EV Caboose "100" w/CupolaCam, 19		130
1926950	N&W EV Caboose "555100" w/CupolaCam, 19		130
1926960	Lionel Lines EV Caboose "6960" w/CupolaCam, 19		130
1926971	Detroit Salt PS-2CD 4427-cu-ft Covered Hopper "5436," 19		100
1926972	Detroit Salt PS-2CD 4427-cu-ft Covered Hopper "5446," 19		100
1926981	Producers Grain PS-2CD 4427-cu-ft Covered Hopper "3926," 19		100
1926982	Producers Grain PS-2CD 4427-cu-ft Covered Hopper "3940," 19		100
1927010	AT&SF 21-inch Passenger Car 4-pack, 19		700
1927020	AT&SF 21-inch Passenger Car 2-pack #1, 19		350
1927030	AT&SF 21-inch Dome Car "550" w/StationSounds, 19		340
1927040	AT&SF 21-inch Passenger Car 2-pack #2, 19		350
1927050	UP Excursion 21-inch Passenger Car Expansion Set, 19		350
1927060	UP Challenger 21-inch Passenger Car Expansion Set, 19		350
1927070	Midnight Special 18-inch Passenger Car 2-pack #1, 18		400
1927080	Midnight Special 18-inch Passenger Car 2-pack #2, 18		400
1927090	Midnight Special 18-inch Passenger Car 2-pack #3, 18		400
1927100	Midnight Special Diner "1305," w/StationSounds, 18		330
1927110	SP 18-inch Passenger Car 2-pack #1, 18-19		400
1927120	SP 18-inch Passenger Car 2-pack #2, 18-19		400
1927130	SP 18-inch Passenger Car 2-pack #3, 18-19		400
1927140	SP 18-inch Passenger Car 2-pack #4, 18-19		400
1927150	NYC Pacemaker 2-car Add-on Set, 19		400
1927160	NYC Pacemaker Diner "617" w/StationSounds, 19		330
1927170	N&W Cavalier 18-inch Passenger Car 2-pack A, 19		400
1927180	N&W Cavalier 18-inch Passenger Car 2-pack B, 19		400
1927190	N&W Cavalier 18-inch Diner "1018" w/StationSounds, 19		330
1927200	611 Excursion Train NS Coach 4-pack, 19		700
1927210	611 Excursion Train Private Car 2-pack A, 19		350
1927220	611 Excursion Train Private Car 2-pack B, 19		350
1927230	611 Excursion Train Dome Car w/StationSounds, 19		340
1927241	611 Excursion Train N&W Tool Car "1407," 19		180
1927242	N&W Cavalier Baggage "110," 19		180
1927243	N&W Cavalier Baggage "114," 19		180
1927251	PC 60-foot Baggage "7533," 19		180
1927252	PC 60-foot Baggage "7551," 19		180
1927261	SP 60-foot Baggage "6340," 19		180
1927262	SP 60-foot Baggage "6344," 19		180
1927271	REA 60-foot Baggage "1631," 19		180
1927272	REA 60-foot Baggage "1650," 19		180
1927281	UP 60-foot Baggage "1830" (Greyhound), 19		180

		Exc	Mint
1927282	UP 60-foot Baggage "1841" (Greyhound), 19		180
1927283	UP 60-foot Baggage "1830" (Yellow), 19		180
1927284	UP 60-foot Baggage "1837" (Yellow), 19		180
1927291	ACL 60-foot Baggage "555," 19		180
1927292	ACL 60-foot Baggage "559," 19		180
1927300	ACL 60-foot Railway Post Office "11," 19		180
1927310	N&W Cavalier Railway Post Office "96," 19		180
1927320	Southern 60-foot Railway Post Office "39," 18-19		160
1927330	AT&SF 60-foot Railway Post Office "65," 19		180
1927340	UP 60-foot Railway Post Office "2062," 19		180
1927351	Polar Express Railway Post Office, White Roof, 19, 22		200
1927352	Polar Express Railway Post Office, Black Roof, 19, 22		200
1927360	LIRR 21-inch Streamlined Coach 4-pack, 19		700
1927370	LIRR 21-inch Streamlined Coach 2-pack, 19		350
1927380	UP 1860s Wood Coach w/RailSounds, 2-pack, 19		350
1927390	Central Pacific 1860s Wood Coach w/RailSounds, 2-pack, 19		350
1927461	Southern 60-foot Baggage "100," 18-19		160
1927462	Southern 60-foot Baggage "109," 18-19		160
1927470	Southern 18-inch Passenger Car 2-pack #1, 18-19		400
1927480	Southern 18-inch Passenger Car 2-pack #2, 18-19		400
1927490	Southern 18-inch Passenger Car 2-pack #3, 18-19		400
1927500	Southern Diner "3168" w/StationSounds, 18-19		330
1927510	MP Sunshine Special 18" Passenger Car 2-pack #1, 18-19		400
1927520	MP Sunshine Special 18" Passenger Car 2-pack #2, 18-19		400
1927530	MP Sunshine Special 18" Passenger Car 2-pack #3, 18-19		400
1927540	MP Sunshine Special Diner "10042" w/StationSounds, 18-19		330
1927550	MP Sunshine Special 60-foot Railway Post Office "45," 18-19		160
1927560	Defense Special Heavyweight Passenger Car 2-pack A, 19		400
1927570	Defense Special Heavyweight Passenger Car 2-pack B, 19		400
1927580	Defense Special Heavyweight Passenger Car 2-pack C, 19		400
1927590	Defense Special Heavyweight Passenger Car 2-pack D, 19		400
1927600	611 Excursion Train NS Coach 2-pack, 19		350
1927610	CP 21-inch Passenger Car 4-pack, 19		700
1927620	CP 21-inch Passenger Car 2-pack, 19		350
1927630	Polar Express Hot Chocolate Car w/StationSounds, 19		330
1927640	Polar Express Abandoned Toy Car, 19		200
1927650	Polar Express 15th Anniversary Coach, 19		200
1927660	Pennsylvania Limited Suetonius Coach, 19		75
1927670	Lionel State Set Add-on 2-pack, 19		530
1927680	Northern Central 1860s Wood Coach w/RailSounds, 2-pack, 19		350
1927690	Woodruff Sleeping and Parlor 1860s Wood Coach, 2-pack, 19		300
1927700	Blue Comet Heavyweight Coach, 19-20		75
1927710	CP 21-inch Diner "550" w/StationSounds, 19		330
1927730	PRR 1860s Wood Coach w/RailSounds, 2-pack, 19		350
1928011	BN Auto Rack "159173," 18-19		80
1928012	BN Auto Rack "159433," 18-19		80
1928021	Conrail Auto Rack "980139," 18-19		80
1928022	Conrail Auto Rack "456249," 18-19		80
1928031	GT Auto Rack "50454," 18-19		80
1928032	GT Auto Rack "50490," 18-19		80
1928041	SP Auto Rack "518027," 18-19		80
1928042	SP Auto Rack "518114,", 18-19		80

		Exc	Mint
___ 1928051	TTX Auto Rack "710866," 18-19		80
___ 1928052	TTX Auto Rack "710877," 18-19		80
___ 1928060	Mickey Mouse Celebration Aquarium Car, 18		100
___ 1928070	NYC Flatcar w/Boat "28070," 18-19		70
___ 1928080	Hot Wheels Fuel 1-Dome Tank Car, 18-19		75
___ 1928091	Branch Line Passenger Car 2-pack, 18-19		75
___ 1928092	James Trucks Wagon Car 2-pack, 18-19		75
___ 1928093	S.C. Ruffey Wagon Car, 18-19		45
___ 1928110	BN Hopper 6-pack, 19		150
___ 1928120	C&NW Hopper 6-pack, 19		150
___ 1928130	CSX Hopper 6-pack, 19-20		150
___ 1928140	PP&L Hopper 6-pack, 19-20		150
___ 1928150	Reading Lines Hopper 6-pack, 19-20		150
___ 1928160	Bethlehem Steel Ore Car 6-pack, 19-20		150
___ 1928170	CN Ore Car 6-pack, 19-20		150
___ 1928180	Erie Mining Ore Car 6-pack, 19		150
___ 1928190	PRR Ore Car 6-pack, 19-20		150
___ 1928200	UP Ore Car 6-pack, 19-20		150
___ 1928210	Malt Tonics Refrigerator Car, 19-22		90
___ 1928220	Anheuser-Busch 1890s Woodside Refrigerator Car, 19		80
___ 1928240	Anheuser-Busch Uni-Body 1-D Tank Car "4271," 19		75
___ 1928250	Anheuser-Busch Barrel Car "28250," 19		80
___ 1928260	Miller High Life Woodside Refrigerator Car, 19-20		80
___ 1928270	Coors Golden Beer Woodside Refrigerator Car, 19-20		80
___ 1928280	Hamm's Beer Woodside Refrigerator Car, 19, 22		90
___ 1928330	Pez Mint Car, 19		80
___ 1928340	John Deere Mower Stockcar, 19		80
___ 1928350	John Deere Flatcar "28350" w/Piggyback Trailers, 19		85
___ 1928360	Scooby-Doo Aquarium Car, 19-20		100
___ 1928370	Spy Vs. Spy Challenge Boxcar, 19		85
___ 1928380	Trick or Treat Boxcar w/HalloweenSounds, 19		80
___ 1928390	Undead Gondola, 19		70
___ 1928400	Polar Express Hero Boy Walking Brakeman Car, 19		100
___ 1928410	Polar Express Reindeer Car, 19		80
___ 1928420	Polar Express Searchlight Car, 19		70
___ 1928430	Polar Express Barrel Car, 19		80
___ 1928440	Sweetest Helper Refrigerator Car, 19-20		80
___ 1928450	Snowball Fight Animated Gondola, 19-20		75
___ 1928460	Santa Mobile Rest Stop Flatcar, 19-20		75
___ 1928470	Santa Freight Lines Christmas Transfer Caboose, 19-20		70
___ 1928480	Santa Freight Lines Santa Finder Searchlight Car, 19-20		65
___ 1928490	Christmas Boxcar 2019, 19		65
___ 1928500	Christmas Music Boxcar, 19		80
___ 1928510	UP Barrel Ramp Car "28510," 19-20		75
___ 1928520	BNSF Maxi-Stack, 18-19		80
___ 1928530	CSX Maxi-Stack, 18-19		80
___ 1928540	TTX Maxi-Stack, 18-19		80
___ 1928550	NPR Flatcar "1937" w/Trailer, 19		70
___ 1928560	Batman & Robin Boxcar, 19-20		80
___ 1928570	Batman Bat-Signal Searchlight Car, 19		70
___ 1928580	Batman The Joker Laughing Gas Missile Car, 19-20		90
___ 1928590	Happy Birthday Scooby-Doo Sound Car, 19-20		85
___ 1928600	Batman Classic Gotham City Villains Boxcar, 19-20		80

		Exc	Mint
1928610	Chevy Auto Rack "1911," 19-20		85 ___
1928620	Chevy Flatcar w/Frames, 19		75 ___
1928630	Looney Tunes Scent-imental Over You Chasing Gondola, 19		80 ___
1928640	Thomas the Tank Engine Boxcar, 19		75 ___
1928650	Percy Boxcar, 19		75 ___
1928660	James Boxcar, 19		75 ___
1928670	Mickey Wish List Boxcar, 19-20		70 ___
1928680	UP Uni-Body 1-D Tank Car "8665," 19-20		70 ___
1928690	Toyota Auto Rack "1937," 19		85 ___
1928700	Toyota Flatcar w/Frames, 19		75 ___
1929040	Anheuser-Busch Barrel Loader, 19		70 ___
1929050	Polar Express Barrel Loader, 19		70 ___
1929060	Polar Express Station Platform, 19-23		55 ___
1929070	Winter Wonderland Station Platform, 19-23		55 ___
1929080	Hot Wheels Crash City Cafe, 18-19		100 ___
1929090	Illuminated Christmas Half-Covered Bridge, 19-23		85 ___
1929100	Defect Detector, 18-23		100 ___
1929110	Halloween House, 18		130 ___
1929130	Elf Tug of War Accessory, 19		75 ___
1929160	Sir Topham Hatt Gateman, 19		120 ___
1929170	Haunted House, 19-22		275 ___
1929230	Burning House, 19-20		120 ___
1929804	Peel and Stick Lights, 4-pack, 19-20		10 ___
1929815	Peel and Stick Lights, 15-pack, 19-20		28 ___
1929904	Peel and Stick LED Lights, 4-pack, 19-20		10 ___
1929915	Peel and Stick LED Lights, 15-pack, 19-20		28 ___
1930010	Steel Coil Load Kit, 18-23		20 ___
1930050	Lumber Load Kit, 19		25 ___
1930060	Millennial People Pack, 18-23		30 ___
1930070	Trick or Treat Figures, 18-23		30 ___
1930080	Halloween Lawn Figures, 18-23		30 ___
1930120	Mickey Mouse Celebration Billboard 3-pack, 18		20 ___
1930130	Thomas & Friends Covered Bridge, 18-19		70 ___
1930140	Trolley House, 19		50 ___
1930150	Budweiser Billboard 3-pack, 19-22		25 ___
1930160	Brown Picket Fence, 19-20		20 ___
1930170	Green Iron Fence, 19-20		20 ___
1930180	Benches, 6-pack, 19-20		10 ___
1930190	Sitting People with Benches, 6-pack, 19-20		23 ___
1930200	Winter Action Figures, 6-pack, 19-20		23 ___
1930210	Sled Kids, 3-pack, 19-20		23 ___
1930220	Sitting People, 6-pack, 19-20		23 ___
1930230	People on Sleigh Figure Pack, 19-20		23 ___
1930240	People Waving, 6-pack, 19-20		23 ___
1930250	People Eating, 6-pack, 19-20		23 ___
1930260	Prisoners (striped), 6-pack, 19-20		23 ___
1930270	Travelers, 6-pack, 19-20		23 ___
1930280	Horses, 4-pack, 19-20		23 ___
1930290	Cows and Calves (brown), 6-pack, 19-20		23 ___
1930300	Unpainted Figures, 36-pack, 19-20		35 ___
1930310	Unpainted Animals, 36-pack, 19-20		35 ___
1930320	Smoking Tony Lighted Figure, 19-20		20 ___
1930330	Railroad Worker with Lamp Lighted Figure, 19-20		20 ___

		Exc	Mint
____	**1930340**	Miner with Headlamp Lighted Figure, 19-20		20
____	**1930350**	Man with Flashlight Lighted Figure, 19-20		20
____	**1930360**	Man with Flashing Jackhammer Lighted Figure, 19-20		20
____	**1930370**	Braga House, 19-20		75
____	**1930380**	Fraser House, 19-20		75
____	**1930390**	Harwell House, 19-20		75
____	**1930400**	Olson House Kit, 19-20		22
____	**1930410**	Morris House Kit, 19-20		22
____	**1930420**	Bishop House Kit, 19-20		22
____	**1930430**	Davis House Kit, 19-20		22
____	**1930440**	Church, 19-20		86
____	**1930450**	Unpainted Steel Coils 2-Pack, 19-23		10
____	**1931060**	L&N USRA 4-8-2 Light Mountain Locomotive "404," CC, 18		1300
____	**1931070**	MP USRA 4-8-2 Light Mountain Locomotive "5307," CC, 18		1300
____	**1931080**	NC&StL USRA 4-8-2 Light Mountain Locomotive "551," CC, 18		1300
____	**1931090**	NH USRA 4-8-2 Light Mountain Locomotive "3301," CC, 18		1300
____	**1931100**	Frisco USRA 4-8-2 Light Mountain Locomotive "1501," CC, 18		1300
____	**1931110**	Soo Line USRA 4-8-2 Light Mountain "4005," CC, 18		1300
____	**1931120**	Southern USRA 4-8-2 Light Mountain "1483," CC, 18		1300
____	**1931130**	Southern USRA 4-8-2 Light Mountain "1495," CC, 18		1300
____	**1931140**	North Pole Central 4-8-2 Light Mountain "1224," CC, 18		1300
____	**1931150**	SP 4-4-2 Atlantic A-6 Locomotive "3001," CC, 18		800
____	**1931160**	SP 4-4-2 Atlantic A-6 Locomotive "3000," CC, 18		800
____	**1931170**	SP 4-4-2 Atlantic A-6 Locomotive "3002," CC, 18		800
____	**1931180**	UP 4-4-2 Atlantic Locomotive "3304," CC, 18		800
____	**1931190**	C&NW 4-4-2 Atlantic Locomotive "394," CC, 18		800
____	**1931200**	IC 4-4-2 Atlantic Locomotive "1003," CC, 18		800
____	**1931210**	Clinchfield 4-6-6-4 Locomotive "675," CC, 18		2,000
____	**1931220**	D&RGW 4-6-6-4 Locomotive "3800," CC, 18		2,000
____	**1931230**	D&RGW 4-6-6-4 Locomotive "3805," CC, 18		2,000
____	**1931240**	UP 4-6-6-4 Challenger Locomotive "3975," CC, 18		2,000
____	**1931250**	UP 4-6-6-4 Challenger Locomotive "3977," CC, 18		2,000
____	**1931260**	UP 4-6-6-4 Challenger Locomotive "3985," CC, 18		2,000
____	**1931270**	UP 4-6-6-4 Challenger Locomotive "3981," CC, 18		2,000
____	**1931280**	UP 4-6-6-4 Challenger Locomotive "3717," CC, 18		2,000
____	**1931290**	UP 4-6-6-4 Challenger Locomotive "3949," CC, 18		2,000
____	**1931300**	Undecorated 4-6-6-4 Challenger Locomotive "9999," CC, 18		2,000
____	**1931311**	UP Vision Auxiliary Water Tender "907853," CC, 18		500
____	**1931312**	UP Vision Auxiliary Water Tender "907856," CC, 18		500
____	**1931313**	UP Vision Auxiliary Water Tender "907857," CC, 18		500
____	**1931314**	UP Vision Auxiliary Water Tender "809," CC, 18		500
____	**1931315**	UP Vision Auxiliary Water Tender "814," CC, 18		500
____	**1931316**	UP Vision Auxiliary Water Tender "903026," CC, 18		500
____	**1931320**	Clinchfield Vision Auxiliary Water Tender "X675," CC, 18		500
____	**1931330**	D&RGW Vision Auxiliary Water Tender "3800A," CC, 18		500
____	**1931340**	N&W 4-8-4 Northern J-Class "600," CC, 19		1500
____	**1931350**	N&W 4-8-4 Northern J-Class "603," CC, 19		1500
____	**1931360**	N&W 4-8-4 Northern J-Class "611" (c1982)," CC, 19		1500
____	**1931370**	N&W 4-8-4 Northern J-Class "611" (c2016)," CC, 19		1500
____	**1931380**	American Freedom Train 4-8-4 "611," CC, 19		1500
____	**1931390**	N&W 4-8-4 Northern J-Class "746," CC, 19		1500
____	**1931400**	C&O 2-10-4 Texas T1 "3001," CC, 19		1500
____	**1931410**	C&O 2-10-4 Texas T1 "3039," CC, 19		1500

		Exc	Mint
1931420	PRR 2-10-4 Texas J1a "6174," CC, 19		1500
1931430	PRR 2-10-4 Texas J1a "6434," CC, 19		1500
1931440	PRR 2-10-4 Texas J1a "6500," CC (artist conception), 19		1500
1931450	NYC 4-6-4 Hudson J3a "5405," CC, 19		1400
1931460	NYC 4-6-4 Hudson J3a "5413," CC, 19		1500
1931470	NYC 4-6-4 Hudson J3a "5418," CC, 19		1400
1931480	NYC 4-6-4 Hudson J3a "5452," CC, 19		1500
1931490	Ely Thomas Two-Truck Shay Locomotive "6," CC, 19		1200
1931500	Lima Stone Two-Truck Shay Locomotive "10," CC, 19		1200
1931510	Lima Locomotive Works Two-Truck Shay "2," CC, 19		1200
1931520	Long Bell Two-Truck Shay Locomotive "5," CC, 19		1200
1931530	NY&P Two-Truck Shay Locomotive "3," CC, 19		1200
1931540	Roaring Camp Two-Truck Shay Locomotive "1," CC, 19		1200
1931550	North Pole Woodworks Two-Truck Shay "25," CC, 19		1200
1931560	Sleepy Hollow Casket, Two-Truck Shay Locomotive "31," CC, 19		1200
1931650	Central Pacific 4-4-0 Hybrid Jupiter, CC (painted), 19		1100
1931660	UP 4-4-0 Hybrid, "119," CC (painted), 19		1100
1931670	Schenectady Locomotive Works 4-4-0 Hybrid, CC (unpainted), 19		1100
1931680	Rogers Locomotive Works 4-4-0 Hybrid, CC (unpainted), 19		1100
1931690	C&O 2-10-4 Texas T1 "3020," CC (weathered), 19		1700
1931700	PRR 2-10-4 Texas J1a "6481," CC (weathered), 19		1700
1931710	B&LE 2-10-4 Texas "643," CC, 19		1500
1931720	CB&Q 2-10-4 Texas "6328," CC, 19		1500
1931730	DM&IR 2-10-4 Texas "717," CC, 19		1500
1931740	KCS 2-10-4 Texas "905," CC, 19		1500
1931750	D&RGW 2-10-4 Texas "1450," CC, 19		1500
1931760	Southern 2-10-4 Texas "5300," CC, 19		1500
1931770	Central Pacific 4-4-0 Hybrid Leviathan, CC (painted), 19		1100
1931780	Northern Central 4-4-0 Hybrid York, CC (painted), 19		1100
1931820	PRR 4-4-0 Hybrid, "573," CC (painted), 19		1100
1932010	ATSF 2-8-4 Berkshire "4101," LionChief Plus 2.0, 19-20		500
1932020	C&O 2-8-4 Berkshire Locomotive "2687," LionChief Plus 2.0, 19		500
1932030	NPR 2-8-4 Berkshire "765," LionChief Plus 2.0, 19-20		500
1932040	Pere Marquette 2-8-4 Berkshire "1225," LionChief Plus 2.0, 19-20		500
1932050	Southern 2-8-4 Berkshire, "2716," LionChief Plus 2.0, 19-20		500
1932080	Disney 2-8-4 Berkshire "2019," LionChief Plus 2.0, 19-20		525
1932090	Polar Express 2-8-4 Berkshire "1225," LionChief Plus 2.0, 19-20		525
1932100	North Pole Central 2-8-4 Berkshire "1224," LionChief Plus 2.0, 19-20		500
1932110	Halloween (ELX) 2-8-4 Berkshire "1031," LionChief Plus 2.0, 19-20		500
1932120	GN 2-4-2 Columbia Locomotive "374," LionChief, 19		200
1932130	PRR 2-4-2 Columbia Locomotive "619," LionChief, 19		200
1932140	AT&SF 2-4-2 Columbia Locomotive "3452," LionChief, 19		200
1932150	Southern 2-4-2 Columbia Locomotive "1412," LionChief, 19		200
1932161	UP 4-8-8-4 Big Boy Locomotive "4012," LionChief Plus 2.0, 19		1200
1932162	UP 4-8-8-4 Big Boy Locomotive "4014," LionChief Plus 2.0, 19		1200
1932163	UP 4-8-8-4 Big Boy Locomotive "4017," LionChief Plus 2.0, 19		1200
1932164	UP 4-8-8-4 Big Boy Locomotive "4018," LionChief Plus 2.0, 19		1200
1932170	UP 4-8-8-4 Big Boy "4000" (Greyhound), LionChief Plus 2.0, 19		1200
1933011	BN Alco RS-11 Diesel "4186," CC, 18		500

		Mint
___ 1933012	BN Alco RS-11 Diesel "4190," CC, 18	500
___ 1933021	CV Alco RS-11 Diesel "3601," CC, 18	500
___ 1933022	CV Alco RS-11 Diesel "3611," CC, 18	500
___ 1933031	Conrail Alco RS-11 Diesel "7640," CC, 18	500
___ 1933032	Conrail Alco RS-11 Diesel "7651," CC, 18	500
___ 1933041	Depew, Lancaster & Western Alco RS-11 Diesel "1800," CC, 18	500
___ 1933042	Depew, Lancaster & Western Alco RS-11 Diesel "1804," CC, 18	500
___ 1933051	L&N Alco RS-11 Diesel "952," CC, 18	500
___ 1933052	L&N Alco RS-11 Diesel "955," CC, 18	500
___ 1933061	SCL Alco RS-11 Diesel "1202," CC, 18	500
___ 1933062	SCL Alco RS-11 Diesel "1210," CC, 18	500
___ 1933081	BN EMD SD40-2 Diesel "6702," CC, 18	550
___ 1933082	BN EMD SD40-2 Diesel "8002," CC, 18	550
___ 1933083	BN non-powered EMD SD40-2 Diesel "6772," 18	300
___ 1933091	FEC EMD SD40-2 Diesel "703," CC, 18	550
___ 1933092	FEC EMD SD40-2 Diesel "713," CC, 18	550
___ 1933093	FEC non-powered EMD SD40-2 Diesel "714,", 18	300
___ 1933101	FURX EMD SD40-2 Diesel "3012," CC, 18	550
___ 1933102	FURX EMD SD40-2 Diesel "3021," CC, 18	550
___ 1933103	FURX non-powered EMD SD40-2 Diesel "3049," 18	300
___ 1933111	Milwaukee Road Bicentennial EMD SD40-2 Diesel "156," CC, 18	550
___ 1933112	Milwaukee Road EMD SD40-2 Diesel "190," CC, 18	550
___ 1933113	Milwaukee Road EMD SD40-2 Diesel "196," CC, 18	550
___ 1933114	Milwaukee Road non-powered EMD SD40-2 Diesel "197," 18	300
___ 1933121	Soo Line "Bandit" EMD SD40-2 Diesel "6301," CC, 18	550
___ 1933122	Soo Line "Bandit" EMD SD40-2 Diesel "6345," CC, 18	550
___ 1933123	Soo Line "Bandit" non-powered EMD SD40-2 Diesel "6362", 18	300
___ 1933131	UP EMD SD40-2 Diesel "3696," CC, 18	550
___ 1933132	UP EMD SD40-2 Diesel "3707," CC, 18	550
___ 1933133	UP non-powered EMD SD40-2 Diesel "B3641," 18	300
___ 1933141	W&LE EMD SD40-2 Diesel "6310," CC, 18	550
___ 1933142	W&LE EMD SD40-2 Diesel "6311," CC, 18	550
___ 1933143	W&LE non-powered EMD SD40-2 Diesel "6347," 18	300
___ 1933151	W&S EMD SD40-2 Diesel "4001," CC, 18	550
___ 1933152	W&S EMD SD40-2 Diesel "4003," CC, 18	550
___ 1933153	W&S non-powered EMD SD40-2 Diesel "4005," 18	300
___ 1933160	AT&SF Alco PA-PA Diesel Set "54-54," CC, 18	1000
___ 1933163	AT&SF Alco PB w/SuperBass Sound "54A," CC, 18	500
___ 1933170	D&RGW Alco PA-PA Diesel Set "6001-6003," CC, 18	1000
___ 1933173	D&RGW Alco PB w/SuperBass Sound "6002," CC, 18	500
___ 1933180	NYC Alco PA-PA Diesel Set "4903-4904," CC, 18	1000
___ 1933183	NYC Alco PB w/SuperBass Sound "4303," CC, 18	500
___ 1933190	PRR Alco PA-PA Diesel Set "5754-5755+B34," CC, 18	1000
___ 1933193	PRR Alco PB w/SuperBass Sound "5754B," CC, 18	500
___ 1933200	SP Alco PA-PA Diesel Set "6034-6039," CC, 18	1000
___ 1933203	SP Alco PB w/SuperBass Sound "5922," CC, 18	500
___ 1933210	UP Alco PA-PA Diesel Set "606-607," CC, 18	1000
___ 1933213	UP Alco PB w/SuperBass Sound "606B," CC, 18	500
___ 1933221	BNSF (ATSF Patch) GE C44-9W Diesel "599," CC, 18	550
___ 1933222	BNSF (ATSF Patch) GE C44-9W Diesel "662," CC, 18	550
___ 1933223	BNSF (ATSF Patch) non-powered GE C44-9W Diesel "604," 18	300
___ 1933231	BNSF GE C44-9W Diesel "703," CC, 18	550
___ 1933232	BNSF GE C44-9W Diesel "4173," CC, 18	550

		Exc	Mint
1933233	BNSF non-powered GE C44-9W Diesel "5282," 18		300 ___
1933241	Pilbara Rail GE C44-9W Diesel "7079," CC, 18		550 ___
1933242	Pilbara Rail GE C44-9W Diesel "7097," CC, 18		550 ___
1933243	Pilbara Rail non-powered GE C44-9W Diesel "7098," 18		300 ___
1933251	Quebec, North Shore & Labrador GE C44-9W "405," CC, 18		550 ___
1933252	Quebec, North Shore & Labrador GE C44-B141 "407," CC, 18		550 ___
1933253	Quebec, North Shore & Labrador non-powered GE C44-9W Diesel "413," 18		300 ___
1933261	UP (SP Patch) GE C44-9W Diesel "9615," CC, 18		550 ___
1933262	UP (SP Patch) GE C44-9W Diesel "9617," CC, 18		550 ___
1933263	UP (SP Patch) non-powered GE C44-9W Diesel "9647," 18		300 ___
1933271	UP GE C44-9W Diesel w/Cheyenne Service Unit Plaque "9700," CC, 18		550 ___
1933272	UP GE C44-9W Diesel "9650," CC, 18		550 ___
1933273	UP non-powered GE C44-9W Diesel "9654," 18		300 ___
1933281	BNSF GE ES44AC Diesel "6411," CC, 19		600 ___
1933282	BNSF GE ES44AC Diesel "6425," CC, 19		600 ___
1933283	BNSF non-powered GE ES44AC Diesel "6438," 19		350 ___
1933291	CitiRail GE ES44AC Diesel "1201," CC, 19		600 ___
1933292	CitiRail GE ES44AC Diesel "1210," CC, 19		600 ___
1933293	CitiRail non-powered GE ES44AC Diesel "1212," 19		350 ___
1933301	GE Demonstrator ES44AC Diesel "2005," CC, 19		600 ___
1933302	GE Demonstrator ES44AC Diesel "2012," CC, 19		600 ___
1933310	Iowa Interstate GE ES44AC Diesel "516," CC, 19		600 ___
1933321	UP GE ES44AC Diesel "7964," CC, 19		600 ___
1933322	UP GE ES44AC Diesel "8109," CC, 19		600 ___
1933323	UP non-powered GE ES44AC Diesel "8140," 19		350 ___
1933324	UP GE ES44AC, Fantasy Greyhound scheme, "8044," CC, 19		600 ___
1933325	UP GE ES44AC Diesel, Fantasy 49er scheme, "8149," CC, 19		600 ___
1933326	UP GE ES44AC Diesel Fantasy "119," CC, 19		600 ___
1933327	UP GE ES44AC Diesel Fantasy Jupiter "60," CC, 19		600 ___
1933331	Allegheny RR EMD GP35 Diesel "305," CC, 19		500 ___
1933332	Allegheny RR EMD GP35 Diesel "306," CC, 19		500 ___
1933341	AT&SF EMD GP35 Diesel "2835," CC, 19		500 ___
1933342	AT&SF EMD GP35 Diesel "2858," CC, 19		500 ___
1933343	AT&SF non-powered EMD GP35 Diesel "2932," 19		300 ___
1933351	C&NW EMD GP35 Diesel "826," CC, 19		500 ___
1933352	C&NW EMD GP35 Diesel "830," CC, 19		500 ___
1933353	C&NW non-powered EMD GP35 Diesel "841," 19		300 ___
1933361	Conrail EMD GP35 Diesel "2398," CC, 19		500 ___
1933362	Conrail EMD GP35 Diesel "3630," CC, 19		500 ___
1933363	Conrail non-powered EMD GP35 Diesel "3692," 19		300 ___
1933371	BNSF EMD GP35 Diesel "2570," CC, 19		500 ___
1933372	BNSF EMD GP35 Diesel "2615," CC, 19		500 ___
1933373	BNSF non-powered EMD GP35 Diesel "2931," 19		300 ___
1933381	Lycoming Valley EMD GP35 Diesel "5510," CC, 19		500 ___
1933382	Lycoming Valley EMD GP35 Diesel "5514," CC, 19		500 ___
1933391	PRR EMD GP35 Diesel "2298," CC, 19		500 ___
1933392	PRR EMD GP35 Diesel "2333," CC, 19		500 ___
1933393	PRR non-powered EMD GP35 Diesel "2356," 19		300 ___
1933401	RF&P EMD GP35 Diesel "131," CC, 19		500 ___
1933402	RF&P EMD GP35 Diesel "134," CC, 19		500 ___
1933403	RF&P non-powered EMD GP35 Diesel "138," 19		300 ___

		Exc	Mint
1933411	Apache RR Alco C-420 Diesel "81," CC, 19		500
1933412	Apache RR Alco C-420 Diesel "82," CC, 19		500
1933413	Apache RR non-powered Alco C-420 Diesel "84," 19		300
1933421	D&H Alco C-420 Diesel "404," CC, 19		500
1933422	D&H Alco C-420 Diesel "414," CC, 19		500
1933423	D&H non-powered Alco C-420 Diesel "204," 19		300
1933430	D&M Alco C-420 Diesel "976," CC, 19		500
1933441	Erie Mining Alco C-420 Diesel "7220," CC, 19		500
1933442	Erie Mining non-powered Alco C-420 Diesel "7221," 19		300
1933451	L&HR Alco C-420 Diesel "21," CC, 19		500
1933452	L&HR Alco C-420 Diesel "23," CC, 19		500
1933453	L&HR non-powered Alco C-420 Diesel "21," CC, 19		300
1933461	LIRR Alco C-420 Diesel "202," CC, 19		500
1933462	LIRR Alco C-420 Diesel "218," CC, 19		500
1933471	P&N Alco C-420 Diesel "2000," CC, 19		500
1933472	P&N Alco C-420 Diesel "2001," CC, 19		500
1933480	NYS&W Alco C-420 Diesel "2010," CC, 19		500
1933490	Alco Demonstrator FA A-A Diesel Set, CC, 19		900
1933498	Alco Demonstrator FB-2 Unit, CC, 19		450
1933499	Alco Demonstrator FB-2 Unit w/RailSounds, 19		430
1933500	C&NW Alco FA A-A Diesel Set, CC, 19		900
1933508	C&NW Alco FB-2 Unit, CC, 19		450
1933509	C&NW Alco FB-2 Unit w/RailSounds, 19		430
1933510	CP Alco FA-2 A-A Diesel Set "4082/4083," CC, 19		900
1933518	CP Alco FB-2 "4469," CC, 19		450
1933519	CP Alco FB-2 Unit w/RailSounds, 19		430
1933520	LV Alco FA A-A Diesel Set, CC, 19		900
1933528	LV Alco FB-2 Unit, CC, 19		450
1933529	LV Alco FB-2 Unit w/RailSounds, 19		430
1933530	MP Alco FA A-A Diesel Set, CC, 19		900
1933538	MP Alco FB-2 Unit, CC, 19		450
1933539	MP Alco FB-2 Unit w/RailSounds, 19		430
1933540	NYC Alco FA A-A Diesel Set, CC, 19		900
1933548	NYC Alco FB-2 Unit, CC, 19		450
1933549	NYC Alco FB-2 Unit w/RailSounds, 19		430
1933550	SP&S Alco FA A-A Diesel Set, CC, 19		900
1933558	SP&S Alco FB-2 Unit, CC, 19		450
1933559	SP&S Alco FB-2 Unit w/RailSounds, 19		430
1933561	LIRR Alco FA Cab Car "607," CC, 19		430
1933562	LIRR Alco FA Cab Car "609," CC, 19		430
1933563	LIRR Alco FA Cab Car "608," CC, 19		430
1933564	LIRR Alco FA Cab Car "610," CC, 19		430
1933571	Milwaukee Road GE Bi-Polar Electric "E-1," CC, 19		1300
1933572	Milwaukee Road GE Bi-Polar Electric "E-2," CC, 19		1300
1933573	Milwaukee Road GE Bi-Polar Electric "E-3," CC, 19		1300
1933574	Milwaukee Road GE Bi-Polar Electric "E-4," CC, 19		1300
1933575	Milwaukee Road GE Bi-Polar Electric "E-5," CC, 19		1300
1933580	GN GE Bi-Polar Electric "5020," CC, 19		1300
1933590	NH GE Bi-Polar Electric "380," CC, 19		1300
1933600	NYC GE Bi-Polar Electric "300," CC, 19		1300
1933610	PRR GE Bi-Polar Electric "4501," CC, 19		1300
1933620	Polar Express GE Bi-Polar Electric "E-25," CC, 19		1300
1933630	NS GE C44-9W Diesel "8520," CC, 18		550

		Exc	Mint
1934011	BNSF GE ET44AC Diesel "3738," LionChief Plus 2.0, 19		400 ___
1934012	BNSF GE ET44AC Diesel "3776," LionChief Plus 2.0, 19		400 ___
1934021	CSX GE ET44AC Diesel "3277," LionChief Plus 2.0, 19		400 ___
1934022	CSX GE ET44AC Diesel "3291," LionChief Plus 2.0, 19		400 ___
1934031	NS GE ET44AC Diesel "3600," LionChief Plus 2.0, 19		400 ___
1934032	NS GE ET44AC Diesel "3619," LionChief Plus 2.0, 19		400 ___
1934041	UP GE ET44AC Diesel "2645," LionChief Plus 2.0, 19		400 ___
1934042	UP GE ET44AC Diesel "2727," LionChief Plus 2.0, 19		400 ___
1934050	BN Alco RS-3 Diesel "4068," LionChief, 19		200 ___
1934060	CNJ Alco RS-3 Diesel "1552," LionChief, 19		200 ___
1934070	Delaware-Lackawanna Alco RS-3 Diesel "4103," LionChief, 19		200 ___
1934080	UP Alco RS-3 Diesel "1219," LionChief, 19		200 ___
1934090	AT&SF EMD FT Diesel A-A Set "123/124," LionChief Plus 2.0, 19		550 ___
1934098	AT&SF EMD FT B Unit, LionChief Plus 2.0, 19		300 ___
1934100	GN EMD FT Diesel A-A Set "400/401," LionChief Plus 2.0, 19		550 ___
1934108	GN EMD FT B Unit, LionChief Plus 2.0, 19		300 ___
1934110	NYC EMD FT A-A Set "1603/1604," LionChief Plus 2.0, 19		550 ___
1934118	NYC EMD FT B Unit, LionChief Plus 2.0, 19		300 ___
1934120	Texas Special FT Diesel A-A "219/220," LionChief Plus 2.0, 19		550 ___
1934128	Texas Special EMD FT B Unit, LionChief Plus 2.0, 19		300 ___
1935010	Area 51 Motorized Trackmobile "51," CC, 19		350 ___
1935020	Bethlehem Steel Motorized Trackmobile "12," CC, 19		350 ___
1935030	BN Motorized Trackmobile, CC, 19		350 ___
1935040	Granite Run Quarries Motorized Trackmobile, CC, 19		350 ___
1935050	Milwaukee Road Motorized Trackmobile, CC, 19		350 ___
1935060	PP&L Motorized Trackmobile "16," CC, 19		350 ___
1935070	AT&SF Motorized Trackmobile "8," CC, 19		350 ___
1935080	SP Motorized Trackmobile "5," CC, 19		350 ___
1935090	WWII U.S. War Bonds Trolley, 19		100 ___
1938010	Mickey Mouse Celebration True Original Boxcar, 18		85 ___
1938030	Well-Stocked Angela Trotta Thomas Boxcar, 18		85 ___
1938040	Jupiter Anniversary Boxcar, 19		85 ___
1938050	Southern Ry. 125th Anniversary Boxcar, 19		85 ___
1938060	Westinghouse Air Brake 150th Anniversary Boxcar, 19		85 ___
1938100	Pez Vintage Boxcar, 19		85 ___
1938110	Looney Tunes Duck Dodgers Boxcar, 19		90 ___
1938120	Looney Tunes Rabbit Season Boxcar, 19		90 ___
1938130	Looney Tunes Road Runner Boxcar, 19		90 ___
1938180	Martin Van Buren Presidential Boxcar, 19		70 ___
1938190	James Buchanan Presidential Boxcar, 19		70 ___
1938200	William McKinley Presidential Boxcar, 19		70 ___
1938210	WWII Kiss the Way Goodbye Boxcar, 19		85 ___
1938220	WWII Sherman Tank Boxcar, 19		85 ___
1938240	WWII Liberty Ships Boxcar, 19		85 ___
1938260	Wings of Angels--Blonde Boxcar, 19		90 ___
1938270	Wings of Angels--Redhead Boxcar, 19		90 ___
1938280	Wings of Angels--Brunette Boxcar, 19		90 ___
1938290	Happy Birthday 2019 Boxcar, 19		95 ___
1938300	Merry Christmas 2019 Boxcar, 19		90 ___
1938310	Angela Trotta Thomas Christmas Boxcar, 19		90 ___
1938320	Personalized Christmas Caboose, 19-20		90 ___
1938340	Happy Birthday Caboose, 19-20		90 ___
1938370	UP Anniversary Boxcar "199," 19		85 ___

		Exc	Mint
___	**1942170**	UP Vision Challenger Boxcar 6-pack #1, 18		390
___	**1942180**	UP Vision Challenger Boxcar 6-pack #2, 18		390
___	**1942190**	UP Vision Challenger Boxcar 6-pack #3, 18		390
___	**1942200**	UP Vision Challenger Boxcar 6-pack #4, 18		390
___	**1942210**	UP Vision Challenger Express Boxcar 6-pack, 18		390
___	**2001090**	LCCA 50th Anniversary Convention Car 2-pack, 20 u		300
___	**2001100**	LCCA 50th Anniversary UP Registration Mint Car, 20 u		75
___	**2001110**	LCCA UP ET44AC Diesel "2020" LionChief Plus 2.0, 20 u		700
___	**2001160**	LCCA 50th Anniversary UP Unibody 1-D Tank Car, 20 u		75
___	**2022010**	Granite Run Quarry Steam Freight Set, LionChief Plus 2.0, 19		350
___	**2022020**	Christmas Candies Steam Freight Set, LionChief Plus 2.0, 19		350
___	**2022030**	Easter Eggspress Steam Freight Set, LionChief Plus 2.0, 19		350
___	**2022040**	Manufacturers Railway Alco S-2 Diesel Freight Set, CC, 19		800
___	**2022050**	George H.W. Bush Funeral Diesel Passenger Train, CC, 19		1200
___	**2022060**	Pennsylvania Fast Freight Electric Set, LionChief Plus 2.0, 19		700
___	**2022070**	B&M E8 Diesel Passenger Set, CC, 20		800
___	**2022080**	Preamble Express Diesel Passenger Set, CC, 20		800
___	**2022090**	Polar Express Elf Steam Work Train Set, LionChief, 20		450
___	**2022100**	Pennsylvania Train Master Diesell Freight Set, CC, 20		900
___	**2022110**	CNJ Red Baron SD40 Diesel Freight Set, CC, 20		850
___	**2022120**	Lionel 120th Deluxe LionChief Plus 2.0 F3 Freight Set, 20		1000
___	**2022130**	SP Vision Stock Express Steam Freight Train Set, CC, 20		2500
___	**2022140**	North Pole Central Snowflake Limited Steam Freight Set, CC, 20		1000
___	**2023010**	Strasburg RR Steam Freight Set, LionChief, 19-20		370
___	**2023020**	Shark Research & Rescue Diesel Freight Set, LionChief, 19		400
___	**2023030**	Budweiser Delivery ET44 Diesel Freight Set, LionChief, 20		370
___	**2023040**	Disney Frozen 2 Steam Freight Set, LionChief, 20-23		450
___	**2023050**	Area 51 ET44 Diesel Freight Set, LionChief, 20, 23		475
___	**2023070**	Lionel Junction North Pole Central Steam Freight Set, LC, 20		330
___	**2023080**	Christmas Light Express Steam Freight Set, LionChief, 20		430
___	**2023090**	Witherslack Hall Steam Passenger Set, LionChief, 20		400
___	**2023100**	GE Tier 4 ET44 Diesel Freight Set, LionChief, 20		400
___	**2023110**	Toy Story Steam Freight Set, LionChief, 20-23		450
___	**2023120**	Lionel Lines LionChief Steam Freight Set, 20		300
___	**2023130**	Star Trek Diesel Freight Set, LionChief, 20		450
___	**2023140**	Polar Express Steam Passenger Set, LionChief, 20		400
___	**2023150**	Alaska GP38 Diesel Freight Set, LionChief, 20		400
___	**2023160**	Baldwin Locomotive Works Steam Freight Set, LionChief, 20		400
___	**2023170**	Hogwarts Express Steam Passenger Set, LionChief, 20		400
___	**2025010**	Lighted FasTrack 10" Straight, 4-pack, 20-23		66
___	**2025020**	Lighted FasTrack O-36 Curve, 4-pack, 20-23		66
___	**2025050**	Merry Christmas FasTrack Girder Bridge, 20-23		35
___	**2025070**	Lighted FasTrack Terminal Track Pack, 20-23		44
___	**2025080**	Lighted FasTrack Oval Track Pack , 20-23		165
___	**2026010**	Side Dump Car 4-pack, 19		160
___	**2026020**	Christmas Side Dump Car 4-pack, 19		160
___	**2026030**	Easter Eggspress Side Dump Car 4-pack, 19		160
___	**2026040**	Ely Thomas Lumber Logging Caboose, "1," 19		45
___	**2026050**	Safety First Logging Caboose, "3," 19		45
___	**2026061**	AT&SF 40' Plug-Door Refrigerator Car, "14180," 19		90
___	**2026062**	AT&SF 40' Plug-Door Refrigerator Car, "14193," 19		90
___	**2026071**	BAR 40' Plug-Door Refrigerator Car, "7728," 19		90
___	**2026072**	BAR 40' Plug-Door Refrigerator Car, "7777," 19		90

2026081	GB&W 40' Plug-Door Refrigerator Car, "21002," 19	90	___
2026082	GB&W 40' Plug-Door Refrigerator Car, "21038," 19	90	___
2026091	PFE 40' Plug-Door Refrigerator Car, "18015," 19	90	___
2026092	PFE 40' Plug-Door Refrigerator Car, "18118," 19	90	___
2026101	Reading 40' Plug-Door Refrigerator Car, "272," 19	90	___
2026102	Reading 40' Plug-Door Refrigerator Car, "278," 19	90	___
2026111	Therm Ice 40' Plug-Door Refrigerator Car, "8907," 19	90	___
2026112	Therm Ice 40' Plug-Door Refrigerator Car, "8910," 19	90	___
2026120	AT&SF PS-1 Boxcar, "17819" w/FreightSounds, 19	135	___
2026130	DT&I PS-1 Boxcar, "14253" w/FreightSounds, 19	135	___
2026140	EL PS-1 Boxcar, B195 "74210" w/FreightSounds, 19	135	___
2026150	GN PS-1 Boxcar, "19038" w/FreightSounds, 19	135	___
2026160	Illinois Terminal PS-1 Boxcar, "8427" w/FreightSounds, 19	135	___
2026170	NYC PS-1 Boxcar, "163194" w/FreightSounds, 19	135	___
2026180	PC PS-1 Boxcar, "253321" w/FreightSounds, 19	135	___
2026190	UP PS-1 Boxcar, "125404" w/FreightSounds, 19	135	___
2026200	B&O I-12 BW Caboose, "C2428," 19	110	___
2026210	B&O I-12 BW Caboose, "C2406," 19	110	___
2026220	B&O I-12 BW Caboose, "C2822," 19	110	___
2026230	B&O I-12 BW Caboose, "C2457," 19	110	___
2026240	Chessie System I-12 BW Caboose, "902440," 19	110	___
2026250	Polar Express I-12 BW Caboose, "C2425," 19	110	___
2026260	Anheuser Busch 8,000-Gallon 1-D Tank Car, "4274," 19	80	___
2026270	Deep Rock 8,000-Gallon 1-D Tank Car, "6516," 19	80	___
2026280	Everett Distilling 8,000-Gallon 1-D Tank Car, "41," 19	80	___
2026290	Hercules Powder 8,000-Gallon 1-D Tank Car, "10673," 19	80	___
2026300	Independence Energy 8,000-Gallon 1-D Tank Car, "1776," 19	80	___
2026310	Sinclair 8,000-Gallon 1-D Tank Car, "13103," 19	80	___
2026320	Amtrak Veterans 60' LED Flag Boxcar, "70042," 19	120	___
2026330	I Love USA 60' LED Flag Boxcar, 19	120	___
2026340	KCS 60' LED Flag Boxcar, "4006,"19	120	___
2026350	NS First Responders 60' LED Flag Boxcar, "9-1-1," 19	120	___
2026360	NS Veterans 60' LED Flag Boxcar, "6920", 19	120	___
2026370	UP 60' LED Flag Boxcar "4141," 19	120	___
2026380	UP Transcontinental 60' LED Flag Boxcar, "150," 19	120	___
2026391	AT&SF 60' Boxcar, "37639," 19	100	___
2026392	AT&SF 60' Boxcar, "37719," 19	100	___
2026401	CP 60' Boxcar, "205502," 19	100	___
2026402	CP 60' Boxcar, "205525," 19	100	___
2026411	DT&I 60' Boxcar, "25525," 19	100	___
2026412	DT&I 60' Boxcar, "25528," 19	100	___
2026421	NYC 60' Boxcar, "56451," 19	100	___
2026422	NYC 60' Boxcar, "56516," 19	100	___
2026431	PRR 60' Boxcar, "11789," 19	100	___
2026432	PRR 60' Boxcar, "11813," 19	100	___
2026441	PC 60' Boxcar, "274570," 19	100	___
2026442	PC 60' Boxcar, "274584," 19	100	___
2026450	Chevrolet 60' Boxcar "26450," 19	100	___
2026460	Ford 60' Boxcar, "26460," 19	100	___
2026470	Area 51 57' Smoking Mechanical Refrigerator Car w/ FreightSounds, 20	200	___
2026480	AT&SF 57' Smoking Mechanical Refrigerator Car w/ FreightSounds, 20	200	___

		Exc	Mint
___ 2026490	BNSF 57' Smoking Mechanical Refrigerator Car w/ FreightSounds, 20		200
___ 2026500	Conrail 57' Smoking Mechanical Refrigerator Car w/ FreightSounds, 20		200
___ 2026510	Halloween Smoking 57' Mechanical Refrigerator Car, 20		200
___ 2026520	PFE 57' Smoking Mechanical Refrigerator Car w/ FreightSounds, 20		200
___ 2026530	UP 57' Smoking Mechanical Refrigerator Car w/ FreightSounds, 20		200
___ 2026541	AT&SF "Beer Car" Insulated Boxcar, "625355," 20		100
___ 2026542	AT&SF "Beer Car" Insulated Boxcar, "625380," 20		100
___ 2026551	BN "Beer Car" Insulated Boxcar, "3069," 20		100
___ 2026552	BN "Beer Car" Insulated Boxcar, "3116,", 20		100
___ 2026561	BNSF "Beer Car" Insulated Boxcar, "782403" w/Graffiti, 20		110
___ 2026562	BNSF "Beer Car" Insulated Boxcar, "782425," 20		100
___ 2026563	BNSF "Beer Car" Insulated Boxcar, "782483," 20		100
___ 2026571	Conrail "Beer Car" Insulated Boxcar, "376045," 20		100
___ 2026572	Conrail "Beer Car" Insulated Boxcar, "376142," 20		100
___ 2026581	Coors "Beer Car" Insulated Boxcar, "24," 20		100
___ 2026582	Coors "Beer Car" Insulated Boxcar, "26," 20		100
___ 2026591	Manufacturers Ry. "Beer Car" Insulated Boxcar, "2520," 20		100
___ 2026592	Manufacturers Ry. "Beer Car" Insulated Boxcar, "2540," 20		100
___ 2026601	SP "Beer Car" Insulated Boxcar, "691783" w/Graffiti, 20		110
___ 2026602	SP "Beer Car" Insulated Boxcar, "691729," 20		100
___ 2026603	SP "Beer Car" Insulated Boxcar, "691745," 20		100
___ 2026611	AT&SF 50' Flatcar, "91156" w/20' Trailers, 20		120
___ 2026612	AT&SF 50' Flatcar, "91220" w/20' Trailers, 20		120
___ 2026621	DT&I 50' Flatcar, "911" w/20' Ford Trailers, 20		120
___ 2026622	DT&I 50' Flatcar, "924" w/20' Ford Trailers, 20		120
___ 2026631	PRR 50' Flatcar, "469469" w/Mason Dixon Trailers, 20		120
___ 2026632	PRR 50' Flatcar, "469625" w/Mason Dixon Trailers, 20		120
___ 2026641	Trailer Train 50' Flatcar, 475231" w/Hennis Trailers, 20		120
___ 2026642	Trailer Train 50' Flatcar, 475293" w/Hennis Trailers, 20		120
___ 2026651	UP 50' Flatcar, "53085" w/Merchants Trailers, 20		120
___ 2026652	UP 50' Flatcar, "53091" w/Merchants Trailers, 20		120
___ 2026661	North Pole Central 50' Flatcar, "2024" w/20' Sled-Ex Trailers, 20		120
___ 2026662	North Pole Central 50' Flatcar, "2025" w/20' Sled-Ex Trailers, 20		120
___ 2026671	Polar Express 50' Flatcar, "122420" w/20' Trailers, 20		125
___ 2026672	Polar Express 50' Flatcar, "122520" w/20' Trailers, 20		125
___ 2026680	Polar Express Elf Work Train, 4-pack, 20		200
___ 2026690	Buffalo, Rochester & Pittsburgh 2-bay Hopper, 3-pack, 20		280
___ 2026700	Blue Coal 2-bay Hopper, 3-pack, 20		280
___ 2026710	NYO&W 2-bay Hopper, 3-pack, 20		280
___ 2026720	Rutland 2-bay Hopper, 3-pack, 20		280
___ 2026730	Waddell Coal 2-bay Hopper, 3-pack, 20		280
___ 2026741	CB&Q Friendship Train PS-1 Boxcar, "36262," 0		75
___ 2026742	C&NW Friendship Train PS-1 Boxcar, "143576," 20		75
___ 2026743	L&N Friendship Train PS-1 Boxcar, "16576," 20		75
___ 2026744	NYC Friendship Train PS-1 Boxcar, "161500," 20		75
___ 2026745	SP Friendship Train PS-1 Boxcar, "97994," 20		75
___ 2026746	UP Friendship Train PS-1 Boxcar, "187989," 20		75
___ 2026750	Chateau Martin Wine Car, "132," 20		100

		Exc	Mint
2026760	Cloverland Dairy Milk Car, "101," 20		100
2026770	D&RGW Milk Car, "1612," 20		100
2026780	Frisco Milk Car, "5009," 20		100
2026790	Reid Ice Cream Milk Car, "103," 20		100
2026800	Scenic Citrus Milk Car, "977," 20		100
2026810	Armour Vision Stockcar 3-pack w/Sound Car, 20		400
2026820	AT&SF Vision Stockcar 3-pack w/Sound Car, 20		400
2026830	CP Vision Stockcar 3-pack w/Sound Car, 20		400
2026840	CB&Q Vision Stockcar 3-pack w/Sound Car, 20		400
2026850	C&NW Vision Stockcar 3-pack w/Sound Car, 20		400
2026860	MKT Vision Stockcar 3-pack w/Sound Car, 20		400
2026870	PRR N5 Caboose, "476998," 20		100
2026880	PRR N5 Caboose, "477714," 20		100
2026890	PRR N5 Caboose, "492418," 20		100
2026900	PC N5 Caboose, "22838," 20		100
2026910	Lionel Lines NE Caboose, "120," 20		115
2026930	NYC Wood Caboose, "19020" w/CupolaCam, 20		190
2026940	NYC Safety Wood Caboose, "18906" w/CupolaCam, 20		190
2026950	Ford 2-bay Hopper, 3-pack, 20		280
2026960	AT&SF Vision Refrigerator Car 3-pack, 20		350
2026970	PFE Vision Refrigerator Car 3-pack, 20		350
2026980	MDT Vision Refrigerator Car 3-pack, 20		350
2026990	PRR Vision Refrigerator Car 3-pack, 20		350
2027011	Christmas Disconnect Passenger Car, Baggage, 19		45
2027012	Christmas Disconnect Passenger Car, Coach, 19		45
2027013	Christmas Disconnect Passenger Car, Diner, 19		45
2027014	Christmas Disconnect Passenger Car, Sleeper, 19		45
2027015	Christmas Disconnect Passenger Car, Observation, 19		45
2027021	NYC Disconnect Passenger Car, Baggage, 19		45
2027022	NYC Disconnect Passenger Car, Coach, 19		45
2027023	NYC Disconnect Passenger Car, Diner, 19		45
2027024	NYC Disconnect Passenger Car, Sleeper, 19		45
2027025	NYC Disconnect Passenger Car, Observation, 19		45
2027031	PRR Disconnect Passenger Car, Baggage, 19		45
2027032	PRR Disconnect Passenger Car, Coach, 19		45
2027033	PRR Disconnect Passenger Car, Diner, 19		45
2027034	PRR Disconnect Passenger Car, Sleeper, 19		45
2027035	PRR Disconnect Passenger Car, Observation, 19		45
2027041	D&RGW Disconnect Passenger Car, Baggage , 19		45
2027042	D&RGW Disconnect Passenger Car, Coach, 19		45
2027043	D&RGW Disconnect Passenger Car, Diner, 19		45
2027044	D&RGW Disconnect Passenger Car, Sleeper, 19		45
2027045	D&RGW Disconnect Passenger Car, Observation, 19		45
2027051	AT&SF Disconnect Passenger Car, Baggage , 19		45
2027052	AT&SF Disconnect Passenger Car, Coach, 19		45
2027053	AT&SF Disconnect Passenger Car, Diner, 19		45
2027054	AT&SF Disconnect Passenger Car, Sleeper, 19		45
2027055	AT&SF Disconnect Passenger Car, Observation, 19		45
2027061	SP Disconnect Passenger Car, Baggage, 19		45
2027062	SP Disconnect Passenger Car, Coach, 19		45
2027063	SP Disconnect Passenger Car, Diner, 19		45
2027064	SP Disconnect Passenger Car, Sleeper, 19		45

		Exc	Mint
___ 2027065	SP Disconnect Passenger Car, Observation, 19		45
___ 2027070	AT&SF California Limited 18" Passenger Car 2-pack, A, 19		400
___ 2027080	AT&SF California Limited 18" Passenger Car 2-pack, B, 19		400
___ 2027090	AT&SF California Limited 18" Passenger Car 2-pack, C, 19		400
___ 2027100	AT&SF California Limited 18" Diner "1406" w/StationSounds, 19		330
___ 2027110	AT&SF Shadow Line 18" Passenger Car 2-pack, 19		400
___ 2027120	Alaska RR 21" Passenger Car 4-pack, 19		720
___ 2027130	Alaska RR 21" Passenger Car 2-pack, 19		420
___ 2027140	Alaska RR 21" Diner, "400" w/StationSounds, 19		330
___ 2027160	Alaska RR VistaVision Camera Dome Car, "501," 19		330
___ 2027170	UP Challenger 21" Passenger Car Expansion 2-pack, 3, 19		360
___ 2027180	NS Executive Train 21" Passenger Car 4-pack, 19		770
___ 2027190	NS Executive Train 21" Passenger Car 2-pack, 19		360
___ 2027200	NS 21" Diner, "Delaware," w/StationSounds, 19		340
___ 2027210	Philadelphia & Reading Observation, 19-20		85
___ 2027220	Ferdinand Magellan Observation, 19		85
___ 2027230	UP Excursion 21" Passenger Car Expansion 2-pack, 3, 19		360
___ 2027240	UP Excursion 21" Passenger Car Expansion 2-pack, 4, 19		360
___ 2027250	Amtrak VistaVision Dome Car, "9463," 19		330
___ 2027260	UP Excursion VistaVision Dome Car, "Colorado Eagle," 19		330
___ 2027270	UP Challenger VistaVision Dome Car, "7005," 19		330
___ 2027280	Auto-Train VistaVision Dome Car, "706," 19		330
___ 2027290	PRR VistaVision Dome Car, "Catenary View," 19		330
___ 2027300	N&W VistaVision Dome Car, "1613," 19		330
___ 2027310	Southern VistaVision Dome Car, "1613," 19		330
___ 2027330	Friendship Train 18" Sleeper 2-pack, 20		400
___ 2027340	American Freedom Train 18" Passenger Car 2-pack, 1, 20		380
___ 2027350	American Freedom Train 18" Passenger Car 2-pack, 2, 20		380
___ 2027360	Chessie Steam Special Passenger Car 2-pack, 1, 20		450
___ 2027370	Chessie Steam Special Passenger Car 2-pack, 2, 20		450
___ 2027380	Chessie Steam Special Passenger Car 2-pack, 3, 20		450
___ 2027390	Chessie Steam Special Passenger Car 2-pack, 4, 20		450
___ 2027400	SP Golden State 21" Passenger Car 4-pack, 20		730
___ 2027410	SP Golden State 21" Passenger Car 2-pack, 20		360
___ 2027420	SP Golden State 21" Diner w/StationSounds, 20		360
___ 2027430	Reading 18" Passsenger Car 2-pack, 1, 20		380
___ 2027440	Reading 18" Passsenger Car 2-pack, 2, 20		380
___ 2027450	Reading 18" Passsenger Car 2-pack, 3, 20		380
___ 2027460	B&M 18" Passenger Car 2-pack, 20		380
___ 2027470	Polar Express 18" Hobo Passenger Car w/Black Roof, 20-22		240
___ 2027480	Polar Express 18" Hobo Passenger Car w/Snow Roof, 20-22		240
___ 2027490	PRR/AT&SF 21" Passenger Car 2-pack, 20		400
___ 2027500	PRR/UP 21" Passenger Car 2-pack, 20		400
___ 2027510	PRR/MP 21" Passenger Car 2-pack, 20		400
___ 2027520	SP Lark 21" Passenger Car 4-pack, 20		730
___ 2027530	SP Lark 21" Passenger Car 2-pack, 20		360
___ 2027540	SP Lark 21" Diner, w/StationSounds , 20		460
___ 2027550	SP Daylight 18" Heavyweight Passenger Car 2-pack, A, 20		400
___ 2027560	SP Daylight 18" Heavyweight Passenger Car 2-pack, B, 20		400
___ 2027570	SP Daylight 18" Heavyweight Passenger Car 2-pack, C, 20		400
___ 2027580	UP 21" Baggage Car, "Promontory," 19		180
___ 2027590	SP Penn-Golden State 21" Passenger Car 2-pack, 20		360
___ 2027600	PRR/Frisco 21" Passsenger Car 2-pack, 20		400

		Exc	Mint
2027610	SP Daylight 18" Heavyweight Diner w/StationSounds, 20		330 ___
2027620	Chessie Steam Special Dome Car w/StationSounds, 20		400 ___
2027630	Lionel Lines 21" VistaVision Dome Car, "Chesterfield," 20		340 ___
2027640	SP Cities 21" VistaVision Dome Car, "3601," 20		340 ___
2027650	SP Daylight VistaVision Dome Car, 20		340 ___
2027660	SP Golden State 21" VistaVision Dome Car, 20		340 ___
2027670	SP Lark 21" VistaVision Dome Car, 20		340 ___
2027680	GN 21" VistaVision Dome Car, "1325," 20		340 ___
2027690	Lionel Lines Vision 21" Baggage, "Madison", 20		350 ___
2027700	SP Vision Baggage Car, 20		350 ___
2027710	SP Vision Baggage Car, Daylight, 20		350 ___
2027720	SP Vision Baggage Car, Golden State, 20		350 ___
2027730	SP Vision Baggage Car, Lark, 20		350 ___
2027740	REA Vision Baggage Car, 20		350 ___
2027750	Lionel Lines 21" Passenger Car 4-pack, 20		730 ___
2027760	Lionel Lines 21" Diner, "Mount Clemens," w/StationSounds , 20		330 ___
2027770	Milwaukee Road 21" VistaVision Dome Car, "60," 20		340 ___
2027780	NYC 21" VistaVision Dome Car, "Hudson Vista," 20		340 ___
2027790	NS 21" VistaVision Dome Car, "50," 20		340 ___
2027800	Polar Express Skiing Hobo Observation w/Black Roof, 20		85 ___
2027810	Great Central Pullman Coach, 20		80 ___
2028010	George H.W. Bush Funeral Mint Car, 19-22		95 ___
2028020	Shark Aquarium Car, "23020," 19		100 ___
2028030	PRR Flatcar w/Trailers, "925030," 19		85 ___
2028040	PRR Walking Brakeman "24095," 19, 22		110 ___
2028060	Ford Auto Rack, "19032020," 20		85 ___
2028090	Finding Nemo Aquarium Car, 20		100 ___
2028100	Inside Out Memory Ball Transport Car, 20-23		100 ___
2028110	Polar Express Elf Bobbing Car, 20-23		90 ___
2028120	Polar Express Hot Cocoa Car, 20-22		200 ___
2028130	Olaf's Personal Flurry 1-D Tank Car, 20-22		90 ___
2028150	Monster Containment Car, 20		80 ___
2028160	Jack O' Lantern Flatcar, 20		80 ___
2028170	Thomas & Friends Nia Boxcar, 20		75 ___
2028180	Thomas & Friends Rebecca Boxcar, 20		75 ___
2028190	Thomas & Friends Gordon Boxcar, 20		75 ___
2028200	Christmas Boxcar 2020, 20		65 ___
2028210	Christmas Music Boxcar 2020, 20		80 ___
2028220	Anheuser Busch Brewing Refrigerator Car, 20-23		90 ___
2028230	Enjoy Budweiser Refrigerator Car, 20-23		90 ___
2028240	Anheuser Busch Cold Storage Car, 20		90 ___
2028250	Miller High Life Woodside Refrigerator Car, 20-23		90 ___
2028260	Coors Banquet Woodside Refrigerator Car, 20-23		90 ___
2028270	Batman vs. The Joker Duel Car, 20-22		90 ___
2028280	Batman Shark Repellent Unibody 1-D Tank Car, 20		75 ___
2028290	Batman Hi-Cube Boxcar, 20		80 ___
2028300	Christmas Light Express Boxcar, "84746," 20-23		100 ___
2028310	Best of Lionel Milk Car, 20		180 ___
2028320	Alien Radioactive Flatcar, 20		85 ___
2028340	Angela Trotta Thomas Gondola w/Presents and Trees, 20		80 ___
2028350	Angela Trotta Thomas Christmas Boxcar, 20		75 ___
2028360	Mickey & Friends Christmas 1-D Tank Car, 20		70 ___
2028380	John Deere Flatcar, "28380" w/3 Tractors, 20		95 ___

		Exc	Mint
___ 2028410	National Lampoon's Christmas Vacation 30th Anniversary Lighted Boxcar, 20		90
___ 2028430	Thomas & Friends 75th Birthday Music Car, 20		80
___ 2028440	A Christmas Story Leg Lamp Boxcar, 20		75
___ 2028450	Angela Trotta Thomas Christmas Hopper, 20		65
___ 2028460	Winter Wonderland Wintry Mix 1-D Tank Car, 20		80
___ 2028470	Polar Express Present Mint Car, 20-23		100
___ 2028480	Angela Trotta Thomas 120th Anniversary Boxcar, 20		75
___ 2028500	Lionel Ale 1-D Tank Car, 20		75
___ 2028510	Thomas Kinkade Santa's Special Delivery Boxcar, "28510," 20		75
___ 2028520	Romulan Ale 1-D Tank Car, 20		80
___ 2028530	Tribble Transport Car, 20		80
___ 2028540	Captain Kirk Boxcar, 20		75
___ 2028550	Captain Picard Boxcar, 20		75
___ 2028570	Pizza Planet Aquarium Car, 20-23		120
___ 2029010	85th Anniversary Gateman, 20		110
___ 2029020	Bluetooth Speaker Bandstand, 20		275
___ 2029030	Next Stop, Santa Passenger Station, 20		100
___ 2029040	End of the Line Passenger Station, 20-23		110
___ 2029050	Polar Express Passsenger Station, 20-23		140
___ 2029060	Chuga Chuga Brew Thru Bar, 20		90
___ 2029160	J Tower Switch Tower, 20		80
___ 2029170	Halloween Freight Station, 20		125
___ 2029180	Christmas Operating Freight Station, 20		125
___ 2029200	Area 51 Search Tower, 20		100
___ 2029210	Santa Tracker Command Tower, 20		100
___ 2029220	Roasted Chestnuts Retreat, 20		125
___ 2029230	Taco Stand, 20		125
___ 2029240	Fake News Stand, 20, 22	125	160
___ 2029250	Strasburg RR Groffs Grove Pep Platform , 19		45
___ 2029260	Strasburg RR East Strasburg Station, 20		100
___ 2029270	Lionelville Freight Station, 20		125
___ 2029280	Area 1 Souvenir Stand, 20		125
___ 2030010	Strasburg RR Cherry Hill Station, 20		20
___ 2030050	Stars & Stripes Billboard, 3-pack, 19-22		25
___ 2030060	Fun with Puns Billboard, 3-pack, 19		20
___ 2030070	Strasburg RR Billboard 3-pack, 20		20
___ 2030130	Crossing Shanty, 20-22		20
___ 2030140	Polar Express Elf Warming Shack, 3 pack, 20-23		60
___ 2030150	Polar Express Barrel Shed, 20, 23		25
___ 2030160	Winter Wonderland Barrel Shed, 20-23		25
___ 2030170	Anheuser Busch Barrel Shed, 20-22		25
___ 2030180	City Park People, 6-pack, 20		23
___ 2030190	Street People, 6-pack, 20		23
___ 2030200	Walking Figures, 6-pack, 20		23
___ 2030210	City People, 6-pack, 20		23
___ 2030220	Highway Lamp Single, 3-pack, 20		27
___ 2030230	Highway Lamp Double, 2-pack, 20-22		30
___ 2030240	Construction Signs, 5-pack, 20-23		9
___ 2030250	Halloween Signs, 5-pack, 20		8
___ 2030260	Christmas Signs, 5-pack, 20-23		9
___ 2030270	Santa's Elves Houses, 3-pack, 20		60
___ 2031010	B&A 4-6-6T, "400," CC, 19		1100

		Exc	Mint
2031020	NYC 4-6-6T, "1297," CC, 19		1100 ___
2031030	CN 4-6-6T, "51," CC, 19		1100 ___
2031040	CNJ 4-6-6T, "231," CC, 19		1100 ___
2031050	DL&W 4-6-6T, "428," CC, 19		1100 ___
2031060	IC 4-6-6T, "205," CC, 19		1100 ___
2031070	NH 4-6-6T, "1850," CC, 19		1100 ___
2031080	US Army Transportation Corps 4-6-6T, "1945," CC, 19		1100 ___
2031090	B&O 2-8-8-4 EM-1, "7609," CC, 19		1700 ___
2031100	B&O 2-8-8-4 EM-1, "7600," CC, 19		1700 ___
2031110	D&RGW 2-8-8-4 EM-1, "224," CC, 19		1700 ___
2031120	DM&IR 2-8-8-4 EM-1, "220," CC, 19		1700 ___
2031130	NP 2-8-8-4 EM-1, "5011," CC, 19		1700 ___
2031140	UP 2-8-8-4 EM-1, "4050," CC, 19		1700 ___
2031150	WM 2-8-8-4 EM-1, "1213," CC, 19		1700 ___
2031160	AT&SF 4-8-4 Northern, "3751," CC, 19		1600 ___
2031170	AT&SF 4-8-4 Northern, "3759," CC, 19		1600 ___
2031180	AT&SF 4-8-4 Northern, "3757," CC, 19		1600 ___
2031190	AT&SF 4-8-4 Northern, "3765," CC, 19		1600 ___
2031200	ACL 4-8-4S Northern, "1800," CC, 19		1600 ___
2031210	Rock Island 4-8-4S Northern, "5100," CC, 19		1600 ___
2031220	D&RGW 4-8-4S Northern, "1802," CC, 19		1600 ___
2031230	MP 4-8-4S Northern, "2202," CC, 19		1600 ___
2031240	Frisco 4-8-4S Northern, "4500," CC, 19		1600 ___
2031250	Frisco 4-8-4S Northern, "4524," CC, 19		1600 ___
2031261	UP 4-8-8-4 Big Boy, "4014," Excursion Version, CC, 19		2200 ___
2031262	UP 4-8-8-4 Big Boy, "4005," CC, 19		2200 ___
2031263	UP 4-8-8-4 Big Boy, "4012," Greyhouse, CC, 19		2200 ___
2031271	Reading 4-8-4 T1, "2107," CC, 20		1700 ___
2031272	Reading 4-8-4 T1, "2111," CC, 20		1700 ___
2031281	Reading 4-8-4 T1, Rambles, "2100," CC, 20		1700 ___
2031282	Reading 4-8-4 T1, Rambles, "2101," CC, 20		1700 ___
2031290	Reading, Blue Mountain & Northern 4-8-4 T1, "2102," CC, 20		1700 ___
2031300	Reading, Blue Mountain & Northern 4-8-4 T1, "2102," CC, 20		1700 ___
2031310	Conrail 4-8-4 T1, "2101," CC, 20		1700 ___
2031320	American Freedom Train Vision 4-8-4 T1, "1," CC, 20		1700 ___
2031330	PRR B6sb 0-4-0, "525," CC, 20		700 ___
2031340	PRR B6sb 0-4-0, "660," CC, 20		700 ___
2031351	PRR B6sb 0-4-0, "711," CC, 20		700 ___
2031352	PRR B6sb 0-4-0, "1644," CC, 20		700 ___
2031360	AT&SF B6sb 0-4-0, "2101," CC, 20		700 ___
2031370	Bethlehem Steet B6sb 0-4-0, "1904," CC, 20		700 ___
2031380	Milwaukee Road B6sb 0-4-0, "1534," CC, 20		700 ___
2031390	GN B6sb 0-4-0, "90," CC, 20		700 ___
2031400	Lionel Lines Vision 4-8-4 GS-4, "120," CC, 20		2000 ___
2031411	SP Vision 4-8-4 GS-1 Brass Hybrid, "4470," CC, 20		2200 ___
2031412	SP Vision 4-8-4 GS-1 Brass Hybrid, "4471," CC, 20		2200 ___
2031421	SP Vision 4-8-4 GS-1 Brass Hybrid, "708," CC, 20		2200 ___
2031422	SP Vision 4-8-4 GS-1 Brass Hybrid, "4403," CC, 20		2200 ___
2031430	Vision 4-8-4 GS-1 Brass Hybrid Pilot, "9999," CC, 20		2200 ___
2031440	SP Vision 4-8-4 GS-2 Black, "4410," CC, 20		2000 ___
2031450	SP Vision 4-8-4 GS-2 Black, "4411," CC, 20		2000 ___
2031460	SP Vision 4-8-4 GS-2 Daylight, "4412," CC, 20		2000 ___
2031470	SP Vision 4-8-4 GS-2 Lark, "4414," CC, 20		2000 ___

		Mint
2031480	SP Vision 4-8-4 GS-3 Daylight, "4416," CC, 20	2000
2031490	SP Vision 4-8-4 GS-3 LAUPT Special, "4426," CC, 20	2000
2031500	SP Vision 4-8-4 GS-3 Daylight, "4423," CC, 20	2000
2031510	SP Vision 4-8-4 GS-3 Golden State, "4428," CC, 20	2000
2031520	SP Lines Vision 4-8-4 GS-4 Daylight, "4449," CC, 20	2000
2031530	SP Vision 4-8-4 GS-4 Daylight, "4449," CC, 20	2000
2031540	American Freedom Train Vision 4-8-4 GS-4, "4449," CC, 20	2000
2031550	BNSF Vision 4-8-4 GS-4, "4449," CC, 20	2000
2031560	SP Vision 4-8-4 GS-4 Daylight, "4439," CC, 20	2000
2031570	SP Lines Vision 4-8-4 GS-5 Daylight, "4458," CC, 20	2000
2031580	SP Vision 4-8-4 GS-5 Daylight, "4459," CC, 20	2000
2031590	SP Lines Vision 4-8-4 GS-6, "4460," CC, 20	2000
2031600	SP Vision 4-8-4 GS-6, "4462," CC, 20	2000
2031610	SP Vision 4-8-4 GS-6, "4467," CC, 20	2000
2031620	WP Vision 4-8-4 GS-6, "481," CC, 20	2000
2031630	WP Vision 4-8-4 GS-6, "486," CC, 20	2000
2031640	Chessie Steam Special Vision GS-4, "4449," CC, 20	2000
2031650	Chessie Steam Special Auxiliary Water Tender w/RailSounds, CC, 20	350
2031660	Conrail Auxiliary Water Tender w/RailSounds, CC, 20	350
2031671	Freedom Train 1975 Auxiliary Water Tender w/RailSounds, CC, 20	350
2031672	Freedom Train 1976 Auxiliary Water Tender w/RailSounds, CC, 20	350
2031673	American Freedom Train Auxiliary Tender, "4449," CC, 20	350
2031680	SP Daylight Auxiliary Water Tender w/RailSounds, CC, 20	350
2031690	Black Auxiliary Water Tender w/RailSounds, CC, 20	350
2031700	UP 4-8-8-4 Big Boy, "4014," First Run Edition, CC, 19	2200
2032010	AT&SF 0-6-0T, "95," LionChief Plus 2.0, 19-20	250
2032020	Brooklyn Eastern District 0-6-0T, "15," LionChief Plus 2.0, 19-20	250
2032030	Bethlehem Steel 0-6-0T, "76," LionChief Plus 2.0, 19-20	250
2032040	D&RGW 0-6-0T, "27," LionChief Plus 2.0, 19-20	250
2032050	PRR 0-6-0T, "2295," LionChief Plus 2.0, 19-20	250
2032100	C&O Lionmaster 2-6-6-6 Allegheny, "1601," CC, 20	1100
2032110	C&O Lionmaster 2-6-6-6 Allegheny, "1607," CC, 20	1100
2032120	C&O Lionmaster 2-6-6-6 Allegheny, "1611," CC, 20	1100
2032130	Virginian Lionmaster 2-6-6-6 Allegheny, "906," CC, 20	1100
2032200	AT&SF 0-8-0, "729," LionChief, 20	220
2032210	GN 0-8-0, "831," LionChief, 20	220
2032220	Reading 0-8-0, "1493," LionChief, 20	220
2032230	SP 0-8-0, "1849," LionChief, 20	220
2033011	B&LE SD38 Diesel, "861," CC, 19	600
2033012	B&LE SD38 Diesel, "863," CC, 19	600
2033021	Conrail SD38 Diesel, "6929," CC, 19	600
2033022	Conrail SD38 Diesel, "6957," CC, 19	600
2033031	CSX SD38 Diesel, "2461," CC, 19	600
2033032	CSX SD38 Diesel, "2463," CC, 19	600
2033041	GTW SD38 Diesel, "6252," CC, 19	600
2033042	GTW SD38 Diesel, "6254," CC, 19	600
2033051	NS SD38 Diesel, "3806," CC, 19	600
2033052	NS SD38 Diesel, "3808," CC, 19	600
2033061	Rail Logix SD38 Diesel, "2001," CC, 19	600
2033062	Rail Logix SD38 Diesel, "2002," CC, 19	600

Item	Description	Exc	Mint
2033070	AT&SF Alco S-4 Diesel Switcher, "1527," CC, 19		500 ___
2033080	EL Alco S-4 Diesel Switcher, "513," CC, 19		500 ___
2033090	Ford Alco S-2 Diesel Switcher, "10013," CC, 19		500 ___
2033100	Morristown & Erie Alco S-2 Diesel Switcher, "14," CC, 19		500 ___
2033110	NYS&W Alco S-2 Diesel Switcher, "206," CC, 19		500 ___
2033120	Nickel Plate Road Alco S-4 Diesel Switcher, "79," CC, 19		500 ___
2033130	NP Alco S-4 Diesel Switcher, "717," CC, 19		500 ___
2033140	Northern Pacific Terminal Alco S-2 Diesel Switcher, "40," CC, 19		500 ___
2033150	Portland Terminal Alco S-2 Diesel Switcher, "1001," CC, 19		500 ___
2033160	SP Alco S-4 Diesel Switcher, "1820," CC, 19		500 ___
2033170	Youngstown Sheet & Tube Alco S-2 Switcher, "1001," CC, 19		500 ___
2033181	CITX SD70M-2 Diesel, "140," CC, 19		600 ___
2033182	CITX SD70M-2 Diesel, "141," CC, 19		600 ___
2033183	CITX SD70M-2 Diesel, "142," unpowered, 19		300 ___
2033191	EMD SD70M-2 Diesel, "74," CC, 19		600 ___
2033192	EMD SD70M-2 Diesel, "75," CC, 19		600 ___
2033193	EMD SD70M-2 Diesel, "76," unpowered, 19		300 ___
2033201	FEC SD70M-2 Diesel, "104," CC, 19		600 ___
2033202	FEC SD70M-2 Diesel, "105," CC, 19		600 ___
2033203	FEC SD70M-2 Diesel, "106," unpowered, 19		300 ___
2033211	NS SD70M-2 Diesel, "2717," CC, 19		600 ___
2033212	NS SD70M-2 Diesel, "2731," CC, 19		600 ___
2033213	NS SD70M-2 Diesel, "2778," unpowered, 19		300 ___
2033221	P&W SD70M-2 Diesel, "4301," CC, 19		600 ___
2033222	P&W SD70M-2 Diesel, "4302," CC, 19		600 ___
2033231	Vermont Ry. SD70M-2 Diesel, "431," CC, 19		600 ___
2033232	Vermont Ry. SD70M-2 Diesel, "432," CC, 19		600 ___
2033240	Alaska RR F7 A-A set, CC, 19		900 ___
2033248	Alaska RR F7B Diesel, "1503," CC, 19		450 ___
2033249	Alaska RR F7B SuperBass Diesel, "1517," CC, 19		440 ___
2033250	BN F7 Diesel A-A set, CC, 19		900 ___
2033258	BN F7B Diesel, "761," CC, 19		450 ___
2033259	BN F7B SuperBass Diesel, "741," CC, 19		440 ___
2033260	CGW F7 Diesel A-A set, CC, 19		900 ___
2033268	CGW F7B Diesel, "114-B," CC, 19		450 ___
2033269	CGW F7B SuperBass Diesel, "114-0," CC, 19		440 ___
2033270	D&RGW F7 Diesel A-A set, CC, 19		900 ___
2033278	D&RGW F7B Diesel, "5652," CC, 19		450 ___
2033279	D&RGW F7B SuperBass Diesel, "5653," CC, 19		440 ___
2033280	NS F9 Diesel A-A set, CC, 19		900 ___
2033288	NS F7B Diesel, "4275," CC, 19		450 ___
2033289	NS F7B SuperBass Diesel, "4276," CC, 19		440 ___
2033290	PC F7 Diesel A-A set, CC, 19		900 ___
2033298	PC F7B Diesel, "3460," CC, 19		450 ___
2033299	PC F7B SuperBass Diesel, "712," CC, 19		440 ___
2033300	Cotton Belt F7 Diesel A-A set, CC, 19		900 ___
2033308	Cotton Belt F7B Diesel, "926," CC, 19		450 ___
2033309	Cotton Belt F7B SuperBass Diesel, "928," CC, 19		440 ___
2033310	UP SD70ACe Diesel, "4141," CC, 19		600 ___
2033319	UP SD70ACe Diesel, "4141," unpowered, 19		300 ___
2033321	UP SD70AH Diesel, "9096," CC, 19		600 ___
2033322	UP SD70AH Diesel, "9069," CC, 19		600 ___
2033323	UP SD70AH Diesel, "9088," CC, 19		600 ___

		Exc	Mint
____ 2033330	KCS SD70ACe Diesel, "4006," CC, 19		600
____ 2033340	Amtrak E8 AA Diesel Set, "4316/249," CC, 20		1000
____ 2033350	DL&W E8 AA Diesel Set, "810/811," CC, 20		1000
____ 2033360	NYC E8 AA Diesel Set, "4038/4041," CC, 20		1000
____ 2033370	PRR E8 AA Diesel Set, "5711/5809," CC, 20		1000
____ 2033380	Southern E8 AA Diesel Set, "6901/6914," CC, 20		1000
____ 2033390	Frisco E8 AA Diesel Set, "2003/2006," CC, 20		1000
____ 2033401	DL&W Train Master Diesel, "853," CC, 20		550
____ 2033402	DL&W Train Master Diesel, "854," CC, 20		550
____ 2033411	FM Demonstrator Train Master Diesel, "TM-3," CC, 20		550
____ 2033412	FM Demonstrator Train Master Diesel, "TM-4," CC, 20		550
____ 2033420	PRR Train Master Diesel, "8703," CC, 20		550
____ 2033431	Southern Train Master Diesel, "6301," CC, 20		550
____ 2033432	Southern Train Master Diesel, "6302," CC, 20		550
____ 2033441	SP Train Master Diesel, "4800," CC, 20		550
____ 2033442	SP Train Master Diesel, "4812," CC, 20		550
____ 2033451	Virginian Train Master Diesel, "55," CC, 20		550
____ 2033452	Virginian Train Master Diesel, "60," CC, 20		550
____ 2033461	CP SD40 Diesel, "740," CC, 20		550
____ 2033462	CP SD40 Diesel, "752," CC, 20		550
____ 2033471	CNJ SD40 Diesel, "3064," CC, 20		550
____ 2033472	CNJ SD40 Diesel, "3069," CC, 20		550
____ 2033481	C&O SD40 Diesel, "7452," CC, 20		550
____ 2033482	C&O SD40 Diesel, "7464," CC, 20		550
____ 2033490	CSX SD40 Diesel, "4617," CC, 20		550
____ 2033501	C&NW SD40 Diesel, "867," CC, 20		550
____ 2033502	C&NW SD40 Diesel, "876," CC, 20		550
____ 2033520	BNSF GE ES44AC Diesel, "5815," CC, 20		550
____ 2033530	CSX GE ES44AC Diesel, "3010," CC, 20		313
____ 2033539	CSX GE ES44AC Diesel, "3010," unpowered, 20		350
____ 2033541	KCS de Mexico GE ES44AC Diesel, "4748," CC, 20		550
____ 2033542	KCS de Mexico GE ES44AC Diesel, "4762," CC, 20		550
____ 2033549	KCS de Mexico GE ES44AC Diesel, "4764," unpowered, 20		350
____ 2033551	SVTX GE ES44AC Diesel, "1912," CC, 20		550
____ 2033552	SVTX GE ES44AC Diesel, "1982," CC, 20		550
____ 2033559	SVTX GE ES44AC Diesel, "1986," unpowered, 20		350
____ 2033560	UP GE ES44AC Diesel, "8003," CC, 20		550
____ 2033571	Christmas ES44AC Diesel, "1224," CC, 20		550
____ 2033572	Christmas ES44AC Diesel, "1225," CC, 20		550
____ 2033590	UP SD70ACe Diesel, "8937," CC, 19		600
____ 2033600	UP SD70AH+B86 Diesel, "1111," CC, 19		600
____ 2033610	CSX First Responders GE ES44AC Diesel, "911," CC, 20		550
____ 2033619	CSX First Responders GE ES44AC Diesel, "911," unpowered, 20		185
____ 2033620	CSX Veterans GE ES44AC Diesel, "1776," CC, 20		550
____ 2033629	CSX Veterans GE ES44AC Diesel, "1776," unpowered, 20		350
____ 2033630	CSX GE ES44AC Diesel, "3194," CC, 20		550
____ 2033639	CSX GE ES44AC Diesel, "3194," unpowered, 20		350
____ 2034010	PRR GG1 Electric, "4935," LionChief Plus 2.0, 19		500
____ 2034020	PRR GG1 Electric, "4877," LionChief Plus 2.0, 19		500
____ 2034030	PRR GG1 Electric, "4872," LionChief Plus 2.0, 19		500
____ 2034040	PRR GG1 Electric, "4890," LionChief Plus 2.0, 19		500
____ 2034050	PRR GG1 Electric, "4916," LionChief Plus 2.0, 19		500
____ 2034061	Conrail LionMaster SD80MAC, "4100" LionChief Plus 2.0, 19		450

		Exc	Mint
2034062	Conrail LionMaster SD80MAC, "4102," LionChief Plus 2.0, 19		450 ___
2034071	CSX LionMaster SD80MAC, "4592," LionChief Plus 2.0, 19		450 ___
2034072	CSX LionMaster SD80MAC, "4594," LionChief Plus 2.0, 19		450 ___
2034081	NS LionMaster SD80MAC Diesel, "7217," LionChief Plus 2.0, 19		450 ___
2034082	NS LionMaster SD80MAC Diesel, "7219," LionChief Plus 2.0, 19		450 ___
2034091	UP LionMaster SD90MAC Diesel, "8025," LionChief Plus 2.0, 19		450 ___
2034092	UP LionMaster SD90MAC Diesel, "8026," LionChief Plus 2.0, 19		450 ___
2034100	NYC F3 AA Diesel Set, "1620/1621," LionChief Plus 2.0, 20		700 ___
2034110	PRR F3 AA Diesel Set, "9542/9542A," LionChief Plus 2.0, 20		700 ___
2034120	UP F3 AA Diesel Set, "1445/1455," LionChief Plus 2.0, 20		700 ___
2034130	SP F3 AA Diesel Set, "6148/6157," LionChief Plus 2.0, 20		700 ___
2034180	Conrail GP38 Diesel, "7670," LionChief, 20		220 ___
2034190	BN GP38 Diesel, "2085," LionChief, 20		220 ___
2034200	Chessie System GP38 Diesel, "3847," LionChief, 20		220 ___
2034210	North Pole Central GP38 Diesel, "1224," LionChief, 20		220 ___
2034220	Lightning McQueen GP38 Diesel, "95," LionChief, 20		220 ___
2035010	ELX Trolley, 20		100 ___
2035020	Fort Collins Trolley, 20		100 ___
2035030	Toy Story Handcar, 20-23		120 ___
2035050	Lionelville Trolley, 20		100 ___
2038010	B&O 190th Anniversary Boxcar, 19		85 ___
2038020	D&RGW 150th Anniversary Boxcar, 19		85 ___
2038030	Casey Jones 120th Anniversary MUSA Boxcar, 20		85 ___
2038040	BN 50th Anniversary MUSA Boxcar, 20		85 ___
2038050	George H.W. Bush Boxcar, 19-20		80 ___
2038060	William Henry Harrison Presidential Boxcar, 20		80 ___
2038070	James Garfield Presidential Boxcar, 20		80 ___
2038080	Battlefield Honor--Berlin Wall Boxcar, 20-23		95 ___
2038090	Battlefield Honor--Candy Bombers Boxcar, 20		90 ___
2038110	Angela Trotta Thomas Well Stocked Shelves Boxcar, Middle Shelf, 19		85 ___
2038120	2020 Happy Birthday Boxcar, 20		90 ___
2038130	Happy Anniversary Boxcar, 20		90 ___
2038140	2020 Merry Christmas Boxcar, 20		90 ___
2038150	Foghorn Leghorn Crockett-Doodle Do Boxcar, 20-23		95 ___
2038160	Picnic With Porky Pig Boxcar, 20-23		95 ___
2038170	Robin Hood Daffy Duck Boxcar, 20-23		95 ___
2038200	Wings of Angels--Jessamyne Rose Boxcar, 20		90 ___
2038210	Wings of Angels--Ashten Goodenough Boxcar, 20		90 ___
2038220	Wings of Angels--Jessie Ray Boxcar, 20		90 ___
2043011	BN 50' Boxcar, "217552" (std O), 20-23		50 ___
2043012	BN 50' Boxcar, "217618" (std O), 20-23		50 ___
2043013	BN 50' Boxcar, "217685" (std O), 20-23		50 ___
2043014	BN 50' Boxcar, "217741" (std O), 20-23		50 ___
2043021	Golden West 50' Boxcar, "767130" (std O), 20-23		50 ___
2043022	Golden West 50' Boxcar, "767150" (std O), 20-23		50 ___
2043023	Golden West 50' Boxcar, "767167" (std O), 20-23		50 ___
2043024	Golden West 50' Boxcar, "767193" (std O), 20-23		50 ___
2043031	KCS 50' Boxcar, "117731" (std O), 20-23		50 ___
2043032	KCS 50' Boxcar, "117756" (std O), 20-23		50 ___
2043033	KCS 50' Boxcar, "117782" (std O), 20-23		50 ___
2043034	KCS 50' Boxcar, "117790" (std O), 20-23		50 ___
2043041	Railbox 50' Boxcar, "10051" (std O), 20-22		50 ___

		Exc	Mint
___ 2043042	Railbox 50' Boxcar, "10189" (std O), 20-22		50
___ 2043043	Railbox 50' Boxcar, "10524" (std O), 20-22		50
___ 2043044	Railbox 50' Boxcar, "10582" (std O), 20-22		50
___ 2043051	MILW Road Centerbeam Flatcar, "6300" (std O), 20-23		50
___ 2043052	MILW Centerbeam Flatcar, "6318" (std O), 20-23		50
___ 2043053	MILW Centerbeam Flatcar, "6336" (std O), 20-23		50
___ 2043054	MILW Centerbeam Flatcar, "6354" (std O), 20-23		50
___ 2043061	Trailer Train Centerbeam Flatcar, "83729" (std O), 20-23		50
___ 2043062	Trailer Train Centerbeam Flatcar, "83741" (std O), 20-23		50
___ 2043063	Trailer Train Centerbeam Flatcar, "83754" (std O), 20-23		50
___ 2043064	Trailer Train Centerbeam Flatcar, "83773" (std O), 20-23		50
___ 2043071	UP Centerbeam Flatcar, "217015" (std O), 20-23		50
___ 2043072	UP Centerbeam Flatcar, "217031" (std O), 20-23		50
___ 2043073	UP Centerbeam Flatcar, "217047" (std O), 20-23		50
___ 2043074	UP Centerbeam Flatcar, "217063" (std O), 20-23		50
___ 2043081	WP Centerbeam Flatcar, "1404" (std O), 20-23		50
___ 2043082	WP Centerbeam Flatcar, "1412" (std O), 20-23		50
___ 2043083	WP Centerbeam Flatcar, "1420" (std O), 20-23		50
___ 2043084	WP Centerbeam Flatcar, "1428" (std O), 20-23		50
___ 2043091	BNSF Bulkhead Flatcar, "545475" (std O), 20-23		50
___ 2043092	BNSF Bulkhead Flatcar, "545512" (std O), 20-23		50
___ 2043093	BNSF Bulkhead Flatcar, "545587" (std O), 20-23		50
___ 2043094	BNSF Bulkhead Flatcar, "545628" (std O), 20-23		50
___ 2043101	GN Bulkhead Flatcar, "160325" (std O), 20-23		50
___ 2043102	GN Bulkhead Flatcar, "160331" (std O), 20-23		50
___ 2043103	GN Bulkhead Flatcar, "160350" (std O), 20-23		50
___ 2043104	GN Bulkhead Flatcar, "160374" (std O), 20-23		50
___ 2043111	NS Bulkhead Flatcar, "118024" (std O), 20-23		50
___ 2043112	NS Bulkhead Flatcar, "118033" (std O), 20-23		50
___ 2043113	NS Bulkhead Flatcar, "118045" (std O), 20-23		50
___ 2043114	NS Bulkhead Flatcar, "118068" (std O), 20-23		50
___ 2043121	Trailer Train Bulkhead Flatcar, "81023" (std O), 20-23		50
___ 2043122	Trailer Train Bulkhead Flatcar, "81094" (std O), 20-23		50
___ 2043123	Trailer Train Bulkhead Flatcar, "81118" (std O), 20-23		50
___ 2043124	Trailer Train Bulkhead Flatcar, "81145" (std O), 20-23		50
___ 2043131	Bethlehem Steel Gondola, "3131" (std O), 20-22		50
___ 2043132	Bethlehem Steel Gondola, "3145" (std O), 20-22		50
___ 2043133	Bethlehem Steel Gondola, "3168" (std O), 20-22		50
___ 2043134	Bethlehem Steel Gondola "3192" w/Covers (std O), 20-23		50
___ 2043141	Chessie System Gondola, "305001" (std O), 20		45
___ 2043142	Chessie System Gondola "305014" w/Covers (std O), 20-23		50
___ 2043143	Chessie System Gondola "305036" w/Covers (std O), 20-23		50
___ 2043144	Chessie System Gondola "305055" w/Covers (std O), 20-23		50
___ 2043151	MKT Gondola "14025" w/Coil Covers (std O), 20-23		50
___ 2043152	MKT Gondola "14032" w/Coil Covers (std O), 20-23		50
___ 2043153	MKT Gondola "14041" w/Coil Covers (std O), 20-23		50
___ 2043154	MKT Gondola "14049" w/Coil Covers (std O), 20-23		50
___ 2043161	Reading Gondola "29061" w/Coil Covers (std O), 20-23		50
___ 2043162	Reading Gondola "29086" w/Coil Covers std O), 20-23		50
___ 2043163	Reading Gondola "29169" w/Coil Covers (std O), 20-23		50
___ 2043164	Reading Gondola "29172" w/Coil Covers (std O), 20-23		50
___ 2043170	BN Rotary Gondola, 4-pack, A, 20		280
___ 2043180	BN Rotary Gondola, 4-pack, B, 20		280

		Exc	Mint
2043190	BN Rotary Gondola, 2-pack, 20		140 ___
2043200	Conrail Rotary Gondola, 4-pack, A, 20		280 ___
2043210	Conrail Rotary Gondola, 4-pack, B, 20		280 ___
2043220	Conrail Rotary Gondola, 2-pack, 20		140 ___
2043230	CSX Rotary Gondola, 4-pack, A, 20		280 ___
2043240	CSX Rotary Gondola, 4-pack, B, 20		280 ___
2043250	CSX Rotary Gondola, 2-pack, 20		140 ___
2043260	NS Rotary Gondola, 4-pack, A, 20		280 ___
2043270	NS Rotary Gondola, 4-pack, B, 20		280 ___
2043280	NS Rotary Gondola, 2-pack, 20		140 ___
2043290	C&NW NE-5 Caboose "606" (std O), 20		60 ___
2043300	Monon NE-5 Caboose "81526" (std O), 20		60 ___
2043310	Monongahela NE-5 Caboose "64" (std O), 20		60 ___
2043320	NH NE-5 Caboose "C-516" (std O), 20		60 ___
2122010	Aliquippa Turn P&LE GP7 Diesel Freight Set, CC, 20		850 ___
2122020	NYC Xplorer Baldwin Sharknose Passenger Set, CC, 20		900 ___
2122030	Southern GP7 Diesel Freight Set, CC, 20		850 ___
2122040	PRR John Bull Display Set, 21		800 ___
2122050	Camden & Amboy John Bull Steam Passenger Set, 21		800 ___
2122060	Uncle Sam John Bull Steam Passenger Set, 21		800 ___
2122070	LV Asa Packer 4-6-2 Pacific Steam Passenger Set, CC, 21		2200 ___
2122080	NYC 1926 Cardinals 4-6-2 Pacific Passenger Set, CC, 21		2100 ___
2122090	Amtrak Acela High Speed Train Set, CC, 21		2500 ___
2122100	Amtrak Acela Concept High Speed Train Set, CC, 21		2500 ___
2122110	MILW High Speed Train Set, CC, 21		2500 ___
2122120	NH High Speed Train Set, CC, 21		2500 ___
2122130	PRR High Speed Train Set, CC, 21		2500 ___
2122140	ATSF High Speed Train Set, CC, 21		2500 ___
2122150	UP High Speed Train Set, CC, 21		2500 ___
2122160	New Hope & Ivyland GP30 Passenger Excursion Set, CC, 21		1000 ___
2122170	ATSF Valley Flyer 4-6-2 Pacific Steam Passenger Set, CC, 21		2200 ___
2122180	Nickel Plate Road Work Train Set, CC, 21		1000 ___
2122190	Polar Express High Speed Train Set, CC, 21		2500 ___
2123010	C&O Steam Freight Set LionChief, 20-23		450 ___
2123030	KCS Tier 4 ET44 Diesel Freight Set LionChief, 21		425 ___
2123040	John Deere GP38 Diesel Freight Set LionChief, 21-23		450 ___
2123060	Hallow's Eve Limited Steam Freight Set LionChief, 21-23		400 ___
2123070	Polar Express Steam Freight Set LionChief, 21-23		400 ___
2123080	Space Launch GP38 Diesel Freight Set LionChief, 21-23		450 ___
2123090	Lionel Junction North Pole Central Steam Freight Set LionChief, Upgraded, 21		325 ___
2123100	Christmas Light Express Steam Freight Set LionChief, Upgraded, 21-23		500 ___
2123110	Toy Story Steam Freight Set LionChief, Upgraded, 21		425 ___
2123120	Star Trek FT Diesel Freight Set LionChief, Upgraded, 21		480 ___
2123130	Polar Express Steam Passenger Set LionChief, Upgraded, 21-23		480 ___
2123140	Harry Potter Hogwarts Express Steam Passenger Set LionChief, Upgraded, 21-23		480 ___
2123150	Frozen II Steam Freight Set LionChief, Upgraded, 21		425 ___
2123160	Area 51 ET44 Diesel Freight Set LionChief, Upgraded, 21		450 ___
2123200	Pennsylvania Keystone Bluetooth 5.0 Steam Freight Set, 21-23		400 ___
2125010	Halloween Girider Bridge, 21-23		35 ___

		Exc	Mint
___ 2126011	B&LE PS-5 Covered Gondola "32001," 20		90
___ 2126012	B&LE PS-5 Covered Gondola "32054," 20		90
___ 2126021	Bethlehem Steel PS-5 Covered Hopper "303025," 20		90
___ 2126022	Bethlehem Steel PS-5 Covered Hopper "303041," 20		90
___ 2126031	BN PS-5 Covered Gondola "577225," 20		90
___ 2126032	BN PS-5 Covered Gondola "577239," 20		90
___ 2126041	DT&I PS-5 Covered Hopper "9502," 20		90
___ 2126042	DT&I PS-5 Covered Hopper "9509," 20		90
___ 2126051	Reading & Northern PS-5 Covered Hopper "3806," 20		90
___ 2126052	Reading & Northern PS-5 Covered Hopper "3810,", 20		490
___ 2126061	UP PS-5 Covered Hopper "229812," 20		90
___ 2126062	UP PS-5 Covered Hopper "903044," 20		90
___ 2126071	Central of Georgia Roof-Hatch Boxcar "6161," 20		95
___ 2126072	Central of Georgia Roof-Hatch Boxcar "6165," 20		95
___ 2126081	C&NW Roof-Hatch Boxcar "108610," 20		95
___ 2126082	C&NW Roof-Hatch Boxcar "108614," 20		95
___ 2126091	Monon Roof-Hatch Boxcar "10249," 20		95
___ 2126092	Monon Roof-Hatch Boxcar "10421," 20		95
___ 2126101	Southern Roof-Hatch Boxcar "26922," 20		95
___ 2126102	Southern Roof-Hatch Boxcar "26961," 20		95
___ 2126111	UP Roof-Hatch Boxcar "284225," 20		95
___ 2126112	UP Roof-Hatch Boxcar "284227," 20		95
___ 2126120	B&LE 100-ton Hopper 2-pack, A, 20		250
___ 2126128	B&LE 100-ton Hopper 2-pack, B, 20		250
___ 2126129	B&LE 100-ton Hopper 2-pack, C, 20		250
___ 2126130	CSX 100-ton Hopper 2-pack, A, 20		250
___ 2126138	CSX 100-ton Hopper 2-pack, B, 20		250
___ 2126139	CSX 100-ton Hopper 2-pack, C, 20		250
___ 2126140	PP&L 100-ton Hopper 2-pack, A, 20		250
___ 2126148	PP&L 100-ton Hopper 2-pack, B, 20		250
___ 2126149	PP&L 100-ton Hopper 2-pack, C, 20		250
___ 2126160	P&LE 100-ton Hopper 2-pack, A, 20		250
___ 2126168	P&LE 100-ton Hopper 2-pack, B, 20		250
___ 2126169	P&LE 100-ton Hopper 2-pack, C, 20		250
___ 2126170	Reading & Northern 100-ton Hopper 2-pack, A, 20		250
___ 2126178	Reading & Northern 100-ton Hopper 2-pack, B, 20		250
___ 2126179	Reading & Northern 100-ton Hopper 2-pack, C, 20		250
___ 2126180	Ann Arbor PS-2 Covered Hopper "800," 20		90
___ 2126190	Central Soya PS-2 Covered Hopper "118," 22		90
___ 2126200	Monon PS-2 Covered Hopper "30648," 20		90
___ 2126210	PRR PS-2 Covered Hopper "257808," 20		90
___ 2126220	T&P PS-2 Covered Hopper "8744," 20		90
___ 2126230	WM PS-2 Covered Hopper "4940," 20		90
___ 2126240	Chessie BW Caboose "C-3010," 20		110
___ 2126250	Conrail BW Caboose "21736," 20		110
___ 2126260	SLSF BW Caboose "1730," 20		110
___ 2126270	L&N BW Caboose "1134," 20		110
___ 2126280	NYC BW Caboose "20284," 20		110
___ 2126290	SP Railroad Police BW Caboose "4762," 20		110
___ 2126300	NYC Pacemaker Expansion Set, 21		500
___ 2126310	American Steel 65' Mill Gondola "1776," 21		100
___ 2126320	Bethlehem Steel 65' Mill Gondola "206320," 21		100
___ 2126330	CP 65' Mill Gondola "337185," 21		100

		Exc	Mint
2126340	Conrail SW8 Diesel Switcher "8657," CC, 21		100
2126350	CSX 65' Mill Gondola "491038," 21		100
2126360	PRR 65' Mill Gondola "442650," 21		100
2126370	B&O Boxcar w/FreightSounds "467434," 21		200
2126380	M&P Boxcar w/FreightSounds "5624," 21		200
2126390	MP Boxcar w/FreightSounds "41260," 21		200
2126400	PRR Boxcar w/FreightSounds "26875," 21		200
2126410	SP Boxcar w/FreightSounds "163285," 21		200
2126420	WP Boxcar w/FreightSounds "220086," 21		200
2126431	BNSF Beer Car "782404," 21		100
2126432	BNSF Beer Car "782480," 21		110
2126441	D&RGW Beer Car "50816," 21		100
2126442	D&RGW Beer Car "50871," 21		100
2126451	Golden West Beer Car "149000," 21		100
2126452	Golden West Beer Car "149008," 21		110
2126461	MP Beer Car "793004," 21		100
2126462	MP Beer Car "793015," 21		100
2126471	UP Beer Car "465304," 21		100
2126472	UP Beer Car "465321," 21		100
2126481	WP Beer Car "67083," 21		100
2126482	WP Beer Car "67055," 21		100
2126490	Nickel Plate Road Work Train Expansion Pack, 21		680
2126500	CP Tool Car "403503," 21		100
2126510	CNJ Tool Car "92083," 21		100
2126520	C&O Tool Car "X509," 21		100
2126530	MKT Tool Car "X-3257," 21		100
2126540	N&W Tool Car "526544," 21		100
2126550	WP Tool Car "MW0995," 21		100
2126560	CP Kitchen Car "410833," 21		150
2126570	CNJ Kitchen Car "92111," 21		150
2126580	C&O Kitchen Car "X41," 21		150
2126590	MKT Kitchen Car "X-3175," 21		150
2126600	N&W Kitchen Car "526030," 21		150
2126610	WP Kitchen Car "MW0912," 21		150
2126621	CP Bunk Car "411213," 21		100
2126622	CP Bunk Car "411919," 21		100
2126631	CNJ Bunk Car "92110," 21		100
2126632	CNJ Bunk Car "92120," 21		100
2126641	C&O Bunk Car "B575," 21		100
2126642	C&O Bunk Car "B579," 21		100
2126651	MKT Bunk Car "X-2121," 21		100
2126652	MKT Bunk Car "X-2122," 21		100
2126661	N&W Bunk Car "525502," 21		100
2126662	N&W Bunk Car "525534," 21		100
2126671	WP Bunk Car "MW0556," 21		100
2126672	WP Bunk Car "MW0761," 21		100
2126680	Polar Express 40' Flatcar w/Bell, 21		100
2127010	NYC Xplorer Coach 2-pack, 20		370
2127020	ATSF WiFi Theater Car "89," 20		340
2127030	BNSF WiFi Theater Car "William Barstow Strong," 20		340
2127040	C&NW WiFi Theater Car "Fox River," 20		340
2127050	KCS WiFi Theater Car "Arthur E. Stilwell," 20		340
2127060	NS WiFi Theater Car "Buena Vista," 20		340

			Exc	Mint
___	2127070	SP WiFi Theater Car "Harriman," 20		340
___	2127080	NYC 1926 Cardinals Passenger Train Expansion Pack, 21		400
___	2127090	NYC 1926 Cardinals "St. Mary of the Lake" Diner w/StationSounds, 21		370
___	2127100	D&RGW Ski Train Power Car, 21-22		370
___	2127110	D&RGW Ski Train Passenger Car 4-pack, 21-22		825
___	2127120	D&RGW Ski Train Passenger Car 2-pack, 21-22		410
___	2127130	D&RGW Ski Train Diner w/StationSounds, 21-22		400
___	2127140	Polar Express High Speed Train Expansion Pack, 21		1000
___	2127150	ATSF Valley Flyer Passenger Train Expansion 2-pack, 21		400
___	2127160	PRR South Wind 21" Passenger Car 4-pack, 20		750
___	2127170	PRR South Wind 21" Passenger Car 2-pack, 20		370
___	2127180	PRR South Wind Diner w/StationSounds, 20		350
___	2127190	PRR "Fleet of Modernism" B60 "7900," 20		190
___	2127200	PC B60 Passenger Car "7705," 20		190
___	2127210	PC B60 Passenger Car "7630," 20		190
___	2127220	Reindeer Express B60 Passenger Car "2124," 20		190
___	2127230	PRR "Fleet of Modernism" 18" Pullman 2-pack, 20		400
___	2127240	Pullman Pool Service 18" Sleeper, Green 2-pack, 20		400
___	2127250	Pullman Pool Service 18" Sleeper, Gray 2-pack, 20		400
___	2127260	PRR South Wind 1947 Expansion Passenger Car 2-pack, 20		370
___	2127270	PRR "Fleet of Modernism" RPO "5260," 20		190
___	2127280	NYC Southwestern Limited 60' Baggage Car "2979," 20		190
___	2127290	NYC Southwestern Limited 60' Baggage Car "8424," 20		190
___	2127300	NYC Southwestern Limited RPO "4814," 20		190
___	2127310	NYC Southwestern Limited 21" Passenger Car 4-pack, 20		750
___	2127320	NYC Southwestern Limited 21" Passenger Car 2-pack, 20		370
___	2127330	NYC Southwestern Limited 21"Diner w/StationSounds, 20		370
___	2127341	Polar Express Sleeping Car "Believe," Black roof, 21		210
___	2127342	Polar Express Sleeping Car "North Pole," Black roof, 21		210
___	2127351	Polar Express Sleeping Car "Believe," White roof, 21		210
___	2127352	Polar Express Sleeping Car "North Pole," White roof, 21		210
___	2127360	D&H 21" Passenger Car 4-pack, 21		750
___	2127370	D&H 21" Passenger Car 2-pack, 21		370
___	2127380	D&H 21" Diner w/StationSounds, 21		370
___	2127390	Amtrak Acela High Speed Train Expansion Set, 21		1000
___	2127400	Amtrak Acela Concept High Speed Train Expansion Set, 21		1000
___	2127410	MILW High Speed Train Expansion Set, 21		1000
___	2127420	NH High Speed Train Expansion Set, 21		1000
___	2127430	PRR Concept High Speed Train Expansion Set, 21		1000
___	2127440	ATSF High Speed Train Expansion Set, 21		1000
___	2127450	UP High Speed Train Expansion Set, 21		1000
___	2127460	E-L 21" Passenger Car 4-pack, 21		750
___	2127470	E-L 21" Passenger Car 2-pack, 21		370
___	2127480	E-L 21" Diner w/StationSounds, 21		370
___	2127490	GM&O 18" Passenger Car 2-pack, A, 21		400
___	2127500	GM&O 18" Passenger Car 2-pack, B, 21		400
___	2127510	GM&O 18" Passenger Car 2-pack, C, 21		400
___	2127520	GM&O 18" Diner w/StationSounds, 21		370
___	2127530	Texas Special 18" Passenger Car 2-pack, A, 21		400
___	2127540	Texas Special 18" Passenger Car 2-pack, B, 21		400
___	2127550	Texas Special 18" Passenger Car 2-pack, C, 21		400
___	2127560	Texas Special 18" Diner w/StationSounds, 21		370

		Exc	Mint
2128010	C&O Walking Brakeman Car "21299," 20-23		110
2128020	Shark Fin Car, 21-23		110
2128030	Monsters Inc. Chasing Gondola, 21-23		90
2128040	Cars Aquarium Car, 21-23		120
2128050	Candy Cane Flatcar, 21		75
2128060	Christmas Tree Flatcar, 21-23		100
2128070	Dump Car w/Presents, 21-23		90
2128080	LL Flatcar w/Handcar, 21-23		135
2128090	Star Trek Dilithium Crystals Hopper w/illumination, 21		90
2128100	Star Trek Chasing Gondola w/Picard, Riker and Q, 21		85
2128110	This Bud's For You Refrigerator Car, 21-23		90
2128120	Those Who Know Bud Refrigerator Car, 21-23		90
2128130	Vintage High Life Refrigerator Car, 21-23		90
2128140	Vintage Coors Refrigerator Car, 21-23		90
2128150	Ford Vintage Boxcar, 21		75
2128160	Chevy Vintage Boxcar, 21		75
2128170	Halloween Sound Car, 21-22		85
2128180	2021 Christmas Music Car, 21		80
2128190	2021 Christmas Boxcar, 21		65
2128200	PRR Flatcar w/Girder Bridge, 21-23		95
2128210	Polar Express Flatcar w/Girder Bridge, 21-23		95
2128220	Batman Aquarium Car, 21-23		120
2128230	Road Runner Aquarium Car, 21-22		120
2128240	Polar Express Operating Present Car, 21-23		100
2128250	SledEx Present Unloading Car, 21-23		100
2128260	North Pole Central Flatcar w/Handcar, 21-22		135
2128270	John Deere Refrigerator Car, 21-22		90
2128280	Polar Express Boxcar, 21-23		85
2128290	Angela Trotta Thomas Christmas Caboose, 21-22		90
2128300	Angela Trotta Thomas Santa Fe Boxcar, 21-23		85
2128310	Angela Trotta Thomas Hudson Boxcar, 21-23		85
2128320	Star Trek Capt. Janeway Boxcar, 21		75
2128330	Star Trek Capt. Sisko Boxcar, 21		75
2128340	Mickey & Friends Christmas Flatcar w/Girders, 21-23		95
2128350	Mickey & Friends Christmas Present Car, 21-23		100
2128360	Space Launch Allis-Chalmers Car w/Capsules, 21-23		85
2129010	Big Tatz Ink, 20-22		100
2129020	Sofa King Mattresses & Furniture, 20-22		110
2129030	Sgt. Stumpy's Red, White & Boom Fireworks, 20-22		300
2129050	Track Laying Crew, 20		100
2129060	Road Crew, 20		100
2129070	Polar Express Present Chute Station, 21-23		200
2129080	SledEx Present Chute Station, 21-22		180
2129090	Angela Trotta Thomas Christmastime Hobby Store, 21-22		300
2129100	Batman Rotary Beacon, 21-22		100
2129110	Classic Rotary Beacon, 21-22		90
2129120	Christmas Rotary Beacon, 21-22		90
2129130	Halloween Rotary Beacon, 21-22		90
2129140	Dr. IP Drips & Sons Plumbing, 20-22		100
2129150	Dominant Jeans , 20-22		120
2129160	McCartney,Äôs Wings, 20		100
2129180	T Rex Elevated Oil Tank, 21		90
2129190	Polar Express Elevated Oil Tank, 21-23		110

		Exc	Mint
____ 2129200	Lionel Ale Elevated Oil Tank, 21-22		110
____ 2129210	Area 51 Elevated Oil Tank, 21-22		110
____ 2129220	Christmas Joy Flagpole, 21-23		45
____ 2129230	Halloween Flagpole, 21-23		45
____ 2129240	Cowens Towing Garage, 21-22		165
____ 2129250	Talking Passenger Station, 21-22		200
____ 2129260	Ford Water Tower, 21		50
____ 2129270	Chevy Water Tower, 21		50
____ 2129280	Halloween Water Tower, 21-22		50
____ 2129290	Christmas Water Tower, 21-23		60
____ 2129300	Area 51 Water Tower, 21-22		60
____ 2129310	John Deere Service Garage, 21-22		180
____ 2129330	Halloween Lighted Half Covered Bridge, 21-22		90
____ 2129340	Chevrolet Flagpole, 21-23		45
____ 2129350	Ford Flagpole, 21-23		45
____ 2129360	Ford Service Station, 21-22		165
____ 2129370	Chevy Service Station, 21-22		165
____ 2129380	Halloween Elevated Oil Tank, 21-23		100
____ 2130010	Frat House, 20		100
____ 2130020	Santa on the Roof House, 21		85
____ 2130030	Cock & Bull Tavern, 21		75
____ 2130040	Russell House, 21		85
____ 2130050	Garage 2-pack, 20		50
____ 2130060	Turner House Kit, 21		50
____ 2130070	Garage Kit, 2-pack, 20		135
____ 2130080	Design-Your-Own-House Kit, 21		60
____ 2130090	Anheuser-Busch Covered Bridge, 21-22		65
____ 2130100	Polar Express Billboard Pack, 21-23		25
____ 2130110	Log Cabin Scented Smoke Fluid, 21-23		9
____ 2130120	Window Shoppers Figures, 21-23		30
____ 2130130	Thru Truss Bridge Kit, 21-23		70
____ 2131010	American Railroads 6-4-4-6 S1 "6100," CC, 20		1600
____ 2131020	PRR 6-4-4-6 S1 "6100," As-Built, CC, 20		1600
____ 2131030	PRR 6-4-4-6 S1 "6100," Calendar, CC, 20		1600
____ 2131040	PRR 6-4-4-6 S1 "6100," Tuscan Red, CC, 20		1600
____ 2131050	B&M 4-6-0 "2074," CC, 20		750
____ 2131060	CP/Railtours 4-6-0 "972," CC, 20		750
____ 2131070	NYC 4-6-0 "1232," CC, 20		750
____ 2131080	Reading & Northern 4-6-0 "225," CC, 20		750
____ 2131090	Rutland 4-6-0 "79," CC, 20		750
____ 2131100	Soo Line 4-6-0 "2645," CC, 20		750
____ 2131110	Southern 4-6-0 "947," CC, 20		375
____ 2131120	T&P 4-6-0 "316," CC, 20		750
____ 2131130	ATSF USRA 2-8-8-2 "1796," CC, 20		1900
____ 2131140	B&O USRA 2-8-8-2 "7150," CC, 20		1900
____ 2131150	Clinchfield USRA 2-8-8-2 "730," CC, 20		1900
____ 2131160	D&RGW USRA 2-8-8-2 "3504," CC, 20		1900
____ 2131170	N&W USRA 2-8-8-2 "2020," CC, 20		1900
____ 2131180	N&W USRA 2-8-8-2 "2050," CC, 20		1900
____ 2131190	N&W USRA 2-8-8-2 "2021," Weathered, CC, 20		2050
____ 2131200	NP USRA 2-8-8-2 "4501," CC, 20		1900
____ 2131210	PRR USRA 2-8-8-2 "377," CC, 20		1900
____ 2131220	UP USRA 2-8-8-2 "3672," CC, 20		1900

		Exc	Mint
2131230	Virginian USRA 2-8-8-2 "702," CC, 20	1900	___
2131240	ACL USRA 4-6-2 Pacific "1504," CC, 21	1500	___
2131250	GM&O USRA 4-6-2 Pacific "5296," CC, 21	1500	___
2131260	GN USRA 4-6-2 Pacific "1385," CC, 21	1500	___
2131270	MKT USRA 4-6-2 Pacific "411," CC, 21	1500	___
2131280	Nickel Plate Road USRA 4-6-2 Pacific "168," CC, 21	1500	___
2131290	SP USRA 4-6-2 Pacific "611," CC, 21	1500	___
2131300	UP USRA 4-6-2 Pacific "3218," CC, 21	1500	___
2131310	ACL USRA Light 2-8-2 "823," CC, 20	1300	___
2131320	Georgia USRA Light 2-8-2 "300," CC, 20	1300	___
2131330	GTW USRA Light 2-8-2 "4070," CC, 20	1300	___
2131340	L&HR USRA Light 2-8-2 "83," CC, 20	1300	___
2131350	Monon USRA Light 2-8-2 "554," CC, 20	1300	___
2131360	SLSF USRA Light 2-8-2 "4003," CC, 20	1300	___
2131370	Southern USRA Light 2-8-2 "4501," CC, 20	1300	___
2131380	Wabash USRA Light 2-8-2 "2202," CC, 20	1300	___
2131390	CNJ Blue Comet 4-6-0 Camelback "770," CC, 21	650	___
2131400	CNJ 4-6-0 Camelback "774," CC, 21	650	___
2131410	D&H 4-6-0 Camelback "810," CC, 21	650	___
2131420	LIRR 4-6-0 Camelback "18," CC, 21	650	___
2131430	NYO&W 4-6-0 Camelback "255," CC, 21	650	___
2131440	Reading 4-6-0 Camelback "652," CC, 21	650	___
2131450	Strasburg 4-6-0 Camelback "771," CC, 21	650	___
2131460	Hallows Eve Limited 4-6-0 Camelback "1313," CC, 21	650	___
2131470	ATSF 2-10-10-2 "3001," CC, 21	2500	___
2131480	ATSF 2-10-10-2 "3009," CC, 21	2500	___
2131490	ATSF Black Bonnet 2-10-10-2 "3005," CC, 21	2500	___
2131500	ATSF Valley Flyer 2-10-10-2 "3008," CC, 21	2500	___
2131510	NYC 4-8-2 L2a Mohawk "2700," CC, 21	1600	___
2131520	NYC 4-8-2 L2a Mohawk "2790," CC, 21	1600	___
2131530	NYC 4-8-2 L2a Mohawk "2728," CC, 21	1600	___
2131540	NYC 4-8-2 L2a Mohawk "2775," CC, 21	1600	___
2131550	NYC 4-8-2 L2a Mohawk "2727," Gray, CC, 21	1600	___
2131560	NYC 4-8-2 L2a Mohawk "2750," Pacemaker, CC, 21	1600	___
2131570	NH 4-8-2 L2a Mohawk "3507," CC, 21	1600	___
2132010	SP LionMaster AC-12 4-8-8-2 Cab-Forward "4294," CC, 20	1300	___
2132020	SP LionMaster AC-12 4-8-8-2 Cab-Forward "4291," CC, 20	1300	___
2132030	SP LionMaster AC-12 4-8-8-2 Cab-Forward "4280," CC, 20	1300	___
2132040	SP LionMaster AC-12 4-8-8-2 Cab-Forward "4290," CC, 20	1300	___
2132050	Christmas 4-4-0 General "1225" LionChief, 21-22	275	___
2132060	Halloween 4-4-0 General "1031" LionChief, 21-22	275	___
2132070	PRR 4-4-0 General "573" LionChief, 21	250	___
2132080	W&A 4-4-0 General "3" LionChief, 21	250	___
2132090	PRR Baby K4 4-6-2 Pacific "1361" LionChief Plus 2.0, 21	550	___
2132100	PRR Baby K4 4-6-2 Pacific "3750" LionChief Plus 2.0, 21	550	___
2132110	PRR Baby K4 4-6-2 Pacific "5400" LionChief Plus 2.0, 21	550	___
2132120	PRR Baby K4 4-6-2 Pacific "5409" LionChief Plus 2.0, 21	550	___
2133010	CRI&P E7 AA Diesel Set "632/635," CC, 20	1000	___
2133019	CRI&P E7B SuperBass, 20	450	___
2133020	SP Golden State E7 AB Diesel Set "6000/6000B," CC, 20	1000	___
2133029	SP Golden State E7B SuperBass "6000C," 20	450	___
2133030	NYC E7 AA Diesel Set "4004/4005," CC, 20	1000	___
2133039	NYC E7B SuperBass "4104," 20	450	___

		Exc	Mint
____ 2133040	PRR E7 AA Diesel Set "5900/5901," CC, 20		1000
____ 2133043	PRR E7B SuperBass "5848B," 20		450
____ 2133049	PRR E7B SuperBass "5900B," 20		450
____ 2133050	ACL E7 AA Diesel Set "540/541," CC, 20		1000
____ 2133059	ACL E7B SuperBass "755," 20		450
____ 2133060	UP E7 AB Diesel Set "927A/928B," CC, 20		1000
____ 2133069	UP E7B SuperBass "929B," 20		450
____ 2133070	SP Lark E7 AB Diesel Set "6004/6004B," CC, 20		1000
____ 2133079	SP Lark E7B SuperBass "6004C," 20		225
____ 2133080	NYC E7 AA Diesel Set "4002/4003," Black, CC, 20		1000
____ 2133089	NYC E7B SuperBass "4102," Black, 20		450
____ 2133090	Bethlehem Steel Genset Diesel Switcher "420," CC, 20		600
____ 2133100	BNSF Genset Diesel Switcher "1228," CC, 20		600
____ 2133110	CSX Genset Diesel Switcher "1300," CC, 20		600
____ 2133120	NS Genset Diesel Switcher "301," CC, 20		600
____ 2133130	PRR Genset Diesel Switcher "9910," CC, 20		600
____ 2133140	UP Genset Diesel Switcher "2706," CC, 20		600
____ 2133151	ATSF GP7 Diesel "2676," CC, 20		500
____ 2133152	ATSF GP7 Diesel "2804," CC, 20		500
____ 2133161	SSW GP7 Diesel "304," CC, 20		500
____ 2133162	SSW GP7 Diesel "320," CC, 20		500
____ 2133171	MEC GP7 Diesel "562," CC, 20		500
____ 2133172	MEC GP7 Diesel "565," CC, 20		500
____ 2133181	NP GP7 Diesel "564," CC, 20		500
____ 2133182	NP GP7 Diesel "566," CC, 20		500
____ 2133191	SAL GP7 Diesel "1700," CC, 20		500
____ 2133192	SAL GP7 Diesel "1760," CC, 20		500
____ 2133201	T&P GP7 Diesel "1110," CC, 20		500
____ 2133202	T&P GP7 Diesel "1118," CC, 20		500
____ 2133210	ATSF Baldwin Sharknose AA Diesel Set "400A/400D," CC, 20		950
____ 2133218	ATSF Baldwin Sharknose Powered B Diesel "400B," CC, 20		430
____ 2133219	ATSF Baldwin Sharknose B Diesel SuperBass "400C," 20		400
____ 2133220	Baldwin Sharknose AA Diesel Set "6000/6001," CC, 20		950
____ 2133228	Baldwin Sharknose Powered B Diesel "6000B," CC, 20		430
____ 2133229	Baldwin Sharknose B Diesel SuperBass "6001B," 20		400
____ 2133230	EJ&E Baldwin Sharknose AA Diesel Set "700A/701A," CC , 20		950
____ 2133238	EJ&E Baldwin Sharknose Powered B Diesel "700B," CC, 20		430
____ 2133239	EJ&E Baldwin Sharknose B Diesel SuperBass "701B," 20		400
____ 2133240	Monongahela Baldwin Sharknose AA Diesel Set "1207/1216," CC, 20		950
____ 2133248	Monongahela Baldwin Sharknose B Diesel "3708," CC, 20		430
____ 2133249	Monongahela Sharknose B Diesel SuperBass "3709," 20		400
____ 2133250	NYC Baldwin Sharknose AA Diesel Set "1206/1213," CC, 20		950
____ 2133258	NYC Baldwin Sharknose Powered B Diesel "3705," CC, 20		430
____ 2133259	NYC Baldwin Sharknose B Diesel SuperBass "3706," 20		400
____ 2133260	PRR Baldwin Sharknose AA Diesel Set "5780A/5781A," CC, 20		950
____ 2133268	PRR Baldwin Sharknose Powered B Diesel "5780B," CC, 20		430
____ 2133269	PRR Baldwin Sharknose B Diesel Superbass "5732B," 22		400
____ 2133270	PRR Baldwin Sharknose AA Diesel Set "9730A/9731A," CC, 20		950
____ 2133278	PRR Baldwin Sharknose Powered B Diesel "9730B," CC, 20		430
____ 2133279	PRR Baldwin Sharknose B Diesel SuperBass "9732B," 20		400
____ 2133280	US Army Baldwin Sharknose AA Set "1775/1776," CC, 20		950
____ 2133288	US Army Baldwin Sharknose Powered B Diesel "1926," CC, 20		430

MODERN 1970-2023

		Exc	Mint
2133289	US Army Baldwin Sharknose B Diesel SuperBass "1941," 20	400	
2133290	UP Genset Diesel Switcher "2709," Graffiti, CC, 20	625	
2133311	ACL SD70ACe Diesel "1840," CC, 21	600	
2133312	ACL SD70ACe Diesel "1967," CC, 21	600	
2133321	ATSF SD70ACe Diesel "1859," CC, 21	600	
2133322	ATSF SD70ACe Diesel "1995," CC, 21	600	
2133330	KCS SD70ACe Diesel "4409 - Heroes," CC, 21	600	
2133331	B&O SD70ACe Diesel "1828," CC, 21	600	
2133332	B&O SD70ACe Diesel "1987," CC, 21	600	
2133341	B&M SD70ACe Diesel "1835," CC, 21	600	
2133342	B&M SD70ACe Diesel "1983," CC, 21	600	
2133351	CP SD70ACe Diesel "1881," CC, 21	600	
2133352	CP SD70ACe Diesel "2021," CC, 21	600	
2133361	GN SD70ACe Diesel "1889," CC, 21	600	
2133362	GN SD70ACe Diesel "1970," CC, 21	600	
2133371	Monon SD70ACe Diesel "1847," CC, 21	600	
2133372	Monon SD70ACe Diesel "1971," CC, 21	600	
2133380	E-L Alco PA AA Diesel Set "862/863," CC, 21	1000	
2133390	GM&O Alco PA AA Diesel Set "290/291," CC, 21	1000	
2133400	MKT Alco PA AA Diesel Set "152A/152C," CC, 21	1000	
2133410	NH Alco PA AA Diesel Set "0760/0761," CC, 21	1000	
2133420	SSW Alco PA AA Diesel Set "300/301," CC, 21	1000	
2133430	D&H Alco PA AA Diesel Set "16/17," CC, 21	1000	
2133441	BNSF GP30 Diesel "2472," CC, 21	530	
2133442	BNSF GP30 Diesel "2826," CC, 21	530	
2133451	C&NW GP30 Diesel "818," CC, 21	530	
2133452	C&NW GP30 Diesel "823," CC, 21	530	
2133461	CSX (Chessie) GP30 Diesel "4126," CC, 21	530	
2133462	CSX (B&O) GP30 Diesel "4131," CC, 21	530	
2133471	KCS GP30 Diesel "4100," CC, 21	530	
2133472	KCS GP30 Diesel "4109," CC, 21	530	
2133481	Reading & Northern GP30 Diesel "2530," CC, 21	530	
2133482	Reading & Northern GP30 Diesel "2531," CC, 21	530	
2133491	Soo GP30 Diesel "700," CC, 21	530	
2133492	Soo GP30 Diesel "703," CC, 21	530	
2133501	UP Veranda Turbine w/SuperBass Tender "61," CC, 21	1650	
2133502	UP Veranda Turbine w/SuperBass Tender "69," CC, 21	1650	
2133510	Alaska Veranda Turbine w/SuperBass Tender "4501," CC, 21	1650	
2133520	GN Veranda Turbine w/SuperBass Tender "5020," CC, 21	1650	
2133530	PRR Veranda Turbine w/SuperBass Tender "6201," CC, 21	1650	
2133540	D&RGW Veranda Turbine w/SuperBass Tender "4010," CC, 21	1650	
2133550	SP Veranda Turbine w/SuperBass Tender "8505," CC, 21	1650	
2133560	US Dept of Defense Veranda Turbine w/SuperBass Tender "1941," CC, 21	1650	
2133570	B&M SW8 Diesel Switcher "801," CC, 21	500	
2133580	Coors Brewing SW8 Diesel Switcher "991," CC, 21	500	
2133590	Conrail SW8 Diesel Switcher "8657," CC, 21	500	
2133600	NYC SW8 Diesel Switcher "9606," CC, 21	500	
2133610	CRI&P SW8 Diesel Switcher "818," CC, 21	500	
2133620	SCL SW8 Diesel Switcher "19," CC, 21	500	
2133630	SP SW8 Diesel Switcher "1102," CC, 21	500	
2133640	Strasburg SW8 Diesel Switcher "8618," CC, 21	500	
2133730	UP Veranda Turbine w/SuperBass Tender "65," CC, 21	1650	

		Exc	Mint
___ 2133740	UP Veranda Turbine w/SuperBass Tender "67," CC, 21		1650
___ 2134010	ACL GP7 Diesel "105" LionChief Plus 2.0, 20-21		375
___ 2134020	MKT GP7 Diesel "93" LionChief Plus 2.0, 20-21		375
___ 2134030	B&O GP7 Diesel "6698" LionChief Plus 2.0, 20-21		375
___ 2134040	CRI&P GP7 Diesel "1274" LionChief Plus 2.0, 20-21		375
___ 2134050	ATSF GE U36B Diesel "8733" LionChief, 21-22		250
___ 2134060	UP GE U36B Diesel "8573" LionChief, 21-22		250
___ 2134070	Seaboard System GE U36B Diesel "5701" LionChief, 21-22		250
___ 2134080	CSX GE U36B Diesel "5871" LionChief, 21-22		250
___ 2134090	LV Alco RS-3 "216" LionChief Plus 2.0, 21		375
___ 2134100	PRR Alco RS-3 "4044" LionChief Plus 2.0, 21		375
___ 2134110	ATSF Alco RS-3 "2098" LionChief Plus 2.0, 21		375
___ 2134120	Southern Alco RS-3 "520" LionChief Plus 2.0, 21		375
___ 2135010	B&O TMCC Speeder, 21		150
___ 2135020	PC TMCC Speeder, 21		150
___ 2135030	ATSF TMCC Speeder, 21		150
___ 2135040	Sperry TMCC Speeder, 21		150
___ 2135050	Polar Express TMCC Speeder, 21-23		165
___ 2135060	Halloween TMCC Speeder, 21-22		165
___ 2135070	Star Trek TMCC Speeder, 21		150
___ 2135080	BNSF TMCC Tamper, 21		200
___ 2135090	BN TMCC Tamper, 21		200
___ 2135100	Conrail TMCC Tamper, 21		200
___ 2135110	CSX TMCC Tamper, 21		200
___ 2135120	NS TMCC Tamper, 21		200
___ 2135130	SP TMCC Tamper, 21		200
___ 2135140	North Pole Central Trolley, 21-23		120
___ 2138010	Kate Shelley Heritage Boxcar, 20		85
___ 2138020	Angela Trotta Thomas Well-Stocked Shelves Boxcar - Bottom Shelf, 20		85
___ 2138030	CP 140th Anniversary Boxcar, 20		85
___ 2138040	Amtrak 50th Anniversary Boxcar, 21		85
___ 2138050	Erie Railroad 170th Anniversary Boxcar, 21		85
___ 2138060	Lyndon B. Johnson Presidential Boxcar, 21		80
___ 2138070	Chester A. Arthur Pesidential Boxcar, 21		80
___ 2138080	Franklin Pierce Presidential Boxcar, 21		80
___ 2138110	Wings of Angels Kacie Boxcar, 21-22		95
___ 2138120	Wings of Angels Victoria Boxcar, 21-22		95
___ 2138130	World War II Africa Campaign Boxcar, 21		85
___ 2138140	World War II Fletcher Class Destroyer Boxcar, 21		85
___ 2138150	2021 Happy Birthday Boxcar, 21		90
___ 2138160	2021 Christmas Boxcar, 21		90
___ 2138170	2021 Anniversary Boxcar, 21		90
___ 2138190	Wings of Angels Jessie Boxcar, 21-22		95
___ 2143011	ATSF Flatcar w/Stakes "90410" (std O), 20-22		55
___ 2143012	ATSF Flatcar w/Stakes "90411" (std O), 20-22		55
___ 2143021	N&W Flatcar w/Stakes "32900" (std O), 20-23		55
___ 2143022	N&W Flatcar w/Stakes "329019" (std O), 20-22		55
___ 2143031	NP Flatcar w/Stakes "69001" (std O), 20-22		55
___ 2143032	NP Flatcar w/Stakes "69123" (std O), 20-22		55
___ 2143041	PRR Flatcar w/Stakes "497918" (std O), 20-22		55
___ 2143042	PRR Flatcar w/Stakes "491301" (std O), 20-22		55
___ 2143051	ADM RBL Refrigerator Car "7014" (std O), 20-22		55

		Exc	Mint
2143052	ADM RBL Refrigerator Car "7019" (std O), 20-23		55 ___
2143061	CN RBL Refrigerator Car "290403" (std O), 20-22		55 ___
2143062	CN RBL Refrigerator Car "290936" (std O), 20-22		55 ___
2143071	FGE RBL Refrigerator Car "363454" (std O), 20-22		55 ___
2143072	FGE RBL Refrigerator Car "363700" (std O), 20-22		55 ___
2143081	PRR RBL Refrigerator Car "19103" (std O), 20-22		55 ___
2143082	PRR RBL Refrigerator Car "19198" (std O), 20-22		55 ___
2143091	CP&LT DD Boxcar "7751" (std O), 21		50 ___
2143092	CP&LT DD Boxcar "7844" (std O), 21		50 ___
2143101	D&M DD Boxcar "2115," 21		50 ___
2143102	D&M DD Boxcar "2127," 21		50 ___
2143111	Port of Tillamook Bay RR DD Boxcar "164" (std O), 21		50 ___
2143112	Port of Tillamook Bay RR DD Boxcar "187" (std O), 21		50 ___
2143121	Sierra RR DD Boxcar "5009" (std O), 21		50 ___
2143122	Sierra RR DD Boxcar "5036" (std O), 21		50 ___
2143131	NYC Gondola w/Ballast Load "632353" (std O), 21		50 ___
2143132	NYC Gondola w/Ballast Load "632361" (std O), 21		50 ___
2143141	N&W Gondola w/Ballast Load "591000" (std O), 21		50 ___
2143142	N&W Gondola w/Ballast Load "591082" (std O), 21		50 ___
2143151	PRR Gondola w/Ballast Load "490075" (std O), 21		50 ___
2143152	PRR Gondola w/Ballast Load "490079" (std O), 21		50 ___
2143161	UP Gondola w/Ballast Load "908467" (std O), 21		50 ___
2143162	UP Gondola w/Ballast Load "908469" (std O), 21		50 ___
2201290	N&W 2-6-6-4 Class A Locomotive "1222," CC, 22		2100 ___
2208010	Legacy Base 3, 22-23		500 ___
2213050	Strasburg RR 2-10-0 Locomotive (1967/2020) "90," CC, 21		1900 ___
2220030	Quonset Hut, 21-23		45 ___
2222010	BNSF SD70MAC Diesel Coal Train Set, CC, 21		900 ___
2222020	UP Rocket Booster Diesel Set, CC, 22		1700 ___
2222030	BN SD45 Hustle Muscle Diesel Freight Set, CC, 21		1100 ___
2222040	Cambria & Indiana SW9 Bicentennial Coal Train Set, CC, 21		1000 ___
2222050	Grand Canyon Ry Steam Passenger Set, CC, 21		1300 ___
2222060	Amtrak Genesis LionChief Plus 2.0 Set, 22		1000 ___
2222070	B&LE Diesel Ore Train Set, CC, 22		1600 ___
2222080	Black River & Western Excursion Passenger Set, CC, 22		1100 ___
2222090	NS 40th Anniversary Diesel Freight Set, CC, 22		1300 ___
2222100	PRR S2 Steam LionChief Plus 2.0 Set, 22		750 ___
2223010	U.S. Army LionChief Bluetooth 5.0 Diesel Freight Set, 21-23		450 ___
2223020	Christmas Celebration LionChief Bluetooth 5.0 Set, 22-23		400 ___
2223040	Emergency Response LionChief Bluetooth 5.0 Set, 22-23		500 ___
2223050	Anheuser Busch LionChief Bluetooth 5.0 Set, 22-23		400 ___
2223060	Lionel Lines LionChief Bluetooth 5.0 Freight Set, 22-23		360 ___
2223070	Great Locomotive Chase Deluxe LC Bluetooth 5.0 Set, 22-23		600 ___
2223110	Graffiti LionChief Bluetooth 5.0 Set, 22-23		500 ___
2226010	Erie Boxcar "82275" w/HoboSounds, 21		190 ___
2226020	RI Boxcar "48582" w/HoboSounds, 21		190 ___
2226030	AT&SF AAR 2-Bay Hopper 2-Pack, 21		200 ___
2226040	Cambria & Indiana Die-cast AAR 2-Bay Hopper 2-Pack, 21		200 ___
2226050	NYC AAR 2-Bay Hopper 2-Pack, 21		200 ___
2226060	NS AAR 2-Bay Hopper 2-Pack, 21		200 ___
2226070	Pittsburg & Shawmut AAR 2-Bay Hopper 2-Pack, 21		200 ___
2226080	Reading AAR 2-Bay Hopper 2-Pack, 21		200 ___

		Exc	Mint
___ 2226090	Alaska Cylindrical Covered Hopper "14500," 21		110
___ 2226100	CSX (ex EL) Cylindrical Covered Hopper "884137," 21		110
___ 2226110	EL Cylindrical Covered Hopper "20021," 21		110
___ 2226120	GM Cylindrical Covered Hopper "61113," 21		110
___ 2226130	NYC Cylindrical Covered Hopper "885950," 21		110
___ 2226140	UP Cylindrical Covered Hopper "221000," 21		110
___ 2226150	CP Caboose "434604" w/CupolaCam, 21		220
___ 2226160	SSW Caboose "3" w/CupolaCam, 21		220
___ 2226170	NP Caboose "10401" w/CupolaCam, 21		220
___ 2226180	SAL Caboose "5754" w/CupolaCam, 21		220
___ 2226190	Soo Caboose "1" w/CupolaCam, 21		220
___ 2226200	North Pole Central Caboose "2521" w/CupolaCam, 21		220
___ 2226210	UP CA-1 Caboose "2664" (brown), 21		150
___ 2226220	UP CA-1 Caboose "2535" (brown), 21		150
___ 2226230	UP CA-1 Caboose "2550" (yellow), 21		150
___ 2226240	UP CA-1 Caboose "2654" (white), 21		150
___ 2226250	SP CA-1 Caboose "703," 21		150
___ 2226260	Great Western CA-1 Caboose "1006," 21		150
___ 2226270	AT&SF 50' Flatcar "91090" w/Fire Truck, 21		160
___ 2226280	C&O 50' Flatcar "81001" w/Fire Truck, 21		160
___ 2226290	NYC 50' Flatcar "506261" w/Fire Truck, 21		160
___ 2226300	PRR 50' Flatcar "469660" w/Fire Truck, 21		160
___ 2226310	Southern 50' Flatcar "51819" w/Fire Truck, 21		160
___ 2226320	UP 50' Flatcar "53026" w/Fire Truck, 21		160
___ 2226330	Ann Arbor 4-Door Hi-Cube Boxcar "10009," 21		130
___ 2226340	CN 4-Door Hi-Cube Boxcar "795101," 21		130
___ 2226350	Ford 4-Door Hi-Cube Boxcar "101," 21		130
___ 2226360	N&W 4-Door Hi-Cube Boxcar "355173," 21		130
___ 2226370	PC 4-Door Hi-Cube Boxcar "237544," 21		130
___ 2226380	WP 4-Door Hi-Cube Boxcar "86011," 21		130
___ 2226390	CN 4-Door Hi-Cube Boxcar w/graffiti, 21		140
___ 2226400	Conrail 4-Door Hi-Cube Boxcar w/graffiti, 21		140
___ 2226410	HLMX 4-Door Hi-Cube Boxcar w/graffiti, 21		140
___ 2226420	NS 4-Door Hi-Cube Boxcar w/graffiti, 21		140
___ 2226430	UP Rocket Booster Flatcar w/Rocket 5-Pack, 22		860
___ 2226440	UP Rocket Booster Flatcar 5-Pack, 22		750
___ 2226451	Bethlehem Steel Coil Car "216451," 22		120
___ 2226452	Bethlehem Steel Coil Car "216489," 22		120
___ 2226461	BNSF Coil Car "534321," 22		120
___ 2226462	BNSF Coil Car "534354," 22		120
___ 2226471	Conrail Coil Car "623603," 22		120
___ 2226472	Conrail Coil Car "623624," 22		120
___ 2226481	Ferromex Coil Car "918040," 22		120
___ 2226482	Ferromex Coil Car "918046," 22		120
___ 2226491	Reading Coil Car "99502," 22		120
___ 2226492	Reading Coil Car "99561," 22		120
___ 2226501	UP Coil Car "242081," 22		120
___ 2226502	UP Coil Car "242118," 22		120
___ 2226510	Bethlehem Steel Coil Car w/Graffiti "216469," 22		130
___ 2226520	BNSF Coil Car w/Graffiti "534370," 22		130
___ 2226530	Conrail (NYC) Coil Car w/Graffiti "623684," 22		130
___ 2226540	Ferromex Coil Car w/Graffiti "918032," 22		130

		Exc	Mint
2226550	NS Coil Car w/Graffiti "167024," 22		130 ___
2226560	Polar Express End Door Boxcar, 22		115 ___
2226571	BN Husky Stack Car "63345," 22		170 ___
2226572	BN Husky Stack Car w/Graffiti "63361," 22		190 ___
2226581	CRLE Husky Stack Car "5462," 22		170 ___
2226582	CRLE Husky Stack Car w/Graffiti "5496," 22		190 ___
2226591	CSX Husky Stack Car "620360," 22		170 ___
2226592	CSX Husky Stack Car w/Graffiti "620365," 22		190 ___
2226601	TT Husky Stack Car "56218," 22		170 ___
2226602	TT Husky Stack Car w/Graffiti "56317," 22		190 ___
2226611	TTX Husky Stack Car "56295," 22		170 ___
2226612	TTX Husky Stack Car w/Graffiti "56363," 22		190 ___
2226621	Pacer Husky Stack Car "6301," 22		170 ___
2226622	Pacer Husky Stack Car w/Graffiti "6325," 22		190 ___
2226630	AT&SF End Door Boxcar "7176," 22		115 ___
2226640	CB&Q End Door Boxcar "48520," 22		115 ___
2226650	Conoco End Door Boxcar "50014," 22		115 ___
2226660	Southern End Door Boxcar "42000," 22		115 ___
2226670	UP End Door Boxcar "161202," 22		115 ___
2226680	Wabash End Door Boxcar "18023," 22		115 ___
2226690	B&O Bobber Caboose "1775," 22		120 ___
2226700	LV Bobber Caboose "2606," 22		120 ___
2226710	Maryland & Pennsylvania Bobber Caboose "2003," 22		120 ___
2226720	Northern Central Bobber Caboose "200," 22		120 ___
2226730	Strasburg Bobber Caboose "1," 22		120 ___
2226740	U.S. Military Bobber Caboose "65," 22		120 ___
2226750	BNSF Anniversary BW Caboose, 22		145 ___
2226760	CSX Fire BW Caboose, 22		145 ___
2226770	CSX Police BW Caboose, 22		145 ___
2226780	CSX Veterans BW Caboose, 22		145 ___
2226790	CN Veterans BW Caboose, 22		145 ___
2226800	CP Veterans BW Caboose, 22		145 ___
2226810	BNSF Illuminated Flag Boxcar, 22		160 ___
2226820	CSX Fire Illuminated Flag Boxcar, 22		160 ___
2226830	CSX Police Illuminated Flag Boxcar, 22		160 ___
2226840	CSX Veterans Illuminated Flag Boxcar, 22		160 ___
2226850	Conrail Veterans Illuminated Flag Boxcar, 22		160 ___
2226860	Montana Rail Link Illuminated Flag Boxcar, 22		160 ___
2226870	AT&SF Vision Line Stockcar 3-Pack, 22		450 ___
2226880	B&O Vision Line Stockcar 3-Pack, 22		450 ___
2226890	NYC Vision Line Stockcar 3-Pack, 22		450 ___
2226900	NP Vision Line Stockcar 3-Pack, 22		450 ___
2226910	Swift Vision Line Stockcar 3-Pack, 22		450 ___
2226920	UP Vision Line Stockcar 3-Pack, 22		450 ___
2226930	N&W 2-Bay Hopper 2-Pack, 22		200 ___
2226940	PRR 2-Bay Hopper 2-Pack, 22		200 ___
2226950	Pennsylvania Coal & Coke 2-Bay Hopper 2-Pack, 22		200 ___
2226960	VGN 2-Bay Hopper 2-Pack, 22		200 ___
2226970	Westmoreland Coal 2-Bay Hopper 2-Pack, 22		200 ___
2226980	West Penn. Power 2-Bay Hopper 2-Pack, 22		200 ___
2226990	North Pole Central End Door Boxcar, 22		115 ___
2226991	UP Desert Victory Illuminated Flag Boxcar, 22		160 ___

		Exc	Mint
2227010	Strasburg RR Observation "Paradise," 21		210
2227020	Philadelphia & Reading Observation "10," 21		210
2227030	Strasburg RR Wood Coach 2-Pack #1 (1990s), 21		400
2227040	Strasburg RR Wood Coach 2-Pack #2 (1990s), 21		400
2227050	Strasburg RR Wood Coach 2-Pack #1 (2000s), 21		400
2227060	Strasburg RR Wood Coach 2-Pack #2 (2000s), 21		400
2227070	PRR Wood Coach 2-Pack #1, 21		400
2227080	PRR Wood Coach 2-Pack #2, 21		400
2227090	B&M Wood Coach 2-Pack #1, 21		400
2227100	B&M Wood Coach 2-Pack #2, 21		400
2227110	LIRR 72' Passenger Coach 2-Pack #1, 21		390
2227120	LIRR 72' Passenger Coach 2-Pack #2, 21		390
2227130	NH 18" Passenger Car 2-Pack #1, 21		420
2227140	NH 18" Passenger Car 2-Pack #2, 21		420
2227150	NH 18" Passenger Car 2-Pack #3, 21		420
2227160	NH 18" Diner w/StationSounds, 21		380
2227170	Strasburg RR B380#1 (1990s), 21		400
2227180	Strasburg RR Wood Coach/Combine 2-Pack #2 (2000s), 21		400
2227190	PRR Wood Coach/Combine 2-Pack, 21		400
2227200	B&M Wood Coach/Combine 2-Pack, 21		400
2227210	Grand Canyon Ry Coach 2-Pack, 21		390
2227220	UP Rocket Train Rider Car "Hialeah," 22		225
2227230	AT&SF Chief Add-On Coach, 22-23		100
2227240	AT&SF Chief Add-On Vista-Dome "501," 22-23		100
2227250	NS Excursion Coach 4-Pack, 22		900
2227260	Amtrak Phase III 21" Passenger Car 4-Pack, 22		900
2227270	Amtrak Phase III 21" Passenger Car 2-Pack, 22		450
2227280	Amtrak Phase III Diner w/StationSounds, 22		400
2227290	Amtrak Amfleet Phase III Coach 2-Pack, 22		400
2227300	Amtrak Amfleet Phase V Coach 2-Pack, 22		400
2227310	Amtrak Amfleet Phase VI Coach 2-Pack, 22		400
2227320	Amtrak Amfleet Phase III Coach/Cab Car 2-Pack, 22		400
2227330	Amtrak Amfleet Phase V Coach 2-Pack, 22		400
2227340	Amtrak Amfleet Phase VI Coach/Cab Car 2-Pack, 22		400
2227350	CSX Business Train 21" Passenger Car 4-Pack, 22		900
2227360	CSX Business Train 18" Passenger Car 2-Pack, 22		500
2227370	CSX Business Train 21" Diner w/StationSounds, 22		400
2227380	Aberdeen, Carolina & Western 21" Passenger Car 2-Pack, 22		450
2227390	Aberdeen, Carolina & Western 18" Passenger Car 2-Pack, 22		500
2227400	MOW Wood Baggage/Coach 2-Pack, 22		450
2227410	MOW Wood Combine/Coach 2-Pack, 22		450
2227420	MOW Wood Coach/Observation 2-Pack, 22		450
2227430	NYC&HR Wood Baggage/Coach 2-Pack, 22		450
2227440	NYC&HR Wood Combine/Coach 2-Pack, 22		450
2227450	NYC&HR Wood Coach/Observation 2-Pack, 22		450
2227460	Southern Wood Baggage/Coach 2-Pack, 22		450
2227470	Southern Wood Combine/Coach 2-Pack, 22		450
2227480	Southern Wood Coach/Observation 2-Pack, 22		450
2227490	Wabash Wood Baggage/Coach 2-Pack, 22		450
2227500	Wabash Wood Combine/Coach 2-Pack, 22		450
2227510	Wabash Wood Coach/Observation 2-Pack, 22		450
2227520	AT&SF Vision Line Horse Car "1995," 22		370
2227530	CP Vision Line Horse Car "4560," 22		370

		Exc	Mint
2227540	L&N Vision Line Horse Car "1507," 22		370 ___
2227550	PRR Vision Line Horse Car "5024," 22		370 ___
2227560	REA Vision Line Horse Car "812," 22		370 ___
2227570	SP Vision Line Horse Car "7200," 22		370 ___
2227580	North Pole Central Vision Reindeer Car, 22		370 ___
2227590	Polar Express Vision Reindeer Car, 22		370 ___
2227600	Bureau of Mines 18" Passenger Car 2-Pack, 22		500 ___
2227610	Wood Chapel Car "Evangel," 22		225 ___
2228020	Angela Trotta Thomas GG1 Boxcar, 21-23		85 ___
2228030	U.S. Army Missile Flatcar, 21-23		90 ___
2228040	Vintage Anheuser Busch Clydesdale Refrigerator Car, 22-23		90 ___
2228050	Budweiser Holiday Stein Refrigerator Car, 22-23		90 ___
2228060	Miller Refrigerator Car, 22		90 ___
2228070	Coors Refrigerator Car, 22		90 ___
2228080	Polar Express Aquarium Car, 22-23		120 ___
2228090	Polar Express Illuminated Boxcar, 22-23		120 ___
2228100	Hallow's Eve Monster Gondola, 22-23		90 ___
2228110	Hallow's Eve Illuminated Caboose, 22-23		90 ___
2228120	Christmas Parade Aquarium Car, 22-23		120 ___
2228130	Christmas Chasing Gondola, 22-23		90 ___
2228140	Night Before Christmas Illuminated Boxcar, 22-23		120 ___
2228150	2022 Christmas Boxcar, 22		70 ___
2228160	2022 Christmas Music Boxcar, 22		85 ___
2228170	Angela Trotta Thomas Christmas Aquarium Car, 22-23		120 ___
2228180	Angela Trotta Thomas Blue Comet Boxcar, 22-23		85 ___
2228190	Angela Trotta Thomas NYC Boxcar, 22-23		85 ___
2228220	Mickey & Friends Christmas Caboose, 22-23		90 ___
2228230	Mickey & Friends Christmas Searchlight Car, 22-23		85 ___
2228250	U.S. Navy Flatcar w/Submarine, 22-23		90 ___
2228270	U.S. Air Force Minuteman Car, 22-23		120 ___
2228280	U.S. Marine Corps Rocket Launcher Car, 22-23		110 ___
2228290	U.S. Army Big Cannon Car, 22-23		110 ___
2228300	Polar Express Caboose, 22-23		90 ___
2228310	North Pole Central Illuminated Hopper, 22-23		100 ___
2228320	Budweiser Tank Car, 22-23		85 ___
2228350	Monsters Inc. Scare Tank Car w/LEDs, 22-23		120 ___
2228360	Incredibles Operating Car, 22-23		120 ___
2228370	Toy Story Woody Walking Brakeman Car, 22-23		120 ___
2228380	John Deere Refrigerator Car, 22-23		90 ___
2228390	John Deere Work Caboose, 22-23		85 ___
2228400	Fourth of July LED Car w/Sounds, 22-23		150 ___
2228410	American Flag LED Car, 22-23		120 ___
2228440	Chevrolet Boxcar, 22-23		85 ___
2228450	Chevrolet Flatcar w/Piggyback Trailers, 22-23		95 ___
2228460	Ford Boxcar, 22-23		85 ___
2228470	Ford Flatcar w/Piggyback Trailers, 22-23		95 ___
2228480	Hallow's Eve Mint Car, 22-23		120 ___
2228490	Ghoul Searchlight Car, 22-23		85 ___
2228500	Graffiti Hi-Cube Boxcar, 22-23		80 ___
2228510	W&A Freight Expansion Pack, 22-23		220 ___
2229010	No. 943 Exploding Ammunition Dump, 21-22		65 ___
2229020	Missile Range, 21-23		80 ___
2229030	Train Orders Building, 21-22		140 ___

		Exc	Mint
2229040	Mission Control Tower, 21-23		130
2229050	Burning House, 21-22		200
2229060	Tough Guy Gym & Fitness, 21-23		160
2229070	Barn, 21-23		180
2229080	Passenger Station, 21-22		150
2229100	Townhouse, 21-23		110
2229110	Thistle Stop Flower Shop, 21-23		160
2229120	Christmas Barn, 21-23		200
2229130	Military Surplus Store, 21-23		160
2229140	Welcome Home Troops Townhouse, 21-23		110
2229150	Fire Station, 22		330
2229160	Private Investigation Building, 22-23		160
2229170	Bail Bonds Building, 22-23		110
2229180	Donuts & Coffee Shop, 22-23		110
2229190	Budweiser Brewery, 22-23		220
2229200	Transfer Station, 22-23		300
2229210	Deer Dash Transfer Station, 22-23		300
2229220	Grim's Repo Depot Transfer Station, 22-23		300
2229230	Western Mercantile, 22-23		80
2229250	Sheriff's Headquarters Building, 22-23		80
2229260	Firefighter Tank Car Accident Training, 22-23		130
2229270	Industrial Water Tower w/Graffiti Decals, 22-23		80
2229280	Polar Express Hot Chocolate Industrial Tower, 22-23		90
2229290	Up on the Rooftop Christmas House, 22-23		100
2229300	Rocket Launch Pad, 22-23		430
2229310	Coaling Station, 22-23		130
2229320	Christmas Coal Works Lighted Coaling Station, 22-23		130
2230010	Vintage Inspired Space Billboards, 21-23		25
2230020	Amtrak Through The Years Billboards, 21-23		25
2230050	Thomas & Friends Christmas Girder Bridge, 22-23		35
2230060	Red Fire Truck, 21-22		80
2230070	Yellow Fire Truck, 21-23		80
2230080	White Fire Truck, 21-23		80
2230090	Black Fire Truck, 21-23		80
2230100	Smoke Fluid Dropper 2-Pack, 21-23		5
2230110	Airplane Accessory 2-Pack, 22-23		14
2230120	Boats 2-Pack, 22-23		14
2230130	Helicopters 2-Pack, 22-23		14
2230140	Railroad Signs 5-Pack, 22-23		9
2230150	Angela Trotta Thomas Christmas Billboards, 22-23		25
2230160	Halloween Billboards, 22-23		25
2230170	Unique Railroad Signs 5-Pack, 22-23		9
2230180	Firefighter Figures and Dog, 22-23		30
2231010	Great Western 2-10-0 Locomotive "90," CC, 21		1900
2231020	Strasburg RR 2-10-0 Locomotive (1990s) "90," CC, 21		1900
2231030	Strasburg RR 2-10-0 Locomotive (2000s) "90," CC, 21		1900
2231040	Great Western 2-10-0 Locomotive (2000s) "90," CC, 21		1900
2231060	SAL 2-10-0 Locomotive "525," CC, 21		1900
2231070	Osage Ry 2-10-0 Locomotive "10," CC, 21		1900
2231080	AT&SF 2-8-0 Locomotive "2535," CC, 21		750
2231090	Buffalo Creek & Gauley 2-8-0 Locomotive "4," CC, 21		750
2231100	C&O 2-8-0 Locomotive "701," CC, 21		750

		Exc	Mint
2231110	MEC 2-8-0 Locomotive "519," CC, 21	750	___
2231120	NYC 2-8-0 Locomotive "960," CC, 21	750	___
2231130	WP 2-8-0 Locomotive "26," CC, 21	750	___
2231141	AT&SF 2-10-4 Locomotive "5011," CC, 22	1750	___
2231142	AT&SF 2-10-4 Locomotive "5022," CC, 22	1750	___
2231150	AT&SF 2-10-4 Locomotive "5001," CC, 22	1750	___
2231160	KCS 2-10-4 Locomotive "902," CC, 22	1750	___
2231170	KCS 2-10-4 Locomotive "905," CC, 22	1750	___
2231180	PRR 2-10-4 Locomotive "6510," CC, 22	1750	___
2231191	SP AC-12 Cab Forward Locomotive "4294," CC, 21	2000	___
2231192	SP AC-12 Cab Forward Locomotive "4281," CC, 21	2000	___
2231200	SP AC-12 Cab Forward "4278" w/black tender, CC, 21	2000	___
2231210	SP AC-12 Cab Forward, Daylight scheme, "4290," CC, 21	2000	___
2231220	SP AC-12 Cab Forward, Lark scheme, "4285," CC, 21	2000	___
2231230	SP AC-12 Cab Forward "4278" w/gray boiler, CC, 21	2000	___
2231241	UP 4-12-2 Locomotive "9000," CC, 21	1700	___
2231242	UP 4-12-2 Locomotive "9023," CC, 21	1700	___
2231250	UP/OSL 4-12-2 Locomotive "9514," CC, 21	1700	___
2231260	UP 4-12-2 Locomotive "9002," CC, 21	1700	___
2231270	UP 4-12-2 Locomotive "9014," CC, 21	1700	___
2231280	C&O 4-12-2 Locomotive "560," CC, 21	1700	___
2231290	D&RGW 4-12-2 Locomotive "1420," CC, 21	1700	___
2231300	MILW 4-12-2 Locomotive "1500," CC, 21	1700	___
2231310	SP 4-12-2 Locomotive "2124," CC, 21	1700	___
2231320	SP&S 4-12-2 Locomotive "651," CC, 21	1700	___
2231340	B&A 2-8-4 Berkshire Locomotive "1401," CC, 22	1600	___
2231350	B&M 2-8-4 Berkshire Locomotive "4019," CC, 22	1600	___
2231360	C&NW 2-8-4 Berkshire Locomotive "2803," CC, 22	1600	___
2231370	AT&SF 2-8-4 Berkshire Locomotive "4198," CC, 22	1600	___
2231380	SP 2-8-4 Berkshire Locomotive "3506," CC, 22	1600	___
2231390	TA&G 2-8-4 Berkshire Locomotive "602," CC, 22	1600	___
2231400	B&M 4-4-2 Atlantic Locomotive "3243," CC, 22	900	___
2231410	MP 4-4-2 Atlantic Locomotive "5521," CC, 22	900	___
2231420	NH 4-4-2 Atlantic Locomotive "1111," CC, 22	900	___
2231430	NYC 4-4-2 Atlantic Locomotive "4751," CC, 22	900	___
2231440	Southern 4-4-2 Atlantic Locomotive "1905," CC, 22	900	___
2231450	Wabash 4-4-2 Atlantic Locomotive "606," CC, 22	900	___
2231460	N&W 2-6-6-4 Class A Locomotive "1218," CC, 22	2100	___
2231470	N&W 2-6-6-4 Class A Locomotive "1238," CC, 22	2100	___
2231480	N&W 2-6-6-4 Class A Locomotive "1200," CC, 22	2100	___
2231490	N&W 2-6-6-4 Class A Locomotive "1210," CC, 22	2100	___
2231500	N&W 2-6-6-4 Class A Locomotive "1211," CC, 22	2100	___
2231510	N&W 2-6-6-4 Class A Locomotive "1201," CC, 22	2100	___
2231520	N&W 2-6-6-4 Class A Locomotive, Pilot," CC, 22	2100	___
2231530	Bethlehem Steel 0-6-0 Locomotive "60," CC, 22	800	___
2231540	SL&SF 0-6-0 Locomotive "3801," CC, 22	800	___
2231550	NYC 0-6-0 Locomotive "222," CC, 22	800	___
2231560	PRR 0-6-0 Locomotive "7007," CC, 22	800	___
2231570	Strasburg 0-6-0 Locomotive "31," CC, 22	800	___
2231580	Terminal RR of St. Louis 0-6-0 Locomotive "160," CC, 22	800	___
2231590	Washington Terminal 0-6-0 Locomotive "32," CC, 22	800	___
2231600	Unpainted brass 2-10-0 Locomotive, CC, 21	1900	___

		Exc	Mint
___ 2232010	NYC 4-6-4 Hudson "5314," LionChief Plus 2.0, 21-22		650
___ 2232020	UP 4-6-4 Hudson "675," LionChief Plus 2.0, 21-22		650
___ 2232030	AT&SF 4-6-4 Hudson "3463," LionChief Plus 2.0, 21-22		650
___ 2232040	Lionel Lines 4-6-4 Hudson "773," LionChief Plus 2.0, 21-22		650
___ 2232050	Bethlehem Steel 0-4-0 Locomotive "76," CC, 22		700
___ 2232060	B&O 0-4-0 Locomotive "37," CC, 22		700
___ 2232070	U.S. Army 0-4-0 Locomotive "491," CC, 22		700
___ 2232080	PRR 0-4-0 Locomotive "477," CC, 22		700
___ 2232090	LIRR 0-4-0 Locomotive "175," CC, 22		700
___ 2232100	B&O 4-6-2 Pacific "5215," LionChief Plus 2.0, 22		650
___ 2232110	D&RGW 4-6-2 Pacific "801," LionChief Plus 2.0, 22		650
___ 2232120	LV 4-6-2 Pacific Locomotive "2101," LionChief Plus 2.0, 22		650
___ 2232130	Reading & Northern 4-6-2 Pacific 425 LionChief Plus 2.0, 22		650
___ 2232140	North Pole Central 4-6-2 Pacific Locomotive "1224," LionChief Plus 2.0, 22-23		650
___ 2233010	BNSF SD70MAC Diesel "9647," CC, 21		650
___ 2233021	BNSF SD70MAC Diesel "9718," CC, 21		650
___ 2233028	BNSF SuperBass SD70MAC Diesel "9829," 21		550
___ 2233031	BNSF SD70MAC Diesel "9721," CC, 21		650
___ 2233032	BNSF SD70MAC Diesel "9789," CC, 21		650
___ 2233038	BNSF SuperBass SD70MAC Diesel "9819," 21		550
___ 2233041	Conrail SD70MAC Diesel "777," CC, 21		650
___ 2233042	Conrail SD70MAC Diesel "780," CC, 21		650
___ 2233048	Conrail SuperBass SD70MAC Diesel "782," 21		550
___ 2233051	CSX SD70MAC Diesel "4551," CC, 21		650
___ 2233052	CSX SD70MAC Diesel "4553," CC, 21		650
___ 2233058	CSX SuperBass SD70MAC Diesel "4558," 21		550
___ 2233061	NS SD70MAC Diesel "1800," CC, 21		650
___ 2233062	NS SuperBass SD70MAC Diesel "1801," 21		550
___ 2233071	P&L SD70MAC Diesel "4501," CC, 21		650
___ 2233072	P&L SD70MAC Diesel "4504," CC, 21		650
___ 2233078	P&L SuperBass SD70MAC Diesel "4523," 21		550
___ 2233081	BN SD45 Diesel "6445," CC, 21		600
___ 2233082	BN SD45 Diesel "6452," CC, 21		600
___ 2233088	BN SuperBass SD45 Diesel "6455," 21		500
___ 2233091	EMD SD45 Diesel "4351," CC, 21		600
___ 2233092	EMD SD45 Diesel "4352," CC, 21		600
___ 2233098	EMD SuperBass SD45 Diesel "4353," 21		500
___ 2233101	Guilford/Springfield Terminal SD45 Diesel "681," CC, 21		600
___ 2233102	Guilford/Springfield Terminal SD45 Diesel "684," CC, 21		600
___ 2233108	Guilford/Springfield Terminal SuperBass SD45 Diesel "685," 21		500
___ 2233111	MILW SD45 Diesel "6," CC, 21		600
___ 2233112	MILW SD45 Diesel "8," CC, 21		600
___ 2233118	MILW SuperBass SD45 Diesel "10," 21		500
___ 2233121	NS SD45 Diesel "1716," CC, 21		600
___ 2233122	NS SD45 Diesel "1766," CC, 21		600
___ 2233128	NS SuperBass SD45 Diesel "1795," 21		500
___ 2233131	PRR SD45 Diesel "6186," CC, 21		600
___ 2233132	PRR SD45 Diesel "6197," CC, 21		600
___ 2233138	PRR SuperBass SD45 Diesel "6202," 21		500
___ 2233141	Alaska DD35 Diesel "5000," CC, 21		700
___ 2233142	Alaska DD35 Diesel "5001," CC, 21		700
___ 2233151	AT&SF DD35 Diesel "1650," CC, 21		700

		Exc	Mint
2233152	AT&SF DD35 Diesel "1652," CC, 21		700 __
2233160	UP DD35 Diesel "71" (Dependable Transportation), CC, 21		700 __
2233170	UP DD35 Diesel "76" (We Can Handle It), CC, 21		700 __
2233180	UP DD35 Diesel "77" (Shield herald), CC, 21		700 __
2233190	UP DD35 Diesel "81" (American flag), CC, 21		700 __
2233200	AT&SF SW1200 Diesel "1441," CC, 21		550 __
2233210	BNSF SW1200 Diesel "3505," CC, 21		550 __
2233220	D&RGW SW1200 Diesel "134," CC, 21		550 __
2233230	EJ&E SW1200 Diesel "306," CC, 21		550 __
2233240	PC SW1200 Diesel "9020," CC, 21		550 __
2233250	US Steel SW1200 Diesel "13," CC, 21		550 __
2233261	FM Demonstrator C-Liner Diesel "4801," CC, 21		600 __
2233262	FM Demonstrator C-Liner Diesel "4802," CC, 21		600 __
2233271	CN C-Liner Diesel "6701," CC, 21		600 __
2233272	CN C-Liner Diesel "6705," CC, 21		600 __
2233281	LIRR C-Liner Diesel "2001," CC, 21		600 __
2233282	LIRR C-Liner Diesel "2003," CC, 21		600 __
2233291	NH C-Liner Diesel "792," CC, 21		600 __
2233292	NH C-Liner Diesel "798," CC, 21		600 __
2233301	NYC C-Liner Diesel "4500," CC, 21		600 __
2233302	NYC C-Liner Diesel "4502," CC, 21		600 __
2233311	PRR C-Liner Diesel "9570," CC, 21		600 __
2233312	PRR C-Liner Diesel "9571," CC, 21		600 __
2233321	Alco Demonstrator RS-27 Diesel "640-2," CC, 22		600 __
2233322	Alco Demonstrator RS-27 Diesel "640-4," CC, 22		600 __
2233331	C&NW Alco RS-27 Diesel "900," CC, 22		600 __
2233332	C&NW Alco RS-27 Diesel "903," CC, 22		600 __
2233341	Conrail Alco RS-27 Diesel "2412," CC, 22		600 __
2233342	Conrail Alco RS-27 Diesel "2414," CC, 22		600 __
2233351	GB&W Alco RS-27 Diesel "316," CC, 22		600 __
2233352	GB&W Alco RS-27 Diesel "318," CC, 22		600 __
2233361	PC Alco RS-27 Diesel, "2407," CC, 22		600 __
2233362	PC Alco RS-27 Diesel, "2409," CC, 22		600 __
2233371	SOO Alco RS-27 Diesel "415," CC, 22		600 __
2233372	SOO Alco RS-27 Diesel "416," CC, 22		600 __
2233380	B&O EMD SW1 Diesel "8408," CC, 22		550 __
2233390	BN EMD SW1 Diesel "97," CC, 22		550 __
2233400	Conrail EMD SW1 Diesel "8408," CC, 22		550 __
2233410	Flambeau Paper EMD SW1 Diesel "1," CC, 22		550 __
2233420	SP EMD SW1 Diesel "1000," CC, 22		550 __
2233430	Turtle Creek EMD SW1 Diesel "462," CC, 22		550 __
2233441	BNSF Heritage ES44AC Diesel "6075," CC, 22		700 __
2233442	BNSF Heritage ES44AC Diesel "6111," CC, 22		700 __
2233449	BNSF Heritage ES44AC Diesel "6179" (nonpowered), 22		400 __
2233451	BC Rail Heritage ES44AC Diesel "3115," CC, 22		700 __
2233459	BC Rail Heritage ES44AC Diesel "3115," (nonpowered), 22		400 __
2233461	EJ&E Heritage ES44AC Diesel "3023," CC, 22		700 __
2233469	EJ&E Heritage ES44AC Diesel "3023" (unpowered), 22		400 __
2233471	IC Heritage ES44AC Diesel "3008," CC, 22		700 __
2233479	IC Heritage ES44AC Diesel "3008" (unpowered), 22		400 __
2233481	WC Heritage ES44AC Diesel "3069," CC, 22		700 __
2233489	WC Heritage ES44AC Diesel "3069" (unpowered), 22		400 __
2233491	CN Veterans ES44AC Diesel "3015," CC, 22		700 __

		Exc	Mint
___	2233492	CN Veterans ES44AC Diesel "3233," CC, 22		700
___	2233499	CN Veterans ES44AC Diesel "3015" (unpowered), 22		400
___	2233501	U.S. Armed Forces ES44AC Diesel "1775," CC, 22		700
___	2233502	U.S. Armed Forces ES44AC Diesel "2022," CC, 22		700
___	2233511	BN EMD SD40-2 Diesel "1876," CC, 22		650
___	2233519	BN EMD SD40-2 Diesel "1876" (unpowered), 22		350
___	2233521	BN EMD SD40-2 Diesel "8002," CC, 22		650
___	2233529	BN EMD SD40-2 Diesel "8002" (unpowered), 22		350
___	2233531	Louisville & Indiana EMD SD40-2 Diesel "3001," CC, 22		650
___	2233539	Louisville & Indiana EMD SD40-2 "3001" (unpowered), 22		350
___	2233541	Maersk/Sealand EMD SD40-2 Diesel "3329," CC, 22		650
___	2233549	Maersk/Sealand EMD SD40-2 Diesel "3329" (unpowered), 22		350
___	2233551	Savage EMD SD40-2 Diesel "8638," CC, 22		700
___	2233559	Savage EMD SD40-2 Diesel "8638" (unpowered), 22		400
___	2233561	UP Desert Victory EMD SD40-2 Diesel "3593," CC, 22		700
___	2233569	UP Desert Victory EMD SD40-2 Diesel "3593" (unpowered), 22		400
___	2233570	B&LE EMD F7 A-B Set "722A/722B," CC, 22		1150
___	2233580	Aberdeen, Carolina & Western EMD F9 A-B Set "271/276," CC, 22		1150
___	2233590	Reading & Northern EMD F9 A-B Set "270/275," CC, 22		1150
___	2233601	CP Veterans EMD SD90MAC Diesel "7020," CC, 22		650
___	2233609	CP Veterans EMD SD90MAC Diesel "7020" (unpowered), 22		400
___	2233611	CP Veterans EMD SD90MAC Diesel "7021," CC, 22		650
___	2233619	CP Veterans EMD SD90MAC Diesel "7021" (unpowered), 22		400
___	2233621	CP Veterans EMD SD90MAC Diesel "7022," CC, 22		650
___	2233629	CP Veterans EMD SD90MAC Diesel "7022" (unpowered), 22		400
___	2233631	CP Veterans EMD SD90MAC Diesel "7023," CC, 22		650
___	2233639	CP Veterans EMD SD90MAC Diesel "7023" (unpowered), 22		400
___	2233641	CP Veterans EMD SD90MAC Diesel "6644," CC, 22		650
___	2233649	CP Veterans EMD SD90MAC Diesel "6644" (unpowered), 22		400
___	2233651	CP Heritage EMD SD90MAC Diesel "7010," CC, 22		650
___	2233652	CP Heritage EMD SD90MAC Diesel "7016," CC, 22		650
___	2233660	EMD Demonstrator SD90MAC Diesel "8204," CC, 22		650
___	2233671	NS (UP Patch) EMD SD90MAC Diesel "7240," CC, 22		650
___	2233672	NS (UP Patch) EMD SD90MAC Diesel "73140," CC, 22		650
___	2233681	San Luis & Rio Grande EMD SD90MAC Diesel "115," CC, 22		650
___	2233682	San Luis & Rio Grande EMD SD90MAC Diesel "116," CC, 22		650
___	2233711	Amtrak F40PH Diesel Phase III "206," CC, 22		630
___	2233712	Amtrak F40PH Diesel Phase III "226," CC, 22		630
___	2233721	Amtrak F40PH Diesel Phase IV "401," CC, 22		630
___	2233722	Amtrak F40PH Diesel Phase IV "404," CC, 22		630
___	2233730	Amtrak F40PH Diesel Phase V "410," CC, 22		630
___	2233740	Amtrak F40PH Diesel Veterans "208," CC, 22		630
___	2233751	CSX Business Train Diesel "CSX-1," CC, 22		630
___	2233752	CSX Business Train Diesel "CSX-2," CC, 22		630
___	2233753	CSX Business Train Diesel "CSX-3," CC, 22		630
___	2233761	D&RGW Ski Train Diesel "242," CC, 22		630
___	2233762	D&RGW Ski Train Diesel "283," CC, 22		630
___	2233770	Amtrak NPCU Phase IV Downeaster "90214" (dummy), 22		500
___	2233780	Amtrak NPCU Diesel Phase IV "90229" (unpowered), 22		500
___	2233790	Amtrak NPCU Diesel Phase V "90413" (unpowered), 22		500
___	2233800	Amtrak NPCU Diesel Veterans "90208" (unpowered), 22		500
___	2233810	AT&SF EMD F7 A-A Set "341/344," CC, 22		1200

		Exc	Mint	
2233818	AT&SF EMD F7 B Unit "345A," CC, 22		600	___
2233819	AT&SF EMD F7 B Unit SuperBass "348A" (unpowered), 22		550	___
2233820	LV EMD F7 A-A Set "562/566," CC, 22		1200	___
2233828	LV EMD F7 B Unit "519," CC, 22		600	___
2233829	LV EMD F7 B Unit SuperBass "521" (unpowered), 22		550	___
2233830	SOO EMD F7 A-A Set "2201A/2201B," CC, 22		1200	___
2233838	SOO EMD F7 B Unit "2201C," CC, 22		600	___
2233839	SOO EMD F7 B Unit SuperBass "2202C" (unpowered), 22		550	___
2233840	SP EMD F7 A-A Set "6475/6476," CC, 22		1200	___
2233848	SP EMD F7 B Unit "8375," CC, 22		600	___
2233849	SP EMD F7 B Unit SuperBass "8376" (unpowered), 22		550	___
2233850	UP EMD F7 A-A Set "1468/1469," CC, 22		1200	___
2233858	UP EMD F7 B Unit "1468B," CC, 22		600	___
2233859	UP EMD F7 B Unit SuperBass "1468C" (unpowered), 22		550	___
2234010	Amtrak Genesis Locomotive "100," LionChief Plus 2.0, 22		550	___
2234020	Amtrak Genesis Locomotive "108," LionChief Plus 2.0, 22		550	___
2234030	Amtrak Genesis Locomotive "160," LionChief Plus 2.0, 22		550	___
2234040	Amtrak Genesis Locomotive "161," LionChief Plus 2.0, 22		550	___
2234050	Amtrak Genesis Phase V "150," LionChief Plus 2.0, 22		550	___
2034060	Amtrak Genesis Phase 1V "111," LionChief Plus 2.0, 21-22		550	___
2234070	Amtrak Genesis Phase III "40," LionChief Plus 2.0, 21-22		550	___
2234080	Amtrak Genesis Locomotive Phase V 50th Anniversary "46," LionChief Plus 2.0, 21-22		550	___
2234090	PRR LionChief 44-Tonner Locomotive "8312," 22-23		250	___
2234100	ATSF LionChief 44-Tonner Locomotive "463," 22-23		250	___
2234110	Ford LionChief 44-Tonner Locomotive "1000," 22-23		250	___
2234120	U.S. Marine Corps LionChief 44-Tonner "234120," 22-23		250	___
2234130	Amtrak LionChief 44-Tonner Locomotive "1100," 22-23		250	___
2234140	ATSF EMD GP20 Diesel "3009," LionChief Plus 2.0, 22-23		500	___
2234150	MILW EMD GP20 Diesel "962," LionChief Plus 2.0, 22-23		500	___
2234160	Conrail EMD GP20 Diesel "2108," LionChief Plus 2.0, 22-23		500	___
2234170	BN EMD GP20 Diesel "2054," LionChief Plus 2.0, 22-23		500	___
2234180	BNSF LionChief Dash-8 Diesel, 22-23		280	___
2234190	NS LionChief Dash-8 Diesel, 22-23		280	___
2234200	CSX LionChief Dash-8 Diesel, 22-23		280	___
2234210	UP LionChief Dash-8 Diesel, 22-23		280	___
2234220	Amtrak Genesis Operation Lifesaver LionChief Plus 2.0, 22		550	___
2235010	Polar Express Trolley, 22-23		120	___
2235020	First Ave Rapid Transit Trolley, 22-23		120	___
2235030	Trippy Trolley, 22		140	___
2235040	AT&SF Doodlebug, LionChief Plus 2.0, 22		400	___
2235050	UP Doodlebug, LionChief Plus 2.0, 22		400	___
2235060	PRR Doodlebug, LionChief Plus 2.0, 22		400	___
2235070	Maryland & Pennsylvania Doodlebug, LionChief Plus 2.0, 22		400	___
2235080	Hallows Eve Limited Doodlebug, LionChief Plus 2.0, 22		400	___
2235090	North Pole Central Doodlebug, LionChief Plus 2.0, 22-23		400	___
2238010	UP 160th Anniversary Boxcar, 21-22		90	___
2238020	Great Locomotive Chase 160th Anniversary Boxcar, 21-22		90	___
2238030	Smithsonian 175th Anniversary Boxcar, 21		90	___
2238040	Rutherford B. Hayes Presidential Boxcar, 22		90	___
2238050	Grover Cleveland Presidential Boxcar, 22		90	___
2238060	Gerald Boxcar Presidential Boxcar, 22		90	___
2238070	2022 Birthday Personalized Boxcar, 22		100	___

		Exc	Mint
___	2238080	2022 Christmas Personalized Boxcar, 22		100
___	2238090	2022 Anniversary Personalized Boxcar, 22		100
___	2238100	World War II General Boxcar, 22-23		95
___	2238110	World War II Aircraft Carrier Boxcar, 22		90
___	2238120	Wings of Angels Sarah Boxcar, 22-23		95
___	2238130	Wings of Angels Lisa Boxcar, 22-23		95
___	2238140	Wings of Angels Raquel Boxcar, 22-23		95
___	2238150	GM Train of Tomorrow Boxcar, 22		90
___	2238160	Rockville Bridge Boxcar, 22		90
___	2238180	Bazooka Joe 75th Anniversary Boxcar, 22		90
___	2238210	MILW Anniversary Boxcar, 22		90
___	2238220	Chevrolet Personalized Boxcar , 22-23		100
___	2238230	Ford Personalized Boxcar, 22-23		100
___	2243010	BNSF Rotary Gondola 4-Pack (std O), 21		360
___	2243020	CSX Rotary Gondola 4-Pack (std O), 21		360
___	2243030	NS Rotary Gondola 4-Pack (std O), 21		360
___	2243040	PRR Rotary Gondola 4-Pack (std O), 21		360
___	2243050	UP Rotary Gondola 4-Pack (std O), 21		360
___	2243060	CSX Rotary Gondola 2-Pack (std O), 21		180
___	2243070	NS Rotary Gondola 2-Pack (std O), 21		180
___	2243080	PRR Rotary Gondola 2-Pack (std O), 21		180
___	2243090	UP Rotary Gondola 2-Pack (std O), 21		180
___	2243101	Ashley, Drew & Northern Modern Boxcar "8134" (std O), 21		60
___	2243102	Ashley, Drew & Northern Modern Boxcar 8145 (std O), 21-23		60
___	2243111	Conrail Modern Boxcar "166255" (std O), 21		60
___	2243112	Conrail Modern Boxcar "166422" (std O), 21		60
___	2243121	RI Modern Boxcar "300032" (std O), 21		60
___	2243122	RI Modern Boxcar "399370" (std O), 21		60
___	2243131	Railbox Modern Boxcar "30284" (std O), 21		60
___	2243132	Railbox Modern Boxcar "30306" (std O), 21		60
___	2243141	UP Modern Boxcar "357416" (std O), 21		60
___	2243142	UP Modern Boxcar "357429" (std O), 21		60
___	2243150	UP Rocket Idler Car 6-Pack, 22		375
___	2243160	B&LE Ore Car 6-Pack #1, 22		200
___	2243170	B&LE Ore Car 6-Pack #2, 22		200
___	2243180	BN Ore Car 6-Pack #1 (std O), 22		200
___	2243190	BN Ore Car 6-Pack #2 (std O), 22		200
___	2243200	C&NW Ore Car 6-Pack #1 (std O), 22		200
___	2243210	C&NW Ore Car 6-Pack #2 (std O), 22		200
___	2243220	DM&IR Ore Car 6-Pack #1 (std O), 22		200
___	2243230	DM&IR Ore Car 6-Pack #2 (std O), 22		200
___	2243240	SOO Ore Car 6-Pack #1 (std O), 22		200
___	2243250	SOO Ore Car 6-Pack #2 (std O), 22		200
___	2243260	UP Ore Car 6-Pack #1 (std O), 22		200
___	2243270	UP Ore Car 6-Pack #2 (std O), 22		200
___	2243281	SSW Insulated Boxcar "30043" (std O), 22		70
___	2243282	SSW Insulated Boxcar "30049" (std O), 22		70
___	2243291	NH State of Maine Insulated Boxcar "45022" (std O), 22		70
___	2243292	NH State of Maine Insulated Boxcar "45064" (std O), 22		70
___	2243301	NP Insulated Boxcar "98583" (std O), 22		70
___	2243302	NP Insulated Boxcar "98621" (std O), 22		70
___	2243311	WM Insulated Boxcar "7" (std O), 22		70
___	2243312	WM Insulated Boxcar "14" (std O), 22		70

		Exc	Mint
2301050	LCCA UP Vision 4-8-8-4 Big Boy Locomotive "4023," CC, 23		2900 ___
2322010	LV Legacy Camelback Steam Freight Set, CC, 23		1100 ___
2322020	WM Hagerstown Hotshot Diesel Freight Set, CC, 22		1600 ___
2322030	PRR Cumberland Valley Wayfreight Set, CC, 22		1500 ___
2322040	UP Vision Big Boy Steam Freight Set, CC, 23		4500 ___
2322050	PRR Iron Hippo Legacy Steam Freight Set, CC, 23		2300 ___
2322060	Union RR Hot Metal Diesel Freight Set, CC, 23		1300 ___
2322070	RI Quad Cities Rocket Legacy Diesel Passenger Set, CC, 23		1000 ___
2322080	ATSF Fast Fruit Express Legacy Steam Freight Set, CC, 23		2500 ___
2323030	ATSF Dash-8 Diesel Auto Rack Set, 22-23		550 ___
2323040	Disney 100 Years of Wonder LionChief Bluetooth 5.0 Steam Passenger Set, CC, 23		530 ___
2323050	Fast Fright Halloween LionChief Bluetooth 5.0 Diesel Freight Set, CC, 23		500 ___
2323060	NYC 2-8-0 LionChief Bluetooth 5.0 Freight Set, CC, 23		450 ___
2323070	Willy Wonka & the Chocolate Factory LionChief Bluetooth 5.0 Steam Freight Set, CC, 23		450 ___
2323080	Texas Special Passenger LionChief Bluetooth 5.0 Set, CC, 23		500 ___
2323090	UP Flyer LionChief Bluetooth 5.0 Steam Freight Set, CC, 23		400 ___
2323100	Winter Wonderland LionChief Bluetooth 5.0 Steam Freight Set, CC, 23		400 ___
2323110	ATSF Super Chief LionChief Bluetooth 5.0 Diesel Set, CC, 23		500 ___
2323130	Gold Mountain LionChief Bluetooth 5.0 Steam Set, CC, 23		470 ___
2325010	Polar Express Ice Track, 23		75 ___
2325030	FasTrack 3" Straight, 22-23		5 ___
2326010	UP Heritage C&NW TOFC Flatcar "231995," 22		150 ___
2326020	UP Heritage D&RGW TOFC Flatcar "231989," 22		150 ___
2326030	UP Heritage MKT TOFC Flatcar "231988," 22		150 ___
2326040	UP Heritage MP TOFC Flatcar "231982," 22		150 ___
2326050	UP Heritage SP TOFC Flatcar "231996," 22		150 ___
2326060	UP Heritage WP TOFC Flatcar "231983," 22		150 ___
2326070	BN 100-ton Hopper 2-pack A, 22		300 ___
2326078	BN 100-ton Hopper 2-pack B, 22		300 ___
2326079	BN 100-ton Hopper 2-pack C, 22		300 ___
2326080	Chessie (B&O) 100-ton Hopper 2-pack, 22		300 ___
2326088	Chessie (C&O) 100-ton Hopper 2-pack, 22		300 ___
2326089	Chessie (WM) 100-ton Hopper 2-pack, 22		300 ___
2326090	D&RGW 100-ton Hopper 2-pack (blue ends), 22		300 ___
2326098	D&RGW 100-ton Hopper 2-pack (white ends), 22		300 ___
2326099	D&RGW 100-ton Hopper 2-pack (blue/white ends), 22		300 ___
2326100	NS 100-ton Hopper 2-pack A, 22		300 ___
2326108	NS 100-ton Hopper 2-pack B, 22		300 ___
2326109	NS 100-ton Hopper 2-pack C, 22		300 ___
2326110	Reading 100-ton Hopper 2-pack A, 22		300 ___
2326118	Reading 100-ton Hopper 2-pack B, 22		300 ___
2326119	Reading 100-ton Hopper 2-pack C, 22		300 ___
2326120	SP 100-ton Hopper 2-pack A, 22		300 ___
2326128	SP 100-ton Hopper 2-pack B, 22		300 ___
2326129	SP 100-ton Hopper 2-pack C, 22		300 ___
2326130	John Deere 60-foot Boxcar "1837," 22		130 ___
2326140	Chevrolet 60-foot Boxcar "236140," 22		130 ___
2326150	Ford 60-foot Boxcar "236150," 22		300 ___
2326160	Reading & Northern 60-foot Boxcar "1998," 22		130 ___

		Exc	Mint
2326170	USMC 60-foot Boxcar "1591," 22		130
2326181	WCOR 60-foot boxcar "6510" 22		140
2326182	WCOR 60-foot Boxcar w/Graffiti "6521," 22		140
2326190	L&NE NE Caboose "583," 22		130
2326200	MC NE Caboose "662," 22		130
2326210	RI NE Caboose "17604," 22		130
2326220	USMC NE Caboose "601750," 22		130
2326230	SSW Hobo Boxcar "35209," 22		210
2326240	Frisco Hobo Boxcar "17350," 22		210
2326250	Ann Arbor Hobo Boxcar "1404," 22		210
2326260	Western of Alabama Hobo Boxcar "18252," 22		210
2326271	PRR N6b Cabin Car "980781," 22		120
2326272	PRR N6b Cabin Car "981530," 22		120
2326273	PRR N6b Cabin Car "492891," 22		120
2326280	C&O Wood Caboose "98076," 22		120
2326290	Strasburg RR Wood Caboose "12," 22		120
2326300	ATSF Vision Refrigerator Car w/RailSounds 3-pack, 23		500
2326310	FGE Vision Refrigerator Car w/RailSounds 3-pack, 23		500
2326320	GN Vision Refrigerator Car w/RailSounds 3-pack, 23		500
2326330	PFE Vision Refrigerator Car w/RailSounds 3-pack, 23		500
2326340	D&RGW Vision Stock Car w/RailSounds 3-pack, 23		500
2326350	PRR Vision Stock Car w/RailSounds 3-pack, 23		500
2326360	T&P Vision Stock Car w/RailSounds 3-pack, 23		500
2326370	UP Vision Stock Car w/RailSounds 3-pack, 23		500
2326380	CP 50-foot Flatcar "505571," w/Reimer Trailer, 23		160
2326390	MILW 50-foot Flatcar "57500," w/ICX Trailer, 23		160
2326400	TTX 50-foot Flatcar "475326," w/Budweiser Trailer, 23		170
2326410	John Deere 50-foot Flatcar "26410," w/Trailer, 23		170
2326420	Lionel 50-foot Flatcar "26420," w/Play World Trailer, 23		160
2326440	UP Vision CA-1 Caboose "2551," 23		300
2326450	UP Vision CA-1 Caboose "2527," 23		300
2326460	Buffalo Creek & Gauley GLA Hopper 2-pack, 23		200
2326470	Interstate GLA Hopper 2-pack, 23		200
2326480	PRR GLA Hopper 2-pack A, 23		200
2326490	PRR GLA Hopper 2-pack B, 23		200
2326500	Westmoreland Coal GLA Hopper 2-pack, 23		200
2326510	PRR N8 Cabin Car "478125," 23		150
2326520	PRR N8 Cabin Car "478172," 23		150
2326530	PRR N8 Cabin Car "478159," 23		150
2326540	PC N8 Cabin Car "4710," 23		150
2326550	Conrail N8 Cabin Car "23236," 23		150
2326560	Union RR Hot Metal Car "14," 23		200
2326570	Area 51 Scale Hot Metal Car "AF-57X," 23		200
2326580	Christmas Hot Chocolate Thermos Car, 23		200
2326590	Polar Express Hot Chocolate Thermos Car, 23		200
2326601	Ann Arbor PS-5 Gondola "2023," 23		120
2326602	Ann Arbor PS-5 Gondola "2058," 23		120
2326611	CN PS-5 Gondola "143035," 23		120
2326612	CN PS-5 Gondola "143211," 23		120
2326621	Conrail PS-5 Gondola "67014," 23		120
2326622	Conrail PS-5 Gondola "67435," 23		120
2326631	Erie PS-5 Gondola "10325," 23		120

		Exc	Mint
2326632	Erie PS-5 Gondola "10359," 23		120 ___
2326641	LV PS-5 Gondola "32953," 23		120 ___
2326642	LV PS-5 Gondola "33059," 23		120 ___
2326651	RI PS-5 Gondola "3050," 23		120 ___
2326652	RI PS-5 Gondola "3091," 23		120 ___
2326660	Christmas Bobber Caboose, 23		110 ___
2326670	C&NW Grain Boxcar "24154," 23		110 ___
2326680	M&StL Grain Boxcar "53150," 23		110 ___
2326690	Soo Grain Boxcar "44968," 23		110 ___
2326700	T&P Grain Boxcar "40814," 23		110 ___
2326710	UP Grain Boxcar "196861," 23		110 ___
2326720	Wabash Grain Boxcar "90090," 23		110 ___
2326770	PRR Vision N8 Cabin Car "478166," 23		300 ___
2326780	PRR Vision N8 Cabin Car "478044," 23		300 ___
2327010	C&O 18" Passenger Car 2-pack A, 22		500 ___
2327020	C&O 18" Passenger Car 2-pack B, 22		500 ___
2327030	C&O 18" Passenger Car 2-pack C, 22		500 ___
2327040	C&O 18" Diner w/StationSounds, 22		430 ___
2327050	The Chessie 21" Passenger Car 4-pack, 22		900 ___
2327060	The Chessie 21" Passenger Car 2-pack, 22		450 ___
2327070	The Chessie 21" Diner w/StationSounds "1971," 22		400 ___
2327080	Strasburg RR Coach (1970s) 2-pack A, 22		450 ___
2327090	Strasburg RR Coach (1970s) 2-pack B, 22		450 ___
2327100	Strasburg RR 18 Heavyweight "Pequea Valley" (brown), 22		250 ___
2327110	Strasburg RR 18 Heavyweight "Pequea Valley" (green), 22		250 ___
2327140	US Army 18" Passenger Car 2-pack A, 22		500 ___
2327150	US Army 18" Passenger Car 2-pack B, 22		500 ___
2327160	US Army 18" Passenger Car 2-pack C, 22		500 ___
2327170	US Army 18" Diner w/StationSounds, 22		430 ___
2327180	CN Wood Passenger Car 2-pack A, 22		450 ___
2327190	CN Wood Passenger Car 2-pack B, 22		450 ___
2327200	CN Wood Passenger Car 2-pack C, 22		450 ___
2327210	Strasburg RR 18" Heavyweight "Pequea Valley," (red), 22		250 ___
2327220	Strasburg RR 18" Heavyweight "Pequea Valley," (gray), 22		250 ___
2327230	Harry Potter "Slytherin" Coach, 23		90 ___
2327240	Harry Potter "Hufflepuff" Coach, 23		90 ___
2327250	Harry Potter "Ravenclaw" Coach, 23		90 ___
2327260	Harry Potter "Gryffindor" Coach, 23		90 ___
2327270	UP Excursion 21" Passenger Car 4-pack, 23		950 ___
2327280	UP Excursion 21" Passenger Car 2-pack, 23		450 ___
2327290	UP Diner w/StationSounds, 23		400 ___
2327300	Aberdeen, Carolina & Western Diner w/StationSounds 2-pack, 23		650 ___
2327310	NYC 20th Century Limited 21" Passenger Car 4-pack, 23		950 ___
2327320	NYC 20th Century Limited 21" Passenger Car 2-pack, 23		450 ___
2327330	NYC 20th Century Limited 21" Diner w/StationSounds 2-pack, 23		650 ___
2327340	North Pole Central 21" Passenger Car 4-pack, 23		950 ___
2327350	North Pole Central 21" Passenger Car 2-pack, 23		450 ___
2327360	North Pole Central 21" Diner w/StationSounds, 23		400 ___
2327370	Texas Special "Anson B. Jones," Add-on Baggage Car, 23		95 ___
2327380	Texas Special "Tulsa," Add-on Coach, 23		100 ___
2327390	Aberdeen, Carolina & Western Dome Car, 23		300 ___

MODERN 1970-2023

		Exc	Mint
___ 2328060	Gold Medal Flour Flatcar w/Milk Container, 22-23		70
___ 2328070	Lionelville Milk Flatcar w/Milk Container, 22-23		70
___ 2328080	Ferromex Auto Rack, 22-23		100
___ 2328090	Southern Auto Rack, 22-23		100
___ 2328100	DC Justice League Lexcorp Kryptonite Hopper, 23		110
___ 2328110	DC Justice League The Flash Mint Car, 23		120
___ 2328120	DC Justice League Wonder Woman Invisible Jet Flatcar, 23		60
___ 2328130	DC Justice League Wayne Enterprises Transport Car, 23		90
___ 2328140	John Deere Tractor Co. Refrigerator Car, 23		90
___ 2328150	John Deere Flatcar "28230," w/Combine, 23		100
___ 2328160	Disney 100 Illuminated Boxcar, 23		150
___ 2328180	Pennywise Peekaboo Car, 23		100
___ 2328190	Exorcist Floating Regan Car, 23		120
___ 2328220	Anheuser-Busch Budweiser Clydesdale Refrigerator Car, 23		90
___ 2328230	Anheuser-Busch Budweiser Military Heritage Refrigerator Car, 23		90
___ 2328240	2023 Christmas Boxcar, 23		85
___ 2328250	Christmas Music Car, 23		150
___ 2328260	Santa's Choice Milk Flatcar w/Milk Carton, 23		70
___ 2328270	Christmas Tree Flatcar, 23		100
___ 2328280	Polar Express Sleigh Bells Mint Car, 23		90
___ 2328290	Polar Express Flatcar w/Hot Chocolate Container, 23		75
___ 2328300	Angela Trotta Thomas Texas Special Boxcar, 23		85
___ 2328310	Angela Trotta Thomas General Boxcar, 23		85
___ 2328320	TTX Maxi Stack w/Container, 23		100
___ 2328330	BNSF Maxi Stack w/Container, 23		100
___ 2328340	Halloween Graffiti Maxi Stack w/Container, 23		100
___ 2328350	Christmas Graffiti Maxi Stack w/Container, 23		100
___ 2328360	Dr. Acula Blood Tonic 1-D Tank Car, 23		100
___ 2328370	Spooky Sounds Illuminated Boxcar, 23		150
___ 2328380	DC Justice League Boxcar, 23		85
___ 2328410	Willy Wonka 1-D Tank Car, 23		100
___ 2328420	Disney 100 Mickey Mouse Vault Moments Boxcar, 23		90
___ 2328430	Disney 100 Minnie Mouse Vault Moments Boxcar, 23		90
___ 2328440	Disney 100 Goofy Vault Moments Boxcar, 23		90
___ 2328450	Disney 100 Donald Duck Vault Moments Boxcar, 23		90
___ 2328460	Christmas Olde Tyme Rolling Stock 3-pack, 23		220
___ 2328470	Gold Mountain 1-D Tank Car, 23		100
___ 2328480	NYC Pacemaker Merchandise Boxcar, 23		120
___ 2328490	Wonka Bar Golden Ticket Boxcar, 23		90
___ 2329010	Roadside Diner, 22-23		150
___ 2329020	Christmas Roadside Diner, 23		160
___ 2329030	Polar Express Illuminated Covered Bridge, 23		80
___ 2329050	Billups Crossing Gate, 22-23		200
___ 2329060	Amtrak Passenger Station, 22-23		170
___ 2329070	Carnival Treats Stand, 22-23		160
___ 2329080	St. Nick's Nog Shoppe Driver-In Diner, 23		400
___ 2329090	Area 51 Drive-In Diner, 23		400
___ 2329100	Franks & Stein's Bar & Ghoul, 23		130
___ 2329110	Roscoe Flattz Automotive & Tire Store, 22-23		130
___ 2329130	Cowen's Family Creamery NE Caboose w/Deck, 22-23		200
___ 2329140	Grandpa's Workshop w/Sounds, 22-23		130
___ 2329150	She Shed w/Sounds, 22-23		130

		Exc	Mint
2329160	Santa's Workshop w/Sounds, 23		130
2329170	Hot Cocoa NE Caboose w/Deck, 23		200
2329190	Disney Christmas Station Platform, 23		55
2329200	Frankenstein's Monster Gateman, 23		130
2329230	Area 51 Hazardous Materials Barrel Loader, 23		80
2329240	Warner Bros. 100th Anniversary Water Tower, 23		90
2329250	John Deere Nothing Runs Like a Deere Flagpole, 23		45
2329270	Prankster Flagpole, 23		45
2329280	Willy Wonka Wonka Bar Packaging Facility, 23		270
2329300	Patriots Salute Gateman, 23		130
2329340	Lionel Theatre, 23		130
2329350	Warner Bros. 100th Anniversary Theatre, 23		130
2329360	Disney 100 Theatre, 23		130
2330010	Unique Road Signs Pack 2, 22-23		9
2330020	Ford Billboard 3-pack, 22-23		25
2330030	Chevrolet Billboard 3-pack, 22-23		25
2330040	Area 51 Glow in the Dark Haz-Mat Barrels, 23		13
2330050	Midway Games 3-pack and Figures, 22-23		120
2330060	Thomas & Friends Billboard Pack, 23		25
2330080	Warner Bros. Classic Movie Billboard Pack, 23		25
2330110	Budweiser Brew Hut, 23		45
2330120	Lionel Ale Quonset Hut, 23		45
2330140	Dasher's Buy and Fly Quonset Hut, 23		45
2330160	Winter Wonderland Scented Smoke Fluid, 23		9
2330170	American Summer Scented Smoke Fluid, 23		9
2330180	Happy Birthday Scented Smoke Fluid, 23		9
2330190	Vanilla Bourbon Scented Smoke Fluid, 23		9
2330200	Maple Syrup Scented Smoke Fluid, 23		9
2330210	Bay Leaf and Tobacco Scented Smoke Fluid, 23		9
2331011	PRR 2-8-2 Mikado L1 Locomotive "496," CC, 22		950
2331012	PRR 2-8-2 Mikado L1 Locomotive "4030," CC, 22		950
2331021	PRR 2-8-2 Mikado L1 Locomotive "1343," CC, 22		950
2331022	PRR 2-8-2 Mikado L1 Locomotive "1627," CC, 22		950
2331030	PRR 2-8-2 Mikado L1 Locomotive "1369," CC, 22		950
2331040	ATSF 2-8-2 Mikado L1 Locomotive "882," CC, 22		1000
2331050	DT&I 2-8-2 Mikado L1 Locomotive "496," CC, 22		950
2331060	L&NE 2-8-2 Mikado L1 Locomotive "501," CC, 22		950
2331070	C&O 4-8-4 Greenbrier Locomotive "614," CC, 22		1700
2331080	C&O 4-8-4 Greenbrier Locomotive "611," CC, 22		1700
2331090	C&O 4-8-4 Greenbrier Locomotive "613," CC, 22		1700
2331100	C&O 4-8-4 Greenbrier Locomotive "612," CC, 22		1700
2331110	Chessie System 4-8-4 Greenbrier Locomotive "614," CC, 22		1700
2331120	Family Lines 4-8-4 Greenbrier Locomotive "614," CC, 22		1700
2331130	CN 2-6-0 Mogul Locomotive "89," CC, 22		800
2331140	Middletown & Hummelstown 2-6-0 Mogul "91," CC, 22		800
2331150	San Luis & Rio Grande 2-6-0 Mogul Locomotive "89," CC, 22		800
2331160	SP 2-6-0 Mogul Locomotive "1760," CC, 22		800
2331170	Strasburg RR 2-6-0 Mogul Locomotive "89," (1970s) CC, 22		800
2331180	Strasburg RR 2-6-0 Mogul Locomotive "89," (2000s), CC, 22		800
2331191	UP Brass Hybrid 4-6-6-4 Challenger Locomotive "3819," CC, 22		2500
2331192	UP Brass Hybrid 4-6-6-4 Challenger "3826," CC, 22		2500
2331193	UP Brass Hybrid 4-6-6-4 Challenger Locomotive, Unnumbered Style 1, CC, 22		2500

		Exc	Mint
___ 2331200	UP Brass Hybrid 4-6-6-4 Challenger Locomotive Pilot, CC, 22		2500
___ 2331211	UP Brass Hybrid 4-6-6-4 Challenger "3836," CC, 22		2500
___ 2331212	UP Brass Hybrid 4-6-6-4 Challenger "3839," CC, 22		2500
2331213	UP Brass Hybrid 4-6-6-4 Challenger Locomotive, Unnumbered, Style 2, CC, 22		2500
___ 2331220	UP Brass Hybrid 4-6-6-4 Challenger Locomotive "3835," (Challenger scheme), CC, 22		2500
___ 2331231	UP Brass Hybrid 4-6-6-4 Challenger "3815," CC, 22		2500
___ 2331232	UP Brass Hybrid 4-6-6-4 Challenger "3828," CC, 22		2500
___ 2331233	UP Brass Hybrid 4-6-6-4 Challenger Locomotive, Unnumbered, Style 3, CC, 22		2500
___ 2331250	UP Vision 4-8-8-4 Big Boy Oil-Burning "4014," CC, 23		2800
___ 2331261	UP Vision 4-8-8-4 Big Boy Locomotive "4000," CC, 23		2900
___ 2331262	UP Vision 4-8-8-4 Big Boy Locomotive "4002," CC, 23		2900
___ 2331263	UP Vision 4-8-8-4 Big Boy Locomotive "4012," CC, 23		2900
___ 2331264	UP Vision 4-8-8-4 Big Boy Locomotive "4014," CC, 23		2900
___ 2331270	UP Vision 4-8-8-4 Big Boy Locomotive "4019," CC, 23		2900
___ 2331280	UP Vision 4-8-8-4 Big Boy Locomotive "4021," CC, 23		2900
___ 2331290	UP Vision 4-8-8-4 Big Boy Locomotive "4024," CC, 23		2900
___ 2331300	Erie Russian 2-10-0 Decapod Locomotive "2445," CC, 23		1300
___ 2331310	Frisco Russian 2-10-0 Decapod Locomotive "1630," CC, 23		1300
___ 2333120	Minneapolis, Northfield & Southern Russian 2-10-0 Decapod Locomotive "505," CC, 23		1300
2331330	Philadelphia & Reading Russian 2-10-0 Decapod Locomotive "1162," CC, 23		1300
___ 2331340	SAL Russian 2-10-0 Decapod Locomotive "544," CC, 23		1300
___ 2331350	USA Russian 2-10-0 Decapod Locomotive "1918," CC, 23		1300
___ 2331361	PRR I1 2-10-0 Decapod Locomotive "531," CC, 23		1500
___ 2331362	PRR I1 2-10-0 Decapod Locomotive "4250," CC, 23		1500
___ 2331371	PRR I1 2-10-0 Decapod Locomotive "4241," CC, 23		1500
___ 2331372	PRR I1 2-10-0 Decapod Locomotive "4652," CC, 23		1500
___ 2331381	PRR I1 2-10-0 Decapod Locomotive "4262," CC, 23		1500
___ 2331382	PRR I1 2-10-0 Decapod Locomotive "4521," CC, 23		1500
___ 2331391	PRR I1 2-10-0 Decapod Locomotive "4258," CC, 23		1500
___ 2331392	PRR I1 2-10-0 Decapod Locomotive "4325," CC, 23		1500
___ 2331401	NYC Dreyfuss J3 4-6-4 Hudson Locomotive "5449," CC, 23		1700
___ 2331402	NYC Dreyfuss J3 4-6-4 Hudson Locomotive "5452," CC, 23		1700
___ 2331411	NYC Dreyfuss J3 4-6-4 Hudson Locomotive "5445," CC, 23		1800
___ 2331412	NYC Dreyfuss J3 4-6-4 Hudson Locomotive "5447," CC, 23		1800
___ 2331420	NYC Dreyfuss J3 4-6-4 Hudson Locomotive "5445," w/short tender, CC, 23		1700
___ 2331430	NYC Dreyfuss J3 4-6-4 Hudson Locomotive "5454," CC, 23		1800
___ 2331451	ATSF 4-8-4 Northern Locomotive "2903," CC, 23		1800
___ 2331452	ATSF 4-8-4 Northern Locomotive "2912," CC, 23		1800
___ 2331453	ATSF 4-8-4 Northern Locomotive "2926," CC, 23		1800
___ 2331460	ATSF 4-8-4 Northern Locomotive Blue Goose "2900," CC, 23		1800
___ 2331470	ATSF 4-8-4 Northern Locomotive Warbonnet "2901," CC, 23		1800
___ 2331480	ATSF 4-8-4 Northern Locomotive Restoration "2926," CC, 23		1800
___ 2331540	Fezziwig RR Legacy 4-6-0 Camelback "1225," CC, 23		700
___ 2331550	DL&W 4-6-0 Camelback Locomotive "1052," CC, 23		700
___ 2331560	Erie 4-6-0 Camelback Locomotive "918," CC, 23		700
___ 2331570	L&NE 4-6-0 Camelback Locomotive "151," CC, 23		700
___ 2331580	Atlantic City RR 4-6-0 Camelback Locomotive "610," CC, 23		700
___ 2331590	PRR 4-6-0 Camelback Locomotive "824," CC, 23		700

	Exc	Mint
2332010 Reading 0-6-0T "1251," LionChief Plus 2.0, 22-23		350 ___
2332020 Alaska 0-6-0T Locomotive "1," LionChief Plus 2.0, 22-23		350 ___
2332030 Lehigh Valley Coal 0-6-0T "126," LionChief Plus 2.0, 22-23		350 ___
2332040 NH 0-6-0T Locomotive "2305," LionChief Plus 2.0, 22-23		350 ___
2335050 Halloween 2-8-2 Mikado "1031," LionChief Plus 2.0, 23		700 ___
2332060 CB&Q 2-8-2 Mikado Locomotive "4978," LionChief Plus 2.0, 23		700 ___
2332070 MILW 2-8-2 Mikado Locomotive "753," LionChief Plus 2.0, 23		700 ___
2332080 UP 2-8-2 Mikado Locomotive "2549," LionChief Plus 2.0, 23		700 ___
2332090 PRR 2-8-2 Mikado Locomotive "9631," LionChief Plus 2.0, 23		700 ___
2332100 NKP 2-10-0 Consolidation Locomotive "455," LionChief, 23		330 ___
2332110 WM 2-10-0 Consolidation Locomotive "754," LionChief, 23		330 ___
2332120 ATSF 2-10-0 Consolidation Locomotive "2517," LionChief, 23		330 ___
2332130 C&O 2-10-0 Consolidation Locomotive "752," LionChief, 23		330 ___
2333040 SP Alco FA-2 AA set "802A/802D," CC, 22		1100 ___
2333050 USMC Alco FA-2 AA set "212/213," CC, 22		1100 ___
2333080 D&H Alco FA-2 AA set "20/21," CC, 22		1100 ___
2333088 D&H Alco FB-2 "20B," CC, 22		550 ___
2333089 D&H Alco FB-2 SuperBass "21B," 22		500 ___
2333090 EL Alco FA-2 AA set "7371/7374," CC, 22		1100 ___
2333098 EL Alco FB-2 "7382," CC, 22		550 ___
2333099 EL Alco FB-2 SuperBass "7383," 22		500 ___
2333100 Halloween Alco FA-2 AA set "1030A/1031A," CC, 22		1100 ___
2333108 Halloween Alco FB-2 "1030B," CC, 22		550 ___
2333109 Halloween Alco FB-2 SuperBass "1031B," 22		500 ___
2333110 L&N Alco FA-2 AA set "311/314," CC, 22		1100 ___
2333118 L&N Alco FB-2 "392," CC, 22		550 ___
2333119 L&N Alco FB-2 SuperBass "394," 22		500 ___
2333120 NYC Alco FA-2 AA set "1175/1176," CC, 22		1100 ___
2333128 NYC Alco FB-2 "3375," CC, 22		550 ___
2333129 NYC Alco FB-2 SuperBass "3376," 22		500 ___
2333130 PRR Alco FA-2 AA set "5760A/5762A," CC, 22		1100 ___
2333138 PRR Alco FB-2 "5760B," CC, 22		550 ___
2333139 PRR Alco FB-2 SuperBass "5762B," 22		500 ___
2333148 SP Alco FB-2 "802B," CC, 22		550 ___
2333149 SP Alco FB-2 SuperBass "802C," 22		500 ___
2333158 USMC Alco FB-2 "212B," CC, 22		550 ___
2333159 USMC Alco FB-2 SuperBass "213B," 22		500 ___
2333160 Montana Rail Link Essential Workers EMD SD70ACe "4404," CC, 22		650 ___
2333170 Montana Rail Link Veterans EMD SD70ACe "4407," CC, 22		650 ___
2333180 PRLX EMD SD70ACe "4834," CC, 22		650 ___
2333190 UP C&NW Heritage EMD SD70ACe "1995," CC, 22		650 ___
2333200 UP D&RGW Heritage EMD SD70ACe "1989," CC, 22		650 ___
2333210 UP MKT Heritage EMD SD70ACe "1988," CC, 22		650 ___
2333220 UP MP Heritage EMD SD70ACe "1982," CC, 22		650 ___
2333230 UP SP Heritage EMD SD70ACe "1996," CC, 22		650 ___
2333240 UP WP Heritage EMD SD70ACe "1983," CC, 22		650 ___
2333251 Central of Georgia FM H-15-44 Diesel "101," CC, 22		600 ___
2333252 Central of Georgia FM H-15-44 Diesel "102," CC, 22		600 ___
2333261 CRI&P FM H-15-44 Diesel "400," CC, 22		600 ___
2333262 CRI&P FM H-15-44 Diesel "401," CC, 22		600 ___
2333271 D&RGW FM H-15-44 Diesel "151," CC, 22		600 ___
2333272 D&RGW FM H-15-44 Diesel "152," CC, 22		600 ___

		Exc	Mint
___ 2333281	KCS FM H-15-44 Diesel "40," CC, 22		600
___ 2333282	KCS FM H-15-44 Diesel "41," CC, 22		600
___ 2333291	Monon FM H-15-44 Diesel "36," CC, 22		600
___ 2333292	Monon FM H-15-44 Diesel "37," CC, 22		600
___ 2333301	UP FM H-15-44 Diesel "1325," CC, 22		600
___ 2333302	UP FM H-15-44 Diesel "1329," CC, 22		600
___ 2333310	Aberdeen, Carolina & Western EMD E8 AA set, CC, 23		1200
___ 2333320	North Pole Central EMD E8 AA set, CC, 23		1200
___ 2333330	Amtrak EMD E8/E9 AA set "410/422," CC, 23		1200
___ 2333340	NYC EMD E8/E9 AA set "4053/4083," CC, 23		1200
___ 2333350	Southern EMD E8/E9 AA set "2923/2925," CC, 23		1200
___ 2333360	SP EMD E8/E9 AA set "6051/6053," CC, 23		1200
___ 2333371	ATSF EMD SD40T-2 "5215," CC, 22		650
___ 2333372	EMD SD40T-2 "5226," CC, 22		650
___ 2333379	ATSF EMD SD40T-2 SuperBass "5238," 22		600
___ 2333381	SP EMD SD40T-2 "8524," CC, 22		650
___ 2333382	SP EMD SD40T-2 "8533," CC, 22		650
___ 2333389	SP EMD SD40T-2 SuperBass "8548," 22		600
___ 2333391	SP EMD SD40T-2 Kodachrome "8286," CC, 22		650
___ 2333392	SP EMD SD40T-2 Kodachrome "8530," CC, 22		650
___ 2333399	SP EMD SD40T-2 SuperBass Kodachrome "8573," 22		600
___ 2333401	NYS&W EMD SD40T-2 "3010," CC, 22		650
___ 2333402	NYS&W EMD SD40T-2 "3012," CC, 22		650
___ 2333409	NYS&W EMD SD40T-2 SuperBass "3016," 22		600
___ 2333411	SP EMD SD40T-2 Black Widow "8520," CC, 22		650
___ 2333412	SP EMD SD40T-2 Black Widow "8525," CC, 22		650
___ 2333419	SP EMD SD40T-2 SuperBass Black Widow "8529," 22		600
___ 2333421	WP EMD SD40T-2 "8625," CC, 22		650
___ 2333422	WP EMD SD40T-2 "8794," CC, 22		650
___ 2333429	WP EMD SD40T-2 SuperBass "8864," 22		600
___ 2333431	BN GE ES44AC "9800," CC, 23		750
___ 2333432	BN GE ES44AC "9810," CC, 23		750
___ 2333439	BN GE ES44AC SuperBass "9819," 23		550
___ 2333441	BNSF GE ES44AC "5555," CC, 23		750
___ 2333442	BNSF GE ES44AC "5570," CC, 23		750
___ 2333449	BNSF GE ES44AC SuperBass "5586," 23		550
___ 2333451	C&NW GE ES44AC "8836," CC, 23		750
___ 2333452	C&NW GE ES44AC "8842," CC, 23		750
___ 2333459	C&NW GE ES44AC SuperBass "8850," 23		550
___ 2333461	Conrail GE ES44AC "4145," CC, 23		750
___ 2333462	Conrail GE ES44AC "4152," CC, 23		750
___ 2333469	Conrail GE ES44AC SuperBass "4163," 23		550
___ 2333471	KCS GE ES44AC "4859," CC, 23		750
___ 2333479	KCS non-powered GE ES44AC "4859," CC, 23		400
___ 2333481	KCS GE ES44AC "4674," CC, 23		750
___ 2333489	KCS non-powered GE ES44AC "4674," CC, 23		400
___ 2333490	BN EMD NW2 Switcher "497," CC, 23		600
___ 2333500	C&O EMD NW2 Switcher "5067," CC, 23		600
___ 2333510	Detroit Terminal EMD NW2 Switcher "115," CC, 23		600
___ 2333520	GN EMD NW2 Switcher "161," CC, 23		600
___ 2333530	Indiana Harbor Belt EMD NW2 Switcher "8827," CC, 23		600
___ 2333540	LV EMD NW2 Switcher "186," CC, 23		600
___ 2333551	ATSF EMD GP20 Diesel "1106," CC, 23		650

		Exc	Mint
2333552	ATSF EMD GP20 Diesel "1171," CC, 23		650
2333561	CB&Q EMD GP20 Diesel "907," CC, 23		650
2333562	CB&Q EMD GP20 Diesel "915," CC, 23		650
2333571	Kyle RR EMD GP20 Diesel "2035," CC, 23		650
2333572	Kyle RR EMD GP20 Diesel "2039," CC, 23		650
2333581	PC EMD GP20 Diesel "2108," CC, 23		650
2333582	PC EMD GP20 Diesel "2109," CC, 23		650
2333591	SSW EMD GP20 Diesel "801," CC, 23		650
2333592	SSW EMD GP20 Diesel "815," CC, 23		650
2333600	KC Terminal EMD GP20 Diesel "WAMX 2005," CC, 23		650
2334010	ATSF EMD NW2 Diesel "2404," CC, 22-23		450
2334020	NYC EMD NW2 Diesel "622," CC, 22-23		450
2334030	GN EMD NW2 Diesel "162," CC, 22-23		450
2334040	SAL EMD NW2 Diesel "1410," CC, 22-23		450
2334050	CN GE ERT44AC Diesel "3810," CC, 23		400
2334060	KCS GE ERT44AC Diesel "5002," CC, 23		400
2334070	BNSF GE ERT44AC Diesel "6337," CC, 23		400
2334080	NS GE ERT44AC Diesel "3657," CC, 23		400
2334090	ATSF EMD FT Diesel "127," CC, 23		300
2334100	NYC EMD FT Diesel "1687," CC, 23		300
2334110	PRR EMD FT Diesel "5888," CC, 23		300
2334120	North Pole Central EMD FT Diesel "1225," CC, 23		300
2335010	MOW TMCC Rail Bonder "M-4," CC, 23		150
2335020	NH TMCC Rail Bonder "18," CC, 23		150
2335030	PE TMCC Rail Bonder "1202," CC, 23		150
2335040	LIRR TMCC Rail Bonder "35040," CC, 23		150
2335050	North Pole Central TMCC Rail Bonder "1225," CC, 23		150
2335060	Angela Trotta Thomas Trolley, 23		120
2335070	Alaska Budd RDC Unit 2-pack "702/712," CC, 23		600
2335080	B&O Budd RDC Unit 2-pack "9902/9917," CC, 23		600
2335090	NH Budd RDC Unit 2-pack "120/42," CC, 23		600
2335100	SP Budd RDC Unit 2-pack "SP-9/SP-11," CC, 23		600
2335110	Polar Express Budd RDC Unit 2-pack "1225/25," CC, 23		600
2335120	Alaska Budd RDC Unit "711," CC, 23		400
2335130	B&O Budd RDC Unit "9918," CC, 23		400
2335140	NH Budd RDC Unit "41," CC, 23		400
2335150	SP Budd RDC Unit "SP-10," CC, 23		400
2335160	Polar Express Budd RDC Unit "24," CC, 23		400
2335190	Disney's Mickey Mouse and Minnie Mouse Handcar, red, 23		200
2338010	Chicago Railroad Fair Boxcar, 22		90
2338030	Millard Fillmore Presidential Boxcar, 23		90
2338040	Zachary Taylor Presidential Boxcar, 23		90
2338050	John Tyler Presidential Boxcar, 23		90
2338060	Chessie System 50th Anniversary Boxcar, 23		90
2338070	Santa Fe Super Chief Anniversary Boxcar, 23		95
2338080	Battle of Midway Boxcar, 23		95
2338100	Personalized Family Boxcar, 23		100
2338110	2023 Happy Birthday Boxcar, 23		100
2338120	2023 Merry Christmas Boxcar, 23		100
2338130	2023 Happy Anniversary Boxcar, 23		100
2338140	Wings of America Ariella Boxcar, 23		95
2338150	Wings of America Jen Boxcar, 23		95
2338160	Wings of America Sarah Boxcar, 2, 23		95

		Exc	Mint
____ 2338170	Happy Birthday Caboose, 23		90
____ 2338180	Merry Christmas Caboose, 23		90
____ 2338200	Disney 100 Celebration Personalized Boxcar, 23		100
____ 2338210	James Webb Space Telescope Boxcar, 23		90
____ 2343011	Reading & Northern Unibody 1-D Tank Car "101275," (std O), 22		75
____ 2343012	Reading & Northern Unibody 1-D Tank Car "2382," (std O), 22		75
____ 2343021	US Army Unibody 1-D Tank Car "18599," (std O), 22		75
____ 2343022	US Army Unibody 1-D Tank Car "18601," (std O), 22		75
____ 2343031	Cargill Unibody 1-D Tank Car "6274," (std O), 22		75
____ 2343032	Cargill Unibody 1-D Tank Car "6281," (std O), 22		75
____ 2343041	GATX Unibody 1-D Tank Car "2658," w/Graffiti (std O), 22		75
____ 2343042	GATX Unibody 1-D Tank Car "2696," w/Graffiti (std O), 22		75
____ 2343051	Procor Unibody 1-D Tank Car "28030," (std O), 22		75
____ 2343052	Procor Unibody 1-D Tank Car "28040," (std O), 22		75
____ 2343061	BN Centerbeam Flatcar "624189," (std O), 23		65
____ 2343062	BN Centerbeam Flatcar "624220," (std O), 23		65
____ 2343071	CSX Centerbeam Flatcar "600700," (std O), 23		65
____ 2343072	CSX Centerbeam Flatcar "600712," (std O), 23		65
____ 2343081	NS Centerbeam Flatcar "120112," (std O), 23		65
____ 2343082	NS Centerbeam Flatcar "120231," (std O), 23		65
____ 2343091	TTX Centerbeam Flatcar "83519," (std O), 23		65
____ 2343092	TTX Centerbeam Flatcar "83593," (std O), 23		65
____ 2343101	WCRC Centerbeam Flatcar "7319," (std O), 23		65
____ 2343102	WCRC Centerbeam Flatcar "7540," (std O), 23		65
____ 79C95204C	Sears Santa Fe Diesel Freight Set, 71 u	150	165
____ 79C9715C	Sears 4-unit Diesel Freight Set, 75 u	50	65
____ 79C9717C	Sears 7-unit Steam Freight Set, 75 u	150	165
____ 79N95223C	Sears 6-unit Diesel Freight Set, 74 u	150	165
____ 79N9552C	Sears 6-unit Steam Freight Set, 72 u	150	165
____ 79N9553C	Sears 6-unit Diesel Freight Set, 72 u	150	165
____ 79N96178C	Sears 4-unit Steam Freight Set, 74 u	50	65
____ 79N97082C	Sears Steam Freight Set, 70 u		NRS
____ 79N97101C	Sears 5-unit Steam Freight Set, 72 u	150	165
____ 79N98765C	Sears Logging Empire Set, 78 u	100	115

Unnumbered Items

		Exc	Mint
	Amtrak Passenger Car Set, 89, 89 u	640	770
	Baltimore & Ohio Set, 94, 96		NRS
	Black Cave Flyer Playmat, 82		8
	Blue Comet Set, 78-80, 87 u	560	620
	Boston & Albany Hudson and Standard O Car Set, 86 u	1500	1700
	Burlington Texas Zephyr Set, 80, 80 u	980	1150
	Cannonball Freight Playmat, 81-82		8
	Chesapeake & Ohio Set, 95-96		NRS
	Chessie System Special Set, 80, 86 u	560	620
	Chicago & Alton Limited Set, 81, 86 u	560	620
	Chicago & North Western Passenger Car Set, 93	385	460
	Commando Assault Train Playmat, 83-84		8
	D&RGW California Zephyr Set, 92, 93		900
	Erie Set (FF 7), 93	385	460
	Erie-Lackawanna Passenger Car Set, 93, 94	940	980
	Favorite Food Freight Set, 81-82	255	355
	Frisco Set (FF 5), 91	405	425
	General Set, 77-80	240	285

	Exc	Mint	
Great Northern Empire Builder Set, 92, 93	620	730	___
Great Northern Set (FARR 3), 81, 81 u	620	690	___
Illinois Central City of New Orleans Set, 85, 87, 93	885	1045	___
Illinois Central Set, 91-92, 95	255	285	___
Jersey Central Set, 86	345	370	___
Joshua Lionel Cowen Set, 80, 80 u, 82	540	580	___
L.A.S.E.R. Playmat, 81-82		8	___
Lionel Lines Madison Car Set, 91, 93	560	620	___
Lionel Lines Set, 82, 84 u, 86, 86 u, 87 u, 94-95	530	620	___
Mickey Mouse Express Set, 77-78, 78 u	1050	1800	___
Milwaukee Road Set (FF 2), 87, 90 u	380	405	___
Mint Set, 79 u, 80-83, 84 u, 86 u, 87, 91 u, 93	940	1073	___
Missouri Pacific Set, 95		390	___
NASCAR Dale Earnhardt Steam Freight Set (TX328RRGMDE), 12-14		300	___
NASCAR Dale Earnhardt Jr. Steam Freight Set (T8828TRAIN), 12-14		300	___
NASCAR Jeff Gordon Steam Freight Set (T2428RRDUJG), 12-14		300	___
NASCAR Jimmy Johnson Steam Freight Set (T4828RRLOJJ), 12-14		300	___
NASCAR Kyle Busch Steam Freight Set (T1828RRMMKB), 12-14		300	___
NASCAR Tony Stewart Steam Freight Set (T1428R-RODTS), 12-14		300	___
New Haven Set, 94-95		400	___
New York Central Set, 89, 91	240	270	___
New York Central 20th Century Limited Set, 83, 83 u, 95	1000	1200	___
Nickel Plate Road Set (FF 6), 92	385	460	___
Norfolk & Western Powhatan Arrow Set, 81, 81 u, 82 u, 91 u	1450	1700	___
Norfolk & Western Powhatan Arrow Passenger Car Set, 95	370	445	___
Northern Pacific Set, 90-92	190	250	___
Pennsylvania Set, 79-80, 79 u, 80 u 81 u, 83 u	1200	1350	___
Pennsylvania Set (FARR 5), 84-85, 89 u	600	660	___
Pennsylvania Set, 87-90, 95	240	270	___
Pere Marquette Set, 93	720	770	___
Rock Island & Peoria Set, 80-82	240	315	___
Rocky Mountain Platform, 83-84		8	___
Santa Fe Set (FARR 1), 79, 79 u	460	580	___
Santa Fe Super Chief Set, 91, 91 u, 92 u, 93, 95	1400	1700	___
Southern Pacific Daylight Diesel Set, 82-83, 82-83 u, 90 u	2150	2300	___
Southern Pacific Daylight Steam Set, 90, 92-93	790	940	___
Southern Ry. Crescent Limited Set, 77-78, 87 u	540	650	___
Southern Ry. Set (FARR 4), 83, 83 u	620	690	___
Spirit of '76 Set, 74-76	600	720	___
Station Platform, 83-84		8	___
Toys 'R' Us Thunderball Freight Set, 75 u		NRS	___
UCS Remote Control Track Section, 70	4	7	___
Union Pacific Overland Route Set, 84, 92 u	770	840	___
Union Pacific Set (FARR 2), 80, 80 u	540	580	___
Union Pacific Set, 94	430	500	___
Wabash Set (FF 1), 86, 87	755	905	___
Western Maryland Set (FF 4), 89	345	405	___

NOTES

NOTES

Section 4
LIONEL CORPORATION TINPLATE

		Exc	Mint
___ 11-1001	No. 400E Locomotive, black, brass trim (std)		900
___ 11-1002	No. 400E Locomotive, gray, nickel trim (std)		900
___ 11-1003	No. 400E Locomotive, gray, brass trim (std)		900
___ 11-1005	No. 390 Locomotive, green (std)		600
___ 11-1006	No. 400E Locomotive, crackle black, brass trim (std)		900
___ 11-1008	No. 400E Locomotive, Lionel Lines (std)		900
___ 11-1009	No. 400E Locomotive, blue, brass trim (std)		900
___ 11-1010	No. 385E Locomotive (std)		700
___ 11-1012	No. 1835E Locomotive, black, nickel trim (std)		700
___ 11-1013	AF No. 4694 Warrior Passenger Set (std)		1400
___ 11-1014	AF No. 4694 Iron Monarch Passenger Set (std)		1250
___ 11-1015	No. 392E Locomotive, black, brass trim (std)		800
___ 11-1016	No. 392E Locomotive, gray, nickel trim (std)		800
___ 11-1017	No. 400E Locomotive, blue, nickel trim (std)		900
___ 11-1018	No. 7 Lionel Locomotive (std)		900
___ 11-1019	No. 6 Pennsylvania Locomotive (std)		900
___ 11-1020	American Flyer No. 4696 Locomotive (std)		1000
___ 11-1021	No. 400E Presidential Locomotive (std)		1000
___ 11-1022	No. 400E Red Comet Locomotive (std)		1000
___ 11-1023	No. 400E Locomotive, blue, brass trim (std)		900
___ 11-1024	No. 400E Locomotive, black, brass trim (std)		900
___ 11-1025	No. 400E Lionel Lines Locomotive (std)		900
___ 11-1026	No. 400E Locomotive, pink (std)		1000
___ 11-1027	No. 400E Locomotive, state green (std)		1000
___ 11-1028	No. 400E Locomotive, black, brass trim (std)		1000
___ 11-1029	No. 6 NYC Locomotive (std)		900
___ 11-1030	No. 6 General Locomotive (std)		900
___ 11-1031	No. 6 Texas Locomotive (std)		950
___ 11-1038	No. 6 B&O Locomotive (std)		900
___ 11-1039	No. 6 Long Island Locomotive (std)		900
___ 11-1040	No. 6 Strasburg Locomotive (std)		900
___ 11-1041	No. 6 PRR Locomotive (std)		900
___ 11-1042	Great Northern Steam Locomotive (std)		1000
___ 11-1043	Lehigh Valley Steam Locomotive (std)		1000
___ 11-1045	PRR Steam Locomotive (std)		1000
___ 11-2003	No. 8E Electric Locomotive, olive green (std)		500
___ 11-2004	No. 8E Electric Locomotive, dark olive green (std)		500
___ 11-2005	No. 8E Electric Locomotive, orange (std)		500
___ 11-2006	No. 8E Electric Locomotive, red/cream (std)		500
___ 11-2007	American Flyer Presidential Passenger Set (std)		1800
___ 11-2008	AF No. 4689 Presidential Locomotive, blue (std)		800
___ 11-2009	Big Brute Electric Engine, zinc chromate (std)		1500
___ 11-2010	Big Brute Electric Engine, green (std)		1500

Lionel Corporation Tinplate		Exc	Mint
11-2015	Super 381 Electric Engine, state green (std)		1300 ___
11-2016	Super 381 MILW Electric Engine (std)		1300 ___
11-2017	No. 408E Electric Locomotive (std)		900 ___
11-2018	No. 408E Electric Locomotive, mojave (std)		900 ___
11-2019	No. 408E Electric Locomotive, pink (std)		900 ___
11-2020	No. 9 Electric Locomotive, green (std)		600 ___
11-2021	No. 9 Electric Locomotive, orange (std)		600 ___
11-2022	No. 9 Electric Locomotive, gray, nickel trim (std)		600 ___
11-2023	No. 9 Electric Locomotive, dark green (std)		600 ___
11-2024	No. 8 Trolley (std)		530 ___
11-2025	No. 9 Trolley (std)		650 ___
11-2026	No. 8 Christmas Trolley (std)		570 ___
11-2027	No. 381E Electric Locomotive, blue (std)		900 ___
11-2028	No. 381E Electric Locomotive, brown (std)		900 ___
11-2029	No. 381E Great Northern Electric Locomotive (std)		900 ___
11-2031	No. 4689 President's Locomotive, red (std)		900 ___
11-2033	Big Brute Electric Locomotive, brown (std)		1600 ___
11-2034	Big Brute Electric Locomotive, orange (std)		1600 ___
11-2038	Super 381 MILW Electric Locomotive (std)		1300 ___
11-2036	Super 381 PRR Electric Locomotive (std)		1300 ___
11-2040	Super 381 Electric Locomotive, two-tone brown (std)		1300 ___
11-2041	Super 381 New Haven Electric Locomotive (std)		1300 ___
11-5001	No. 384 Locomotive Passenger Set, black, brass trim (std		600 ___
11-5002	No. 384 Locomotive Christmas Freight Set (std)		600 ___
11-5003	No. 384 Locomotive LV Passenger Set (std)		600 ___
11-5004	No. 384 Locomotive NYC Freight Set (std)		600 ___
11-5006	No. 384E Locomotive Girl's Passenger Set (std)		600 ___
11-5007	No. 386 Freight Set (std)		600 ___
11-5008	No. 340E Coal Freight Set (std)		600 ___
11-5009	No. 342E Baby State Passenger Set (std)		600 ___
11-5010	No. 384E Blue Comet Passenger Set (std)		600 ___
11-5011	No. 386 Christmas Freight Set (std)		600 ___
11-5012	No. 342E Passenger Set (std)		600 ___
11-5013	No. 318E Christmas Freight Set (std)		600 ___
11-5014	No. 384E PRR Steam Passenger Set (std)		600 ___
11-5501	No. 263E Steam Christmas Freight Set (O)		600 ___
11-5502	No. 263E Steam B&O Freight Set (O)		600 ___
11-5505	No. 249E Christmas Steam Passenger Set (O)		500 ___
11-5506	No. 299 Freight Set (O)		450 ___
11-5507	No. 269E Distant Control Freight Set (O)		500 ___
11-5508	Celebration Passenger Set (O)		480 ___
11-5509	No. 269E Christmas Distant Control Freight Set (O)		500 ___
11-5510	No. 269E Distant Control Freight Set (O)		500 ___
11-6001	No. 263E Locomotive, black, brass trim (O)		430 ___
11-6002	No. 263E Locomotive, blue (O)		430 ___
11-6003	No. 277W Remote Control Work Train (O)		680 ___

			Exc	Mint
___	11-6004	Blue Comet Distant Control Passenger Set (O)		650
___	11-6005	No. 275W Distant Control Freight Set (O)		600
___	11-6006	UP Streamliner Passenger Set, silver (O)		800
___	11-6007	UP Streamliner Passenger Set, yellow (O)		800
___	11-6008	No. 249E Steam Passenger Set, black, brass trim (O)		600
___	11-6009	No. 249E Steam Passenger Set, blue (O)		600
___	11-6010	No. 249E Steam Passenger Set, gray, nickel trim (O)		600
___	11-6012	No. 260E Locomotive, black, brass trim (O)		430
___	11-6013	No. 255E Locomotive, gray, nickel trim (O)		430
___	11-6014	No. 255E Lionel Lines Locomotive (O)		430
___	11-6015	No. 279E Distant Control Passenger Set (O)		750
___	11-6016	No. 295E Distant Control Passenger Set (O)		750
___	11-6017	Hiawatha Distance Control Streamliner Set (O)		900
___	11-6018	Hiawatha Passenger Train Set (O)		900
___	11-6019	Hiawatha Distance Control Freight Set (O)		900
___	11-6020	UP City of Denver Passenger Set, green (O)		590
___	11-6021	UP City of Denver Passenger Set, yellow/brown (O)		700
___	11-6022	No. 262E Locomotive, black, brass trim (O)		300
___	11-6023	No. 262E Locomotive, black, nickel trim (O)		300
___	11-6024	No. 260E Locomotive, black, brass trim (O)		450
___	11-6025	No. 214 Armored Motor Car Set (O)		400
___	11-6028	No. 256 Electric Locomotive, orange (O)		450
___	11-6029	No. 214 Armored Motor Car Set (O)		400
___	11-6030	No. 295E Distant Control Passenger Set (O)		750
___	11-6031	No. 279E NYC Distance Control Passenger Set (O)		700
___	11-6033	No. 265E Commodore Vanderbilt Locomotive (O)		430
___	11-6036	No. 263E Baby Blue Comet Locomotive (O)		460
___	11-6037	Girls Freight Set (O)		830
___	11-6038	No. 284E Distant Control Freight Set (O)		700
___	11-6039	No. 616 Flying Yankee Passenger Set, black/chrome (O)		590
___	11-6040	No. 616 Flying Yankee Passenger Set, red/chrome (O)	215	590
___	11-6041	No. 616 Flying Yankee Passenger Set, green/chrome (O)		590
___	11-6046	No. 279E Distant Control Passenger Set (O)		700
___	11-6047	No. 264 Red Comet Locomotive (O)		460
___	11-6048	No. 263E Baby Blue Comet Locomotive, brass trim (O)		500
___	11-6050	No. 256 New Haven Electric Locomotive (O)		500
___	11-6051	No. 256 Great Northern Electric Locomotive (O)		500
___	11-6052	No. 263E Locomotive, black, nickel trim (O)		500
___	11-6053	No. 263E Chessie Locomotive (O)		500
___	11-6054	No. 263E Southern Locomotive (O)		500
___	11-6055	Boys Freight Set (O)		900
___	11-6056	No. 261E Lionel Lines Locomotive and Tender (O)		350
___	11-6057	No. 216E Locomotive and Tender (O)		350
___	11-6061	No. 256 MILW Electric Locomotive (O)		500
___	11-6062	No. 256 PRR Electric Locomotive (O)		500
___	11-30004	No. 213 Cattle Car, cream/maroon (std)		130

Lionel Corporation Tinplate		Exc	Mint
11-30005	No. 213 Cattle Car, terra-cotta/green (std)		130
11-30006	No. 214 Boxcar, cream/orange (std)		130
11-30007	No. 214 Boxcar, yellow/brown (std)		130
11-30008	No. 214R Refrigerator Car, white/blue (std)		130
11-30009	No. 215 Tank Car, silver, nickel trim (std)		130
11-30010	No. 215 Tank Car, green, brass trim (std)		130
11-30011	No. 215 Tank Car, white (std)		130
11-30012	No. 216 Hopper Car, red (std)		130
11-30013	No. 217 Caboose, orange/maroon (std)		140
11-30014	No. 217 Caboose, red (std)		160
11-30015	No. 513 Cattle Car, green/orange, brass trim (std)		100
11-30016	No. 514 Boxcar, cream/orange (std)		100
11-30017	No. 514R Refrigerator Car, ivory/peacock, brass trim (std)		100
11-30018	No. 515 Tank Car, terra-cotta, brass trim (std)		100
11-30019	No. 516 Hopper Car, red, brass trim (std)		120
11-30020	No. 517 Caboose, pea green/red (std)		120
11-30021	No. 212 Gondola, maroon (std)		110
11-30022	No. 212 Gondola, pea green (std)		110
11-30023	No. 513 Cattle Car, cream/maroon, nickel trim (std)		100
11-30024	No. 514R Refrigerator Car, white/blue, nickel trim (std)		100
11-30025	No. 515 Tank Car, silver, nickel trim (std)		100
11-30026	No. 516 Hopper Car, red, nickel trim (std)		100
11-30027	No. 517 Caboose, red, nickel trim (std)		120
11-30028	No. 520 Floodlight Car, green, nickel trim (std)		130
11-30029	No. 520 Floodlight Car, terra-cotta, brass trim (std)		130
11-30030	No. 514R Christmas Refrigerator Car, (std)		100
11-30031	No. 514 Christmas Boxcar (std)		100
11-30032	No. 515 MTH/Lionel Tank Car (std)		100
11-30033	No. 211 Flatcar, black, brass trim, with wood (std)		120
11-30034	No. 211 Flatcar, black, nickel trim, with wood (std)		120
11-30035	No. 218 Dump Car, mojave, nickel trim (std)		140
11-30036	No. 218 Dump Car, mojave, brass trim (std)		140
11-30037	No. 219 Crane Car, white (std)		200
11-30038	No. 219 Crane Car, yellow, nickel trim (std)		200
11-30039	No. 219 Crane Car, yellow (std)		380
11-30042	No. 514 Boxcar, red/black (std)		100
11-30043	No. 512 Gondola, peacock, brass trim (std)		80
11-30044	No. 512 Gondola, green, nickel trim (std)		80
11-30045	No. 514 Boxcar, yellow/brown (std)		100
11-30046	No. 511 Flatcar, black, brass trim, with wood (std)		100
11-30047	No. 511 Flatcar, black, nickel trim, with wood (std)		100
11-30048	No. 216 Hopper Car, dark green (std)		130
11-30050	No. 219 Crane Car, white, brass trim (std)		380
11-30051	No. 514R NYC Refrigerator Car (std)		100
11-30055	No. 212 Gondola, gray (std)		110
11-30056	No. 213 Cattle Car, mojave/maroon (std)		130

	Lionel Corporation Tinplate	Exc	Mint
____	**11-30057** No. 213 Cattle Car, terra-cotta/maroon (std)		130
____	**11-30058** No. 214 Boxcar, terra-cotta/black, brass trim (std)		130
____	**11-30059** No. 214R Refrigerator Car, white/peacock, brass trim (std		130
____	**11-30060** No. 214R Refrigerator Car, ivory/peacock, brass trim (std)		130
____	**11-30061** No. 215 Tank Car, silver, brass trim (std)		130
____	**11-30062** No. 215 Tank Car, silver, nickel trim (std)		130
____	**11-30063** No. 217 Caboose, olive green (std)		140
____	**11-30064** No. 217 Lionel Lines Caboose (std)		140
____	**11-30065** No. 217 Caboose, pea green/red (std)		140
____	**11-30066** No. 217 Caboose, red/peacock (std)		160
____	**11-30067** No. 218 Dump Car, gray (std)		140
____	**11-30068** No. 218 Dump Car, pea green (std)		140
____	**11-30069** No. 218 Dump Car, peacock (std)		140
____	**11-30070** No. 219 Crane Car, peacock/dark green (std)		200
____	**11-30071** No. 219 Lionel Lines Crane Car (std)		380
____	**11-30072** No. 220 Floodlight Car, green, nickel trim (std)		140
____	**11-30073** No. 220 Floodlight Car, terra-cotta, brass trim (std)		140
____	**11-30074** No. 513 Cattle Car, orange/pea green (std)		100
____	**11-30075** No. 514 Christmas Boxcar (std)		100
____	**11-30076** No. 514R Refrigerator Car, ivory/blue (std)		100
____	**11-30077** No. 515 Tank Car, cream (std)		100
____	**11-30078** No. 515 Tank Car, ivory (std)		100
____	**11-30079** No. 515 Tank Car, orange (std)		100
____	**11-30080** No. 516 Christmas Hopper Car (std)		120
____	**11-30081** No. 516 Hopper Car, red (std)		120
____	**11-30082** No. 517 Caboose, red/black (std)		120
____	**11-30083** No. 520 Floodlight Car, green, nickel trim (std)		130
____	**11-30087** No. 516 Hopper Car, red, brass trim (std)		100
____	**11-30088** AF 4018 Automobile Car, white/blue (std)		150
____	**11-30089** AF 4020 Stock Car, blue (std)		150
____	**11-30090** AF 4006 Hopper Car, red (std)		150
____	**11-30091** AF 4017 Sand Car, green (std)		150
____	**11-30092** AF 4010 Tank Car, cream/blue (std)		150
____	**11-30093** AF 4022 Machine Car, orange (std)		110
____	**11-30094** AF 4021 Caboose, red (std)		160
____	**11-30095** AF 4018 Automobile Car, orange/maroon (std)		130
____	**11-30096** AF 4022 Machine Car, blue (std)		110
____	**11-30097** AF 4022 Machine Car, orange/green (std)		110
____	**11-30098** AF 4010 Tank Car, blue (std)		130
____	**11-30099** AF 4017 Sand Car, maroon (std)		130
____	**11-30100** AF 4006 Hopper Car, green (std)		130
____	**11-30101** AF 4020 Stock Car, cream/maroon (std)		130
____	**11-30102** AF 4021 Caboose, red/maroon (std)		140
____	**11-30103** AF 4021 Caboose, cream/red (std)		140
____	**11-30104** No. 215 Tank Car (std)		130
____	**11-30105** No. 214R Refrigerator Car (std)		130

Lionel Corporation Tinplate	Exc	Mint
11-30107	No. 214R Altoona 36 Lager Refrigerator Car (std)		130 ___
11-30108	No. 214R Budweiser Refrigerator Car (std)		140 ___
11-30109	No. 214R Burp-oh Beer Refrigerator Car (std)		130 ___
11-30110	No. 214R Hood's Dairy Refrigerator Car (std)		130 ___
11-30111	No. 214R Old Reading Refrigerator Car (std)		130 ___
11-30112	No. 214R Palisades Park Refrigerator Car (std)		130 ___
11-30113	No. 214 Circus Boxcar (std)		130 ___
11-30114	No. 214 M&M's Christmas Boxcar (std)		140 ___
11-30115	No. 215 Budweiser Tank Car (std)		140 ___
11-30116	No. 215 Freedomland Tank Car (std)		130 ___
11-30117	No. 215 Gulf Tank Car (std)		130 ___
11-30118	No. 215 Tropicana Tank Car (std)		130 ___
11-30119	No. 513 UP Cattle Car (std)		100 ___
11-30120	No. 513 WM Cattle Car (std)		100 ___
11-30121	No. 514 B&O Boxcar (std)		100 ___
11-30122	No. 514 State of Maine Boxcar (std)		120 ___
11-30123	No. 514R PFE Refrigerator Car (std)		100 ___
11-30124	No. 514R Tropicana Refrigerator Car (std)		120 ___
11-30125	No. 515 Anheuser Busch Tank Car (std)		110 ___
11-30126	No. 515 Hooker Chemicals Tank Car (std)		100 ___
11-30127	No. 516 Blue Coal Hopper Car (std)		100 ___
11-30128	No. 516 Waddell Coal Hopper Car (std)		120 ___
11-30129	No. 517 Pennsylvania Caboose (std)		120 ___
11-30130	No. 517 Santa Fe Caboose (std)		140 ___
11-30131	No. 215 Lionel Lines Tank Car (std)		130 ___
11-30134	No. 515 Christmas Tank Car (std)		100 ___
11-30136	No. 214 Christmas Boxcar (std)		150 ___
11-30137	No. 214 UP Boxcar (std)		150 ___
11-30138	No. 214R Horlacher's Brewing Refrigerator Car (std)		150 ___
11-30139	No. 214R Coors Refrigerator Car (std)		140 ___
11-30140	No. 215 Keystone Gasoline Tank Car (std)		150 ___
11-30141	No. 215 Texaco Tank Car (std)		150 ___
11-30142	No. 216 Peabody Hopper Car (std)		130 ___
11-30143	No. 216 Pennsylvania Power & Light Hopper Car (std)		130 ___
11-30144	No. 213 Cattle Car (std)		130 ___
11-30146	No. 217 Jersey Central Caboose (std)		140 ___
11-30147	No. 214 Jersey Central Boxcar (std)		130 ___
11-30148	No. 214 U.S. Army Boxcar (std)		130 ___
11-30149	No. 215 MTH/Lionel Tank Car		130 ___
11-30150	No. 212 Lionel Lines Gondola (std)		130 ___
11-30151	No. 212 Circus Gondola (std)		130 ___
11-30152	No. 212 NYC Gondola (std)		130 ___
11-30153	No. 214 MKT Boxcar (std)		150 ___
11-30154	No. 214 NYC Boxcar (std)		150 ___
11-30155	No. 215 C&O Tank Car (std)		150 ___
11-30156	No. 215 Shell Tank Car (std)		150 ___

	Lionel Corporation Tinplate	Exc	Mint
___	11-30157	No. 216 Hopper Car, red, brass trim (std)		150
___	11-30158	No. 216 LV Hopper Car (std)		150
___	11-30159	No. 217 Pennsylvania Caboose (std)		160
___	11-30160	No. 219 B&O Crane Car (std)		220
___	11-30161	No. 219 Crane Car, ivory/red (std)		400
___	11-30162	No. 219 Lionel Lines Crane Car (std)		220
___	11-30163	No. 219 Crane Car, red/silver (std)		400
___	11-30164	No. 514R Christmas Refrigerator Car (std)		120
___	11-30168	No. 515 PRR Tank Car (std)		120
___	11-30169	No. 515 Texaco Tank Car (std)		120
___	11-30170	No. 515 Esso Tank Car (std)		120
___	11-30180	No. 219 Crane Car, black/cream (std)		220
___	11-30182	No. 217 NYC Illuminated Caboose (std)		160
___	11-30185	No. 212 Gondola, pea green (std)		150
___	11-30193	No. 514R Altoona Brewing Refrigerator Car (std)		120
___	11-30194	No. 514R PFE Refrigerator Car (std)		120
___	11-30195	No. 514R REA Refrigerator Car (std)		120
___	11-30196	No. 514R Robin Hood Beer Refrigerator Car (std)		120
___	11-30197	No. 514 UP Boxcar (std)		120
___	11-30198	No. 514 Santa Fe Boxcar (std)		120
___	11-30199	No. 514 PRR Boxcar (std)		120
___	11-30200	No. 514 B&O Boxcar (std)		120
___	11-30201	No. 215-3 Shell 3-D Tank Car (std)		150
___	11-30202	No. 215-3 Mazda Lamps 3-D Tank Car (std)		150
___	11-30203	No. 215-3 Celanese Chemicals 3-D Tank Car (std)		150
___	11-30204	No. 215-3 Clark Oil 3-D Tank Car (std)		150
___	11-30205	No. 215-2 Sterling Fuels 2-D Tank Car (std)		150
___	11-30206	No. 215-2 Philadelphia Quartz 2-D Tank Car (std)		150
___	11-30207	No. 215-2 Cook's Paints 2-D Tank Car (std)		150
___	11-30208	No. 215-2 Hercules 2-D Tank Car (std)		150
___	11-30209	No. 216-1 PRR Covered Hopper (std)		150
___	11-30210	No. 216-1 P&LE Covered Hopper (std)		150
___	11-30211	No. 216-1 Jack Frost Covered Hopper (std)		150
___	11-30212	No. 216-1 GE Lamps Covered Hopper (std)		150
___	11-30213	No. 212-1 PRR Covered Gondola Car (std)		150
___	11-30214	No. 212-1 Covered Gondola Car (std)		150
___	11-30215	No. 212-1 NYC Covered Gondola Car (std)		150
___	11-30216	No. 212-1 GN Covered Gondola Car (std)		150
___	11-30217	No. 211 Flatcar with wheel load (std)		150
___	11-30218	No. 211 Altoona Shops Flatcar with wheel load (std)		150
___	11-30219	No. 211 Baldwin Flatcar with wheel load (std)		150
___	11-30220	No. 211 Lima Flatcar with wheel load (std)		150
___	11-30221	No. 217-1 Chessie Bay Window Caboose (std)		160
___	11-30222	No. 217-1 UP Bay Window Caboose (std)		160
___	11-30223	No. 217-1 NYC Bay Window Caboose (std)		160
___	11-30224	No. 217-1 Long Island Bay Window Caboose (std)		160

Lionel Corporation Tinplate		Exc	Mint
11-30225	PRR Automobile Car (std)		150 ___
11-30227	Shell Tank Car (std)		150 ___
11-30230	Waddell Coal Hopper (std)		150 ___
11-30232	PRR Caboose (std)		160 ___
11-40001	Presidential Passenger Set, blue (std)		1200 ___
11-40002	No. 339 Pullman Car, green (std)		150 ___
11-40003	No. 332 Mail/Baggage Car, green (std)		150 ___
11-40004	No. 332 LV Ithaca Baggage Car		150 ___
11-40005	No. 339 LV Easton Passenger Coach		150 ___
11-40007	300 Series 3-Car Passenger Set, blue/silver (std)		400 ___
11-40009	3-Car State Passenger Set, green (std)		1200 ___
11-40010	Pennsylvania State Baggage Car, green (std)		400 ___
11-40011	Illinois State Coach, green (std)		400 ___
11-40012	Solarium State Car, green (std)		400 ___
11-40013	MILW 3-Car State Passenger Set (std)		1200 ___
11-40014	MILW State Baggage Car (std)		400 ___
11-40015	MILW State Passenger Coach (std)		400 ___
11-40016	MILW Solarium State Car (std)		400 ___
11-40017	3-Car Showroom Passenger Set, green (std)		1500 ___
11-40018	Showroom Passenger Coach, green (std)		500 ___
11-40019	3-Car Showroom Passenger Set, zinc chromate (std)		1500 ___
11-40020	Showroom Passenger Coach, zinc chromate (std)		500 ___
11-40021	3-Car Blue Comet Passenger Set (std)		1100 ___
11-40022	No. 432 Olbers Blue Comet Baggage Car (std)		380 ___
11-40023	No. 419 Tuttle Blue Comet Passenger Coach (std)		380 ___
11-40024	No. 4343 Diner Car		180 ___
11-40025	339 Series Passenger Car, pink		130 ___
11-40026	332 Series Baggage Car, pink		130 ___
11-40027	309 Series 3-Car State Passenger Set, brown (std)		1200 ___
11-40028	Pennsylvania State Baggage Car, brown (std)		400 ___
11-40029	Illinois State Passenger Coach, brown (std)		400 ___
11-40030	Solarium State Car, brown (std)		400 ___
11-40031	State 3-Car Passenger Set, blue (std)		1200 ___
11-40032	Pennsylvania State Baggage Car, blue (std)		400 ___
11-40033	Illinois State Passenger Coach, blue (std)		400 ___
11-40034	Solarium State Car, blue (std)		400 ___
11-40035	309 Series 3-Car Passenger Set, blue (std)		400 ___
11-40036	309 Series 3-Car Passenger Set, green (std)		400 ___
11-40037	309 Series 3-Car Passenger Set, red (std)		400 ___
11-40038	No. 309 Passenger Coach (std)		140 ___
11-40039	No. 310 Baggage Car (std)		140 ___
11-40040	3-Car Blue Comet Passenger Set, nickel trim (std)		1100 ___
11-40041	No. 432 Blue Comet Baggage Car, nickel trim (std)		380 ___
11-40042	No. 423 Blue Comet Passenger Coach, nickel trim (std)		380 ___
11-40043	3-Car Stephen Girard Set, brass trim (std)		600 ___
11-40044	No. 4427 Stephen Girard Baggage Car, brass trim (std)		200 ___

	Lionel Corporation Tinplate	Exc	Mint
___	**11-40045** No. 427 Stephen Girard Passenger Coach, brass trim (std)		200
___	**11-40046** 3-Car Stephen Girard Set, nickel trim (std)		600
___	**11-40047** No. 4427 Stephen Girard Baggage Car, nickel trim (std)		200
___	**11-40048** No. 427 Stephen Girard Passenger Coach, nickel trim (std)		200
___	**11-40049** No. 418 3-Car Passenger Set, green, brass trim (std)		600
___	**11-40050** No. 418 Diner, green, brass trim (std)		200
___	**11-40051** No. 418 3-Car Passenger Set, orange, brass trim (std)		600
___	**11-40052** No. 418 Diner, orange brass trim (std)		200
___	**11-40053** No. 418 3-Car Passenger Set, mojave, brass trim (std)		600
___	**11-40054** No. 418 Diner, mojave, brass trim (std)		200
___	**11-40055** No. 418 3-Car Passenger Set, pink, brass trim (std)		600
___	**11-40056** No. 418 Diner, pink, brass trim (std)		200
___	**11-40057** Lionel 3-Car Pullman Passenger Set (std)		700
___	**11-40058** Pennsylvania 3-Car Pullman Passenger Set (std)		700
___	**11-40059** No. 332 Baggage Car (std)		140
___	**11-40060** No. 339 Passenger Coach (std)		140
___	**11-40061** Great Northern State 3-Car Passenger Set (std)		1200
___	**11-40062** Great Northern State Baggage Car (std)		430
___	**11-40063** Great Northern State Passenger Coach (std)		430
___	**11-40064** Great Northern State Solarium Car (std)		430
___	**11-40065** Presidential 3-Car Passenger Set (std)		1200
___	**11-40066** Presidential Baggage Car (std)		430
___	**11-40067** Presidential Passenger Coach (std)		430
___	**11-40068** Red Comet 3-Car Passenger Set (std)		1140
___	**11-40069** Red Comet Baggage Car (std)		400
___	**11-40070** Red Comet Passenger Coach (std)		400
___	**11-40072** President's Passenger Set, red (std)		1300
___	**11-40073** No. 310 Baggage Car (std)		140
___	**11-40074** No. 309 Passenger Coach (std)		140
___	**11-40076** Green Comet 3-Car Passenger Set (std)		1140
___	**11-40077** NYC 3-Car Passenger Set, brown (std)		700
___	**11-40078** General 3-Car Pullman Passenger Set (std)		700
___	**11-40079** Green Comet Baggage Car (std)		400
___	**11-40080** Green Comet Passenger Coach (std)		400
___	**11-40081** Showroom 3-Car Passenger Set, brown (std)		1600
___	**11-40082** Showroom Passenger Coach, brown (std)		540
___	**11-40083** Showroom 3-Car Passenger Set, orange (std)		1600
___	**11-40084** Showroom Passenger Coach, orange (std)		540
___	**11-40095** 3-car B&O Pullman Passenger Set (std)		700
___	**11-40096** 3-car Long Island Pullman Passenger Set (std)		700
___	**11-40097** 3-car Strasburg Pullman Passenger Set (std)		700
___	**11-40098** 3-car PRR Pullman Passenger Set (std)		700
___	**11-40099** 3-car MILW State Passenger Set (std)		1200
___	**11-40100** MILW State Solarium Car (std)		400
___	**11-40101** MILW State Passenger Coach (std)		400
___	**11-40102** MILW State Baggage Car (std)		400

Lionel Corporation Tinplate		Exc	Mint
11-40103	3-car PRR State Passenger Set (std)		1200 ___
11-40104	PRR State Solarium Car (std)		400 ___
11-40105	PRR State Passenger Coach (std)		400 ___
11-40106	PRR State Baggage Car (std)		400 ___
11-40107	3-car State Passenger Set, two-tone brown (std)		1200 ___
11-40108	State Solarium Car, two-tone brown (std)		400 ___
11-40109	State Passenger Coach, two-tone brown (std)		400 ___
11-40110	State Baggage Car, two-tone brown (std)		400 ___
11-40111	3-car Great Northern Presidential Set (std)		1200 ___
11-40112	Great Northern Presidential Diner (std)		400 ___
11-40113	3-car Lehigh Valley Presidential Set (std)		1200 ___
11-40114	Lehigh Valley Presidential Diner (std)		400 ___
11-40115	3-car New Haven State Passenger Set (std)		1200 ___
11-40116	New Haven State Solarium Car (std)		400 ___
11-40117	New Haven State Passenger Coach (std)		400 ___
11-40118	New Haven State Baggage Car (std)		400 ___
11-60033	No. 607 Christmas Coach Passenger (O)		90 ___
11-70002	No. 2814 Boxcar, cream/orange (O)		80 ___
11-70003	No. 2814R Refrigerator Car, white/brown (O)		80 ___
11-70004	No. 2814R Christmas Refrigerator Car (O)		80 ___
11-70005	No. 2814R Refrigerator Car, Ivory/peacock (O)		80 ___
11-70006	No. 2815 Tank Car, silver (O)		90 ___
11-70007	No. 2815 Tank Car, orange, nickel trim (O)		80 ___
11-70008	No. 2817 Caboose, red/green (O)		90 ___
11-70009	No. 2815 Christmas Tank Car (O)		80 ___
11-70010	No. 2813 Cattle Car, cream/maroon (O)		80 ___
11-70011	No. 2812 Gondola, apple green (O)		80 ___
11-70012	No. 2811 Flatcar, silver (O)		70 ___
11-70013	No. 2816 Hopper Car, red (O)		90 ___
11-70014	No. 2816 Hopper Car, olive green (O)		80 ___
11-70015	No. 2820 Floodlight Car, terra-cotta (O)		90 ___
11-70016	No. 2815 Sunoco Tank Car (O)		80 ___
11-70017	No. 2810 Crane Car, terra-cotta/maroon (O)		180 ___
11-70018	No. 2811 Flatcar, maroon (O)		70 ___
11-70019	No. 2814R MTH/Lionel Refrigerator Car (O)		90 ___
11-70024	No. 2814 Christmas Boxcar (O)		80 ___
11-70025	No. 2814 Boxcar, cream/orange (O)		80 ___
11-70026	No. 2814 Boxcar, orange/brown (O)		80 ___
11-70027	No. 2814 Boxcar, white brown (O)		80 ___
11-70028	No. 2816 Christmas Hopper Car (O)		80 ___
11-70029	No. 2817 Caboose, red/brown (O)		90 ___
11-70030	No. 2812 Gondola, dark orange (O)		70 ___
11-70031	No. 813 Cattle Car, brown (O)		80 ___
11-70032	No. 2816 Hopper Car, black (O)		80 ___
11-70033	No. 2820 Floodlight Car, light green (O)		90 ___
11-70034	No. 2814R Refrigerator Car, white/brown (O)		80 ___

		Exc	Mint
___	**11-70035** No. 2651 Flatcar, green (O)		60
___	**11-70036** No. 2652 Gondola, red (O)		60
___	**11-70037** No. 2653 Hopper Car, black (O)		60
___	**11-70038** No. 2654 Shell Tank Car, yellow (O)		60
___	**11-70039** No. 2655 Boxcar, yellow/brown (O)		60
___	**11-70040** No. 2656 Cattle Car, red/brown (O)		60
	11-70041 No. 2657 Caboose, red/maroon (O)		60
___	**11-70042** No. 659 Dump Car, green (O)		60
___	**11-70043** No. 659 Dump Car, orange (O)		60
___	**11-70045** No. 2814 Boxcar, yellow/brown (O)		90
___	**11-70046** No. 2817 Caboose, red (O)		100
___	**11-70047** No. 2814 Christmas Boxcar (O)		80
___	**11-70048** No. 2815 Christmas Tank Car (O)		90
___	**11-70049** No. 2814R Refrigerator Car, silver frame (O)		90
___	**11-70050** No. 2814R Refrigerator Car, black frame (O)		80
___	**11-70051** No. 2817 Caboose, red/maroon (O)		90
___	**11-70052** No. 2654 Shell Tank Car, gray (O)		60
___	**11-70053** No. 2654 Shell Tank Car, black (O)		60
___	**11-70054** No. 2653 Hopper Car, green (O)		60
___	**11-70055** No. 2653 Hopper Car, red (O)		60
___	**11-70056** No. 2655 Boxcar, yellow/maroon (O)		60
___	**11-70057** No. 2655 Boxcar, yellow/brown (O)		60
___	**11-70058** No. 2656 Cattle Car, gray/red (O)		60
___	**11-70059** No. 2656 Cattle Car, burnt orange (O)		60
___	**11-70060** No. 659 Dump Car, blue (O)		60
___	**11-70061** No. 900 Ammunition Car, gray (O)		60
___	**11-70064** No. 2814R Hoods Dairy Refrigerator Car (O)		80
___	**11-70065** No. 2814R Isaly's Refrigerator Car (O)		80
___	**11-70066** No. 2814R Sheffield Farms Refrigerator Car (O)		90
___	**11-70067** No. 2814R Palisades Park Refrigerator Car (O)		80
___	**11-70068** No. 2654 UP Tank Car, yellow (O)		60
___	**11-70069** No. 2654 M&M's Tank Car (O)		70
___	**11-70070** No. 2654 Baker's Chocolate Tank Car (O)		60
___	**11-70071** No. 2654 Budweiser Tank Car (O)		70
___	**11-70072** No. 2655 Delaware & Hudson Boxcar (O)		60
___	**11-70073** No. 2655 Railbox Boxcar (O)		60
___	**11-70074** M&M's Christmas Boxcar (O)		70
___	**11-70076** No. 2654 Lionel Lines Tank Car, orange/blue (O)		70
___	**11-70078** No. 900 Ammunition Car, green (O)		60
___	**11-70079** No. 2820 Lionel Lines Floodlight Car, black/orange (O)		120
___	**11-70080** No. 2820 U.S. Army Air Corps Floodlight Car (O)		120
___	**11-70081** No. 2810 Crane Car, yellow/red (O)		180
___	**11-70082** No. 2810 Crane Car, white/red (O)		180
___	**11-70083** No. 2660 Crane Car, cream/red (O)		100
___	**11-70084** No. 2660 Crane Car, terra-cotta/maroon (O)		100
___	**11-70085** No. 2660 Crane Car, yellow/red (O)		100

Lionel Corporation Tinplate		Exc	Mint
11-70086	No. 2660 Crane Car, peacock/dark green (O)		100
11-70087	No. 2813 Lionel Lines Cattle Car, cream/tuscan (O)		90
11-70088	No. 2813 Lionel Lines Cattle Car, terra cotta/pea green (O		90
11-70089	No. 2810 B&O Crane Car (O)		180
11-70091	No. 2815 Lionel Lines Tank Car, cream, orange/blue (O)		80
11-70092	No. 2810 Crane Car, blue (O)		180
11-70095	No. 2820 LL Floodlight Car, black/peacock (O)		120
11-70096	No. 2814 Southern Boxcar (O)		90
11-70097	No. 2814 Chessie Boxcar (O)		90
11-70098	No. 2814 Blue Comet Boxcar, nickel trim (O)		90
11-70099	No. 2814 Blue Comet Boxcar, brass trim (O)		90
11-70102	No. 2654 Mobilgas Tank Car (O)		70
11-70103	No. 2654 Esso Tank Car (O)		70
11-70104	No. 2653 Blue Coal Hopper (O)		70
11-70105	No. 2653 Peabody Hopper (O)		70
11-70106	No. 2655 Altoona Brewing Boxcar (O)		70
11-70107	No. 2655 Hood's Grade A Milk Boxcar (O)		70
11-70108	No. 2655 Lionel Lines Boxcar (O)		70
11-70109	No. 2657 Lionel Lines Caboose, green/red (O)		70
11-70110	No. 2657 Lionel Lines Caboose, orange/red (O)		70
11-70113	No. 2814 PRR Boxcar (O)		90
11-70114	No. 2814 ATSF Grand Canyon Boxcar (O)		90
11-70115	No. 2814 Long Island Boxcar (O)		90
11-70116	No. 2814 Alaska Boxcar (O)		90
11-70117	No. 2814R M. K. Goetz Brewing Refrigerator Car (O)		90
11-70118	No. 2814R Gerber Refrigerator Car (O)		90
11-70119	No. 2814R Roberts & Oake Meats Refrigerator Car (O)		90
11-70120	No. 2814R Sullivan's Packing Refrigerator Car (O)		90
11-70121	No. 2816 Western Maryland Coal Car (O)		90
11-70122	No. 2816 P&LE Coal Car (O)		90
11-70123	No. 2816 Waddell Mining Coal Car (O)		90
11-70124	No. 2816 Blue Coal Car (O)		90
11-70125	No. 2815 Clark Oil Tank Car (O)		90
11-70126	No. 2815 Celanese Chemicals Tank Car (O)		90
11-70127	No. 2815 Shell Tank Car (O)		90
11-70128	No. 2815 Cook's Paints Tank Car (O)		90
11-70129	No. 2817 C&O Caboose (O)		100
11-70130	No. 2817 Long Island Caboose (O)		100
11-70131	No. 2817 Southern Caboose (O)		100
11-70132	No. 2817 Jersey Central Caboose (O)		100
11-70133	No. 2814R Gerber Refrigerator Car (O)		90
11-70144	No. 2815 Shell Tank Car (O)		90
11-70154	No. 2814 ATSF Grand Canyon Boxcar (O)		90
11-80001	2600 Series 4-Car Blue Comet Passenger Set (O)		430
11-80002	UP Articulated Baggage Car, silver (O)		150
11-80003	UP Articulated Baggage Car, yellow (O)		150

Lionel Corporation Tinplate	Exc	Mint
11-80004	UP Articulated Coach, silver (O)		150
11-80005	UP Articulated Coach, yellow (O)		150
11-80006	No. 2613 Series Pullman Coach, blue (O)		110
11-80007	2600 Series 3-Car Passenger Set, red (O)		300
11-80008	2600 Series 3-Car Passenger Set, green (O)		300
11-80009	Milwaukee Road Articulated Baggage Car (O)		150
11-80010	Milwaukee Road Articulated Coach (O)		150
11-80011	Articulated Streamliner Baggage Car (O)		150
11-80012	Articulated Streamliner Coach (O)		150
11-80013	No. 2613 Series Pullman Coach, red (O)		100
11-80014	No. 2613 Series Pullman Coach, green (O)		100
11-80015	No. 605 Christmas Baggage Car (O)		90
11-80016	710 Series 3-Car Passenger Set, blue (O)		350
11-80017	No. 710 Series Baggage Car, blue (O)		120
11-80018	No. 710 Series Passenger Coach, blue (O)		120
11-80019	710 Series 3-Car Passenger Set, orange (O)		350
11-80020	No. 710 Series Baggage Car, orange (O)		120
11-80021	No. 710 Series Passenger Coach, orange (O)		120
11-80022	710 Series 3-Car Passenger Set, red (O)		350
11-80023	No. 710 Series Baggage Car, red (O)		120
11-80024	No. 710 Series Passenger Coach, red (O)		120
11-80025	No. 1695 3-Car Passenger Set, blue/silver (O)		350
11-80026	No. 1685 Passenger Car, blue/silver (O)		120
11-80027	1695 Series 3-Car Passenger Set, red/maroon (O)		380
11-80028	No. 1695 Passenger Coach, red/maroon (O)		130
11-80029	City of Denver Coach, yellow/green (O)		110
11-80030	City of Denver Coach, green (O)		110
11-80031	No. 605 Baggage Car (O)		90
11-80032	No. 607 Passenger Coach (O)		90
11-80034	No. 2613 NYC Pullman Car, LCCA 2012 Convention (O)		100
11-80036	No. 605 Red Comet Baggage Car (O)		90
11-80039	600 Series 3-Car Red Comet Passenger Set (O)		270
11-80040	2600 Series 4-Car Blue Comet Passenger Set, brass trim		430
11-80041	No. 2613 Pullman Coach, brass trim (O)		110
11-80042	Flying Yankee Chrome Coach (O)		110
11-80047	710 Series 3-Car NH Passenger Set (O)		400
11-80048	710 Series 3-Car GN Passenger Set (O)		400
11-80049	2600 Series 4-Car Chessie Passenger Set (O)		430
11-80050	2600 Series 4-Car Southern Passenger Set (O)		430
11-80051	No. 2613 Chessie Pullman Coach (O)		110
11-80052	No. 2613 Southern Pullman Coach (O)		110
11-80053	No. 710 NH Baggage Car (O)		140
11-80054	No. 710 NH Passenger Coach (O)		140
11-80055	No. 710 GN Baggage Car (O)		140
11-80056	No. 710 GN Passenger Coach (O)		140
11-80059	710 Series 3-car MILW Passenger Set (O)		400

Lionel Corporation Tinplate		Exc	Mint
11-80060	No. 713 MILW Baggage Car (O)		140 ___
11-80061	No. 710 MILW Passenger Coach (O)		140 ___
11-80062	710 Series 3-car PRR Passenger Set (O)		400 ___
11-80063	No. 713 PRR Baggage Car (O)		140 ___
11-80064	No. 710 PRR Passenger Coach (O)		140 ___
11-90001	No. 300 Hellgate Bridge, green/cream		500 ___
11-90002	No. 300 Hellgate Bridge, silver/white		500 ___
11-90003	No. 092 Signal Tower, cream/red		70 ___
11-90006	No. 437 Switch Tower		280 ___
11-90007	No. 155 Freight Shed		330 ___
11-90008	No. 116 Passenger Station		400 ___
11-90009	No. 438 Signal Tower		150 ___
11-90010	No. 192 Villa Set		200 ___
11-90011	No. 191 Villa		70 ___
11-90012	No. 54 Street Lamp Set, green		45 ___
11-90013	No. 54 Street Lamp Set, red		45 ___
11-90014	No. 56 Gas Lamp Set, green		35 ___
11-90015	No. 56 Gas Lamp Set, maroon		35 ___
11-90016	No. 57 Corner Lamp Set, black		40 ___
11-90017	No. 57 Corner Lamp Set, red		35 ___
11-90018	No. 58 Lamp Set, single arc, cream		35 ___
11-90019	No. 58 Lamp Set, single arc, dark green		35 ___
11-90020	No. 59 Gooseneck Lamp Set, black		40 ___
11-90021	No. 59 Gooseneck Lamp Set, maroon		40 ___
11-90022	No. 1184 Bungalow (std)		200 ___
11-90023	No. 1184 Bungalow (std)		200 ___
11-90024	No. 1189 Villa (std)		300 ___
11-90025	No. 1191 Villa (std)		300 ___
11-90026	No.165 Magnetic Crane		300 ___
11-90027	No. 441 Weighing Station (std)		380 ___
11-90028	No. 69 Operating Warning Bell		50 ___
11-90029	No. 78 Automatic Control Signal (std)		70 ___
11-90030	No. 79 Flashing Railroad Signal		70 ___
11-90031	No. 80 Operating Semaphore		70 ___
11-90032	No. 63 Lamp Post Set, aluminum		50 ___
11-90033	No. 87 Railroad Crossing Signal		50 ___
11-90034	No. 92 Floodlight Tower Set		160 ___
11-90035	No. 94 High Tension Tower Set		150 ___
11-90036	No. 76 Automatic Block Signal (std)		70 ___
11-90037	No. 163 Freight Accessory Set, green cart		100 ___
11-90038	No. 163 Freight Accessory Set, orange cart		100 ___
11-90039	No. 208 Tools and Chest, dark gray		80 ___
11-90040	No. 208 Tools and Chest, silver		80 ___
11-90041	No. 550 Miniature Figures		100 ___
11-90042	No. 64 Lamp Post Set, light green		30 ___
11-90043	No. 85 Race Car Set	300	700 ___

	Lionel Corporation Tinplate	Exc	Mint
____	11-90044 Straight Race Car Track Section		20
____	11-90045 Inside Curve Race Car Track Section		20
____	11-90046 Outside Curve Race Car Track Section		20
____	11-90047 No. 55 Airplane & No. 49 Airport Set with mat		800
____	11-90048 No. 49 Airport Mat		60
____	11-90049 No. 90 Flagpole		50
____	11-90050 No. 205 Merchandise Containers, 3 pieces (std)		130
____	11-90052 No. 442 Diner		160
____	11-90053 No. 43 Runabout Boat, red/white		450
____	11-90054 No. 44 Speed Boat		450
____	11-90055 No. 71 Telegraph Post Set, gray/red		80
____	11-90056 Teardrop Lamp Set, pea green		20
____	11-90057 No. 46 Crossing Gate		40
____	11-90058 Small Oil Drum Set		20
____	11-90060 No. 115 Passenger Station, beige/pea green		300
____	11-90061 No. 115 Passenger Station, cream, orange/blue		300
____	11-90062 No. 134 Lionel City Station with stop		330
____	11-90063 No. 444 Roundhouse Section		500
____	11-90064 No. 200 Turntable, red/black		200
____	11-90065 No. 89 Flagpole, blue base (std)		50
____	11-90066 No. 89 Flagpole, white base (std)		50
____	11-90067 No. 89 American Flag Pole, white base (std)		50
____	11-90068 Operating Industrial Crane		350
____	11-90069 Operating Industrial Crane, TCA 2010 Convention		350
____	11-90070 No. 552 Diner, orange/blue		200
____	11-90071 No. 552 Diner, white/blue		200
____	11-90072 No. 911 Country Estate, cream/red		140
____	11-90073 No. 911 Country Estate, red/green		140
____	11-90074 No. 912 Suburban Home, ivory/peacock		140
____	11-90075 No. 912 Suburban Home, mustard/green		140
____	11-90076 No. 913 Landscaped Bungalow, white/maroon		110
____	11-90077 No. 913 Landscaped Bungalow, light green/peacock		110
____	11-90078 AF No. 2050 Old Glory Flag Pole		100
____	11-90079 No. 43 Runabout Boat, orange/blue		400
____	11-90084 No. 57 Lamp Post Set, Lionel & American Flyer Aves.		40
____	11-90085 No. 57 Lamp Post Set, orange, 21st St. & Fifth Ave.		40
____	11-90086 AF No. 2013 Corner Lamp Set, yellow		40
____	11-90089 No. 436 Power Station, cream		150
____	11-90090 No. 436 Power Station, terra-cotta		150
____	11-90094 No. 438 Signal Tower		160
____	11-90095 No. 116 Passenger Station		400
____	11-90096 No. 1184 Bungalow, gray/green		200
____	11-90097 No. 1184 Bungalow, white/maroon		200
____	11-90098 No. 1189 Villa (std)		300
____	11-90099 No. 1191 Villa (std)		300

Lionel Corporation Tinplate

		Exc	Mint
11-90100	No. 442 Diner		160 ___
11-90101	No. 54 Lamp Post Set, pea green		45 ___
11-90102	No. 54 Lamp Post Set, state brown		45 ___
11-90103	No. 58 Lamp Post Set, peacock		35 ___
11-90104	No. 58 Lamp Post Set, orange		35 ___
11-90105	No. 59 Lamp Post Set, dark green		40 ___
11-90106	No. 59 Lamp Post Set, light green		40 ___
11-90107	No. 92 Floodlight Tower Set		170 ___
11-90108	No. 79 Flashing Signal		70 ___
11-90109	No. 69 Warning Signal		50 ___
11-90110	No. 94 High Tension Tower Set		170 ___
11-90111	No. 57 Corner Lamp Set, orange, Lionel		40 ___
11-90112	No. 57 Corner Lamp Set, blue, Lionel		40 ___
11-90113	No. 57 Corner Lamp Set, blue/yellow		40 ___
11-90114	No. 152 Operating Crossing Gate		40 ___
11-90115	No. 153 Operating Block Signal		40 ___
11-90116	No. 154 Highway Flashing Signal		40 ___
11-90117	No. 437 Switch Signal Tower, cream/orange		300 ___
11-90118	No. 437 Switch Signal Tower, terra-cotta/green		300 ___
11-90119	AF No. 4230 Roadside Flashing Signal		100 ___
11-90120	No. 200 Turntable, gray/green		200 ___
11-90121	No. 200 Turntable, orange/blue		200 ___
11-90122	No. 437 Switch Tower		280 ___
11-90123	No. 98 Coal Bunker		180 ___
11-99030	No. 25 Illuminated Track Bumpers (std)		60 ___

Section 5
MODERN TINPLATE

		Exc	Mint
O Gauge Classics			
____ 1-263E	Lionel Lines Blue Comet 2-4-2 Locomotive		NRS
____ 350E	Lionel Lines Hiawatha 4-4-2 Locomotive	113	200
____ 882	Lionel Lines Combination Car		NRS
____ 883	Lionel Lines Passenger Car		NRS
____ 884	Lionel Lines Observation Car		NRS
____ 1612	Lionel Lines Passenger Car		NRS
____ 1613	Lionel Lines Passenger Car		NRS
____ 1614	Lionel Lines Baggage Car		NRS
____ 1615	Lionel Lines Observation Car		NRS
____ 51000	Milwaukee Road Hiawatha Set, 88 u	353	882
____ 51001	Lionel #44 Freight Special Set, 89	230	600
____ 51004	Blue Comet Set, 91		1600
____ 51100	Lionel Lines Electric Locomotive "44E," 89		NRS
____ 51201	Rail Chief Passenger Cars, set of 4, 90	150	458
____ 51202	Lionel Lines Combination Car "892"		NRS
____ 51203	Lionel Lines Passenger Car "893"		NRS
____ 51204	Lionel Lines Passenger Car "894"		NRS
____ 51205	Lionel Lines Observation Car "895"		NRS
____ 51400	Lionel Lines Boxcar "8814," 89		NRS
____ 51500	Lionel Lines Hopper "8816," 89		NRS
____ 51700	Lionel Lines Caboose "8817," 89		NRS
____ 51800	Lionel Lines Searchlight Car "8820," 89		NRS
____ 51900	Signal Bridge and Control Panel, 89 u		399
Standard Gauge Classics			
____ 1-318E	Lionel Lines Electric Locomotive	180	600
____ 1-4390	American Flyer West Point Baggage Car		NRS
____ 1-4391	American Flyer Academy Passenger Car		NRS
____ 1-4392	American Flyer Army/Navy Observation Car		NRS
____ 5130	Lionel Lines Flatcar with lumber		NRS
____ 5140	Lionel Lines Reefer		NRS
____ 5150	Lionel Lines Shell Tank Car		NRS
____ 5160	Lionel Lines Caboose		NRS
____ 13001	1-318E Freight Express Train Set, 90-91		960
____ 13002	Fireball Express Set, 90 u		1600
____ 13003	American Flyer Mayflower Passenger Car Set, 92		2000
____ 13004	Milwaukee Road Hiawatha Passenger Set, 44928		2000
____ 13008	NYC Commodore Vanderbilt Passenger Set, 2		1600
____ 13100	Lionel Lines 2-4-2 Locomotive "1-390E," 88 u		610
____ 13101	Lionel Lines 2-4-0 Locomotive "1-384E," 89 u	325	750
____ 13102	Lionel Lines Electric Locomotive "1-381E," 89 u	440	1490

		Exc	Mint
13103	Lionel Lines Blue Comet 4-4-4 Locomotive, 90		1350
13104	Lionel Lines "Old #7" 4-4-0 Locomotive, 90		900
13106	Lionel Lines Fireball Express 2-4-2 Locomotive		NRS __
13107	Lionel Lines Electric Locomotive "1-408E," 91		880 __
13108	Lionel Lines 4-4-4 Locomotive "2-400E," Gray, 91		1100 __
13109	American Flyer Mayflower Electric Locomotive, 92		2500 __
13200	Lionel Lines Searchlight Car "1520," 89 u	55	155 __
13300	Lionel Lines Gondola "1512," 89 u		75 __
13303	Lionel Lines Sunoco Tank Car "1-215," 92		135 __
13400	Lionel Lines Baggage Car "323," 88 u		155 __
13401	Lionel Lines Passenger Car "324," 88 u		135 __
13402	Lionel Lines Observation Car "325," 88 u	35	135 __
13403	Lionel Lines State Passenger Car Set, 89 u		1100 __
13404	Lionel Lines California Passenger Car "1412," 90	200	360 __
13405	Lionel Lines Colorado Passenger Car "1413," 90	200	360 __
13406	Lionel Lines New York Observation Car "1416," 90	200	360 __
13407	Lionel Lines Illinois Passenger Car "1414," 90	175	450 __
13408	Lionel Lines Blue Comet Passenger Car Set, 90		1500 __
13409	Lionel Lines Faye Passenger Car "1420"		NRS __
13410	Lionel Lines Westphal Passenger Car "1421"		NRS __
13411	Lionel Lines Tempel Observation Car "1422"		NRS __
13412	Lionel Lines "Old #7" Passenger Car Set, 90		800 __
13413	Lionel Lines Combination Car "183"		NRS __
13414	Lionel Lines Passenger Car "184"		NRS __
13415	Lionel Lines Observation Car "185"		NRS __
13416	Lionel Lines New Jersey Baggage Car "326"		NRS __
13417	Lionel Lines Connecticut Passenger Car "327"		NRS __
13418	Lionel Lines New York Observation Car "328"		NRS __
13420	Lionel Lines State Passenger Car Set, 91		1300 __
13421	Lionel Lines California Passenger Car "2412," 90	200	360 __
13422	Lionel Lines Colorado Passenger Car "2413," 90	200	360 __
13423	Lionel Lines Illinois Passenger Car "2414," 92 u	200	817 __
13424	Lionel Lines New York Observation Car "2416", 92	200	360 __
13425	Lionel Lines Barnard Passenger Car "1423", 91 u		1350 __
13600	Lionel Lines Cattle Car "1513," 89 u		90 __
13601	"Season's Greetings" Boxcar, 89 u		105 __
13602	"Season's Greetings" Boxcar, 90 u		100 __
13604	"Season's Greetings" Boxcar, 91 u		110 __
13605	Lionel Lines Boxcar "1-214," 92		155 __
13700	Lionel Lines Caboose "1517," 89 u		105 __
13702	Lionel Lines Caboose "1217," 91		115 __
13800	Lionelville Passenger Station, 88 u		390 __
13801	Lionelville Station "126," 89 u		290 __
13804	Lionelville Switch Tower "437," 91		400 __
13900	Electric Rapid Transit Trolley "200," 89 u		290 __
13901	Electric Rapid Transit Trolley Trailer "201," 89 u		150 __

Section 6
CLUB CARS AND SPECIAL PRODUCTION

		Exc	Mint
ARTRAIN			
17885	1-D Tank Car, 90	55	65
17891	GTW 20th Anniversary Boxcar, 91	70	75
19425	CSX Flatcar with "Art in Celebration" trailer, 96	40	80
52013	Norfolk Southern Flatcar with trailer, 92	160	228
52024	Conrail Auto Carrier, 93	80	90
52049	BN Gondola with coil covers, 94	50	56
52097	Chessie System Reefer, 95	20	34
52140	Union Pacific Bunk Car, 97	20	37
52165	SP Caboose "6256," 98	30	60
52197	Santa Fe GP38 Diesel, 99	125	243
52227	"Artistry in Space" Boxcar, 00	40	75
52255	30th Anniversary Flatcar with billboard, 01	50	100
52283	Paint Vat Car, 02	30	59
52331	Flatcar with "America's Railways" trailer, 03	75	150
52349	Hometown Art Museum Hopper, purple, 04	20	35
52350	"Native Views" 3-bay Hopper, 04	35	65
52411	"35 Years" 1-D Tank Car, 06	20	35
CARNEGIE SCIENCE CENTER			
25085	Miniature Railroad & Village Boxcar, 09	25	50
26750	Great Miniature Railroad & Village Boxcar, 99	40	78
36202	Great Miniature Railroad 80th Anniversary Boxcar, 00	55	110
36234	Great Miniature Railroad & Village Boxcar, 01	25	50
52277	Carnegie Science Center 10th Anniversary Boxcar, 02	30	60
52332	Miniature Railroad & Village Boxcar, 03	30	58
52362	Miniature Railroad & Village 50th Anniversary Boxcar, 04	25	50
52399	Miniature Railroad & Village Express Boxcar, 05	25	50
52432	Miniature Railroad & Village Boxcar, 06	25	50
52510	Miniature Railroad & Village Caboose, 08	25	50
CHICAGOLAND RAILROAD CLUB			
52081	C&NW Boxcar "6464-555," 96	40	68
52101	BN Maxi-Stack Flatcar "64287" with containers, 97	40	82
52102	SF Extended Vision Caboose, red roof, 96	40	75
52103	SF Extended Vision Caboose, black roof, 96	40	75
52120	Shedd Aquarium Car "3435-557," 98	34	79
52148	REA/Santa Fe Operating Boxcar, 99	15	70
52170	SP Operating Boxcar "52170-561," 99	35	65
52171	UP Operating Boxcar "52171-561," 99	35	65
52178	Burlington Operating Boxcar "52178-559," 00	35	70
52179	ACL Operating Boxcar "52179-560," 00	40	73
52215	C&NW 3-bay Cylindrical Hopper, 01	30	60
52216	C&NW Cylindrical Hopper, 02	30	60

CLUB CARS AND SPECIAL PRODUCTION

		Exc	Mint	
52223	REA/Santa Fe Centennial Operating Boxcar, 00	35	65	___
52251	PRR Express Car, green, 01	35	67	___
52259	MP GP20 Diesel, traditional, 01	125	250	___
52292	PRR Express Car, Tuscan red, 02	25	50	___
52327	City of Los Angeles Express Car, 04	35	65	___
52328	City of New Haven Express Car, 04	30	55	___
52363	City of New Orleans Express Car, 04	30	55	___
52364	City of New York Express Car, 04	35	65	___
52388	Great Northern Tool Car, 06	25	48	___
52389	Great Northern Crew Car, 06	25	48	___
52390	Great Northern Welding Caboose, 06	40	78	___
52391	Great Northern Racing Crew Car, 06	25	48	___
52426	City of San Francisco Express Car, 07	30	55	___
52427	Rock Island Rocket Express Car, 07	30	55	___
52475	Western Pacific UP Heritage Boxcar, 07	30	60	___

CLASSIC TOY TRAINS

		Exc	Mint	
52126	MILW Boxcar "21027" with CTT Logo, 97	25	50	___

DEPT. 56

		Exc	Mint	
16270	Heritage Village Boxcar "9796," 96	30	56	___
52096	Snow Village Boxcar "9756," 95	45	85	___
52139	Square Window Caboose "6256," 97	35	72	___
52157	Holly Brothers 3-D Tank Car, 98	45	85	___
52175	4-6-4 Hudson Locomotive, CC, 99	175	350	___
52199	4-bay Hopper "6756," 00	30	53	___
52254	"Happy Holidays" Gondola, 01	20	35	___

EASTWOOD AUTOMOBILIA

		Exc	Mint	
16275	Radio Flyer Boxcar "16275," 96	25	50	___
16757	Johnny Lightning Auto Carrier "3435," 96	45	90	___
16985	Flatcar with 2 Ford vans, 97	25	49	___
52044	Mogen David Wine Vat Car, 95	21	30	___
52083	PRR Flatcar "21697" with tanker, 95	20	41	___
52130	Flatcar with Hot Wheels tanker, 97	30	60	___

HOUSTON TINPLATE OPERATORS SOCIETY (HTOS)

		Exc	Mint	
8900	Sam Houston Mint Car, 00	60	120	___
8901	Miracle Petroleum 1-D Tank Car, 01	50	100	___
8902	USS Houston Submarine Car, 02	50	100	___
8903	Railway Express Boxcar, 03	50	100	___
8904	Lone Star Bay Window Caboose, 04	50	100	___
8999	Lone Star Aquarium Car, mermaid or trout, 99	53	105	___

INLAND EMPIRE TRAIN COLLECTORS ASSOCIATION (IETCA)

		Exc	Mint	
1979	Boxcar, 79	5	15	___
1980	SP-type Caboose, 80	5	14	___
1981	Quad Hopper, 81	5	14	___

CLUB CARS AND SPECIAL PRODUCTION

		Exc	Mint
___ 1982	3-D Tank Car, 82	5	14
___ 1983	Reefer, 83	5	14
___ 1986	Bunk Car, 86	5	14
___ 7518	Carson City Mint Car, 84	36	43

LIONEL CENTRAL OPERATING LINES (LCOL)

		Exc	Mint
___ 1981	Boxcar, 81	10	23
___ 1986	Work Caboose, shell only, 86	5	14
___ 5724	Pennsylvania Bunk Car, 84	30	39
___ 6508	Canadian Pacific Crane Car, 83	20	40
___ 6907	NYC Wood-sided Caboose, 97	25	50
___ 9184	Erie Bay Window Caboose, 82	17	21
___ 9475	D&H "I Love NY" Boxcar, 85	20	34
___ 16342	CSX Gondola with coil covers, 92	10	20
___ 17221	NYC Boxcar, 95	15	30

LIONEL COLLECTORS ASSOCIATION OF CANADA (LCAC)

		Exc	Mint
___ 5710	Canadian Pacific Refrigerator Car, 83		215
___ 5714	Michigan Central Refrigerator Car, 85	120	150
___ 6100	Ontario Northland Covered Quad Hopper, 82		250
___ 8103	Toronto, Hamilton & Buffalo Boxcar, 81		150
___ 8204	Algoma Central Boxcar, 82		150
___ 8507/08	Canadian National F3 Diesel AA, shells only, 85		400
___ 8912	Canada Southern Operating Hopper, 89		95
___ 9413	Napierville Junction Boxcar, 80		10
___ 9718	Canadian National Boxcar, 79		20
___ 17893	BAOC 1-D Tank Car "914," 91		120
___ 52004	Algoma Central Gondola "9215" with coil covers, 92	70	90
___ 52005	Canadian National F3 Diesel B Unit "9517," 93		30
___ 52006	Canadian Pacific Boxcar "930016" (std O), 93	63	149
___ 52115	Wabash Lake Railway 2-tier Auto Carrier "9519," 98		100
___ 52125	TH&B Gondola 2-pack, 99		90
___ 86009	Canadian National Bunk Car, 86		115
___ 87010	Canadian National Express Reefer, 87		115
___ 88011	Canadian National Caboose (std O), 88		500
___ 830005	Canadian National Boxcar, 83		300
___ 840006	Canadian Wheat Board Covered Quad Hopper, 84		165
___ 900013	Canadian National Flatcar with trailers, 90		225

LIONEL COLLECTORS CLUB OF AMERICA (LCCA)

■ LCCA National Convention Cars

		Exc	Mint
___ 6112	Commonwealth Edison Quad Hopper with coal, 83	49	78
___ 6323	Virginia Chemicals 1-D Tank Car, 86	47	63
___ 6567	Illinois Central Gulf Crane Car "100408," 85	55	63
___ 7403	LNAC Boxcar, 84	21	24
___ 9118	Corning Covered Quad Hopper, 74	65	92

CLUB CARS AND SPECIAL PRODUCTION

		Exc	Mint	
9155	Monsanto 1-D Tank Car, 75	38	47	___
9159UP	UP Refrigerator Car, 10	50	100	___
9212	Seaboard Coast Line Flatcar with trailers, 76	22	31	___
9259	Southern Bay Window Caboose, 77	11	41	___
9358	Sands of Iowa Covered Quad Hopper, 80	24	33	___
9435	Central of Georgia Boxcar, 81	25	29	___
9460	D&TS Automobile Boxcar, 82	25	34	___
9701	Baltimore & Ohio Automobile Boxcar, 72	85	170	___
9727	TA&G Boxcar, 73	105	134	___
9728	Union Pacific Stock Car, 78	23	26	___
9733	Airco Boxcar with tank car body, 79	37	50	___
17870	East Camden & Highland Boxcar (std O), 87	29	33	___
17873	Ashland Oil 3-D Tank Car, 88	55	70	___
17876	Columbia, Newberry & Laurens Boxcar (std O), 89	32	40	___
17880	D&RGW Wood-sided Caboose (std O), 90	43	55	___
17887	Conrail Flatcar with Armstrong Tile trailer (std O), 91	30	49	___
17888	Conrail Flatcar with Ford trailer (std O), 91	42	80	___
17892	Conrail Flatcar with Armstrong and Ford Trailers (std O), 91	70	140	___
17899	NASA Tank Car "190" (std O), 92	47	53	___
27019	Imco PS-2 Covered Hopper, 09	25	50	___
52023	D&TS 2-bay ACF Hopper "2601" (std O), 93	27	40	___
52038	Southern Hopper "360794" w/Coal (std O), 94	36	46	___
52074	Iowa Beef Packers Refrigerator Car "197095" (std O), 95	15	32	___
52090	Pere Marquette DD Boxcar "71996" (std O), 96	25	52	___
52110	CStPM&O Boxcar "71997" (std O), 97	18	52	___
52151	Amtrak Express Baggage Boxcar "71998" (std O), 98	35	64	___
52176	Fort Worth & Denver Boxcar "8277" (std O), 99	30	55	___
52195	Double-stack Car with 2 containers, 00	50	100	___
52244	Louisville & Nashville Horse Car "2001," 01	25	50	___
52266	PRR "Coal Goes To War" Hopper "707025," 02	45	86	___
52267	PRR "Coal Goes To War" Hopper "707026," 02	45	92	___
52299	Las Vegas Mint Car, 03	23	80	___
52343	MILW Milk Car, orange, 04	43	130	___
52344	MILW Milk Car, blue, 04	50	172	___
52393	MKT Speeder, yellow, nonpowered, 05	10	20	___
52394	Frisco Speeder, red, powered, 05	10	25	___
52395	Frisco Flatcar, silver, powered, 05	10	25	___
52396	Frisco Flatcar with 2 speeders, 05	65	125	___
52412	UP Auxiliary Power Car, 06	30	55	___
52455	C&NW/UP Tank Car, 07	55	110	___
52491	PS-2 Covered Hopper 2-pack, 08	70	140	___
52507	NYC Water Tower, 08	45	83	___
52514	ATSF Mint Car with Gold, 09	140	275	___
52543	BNSF Mechanical Reefer, 09	70	140	___
52559	UP Cylindrical Hopper, 10	50	100	___

	CLUB CARS AND SPECIAL PRODUCTION	Exc	Mint
___ 52562	D&RGW Uranium Transport Mint Car, 10	115	230
___ 58560	Southern Boxcar, 13	45	90
___ 72511	Alamo Mint Car, 11	75	150
___ 75511	Federal Reserve Mint Car, 11	100	200

■ LCCA Meet Specials

		Exc	Mint
___ 1130	Tender, 76	5	15
___ 6014-900	Frisco Boxcar (O27), 75	17	30
___ 6483	Jersey Central SP-type Caboose, 82	24	28
___ 9016	Chessie System Hopper (O27), 79	16	20
___ 9036	Mobilgas 1-D Tank Car (O27), 78	20	22
___ 9142	Republic Steel Gondola, green or blue, with canisters, 77	15	23

■ Other LCCA Production

		Exc	Mint
___ 4001	RJ Corman Boxcar, 99	40	80
___ 4002	RJ Corman Boxcar, 99	20	40
___ 6464-2002	Maddox Retirement Boxcar, 02	50	100
___ 8068	Rock Island GP20 Diesel, 80	85	120
___ 9739	D&RGW Boxcar, 78	17	25
___ 9771	Norfolk & Western Boxcar, 77	15	32
___ 14154	Water Tower with LCCA plaque, 04	45	90
___ 17174	Great Northern 3-Bay Hopper, 03	10	25
___ 17234	Port Huron & Detroit Boxcar, 00	25	45
___ 17377	American Railway Express Reefer "302," 06	25	48
___ 17412	Gondola, blue, 02	15	28
___ 17895	LCCA Tractor, 91	13	21
___ 17896	Lancaster Lines Tractor, 91	22	30
___ 18090	D&RGW 4-6-2 Pacific Locomotive and Tender, 90	230	303
___ 18483	C&O Ballast Tamper, 07	40	73
___ 18490	UP Ballast Tamper, yellow, 06	65	125
___ 19998	Seasons Greetings Boxcar, 03	20	40
___ 26023	Flatcar with bulldozer, 04	30	53
___ 26024	Flatcar with scraper, 04	35	63
___ 26049	Speedboat Willie Flatcar with boat, 05	25	45
___ 26132	UP 1-D Tank Car, 06	15	27
___ 26780	Operating Giraffe Car, green or pink, 05	35	70
___ 26791	UP Chase Gondola, red, 03	15	32
___ 26791	Rio Grande Chase Gondola, black, 06	15	32
___ 26795	Mrs. O'Leary's Dairy Farm Stock Car, 07	50	100
___ 26834	La Cosa Nostra Railway Operating Ice Car, 07	25	75
___ 29232	Lenny the Lion Hi-Cube, signed by Lenny Dean, 98	35	63
___ 52025	Madison Hardware Tractor and Trailer, 93	13	18
___ 52039	Track 29 Bumper, 94	10	20
___ 52055	SOVEX Tractor and Trailer, 94	15	22
___ 52056	Southern Tractor and Trailer, 94	17	23

CLUB CARS AND SPECIAL PRODUCTION

		Exc	Mint	
52091	Lenox Tractor and Trailer, 95	5	14	___
52092	Iowa Interstate Tractor and Trailer, 95	10	20	___
52100	Grand Rapids Station Platform, 98	10	23	___
52107	On-track Pickup, orange, 96	25	50	___
52108	On-track Van, blue, 96	20	35	___
52131	Beechcraft Airplane, blue, 97	10	25	___
52138	Beechcraft Airplane, orange, 97	10	25	___
52152	Ben Franklin and Liberty Bell Reefer, 98	60	120	___
52153	6414 Auto Set, 4-pack, 98	35	72	___
52206	SD40 Diesel and Extended Vision Caboose, 00	325	650	___
52257	Season's Greetings Gondola, 01	20	36	___
52273	Flatcar with submarine, 02	110	219	___
52300	Halloween General Train, 04	180	360	___
52348	Halloween General Sheriff and Outlaw Car, 04	60	115	___
52405	Halloween General Add-on Cars, 06	80	160	___
52406	Halloween General Cannon, 08	70	135	___
52423	New Haven Alco Diesel Passenger Set, 09	316	510	___
52468	Postwar "2434" Passenger Coach, 09	40	75	___
52469	Postwar "2432" Passenger Coach, 09	40	75	___
52581	Texas Special Milk Car, 10	55	110	___
52582	Gondola with dinosaurs, 12	25	45	___
58526	Texas Special Cow and Calf SW9 Switchers, 14		375	___
58549	Texas Special Diamonds Mint Car, 14	40	75	___
58599	UP Cylindrical Hopper, 11	27	55	___

LIONEL OPERATING TRAIN SOCIETY (LOTS)

■ LOTS National Convention Cars

		Exc	Mint	
303	Stauffer Chemical 1-D Tank Car, 85	85	210	___
3764	Kahn's Brine Tank Reefer, 81	70	85	___
6111	L&N Covered Quad Hopper, 83	37	42	___
6211	C&O Gondola with canisters, 86	60	90	___
9414	Cotton Belt Boxcar, 80	39	55	___
16812	Grand Trunk 2-Bay ACF Hopper (std O), 96	30	60	___
16813	Pennsylvania Power & Light Hopper with coal (std O), 97	40	78	___
17874	Milwaukee Road Log Dump Car "59629," 88	90	148	___
17875	Port Huron & Detroit Boxcar "1289," 89	40	48	___
17882	B&O DD Boxcar "298011" with ETD, 90	55	65	___
17890	CSX Auto Carrier "151161," 91	45	80	___
18890	Union Pacific RS3 Diesel "8805," 89	120	145	___
19960	Western Pacific Boxcar "1952" (std O), 92	47	66	___
38356	Dow Chemical 3-D Tank Car, 87	85	125	___
52014	BN TTUX Flatcar Set with N&W trailers, 93	165	205	___
52041	BN TTUX Flatcar Set with Conrail trailers, 94	60	85	___
52067	Burlington Operating Ice Car "50240," 95	30	60	___
52135	ATSF Refrigerator Car "22739," 98	30	55	___

CLUB CARS AND SPECIAL PRODUCTION

		Exc	Mint
___ 52162	Gulf Mobile & Ohio DD Boxcar "24580," 99	35	65
___ 52196	CP Maxi-Stack Flatcar "524115" with 2 containers, 00	50	95
___ 52234	WM Well Car with transformer, 01	30	60
___ 52261	Schlitz Beer Refrigerator Car "92132," 2	30	60
___ 52281	PRR Operating Boxcar, 03	30	55
___ 52342	Southern Stock Car, sound, 04	30	57
___ 52346	D&H PS-2 Cement Hopper, 06	35	65
___ 52347	ATF SD80MAC Diesel, CC, 04	175	350
___ 52380	Virginian Coal Hopper "2605" with ETD, 05	25	50
___ 52381	Virginian Coal Hopper "2606" with ETD, 05	25	50
___ 52382	ATSF Extended View Caboose, 05	165	325
___ 52425	SP&S Boxcar (std O), 07	54	90
___ 52474	NYC Evans Auto Loader with 4 Studebakers, 08	40	82
___ 52550	NC&StL Dixieland Boxcar, 09	40	73
___ 52553	Tennessee Aquarium Car, 09	15	52
___ 52566	NH State of Maine Boxcar, 10	30	62
___ 52580	Robin Hood Beer Double-sheathed Boxcar, 11	40	80
___ 58505	Genesee Beer & Ale Boxcar, 12	35	65
___ 58553	UP Maxi-Stack Car with WP feather containers, 13	40	75
___ 58575	H. J. Heinz Double-sheathed Boxcar, 14	35	70
___ 80948	Michigan Central Boxcar, 82	145	230
___ 121315	Pennsylvania Hi-Cube Boxcar, 84	125	343

■ LOTS Meet Specials

		Exc	Mint
___ 52413	Saratoga Brewery Reefer, 06	30	60
___ 52456	Alpenrose Dairy Milk Car, 07	50	95
___ 52506	Studebaker Automobile Parts Boxcar, 08	40	75
___ 52552	Radioactive Waste Removal Car, 09	45	86

■ Other LOTS Production

		Exc	Mint
___ 1223	Seattle & North Coast Hi-Cube Boxcar, 86	300	400
___ 52042	BN TTUX Flatcar "637500C" with CN trailer, 94	50	60
___ 52048	Canadian National Tractor and Trailer "197993," 94	28	33
___ 52129	Lighted Billboard with Angela Trotta Thomas art, 97	15	28
___ 52217	LOTS/LCCA 2000 Convention Billboard, 00	5	10
___ 52260	National Aquarium in Baltimore Car, 01	55	110
___ 52280	More Precious than Gold Mint Car, 02	45	90
___ 52309	Patriotic Tank Car, 03	35	68
___ 52359	Silver Anniversary Ore Car "1979," 04	20	40
___ 52360	Silver Anniversary Ore Car "2004," 04	20	40
___ 52419	Touring Layout Aquarium Car, 05	45	90
___ 52523	Santa Fe Flatcar with trailer and tractor, 08	45	88
___ 52567	Santa Fe ACF 2-bay Hopper, 10	30	58
___ 52590	Santa Fe Warbonnet Mint Car, 11	40	75
___ 58535	Santa Fe ACF Transparent Boxcar, 12	40	75

	CLUB CARS AND SPECIAL PRODUCTION	Exc	Mint	
58566	Virginia & Truckee Carson City Mint Car, 13	35	70	___

LIONEL CENTURY CLUB (LCC)

		Exc	Mint	
14532	PRR Sharknose Diesel AA Set, LCC II, 00	350	690	___
18053	2-8-4 Berkshire Locomotive "726," 97	360	705	___
18057	6-8-6 PRR S2 Steam Turbine Locomotive "671," 98	320	568	___
18058	4-6-4 Hudson Locomotive "773," 97	274	840	___
18068	Tender for PRR Steam Turbine Locomotive "671," 99	105	210	___
18135	NYC F3 Diesel AA Set, 99	325	650	___
18178	NYC F3 Diesel B Unit, 99	115	230	___
18314	PRR GG1 Electric "2332," 97	490	560	___
18340	Fairbanks-Morse Train Master Set, LCC II, 00	450	900	___
24510	PRR Sharknose Diesel B Unit, LCC II, 00	100	200	___
28069	NYC 4-8-6 Niagara Locomotive "6024," CC, LCC II, 00	460	920	___
29173	Empire State Express Passenger Car 4-pack, LCC II, 02	175	350	___
29178	Empire State Express Passenger Car 2-pack, LCC II, 02	90	175	___
29181	Empire State Express Diner, LCC II, 02	100	200	___
29204	Boxcar "1900-2000," 96	165	331	___
29226	Berkshire Boxcar, 97	115	145	___
29227	GG1 Boxcar, 98	30	55	___
29228	PRR Turbine Boxcar "671," 99	30	60	___
29248	F3 Boxcar "2333," 99	35	67	___
31716	Niagara Milk Train Set, LCC II, 00	150	300	___
31726	PRR Sharknose Coal Train Set, LCC II, 00	90	180	___
31731	Train Master Freight Train Set, LCC II, 00	90	180	___
38000	NYC 4-6-4 Hudson Empire State Locomotive, LCC II, 02	495	990	___
39201	Hudson Boxcar "773," 00	30	58	___
39215	Niagara Boxcar, LCC II, 01	25	48	___
39217	Boxcar, LCC II, 00	30	60	___
39218	Gold Boxcar, LCC II, 00	45	85	___
39237	M-10000 Boxcar, LCC II, 00	35	70	___
39246	PRR Sharknose Boxcar, LCC II, 00	30	55	___
39265	Fairbanks-Morse Train Master Boxcar, LCC II, 00	30	60	___
39266	Empire State Boxcar, LCC II, 00	20	40	___
51007	UP M-10000 4-car Passenger Set, LCC II, 00	600	970	___
51249	UP Overland Route Sleeper Car, LCC II, 02	60	120	___

LIONEL RAILROADER CLUB (LRRC)

		Exc	Mint	
780	Boxcar, 82	55	67	___
781	Flatcar with trailers, 83	40	50	___
782	1-D Tank Car, 85	40	43	___
784	Covered Quad Hopper, 84	50	60	___
11183	Lincoln Funeral Train	400	800	___
11319	PRR Tuscan K4 Locomotive, CC	450	900	___
11320	PRR Tuscan K4 Locomotive	375	750	___
12875	Tractor and Trailer, 94	13	18	___

			Exc	Mint
	CLUB CARS AND SPECIAL PRODUCTION			
___	12921	Illuminated Station Platform, 95	19	22
___	14274	Water Tower, 07	10	20
___	15034	50th Anniversary Mail Car, 10	25	50
___	15035	Holiday Boxcar, 10	25	50
___	16800	Ore Car, yellow, 86	60	69
___	16801	Bunk Car, blue, 88	20	33
___	16802	Tool Car, 89	24	35
___	16803	Searchlight Car, 90	23	27
___	16804	Bay Window Caboose, 91	25	30
___	16839	Covered Bridge, 11	25	50
___	18680	4-6-4 Hudson Locomotive, 00	150	300
___	18684	4-6-2 Pacific Locomotive, 99	110	220
___	18818	GP38-2 Diesel, 92	100	117
___	19399	Christmas Boxcar, 13	30	60
___	19437	Flatcar with trailer, 97	30	55
___	19473	Operating Log Dump Car "3351," 99	20	38
___	19685	Western Union Dining Car, 02	24	47
___	19695	Western Union 1-D Tank Car, 03	10	22
___	19774	Porthole Caboose, 99	25	49
___	19775	Stock Car, 99	25	51
___	19924	Boxcar, 93	10	22
___	19930	Quad Hopper with coal, 94	14	20
___	19935	1-D Tank Car, 95	19	24
___	19940	Vat Car, 96	15	32
___	19953	6464 Boxcar, 97	20	35
___	19965	Aquarium Car "3435," 99	30	56
___	19966	Gondola "9820" (std O), 98	18	32
___	19978	Gold Membership Boxcar, 99	25	46
___	19991	Gold Membership Boxcar, 00	35	65
___	19992	Western Union Tool Car "3550," 00	25	50
___	19993	Gold Membership Boxcar, 01	35	65
___	19994	Western Union Passenger Car "1307," 01	30	60
___	19995	25th Anniversary Boxcar (std O), 01	25	49
___	24217	Animated Billboard, 08	15	30
___	25631	Lincoln Train Passenger Car 2-pack, 13	150	300
___	25635	Red Passenger Car 3-pack, 12	210	420
___	25639	Red Arrow Diner, 12	70	140
___	26089	Western Union Gondola with handcar, 05	35	65
___	26165	Western Union Refrigerator Car, 04	15	30
___	26382	Flatcar with tractor and tanker, 08	30	60
___	26413	Commemorative 4-bay Hopper, 08	35	68
___	26636	6830 50th Anniversary Flatcar with submarine, 11	30	55
___	26637	6640 50th Anniversary USMC Missile Launching Car, 11	35	65
___	27940	Postwar 6469 Liquified Gas Tank Car, 13	25	50
___	27943	Postwar 6416 Boat Loader, 13	25	50

CLUB CARS AND SPECIAL PRODUCTION

		Exc	Mint	
27944	Postwar 3413 Mercury Capsule Launch Car, 13	30	60	___
27945	Postwar 6446-60 LV Covered Quad Hopper, 13	30	55	___
28062	4-6-4 Hudson Locomotive, 00	575	1150	___
28571	GP9 Diesel, CC, 07	125	250	___
28665	Western Union 2-8-4 Berkshire Locomotive "665," 05	63	175	___
29200	Lionel Boxcar "9700," 96	20	38	___
29313	3409 50th Anniversary Helicopter Car, 11	35	70	___
29657	6413 50th Anniversary Mercury Capsule Car, 12	30	55	___
29658	6465 50th Anniversary Cities Service 2-D Tank Car, 12	25	50	___
29931	Holiday Boxcar, 05	10	25	___
29939	30th Anniversary Boxcar, 06	25	50	___
29941	Holiday Boxcar, 06	10	25	___
29946	Holiday Boxcar, 07	20	37	___
29947	Commemorative Boxcar, 07	15	30	___
29957	Holiday Boxcar, 08	25	50	___
29977	Holiday Boxcar, 11	30	60	___
36521	Western Union Searchlight Caboose, 05	15	32	___
36769	4th of July Boxcar with illumination, 03	35	70	___
37968	Clock Tower with wreath, 11	25	43	___
39249	Holiday Boxcar, 03	15	30	___
39264	Holiday Boxcar, 04	25	50	___
39352	6445 50th Anniversary Fort Knox Mint Car, 12	35	70	___
39353	50th Anniversary Santa Fe Boxcar, 11	30	55	___
39496	6475 50th Anniversary Vat Car, 10	30	60	___
58632	1955 Maintenance of Way Truck, 13	85	165	___
81116	Polar Express Operating Billboard, 14	30	60	___
81117	Polar Express Flatcar with silver bell, 14	25	45	___

LIONEL RAILROAD CLUB MILWAUKEE

		Exc	Mint	
52116	MILW Flatcar "194797," black, with tractor and trailer, 97	40	71	___
52163	CMStP&P Hiawatha DD Automobile Boxcar, 98	25	63	___
52180	MILW Flatcar "194799," Tuscan, with trailer, 99	25	70	___
52228	CMStP&P 1-D Water Tank Car "908309," 00	25	50	___
52229	MILW 1-D Diesel Fuel Tank Car "907797," 00	25	50	___
52230	1-D Tank Car 2-pack, 00	70	142	___
52246	CMStP&P Olympian"Boxcar "194701," 01	19	61	___
52265	MILW/Zoological Society Aquarium Car "4701," orange, 02	30	55	___
52278	MILW/Zoological Society Aquarium Car "4702," blue, 03	50	95	___
52297	MILW Refrigerator Car "194703," yellow, 03	35	67	___
52298	MILW Flatcar "194704" with orange trailer, 04	60	115	___
52337	MILW/Zoological Society Motorized Aquarium Car, 04	45	90	___
52368	MILW Flatcar "472004," black, 05	35	65	___
52369	MILW Trailer Train Auto Carrier "194705," 05	45	85	___
52370	CMStP&P Milk Car "364," tan, 05	57	86	___
52387	CMStP&P Flatcar "194706," gray, 06	30	59	___

CLUB CARS AND SPECIAL PRODUCTION	Exc	Mint
52400 MILW PS-2 2-Bay Hopper "99607," orange, 06	45	85
52401 MILW PS-2 2-Bay Hopper "98809," yellow, 06	33	73
52402 CMStP&P URTX Operating Ice Car "4706," 06	54	85
52428 CMStP&P 0-4-0 Switcher and Caboose Set, 60th Anniversary, 06	140	275
52429 CMStP&P 0-4-0 Switcher, 06	100	200
52430 CMStP&P Offset Cupola Caboose, 06	20	65
52458 MILW Stock Car "102721" (std O), 07	24	69
52466 CMStP&P Stock Car "105254" (std O), 07	35	76
52551 MILW "Big M" DD Boxcar "200947," yellow, 09	30	60
52572 MILW Reiman Aquarium Car, 11	40	75
52599 MILW 2-Bay ACF Hopper, 12	30	60
58563 CMStP&P Round-Roof Boxcar, 13	30	73
58591 MILW Flatcar "58591" with auto frames, 14	30	60

LONG ISLAND TOY TRAIN LOCOMOTIVE ENGINEERS

58520 Entenmann's Vat Car, 12	35	65
58556 Flatcar with U.S. Navy airplane, 13	30	70
58562 Entenmann's Quad Hopper, 14	40	74

NASSAU LIONEL OPERATING ENGINEERS (NLOE)

8389 Long Island Boxcar, 89	70	100
8390 Long Island Covered Quad Hopper, 90	70	100
8391A Long Island Bunk Car, 91	70	90
8391B Long Island Tool Car, 91	70	90
8392 Long Island 1-D Tank Car, 92	80	105
52007 Long Island RS3 Diesel "1552," 93	120	250
52019 Long Island Boxcar, 93	39	65
52020 Long Island Bay Window Caboose, 93	65	95
52026 Long Island Flatcar "8394" with Grumman trailer, 94	275	465
52061 Long Island Stern's Pickle Products Vat Car "8395," 95	100	200
52072 Grumman Tractor, 94	40	75
52076 Long Island Observation Car "8396," 96	175	350
52112 Long Island Ronkonkoma Vista Dome Car "9783," 97	150	300
52122 Meenan Oil 1-D Tank Car "8397" (std O), 97	30	60
52123 Long Island Hicksville Diner Car "9883," 98	150	300
52144 Long Island Flatcar with Grumman van, 99	50	94
52145 Long Island Jamaica Passenger Coach, 99	150	300
52145 Long Island Penn Station Passenger Coach, 99	150	300
52166 Long Island Flatcar "8398" with Grumman trailer, 98	40	77
52186 Grucci Fireworks Boxcar, 00	35	72
52232 Central RR of Long Island Boxcar, 01	30	60
52256 New York & Atlantic Boxcar "8302," 02	30	58
52296 Long Island Flatcar with Republic tanker, 03	40	78
52329 New York & Atlantic Caboose, 04	40	80
52341 Long Island Flatcar with Pan Am trailer, 05	45	85
52365 Long Island Flatcar with Lilco transformer, 04	70	135

CLUB CARS AND SPECIAL PRODUCTION

		Exc	Mint	
52420	Long Island 80th Anniversary Boxcar, 06	25	45	___
52480	Long Island Flatcar with pipes, 08	25	50	___
52489	Long Island Flatcar with P.C. Richard & Son trailer, 07	35	67	___
52555	Martha Clara Vineyards Vat Car, 09	30	58	___
52568	Flatcar with NY Islanders refrigerated trailer, 10	30	62	___
52586	Flatcar with Cradle of Aviation Museum trailer, 11	30	52	___
52592	Petland Discounts Aquarium Car, 11	35	70	___
58500	Nassau County Firefighters Museum Tank Car, 12	30	55	___
58567	Nathan's Famous Refrigerator Car, "83131," 13	40	74	___
58568	Nathan's Famous Refrigerator Car, "83132," 13	40	74	___

RAILROAD MUSEUM OF LONG ISLAND

52416	RMLI 15th Anniversary LIRR Boxcar, 05	85	170	___
52433	Atlantis Marine World Aquarium Car, 06	75	145	___
52453	North Fork Bank Mint Car, 07	45	90	___
52497	LIRR Flatcar with Entenmann's trailer and tractor, 08	55	110	___
52498	Boeing Fairchild Container Car, 10	40	75	___
52548	RMLI "Celebrating 175 Years of Railroading" Boxcar, 09	45	90	___
52557	Entenmann's Operating Boxcar, 10	45	90	___
52570	Riverhead Building Supply Boxcar, 11	30	60	___
52571	Riverhead Visitor's Center Boxcar, 11	30	60	___
52577	King Kullen Boxcar, 11	30	60	___
52595	J. P. Holland Submarine Car, 12	30	60	___
58521	Wonder Bread PS-2 Covered Hopper, 12	30	60	___
58551	Flatcar with White Castle refrigerated trailer, 13	30	60	___
58554	RCA Operating Radar Car, 13	30	60	___

ST. LOUIS LIONEL RAILROAD CLUB (ST. LOUIS LRRC)

52099	MP Flatcar with St. Louis trailer, 96	35	65	___
52104	St. Louis tractor and trailer, 96	10	20	___
52117	Wabash Flatcar with REA tractor and trailer, 97	35	65	___
52136A	Christmas Tractor and Trailer, 97		100	___
52136B	Frisco Tractor and Trailer, 98		100	___
52147	Frisco Campbell TOFC Flatcar, 98	40	75	___
52150	Frisco Campbell TOFC Flatcar, 98	65	130	___
52167	ATSF Flatcar "831999" with Navajo trailer, 99	40	75	___
52190	IC Flatcar with trailers, 00	40	80	___
52222	Cotton Belt Flatcar with SP tractor and trailer, 01	25	50	___
52224A	SP Flatcar with Navajo tractor and trailer, 01	15	25	___
52224B	SP Flatcar with service tractor and trailer, 01	15	25	___
52258	UP Flatcar with UP tractor and trailer, 02	30	55	___
52290	UP Flatcar with tractor trailer, 03	40	75	___
52336	U.S. Army Flatcar with tanker truck, 04	65	125	___
52371	NYC Flatcar with Fire Company tanker truck, 05	75	145	___
52392	PRR Flatcar with Hood's Milk tanker truck, 06	50	100	___
52440	U.S.M.C. Flatcar with tractor and trailer, 07	70	135	___

			Exc	Mint
___	52490	Silver Special Flatcar with USA tractor and trailer, 08	50	100
___	52513	Frisco Flatcar with U.S.A.F. trailer, 09	60	120

TRAIN COLLECTORS ASSOCIATION (TCA)

■ TCA National Convention Cars

			Exc	Mint
___	511	St. Louis Baggage Car, 81	36	41
___	2671-1968	TCA Tender, shell only, 68	10	54
___	5734	REA Refrigerator Car, 85	42	51
___	6315	Pittsburgh 1-D Tank Car, 72	55	60
___	6436-1969	Open Quad Hopper, red, 69	39	65
___	6464-1965	Pittsburgh Boxcar, blue, 65	125	182
___	6464-1970	Chicago Boxcar, 70	55	85
___	6464-1971	Disneyland Boxcar, 71	210	240
___	6517-1966	Bay Window Caboose, 66	163	268
___	6926	New Orleans Extended Vision Caboose, 86	27	39
___	7205	Denver Combination Car, 82	37	50
___	7206	Louisville Passenger Car, 83	40	55
___	7212	Pittsburgh Passenger Car, 84	41	50
___	7812	Houston Stock Car, 77	12	25
___	8476	4-6-4 Hudson Locomotive "5484," 85	255	310
___	9123	Dearborn 3-tier Auto Carrier, 73	25	36
___	9319	Silver Jubilee Mint Car, 79	60	130
___	9544	Chicago Observation Car, 80	25	50
___	9611	Boston Hi-Cube Boxcar, 78	21	26
___	9774	Orlando "Southern Belle" Boxcar, 75	15	35
___	9779	Philadelphia Boxcar "9700-1976," 76	26	34
___	9864	Seattle Refrigerator Car, 74	37	52
___	11737	TCA 40th Anniversary F3 Diesel ABA Set, 93	368	528
___	17879	Valley Forge Dining Car, 89	30	60
___	17883	New Georgia Passenger Car, 90	52	64
___	17898	Wabash Refrigerator Car "21596," 92	41	44
___	19211	Vermont Railway Flatcar 2-pack with 4 trailers, 08	80	160
___	52008	Bucyrus Erie Crane Car, 93	44	49
___	52035	Yorkrail GP9 Diesel "1750," shell only, 94	44	55
___	52036	TCA 40th Anniversary Bay Window Caboose, 94	35	40
___	52037	Yorkrail GP9 Diesel "1754," 94	125	150
___	52059	Clinchfield Quad Hopper "16413" with coal, 94	85	110
___	52062	Skytop Observation Car, 95	210	360
___	52085	Full Vista Dome Car, 96	60	115
___	52106	City of Phoenix Diner, 97	56	100
___	52142	Massachusetts Central Maxi-Stack Flatcar "5100-01," 98	60	120

CLUB CARS AND SPECIAL PRODUCTION		Exc	Mint	
52143	City of Providence Passenger Car, 98	76	140	__
52146	Ocean Spray Refrigerator Car, 98	120	235	__
52155	City of San Francisco Baggage Car, 99	70	140	__
52191	City of Grand Rapids Aluminum Passenger Car, 00	70	135	__
52210	Rico Station, 00	15	29	__
52220	City of Chattanooga Vista Dome Car, 01	70	140	__
52221	Norfolk Southern Boxcar, 01	25	50	__
52237	Lionel Gondola, yellow, 01	55	110	__
52238	Lionel Gondola, red, 01	55	110	__
52239	Lionel Gondola, silver, 01	55	110	__
52240	Lionel Gondola 3-pack, 01	155	330	__
52241	Lionel Gondola, black, 02	10	15	__
52242	Lionel Gondola, blue, 02	20	35	__
52250	City of Chicago Combination Car, 02	65	130	__
52272	Lionel Gondola, gold, 02	40	80	__
52276	California Gold Mint Car, 03	35	65	__
52333	Harmony Dairy Milk Car, 04	45	90	__
52338	Lionel 50th Anniversary Mint Car, 04	40	75	__
52339	50th Anniversary Convention Banquet Car with coin, 04	188	360	__
52340	Train Order Building, 04	45	90	__
52373	Montana Rail Link 2-car Set, 05	45	90	__
52374	Montana Rail Link 2-Bay Hopper, 05	25	50	__
52375	Montana Rail Link Flatcar with pulp-wood logs, 05	25	50	__
52376	GN Refrigerator Car, 05	30	60	__
52403	T&P Stock Car (std O), 06	40	75	__
52414	Flatcar with 3 snowmobiles, 07	40	80	__
52481	Ben & Jerry's Refrigerator Car, 08	50	95	__
52500	ATSF Grand Canyon Reefer, 09	30	60	__
52508	Celebrate America Mint Car, 09	50	95	__
58544	St. Louis Refrigerator Car, 13	50	85	__
58547	Cotton Belt Blue Streak Merchandise Boxcar, 13	40	75	__
58571	Bethlehem Steel PS-1 Boxcar, 14	40	80	__
58572	Reading Philadelphia Mint Car, 14	40	80	__

■ TCA Museum-Related and Other Cars

1018-1979	Mortgage Burning Hi-Cube Boxcar, 79	32	35	__
5731	L&N Refrigerator Car, 90	50	95	__
7780	TCA Museum Boxcar, 80	15	26	__
7781	Hafner Boxcar, 81	15	26	__
7782	Carlisle & Finch Boxcar, 82	15	26	__
7783	Ives Boxcar, 83	15	26	__
7784	Voltamp Boxcar, 84	15	23	__
7785	Hoge Boxcar, 85	15	23	__
9771	Norfolk & Western Boxcar, 77	24	31	__
16811	Rutland Boxcar "5477096," 96	18	47	__

CLUB CARS AND SPECIAL PRODUCTION		Exc	Mint
___ 52045	Pennsylvania Dutch Milk Car "61052," 94	45	90
___ 52051	Baltimore & Ohio Sentinel Boxcar "6464095," 95	36	42
___ 52052	TCA 40th Anniversary Boxcar, 94	45	90
___ 52063	NYC Pacemaker Boxcar "6464125," 95	175	345
___ 52064	Missouri Pacific Boxcar "6464150," 95	185	370
___ 52065	Pennsylvania Dutch Grain Operating Boxcar "9208," 96	50	100
___ 52118	Rio Grande Boxcar "5477097," 97	30	53
___ 52119	TCA Museum 20th Anniversary Boxcar, 97	35	70
___ 52128	Pennsylvania Dutch Pretzels Boxcar, 99	40	80
___ 52172	L&N "Share the Freedom" Boxcar "5477099," 99	25	56
___ 52198	Frisco Boxcar "5477000," 00	25	43
___ 52215	Museum Work Train Gondola with pipes, 03	30	53
___ 52226	Angela Trotta Thomas Boxcar "2000," 01	50	100
___ 52243	Museum Work Train 1-D Tank Car, 01	25	50
___ 52271	Museum Work Train Flatcar with wheel load, 02	10	20
___ 52289	National Toy Train Museum 25th Anniversary Bullion Car, 02	40	75
___ 52295	National Toy Train Museum Gondola with pipes, 03	10	16
___ 52310	Museum Work Train Boxcar, 04	30	53
___ 52311	50th Anniversary Golden Express Freight Set, 04	233	450
___ 52372	Museum Work Train Baggage Car, 05	35	70
___ 52408	N&W Caboose, 06	30	55
___ 52409	Museum Work Train Idler Caboose, 06	35	68
___ 52437	Museum Work Train Crane Car, 07	40	78

TCA Bicentennial Special Set

		Exc	Mint
___ 1973	Bicentennial Observation Car, 76	34	50
___ 1974	Bicentennial Passenger Car, 76	34	50
___ 1975	Bicentennial Passenger Car, 76	34	50
___ 1976	Bicentennial U36B Diesel, 76	115	165

Atlantic Division

		Exc	Mint
___ 1980	Atlantic Division Flatcar with trailers, 80	28	34
___ 6101	Burlington Northern Covered Quad Hopper, 82	21	34
___ 9186	Conrail N5c Caboose, 79	22	30
___ 9193	Budweiser Vat Car, 84	80	110
___ 9466	Wanamaker Boxcar, 83	105	135
___ 9788	Lehigh Valley Boxcar, 78	19	24

Desert Division

		Exc	Mint
___ 52088	Desert Division 25th Anniversary On-track Step Van, 96	60	120
___ 52105	Superstition Mountain Operating Gondola "61997," 97	40	80
___ 52442	Verde Canyon Boxcar, 07	30	55
___ 52443	Grand Canyon Boxcar, 07	30	55

■ Dixie Division

		Exc	Mint
52127	Dixie Division 10th Anniversary Southern 3-Bay Hopper, 98	35	70
52444	Dixie Division 20th Anniversary PS-1 Boxcar, 06	40	80

■ Eastern Division

		Exc	Mint
9412	Richmond, Fredericksburg & Potomac Boxcar, 79		26
9740	Chessie System Boxcar, 76		23
9771	Norfolk & Western Boxcar, 78		30
9783	B&O Time-Saver Boxcar, 77		30

■ Fort Pitt Division

		Exc	Mint
1984-30X	Heinz Ketchup Boxcar, 84	250	500

■ Great Lakes Division

		Exc	Mint
1983	Churchill Downs Boxcar, 83	100	200
1983	Churchill Downs Refrigerator Car, 83	125	250
9740	Chessie System Boxcar, 76	10	23

■ Great Lakes Division: Detroit-Toledo Chapter

		Exc	Mint
8957	Burlington Northern GP20 Diesel, 80	115	230
8958	Burlington Northern GP20 Diesel Dummy, 80	75	150
9119	Detroit & Mackinac Covered Quad Hopper, 77	19	22
9272	New Haven Bay Window Caboose, 79	19	22
9401	Great Northern Boxcar, 78	10	23
9730	CP Rail Boxcar, 76	10	27
52000	Detroit-Toledo Division Flatcar with trailer, 92	70	85

■ Great Lakes Division: Three Rivers Chapter

		Exc	Mint
9113	Norfolk & Western Quad Hopper, 76	27	30

■ Great Lakes Division: Western Michigan Chapter

		Exc	Mint
9730	CP Rail Boxcar, 74	10	25

■ Lake & Pines Division

		Exc	Mint
52018	3-M Boxcar, 93	225	450

■ Lone Star Division

		Exc	Mint
7522	New Orleans Mint Car with coin, 86	210	420
52093	Lone Star Division Boxcar "6464696," 96	15	32
52585	Texas Special Mint Car, 11	3535	62
58512	SP Daylight Mint Car, 12		65
58552	Texas Special Mint Car with silver bars, 12	35	65

■ Lone Star Division: North Texas Chapter

		Exc	Mint
___ 9739	D&RGW Boxcar, 76	10	20

■ Metropolitan Division (METCA)

		Exc	Mint
___ 10	Jersey Central F3 A Unit, shell only, 71	10	25
___ 9272	New Haven Bay Window Caboose, 79	21	25
___ 9754	NYC Pacemaker Boxcar, 76	15	31
___ 52485	NYC Mint Car with copper load, 8	60	120
___ 52486	Pennsylvania Mint Car, green, 9	60	125
___ 52487	Pennsylvania Mint Car, Tuscan, 9	60	125
___ 52488	NYC Lightning Stripe Mint Car, 10	30	60
___ 52574	Fort Knox 50th Anniversary Mint Car, 11	50	100
___ 52583	B&O Capitol Dome Mint Car, 11	50	100
___ 52596	LIRR Mint Car, 12	50	100
___ 58523	Blue Comet Mint Car, 13	35	69
___ 58534	Jersey Central Mint Car, 13	35	69
___ 58569	Erie Lackawanna Mint Car, 14	35	69

■ Midwest Division

		Exc	Mint
___ 4	C&NW F3 Diesel A Unit, shell only, 77	40	80
___ 5	Midwest Division Covered Quad Hopper, 78	25	43
___ 1287	C&NW Reefer, 84		NRS
___ 7600	Frisco "Spirit of '76" N5c Caboose "00003," 76	20	38
___ 9872	PFE Refrigerator Car "00006," 79	205	410

■ Midwest Division: Museum Express

		Exc	Mint
___ 9264	ICG Covered Quad Hopper, 78	22	26
___ 9289	C&NW N5c Caboose, 80	37	44
___ 9785	Conrail Boxcar, 77	20	35
___ 9786	C&NW Boxcar, 79	10	20

■ New England Division (NETCA)

		Exc	Mint
___ 1203	Boston & Maine NW2 Diesel, shell only, 72	35	65
___ 5710	Canadian Pacific Refrigerator Car, 82	38	45
___ 5716	Vermont Central Refrigerator Car, 83	25	30
___ 6124	Delaware & Hudson Covered Quad Hopper, 84	25	30
___ 8051	Hood's Milk Boxcar, 86	44	75
___ 9181	Boston & Maine N5c Caboose, 77	23	35
___ 9400	Conrail Boxcar, Tuscan or blue, 78	23	27
___ 9415	Providence & Worcester Boxcar, 79	28	34
___ 9423	NYNH&H Boxcar, 80	25	30
___ 9445	Vermont Northern Boxcar, 81	29	39
___ 9753	Maine Central Boxcar, 75	24	34
___ 9768	Boston & Maine Boxcar, 76	32	39

CLUB CARS AND SPECIAL PRODUCTION		Exc	Mint	
9785	Conrail Boxcar, 78	22	26	___
16911	B&M Flatcar with trailer, 95	75	150	___
22677	B&M Baked Beans Boxcar, 10	25	45	___
52001	B&M Quad Hopper with coal, 92	50	75	___
52016	B&M Gondola with coil covers, 93	55	65	___
52043	L.L. Bean Boxcar, 94	115	215	___
52080	B&M Flatcar "91095" with trailer, 95	10	215	___
52111	Ben & Jerry's Flatcar with trailer, 96	160	313	___
52212	Berkshire Brewing Refrigerator Car, 00	80	155	___
52236	Moxie Boxcar, 01	80	160	___
52270	Jenney Manufacturing Tank Car, 02	75	150	___
52306	NH Flatcar with New England Transportation trailer, 03	75	150	___
52352	Poland Spring Boxcar, 04	65	131	___
52379	CP Rail with W.B. Mason trailer, 05	40	75	___
52383	Fisk Tire Boxcar, 05	55	108	___
52397	D&H Flatcar with Vermont Railway trailer, 06	45	90	___
52418	Indian Motocycle Boxcar, 06	95	190	___
52434	New England Central Flatcar with Cabot's trailer, 07	50	95	___
52448	Oilzum Tanker 2-pack, 08	55	105	___
52457	Cape Cod Potato Chip Boxcar, 07	50	93	___
52484A	Cabot's Refrigerator Car, 08	100	250	___
52484B	Bay State Beer Refrigerator Car, 09	45	90	___
52589	B&M Flatcar with Howard Johnson trailer, 11	50	100	___
58522	Grafton & Upton Flatcar with Spag's trailer, 12	45	90	___

■ Ozark Division: Gateway Chapter

5700	Oppenheimer Reefer, 81	55	110	___
9068	Reading Bobber Caboose, 76	10	20	___
9601	Illinois Central Gulf Hi-Cube Boxcar, 77	10	21	___
9767	Railbox Boxcar, 78	10	20	___
52003	Meet Me In St. Louis Flatcar with trailer, 92	260	520	___

■ Pacific Northwest Division

52077	Great Northern Hi-Cube Boxcar "9695," 95	230	460	___

■ Rocky Mountain Division

1971-1976	Rocky Mountain Division Refrigerator Car, 76	40	75	___

■ Sacramento Sierra Chapter

6401	Virginian Bay Window Caboose, 84	20	35	___
9301	U.S. Mail Operating Boxcar, 76	26	38	___
9414	Cotton Belt Boxcar, 80	20	35	___
9427	Bay Line Boxcar, 81	15	30	___
9444	Louisiana Midland Boxcar, 82	20	35	___
9452	Western Pacific Boxcar, 83	20	35	___

CLUB CARS AND SPECIAL PRODUCTION		Exc	Mint
____ 9705	D&RGW Boxcar, 75	20	38
____ 9723	Western Pacific Boxcar, 73	15	29
____ 9726	Erie-Lackawanna Boxcar, 79	10	23
____ 9730	CP Rail Boxcar, 77	15	30
____ 9785	Conrail Boxcar, 78	10	22

■ Southern Division

		Exc	Mint
____ 1976	FEC F3 Diesel ABA, shells only, 76	140	275
____ 1986	Southern Division Bunk Car, 86	15	30
____ 6111	L&N Covered Quad Hopper, 83	20	22
____ 9287	Southern N5c Caboose, 77	15	22
____ 9352	Trailer Train Flatcar with circus trailers, 80	29	55
____ 9403	Seaboard Coast Line Boxcar, 78	10	18
____ 9405	Chattahoochie Boxcar, 79	10	21
____ 9443	Florida East Coast Boxcar, 81	10	23
____ 9471	ACL Boxcar, 84	10	23
____ 9482	Norfolk & Southern Boxcar, 85	10	23
____ 16606	Southern Searchlight Car, 88	17	24
____ 19942	Southern Division 30th Anniversary Boxcar, 96	10	20

■ Western Division

		Exc	Mint
____ 52275	Western Pacific Boxcar, 03	55	105

TOY TRAIN OPERATING MUSEUM (GADSDEN-PACIFIC DIVISION)

		Exc	Mint
____ 17872	Anaconda Ore Car, 88	60	72
____ 17878	Magma Ore Car, 89	45	55
____ 17881	Phelps Dodge Ore Car, 90	36	40
____ 17886	Cyprus Ore Car, 91	26	31
____ 19961	Inspiration Consolidated Copper Ore Car, 92	23	30
____ 52011	Tucson, Cornelia & Gila Bend Ore Car, 93	20	29
____ 52027	Pinto Valley Mine Ore Car, 94	20	29
____ 52071	Copper Basin Railway Ore Car, 95	15	30
____ 52089	SMARRCO Ore Car, 96	10	26
____ 52124	El Paso & Southwestern Ore Car, 97	20	40
____ 52164	SP Ore Car, 98	20	35
____ 52177	Arizona Southern Ore Car, 99	20	35
____ 52213	BHP Copper Ore Car, 00	15	29
____ 52248	Tombstone & Western Ore Car, 01	20	40
____ 52279	Dragoon & Northern Ore Car, 02	25	50
____ 52307	Twin Buttes Ore Car, 03	20	35
____ 52358	AJO & Southwestern Ore Car, 04	25	45
____ 52386	Ray & Gila Bend Ore Car, 05	25	45
____ 52421	Calabasas, Tuscon & Northwestern Ore Car, 06	25	45
____ 52473	Mascot & Western Ore Car, 07	45	90
____ 52524	Tucson, Globe & Northern Ore Car, 08	20	42
____ 52558	Port of Tucson Ore Car, 09	25	45
____ 52579	Rosemont Copper Ore Car, 10	20	40

CLUB CARS AND SPECIAL PRODUCTION		Exc	Mint
52588	ASARCO Ore Car, 11	20	40 ___
58513	Freeport-McMoRan Ore Car, 12	20	40 ___
58557	San Pedro & Southwestern Ore Car, 13	20	40 ___
58583	Arizona Eastern Ore Car, 14	20	42 ___

TOY TRAIN OPERATING SOCIETY (TTOS)

■ TTOS National Convention Cars

		Exc	Mint
1984	Sacramento Northern Boxcar, 84	65	85 ___
1985	Snowbird Covered Quad Hopper, 85	42	55 ___
6017	SP-type Caboose, blue, 68	125	210 ___
6017	SP-type Caboose, brown, 69	200	300 ___
6057	SP-type Caboose, orange, 69	125	210 ___
6076	Santa Fe Hopper (O27), 70	45	103 ___
6167-1967	Hopper, olive drab with gold lettering, 67	25	85 ___
6257	SP-type Caboose, red, 69	125	210 ___
6476-1	LV Hopper, gray, 69	45	73 ___
6582	Portland Flatcar with wood, 86	44	55 ___
9326	Burlington Northern Bay Window Caboose, 82	15	25 ___
9347	Niagara Falls 3-D Tank Car, 79	38	46 ___
9355	Delaware & Hudson Bay Window Caboose, 82	25	50 ___
9361	C&NW Bay Window Caboose, 82	47	55 ___
9382	Florida East Coast Bay Window Caboose, 82	35	70 ___
9512	Summerdale Junction Passenger Car, 74	38	53 ___
9520	Phoenix Combination Car, 75	29	33 ___
9526	Snowbird Observation Car, 76	36	51 ___
9535	Columbus Baggage Car, 77	33	51 ___
9678	Hollywood Hi-Cube Boxcar, 78	25	32 ___
9868	Oklahoma City Refrigerator Car, 80	36	44 ___
9883	Phoenix Refrigerator Car, 83	25	50 ___
17871	NYC Flatcar "81487" with Kodak and Xerox trailers, 87	185	217 ___
17877	MKT 1-D Tank Car "3739469," 89	55	70 ___
17884	Columbus & Dayton Terminal Boxcar (std O), 90	32	41 ___
17889	SP Flatcar "15791" (std O) with trailer, 91	43	63 ___
19963	Union Equity 3-Bay ACF Hopper "86892" (std O), 92	30	38 ___
52010	Weyerhaeuser DD Boxcar "838593" (std O), 93	25	42 ___
52029	Ford 1-D Tank Car "12" (O27), 94	33	40 ___
52030	Ford Gondola "4023" (O27), 94	23	29 ___
52031	Ford Hopper "1458" (O27), 94	28	33 ___
52057	Western Pacific Boxcar "64641995," 95	45	48 ___
52087	New Mexico Central Boxcar "64641996," 96	30	55 ___
52114	NYC Flatcar with Gleason and SASIB trailers, 97	30	58 ___
52149	Conrail Flatcar with Blum coal shovel, 98	30	60 ___
52192	SP Crane and Gondola Set, 00	40	75 ___
52193	SP Gondola "6060," 00	25	50 ___

CLUB CARS AND SPECIAL PRODUCTION		Exc	Mint
___ 52194	SP Crane Car "7111," 00	40	35
___ 52231	British Columbia 1-D Tank Car, 01	15	25
___ 52288	D&RGW Cookie Box Boxcar, 03	10	20
___ 52293	D&RGW 1-D Tank Car, 03	20	40
___ 52378	Las Vegas & Tonopah Boxcar, 05	35	70
___ 52410	SP Flatcar with 2 trailers, 06	35	70
___ 52441	Pennsylvania Operating Hopper, 07	30	60
___ 52445	Pennsylvania Boxcar, 07	35	68
___ 52545	Erie "6464" Boxcar, 09	25	50
___ 58333	Sierra Railroad Sierra Beer Boxcar, 13	35	70

■ TTOS Division Cars

		Exc	Mint
___ 52009	Sacramento Valley Division WP Boxcar, 93	34	44
___ 52040	Wolverine Division GTW Flatcar w/Tractor and trailer, 94	42	51
___ 52058	Central California Division Santa Fe Boxcar, 95	32	42
___ 52086	Canadian Division Pacific Great Eastern Boxcar, 96	15	48
___ 52113	Northeastern Division Genesee & Wyoming 3-Bay Hopper, 97	20	34
___ 52264	New Mexico Division Durango & Silverton Operating Hopper, 2	30	55

■ TTOS Southwestern Division

		Exc	Mint
___ 19962	Southern Pacific 3-bay ACF Hopper "496035" (std O), 92	50	65
___ 52047	Cotton Belt Wood-sided Caboose (std O), smoke, 93-94	60	68
___ 52073	Pacific Fruit Express Refrigerator Car "459402" (std O), 95	30	65
___ 52098	National Bureau of Standards Boxcar (std O), 96	25	47
___ 52121	Mobilgas Tank Car "238" (std O), 97	40	75
___ 52154	Pacific Fruit Express Refrigerator Car "459403" (std O), 98	30	53
___ 52205	SP Overnight Merchandise Service Boxcar 5-pack, 00	95	185
___ 52287	Operating MX Missile Car, 02	30	55
___ 52385	Ward Kimball Boxcar, 05	30	55
___ 52431	Operating MX Missile Car, 06	30	60
___ 52476	Life Savers Tank Car, 07	45	85
___ 52515	Life Savers Wild Cherry Tank Car, 08	40	77
___ 52565	Life Savers Pep O Mint Tank Car, 09	30	60
___ 52569	Life Savers Butter Rum Tank Car, 10	30	62
___ 52591	Life Savers Wint O Green Tank Car, 11	30	62
___ 58545	Life Savers Bay Window Caboose, 13	40	82

■ Other TTOS Production

		Exc	Mint
___ 1983	Phoenix 3-D Tank Car, 83	50	100
___ 17894	Southern Pacific Tractor, 91	17	21
___ 27148	BNSF PS-2 Hopper "4427," 06	25	50
___ 52021	Weyerhaeuser Tractor and Trailer, 93	24	31
___ 52022	Union Pacific Boxcar, 93	200	400
___ 52032	Ford 1-D Tank Car (027) with Kughn inscription, 94	70	95
___ 52046	ACL Boxcar "16247," 94	55	110
___ 52053	Carail Boxcar, 94	50	55

CLUB CARS AND SPECIAL PRODUCTION

		Exc	Mint	
52068	Toy Train Parade Contadina Boxcar "16245," 94	30	55	___
52078	Southern Pacific SD9 Diesel "5366," 96	120	235	___
52079	Southern Pacific Bay Window Caboose, 96	45	55	___
52084	Union Pacific I-Beam Flatcar "16380" with load, 95	80	155	___
52384	Transparent Damage Control Boxcar, 03	35	71	___
52451	Pennsylvania "X2454" Boxcar, 07	107	175	___
52505	Forest Service/Smokey Bear Flatcar with airplane, 08	25	45	___
52525	SP "X6454" Boxcar, 08	25	50	___
52526	SP "X6454" Boxcar, 08	80	165	___
52547	C&NW Refrigerator Car, 09	44	84	___

VIRGINIA TRAIN COLLECTORS (VTC)

		Exc	Mint	
7679	Boxcar, 79		17	___
7681	N5c Caboose, 81		23	___
7682	Covered Quad Hopper, 82		26	___
7683	Virginia Fruit Express Reefer, 83		26	___
7684	Vitraco 3-D Tank Car, 84		26	___
7685	Boxcar, 85		27	___
7686	GP7 Diesel, 86		100	___
7692-1	Baggage Car (027), 92	35	45	___
7692-2	Combination Car (027), 92	35	45	___
7692-3	Dining Car (027), 92	35	45	___
7692-4	Passenger Car (027), 92	35	45	___
7692-5	Vista Dome Car (027), 92	35	45	___
7692-6	Passenger Car (027), 92	35	45	___
7692-7	Observation Car (027), 92	35	45	___
7696	20th Anniversary Station, 96		65	___
52060	Tender "7694" with whistle, 94		70	___

Section 7
BOXES 1945-1969

		Good P-5	Exc P-7
20	90-Degree Crossover, 45-61	3	8
20	"O" 90 Degree Crossover	7	12
020X	45-Degree Crossover	3	8
020X	"O" 45 Degree Crossover	8	13
22	Switch Controller	2	3
22	Remote Control Switches, pair (with both inserts)	4	10
22	Remote Control Switches, pair (yellow, with both inserts)	4	10
022A	Remote Control Switches, pair (with both inserts)	7	14
25	Bumper	2	5
26	Bumper	2	5
30	Water Tower	11	30
35	Boulevard Lamp	4	11
36	Operating Car Remote Control Set	5	13
37	Uncoupling Track Set	2	5
38	Operating Water Tower	22	76
40	Hookup Wire, 8 reels (dealer box)	33	118
41	U.S. Army Switcher	14	44
42	Manual Switches	3	17
42	Picatinny Arsenal Switcher	25	78
44	U.S. Army Mobile Launcher	21	73
44	U.S. Army Mobile Launcher (with orange sleeve)	38	153
45	U.S. Marines Mobile Launcher	35	107
45/45N	Automatic Gateman	5	19
48	Super O Insulated Straight Track, 6 pieces (dealer box)	12	35
49	Super O Insulated Curved Track, 6 pieces (dealer box)	11	32
50	Section Gang Car (early classic)	11	31
50	Section Gang Car (brown corrugated)	5	14
50	Section Gang Car (orange picture)	13	35
51	Navy Yard Switcher	19	54
52	Fire Car	26	70
53	Rio Grande Snowplow	30	82
54	Ballast Tamper	14	39
55	PRR Tie-Jector Car	13	38
56	Lamp Post	3	12
56	M&StL Mine Transport	36	125
57	AEC Switcher	53	210
58	Lamp Post	6	21
58	Great Northern Rotary Snow Blower	49	161
59	Minuteman Switcher	67	227
60	Lionelville Rapid Transit Trolley (classic)	11	36
60	Lionelville Rapid Transit Trolley (brown corrugated)	8	26
64	Highway Lamp Post	7	24
65	Handcar	27	128

BOXES		Good P-5	Exc P-7	
68	Executive Inspection Car	25	60	___
69	Maintenance Car	24	65	___
70	Yard Light	4	11	___
71	Lamp Post	2	6	___
75	Goose Neck Lamps	3	12	___
76	Boulevard Street Lamps	5	20	___
76	Boulevard Street Lamps (Hillside checkerboard)	17	60	___
89	Flagpole	4	23	___
91	Circuit Breaker	6	23	___
92	Circuit Breaker		10	___
93	Water Tower	11	31	___
97	Coal Elevator	16	48	___
108	Trestle Set (overstamped)	8	22	___
110	Graduated Trestle Set	1	4	___
111	Elevated Trestle Set	4	11	___
112	Remote Control Switches, pair (Super O)	6	16	___
112LH	Remote Control Super O Switch, left-hand	5	14	___
112RH	Remote Control Super O Switch, right-hand	5	15	___
114	Newsstand with horn	7	25	___
115	Passenger Station (113-1, Star Corp. stamped on box)	30	123	___
118	Newsstand with whistle	7	21	___
122	Lamp Assortment	16	83	___
123	Lamp Assortment	15	83	___
123-60	Replacement Lamp Assortment	5	55	___
125	Whistle Shack	5	16	___
128	Animated Newsstand	10	26	___
130	60-degree Crossing (Super O)	2	6	___
132	Passenger Station	9	22	___
133	Passenger Station	9	21	___
138	Water Tower	11	30	___
140	Automatic Banjo Signal (classic)	4	11	___
142	Manual Switches, pair (Super O)	5	19	___
145	Automatic Gateman (brown corrugated)	7	18	___
145	Automatic Gateman (cellophane), 66	11	38	___
148	Dwarf Trackside Signal	5	17	___
150	Telegraph Pole Set	4	13	___
151	Automatic Semaphore	3	9	___
151	Automatic Semaphore (narrower box, earlier postwar)	7	18	___
151	Automatic Semaphore (blister pack enclosure)	17	58	___
152	Automatic Crossing Gate	3	26	___
153	Automatic Block Control Signal	5	12	___
154	Automatic Highway Signal (cellophane)	5	18	___
154	Automatic Highway Signal (all other boxes)	3	9	___
155	Blinking Light Signal	8	32	___
156	Station Platform	11	35	___
157	Station Platform	8	23	___

|---|---|---|---|
___ 160	Unloading Bin	19	75
___ 161	Mail Pickup Set (with liner)	11	35
___ 163	Single Target Block Signal (white box)	17	49
___ 164	Log Loader	18	48
___ 167	Whistle Controller	2	5
___ 175	Rocket Launcher	20	52
___ 175-50	Rocket, separate sale	51	147
___ 175-50	Dealer Display Box, 6 rockets	75	402
___ 182	Magnetic Crane	22	66
___ 192	Operating Control Tower	38	138
___ 193	Industrial Water Tower	11	39
___ 195	Floodlight Tower	6	21
___ 195	Floodlight Tower (cellophane)	7	32
___ 195-75	Floodlight Extension, 8-bulb (classic)	7	32
___ 195-75	Floodlight Extension, 8-bulb (white box)	10	48
___ 197	Rotating Radar Antenna	10	38
___ 197-15	Separate Sale Radar Head	31	87
___ 199	Microwave Relay Tower	6	30
___ 202	UP Alco Diesel A Unit	11	42
___ 204	Santa Fe Alco AA Set (master carton)	74	207
___ 204	Santa Fe Alco AA Set (P and T boxes)	23	108
___ 204P	Santa Fe A Unit	16	43
___ 204T	Santa Fe Diesel Dummy A Unit	20	55
___ 208	Santa Fe Alco AA Set (master carton)	46	232
___ 208	Santa Fe Alco AA Set (P and T boxes)	25	101
___ 208P	Santa Fe Alco A Unit	17	64
___ 208T	Santa Fe Alco Dummy A Unit	32	76
___ 209	New Haven Alco AA Set (master carton)	89	360
___ 209	New Haven Alco AA Set (P and T boxes)	72	262
___ 209P	New Haven Alco A Unit	23	84
___ 209T	New Haven Diesel Dummy A Unit	43	140
___ 210	Texas Special Alco AA Set (P and T boxes)	15	61
___ 210P	Texas Special Alco A Unit	6	27
___ 210T	Texas Special Alco Dummy A Unit	16	42
___ 211	Texas Special Alco AA Set (P and T boxes)	23	94
___ 211P	Texas Special Alco A Unit (brown corrugated)	14	45
___ 212	Santa Fe AA Master Carton		170
___ 212P	USMC Alco Diesel A Unit	31	104
___ 212T	USMC Diesel Dummy A Unit	194	669
___ 214	Plate Girder Bridge (classic)	3	8
___ 214	Plate Girder Bridge (Hillside orange picture)	7	23
___ 216	Burlington Alco Diesel A Unit	27	93
___ 217	B&M Alco AB Set (C and P boxes)	33	135
___ 217C	B&M Alco B Unit	15	50
___ 217P	B&M Alco A Unit	12	43
___ 217-16	Sleeve for 217 and 218 outer boxes	26	81

BOXES		Good P-5	Exc P-7
218	Santa Fe Alco AA Set (master carton)	18	83 ___
218C	Santa Fe Alco Diesel B Unit	20	76 ___
218P	Santa Fe Alco Diesel A Unit	17	59 ___
218T	Santa Fe Diesel Dummy A Unit	21	62 ___
220	Santa Fe Alco AA Set (P and T boxes)	19	83 ___
220T	Santa Fe Alco Dummy A Unit	20	90 ___
221	2-6-4 Locomotive	17	72 ___
221T	Tender	10	40 ___
221W	Whistling Tender	14	44 ___
223P	Santa Fe Alco A Unit	15	56 ___
224	2-6-2 Locomotive	18	76 ___
224	U.S. Navy Alco AB Set (C and P boxes)	33	187 ___
224C	U.S. Navy B Unit	45	102 ___
224P	U.S. Navy Alco A unit	31	139 ___
225	C & O Alco Diesel A Unit	12	49 ___
226	B&M Alco Diesel AB Set (C and P boxes)	24	100 ___
226C	B&M Alco Diesel B Unit	13	30 ___
226P	B&M Alco Diesel A Unit	10	43 ___
228P	CN Alco Diesel A Unit	20	70 ___
229C	M&StL Alco B Unit	13	45 ___
229P	M&StL Alco A Unit (brown corrugated)	9	36 ___
230P	C&O Alco A Unit	15	53 ___
231P	Rock Island Alco A Unit	9	67 ___
233	2-4-2 Scout Locomotive	15	35 ___
234W	Whistle Tender	11	31 ___
235	2-4-2 Scout Locomotive	21	79 ___
236	2-4-2 Scout Locomotive	8	32 ___
237	2-4-2 Scout Locomotive	8	31 ___
238	Engine and Tender Master Carton	15	34 ___
239	2-4-2 Scout Locomotive	18	39 ___
243	2-4-2 Scout Locomotive	8	30 ___
243W	Tender	8	25 ___
244T	Tender (overstamped 1625T box)	23	68 ___
245	2-4-2 Scout Locomotive	18	50 ___
246	2-4-2 Scout Locomotive	11	35 ___
247	2-4-2 Scout Locomotive	11	35 ___
247T	Tender	7	25 ___
248	2-4-2 Scout Locomotive	9	43 ___
249	2-4-2 Scout Locomotive	14	40 ___
250	2-4-2 Scout Locomotive	10	28 ___
250T	Tender	7	23 ___
252	Crossing Gate	3	9 ___
253	Block Control Signal	4	12 ___
256	Illuminated Freight Station	13	31 ___
257	Freight Station with diesel horn	10	28 ___
260	Bumper (Hagerstown checkerboard)	5	14 ___

BOXES		Good P-5	Exc P-7
____ 260	Bumper (all other boxes)	2	5
____ 262	Highway Crossing Gate	4	22
____ 264	Operating Forklift Platform	21	61
____ 282	Portal Gantry Crane	27	72
____ 299	Code Transmitter Beacon Set	11	39
____ 308	Railroad Sign Set	3	11
____ 309	Yard Sign Set	3	11
____ 310	Billboard Set	2	6
____ 313	Bascule Bridge	36	145
____ 314	Scale Model Girder Bridge	5	14
____ 315	Illuminated Trestle Bridge	22	71
____ 316	Trestle Bridge	7	24
____ 317	Trestle Bridge	6	18
____ 321	Trestle Bridge	5	15
____ 321-100	Trestle Bridge	9	22
____ 332	Arch-Under Trestle Bridge	5	15
____ 334	Operating Dispatching Board	11	44
____ 342	Culvert Loader	27	83
____ 345	Culvert Unloader	25	81
____ 348	Manual Culvert Unloader	21	60
____ 350	Engine Transfer Table	17	51
____ 350-50	Transfer Table Extension	15	50
____ 352	Ice Depot	20	67
____ 353	Trackside Control Signal	5	15
____ 356	Operating Freight Station	9	35
____ 356-35	Baggage Trucks Set	12	40
____ 362	Barrel Loader	7	23
____ 362-78	Wooden Barrels	2	5
____ 364	Conveyor Lumber Loader	8	27
____ 365	Dispatching Station	14	39
____ 375	Turntable	23	77
____ 394	Rotary Beacon	6	21
____ 394-37	Rotating Beacon Cap	2	6
____ 395	Floodlight Tower	6	22
____ 397	Operating Coal Loader	10	33
____ 397	Operating Coal Loader (separate label on box)	15	42
____ 400	B&O Passenger Rail Diesel Car	20	50
____ 404	B&O Baggage-Mail Rail Diesel Car	35	81
____ 410	Billboard Blinker	4	15
____ 413	Countdown Control Panel	6	17
____ 415	Diesel Fueling Station	13	38
____ 419	Heliport Control Tower	34	115
____ 443	Missile Launching Platform	11	29
____ 445	Switch Tower	8	20
____ 448	Missile Firing Range Set	14	47
____ 450	Operating Signal Bridge	4	15

BOXES		Good P-5	Exc P-7	
452	Overhead Gantry Signal	10	37	___
455	Operating Oil Derrick	19	65	___
456	Coal Ramp	17	42	___
460	Piggyback Transportation Set	15	40	___
460-150	Two Trailers	66	212	___
461	Platform with truck and trailer	11	42	___
462	Derrick Platform Set	46	153	___
464	Lumber Mill	10	38	___
465	Sound Dispatching Station	11	35	___
470	Missile Launching Platform	8	26	___
494	Rotating Beacon (classic)	6	22	___
497	Coaling Station	20	51	___
600	MKT NW2 Switcher	23	63	___
601	Seaboard NW2 Switcher	25	76	___
602	Seaboard NW2 Switcher	29	95	___
610	Erie NW2 Switcher	16	58	___
611	Jersey Central NW2 Switcher (overstamped 621 box)	50	108	___
613	UP NW2 Switcher	29	88	___
614	Alaska NW2 Switcher	52	186	___
616	Santa Fe NW2 Switcher	22	111	___
617	Santa Fe NW2 Switcher	33	104	___
621	Jersey Central NW2 Switcher	22	69	___
622	Santa Fe NW2 Switcher	33	95	___
623	Santa Fe NW2 Switcher	18	80	___
624	C&O NW2 Switcher	26	71	___
625	LV GE 44-ton Switcher	76	293	___
626	B&O GE 44-ton Switcher	43	182	___
628	Northern Pacific GE 44-ton Switcher	20	81	___
629	Burlington GE 44-ton Switcher	41	178	___
634	Santa Fe NW2 Switcher	26	145	___
637	2-6-4 Locomotive	15	48	___
637LTS	2-6-4 Locomotive and Tender (master carton)	48	194	___
646	4-6-4 Locomotive	21	61	___
665	4-6-4 Locomotive	21	53	___
665LTS	4-6-4 Locomotive and Tender (master carton)	60	248	___
671	6-8-6 Steam Turbine Locomotive	27	76	___
671R	6-8-6 Steam Turbine Locomotive	46	130	___
671W	Whistle Tender	15	118	___
671-75	Smoke Lamp, 12 volt	2	6	___
675	2-6-2 Locomotive (classic), 47-49	20	89	___
675	2-6-2 Locomotive (brown corrugated), 52	33	97	___
681	6-8-6 Steam Turbine Locomotive	42	133	___
681LTS	6-8-6 Steam Turbine and Tender (master carton)	163	513	___
682	6-8-6 Steam Turbine Locomotive	41	134	___
682LTS	6-8-6 Steam Turbine and Tender (master carton)	375	850	___
685	4-6-4 Hudson Locomotive	25	66	___

BOXES		Good P-5	Exc P-7
____ 685LTS	4-6-4 Hudson Locomotive and Tender (master carton)	160	463
____ 726	2-8-4 Berkshire Locomotive, 46	58	156
____ 726	2-8-4 Berkshire Locomotive (after 1946)	42	112
____ 726RR	2-8-4 Berkshire Locomotive	25	71
____ 736	2-8-4 Berkshire Locomotive, 50	31	89
____ 736	2-8-4 Berkshire Locomotive (after 1950)	25	71
____ 736X	2-8-4 Berkshire Locomotive	31	93
____ 736LTS	2-8-4 Berkshire Locomotive and Tender (master carton)	59	232
____ 736W	Pennsylvania Tender	15	58
____ 746	N&W 4-8-4 Locomotive	59	174
____ 746LTS	N&W 4-8-4 Locomotive and Tender (master carton)	241	586
____ 746W	N&W Whistle Tender	35	148
____ 746WX	N&W Whistle Tender, long stripe	50	136
____ 760	Curved Track	8	24
____ 773	4-6-4 Hudson Locomotive, 50	97	288
____ 773	4-6-4 Hudson Locomotive, 64-66	66	165
____ 773LTS	4-6-4 Hudson and Tender (master carton), 50	131	581
____ 773LTS	4-6-4 Hudson and Whistle Tender (master carton), 64-66	101	321
____ 773W	NYC Tender	27	86
____ 810	Milwaukee Road Freight Set	75	500
____ 920	Scenic Display Set	15	43
____ 920-2	Tunnel Portals	6	20
____ 927	Lubricating Kit	2	6
____ 928	Maintenance and Lubricating Kit	5	25
____ 943	Ammo Dump	4	13
____ 951	Farm Set	15	44
____ 952	Figure Set	11	35
____ 953	Figure Set	15	45
____ 957	Farm Building and Animal Set	18	52
____ 959	Barn Set	17	49
____ 960	Barnyard Set	10	58
____ 961	School Set	30	182
____ 963	Frontier Set	18	65
____ 965	Farm Set	14	53
____ 966	Firehouse Set	14	53
____ 969	Construction Set	11	44
____ 970	Ticket Booth	11	44
____ 972	Landscape Tree Assortment	10	35
____ 981	Freight Yard Set	11	36
____ 983	Farm Set	14	47
____ 984	Railroad Set	14	55
____ 986	Farm Set	20	87
____ 987	Town Set		185
____ 1000W	Steam Freight Set	30	95
____ 1001	Diesel Freight Set	18	65
____ 1001	2-4-2 Scout Locomotive	7	33

BOXES		Good P-5	Exc P-7
1001T	Tender	5	13 ___
1002	Gondola	3	8 ___
X1004	PRR Baby Ruth Boxcar	3	8 ___
1005	Sunoco 1-D Tank Car	3	8 ___
1007	LL SP-type Caboose	3	8 ___
1009	Manumatic Track Section	4	12 ___
1019	Remote Control Track Set (027)	4	8 ___
1024	Manual Switches for 027 Track Set	6	15 ___
1024	Manual Switches	3	6 ___
1025	Illuminated Bumper (027)	1	5 ___
1032	Transformer, 75 watts	2	6 ___
1033	Transformer, 90 watts	3	10 ___
1034	Transformer, 75 watts	2	8 ___
1041	Transformer, 50 watts	2	7 ___
1041	Transformer, 60 watts	2	8 ___
1043	Transformer, 50 watts	3	8 ___
1043-500	Transformer, 50 watts, ivory	30	79 ___
1044	Transformer, 90 watts	3	10 ___
1045	Operating Watchman	5	21 ___
1047	Operating Switchman	26	85 ___
1060	2-4-2 Locomotive (brown corrugated)	17	78 ___
1107	Steam Freight Set	15	49 ___
1109	Steam Freight Set	13	40 ___
1110	2-4-2 Locomotive	5	21 ___
1112	Scout Set	8	25 ___
1113	Scout Set	14	39 ___
1117	Scout Steam Freight Set	14	35 ___
1119	Scout Set	11	35 ___
1120	2-4-2 Scout Locomotive	5	17 ___
1121	027 Remote Control Switches, pair	3	8 ___
1121LH	027 Remote Control Switch, left-hand	3	8 ___
1121RH	027 Remote Control Switch, right-hand	3	8 ___
1122	027 Remote Control Switches, pair	3	10 ___
1130	2-4-2 Locomotive	6	22 ___
1130T	Tender (classic)	5	14 ___
1130T	Tender (orange perforated)	13	35 ___
1130T-500	Tender, pink, from Girls Set	47	162 ___
1232	Transformer, 75 watts, made for export	4	12 ___
1407B	Steam Switcher Work Set	50	268 ___
1417WS	Steam Work Train Set	28	145 ___
1423W	Steam Freight Set	22	120 ___
1425B	Steam Switcher Freight Set	54	224 ___
1429WS	Steam Freight Set	35	138 ___
1431	Steam Freight Set	26	75 ___
1432W	027 Steam Passenger Set	55	251 ___
1433W	Steam Freight Set	14	37 ___

BOXES		Good P-5	Exc P-7
___ 1435WS	Steam Freight Set	10	35
___ 1447WS	Turbine Locomotive Set	41	138
___ 1451WS	O27 Steam Freight Set	25	110
___ 1453WS	O27 Steam Freight Set	19	71
___ 1455WS	Steam Freight Set	21	74
___ 1457B	Santa Fe Freight Set (marked "1457"), 49	37	142
___ 1457B	Santa Fe Freight Set, 50	40	151
___ 1459WS	Steam Freight Set	30	85
___ 1463WS	Steam Freight Set	36	85
___ 1464W	Union Pacific Diesel Passenger Set	127	485
___ 1465	Steam Freight Set	23	76
___ 1467W	Union Pacific Freight Set	44	134
___ 1469WS	Steam Freight Set	25	77
___ 1471	Steam Freight Set	20	70
___ 1471WS	Steam Freight Set	22	66
___ 1473WS	Steam Freight Set	25	66
___ 1475WS	Steam Freight Set	19	80
___ 1479WS	Steam Freight Set	26	96
___ 1481WS	Steam Freight Set	22	75
___ 1483WS	Steam Freight Set	30	93
___ 1485WS	Steam Freight Set	21	65
___ 1500	Steam Freight Set	13	49
___ 1502WS	Steam Freight Set	158	496
___ 1503WS	Steam Freight Set	30	69
___ 1505WS	Steam Freight Set	30	87
___ 1507WS	Steam Freight Set	30	80
___ 1511S	Steam Freight Set	21	63
___ 1513S	Steam Freight Set	25	77
___ 1515WS	Steam Freight Set	35	99
___ 1517W	Texas Special Freight Set	47	155
___ 1519WS	Steam Freight Set	44	154
___ 1520W	Texas Special Passenger Set	170	651
___ 1521WS	Steam Work Train Set	64	225
___ 1523	Diesel Freight Set	44	162
___ 1525	Diesel Freight Set	23	65
___ 1527	O27 Steam Work Train Set	42	147
___ 1529	Pennsylvania Diesel Freight Set	66	204
___ 1531W	Diesel Freight Set	33	99
___ 1533WS	Steam Freight Set	25	70
___ 1534W	Burlington Diesel Passenger Set	166	508
___ 1535W	Diesel Freight Set	78	250
___ 1536W	Diesel Passenger Set	75	422
___ 1537WS	Steam Freight Set	55	191
___ 1538WS	Hudson Passenger Set	230	755
___ 1539W	Santa Fe Diesel Freight Set	80	216
___ 1541WS	Steam Freight Set	50	157

BOXES		Good P-5	Exc P-7	
1542	Electric Freight Set	14	62	___
1543	Lehigh Valley Freight Set	15	60	___
1547S	Steam Freight Set	22	65	___
1549	Steam Work Train Set	29	85	___
1551W	Diesel Freight Set	10	43	___
1552W	Diesel Passenger Set	65	242	___
1553W	Diesel Freight Set	30	71	___
1555WS	027 Steam Freight Set	29	61	___
1557	Diesel Freight Set	27	80	___
1559W	MILW Diesel Freight Set	33	88	___
1561WS	Steam Freight Set	23	55	___
1562W	Burlington GP7 Diesel Passenger Set	40	133	___
1569	UP Diesel Freight Set	18	58	___
1571	LV Diesel Freight Set	21	63	___
1573	Steam Freight Set	24	67	___
1575	Diesel Freight Set	26	62	___
1577S	Steam Freight Set	32	75	___
1578S	Steam Passenger Set	158	509	___
1579S	Steam Freight Set	28	70	___
1581	Jersey Central Mixed Set	24	74	___
1583WS	Steam Freight Set	22	67	___
1585W	Diesel Freight Set	26	73	___
1586	Diesel Passenger Set	33	100	___
1587S	Girls Train Set	444	1294	___
1589WS	027 Steam Freight Set	36	124	___
1590	Steam Freight Set	17	64	___
1591	USMC Military Set	122	599	___
1593	UP Diesel Work Train Set	30	90	___
1599W	Texas Special Freight Set	28	91	___
1600	Diesel Passenger Set	148	564	___
1601W	Wabash GP7 Diesel Set	46	218	___
1603WS	Steam Freight Set	33	88	___
1605W	Santa Fe Diesel Freight Set	41	140	___
1607WS	Steam Work Train Set	13	44	___
1608W	New Haven Passenger Set	107	539	___
1609W	Steam Freight Set	26	83	___
1611	027 Alaska Diesel Freight Set	60	192	___
1612	027 General Set	30	103	___
1613S	Steam Freight Set	27	87	___
1615	B&M Diesel Freight Set	24	73	___
1615	0-4-0 Locomotive	18	48	___
1615LTS	0-4-0 Locomotive and Tender (master carton)	61	170	___
1615T	Tender	10	48	___
1617S	Steam Work Train	63	140	___
1619W	Santa Fe Diesel Freight Set	36	97	___
1621WS	027 Steam Freight Set (brown corrugated)	58	202	___

BOXES		Good P-5	Exc P-7
____ 1621WS	027 Steam Freight Set (suitcase)	37	110
____ 1623W	NP Diesel Freight Set	54	195
____ 1625	0-4-0 Locomotive	32	116
____ 1625T	Tender	29	79
____ 1625WS	Steam Freight Set	30	102
____ 1626W	Santa Fe Diesel Passenger Set	89	205
____ 1627S	Stream Freight Set	20	41
____ 1629WS	C&O Diesel Freight Set	20	88
____ 1631WS	027 Steam Freight Set	21	66
____ 1633	U.S. Navy Diesel Freight Set	103	339
____ 1635WS	Steam Freight Set	41	135
____ 1637	Santa Fe Diesel Freight Set	22	66
____ 1639WS	Steam Freight Set	16	38
____ 1640-100	Presidential Kit	15	54
____ 1643	C&O Diesel Freight Set	14	48
____ 1645	Diesel Freight Set	36	95
____ 1647	U.S. Marines Military Set	40	119
____ 1648	Steam Freight Set	8	40
____ 1649	Santa Fe Diesel Freight Set	22	64
____ 1650	Steam Military Set	31	89
____ 1651	Passenger Train Set	37	131
____ 1654	2-4-2 Locomotive	8	28
____ 1654W	Whistle Tender	14	23
____ 1655	2-4-2 Locomotive	15	40
____ 1656	0-4-0 Locomotive	26	110
____ 1656LTS	4-4-0 Locomotive and Tender (master carton)	50	205
____ 1665	0-4-0 Locomotive	38	152
____ 1666	2-6-2 Locomotive	15	56
____ 1682T	Tender	5	21
____ 1800	General Gift Pack	23	124
____ 1805	Marine Land Sea and Air Gift Pack	813	1398
____ 1809	Western Gift Pack	12	60
____ 1862	4-4-0 Civil War General Locomotive	24	79
____ 1862T	Tender	13	47
____ 1865	Western & Atlantic Coach	10	42
____ 1866	Western & Atlantic Mail-Baggage Car	10	42
____ 1872	4-4-0 Civil War General Locomotive	40	100
____ 1872LTS	4-4-0 Locomotive and Tender (master carton)	100	400
____ 1872T	Tender	16	47
____ 1875	Western & Atlantic Coach	40	155
____ 1875W	Western & Atlantic Coach, whistle	19	108
____ 1876	Western & Atlantic Baggage Car	17	69
____ 1877	Flatcar with fence and horses	13	42
____ 2001	Track Make-up Kit (027)	800	2000
____ 2002	Track Make-up Kit (027)	600	1400
____ 2016	2-6-4 Locomotive	10	33

BOXES		Good P-5	Exc P-7	
2018	2-6-4 Locomotive	11	32	___
2018-14	Sleeve for Outer Box	6	20	___
2020	6-8-6 Steam Turbine Locomotive	18	68	___
2020W	Tender	11	60	___
2023	Union Pacific Alco AA Set (master carton), 50	31	109	___
2023	Union Pacific Alco AA Set (master carton), 51	30	98	___
2025	2-6-2 or 2-6-4 Locomotive	15	73	___
2026	2-6-2 or 2-6-4 Locomotive	13	50	___
2028	Pennsylvania GP7 Diesel	33	126	___
2029	2-6-4 Locomotive	15	50	___
2031	Rock Island Alco AA Set (master carton), 52	60	165	___
2032	Erie Alco AA Set (master carton)	42	112	___
2033	Union Pacific Alco AA Set (master carton)	31	93	___
2034	2-4-2 Scout Locomotive	10	42	___
2035	2-6-4 Locomotive	20	66	___
2036	2-6-4 Locomotive	14	49	___
2036LTS	2-6-4 Locomotive and Tender (master carton)	450	1762	___
2037	2-6-4 Locomotive (brown corrugated)	11	34	___
2037-500	2-6-4 Locomotive, pink, from Girls Set	74	330	___
2046	4-6-4 Locomotive	22	72	___
2046LTS	4-6-4 Locomotive and Tender (master carton)	90	297	___
2046T	Lionel Lines Tender, for export	21	72	___
2046W	Lionel Lines Tender (early classic, with liner)	17	65	___
2046W	Lionel Lines Tender (marked "2046")	21	80	___
2046W	Pennsylvania Tender	30	99	___
2046W-50	Pennsylvania Tender	12	55	___
2055	4-6-4 Locomotive	21	64	___
2055LTS	4-6-4 Locomotive and Tender (master carton)	67	219	___
2056	4-6-4 Locomotive	18	54	___
2065	4-6-4 Locomotive	18	57	___
2103W	Steam Freight Set	25	90	___
2105WS	Steam Freight Set	39	127	___
2113WS	Steam Freight Set	48	204	___
2120WS	Steam Passenger Set	100	565	___
2121WS	Steam Freight Set	34	162	___
2124W	GG1 Passenger Set	160	1053	___
2125WS	Steam Freight Set	58	110	___
2126WS	Steam Turbine Passenger Set	80	665	___
2129WS	Steam Freight Set	113	600	___
2136WS	Steam Passenger Set	39	152	___
2139W	GG1 Freight Set	151	778	___
2140WS	Steam Turbine Passenger Set	91	669	___
2141WS	Steam Turbine Freight Set	35	189	___
2145WS	Steam Freight Set	99	283	___
2146W	Berkshire Passenger Set	69	525	___
2147WS	Steam Freight Set	53	140	

BOXES		Good P-5	Exc P-7
____ 2148WS	Hudson Passenger Set	450	1531
____ 2149	Santa Fe Diesel Freight Set	86	397
____ 2151W	F3 Freight Set	58	280
____ 2153WS	Steam Freight Set	53	185
____ 2155WS	Berkshire Freight Set	48	202
____ 2159W	GG1 Freight Set	114	503
____ 2161W	Santa Fe Twin Diesel Freight Set	40	161
____ 2163WS	Steam Freight Set	40	160
____ 2165WS	Steam Freight Set	40	139
____ 2167WS	Steam Freight Set	36	147
____ 2171W	NYC Diesel Freight Set	30	170
____ 2173WS	Steam Freight Set	47	151
____ 2175W	Santa Fe Diesel Freight Set	42	166
____ 2177WS	Steam Freight Set	18	63
____ 2179WS	Steam Freight Set	27	75
____ 2183WS	Steam Freight Set	34	113
____ 2185W	NYC Diesel Freight Set	33	107
____ 2187WS	Steam Freight Set	19	75
____ 2190W	Santa Fe Diesel Passenger Set	36	154
____ 2191W	Santa Fe Diesel Freight Set	37	160
____ 2193W	NYC Diesel Freight Set	36	118
____ 2201WS	Steam Freight Set	41	125
____ 2203WS	Steam Freight Set	50	229
____ 2205WS	Steam Freight Set	28	95
____ 2207W	Santa Fe Diesel Freight Set	36	133
____ 2209W	NYC Diesel Freight Set	41	129
____ 2211WS	Steam Freight Set	30	128
____ 2213WS	Steam Freight Set	35	116
____ 2217WS	Steam Turbine Freight Set	62	212
____ 2219W	Diesel Freight Set	74	315
____ 2221WS	Steam Freight Set	34	133
____ 2222WS	Hudson Passenger Set	111	530
____ 2223W	Lackawanna FM Freight Set	131	446
____ 2225T	Tender	18	77
____ 2225WS	Steam Freight Set	43	170
____ 2226W	Tender	36	111
____ 2226WX	Lionel Lines Tender	40	118
____ 2227W	Santa Fe Diesel Freight Set	63	287
____ 2229W	NYC Diesel Freight Set	34	125
____ 2231W	Southern Diesel Freight Set	74	286
____ 2234W	Santa Fe Passenger Set	59	314
____ 2235W	Milwaukee Road Diesel Freight Set	42	168
____ 2237WS	Steam Freight Set	36	154
____ 2239W	Illinois Central Freight Set	95	410
____ 2240	Wabash F3 AB Set (C and P boxes)	58	249
2240	Wabash F3 AB Set (master carton)	122	695

		Good P-5	Exc P-7	
2240C	Wabash F3 B Unit	40	166	___
2240P	Wabash F3 A Unit	29	95	
2241WS	Steam Freight Set	23	82	
2242	New Haven F3 AB Set (C and P boxes)	91	513	
2242	New Haven F3 AB Set (master carton)	288	933	
2242C	New Haven F3 B Unit	78	319	
2242P	New Haven F3 A Unit	82	301	
2243	Santa Fe F3 AB Set (C and P boxes)	30	97	
2243	Santa Fe F3 AB Set (master carton)	42	132	
2243C	Santa Fe F3 B Unit	23	77	
2243P	Santa Fe F3 A Unit	24	82	
2243W	Diesel Freight Set	34	135	
2244W	Wabash Passenger Set	201	865	
2245	Texas Special F3 AB Set (C and P boxes)	55	196	
2245	Texas Special F3 AB Set (master carton)	275	788	
2245C	Texas Special F3 B Unit	34	119	
2245P	Texas Special F3 A Unit	22	83	
2247W	Wabash F3 Diesel Freight Set	67	268	___
2251W	Diesel Freight Set	43	170	___
2254W	Pennsylvania GG1 Passenger Set, 55	242	1062	
2255W	Diesel Work Train Set	50	140	
2257	SP-type Caboose	4	17	
2257WS	Steam Freight Set	27	116	
2259W	New Haven Electric Freight Set	40	162	
2261WS	Steam Freight Set	25	90	
2263W	New Haven Freight Set	42	193	
2265WS	Steam Freight Set	31	112	___
2267W	Diesel Freight Set	51	205	
2269W	B&O Diesel Freight Set	113	663	___
2270W	Jersey Central Passenger Set	304	1108	
2271W	Pennsylvania GG1 Freight Set	67	335	___
2273W	Milwaukee Road Diesel Freight Set	101	536	___
2274W	Pennsylvania Passenger Set	196	797	___
2275W	Wabash GP7 Freight Set	49	131	___
2276W	Budd Passenger Set	54	317	___
2277WS	Work Train Set	36	170	___
2279W	NH Electric Freight Set	68	215	___
2283W	Steam Freight Set	30	120	___
2285W	Diesel Freight Set	87	229	___
2289WS	Berkshire Super O Freight Set	45	192	___
2291W	Rio Grande Diesel Freight Set	116	585	___
2292WS	Steam Passenger Set	110	582	___
2293W	Pennsylvania GG1 Freight Set	167	916	___
2295WS	N&W Steam Freight Set	181	772	___
2296W	Canadian Pacific Passenger Set	330	1161	___
2297WS	N&W Steam Freight Set	129	689	

	BOXES		Good P-5	Exc P-7
___	2321	Lackawanna FM Train Master Diesel	39	155
___	2322	Virginian FM Train Master Diesel	37	123
___	2328	Burlington GP7 Diesel	29	185
___	2329	Virginian Electric Locomotive	56	208
___	2330	Pennsylvania GG1 Electric Locomotive	57	258
___	2331	Virginian FM Train Master Diesel	37	144
___	2332	Pennsylvania GG1 Electric Locomotive	38	119
___	2333	NYC F3 AA Set (master carton)	45	142
___	2333	NYC F3 AA Set (P and T boxes)	39	154
___	2333P	NYC F3 A Unit (brown corrugated)	21	78
___	2333	Santa Fe F3 AA Set (master carton)	51	172
___	2333	Santa Fe F3 AA Set (P and T boxes)	35	97
___	2333P	Santa Fe F3 A Unit	17	73
___	2333T	Santa Fe F3 Dummy A Unit	27	82
___	2337	Wabash GP7 Diesel, 58	30	141
___	2338	MILW GP7 Diesel (classic)	25	104
___	2338	MILW GP7 Diesel (brown corrugated)	16	56
___	2338X	MILW GP7 Diesel (brown corrugated marked "2338X")	27	94
___	2339	Wabash GP7 Diesel, 57	34	114
___	2340-1	Pennsylvania GG1 Electric, tuscan	63	221
___	2340-25	Pennsylvania GG1 Electric, green, gold stripes	31	141
___	2341	Jersey Central FM Train Master Diesel	224	772
___	2343	Santa Fe F3 AA Set (master carton)	43	150
___	2343	Santa Fe F3 AA Set (P and T boxes)	37	122
___	2343C	Santa Fe F3 B Unit	23	93
___	2343P	Santa Fe F3 A Unit	21	57
___	2343T	Santa Fe F3 Dummy Unit	28	85
___	2344	NYC F3 AA Set (master carton)	69	269
___	2344	NYC F3 AA Set (P and T boxes)	57	194
___	2344C	NYC F3 B Unit	35	90
___	2344P	NYC F3 A Unit	47	113
___	2344T	NYC F3 Dummy Unit	32	184
___	2345	Western Pacific F3 AA Set (master carton)	175	668
___	2345	Western Pacific F3 AA Set (P and T boxes, brown corrugated)	50	311
___	2345P	Western Pacific F3 A Unit	38	140
___	2345T	Western Pacific F3 Dummy A Unit	70	207
___	2346	B&M GP9 Diesel	35	119
___	2347	C&O GP9 Diesel	550	1425
___	2348	M&StL GP9 Diesel	36	136
___	2349	Northern Pacific GP9 Diesel	63	212
___	2349-12	Sleeve for 2349 and 2359 outer boxes	24	101
___	2350	New Haven EP-5 Electric Locomotive	29	91
___	2351	Milwaukee Road EP-5 Electric Locomotive	41	141
___	2352	Pennsylvania EP-5 Electric Locomotive	50	188
___	2353	Santa Fe F3 AA Set (master carton)	60	194

		Good P-5	Exc P-7
2353	Santa Fe F3 AA Set (P and T boxes)	43	169
2353P	Santa Fe F3 A Unit (brown corrugated)	22	63
2353T	Santa Fe F3 Dummy Unit	26	97
2354	NYC F3 AA Set (master carton)	52	256
2354P	NYC F3 A Unit (brown corrugated)	37	111
2354T	NYC F3 Dummy Unit	32	130
2355	Western Pacific F3 AA Set (master carton)	93	401
2355	Western Pacific F3 AA Set (P and T boxes)	60	240
2355P	Western Pacific F3 A Unit	42	131
2355T	Western Pacific F3 Dummy A Unit	44	153
2356	Southern F3 AA Set (master carton)	88	417
2356C	Southern F3 B Unit	56	201
2356P	Southern F3 A Unit	35	121
2356T	Southern F3 Dummy Unit	57	211
2357	SP-type Caboose	5	16
2358	Great Northern EP-5 Electric Locomotive	64	216
2358-12	Outer Box Sleeve	48	160
2359	Boston & Maine GP9 Diesel	25	91
2360-10	Pennsylvania GG1 Electric Locomotive, tuscan	75	255
2360-25	Pennsylvania GG1 Electric Locomotive, green	46	191
2363	Illinois Central F3 AB Set (master carton)	160	604
2363	Illinois Central F3 AB Set (C and P boxes)	81	337
2363C	Illinois Central F3 B Unit	50	139
2363P	Illinois Central F3 A Unit	32	106
2365	C&O GP7 Diesel	21	74
2367	Wabash F3 AB Diesel Set Master Carton	45	89
2367C	Wabash F3 B Unit	48	234
2367P	Wabash F3 A Unit	44	160
2368	B&O F3 AB Set (master carton)	232	871
2368C	B&O F3 B Unit	69	275
2368P	B&O F3 A Unit	39	193
2373	CP F3 AA Set (P and T boxes)	169	497
2373P	CP F3 A Unit	49	177
2373T	CP F3 Dummy A Unit	70	197
2378	Milwaukee Road F3 AB Set (master carton)	167	768
2378C	Milwaukee Road F3 B Unit	76	267
2378P	Milwaukee Road F3 A Unit	63	249
2379	Denver & Rio Grande Western F3 AB Set (master carton)	179	706
2379C	Denver & Rio Grande Western F3 B Unit	43	181
2379P	Denver & Rio Grande Western F3 A Unit	43	161
2383	Santa Fe F3 AA Units (master carton)	55	280
2383P	Santa Fe F3 A Unit	23	77
2383T	Santa Fe F3 Dummy Unit	29	91
2400	Maplewood Pullman Car	16	51
2401	Hillside Observation Car	16	51
2402	Chatham Pullman Car	16	52

BOXES		Good P-5	Exc P-7
____ 2403B	Tender with bell	29	83
____ 2404	Santa Fe Vista Dome Car	15	45
____ 2405	Santa Fe Pullman Car	15	45
____ 2406	Santa Fe Observation Car	15	46
____ 2408	Santa Fe Vista Dome Car	14	45
____ 2409	Santa Fe Pullman Car	15	45
____ 2410	Santa Fe Observation Car	14	46
____ 2411	Lionel Lines Flatcar	10	32
____ 2412	Santa Fe Vista Dome Car	15	47
____ 2414	Santa Fe Pullman Car	15	47
____ 2416	Santa Fe Observation Car (orange perforated)	18	66
____ 2416	Santa Fe Observation Car (orange picture)	15	46
____ 2419	DL&W Work Caboose	11	36
____ 2420	DL&W Work Caboose with searchlight	22	53
____ 2421	Maplewood Pullman Car	14	44
____ 2422	Chatham Pullman Car	14	44
____ 2423	Hillside Observation Car	15	45
____ 2426W	Hudson Tender (early classic)	76	257
____ 2426W	Hudson Tender (middle classic)	66	226
____ 2429	Livingston Pullman Car	22	68
____ 2430	Pullman Car, blue	15	44
____ 2431	Observation Car, blue	15	45
____ 2432	Clifton Vista Dome Car	13	43
____ 2434	Newark Pullman Car	14	42
____ 2435	Elizabeth Pullman Car	20	55
____ 2436	Mooseheart Observation Car	13	42
____ 2436	Mooseheart Observation Car (classic)	13	40
____ 2440	Pullman Car, green	13	41
____ 2441	Observation Car, green	13	41
____ 2442	Pullman Car, brown	14	44
____ 2442	Clifton Vista Dome Car	16	46
____ 2443	Observation Car, brown	10	40
____ 2444	Newark Pullman Car	15	47
____ 2445	Elizabeth Pullman Car	30	97
____ 2446	Summit Observation Car	15	46
____ 2452	Pennsylvania Gondola	6	20
____ 2452X	Pennsylvania Gondola	5	15
____ X2454	Pennsylvania Boxcar (marked "Box Car")	11	36
____ X2454	Pennsylvania Boxcar (marked "Merchandise Car")	20	62
____ 2456	Lehigh Valley Hopper	5	21
____ 2457	Pennsylvania N5-type Caboose	7	33
____ 2458	Pennsylvania Automobile Boxcar	11	36
____ 2460	Bucyrus Erie Crane Car (with toymakers logo)	14	51
____ 2460	Bucyrus Erie Crane Car (without toymakers logo)	27	112
____ 2461	Transformer Car	15	47
____ 2465	Sunoco 2-D Tank Car	4	11

BOXES		Good P-5	Exc P-7	
2466T	Tender	5	26	
2466W	Tender	11	37	
2466WX	Tender	12	41	
2472	PRR N5-type Caboose	4	21	
2481	Plainfield Pullman Car	38	148	
2482	Westfield Pullman Car	38	147	
2483	Livingston Observation Car	38	147	
2501W	M&StL Diesel Freight Set	37	209	
2502W	Budd RDC Set	112	205	
2503WS	Super O Steam Freight Set	28	111	
2505W	Super O Electric Freight Set	56	258	
2507W	New Haven Diesel Freight Set	59	389	
2509WS	Super O Steam Freight Set	37	220	
2511W	Pennsylvania Electric Work Set	51	242	
2513W	Virginian Rectifier Set	71	383	
2515WS	Super O Steam Freight Set	84	385	
2517W	Rio Grande Diesel Freight Set	74	419	
2518W	Pennsylvania Electric Passenger Set	107	577	
2519W	Virginian Train Master Super O Freight Set	46	390	
2521	President McKinley Observation Car	21	78	
2521WS	Super O Steam Freight Set	48	272	
2522	President Harrison Vista Dome Car	23	82	
2523	President Garfield Pullman Car	23	82	
2523W	Santa Fe Super O Freight Set	44	282	
2525WS	Super O Steam Work Train Set	131	516	
2526W	Santa Fe Passenger Set	43	368	
2527	Missile Launcher Set, yellow	20	80	
2528WS	Super O General Set	37	162	
2530	REA Baggage Car	27	96	
2530	REA Baggage Car (orange perforated)	81	340	
2531	Silver Dawn Observation Car	17	57	
2531WS	Super O Steam Freight Set	41	171	
2532	Silver Range Vista Dome Car	17	60	
2533	Silver Cloud Pullman Car	18	57	
2533W	Super O GN Electric Freight Set	94	498	
2534	Silver Bluff Pullman Car	17	57	
2535WS	Steam Freight Set	50	190	
2537W	New Haven Freight Set	55	321	
2541	Alexander Hamilton Observation Car	24	78	
2541W	Santa Fe Super O Freight Set	178	572	
2542	Betsy Ross Vista Dome Car	22	79	
2543	William Penn Pullman Car	21	79	
2543WS	Berkshire Freight Set	111	445	
2544	Molly Pitcher Pullman Car	21	79	
2544W	Santa Fe Passenger Set	118	744	
2545WS	Super O Military Set	160	819	

BOXES		Good P-5	Exc P-7
___ 2547WS	Super O Steam Freight Set	35	184
___ 2549W	Super O Military Set	45	210
___ 2550	B&O Baggage-Mail Rail Diesel Car	38	141
___ 2551	Banff Park Observation Car	29	101
___ 2551W	GN Electric Set	115	549
___ 2552	Skyline 500 Vista Dome Car	29	97
___ 2553	Blair Manor Pullman Car	49	182
___ 2553WS	Berkshire Freight Set	53	272
___ 2554	Craig Manor Pullman Car	56	176
___ 2555	Sunoco 1-D Tank Car	10	40
___ 2555	Sunoco 1-D Tank Car (overstamped 2755 box)	23	81
___ 2559	B&O Passenger Rail Diesel Car	37	117
___ 2560	Lionel Lines Crane Car	17	51
___ 2561	Vista Valley Observation Car	34	109
___ 2561	Vista Valley Observation Car (orange perforated)	52	144
___ 2562	Regal Pass Observation Car	32	115
___ 2562	Regal Pass Observation Car (orange perforated)	50	148
___ 2563	Indian Falls Pullman Car	36	143
___ 2570	Super O Santa Fe Work Train Set	54	203
___ 2572	Boston & Maine Military Set	38	158
___ 2574	Santa Fe Military Set	63	273
___ 2625	Irvington Pullman Car	42	115
___ 2627	Madison Pullman Car	28	115
___ 2628	Manhattan Pullman Car	29	113
___ 2671T	Pennsylvania Tender, for export	18	59
___ 2671W	Pennsylvania Tender	22	72
___ 2671WX	Lionel Lines Tender	26	72
___ 2755	Sunoco 1-D Tank Car	16	52
___ X2758	PRR Automobile Boxcar	10	34
___ 2855	Sunoco 1-D Tank Car	33	115
___ 3330	Flatcar with submarine kit	20	68
___ 3330-100	Operating Submarine Kit, separate sale	48	167
___ 3349	Turbo Missile Launch Car	7	40
___ 3356	Operating Horse Car and Corral Set (classic)	13	66
___ 3356	Operating Horse Car and Corral Set (orange picture)	18	63
___ 3356-2	Horse Car	65	426
___ 3356-100	Black Horses (classic)	4	13
___ 3356-100	Black Horses (white box)	8	22
___ 3356-150	Horse Car Corral	69	626
___ 3357	Hydraulic Maintenance Car	10	33
___ 3357-27	Trestle Components for Cop and Hobo Car	7	24
___ 3359	Lionel Lines Twin-bin Coal Dump Car	12	39
___ 3360	Operating Burro Crane	18	61
___ 3361	Operating Log Dump Car	5	21
___ 3361X	Operating Log Dump Car	6	27
___ 3362	Helium Tank Unloading Car	14	39

BOXES		Good P-5	Exc P-7	
3362/3364	Operating Unloading Car (Hagerstown checkerboard)	20	50	___
3364	Log Unloading Car	9	28	___
3366	Circus Car Corral Set	37	135	___
3366-100	White Horses	10	32	___
3370	W&A Outlaw Car	9	33	___
3376	Bronx Zoo Car	13	38	___
3376-160	Bronx Zoo Car, green	17	49	___
3410	Helicopter Car	14	63	___
3413	Mercury Capsule Car	18	65	___
3419	Helicopter Car	18	105	___
3424	Wabash Operating Boxcar	19	58	___
3424-75	Low Bridge Signal (marked "3424-75" or overstamped on 3424-100 box)	77	246	___
3424-100	Low Bridge Signal	5	17	___
3428	U.S. Mail Operating Boxcar	11	44	___
3434	Poultry Dispatch Car	24	61	___
3435	Traveling Aquarium Car	29	103	___
3444	Erie Operating Gondola	10	28	___
3451	Operating Log Dump Car	8	27	___
3454	PRR Operating Merchandise Car	21	89	___
3456	N&W Operating Hopper	13	39	___
3459	LL Operating Coal Dump Car (without toymakers logo)	21	69	___
3459	LL Operating Coal Dump Car (with toymakers logo)	16	51	___
3461	LL Operating Log Car	9	27	___
3461X	Automatic Lumber Car	13	45	___
3461-25	Lionel Lines Operating Log Car, green	14	60	___
3462	Automatic Milk Car	11	51	___
3462-70	Milk Cans	2	10	___
3464	NYC Operating Boxcar	5	16	___
3464	Santa Fe Operating Boxcar	5	12	___
3469	LL Operating Coal Dump Car	12	42	___
3469X	LL Operating Coal Dump Car	9	22	___
3470	Target Launching Car	13	42	___
3472	Automatic Milk Car	12	36	___
3474	Western Pacific Operating Boxcar	11	45	___
3482	Automatic Milk Car	13	45	___
3484	Pennsylvania Operating Boxcar	11	28	___
3484-25	ATSF Operating Boxcar	10	35	___
3494	NYC Operating Boxcar	14	41	___
3494-150	Missouri Pacific Operating Boxcar	15	46	___
3494-275	State of Maine Operating Boxcar	12	45	___
3494-550	Monon Operating Boxcar	44	180	___
3494-625	Soo Operating Boxcar	46	179	___
3509	Satellite Launching Car	13	54	___
3512	Fireman and Ladder Car	17	92	___
3519	Satellite Launching Car	12	37	___

| --- | --- | --- | --- |
___ 3520	Searchlight Car	10	30
___ 3530	GM Generator Car	17	52
___ 3530-50	Searchlight with pole and base, separate sale	41	100
___ 3535	Security Car with searchlight	13	48
___ 3540	Operating Radar Car	22	69
___ 3545	Operating TV Monitor Car	21	100
___ 3559	Operating Coal Dump Car	12	34
___ 3562-1	ATSF Operating Barrel Car	27	209
___ 3562-25	ATSF Operating Barrel Car, gray	13	43
___ 3562-50	ATSF Operating Barrel Car, yellow	15	49
___ 3562-75	ATSF Operating Barrel Car, orange	19	49
___ 3619	Helicopter Reconnaissance Car	12	48
___ 3620	Searchlight Car with insert	13	38
___ 3650	Extension Searchlight Car	11	33
___ 3656	Operating Cattle Car	11	37
___ 3656	Stockyard with cattle (set box with car box)	16	66
___ 3656-9	Cattle (marked "3656" on 4 sides, unnumbered tuck flaps)	6	16
___ 3656-9	Cattle (marked "3656" on 4 sides, "3656-44" on 1 tuck flap)	3	10
___ 3656-9	Cattle (marked "3656-34" on 4 sides, "3656-44" on 1 tuck flap)	3	10
___ 3656-9	Cattle (marked "3656" on 4 sides, "3656-44" on 1 tuck flap, OPS markings)	6	19
___ 3656-9	Cattle (unnumbered sides, marked "3656-44" on 1 tuck flap)	7	20
___ 3656-9	Cattle (unnumbered sides, marked "3656-34" on 1 tuck flap)	11	29
___ 3656-150	Corral Platform, separate sale	120	536
___ 3662	Automatic Milk Car (classic), 55	15	114
___ 3662	Automatic Milk Car (orange picture), 64	19	65
___ 3662	Automatic Milk Car (white box), 66	24	78
___ 3665	Minuteman Operating Car	17	47
___ 3672	Bosco Operating Milk Car	50	175
___ 3820	USMC Operating Submarine Car	23	67
___ 3830	Operating Submarine Car	16	42
___ 3854	Automatic Merchandise Car	74	480
___ 3927	Lionel Lines Track Cleaning Car	7	26
___ 4109WS	Electronic Control Set	90	485
___ 4357	SP-type Caboose, electronic	27	96
___ 4452	PRR Gondola, electronic	26	90
___ 4454	Baby Ruth PRR Boxcar, electronic	26	105
___ 4457	PRR N5-type Caboose, tintype, electronic	25	93
___ 4671W	Tender	37	136
___ 5160	Viewing Stand	12	52
___ 5459	LL Coal Dump Car, electronic	25	126
___ 6001T	Tender	3	9
___ 6002	NYC Gondola	2	7

BOXES		Good P-5	Exc P-7	
6004	Baby Ruth PRR Boxcar	3	10	___
6007	Lionel Lines SP-type Caboose	2	8	___
6009	Remote Control Uncoupling Track	2	6	___
6012	Gondola	3	9	___
6014	Boxcar	3	10	___
6014-60	Frisco Boxcar, white (middle classic)	7	20	___
6014-60	Frisco Boxcar, white	5	16	___
6014-85	Bosco or Frisco Boxcar, orange (classic)	8	25	___
6014-85	Boxcar (Hagerstown production)		19	___
6014-100	Airex Boxcar, red	8	25	___
6014-100	Airex Boxcar, red (orange perforated)	12	35	___
6014-150	Wix Boxcar	43	173	___
6014-335	Frisco Boxcar	6	22	___
6014-410	Frisco Boxcar	12	59	___
6015	Sunoco 1-D Tank Car	4	12	___
6017	Lionel Lines SP-type Caboose	2	8	___
6017-1	Caboose	8	22	___
6017-50	USMC SP-type Caboose (box marked "6017-60")	16	62	___
6017-60	USMC SP-type Caboose	5	18	___
6017-85	Lionel Lines SP-type Caboose, gray	12	36	___
6017-100	B&M SP-type Caboose	14	50	___
6017-185	ATSF SP-type Caboose	5	19	___
6017-200	U.S. Navy SP-type Caboose	36	550	___
6017-235	ATSF SP-type Caboose	12	36	___
6019	Remote Control Track	2	6	___
6020W	Tender	8	36	___
6024	Nabisco Shredded Wheat Boxcar	5	27	___
6024-60	RCA Whirlpool Boxcar	18	63	___
6025	Gulf 1-D Tank Car (classic)	6	16	___
6025-60	Gulf 1-D Tank Car	5	22	___
6025-60	Gulf 1-D Tank Car (classic, overstamped 6024 box)	11	44	___
6025-85	Gulf 1-D Tank Car (classic)	7	38	___
6026T	Lionel Lines Tender	6	21	___
6026W	Lionel Lines Tender (classic or picture)	11	39	___
6027	Alaska SP-type Caboose	55	239	___
6029	Remote Control Uncoupling Track (classic)	2	7	___
6029	Remote Control Uncoupling Track (orange picture)	7	20	___
6032	Short Gondola	3	11	___
6034	Boxcar (Hagerstown production)	2	9	___
X6034	Baby Ruth PRR Boxcar	3	11	___
6035	Sunoco 1-D Tank Car	4	11	___
6037	Lionel Lines SP-type Caboose	2	7	___
6050	Lionel Savings Bank Boxcar	7	26	___
6050-110	Swift Boxcar	7	26	___
6057	Lionel Lines SP-type Caboose	5	26	___

BOXES		Good P-5	Exc P-7
___ 6059	M&StL SP-type Caboose	7	22
___ 6059-50	M&StL SP-type Caboose (Hagerstown checkerboard)	9	29
___ 6062	NYC Gondola	5	18
___ 6066T	Tender	7	20
___ 6110	2-4-2 Locomotive	6	24
___ 6111-75	Flatcar with logs	12	52
___ 6111-110	Flatcar	16	55
___ 6112-1	Canister Car	9	30
___ 6112-25	Canister Set	9	31
___ 6112-85	Short Gondola (marked "Canister Car")	5	23
___ 6112-110	Gondola Car with Canisters	6	29
___ 6112-135	Short Gondola (marked "Canister Car")	6	26
___ 6119	DL&W Work Caboose, red	5	21
___ 6119-25	DL&W Work Caboose, orange	8	28
___ 6119-50	DL&W Work Caboose, brown	10	31
___ 6119-75	DL&W Work Caboose	10	34
___ 6119-100	DL&W Work Caboose (classic)	8	28
___ 6119-100	DL&W Work Caboose (picture, perforated, or window)	13	70
___ 6121	Flatcar with pipes	12	44
___ 6121-60	Flatcar with pipes	15	56
___ 6121-85	Flatcar with pipes (classic)	15	55
___ 6130	ATSF Work Caboose (cellophane)	11	40
___ 6130	ATSF Work Caboose (Hagerstown checkerboard)	14	43
___ 6130	ATSF Work Caboose (all other boxes)	6	26
___ 6149	Remote Control Uncoupling Track, 64-69	2	6
___ 6151	Flatcar with patrol truck	11	42
___ 6162-60	Alaska Gondola	31	147
___ 6162-110	NYC Gondola, blue (orange picture)	10	33
___ 6162-110	NYC Gondola, red, separate sale (orange picture with label)	20	67
___ 6167-85	Union Pacific SP-type Caboose	17	61
___ 6175	Flatcar with rocket	9	36
___ 6220	Santa Fe NW2 Switcher	22	90
___ 6250	Seaboard NW2 Switcher	31	121
___ 6257	SP-type Caboose	4	10
___ 6257X	SP-type Caboose	12	36
___ 6257-25	SP-type Caboose	4	12
___ 6257-50	SP-type Caboose	5	13
___ 6262	Flatcar with wheel load	9	33
___ 6264	Flatcar with lumber, separate sale	42	136
___ 6311	Flatcar with pipes	13	45
___ 6315	Gulf 1-D Chemical Tank Car (classic)	14	43
___ 6315	Gulf 1-D Chemical Tank Car (Hagerstown checkerboard)	20	50
___ 6315-60	Gulf 1-D Chemical Tank Car (orange picture)	10	34
___ 6342	NYC Gondola	27	112
___ 6343	Barrel Ramp Car	11	36

		Good P-5	Exc P-7
6346	Alcoa Quad Hopper	12	37
6356	NYC Stock Car	11	31
6357	SP-type Caboose (classic)	5	15
6357	SP-type Caboose (orange perforated)	8	20
6357	SP-type Caboose (orange perforated, overstamped)	16	66
6357-50	ATSF SP-type Caboose	130	483
6361	Timber Transport Car	13	40
6361	Timber Transport Car (Hagerstown checkerboard)	16	62
6362	Truck Car	10	39
6376	LL Circus Stock Car	11	41
6401	Flatcar, gray	25	97
6403B	Tender with bell	21	66
6405	Flatcar with piggyback van	8	28
6407	Flatcar with rocket	101	730
6411	Flatcar with logs	5	22
6413	Mercury Capsule Carrying Car	17	57
6414	Evans Auto Loader (classic)	19	53
6414	Evans Auto Loader (orange picture)	27	82
6414	Evans Auto Loader (orange picture, overstamped 6416 box)	31	97
6414	Evans Auto Loader (orange perforated), 59	20	84
6414	Evans Auto Loader (cellophane), 66	24	157
6414-25	Four Automobiles, separate sale	157	428
6414-85	Evans Auto Loader (orange picture)	124	452
6415	Sunoco 3-D Tank Car (classic)	8	22
6415	Sunoco 3-D Tank Car (orange picture)	15	40
6415	Sunoco 3-D Tank Car (cellophane)	21	76
6415	Sunoco 3-D Tank Car (Hillside checkerboard)	19	52
6415	Sunoco 3-D Tank Car (orange picture with label)	33	93
6416	Boat Transport Car	36	121
6417	PRR N5c Porthole Caboose	4	27
6417-25	Lionel Lines N5c Porthole Caboose	7	26
6417-50	Lehigh Valley N5c Porthole Caboose	22	80
6418	Machinery Car	17	58
6419	DL&W Work Caboose	9	33
6419-25	DL&W Work Caboose	6	24
6419-50	DL&W Work Caboose	9	34
6419-100	N&W Work Caboose	29	73
6420	DL&W Work Caboose with searchlight	14	41
6424	Twin Auto Flatcar	13	41
6424-60	Twin Auto Flatcar	16	36
6424-85	Twin Auto Flatcar	12	57
6424-110	Twin Auto Flatcar	21	93
6425	Gulf 3-D Tank Car	10	32
6427	Lionel Lines N5c Porthole Caboose	8	21
6427-1	Lionel Lines N5c Porthole Caboose	10	31

BOXES		Good P-5	Exc P-7
___ 6427-60	Virginian N5c Porthole Caboose	61	265
___ 6427-500	PRR N5c Porthole Caboose, sky blue, from Girls Set	37	126
___ 6428	U.S. Mail Boxcar	13	45
___ 6429	DL&W Work Caboose	34	142
___ 6430	Flatcar with trailers	12	45
___ 6431	Flatcar with vans and tractor (cellophane), 66	48	164
___ 6434	Poultry Dispatch Stock Car	15	47
___ 6436	Lehigh Valley Open Quad Hopper, black	9	43
___ 6436-25	Lehigh Valley Open Quad Hopper, maroon	9	92
___ 6436-110	Lehigh Valley Open Quad Hopper, red	12	33
___ 6436-500	Lehigh Valley Open Quad Hopper, lilac, from Girls Set	42	136
___ 6436-1969	TCA Hopper (Hagerstown checkerboard)	14	44
___ 6437	PRR N5c Porthole Caboose	7	21
___ 6440	Flatcar with vans	14	42
___ 6440	Green Pullman Car	11	43
___ 6441	Green Observation Car	11	42
___ 6442	Brown Pullman Car	11	43
___ 6443	Brown Observation Car	11	43
___ 6445	Fort Knox Gold Reserve Car	16	47
___ 6446	N&W Covered Quad Hopper	8	31
___ 6446	N&W Covered Quad Hopper (orange picture)	15	61
___ 6446-25	N&W Covered Quad Hopper	11	37
___ 6446-60	Lehigh Valley Covered Quad Hopper	69	353
___ 6447	PRR N5c Porthole Caboose	55	254
___ 6448	Exploding Target Range Boxcar	8	32
___ 6452	Pennsylvania Gondola	3	13
___ X6454	Santa Fe, NYC, or Baby Ruth Boxcar	6	25
___ X6454	PRR Boxcar	6	25
___ X6454	PRR Boxcar (classic, overstamped 3464 box)	11	35
___ X6454	SP Boxcar	6	25
___ X6454	Erie Boxcar	7	30
___ 6456	Lehigh Valley Short Hopper	6	15
___ 6456-25	LV Short Hopper ("25" rubber-stamped on end flaps)	8	67
___ 6456-75	Lehigh Valley Short Hopper	32	127
___ 6457	SP-type Caboose	6	15
___ 6460	Bucyrus Erie Crane Car	13	44
___ 6460-25	Bucyrus Erie Crane Car, red cab	16	51
___ 6461	Transformer Car	8	30
___ 6462	NYC Gondola, black	3	10
___ 6462-25	NYC Gondola, green	6	17
___ 6462-75	NYC Gondola, red	4	13
___ 6462-100	NYC Gondola, red	15	40
___ 6462-125	NYC Gondola, red plastic	4	14
___ 6462-500	NYC Gondola, pink, from Girls Set	43	132
___ 6463	Rocket Fuel 2-D Tank Car	11	46

BOXES		Good P-5	Exc P-7	
6464-1	Western Pacific Boxcar	12	43	___
6464-25	Great Northern Boxcar	15	45	___
6464-50	M&StL Boxcar	15	44	___
6464-50	M&StL Boxcar (overstamped with "S" and "Silver")	18	53	___
6464-75	Rock Island Boxcar	11	40	___
6464-100	Western Pacific Boxcar	23	96	___
6464-125	NYC Pacemaker Boxcar	17	62	___
6464-150	Missouri Pacific Boxcar	15	56	___
6464-175	Rock Island Boxcar	13	70	___
6464-175	Rock Island Boxcar (overstamped with "S" and "Silver")	37	163	___
6464-200	Pennsylvania Boxcar	13	67	___
6464-200	Pennsylvania Boxcar (Hagerstown checkerboard)	21	62	___
6464-225	Southern Pacific Boxcar	14	46	___
6464-250	Western Pacific Boxcar (orange picture with label)	43	142	___
6464-250	Western Pacific Blue Feather Boxcar (classic for 6464-100), 54	84	447	___
6464-250	Western Pacific Boxcar (cellophane)	21	83	___
6464-275	State of Maine Boxcar	17	97	___
6464-300	Rutland Boxcar, 55	22	96	___
6464-325	B&O Sentinel Boxcar	57	207	___
6464-350	MKT Boxcar	35	204	___
6464-375	Central of Georgia Boxcar	16	53	___
6464-400	B&O Time-Saver Boxcar	12	41	___
6464-425	New Haven Boxcar (classic)	10	41	___
6464-425	New Haven Boxcar (Hagerstown)	13	42	___
6464-450	Great Northern Boxcar	12	51	___
6464-450	Great Northern Boxcar (cellophane)	17	60	___
6464-475	B&M Boxcar (classic)	10	46	___
6464-475	B&M Boxcar (orange picture)	20	77	___
6464-500	Timken Boxcar	18	79	___
6464-510	NYC Pacemaker Boxcar	74	258	___
6464-515	MKT Boxcar	72	257	___
6464-525	M&StL Boxcar	11	43	___
6464-650	D&RGW Boxcar (cellophane)	15	66	___
6464-700	Santa Fe Boxcar	16	55	___
6464-725	New Haven Boxcar (orange picture, "735" on box)	11	38	___
6464-725	New Haven Boxcar (Hagerstown checkerboard)	19	67	___
6464-825	Alaska Boxcar	45	217	___
6464-900	NYC Boxcar	10	38	___
6464-960	TCA Boxcar, 1965	48	95	___
6465	Gulf 2-D Tank Car, black (classic)	5	14	___
6465	Sunoco 2-D Tank Car (classic, overstamped 2465 box)	5	18	___
6465	Sunoco 2-D Tank Car (classic, overstamped 6555 box)	5	17	___
6465-60	Gulf 2-D Tank Car (classic)	5	18	___
6465-60	Sunoco 2-D Tank Car (classic)	3	12	___
6465-85	Lionel Lines 2-D Tank Car (orange perforated)	28	180	___

BOXES		Good P-5	Exc P-7
___ 6465-110	Cities Service 2-D Tank Car (orange perforated)	13	48
___ 6465-160	Lionel Lines Tank Car (orange picture)	35	126
___ 6466T	Lionel Lines Tender	6	19
___ 6466W	Lionel Lines Tender (with liner)	13	41
___ 6466WX	Lionel Lines Tender (with liner)	16	46
___ 6467	Miscellaneous Car	15	42
___ 6468	B&O Auto Boxcar, tuscan (marked "X")	40	154
___ 6468	B&O Auto Boxcar, blue	10	31
___ 6468-25	NH Auto Boxcar	13	42
___ 6469	Liquified Gas Tank Car	21	83
___ 6470	Explosives Boxcar	11	40
___ 6472	Refrigerator Car	6	21
___ 6473	Horse Transport Car	9	33
___ 6473	Horse Transport Car (end flaps half white, half orange)	23	93
___ 6475	Pickles Vat Car (orange picture)	20	65
___ 6476	Lehigh Valley Short Hopper	6	19
___ 6476	Lehigh Valley Short Hopper (orange perforated)	13	42
___ 6476-85	Lehigh Valley Short Hopper	15	52
___ 6476-135	Lehigh Valley Short Hopper	8	29
___ 6476-160	Lehigh Valley Short Hopper (Hagerstown checkerboard)	9	27
___ 6477	Miscellaneous Car with pipes	11	42
___ 6482	Refrigerator Car	8	34
___ 6500	Flatcar with Bonanza airplane	88	280
___ 6501	Flatcar with jet boat	25	70
___ 6511	Flatcar with pipes	9	28
___ 6512	Cherry Picker Car	13	40
___ 6517	Lionel Lines Bay Window Caboose	15	39
___ 6517-60	Bay Window Caboose (TCA)	30	127
___ 6517-75	Erie Bay Window Caboose	54	236
___ 6518	Transformer Car	16	45
___ 6519	Allis-Chalmers Flatcar (classic)	21	78
___ 6519	Allis-Chalmers Flatcar (orange perforated)	31	116
___ 6520	Searchlight Car (2 City)	12	41
___ 6520	Searchlight Car (3 City)	33	124
___ 6530	Firefighting Instruction Car	17	61
___ 6536	M&StL Open Quad Hopper	17	65
___ 6544	Missile Firing Car	21	75
___ 6555	Sunoco 1-D Tank Car	13	34
___ 6556	MKT Stock Car	44	161
___ 6557	SP-type Smoking Caboose	25	108
___ 6560	Bucyrus Erie Crane Car (Hagerstown checkerboard)	19	63
___ 6560	Bucyrus Erie Crane Car (all other boxes)	12	40
___ 6560-25	Bucyrus Erie Crane Car, 8-wheel (with liner)	14	47
___ 6561	Cable Car, 2 reels	9	37
___ 6562-1	NYC Gondola, gray	7	23
___ 6562-25	NYC Gondola, red	5	25

BOXES		Good P-5	Exc P-7	
6562-50	NYC Gondola, black	6	20	___
6572	REA Reefer (classic)	13	51	
6572	REA Reefer (orange picture)	14	41	
6636	Alaska Open Quad Hopper	14	61	___
6646	Lionel Lines Stock Car	7	22	___
6650	IRBM Rocket Launcher	9	32	___
6654W	Whistle Tender	8	26	
6656	Stock Car	10	36	
6657	Rio Grande SP-type Caboose	23	90	
6660	Boom Car	12	45	___
6670	Derrick Car	14	50	
6672	Santa Fe Refrigerator Car	9	29	___
6736	Detroit & Mackinac Open Quad Hopper	16	49	
6800	Flatcar with airplane (classic)	17	51	___
6800	Flatcar with airplane (orange perforated)	17	62	
6800-60	Airplane, separate sale	71	205	
6801	Flatcar with brown and white boat	9	33	
6801-50	Flatcar with yellow and white boat	10	39	
6801-60	Boat, separate sale	31	92	___
6801-75	Flatcar with blue and white boat	11	41	
6802	Flatcar with girders (late classic)	7	27	___
6802	Flatcar with girders (orange perforated)	17	54	___
6803	Flatcar with USMC tank and sound truck	28	98	___
6804	Flatcar with USMC trucks	26	89	___
6805	Atomic Energy Disposal Flatcar	19	78	
6806	Flatcar with USMC trucks	28	96	
6807	Flatcar with boat	23	85	
6808	Flatcar with military units	27	95	
6809	Flatcar with USMC trucks	27	94	
6810	Flatcar with trailer	8	32	___
6812	Track Maintenance Car	16	61	___
6814	Rescue Caboose	19	65	___
6816	Flatcar with Allis-Chalmers bulldozer	45	191	
6816-100	Allis-Chalmers bulldozer	122	421	
6817	Flatcar with Allis-Chalmers motor scraper	52	181	
6818	Flatcar with transformer	7	27	___
6819	Flatcar with helicopter	10	49	___
6820	Aerial Missile Transport Car with helicopter	67	245	___
6821	Flatcar with crates	6	27	___
6822	Searchlight Car	7	26	___
6823	Flatcar with IRBM missiles	17	63	___
6825	Flatcar with arch trestle bridge	7	23	___
6826	Flatcar with Christmas trees	20	63	
6827	Flatcar with Harnischfeger power shovel	27	105	
6827-100	Harnischfeger Power Shovel	32	81	___

BOXES		Good P-5	Exc P-7
____ 6828	Flatcar with Harnischfeger crane (cellophane, no crane kit box)	31	86
____ 6828	Flatcar with Harnischfeger crane (orange picture, no crane kit box)	19	72
____ 6828	Harnischfeger Crane Kit, used with flatcar	17	74
____ 6828-100	Harnischfeger Crane, separate sale	43	154
____ 6830	Flatcar with submarine	19	61
____ 6844	Missile Carrying Car	17	75
____ 11001	Steam Freight Set (advance catalog 1962)	6	26
____ 11011	Diesel Freight Set	22	70
____ 11201	Steam Freight Set	14	50
____ 11212	Diesel Freight Set	25	77
____ 11222	O27 Steam Freight Set	20	51
____ 11232	NH Diesel Freight Set	22	73
____ 11242	Steam Freight Set	19	58
____ 11252	Diesel Space Set	28	68
____ 11268	Military Set	30	98
____ 11278	Steam Freight Set	21	66
____ 11288	Steam Freight Set	31	104
____ 11321	Diesel Freight Set	17	34
____ 11331	Steam Freight Set	12	40
____ 11341	Diesel Freight Set	10	26
____ 11375	O27 Steam Freight Set	13	55
____ 11415	Steam Freight Set (advance catalog 1963)	21	109
____ 11420	Steam Freight Set	8	30
____ 11430	Steam Freight Set	20	65
____ 11440	Diesel Freight Set	16	55
____ 11450	Steam Freight Set	20	62
____ 11460	Steam Freight Set	13	39
____ 11480	Diesel Freight Set	70	225
____ 11490	Santa Fe Passenger Set	30	105
____ 11500	Steam Freight Set	29	91
____ 11520	Steam Freight Set	27	76
____ 11530	Diesel Freight Set	43	83
____ 11540	Steam Freight Set	13	33
____ 11550	Steam Freight Set	19	53
____ 11560	Texas Special Set	10	37
____ 11590	Santa Fe Passenger Set	25	87
____ 11710	Steam Freight Set	23	75
____ 11750	Steam Freight Set	22	79
____ 12710	Steam Freight Set	31	126
____ 12730	Santa Fe Diesel Freight Set	44	155
____ 12760	Berkshire Freight Set	77	288
____ 12780	Santa Fe Passenger Set	106	409
____ 12800	B&M Diesel Freight Set	25	80
____ 12800X	B&M Diesel Freight Set	44	173

BOXES		Good P-5	Exc P-7	
12820	Virginian Train Master Freight Set	69	265	___
12840	Steam Freight Set	42	187	___
12850	Diesel Freight Set	40	171	___
13008	Super O Introductory Set	24	88	___
13018	Santa Fe Space-age Military Set	165	643	___
13028	Super O Space Set	61	249	___
13048	Super O Steam Freight Set	44	260	___
13058	Santa Fe Space-age Military Set	74	355	___
13088	Santa Fe Passenger Set	249	796	___
13098	Steam Freight Set	67	251	___
13108	Santa Fe Space Set	60	168	___
13118	Berkshire Freight Set	69	287	___
13128	Santa Fe Space-age Military Set	150	523	___
13150	Hudson Freight Set	261	868	___
A	Transformer, 90 watts	4	11	___
CO-1	Track Clips, 100	4	13	___
CTC	Master Carton		167	___
ECU-1	Electronic Control Unit	30	114	___
KW	Transformer, 190 watts	5	18	___
KW	Transformer, 190 watts (yellow)	6	19	___
LTC	Lockon	1	5	___
LW	Transformer, 125 watts	5	15	___
R	Transformer, 110 watts	5	12	___
RCS	Remote Control Track	2	7	___
RW	Transformer, 110 watts	5	17	___
S	Transformer, 80 watts	4	19	___
SW	Transformer, 130 watts	5	15	___
TW	Transformer, 175 watts	4	21	___
UCS	Remote Control Track (O)	2	5	___
UTC	Lockon	4	9	___
VW	Transformer, 150 watts	6	18	___
Z	Transformer, 250 watts	25	83	___
ZW	Transformer, 250 Watts	10	23	___
ZW	Transformer, 275 watts (classic)	10	35	___
ZW	Transformer, 275 watts (orange, with inserts)	11	38	___
ZW	Transformer, 275 watts (yellow, with inserts)	12	38	___
ZW	Transformer, 275 watts (yellow, with inserts)	12	38	___
ZW	Transformer, 275 watts (classic)	11	35	___
ZW	Transformer, 275 watts (orange, with inserts)	11	35	___
ZW	Transformer, 275 watts (yellow, with inserts)	13	35	___

Section 8
CATALOGED SETS 1945-1969

		Good	Exc
463W	Steam Freight Set, 45		793
1000W	027 Steam Freight Set, 55	159	365
1001	027 Diesel Freight Set, 55	59	238
1105	027 Diesel Freight Set (1055, 6042, 6044, 6045, 6047), 59		145
1107	027 Diesel Freight Set (1055, 6042, 6044, 6047), 60	56	120
1111	027 Scout Freight Set, 48		225
1112	027 Scout Freight Set, 48	61	250
1113	027 Scout Freight Set, 50	62	127
1115	027 Scout Freight Set, 49	42	172
1117	027 Scout Freight Set, 49	50	172
1119	027 Freight Scout Set, 51-52	55	160
1123	027 Steam Freight Set (1060, 1060T, 6042, 6406, 6067), 60-62	50	98
1400	027 Steam Passenger Set, 46	110	777
1400W	027 Steam Passenger Set, 46	63	720
1401	027 Steam Freight Set, 46		120
1401W	027 Steam Freight Set, 46	60	220
1402	027 Steam Passenger Set, 46		550
1402W	027 Steam Passenger Set, 46	125	550
1403	027 Steam Freight Set, 46		515
1403W	027 Steam Freight Set, 46		500
1405	027 Steam Freight Set, 46		145
1405W	027 Steam Freight Set, 46		280
1407B	027 Steam Switcher Set, 46		1933
1409	027 Steam Freight Set, 46		425
1409W	027 Steam Freight Set, 46		435
1411W	027 Steam Freight Set, 46	188	1008
1413WS	027 Steam Freight Set, 46		350
1415WS	027 Steam Freight Set, 46		530
1417WS	027 Steam Work Train Set, 46		720
1419WS	027 Steam Freight Set, 46		880
1421WS	027 Steam Freight Set, 46		1100
1423W	027 Steam Freight Set, 48-49		239
1425B	027 Steam Switcher Freight Set, 48	267	711
1425B	027 Steam Switcher Freight Set, 49		825
1426WS	027 Steam Passenger Set, 48-49	236	779
1427WS	027 Steam Freight Set, 48	169	294
1429WS	027 Steam Freight Set, 48	200	530
1430WS	027 Steam Passenger Set, 48-49		894
1431	027 Steam Freight Set, 47		235
1431W	027 Steam Freight Set, 47	55	168
1432	027 Steam Passenger Set, 47		850
1432W	027 Steam Passenger Set, 47		795
1433	027 Steam Freight Set, 47		521
1433W	027 Steam Freight Set, 47	237	378
1434WS	027 Steam Passenger Set, 47		555
1435WS	027 Steam Freight Set, 47		240
1437WS	027 Steam Freight Set, 47	95	611
1439WS	027 Steam Freight Set, 47		470
1441WS	027 Steam Work Train Set, 47		1225
1443WS	027 Steam Freight Set, 47		400

		Good	Exc	
1445WS	027 Steam Freight Set, 48	163	363	___
1447WS	027 Steam Work Train Set, 48		460	___
1447WS	027 Steam Work Train Set, 49	238	1463	___
1449WS	027 Steam Freight Set, 48		430	___
1451WS	027 Steam Freight Set, 49	75	290	___
1453WS	027 Steam Freight Set, 49		386	___
1455WS	027 Steam Freight Set, 49		335	___
1457B	027 Diesel Freight Set, 49-50		710	___
1459WS	027 Steam Freight Set, 49		1090	___
1461S	027 Steam Freight Set, 50		175	___
1463W	027 Steam Freight Set, 50		268	___
1463WS	027 Freight Set, 51	88	244	___
1464W	027 UP Diesel Passenger Set, 50	563	1606	___
1464W	027 UP Passenger Set, 51		880	___
1464W	027 UP Passenger Set, 52-53		813	___
1465	027 Steam Freight Set, 52	75	264	___
1467W	027 UP Diesel Freight Set, 50-51	126	795	___
1467W	027 Erie Diesel Freight Set, 52-53	79	641	___
1469WS	027 Steam Freight Set, 50-51	187	329	___
1471WS	027 Steam Freight Set, 50-51	142	450	___
1473WS	027 Steam Freight Set, 50	110	560	___
1475WS	027 Steam Freight Set, 50		615	___
1477S	027 Steam Freight Set, 51-52	75	249	___
1479WS	027 Steam Freight Set, 52	234	396	___
1481WS	027 Steam Freight Set, 51	230	469	___
1483WS	027 Steam Freight Set, 52	527	1023	___
1484WS	027 Steam Passenger Set, 52		705	___
1485WS	027 Steam Freight Set, 52		270	___
1500	027 Steam Freight Set, 53	43	193	___
1500	027 Steam Freight Set, 54		172	___
1501S	027 Steam Freight Set, 53	95	234	___
1502WS	027 Steam Passenger Set, 53	375	1523	___
1503WS	027 Steam Freight Set, 53-54	216	442	___
1505WS	027 Steam Freight Set, 53	407	592	___
1507WS	027 Steam Freight Set, 53	225	558	___
1509WS	027 Steam Freight Set, 53		500	___
1511S	027 Steam Freight Set, 53	91	250	___
1513S	027 Steam Freight Set, 54-55	83	248	___
1515WS	027 Steam Freight Set, 54	212	488	___
1516WS	027 Passenger Set, 54	208	650	___
1517W	027 Diesel Freight Set, 54	625	2075	___
1519WS	027 Steam Freight Set, 54		615	___
1520W	027 Texas Special Passenger Set, 54	934	2100	___
1521WS	027 Steam Work Train Set, 54		758	___
1523	027 Diesel Work Train Set, 54	138	671	___
1525	027 Diesel Freight Set, 55		245	___
1527	027 Steam Work Train Set, 55	276	554	___
1529	027 PRR Diesel Freight Set, 55	320	652	___
1531W	027 Diesel Freight Set, 55	288	1094	
1533WS	027 Steam Freight Set, 55		429	___
1534W	027 Diesel Passenger Set, 55	288	1000	___
1535W	027 Diesel Freight Set, 55		1650	___
1536W	027 Texas Special Passenger Set, 55	240	1800	___

			Good	Exc
SETS				
___ **1537WS**	O27 Steam Freight Set, 55			508
___ **1538WS**	O27 Steam Passenger Set, 55			900
___ **1539W**	O27 Santa Fe Diesel Freight Set, 55			850
___ **1541WS**	O27 Steam Freight Set, 55			600
___ **1542**	O27 Electric Freight Set, 56		108	322
___ **1543**	O27 Diesel Freight Set, 56		133	255
___ **1545**	O27 Diesel Freight Set, 56			265
___ **1547S**	O27 Steam Freight Set, 56			125
___ **1549**	O27 Steam Work Train Set, 56			980
___ **1551W**	O27 Diesel Freight Set, 56			566
___ **1552**	O27 Diesel Passenger Set, 56		183	842
___ **1553W**	O27 MILW Diesel Freight Set, 56		0	505
___ **1555WS**	O27 Steam Freight Set, 56		187	357
___ **1557W**	O27 Diesel Work Train Set, 56		334	466
___ **1559W**	O27 MILW Diesel Freight Set, 56			800
___ **1561WS**	O27 Steam Freight Set, 56			733
___ **1562W**	O27 Diesel Passenger Set, 56		769	2089
___ **1563W**	O27 Wabash Diesel Freight Set, 56			1570
___ **1565WS**	O27 Steam Freight Set, 56		311	535
___ **1567W**	O27 Santa Fe Diesel Freight Set, 56			1200
___ **1569**	O27 UP Diesel Freight Set, 57		63	220
___ **1571**	O27 LV Diesel Freight Set, 57			390
___ **1573**	O27 Steam Freight Set, 57		85	212
___ **1575**	O27 MP Diesel Freight Set, 57		118	320
___ **1577S**	O27 Steam Freight Set, 57		126	235
___ **1578S**	O27 Steam Passenger Set, 57		216	775
___ **1579S**	O27 Steam Freight Set, 57			260
___ **1581**	O27 Jersey Central Diesel Freight Set, 57			495
___ **1583WS**	O27 Steam Freight Set, 57		78	268
___ **1585W**	O27 Seaboard Diesel Freight Set, 57			493
___ **1586**	O27 Santa Fe Diesel Passenger Set, 57		213	670
___ **1587S**	O27 Steam Freight Set (Girls Set), 57-58		1288	3706
___ **1589WS**	O27 Steam Freight Set, 57		123	500
___ **1590**	O27 Steam Freight Set, 58		87	457
___ **1591**	O27 Military Set, 58			1719
___ **1593**	O27 UP Diesel Work Set, 58			590
___ **1595**	O27 Military Set, 58			2050
___ **1597S**	O27 Steam Freight Set, 58			355
___ **1599**	O27 Texas Special Freight Set, 58			529
___ **1600**	O27 Burlington Diesel Passenger Set, 58			750
___ **1601W**	O27 Wabash Diesel Freight Set, 58			766
___ **1603WS**	O27 Steam Freight Set, 58			433
___ **1605W**	O27 Santa Fe Diesel Freight Set, 58			945
___ **1607WS**	O27 Steam Work Train Set, 58			483
___ **1608W**	O27 NH Diesel Passenger Set, 58		825	1865
___ **1609**	O27 Steam Freight Set, 59-60		75	177
___ **1611**	O27 Alaska Diesel Freight Set, 59		158	494
___ **1612**	O27 General Set, 59-60		192	399
___ **1613S**	O27 B&O Steam Freight Set, 59			254
___ **1615**	O27 B&M Diesel Freight Set, 59		320	613
___ **1617S**	O27 Steam Work Train Set, 59			800
___ **1619W**	O27 Santa Fe Diesel Freight Set, 59		225	975
___ **1621WS**	O27 Steam Freight Set, 59		255	587

SETS		Good	Exc
1623W	O27 NP Diesel Freight Set, 59		1600 ___
1625WS	O27 Steam Freight Set, 59		563 ___
1626W	O27 Santa Fe Diesel Passenger Set, 59		875 ___
1627S	O27 Steam Freight Set, 60	23	175 ___
1629	O27 C&O Diesel Freight Set, 60	120	361 ___
1631WS	O27 Steam Freight Set, 60	192	275 ___
1633	O27 U.S. Navy Diesel Freight Set, 60	477	1199 ___
1635WS	O27 Steam Freight Set, 60		400 ___
1637W	O27 Santa Fe Diesel Freight Set, 60	459	676 ___
1639WS	O27 Steam Freight Set, 60		1250 ___
1640W	O27 Santa Fe Diesel Passenger Set, 60	150	750 ___
1641	O27 Steam Freight Set, 61		175 ___
1642	O27 Steam Freight Set, 61		225 ___
1643	O27 C&O Diesel Freight Set, 61		328 ___
1644	O27 General Set, 61	53	375 ___
1645	O27 Diesel Freight Set, 61		250 ___
1646	O27 Steam Freight Set, 61		325 ___
1647	O27 U.S. Marines Military Set, 61	685	1203 ___
1648	O27 Steam Freight Set, 61	168	1120 ___
1649	O27 Santa Fe Diesel Freight Set, 61		538 ___
1650	O27 Steam Military Set, 61	105	506 ___
1651	O27 Santa Fe Diesel Passenger Set, 61		671 ___
1800	General Gift Pack, 59-60	231	395 ___
1805	O27 Military Set (Land-Sea and Air Gift Pack), 60	585	1795 ___
1809	Western Gift Pack, 61		300 ___
1810	Space Age Gift Pack, 61	596	1165 ___
2100	Steam Passenger Set, 46		550 ___
2100W	Steam Passenger Set, 46	330	640 ___
2101	Steam Freight Set, 46		350 ___
2101W	Steam Freight Set, 46		395 ___
2103W	Steam Freight Set, 46		467 ___
2105WS	Steam Freight Set, 46		464 ___
2110WS	Steam Passenger Set, 46		1875 ___
2111WS	Steam Freight Set, 46		895 ___
2113WS	Steam Freight Set, 46		2093 ___
2114WS	Steam Passenger Set, 46	782	2500 ___
2115WS	Steam Work Train Set, 46	422	1288 ___
2120S	Steam Passenger Set, 47		500 ___
2120WS	Steam Passenger Set, 47		500 ___
2121S	Steam Freight Set, 47		400 ___
2121WS	Steam Freight Set, 47		405 ___
2123WS	Steam Freight Set, 47		645 ___
2124W	PRR Electric Passenger Set, 47		3200 ___
2125WS	Steam Freight Set, 47		568 ___
2126WS	Steam Passenger Set, 47	463	1950 ___
2127WS	Steam Work Train Set, 47		670 ___
2129WS	Steam Freight Set, 47		2250 ___
2131WS	Steam Work Train Set, 47		1200 ___
2133W	Diesel Freight Set, 48		1350 ___
2135WS	Steam Freight Set, 48		403 ___
2135WS	Steam Freight Set, 49	230	514 ___
2136WS	Steam Passenger Set, 48		674 ___
2136WS	Steam Passenger Set, 49	86	802 ___

SETS		Good	Exc
____ 2137WS	Steam Freight Set, 48	263	720
____ 2139W	PRR Electric Freight Set, 48		1425
____ 2139W	PRR Electric Freight Set, 49	475	1360
____ 2140WS	Steam Passenger Set, 48-49	225	1600
____ 2141WS	Steam Freight Set, 48	188	519
____ 2143WS	Steam Work Train Set, 48		795
____ 2144W	PRR Electric Passenger Set, 48-49	925	1957
____ 2145WS	Steam Freight Set, 48		815
____ 2146WS	Steam Passenger Set, 48-49	500	2000
____ 2147WS	Steam Freight Set, 49	125	454
____ 2148WS	Hudson Passenger Set, 50	1150	5800
____ 2149B	Diesel Work Train Set, 49		690
____ 2150WS	Steam Passenger Set, 50		1000
____ 2151W	Diesel Freight Set, 49		1078
____ 2153WS	Steam Work Train Set, 49		1010
____ 2155WS	Steam Freight Set, 49		1053
____ 2159W	Electric Freight Set, 50	875	2514
____ 2161W	Santa Fe Diesel Freight Set, 50		1350
____ 2163WS	Steam Freight Set, 50		550
____ 2163WS	Steam Freight Set, 51	363	1164
____ 2165WS	Steam Freight Set, 50		678
____ 2167WS	Steam Freight Set, 50-51	110	618
____ 2169WS	Hudson Freight Set, 50	0	3205
____ 2171W	NYC Diesel Freight Set, 50		1335
____ 2173WS	Steam Freight Set, 50	177	593
____ 2173WS	Steam Freight Set, 51		523
____ 2175W	Santa Fe Diesel Freight Set, 50	285	836
____ 2175W	Santa Fe Diesel Freight Set, 51	271	860
____ 2177WS	Steam Freight Set, 52	118	342
____ 2179WS	Steam Freight Set, 52	166	564
____ 2183WS	Steam Freight Set, 52	313	945
____ 2185W	NYC Diesel Freight Set, 50		960
____ 2185W	NYC Diesel Freight Set, 51		1018
____ 2187WS	Steam Freight Set, 52	280	650
____ 2189WS	Steam Freight Set, 52		580
____ 2190W	Santa Fe Diesel Passenger Set, 52		1900
____ 2190W	Santa Fe Diesel Passenger Set, 53	235	1919
____ 2191W	Santa Fe Diesel Freight Set, 52		1355
____ 2193W	NYC Diesel Freight Set, 52	388	1273
____ 2201WS	Steam Freight Set, 53	233	621
____ 2203WS	Steam Freight Set, 53	447	1219
____ 2205WS	Steam Freight Set, 53	371	1123
____ 2207W	Santa Fe Diesel Freight Set, 53	614	1563
____ 2209W	NYC Diesel Freight Set, 53	714	1433
____ 2211WS	Steam Freight Set, 53		740
____ 2213WS	Steam Freight Set, 53	325	1274
____ 2217WS	Steam Freight Set, 54	583	1210
____ 2219W	Diesel Freight Set, 54	870	1543
____ 2221WS	Steam Freight Set, 54		500
____ 2222WS	Steam Passenger Set, 54	1423	2613
____ 2223W	Diesel Freight Set, 54	1659	3132
____ 2225WS	Steam Work Train Set, 54	223	960
____ 2227W	Santa Fe Diesel Freight Set, 54	777	1614
____ 2229W	NYC Freight Set, 54	650	1525

SETS		Good	Exc	
2231W	Southern Diesel Freight Set, 54	797	2829	___
2234W	Santa Fe Diesel Passenger Set, 54	248	1990	___
2235W	MILW Diesel Freight Set, 55	188	654	___
2237WS	Steam Freight Set, 55		393	___
2239W	Illinois Central Diesel Freight Set, 55	288	1366	___
2241WS	Steam Freight Set, 55		615	___
2243W	Diesel Freight Set, 55	488	1375	___
2244W	Wabash Diesel Passenger Set, 55	2463	3650	___
2245WS	Steam Freight Set, 55		1150	___
2247W	Wabash Diesel Freight Set, 55	1596	2583	___
2249WS	Steam Freight Set, 55	341	872	___
2251W	Diesel Freight Set, 55	1500	3745	___
2253W	PRR Electric Freight Set, 55	950	2788	___
2254W	PRR Electric Passenger Set, 55		5500	___
2255W	Diesel Work Train Set, 56	224	843	___
2257WS	Steam Freight Set, 56	95	500	___
2259W	NH Electric Freight Set, 56		692	___
2261WS	Steam Freight Set, 56	285	636	___
2263W	NH Electric Freight Set, 56	162	978	___
2265WS	Steam Freight Set, 56		1003	___
2267W	Diesel Freight Set, 56		2210	___
2269W	B&O Diesel Freight Set, 56		2967	___
2270W	Jersey Central Diesel Passenger Set, 56	877	5730	___
2271W	PRR Electric Freight Set, 56	1094	2288	___
2273W	MILW Diesel Freight Set, 56	2036	4480	___
2274W	PRR Electric Passenger Set, 56	1493	3834	___
2275W	Wabash Diesel Freight Set, 57	115	820	___
2276W	Budd RDC Set, 57	1019	2035	___
2277WS	Steam Work Train Set, 57		585	___
2279W	NH Electric Freight Set, 57	340	837	___
2281W	Santa Fe Diesel Freight Set, 57		1040	___
2283WS	Steam Freight Set, 57		750	___
2285W	Diesel Freight Set, 57	525	2132	___
2287W	MILW Electric Freight Set, 57	1200	2000	___
2289WS	Super O Steam Freight Set, 57	553	1300	___
2291W	Super O Rio Grande Diesel Freight Set, 57	1532	2617	___
2292WS	Super O Steam Passenger Set, 57	1000	1982	___
2293W	Super O PRR Electric Freight Set, 57		2400	___
2295WS	Super O Steam Freight Set, 57	1050	2157	___
2296W	Super O CP Diesel Passenger Set, 57	870	3913	___
2297WS	Super O Steam Freight Set, 57		2300	___
2501W	Super O Diesel Work Train Set, 58	188	914	___
2502W	Super O Budd RDC Set, 58		2250	___
2503WS	Super O Steam Freight Set, 58	150	715	___
2505W	Super O Electric Freight Set, 58		1400	___
2507W	Super O Diesel Freight Set, 58	1175	2600	___
2509WS	Super O Steam Freight Set, 58		927	___
2511W	Super O Electric Work Set, 58		1100	___
2513W	Super O Electric Freight Set, 58	1633	3000	___
2515WS	Super O Steam Freight Set, 58		892	___
2517W	Super O Rio Grande Diesel Freight Set, 58	1275	2625	___
2518W	Super O PRR Electric Passenger Set, 58		1850	___
2519W	Super O Diesel Freight Set, 58	1267	3400	___

	SETS		Good	Exc
___	2521WS	Super O Steam Freight Set, 58	1000	2409
___	2523W	Super O Santa Fe Diesel Freight Set, 58		1300
___	2525WS	Super O Steam Work Train Set, 58	1358	3448
___	2526W	Super O Santa Fe Diesel Passenger Set, 58	888	4034
___	2527	Super O Missile Launcher Set, 59-60	482	861
___	2528WS	Super O General Set, 59-61	492	854
___	2529W	Super O Electric Work Train Set, 59	650	1967
___	2531WS	Super O Steam Freight Set, 59	650	1294
___	2533W	Super O GN Electric Freight Set, 59		1910
___	2535WS	Super O Steam Freight Set, 59		840
___	2537W	Super O NH Diesel Freight Set, 59	332	2500
___	2539WS	Super O Steam Freight Set, 59		1483
___	2541W	Super O Santa Fe Diesel Freight Set, 59	398	2400
___	2543WS	Super O Steam Freight Set, 59		1590
___	2544W	Super O Santa Fe Diesel Passenger Set, 59-60	1370	2490
___	2545WS	Super O Military Set, 59		3000
___	2547WS	Super O Steam Freight Set, 60		484
___	2549W	Super O Military Set, 60	580	1237
___	2551W	Super O GN Electric Freight Set, 60	1150	3392
___	2553WS	Super O Steam Freight Set, 60	1077	2672
___	2555W	Super O Santa Fe Freight Set with matching HO Set, 60		10000
___	2570	Super O Santa Fe Work Train Set, 61	543	875
___	2571	Super O Steam Freight Set, 61		520
___	2572	Super O B&M Diesel Freight Set, 61		813
___	2573	Super O Steam Freight Set, 61	650	1433
___	2574	Super O Santa Fe Diesel Freight Set, 61	750	1875
___	2575	Super O PRR Electric Freight Set, 61	1250	3300
___	2576	Super O Santa Fe Diesel Passenger Set, 61		3030
___	4109WS	Electronic Control Set, 46-47		1493
___	4110WS	Electronic Control Set, 48-49	265	2500
___	11011	027 Diesel Freight Set, 62		286
___	11201	027 Steam Freight Set, 62		129
___	11212	027 Santa Fe Diesel Freight Set, 62		375
___	11222	027 Steam Freight Set, 62		243
___	11232	027 NH Diesel Freight Set, 62		535
___	11242	027 Steam Freight Set, 62		167
___	11252	027 Texas Special Space Set, 62	190	477
___	11268	027 C&O Diesel Freight Set, 62	817	1425
___	11278	027 Steam Freight Set, 62		239
___	11288	027 Space Set, 62	500	1215
___	11298	027 Steam Freight Set, 62		565
___	11308	027 Santa Fe Diesel Passenger Set, 62		730
___	11311	027 Steam Freight Set, 63		232
___	11321	027 Rio Grande Diesel Freight Set, 63		400
___	11331	027 Steam Freight Set, 63	35	105
___	11341	027 Santa Fe Diesel Freight Set, 63		831
___	11351	027 Steam Freight Set, 63		190
___	11361	027 Texas Special Space Set, 63		750
___	11375	027 Steam Freight Set, 63		700
___	11385	027 Santa Fe Space Set, 63		2000
___	11395	027 Steam Freight Set, 63		600
___	11405	027 Santa Fe Diesel Passenger Set, 63		750
___	11420	027 Steam Freight Set, 64		200

SETS		Good	Exc	
11430	027 Steam Freight, 64	97	170	___
11440	027 Rio Grande Diesel Freight Set, 64	143	291	___
11450	027 Steam Freight Set, 64	98	298	___
11460	027 Steam Freight Set, 64		150	___
11470	027 Steam Freight Set, 64	91	305	___
11480	027 Diesel Freight Set, 64		619	___
11490	027 Diesel Passenger Set, 64-65		397	___
11500	027 Steam Freight Set, 64		438	___
11500	027 Steam Freight Set, 65		275	___
11500	027 Steam Freight Set, 66	105	275	___
11510	027 Steam Freight Set, 64		300	___
11520	027 Steam Freight Set, 65-66		143	___
11530	027 Santa Fe Diesel Freight, 65-66	113	439	___
11540	027 Steam Freight Set, 65-66		260	___
11550	027 Steam Freight Set, 65-66	60	207	___
11560	027 Texas Special Freight Set, 65-66	132	360	___
11590	027 Santa Fe Diesel Passenger Set, 66		646	___
11600	027 Steam Freight Set, 68		1280	___
11710	027 Steam Freight Set, 69	103	173	___
11720	Diesel Freight Set, 69	100	746	___
11730	027 UP Diesel Freight Set, 69		800	___
11740	027 RI Diesel Freight Set, 69		310	___
11750	027 Steam Freight Set, 69		360	___
11760	027 Steam Freight Set, 69		355	___
12502	Prairie-Rider Gift Pack, 62		600	___
12512	Enforcer Gift Pack, 62		1100	___
12700	Steam Freight Set, 64		1000	___
12710	Steam Freight Set, 64-66		1063	___
12720	Santa Fe Diesel Freight Set, 64		1500	___
12730	Santa Fe Diesel Freight Set, 64-66	448	1136	___
12740	Santa Fe Diesel Freight Set, 64		1500	___
12760	Steam Freight Set, 64		1100	___
12780	Santa Fe Diesel Passenger, 64-66	1108	4678	___
12800	B&M Diesel Freight Set, 65-66	355	834	___
12820	Diesel Freight Set, 65	1017	2508	___
12840	Steam Freight Set, 66	771	1791	___
12850	Diesel Freight Set, 66	850	2700	___
13008	Super O Steam Freight Set, 62		500	___
13018	Super O Santa Fe Diesel Freight Set, 62	646	1200	___
13028	Super O Space Set, 62		1000	___
13036	Super O General Set, 62	490	1160	___
13048	Super O Steam Freight Set, 62	360	941	___
13058	Super O Space Set, 62	800	2048	___
13068	Super O PRR Electric Freight Set, 62		3200	___
13078	Super O PRR Electric Passenger Set, 62		3500	___
13088	Super O Santa Fe Diesel Passenger Set, 62	1250	3300	___
13098	Super O Steam Freight Set, 63		2000	___
13108	Super O Santa Fe Space Set, 63		1000	___
13118	Super O Steam Freight Set, 63		1500	___
13128	Super O Santa Fe Space Set, 63		1750	___
13138	Super O PRR Electric Freight Set, 63		3800	___
13148	Super O Santa Fe Diesel Passenger Set, 63		2500	___
13150	Super O Hudson Steam Freight Set, 64-66	1538	4450	___

ABBREVIATIONS

Descriptions

AAR	Association of American Railroads (truck type)
AEC	Atomic Energy Commission
AF	American Flyer
CC	Command Control
DD	Double-door
EMD	Electro-Motive Division
ETD	End-of-train device
FARR	Famous American Railroad Series
FF	Fallen Flag Series
FM	Fairbanks-Morse
GE	General Electric
LL	Lionel Lines
MOW	Maintenance-of-way
MU	Multiple unit (commuter cars)
O	Lionel gauge (1¼" between outside rails)
OO	Lionel gauge (¾" between outside rails)
PFE	Pacific Fruit Express
REA	Railway Express Agency
SSS	Service Station Special
std	Standard gauge (2⅛" between outside rails)
std O	Standard O (scale length and dimension)
TMCC	TrainMaster Command Control
USMC	United States Marine Corps
1-D	One dome
2-D	Two dome
3-D	Three dome

Railroad names

ACL	Atlantic Coast Line	LV	Lehigh Valley
ATSF	Atchison, Topeka & Santa Fe	MEC	Maine Central
B&A	Boston & Albany	MILW	Milwaukee Road
BAR	Bangor & Aroostook	MKT	Missouri-Kansas-Texas (Katy)
B&LE	Bessemer & Lake Erie	MNS	Minnesota, Northfield & Southern
B&M	Boston & Maine		
BN	Burlington Northern	MP	Missouri Pacific
BNSF	Burlington Northern Santa Fe	M&StL	Minneapolis & St. Louis
B&O	Baltimore & Ohio	NdeM	Nacionales de Mexico Railway
CB&Q	Chicago, Burlington & Quincy		
CMStP&P	Chicago, Milwaukee, St. Paul & Pacific (Milwaukee Road)	NH	New Haven
		NKP	Nickel Plate Road
CN	Canadian National	NOT&M	New Orleans, Texas & Mexico
CGW	Chicago Great Western	NP	Northern Pacific
CNJ	Central of New Jersey	NS	Norfolk Southern
C&NW	Chicago & North Western	N&W	Norfolk & Western
C&O	Chesapeake & Ohio	NWP	Northwestern Pacific
CP	Canadian Pacific	NYC	New York Central
CRI&P	Chicago, Rock Island & Pacific (Rock Island)	NYO&W	New York, Ontario & Western
		NYNH&H	New York, New Haven & Hartford (New Haven)
C&S	Colorado & Southern		
CUVA	Cuyahoga Valley Railway	OSL	Oregon Short Line
D&H	Delaware & Hudson	P&LE	Pittsburgh & Lake Erie
D&RGW	Denver & Rio Grande Western	PC	Penn Central
DT&I	Detroit, Toledo & Ironton	PRR	Pennsylvania Railroad
DM&IR	Duluth, Missabe & Iron Range	PMKY	Pittsburgh, McKeesport & Youghiogheny
		PTM	ST Rail System
E-L	Erie-Lackawanna (Erie-Lack.)	RFP	Richmond, Fredericksburg & Potomac
FEC	Florida East Coast		
FWD	Fort Worth & Denver	SF	Santa Fe
FY&P	Franklin & Pittsylvania	SLSF	St. Louis-San Francisco (Frisco)
GM&O	Gulf, Mobile & Ohio		
GN	Great Northern	SP	Southern Pacific
GN&W	Genesee & Wyoming	SSW	St. Louis Southwestern (Cotton Belt)
GTW	Grand Trunk Western		
IC	Illinois Central	T&P	Texas & Pacific
ICG	Illinois Central Gulf	TP&W	Toledo, Peoria & Western
IGN	International-Great Northern	UP	Union Pacific
KCS	Kansas City Southern	WM	Western Maryland
L&N	Louisville & Nashville	WP	Western Pacific
LNE	Lehigh & New England